Hickman

Integrated principles of zoology

Second edition

Integrated

Second edition

principles of zoology

Cleveland P. Hickman, Ph.D.

Professor and Head of the Department of Zoology
DePauw University, Greencastle, Indiana

With 639 illustrations

The C. V. Mosby Company

St. Louis   1961

To the memory of

J. R. H.

Who shared with the author many glorious

adventures in zoological study

To live with them is far less sweet
Than to remember thee!

Preface
to second edition

This second edition is a thorough revision. However, the general plan of the first edition has been largely retained. Although the success of the first edition has been convincing proof that the basic organization of the book is what it should be—an integration of the major principles of zoological study—experience in many classrooms has shown where improvements could be made.

Some minor changes have been made in the over-all organization. Part I deals with the structural and functional organization of animals. In this part are presented the general plan of zoological study, the energy relations of protoplasm, methods of zoological study, and the architectural pattern of an animal. Certain biological concepts and generalizations are introduced and their applications to zoology are pointed out and integrated.

Part II presents the morphological and physiological features of the major phyla. This part demonstrates the many patterns of animals and how they achieve similar aims by unlike methods. Emphasis is placed upon the gradual unfolding of the evolutionary blueprint by showing the contributions of each major group to this blueprint. Every effort has been made to use the most recent classification.

Part III, a summary of the various organ systems, might be considered a synthesis of the architectural patterns. Here the student can see the unifying principles of bodily structures and the common underlying plan of the organism as a unit. He can also see how the human body fits into the evolutionary scheme.

Part IV deals with the continuity of life as revealed by a study of development, heredity, and evolution. Here specific details of the animal's origin, the relations between successive generations, and the evolutionary process are appraised.

Part V discusses the adaptive and environmental relations of organisms. The numerous means or adaptations by which animals solve their problems, the interrelationships between organisms and their environment, the distribution of animals over the face of the earth, and the specific behavior patterns of animals are dealt with in this section.

Part VI shows the historical development of zoology by presenting chronologically the origin of the great concepts and key discoveries, many of which are referred to in the proper setting of text discussion.

The illustrations have undergone thorough revision. Some of the older ones have been retained because of their usefulness, but many have been modified or replaced by better ones. A large number of new ones have been added. Approximately one-half of the figures are new. The purpose of these drawings and photographs is to explain and clarify as well as to direct the student's attention to vital points. The new drawings were made by skilled artists directly under my supervision, often from dissected specimens so that frequently overlooked details could be included. Although accuracy was the major objective, esthetic qualities are also stressed. Often the legends are a part of the engraving itself in order to stimulate the student's interest and to call his attention to important concepts. Comparative schemes of bodily structures and important conceptual relations have been highlighted in this manner.

The newer concepts of biological investigation have been carefully considered and recent advances covered and appraised in the light of present information. Molecular biology and animal behavior, two live subjects in current biological investigations, have been given adequate treatment at the introductory level. Some recently discovered and appraised groups, such as phylum Pogonophora and the mollusk class Monoplacophora, have been given consideration. Newer interpretations of old subjects are presented wherever justified. Every effort within the limits of space has been used to bring the revision up to date.

Other features which add to the effectiveness of the text as a teaching tool have been included. A glossary of difficult terms, including pronunciations, derivations, and definitions, has been added. More terms have been added to the lists of derivation and meaning of basic terminology at the ends of the chapters where the student may consult them while they are fresh in his mind. The annotated references at the ends of the chapters now include the latest treatises and monographs. It is my hope tha some students will be inspired to read beyond the material of the text. New concepts and key discoveries from this period of rapid advancement in life sciences bring the section at the end of the book up to date; many older concepts not included in the first edition have also been incorporated.

The life sciences have arrived at that stage when many revealing concepts have blossomed out within a relatively short time. After a long period of growth and development of vast bodies of information, the time has seemed ripe for a synthesis of this material into conceptual schemes which are beginning to have basic meanings. Many pieces of the jigsaw puzzle of the life process are now being fitted into place. The strides which have been made in understanding cellular metabolism, the finer organization of the gene, and the behavior patterns of animals are all evidences of this advancement. We now have clearer ideas about many biological phenomena, but there is no place for dogmatic attitudes and modes of thinking. Each insight reveals further mystery; each vista opens up another. No problem has been fully solved. This is what makes zoology an exciting and challenging science. The really great discoveries lie ahead, and no authoritarian viewpoint has the slightest justification in any branch of scientific study.

The writing of a zoology textbook presents many problems. Zoology, in common with other sciences, is becoming increasingly complex. Its study is intimately linked up with that of other scientific disciplines, and a knowledge of many branches of learning is necessary for effective investigations in the life sciences. The teacher's problem is to reduce this complexity to simple and comprehensible schemes of relations. The organization pattern of even the simplest animal is so intricate that man has only recently acquired the power to understand a little of its nature. Some meaningful scheme should be followed for making order out of chaos. This book has tried partly to resolve this problem by the evolutionary approach. Throughout this text the evolutionary principle has been the cardinal one around which the variations of animal patterns are built. It is my belief that the complexity of variations can be appreciated only when the evolutionary sequences from the simple to the complex are presented. In no other way can the student understand structural and functional differences among organisms.

Cleveland P. Hickman

Acknowledgments

A revision of this kind is the work of many minds. Suggestions and critical comments from teachers who used the first edition have come from all parts of the country. Some have gone through the book page by page indicating omissions and suggesting improvements. Others have indicated on tape their ideas for increasing the effectiveness of the text. Constructive criticisms from hundreds of my own students have been invaluable. All these individuals have shown a warm interest in the general plan of the book and its method of presentation. For all this help the author expresses his utmost gratitude.

In a more specific way the following persons have made major contributions to the actual revision process. A number of talented artists have been responsible for the revealing and authoritative drawings. Most of this work was done by Patricia Simpson and Delbert L. Michel. Others who helped with drawings were Virginia Spanagel, Meredith L. Miller, Neal A. Cochran, Virginia Jones, and Frances M. Hickman. Most of the manuscript was typed by Sue Proud and Joanne Helmerich. As in the first edition, my wife, Frances M. Hickman, has had to carry the exacting and heavy work of preparing and proofreading the manuscript. Helping her in this work were Elizabeth A. Weber and Kenneth B. Welliver.

Many illustrations have been contributed by a number of persons. Others have been borrowed from publishers and organizations. Credit is given to all these in the legends. I also wish to thank Mr. Murray A. Newman of the Vancouver Public Aquarium for his many courtesies while we photographed animal forms in the aquarium during the summer of 1958.

It is a pleasure to express my appreciation to the following teachers and specialists in the various branches of biological study who have generously checked certain sections of the revised manuscript and made critical comments and suggestions: C. L. Bieber (*Paleontology*), C. J. D. Brown (*Osteichthyes*), E. L. Cockrum (*Mammals*), P. A. Dehnel (*Mollusca, Echinodermata*), R. W. Dexter (*Crustaceans*), F. Fuller (*Cellular Physiology*), C. P. Hickman, Jr. (*Reproduction* and *Endocrinology*), C. H. Lowe, Jr. (*Amphibians* and *Reptiles*), G. O. Mackie (*Coelenterata*), W. E. Martin (*Platyhelminthes*), R. Rector (*Animal Behavior*), A. E. Reynolds (*Evolution* and *Genetics*), H. W. Schoenborn (*Protozoa*), J. F. Vernberg (*Ecology*).

Others who made evaluations of the first edition and definite suggestions for the revision as a whole are J. T. Bagnara, W. H. Brown, J. Heath, D. Heyneman, and W. D. Ivey.

Contents

part one   STRUCTURAL AND FUNCTIONAL ORGANIZATION
OF ANIMAL LIFE

1. Introduction—the science of zoology, 17

2. Energy relations and the nature of protoplasm, 35

3. The cell as unit of protoplasmic organization, 51

4. Architectural pattern of an animal, 71

5. Some important biological principles and concepts, 90

part two   MORPHOLOGICAL AND PHYSIOLOGICAL
PRINCIPLES OF ANIMAL LIFE AS REVEALED
BY THE VARIOUS GROUPS (PHYLA)

6. Phylum Protozoa, 101

7. Phylum Porifera, 138

8. Phylum Coelenterata (Cnidaria), 150

9. Phylum Ctenophora, 179

10. Phylum Platyhelminthes, 184

11. Phylum Rhynchocoela (Nemertina), 211

12. Phylum Aschelminthes, 217

13. Phylum Acanthocephala, 234

14. Phyla of uncertain relationships (miscellaneous phyla), 239

15. Phylum Annelida, 251

16. Phylum Arthropoda—subphylum Chelicerata and minor groups, 273

17. Phylum Arthropoda—subphylum Mandibulata—except insects, 293

18. Phylum Arthropoda—subphylum Mandibulata—insects, 314

19. Phylum Mollusca, 345

20. Phylum Echinodermata, 372

21. Phyla Hemichordata and Pogonophora, 392

22. Phylum Chordata—ancestry and evolution; general characteristics; protochordates, 401

23. Phylum Chordata—classes Cyclostomata and Chondrichthyes, 431

24. Phylum Chordata—class Osteichthyes, 441

25. Phylum Chordata—classes Amphibia and Reptilia, 457

26. Phylum Chordata—the frog as a vertebrate type, 488

27. Phylum Chordata—class Aves, 518

28. Phylum Chordata—class Mammalia, 547

part three   RÉSUMÉ OF ORGAN SYSTEMS WITH
PARTICULAR REFERENCE TO MAN

29. Support, protection, and movement, 587

30. Digestive, circulatory, respiratory, and excretory systems, 609

31. Nervous and sensory systems, 648

32. Reproductive and endocrine systems, 671

part four   ORIGIN AND RELATIONSHIP OF ANIMALS

33. Principles of development, 703

34. Principles of inheritance, 721

35. Applied genetics; human heredity, 746

36. The record of fossils (paleontology), 760

37. Principles of variation and organic evolution, 772

part five   ADAPTIVE AND ENVIRONMENTAL
RELATIONS OF ANIMALS

38. Relation of animals to their environment (ecology), 809

39. Distribution of animals (zoogeography), 843

40. Some interesting and striking adaptations, 851

41. Animal behavior patterns, 869

part six   DEVELOPMENT OF ZOOLOGY

42. Origin of basic concepts and key discoveries in biology,
including books that have influenced zoology, 889

Glossary, 932

Part One

Structural and functional organization of animal life

chapter 1

Introduction—the science of zoology

DEFINITION OF ZOOLOGY

Zoology (Gr. *zoion*, animal, + *logos*, study) is the branch of the life sciences that deals with the animal organism as contrasted to botany, the science that is concerned with the plant organism. Both zoology and botany make up the science of biology (Gr. *bios*, life, + *logos*, study) or the study of living things, and the distinction between animals and plants is mainly one of convention rather than of basic differences. The biological sciences are empirical, that is, knowledge about them is acquired by observation and experimentation. They have their own conceptual schemes and laws and their own methods of research which must meet the same requirements imposed upon all scientific investigation. Theories and hypotheses must be testable and must be verified in a life science as in any other science. Both zoology and botany seek to establish exact and quantitative principles for the basic organization of living systems. At present a life science must be considered a descriptive science in contrast to an exact one like physics and may well remain so because of the complexity and variety of living organisms.

RELATION OF ZOOLOGY TO OTHER SCIENCES

All the sciences are interrelated. Although biology uses physics, chemistry, and other physical sciences in explaining its phenomena, biological principles are not merely an application of physicochemical laws. The laws of many life processes have no counterparts in physics or chemistry. Many biological concepts can be expressed mathematically but others cannot. Biological sciences at present are often restricted to mere descriptive statements of general phenomena without quantitative connotation. Biological systems are represented by many levels of organization, not all of which have been resolved into concise concepts and testable theories. Many branches of study serve to connect biology to other sciences, such as paleontology, biophysics, and biochemistry. There has been a marked trend for some time toward a synthesis of the biological sciences with other sciences.

WHAT ARE YOUR INTERESTS IN ZOOLOGY?

Zoology is a complex science with myriads of problems yet to solve. This alone is a challenge to an enquiring mind, but there are also other motives for zoological study.

1. Man is the product of the biological heritage of the past. He is part of the animal kingdom and a product of the evolutionary process. He is limited by the potentialities of living matter, for his roots are found in his biological background. No

group of animals stands alone and isolated from other groups; all are links in a sequence of life patterns, many of which have been displaced by other patterns in the long evolutionary process. Much information about man is obtained by studying other animals, for there is an underlying unity of structure and function throughout the animal kingdom.

2. Zoology is of practical importance because of our dependence upon animals for many products and uses, such as food, clothing, sources of drugs, subjects of experimentation, building materials, and scores of lesser things. Genetics, one of the branches of zoology, has been a factor in producing better domestic animals and even promises some progress in the improvement of the human stock.

3. A study of zoology is necessary for preprofessional work in medicine, dentistry, nursing, veterinary science, dietetics, agriculture, sanitary engineering, conservation, and many other fields. Medical sciences have profited from zoological discoveries, for concepts formed by studying one group of animals can be applied also to other groups, including man.

4. Zoological study furnishes the basis for psychological and sociological studies. At present there is a lively study of animal behavior and its implications of human application, which is indicative of this interest. Animal sociology is rapidly becoming a branch of zoology in its own right.

5. An interest in living forms is basic. Primitive man followed the chase from necessity; modern man does it as a relief from the tension of organized society and for the sheer love of hunting and fishing. This is one of the reasons for setting aside wilderness recreation areas.

6. Animals influence man's welfare in harmful ways. Parasites injure man and his domestic animals. Many animals carry disease (vectors) and others are themselves disease agents, such as those causing malaria. Destruction of crops and fruit by insect pests is a problem for agriculture everywhere.

7. All animals, including man, fit into a balance of nature. This is the web of life in which all plant and animal life fits into a pattern of environmental relationships. One of our problems has been to understand this relationship which is so often disturbed by man's blundering.

8. The study of zoology is an excellent discipline for your mind. This is true for all sciences, but it is particularly true of the life sciences that have a unique role in man's cultural pattern. Biological concepts influence your thinking in every realm of human interest. For instance, the concept of evolution, or the transformation of organisms from one type to another during geological eras, has affected concepts in philosophy, psychology, sociology, religion, and many other disciplines. One of the fascinating facets of biological study is the ever-changing nature of its concepts. The zoologist may at unguarded moments make dogmatic statements, but basically absolutism is nonexistent in biological phenomena. Much biological investigation may be done with practical objectives in mind, but a greater amount is motivated by curiosity and an urge to explain what lies beyond our present knowledge of the life process.

DISTINCTIONS BETWEEN THE LIVING AND THE NONLIVING

It is not always easy to distinguish between the living and the nonliving. The terms inorganic for the nonliving (inanimate) and organic for the living (animate) substances are commonly used. Both organic and inorganic matter have the same chemical elements, although living matter has fewer elements represented. Man once believed that the world around him was all alive; his concept of a distinction between the organic and inorganic must have evolved gradually out of his thinking, especially about his own body. Almost any single criterion one may use for living substance can also apply to the nonliving. If we restrict the differences to individual phenomena, no real distinction can be made between the two concepts. The real properties of living things are due partly to their compounds (the way in which chemical elements are put together) and partly to the organization of the whole (the organism). Many compounds associated with organic life have been made synthetically, but the secret of life lies in how these compounds are integrated to form dynamic life. Organization, however, is not the cause of life but is the result of it. Protoplasm or living substance is endowed with the characteristic criteria of life—contractility, growth, irritability, and reproduction. Some animals do these things without muscle, stomach, nervous system, and germ cells; higher forms develop specialized structures for these functions.

Both living and nonliving matter may be organized in the form of systems, which implies the coordination and integration of processes into a functional whole, but living systems are essentially open systems, that is, they have a mutual exchange of energy materials with their environment. Changes in the environment can thus affect life wherever it is found. A living organism is in constant change; it is never the same at any two instances.

The extensive study of viruses in recent years has focused attention upon these pathogenic agents as possible examples of borderline forms between the animate and the inanimate. Viruses cause many common diseases in man and the animals, such as smallpox, measles, and influenza, as well as many plant diseases. One of the latter is tobacco mosaic disease, which has been extensively studied. Viruses can be crystallized, in which form they can be kept for an indefinite period and can be subjected to temperatures that would kill ordinary organisms; yet when these crystals are placed on tobacco leaves with the proper moisture they will grow, reproduce, and undergo mutations (hereditary changes). Although most viruses are small, a few, such as the smallpox virus, are actually larger than some bacteria. They share with genes (hereditary units) the distinction of being the smallest biological systems capable of self-duplication.

WHAT IS AN ANIMAL?

The simple dictionary definition of an animal is not satisfactory to a biologist who appraises the living organism from its organization, properties, and historical character. The more we know about an animal the greater the difficulty in defining it. A definition of an animal that would exclude all plants cannot be made within the limits of a short, logical statement. Perhaps we should confine ourselves to defining any living organism and thus avoid debatable grounds which arise when different organic types are considered. For instance, certain basic differences between higher animals and higher plants are apparent and distinctive, but among the lower forms of both the plant and animal kingdoms the members grade imperceptibly into each other. The acellular or single-celled forms of both are now often lumped together under the Protista (Gr. *protistos*, first of all), a term proposed long ago by Haeckel. In general, plants are characterized by cellulose cell walls, synthesis of complex organic foodstuffs by photosynthesis (holophytic nutrition), inconstant body form, limited movement, and external organs; and animals are characterized by an absence of cellulose cell walls, a fairly constant body form, holozoic nutrition (ingestion and digestion of organic matter), mostly internal organs, pronounced movement, and definite irritability.

On the basis of what was stated about the living and the nonliving, we may tentatively define an organism as a physicochemical system of specific and varying levels of organization patterns, self-regulative, self-perpetuating, and in continuous adjustment with its environment.

WHERE ARE ANIMALS FOUND?

Lamarck, the noted French naturalist, called that region of our planet where living organisms occur the **biosphere**. The biosphere is made up of both fresh and salt water, surfaces, depths below the surface, and the air. The biosphere extends down in the ocean to more than 30,000 feet and below the land surface from 1,000 to 3,000 feet (bacteria). In the atmosphere, the biosphere extends vertically 40,000 to 50,000 feet, where bacteria and other small organisms have been collected. Terrestrial (land surface) forms, such as spiders, have been collected at altitudes of 22,000 feet on Mt. Everest. Birds have been known to fly at altitudes of 25,000 to 30,000 feet. Bacteria and animals have a greater vertical distribution than green plants which are rarely found a few hundred feet below the surface of water because of lack of light. Within the range of the biosphere environmental conditions may vary greatly; yet some animals adjust to extreme physical conditions. Deep-sea fishes are subjected to thousands of pounds' pressure per square inch of body surface; brine shrimp are found in Great Salt Lake which has a salt concentration eight to ten times that of the sea. Certain fishes and crustaceans are known to occur in hot springs. Some fishes are adjusted to both a fresh-water and a salt-water existence and spend part of their life cycle in each.

In what part of the biosphere is life most abundant? Four fifths of all known species of animals are terrestrial, although the sea covers 71% of the earth's surface. In numbers of individuals also, land forms are more common. There are, however, more structural types (major groups) in the sea. There are certain regions within the biosphere that will not support life at all or else in negligible amounts, such as the Dead Sea, the depths of the Black Sea, and shifting sandy regions, which have highly unfavorable conditions of existence (toxic salt content, lack of food relations, etc.)

WHY SO MANY VARIETIES OF ANIMALS?*

More than a million species of animals have been named to date and the number increases by thousands each year. Animal species outnumber plant species about four to one. According to the fossil record each succeeding period in geological history has shown a greater variety of life, although the rate of expansion of animal diversity has not always been the same in all ages. While many aspects of the past may always remain obscure, certain marked trends are noticeable. The evidence at hand indicates the organic world has passed progressively from simpler to more complex forms. Although there is a great multiplicity of animal types, they are not connected by all gradations of intermediate or transition forms. Organisms as we know them represent separate and distinct species. What has been the cause of this diversity of animal life? The answer lies in one of the most important principles in biology—evolution. This principle states that all living organisms have arisen from common ancestors through a gradual transformation of types brought about by change and diversification. Every organism thus has a historical background which must be understood in order to appreciate its origin and nature. Briefly, the evolutionary theory may be outlined as follows: chance variations appear now and then in organisms. These variations may be useful, harmful, or indifferent to the welfare of the animal or plant. If harmful, the variation will be eliminated by natural selection; if beneficial, the organism may gain some slight advantage over the others in the struggle for existence and thus may have a better chance to survive and reproduce its kind. Over long periods of time such a process could result in forms quite different from their ancestor, or a new species. Evolution therefore has two main features: (1) the production of diversity among organisms for different ecological niches and (2) the origin of adaptations which fit organisms for efficient adjustment to their environments.

HOW INFORMATION ABOUT ANIMALS IS FOUND

Knowledge about animals is acquired by the same methods used by other sciences, that is, by close observation, by controlled experiments, by careful analysis and arrangement of facts, by determin-

*Refer to Chapter 5, Principle 18.

ing relationships between facts, and by the formulation of concepts which have wide application to other problems in that field of study. Almost anyone with ordinary abilities and skills plus lively curiosity and patience can make new discoveries in an extensive field such as the biological sciences, but it is quite a different matter to fit these facts into conceptual schemes which have fruitful meanings. Perhaps the greatest shortcomings in scientific investigation are the inability to think things through to logical conclusions and to see relationships where none appear to exist. Often complicated and involved explanations and conclusions are advanced when simpler ones would suffice. A good principle of scientific logic is "Occam's Razor" (after a scholastic scholar of the fourteenth century) which states that of several possible explanations, the one that is simplest and requires the fewest assumptions is usually the most probable.

No set procedures as outlined in a so-called "scientific method," will necessarily produce startling discoveries if the subjective attitude of the investigator is not scientific. Many great scientific facts have been discovered quite by accident when a keen-minded investigator with a wide background of experience in the field was around to see the hidden relationships. All scientists do not follow the same procedures in their investigations any more than they follow the same pattern of thinking. In general, however, good scientists formulate hypotheses from their accumulated facts; they test out their theories and reject those that do not apply; they repeat their experiments; they are cautious about generalizations; and they do not hesitate to seek the advice and observations of others competent in that field. Above all, they have a great motive force to pry out secrets and to satisfy their curiosity. Finally, they are eager to communicate their findings to the world of science, not necessarily through pride of personal achievements but that others may profit thereby and that the frontiers of knowledge in that particular field may be advanced.

THE MANY FACETS OF ZOOLOGICAL STUDY

The content and scope of zoology has steadily increased. In their early development, zoology and botany were never far removed from practical applications. Plants were studied as sources for drugs in medical practice. The human body was studied for medical purposes, and to understand it better, comparative studies of other animals were also made. But, in addition, even early man observed animals and collected them. He did this because of curiosity, with little regard to practical importance. Collectors and naturalists have always played important roles in the progress of zoology. In the early development of the zoological sciences, natural history, structure, function, and taxonomy comprised the major part of the field. Later, evolution and genetics were emphasized, each mutually helpful in understanding the other. Recent trends of zoological study have swung toward functional discoveries along such lines as endocrinology, biochemistry, and experimental embryology. There is now a marked tendency to study the substance out of which cells and tissues are made. Chemical analysis has been carried to the point where we may be said to have a form of molecular biology. All this advancement has necessitated a subdivision of zoology into many branches. This means a high degree of specialization, so that no one person can hope to grasp all phases of such an extensive science.

Major subdivisions of zoology

Systematic zoology. This group includes taxonomy or classification, ecology, distribution, and the evolution of animals.

Morphology. Structural aspects are stressed in this group, which includes comparative anatomy, histology, cytology, embryology, and paleontology.

Physiology. This group has to do with the functional considerations of the organism. It includes general physiology, physiological chemistry, and animal behavior or psychology.

Experimental zoology. This group is a

broad one and includes those subdivisions that are concerned with experimental alterations of the patterns of organisms. It includes genetics, experimental morphology, and embryology.

Such groupings cannot be arbitrary, for there is much overlapping and interrelation among the various fields of zoological investigation. For example, cytogenetics represents the close dependence of two branches of study, cytology and genetics, that were formerly considered more or less separately. As specialization increases, branches of study become more and more restricted in their scope. We thus have protozoology, the study of protozoans; entomology, the study of insects; parasitology, the study of parasites; and many others.

Some other subdivisions of zoology

anatomy (Gr. *ana,* up, + *tome,* cutting) The study of animal structure as revealed by gross dissection.

anatomy, comparative The study of various animal types from the lowest to the highest with the aim of establishing homologies and the origin and modifications of body structures.

biochemistry (Gr. *bios,* life, + *chemos,* fluid) The study of the chemical make-up of animal tissues.

cytology (Gr. *kytos,* hollow vessel) The study of the minute parts and functions of cells.

ecology (Gr. *oikos,* house) The study of animals in relation to their surroundings.

embryology (Gr. *embryon,* embryo) The study of the formation and early development of the organism.

endocrinology (Gr. *endon,* within, + *krinein,* to separate) The science of hormone action in organisms.

entomology (Gr. *entomon,* insect) The study of insects.

genetics (Gr. *genesis,* origin) The study of the laws of inheritance.

helminthology (Gr. *helmins,* worm) The study of worms, with especial reference to the parasitic forms.

herpetology (Gr. *herpein,* to creep) The study of reptiles, although the term sometimes includes both reptiles and amphibians.

histology (Gr. *histos,* tissue) The study of structure as revealed by the microscope.

ichthyology (Gr. *ichthys,* fish) The study of fishes.

morphology (Gr. *morphe,* form) The study of organic form, with special reference to ideal types and their expression in animals.

ornithology (Gr. *ornis,* bird) The study of birds.

paleontology (Gr. *palaios,* ancient, + *onto,* existing) The study of past life as revealed by fossils.

parasitology (Gr. *para,* beside, + *sitos,* foods) The study of parasitic organisms.

physiology (Gr. *physis,* nature) The study of animal functions.

taxonomy (Gr. *taxis,* organization, + *nomos,* law) The study of the classification of animals.

zoogeography (Gr. *zoon,* animal, + *ge,* earth + *graphein,* to write) The study of the principles of animal distribution.

METHODS USED BY ZOOLOGISTS

Difficulties of biological investigation

Investigation in the biological sciences does not lend itself to the preciseness of the physical sciences, such as chemistry and physics. There are several reasons for this. One is the variation in biological material. Biological units do not always behave in the same way. Two healthy animals of the same age, size, and environment may react very differently to some experimental factor. The reactions cannot be predicted with the same success as that of the mathematical sciences.

From this standpoint the student can see some of the difficulties that confront the medical profession in the treatment of disease. A drug may be highly effective in one individual; in another it may react in an entirely different manner. When one considers the wide variations in age, weight, and diseases of those the doctor treats, the impossibility of getting uniform results is even more apparent.

Many medical men, therefore, despair of making medicine a science in the true sense of the word. The factor of human variation, the impossibility of conducting medical procedures under controlled conditions, and the lack of absolute rules in experimental work—all of these explain why biological investigation has not yet solved some diseases such as cancer.

Development of experimental methods and techniques

Whenever a biological problem is discovered, observed, and described, the logical follow-up is controlled experimentation using a single variable factor. The past seventy-five years have seen great advancement in biological experimentation. There still remain several fields in biology where little has been done in an experimental way, for example, evolution and taxonomy. In others, such as genetics, embryology, and cellular physiology, much has been accomplished by biological workers all over the world.

When the experimental method gained a foothold, workers in biology were alert to new techniques whenever they saw them. Only a few months after the discovery of x-rays in 1895, these wonderful rays were used to photograph the living skeleton. A short time later Cannon of Harvard used these rays to study the movements of the alimentary canal, and soon they were employed in treating cancer. The use of tagged atoms has become important in biochemistry. Much importance is being given to mathematics as a tool. Whether the life process can be expressed as a mathematical formula may be doubted, but many phases of it can be so expressed. One of the earliest techniques derived from the physical sciences was the practical application of optics to the compound microscope.

As biological research becomes more specialized, equipment becomes more complicated and expensive, a problem in many laboratories. It has been said that the test of a really clever research worker is the ability to perform outstanding research with simple apparatus. Most research workers admire research results obtained by simple methods. The more complicated the apparatus, the more chances there are for things to go wrong.

Factors responsible for scientific progress

The layman often takes scientific discoveries for granted, little realizing the careful planning and the many disappointments that go into the make-up of every important discovery. Moreover, specialization demands skills and thorough training along special lines. At the present time, biochemistry holds a prominent place, and those who expect to achieve in this field must be well drilled in the chemical sciences.

The development of the zoological sciences has gone hand in hand with improvements in techniques and tools. A single new technique may open up a whole world of research. A number of the major techniques that have profoundly influenced the progress of biological investigation are given in the following outline.

Microscope

The major objectives in the development of the microscope and its use have been magnification, resolution, and definition. The following represents the chief advances in the improvement of the microscope:

1. First compound microscope (Janssen, 1590; Galileo, 1610)
2. Microscope with condenser (1635)
3. Huygenian ocular (Huygens, 1660)
4. Substage mirror (Hertzel, 1712)
5. Achromatic lens (Dolland, 1757; Amici, 1812)
6. Polarizing microscope (Talbot, 1834)
7. Binocular miscroscope (single objective with double oculars) (Riddell, 1853)
8. Water immersion objective (Amici, 1840)
9. Oil immersion objective (Wenham, 1870)
10. Compensating oculars (1886)
11. Apochromatic objectives (1886)
12. Iris diaphragm (Bausch and Lomb, 1887)
13. Abbé condenser (Abbé, 1888)
14. Double objective binocular microscope (Greenough, 1892)
15. Ultramicroscope (darkfield) (Zsigmondy, 1900)
16. Electron microscope (Knoll and Ruska, 1931)
17. Phase contrast microscope (Zernicke, 1935)
18. Reflecting microscope (Burch, 1943)

Kymograph

This instrument, first introduced by Ludwig (1847), is for recording neuromuscular and other mechanical changes.

Microtome

This is an instrument for cutting thin sections of tissues. There are two kinds:

1. Sliding microtome (His, 1866)
2. Automatic rotary (1880)

Reconstruction models

The method of constructing models of anatomical structures by wax duplications of serial sections was first developed by Born (1883), but many variant forms have been developed since, such as plastic injections and corrosion techniques.

Intra-vitam staining

Ehrlich (1885) used certain dyes, such as methylene blue, to stain living nervous and other tissues.

Freezing-drying fixation

This method was first introduced by Altmann (1890) but was greatly improved by Gersh (1932). It reduces the physical and chemical alteration in tissue characteristics. The tissue is first frozen in liquid air and then dried under high vacuum.

Radiography (x-rays)

First discovered by Roentgen (1895), x-ray photography in all its forms makes possible valuable studies of otherwise hidden structures.

Silver impregnation

The employment of silver salts and their subsequent reduction by photographic developers was developed by Cajal (1903) in the demonstration of nervous tissue.

Tissue culture

The cultivation of tissue cells outside the body, first perfected by Harrison (1907), enables studies to be made which would be impossible otherwise.

Micromanipulation

The employment of fine needles and pipettes on minute structures such as cells, nerves, and blood vessels under the microscope by mechanical manipulation was developed by Barber (1914) and Chambers (1922).

Cathode ray oscillograph

This instrument, developed by Gasser and Erlanger (1920), records small variations in electrical potential induced by nerve or other activity. The results of such activity can be shown on a fluorescent screen or photographed.

Radioactive tracers

Radioactive tracers were first applied to biological studies by de Hevesy (1923). This technique makes possible the detection of radioactive isotopes in various tissues so their fate in body metabolism can be determined.

Transparent ear chamber

This makes possible the study of tissues and organs within the living intact body and was developed by Sandison (1924) and Clark (1930).

Micro-incineration

This is a method of incinerating tissues so that only the mineral framework of tissues is preserved. It was developed by Policard (1927) and Scott (1935).

Quartz-rod illumination

This technique, introduced by Knisely (1936), allows an object to be illuminated at a considerable distance from the source of light.

HOW ANIMALS ARE CLASSIFIED (TAXONOMY)

Hundreds of thousands of different species have been described to date and the number is constantly increasing. The necessity of arranging this array of forms into some sort of order is obvious. Classification, or taxonomy, is the science of the orderly arrangement of animals according to some scheme of likenesses and differences among the various groups. At first, cataloguing animals was for convenience, so that their names could be easily found, very much as one would classify an odd assortment of letters. Animals were classified in various ways, such as those that were harmful or useful, those that lived on land or in the water, or those that dwelt in trees or on the surface of the land, etc. How they were classified depended upon what qualities the classifier had in mind. However, as knowledge of animal life increased, classification took on other fundamental purposes. It was found, for instance, that in spite of the great diversity there were patterns of similarity among the groups of animals. Animals were classified according to nice discriminations of structure, so that anatomical similarities and dissimilarities were carefully noted. With the establishment of the theory of evolution, anatomical distinctions alone were not considered sufficent. Taxonomy gradually became concerned with the relationship or kinship of animals to each other, so that the degree of homologous resemblances between animals determined the groups in which they were placed. The evolutionary concept has really afforded the cue for the modern arrangement of animals into groups. Modern taxonomy, therefore, expresses not merely a convenient cataloguing of animals but also the degree of kinship among them. By emphasizing the ancestral relationship of organisms taxonomy loses its artificial nature and has been given greater recognition in modern biology.

Importance of taxonomy

Taxonomy aims to apply a name tag to every species of animal in the animal kingdom. Since each species has a universal scientific name, students of all languages know what animal is meant when the scientific name is designated. Common names vary with the different languages or even in different parts of one country, but the scientific ones are universal. The woodpecker, *Colaptes auratus luteus,* for instance, is called the golden-winged woodpecker, the flicker, the high-hole, etc., depending upon the part of the United States in which it is found. But it has only one valid scientific name wherever it is found.

Early history of taxonomy

Although Aristotle, the great Greek philosopher and student of zoology, attempted to classify animals on the basis of their structural similarities, little was done about the grouping of animals until the English naturalist, John Ray (1627-1705), brought forth his system of classification. He employed structural likenesses as the basis of his classification and worked out a number of groups. He seems to have been the first biologist to have a modern concept of species and paved the way for the work of Carolus Linnaeus (1707-1778), who gave us the modern scheme of classification. Linnaeus was a Swedish botanist connected with the University of Uppsala. He had a great talent for collecting and classifying objects, especially flowers. Through the collaboration of workers in all parts of the world, Linnaeus worked out a fairly extensive system of classification for both plants and animals. His scheme of classification was published in his great classical work, *Systema Naturae,* which had gone through ten editions by 1758. Linnaeus emphasized structural features of plants and animals in his methods of classification. His classification at first was largely arbitrary and artificial, and he believed strongly in the fixity of species. He divided the animal kingdom down to species, and according to his scheme each species was given a distinctive name. He recognized four **classes** of vertebrates and two classes of invertebrates. These classes were divided by him into **orders**, the orders into **genera**, and the latter into **species**. Since his knowledge of animals was limited, his lower groups, such as the genera, were very inclusive and included animals now placed in several orders or families. As a result of this, much of his classification has been drastically altered, yet the basic principle of his scheme is followed at the present time.

Although Linnaeus recognized four units in classification—class, order, genus, and species—since his time other major units of grouping have been added, such as the **phylum** and the **family**. Additional categories are often used when the major units can be subdivided into finer distinctions, such as **subphylum, subclass, suborder, subfamily, subgenus,** and **subspecies.**

Binomial nomenclature and the naming of animals

Linnaeus early adopted the use of two names for each species, the genus name and the species name. These words are from Latin or in Latinized form, because Latin was the language of scholars and is universally understood. The generic name is usually a noun and the specific name an adjective. For instance, the scientific name of the common robin is *Turdus migratorius* (L. *turdus*, thrush; *migratorius*, of the migratory habit). This usage of two names to designate a species is called **binomial nomenclature.** But there are times when a species is divided into subspecies, in which case a **trinomial nomenclature** is employed. Thus to distinguish the southern form of the robin from the eastern robin, the scientific term *Turdus migratorius achrustera* (duller color) is employed for the southern type. Taxonomic ranks lower than subspecies are sometimes employed where four words are used in the scientific name, the last one usually standing for **variety.** In this latter case the nomenclature is **quadrinomial.** The trinomial and quadrinomial nomenclatures are really additions to the Linnaean system which is basically binomial.

Basis for formation of taxonomic units

Taxonomy, as already mentioned, is not merely a convenient method for cataloguing animals. It is based upon the resemblances and differences between different animals and emphasizes the natural relationships among the various animal types. Taxonomy is thus tied in with the evolutionary concept.* Resemblances between animals may be due mainly to homology (similarity of origin) or to convergence (independent adaptation). The idea is that descent from a common ancestor makes for similarity in character, and the more recent this descent the closer the animals are grouped in taxonomic units. For instance, the genera of a particular family show less diversity than do the families of an order. Families must take more time to become diverse and thus their common ancestor must have been more remote than that of the genera. The same principle applies to the higher categories and therefore we should expect the common ancestors of the various phyla to be much older than those of classes. This principle, however, cannot be applied too

---

*Refer to Chapter 5, Principle 18.

26

rigidly to all groups of animals, for some have been much faster in their evolution than others. As we shall see later, some mollusks have taxonomic categories which have changed little in the course of millions of years. Some of their genera are actually much older than orders and classes in other groups. The rate of evolution has not always been the same for all groups.

Why classification varies among different authorities

Taxonomic categories are the outcome of changing concepts of classification and therefore are subject to man's diverse judgments. One might expect differences of opinion among taxonomists. (1) It is very difficult to appraise all the fine distinctions among animals. The fact that two animals have similar characteristics does not establish their relationship. The similar characteristics may have developed entirely independently of each other, by convergent evolution, with no common ancestry involved. Taxonomists do not always agree about these lines of descent. (2) Many thousands of new species are named each year. Not all of these are well defined and more will have to be found out about them before they are firmly established in animal classification. For this reason much of the work of the taxonomist consists of revising what has already been described rather than describing new species. (3) There is some diversity of opinion among zoologists about subdivision of groups. Some are "splitters," inclined to much subdivision; others are "lumpers," preferring to lump together minor groups. (4) The **law of priority** also brings about frequent changes. The first name proposed for a taxonomic unit which is published and meets other proper specifications has priority over all subsequent names proposed. These rejected duplicate names are called **synonyms.** It is amazing sometimes to find that species which have been well established for years must undergo a change in terminology when some industrious systematist discovers that on the basis of priority, or for some other reason, the species are misnamed.

What is a species?

The **species** is the basic unit used in taxonomic studies and applies to a particular kind of animal or plant that possesses definite morphological and physiological characteristics. The term species is difficult to define. A certain amount of variation among the individuals of a species must be allowed, but in general there are certain common characters shared by all members of a particular species. Such characteristics are those that are inherited with regularity, and variations that are caused by environmental differences are largely ignored in the make-up of a true species. Among the characteristics a true species possesses are (1) the presence of definite structures differing from those of other groups, (2) the presence of more or less definite geographical ranges, and (3) a marked tendency not to interbreed with other species. There are many exceptions, for interbreeding does occur, although it is not common under natural conditions.

Genetically, if the genes of all the individuals of a species were alike, we should expect a uniformity of characters, except those due to environmental or other causes, throughout the taxonomic group. But the various individuals that make up a species are often heterozygous and may produce types different from the parents. Even though the individuals of a species had the same genes to start with, in the course of evolution mutations of genes now and then would account for the appearance of new variations which in time could lead to new varieties and even new species. Formerly, taxonomists stressed the type concept, which means that a species description is based upon a single standard specimen called the type. All members of that species are supposed to conform to that type. This concept is gradually being replaced by the population concept which involves the study of many specimens throughout the range of a species. No one specimen can be considered as typical.

Rules of scientific nomenclature

To prevent confusion in the field of taxonomy and to lay down a uniform code of rules for the classification of animals, there was established in 1898 an International Commission on Zoological Nomenclature. This Commission meets from time to time to formulate rules and to make decisions in connection with taxonomic work. It is the duty of the commission to decide which taxonomic categories are to be recognized as valid.

The Basic Rules of Nomenclature laid down by the International Commission on Zoological Nomenclature are as follows:

1. The system of nomenclature adopted is the binomial system as described by Linnaeus in the tenth edition of his *Systema Naturae* (1758). This system is modified in some cases to include a trinomial nomenclature when a subspecific name is used.

2. Zoological nomenclature is independent of botanical nomenclature and may employ the same names for taxonomic units, but this procedure is not recommended.

3. The scientific names of animals must be either Latin or Latinized in form.

4. The genus name is a single word, nominative singular, and begins with a capital letter.

5. The species name may be a single or compound word, is printed with an initial lower case letter, and is usually an adjective in grammatical agreement with the generic name. In case the species name is derived from a personal name, it may be written with a capital initial letter. When a subspecies name is used it also has an initial small letter.

6. The author of a scientific name is the one who first definitely published the name in connection with a description of the animal. The author's name should follow the species name and should rarely be abbreviated.

7. The law of priority states that the first published name in connection with a genus, species, or subspecies is the one recognized. All duplicate names are called synonyms.

8. When the genus name is not the one under which a species is placed by the original author, or if the generic name is changed, the original author's name is placed in parentheses. For instance, the name *Rana gryllus* was given by Le Conte to the common cricket frog, but it is now *Acris gryllus* (Le Conte) since the generic name has been changed.

9. A type specimen is the particular specimen or specimens on which the name of the species was established. It is customary for taxonomists to place such types in public museums or other places where they can be available to those who are interested. Such types must retain their original name even if the species is later divided. Whenever a new genus is described, one species is taken as the type of the genus and also retains the original name in case the genus is later divided into two or more genera. No two genera of animals may have the same name.

10. The name of a family is formed by adding *idae* to the stem of the name of the type genus; the name of a subfamily, by adding *inae*.

Some examples of scientific nomenclature

The examples listed in Table 1 will give you some idea of how animals are classified on the basis of relationship and likeness. Of all animals the anthropoid apes are generally agreed to be nearest man in relationship and structural features. In contrast to man and the gorilla are the frog, also a vertebrate like the others but diverging from them much earlier, and the little katydid, which is not a chordate but belongs to a lower phylum.

Major groups of animals (phyla)

The number of different categories or taxonomic units naturally varies and is never stable. Revisions are constantly being made and shifts are made from one category to another. A recent survey of the higher taxonomic units reveals that there are about 30 phyla, 68 classes, and 350 orders. The following list represents the chief phyla of the animal kingdom:

Protozoa

The single-celled animals. Acellular or cellular; of single cells or in colonies; mostly microscopic. 15,000 to 30,000 species.

Mesozoa

Cellular endoparasites of simple metazoan (many-celled) structure; no organs or tissues. 45 species.

Porifera

The sponges. Body usually irregular in shape and provided with numerous pores and canals; radially symmetrical or asymmetrical. 5,000 species.

Cnidaria or Coelenterata

The jellyfish, sea anemones, and corals. Saclike gastrovascular cavity; nematocysts; two or three layers of cells; radially symmetrical. 10,000 species.

Table 1 Examples of classification of animals

	Man	*Gorilla*	*Grass frog*	*Katydid*
Phylum	Chordata	Chordata	Chordata	Arthropoda
Subphylum	Vertebrata	Vertebrata	Vertebrata	
Class	Mammalia	Mammalia	Amphibia	Insecta
Subclass	Eutheria	Eutheria		
Order	Primates	Primates	Salientia	Orthoptera
Suborder	Anthropoidea	Anthropoidea		
Family	Hominidae	Simiidae	Ranidae	Tettigoniidae
Subfamily			Raninae	
Genus	Homo	Gorilla	Rana	Scudderia
Species	sapiens	gorilla	pipiens	furcata
Subspecies			pipiens	Brunner

Ctenophora

The comb jellies. Ciliated comb plates; biradial symmetry; adhesive cells (colloblasts). 100 species.

Platyhelminthes

The flatworms, including flukes and tapeworms. Elongated flat bodies; bilateral symmetry; digestive tract branched or absent. 6,000 species.

Rhynchocoela

The ribbon worms. Body wormlike and flattened or cylindrical; eversible proboscis; bilateral symmetry. 550 species.

Acanthocephala

The spiny-headed worms. Body wormlike, cylindrical, and hollow; no gastric cavity; bilateral symmetry. 300 species.

Aschelminthes

The roundworms. Body mostly wormlike; tough cuticle; pseudocoel; bilateral symmetry. 12,000 species.

Entoprocta

Body of calyx and slender stalk; sessile; solitary or colonial; pseudocoel; anus inside circlet of tentacles; bilateral symmetry. 60 species.

Ectoprocta (bryozoa)

The moss animals. Sessile mosslike colonies; each zooid enclosed in exoskeletal case; anus outside of circlet of tentacles; bilateral symmetry. 4,000 species.

Brachiopoda

The lamp shells. Body enclosed in dorsal and ventral shells; sessile; lophophore; bilateral symmetry. 120 species.

Annelida

The segmented worms. Body wormlike and segmented; setae; coelom; bilateral symmetry. 6,500 species.

Arthropoda

The crustaceans, insects, spiders, and others. Body segmented; somites often specialized; jointed appendages; bilateral symmetry. 750,000 species.

Mollusca

The clams, oysters, snails, and squids. Body soft and mainly unsegmented; limy shell present or absent; bilateral symmetry. 70,000 species.

Echinodermata

The sea stars, sea urchins, sea cucumbers, and sea lilies. Body unsegmented and usually in parts of 5's; endoskeleton of plates; secondary radial symmetry; water vascular system. 5,000 species.

Chaetognatha

The arrow worms. Body arrow-shaped; postanal tail; lateral fins; bilateral symmtery. 30 species.

Pogonophora

The beard worms. Body wormlike, encased in tube; body divided into protosome, mesosome, and metasome; usually many tentacles; no digestive tract; bilateral symmetry. 22 species.

Hemichordata

The tongue worms. Body wormlike and divided into proboscis, collar, and trunk; bilateral symmetry. 100 species.

Chordata

The lampreys, fishes, amphibians, reptiles, birds, and mammals. Body segmented with axial notochord; dorsal tubular nervous system; paired gill slits; bilateral symmetry. 60,000 species.

Phylogeny of animals*

Phylogeny is the science of ancestral history and racial relationships. Evolutionary evidence indicates that the many diverse animals discussed in the previous pages have evolved to their present form and behavior as the result of gradual change over an immense period of geological time. As you study the various groups of animals throughout this text you will note that the interpretation of animal relationships is based upon many factors, such as the resemblance of like structures or body plans, similarity of development and biochemistry, comparison of homologous parts, pooled hereditary constitutions of populations, behavior patterns, and many others.

Exact relationships of the members of the animal kingdom are often vague or nonexistent according to our present knowledge. This is especially the case with the large major groups (phyla) where there is much disagreement among authorities. Within smaller taxonomic

---

*Refer to Chapter 5, Principles 18 and 19.

units (species, genera, orders, etc.) relationships have been more definitely established. The student should therefore remember that the sequence zoologists present does not indicate that each group has arisen directly from the one which has preceded it. Most existing forms are related indirectly to each other through common ancestors which are now extinct. Most common ancestors were sufficiently generalized in structure to give rise to many divergent groups, but such ancestors have either undergone evolution or else become extinct because of their inability to adapt to a changing environment. The closing of the gaps in relationships is very much like supplying the missing parts of a jigsaw puzzle. If many parts are gone, the problem becomes complicated. However, if similarity of structure and development means anything in an evolutionary interpretation,

then it is obvious that certain groups are closely connected because the evidence stands out clearly. It is a generalization widely accepted in biology that if two different organisms share many common traits it is logical to assume that there is a relationship basis for this similarity and that it has not been due to convergent or coincidental evolution.

With all the shortcomings any phylogenetic tree (Figure 1) must possess, such a scheme of hypothetical relations has some value in visualizing the evolutionary picture, provided it is not stressed too dogmatically. Many lines of evidence will be pointed out in the discussions of the various invertebrate phyla. The phylogenetic tree here presented on the basis of these evidences may serve to tie the phyla together in the evolutionary blueprint.

No one can appreciate the evolutionary

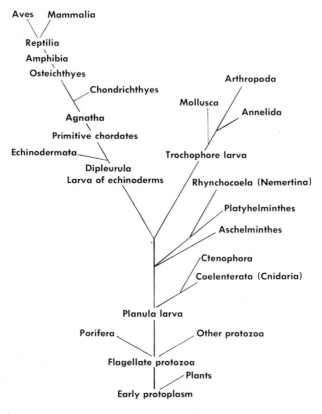

Figure 1. Hypothetical diagram of possible relationships of principal animal groups.

Table 2 Geological time scale

Era	Period	Epoch	Time at beginning of each period (millions of years)	Geological events and climate	Biological characteristics
Cenozoic (Age of Mammals)	Quaternary	Recent	0.025	End of fourth ice age; climate warmer	Dominance of modern man; modern species of animals and plants
	Quaternary	Pleistocene	0.6 to 1.0	Four ice ages with valley and sheet glaciers covering much of North America and Eurasia; continents in high relief; cold and mild climates	Modern species; extinction of giant mammals and many plants; development of man
	Tertiary	Pliocene	12	Continental elevation; volcanic activity; dry and cool climate	Modern genera of mammals; emergence of man from man-apes; peak of mammals; invertebrates similar to modern kinds
	Tertiary	Miocene	25	Development of plains and grasslands; moderate climates; sierra mountains renewed	Modern subfamilies rise; development of grazing mammals, first man-apes; temperate kind of plants; saber-toothed cat
	Tertiary	Oligocene	34	Mountain building; mild climates	Primitive apes and monkeys; whales; rise of most mammal families; temperate kind of plants; archaic mammals extinct
	Tertiary	Eocene	55	Land connection between North America and Europe during part of epoch; mountain erosion; heavy rainfall	Modern orders of mammals; adaptive radiation of placental mammals; subtropical forests; first horses
	Tertiary	Paleocene	75	Mountain building; temperate to subtropical climates	Dominance of archaic mammals; modern birds; dinosaurs all extinct; placental mammals; subtropical plants; first tarsiers and lemurs
Mesozoic (Age of Reptiles)	Cretaceous		130	Spread of inland seas and swamps; mountains (Andes, Himalayas, Rocky, etc.) formed; mild to cool climate	Extinction of giant land and marine reptiles; pouched and placental mammals rise; flowering plants; gymnosperms decline
	Jurassic		180	Continents with shallow seas; Sierra Nevada Mountains	Giant dinosaurs; reptiles dominant; first mammals; first toothed birds
	Triassic		230	Continents elevated; widespread deserts; red beds	First dinosaurs; marine reptiles; mammal-like reptiles; conifers dominant

(Continued on next page.)

Introduction—science of zoology 31

Table 2 Geological time scale—cont'd

Era	Period	Epoch	Time at beginning of each period (millions of years)	Geological events and climate	Biological characteristics
Paleozoic	Permian		260	Rise of continents; widespread mountains; Appalachians formed; cold, dry, and moist climate; glaciation; red beds	Adaptive radiation of reptiles which displace amphibians; many marine invertebrates extinct; modern insects; evergreens appear
(Age of Amphibians)	Pennsylvanian		310	Shallow inland seas; glaciation in Southern Hemisphere; warm, moist climate, coal swamp-forests	Origin of reptiles; diversification in amphibians; gigantic insects
	Mississippian		350	Inland seas; mountain formation; warm climates; hot swamp lands	Amphibian radiation; insects with wings; sharks and bony fish; crinoids
(Age of Fishes)	Devonian		400	Small inland seas; mountain formation; arid land; heavy rainfall	First amphibians; mostly fresh-water fish; lungfish and sharks; forests and land plants; brachiopods; wingless insects; bryozoans and corals
	Silurian		425-430	Continental seas; relatively flat continents; mild climates; land rising; mountains in Europe	Eurypterids; fish with lower jaws; brachiopods; graptolites; invasion of land by arthropods and plants
	Ordovician		475	Oceans greatly enlarge; submergence of land; warm mild climates into highest latitudes	Ostracoderms (first vertebrates); brachiopods; cephalopods; trilobites abundant; land plants; graptolites
(Age of Invertebrates)	Cambrian		550	Lowlands; mild climates	Marine invertebrates and algae; all invertebrate phyla and many classes; abundant fossils; trilobites dominant
Proterozoic (Precambrian)			2000	Volcanic activity; very old sedimentary rocks; mountain building; glaciations; erosions; climate warm moist to dry cold	Fossil algae 2.6 billion years old; sponge spicules: worm burrows; soft-bodied animals; autotrophism established
Archeozoic (Precambrian)			4000-4500	Lava flows; granite formation; sedimentary deposition; erosion	Origin of life; heterotrophism established

blueprint without some acquaintance with paleontology or the historical record of fossils. For this and other reasons, a geological time scale (Table 2) is presented here for ready reference when mention is made of the racial history of the various groups. Details of this time scale will be discussed in Chapter 36, The Record of Fossils (Paleontology).

ANNOTATED REFERENCES

Arber, A. 1954. The Mind and the Eye. New York, Cambridge University Press. *This small work is a general analysis of the nature of biological research.*

Bates, M. 1960. The Forest and the Sea. New York, Random House. *Written in a popular style, this revealing book will give the inquisitive student much to think about in man's relations to the world around him. It is an excellent introduction to the study of ecology.*

Beck, W. S. 1957. Modern Science and the Nature of Life. New York, Harcourt, Brace & Co.

Blumenstock, D. I. 1959. The Ocean of Air. New Brunswick, Rutgers University Press. *The atmosphere as a biological environment is presented in this revealing book.*

Cain, A. J. 1954. Animal Species and Their Evolution. New York, Hutchinson's University Library. *This small book gives a comprehensive account of animal species and the present-day concept of classification. In this work the advanced student will get a good up-to-date view of the relation of speciation to the evolutionary process.*

Calder, R. 1954. Science in Our Lives. East Lansing, Michigan State College Press. *This is a fascinating account of scientific discoveries and the impact these discoveries have had on our lives. The author stresses the fact that the essentials of a great scientific discovery depend upon three factors—the method, the man, and the moment. Is not this last factor mainly responsible for independent discovery by more than one worker? All students should read this little book.*

Calman, W. T. 1949. The Classification of Animals, an Introduction to Zoological Taxonomy. London, Methuen & Co., Ltd. *An excellent and clearly written statement of taxonomic principles suitable for the beginning student in zoology.*

Cannon, W. B. 1945. The Way of an Investigator. New York, W. W. Norton & Co., Inc.

Conant, J. B. 1951. Science and Common Sense. New Haven, Yale University Press. *This masterly treatise deals with all science, but*

Chapters 8 and 9 are devoted to the living organisms. The nature of the control experiment and the methods biologists have employed are explained. The history of the investigations on spontaneous generation is used as an example. The beginning student in biology will derive great inspiration from this book.

Conant, J. B. 1957. Harvard Case Histories in Experimental Science. 2 volumes. Cambridge, Harvard University Press.

Gabriel, M. L., and S. Fogel (editors). 1955. Great Experiments in Biology. Englewood Cliffs, N. J., Prentice-Hall, Inc. *This work should be studied by every student of biology, for this anthology covers those biological experiments which have led to some of the most fundamental generalizations in the field of biology.*

Hall, T. S. 1951. A Source Book in Animal Biology. New York, McGraw-Hill Book Co., Inc. *An excellent biological anthology of great selections from the leading biologists of all times. Suitable for the beginning student.*

Jaeger, E. C. 1955. A Source-Book of Biological Names and Terms, ed. 3. Springfield, Ill., Charles C Thomas, Publisher. *This is a useful book for all students who are interested in the meaning and derivation of biological terms. It is perhaps the best in the field.*

Kinhead, E. 1955. Spider, Egg, and Microcosm. New York, Alfred A. Knopf, Inc. *This book is really the candid portraits of three outstanding Russian-born Americans — Petrunkevitch, Romanoff, and Vishniac. All three have made their mark in certain biological fields, the first with spiders, the second with the bird's egg, and the last with the photography of protozoans.*

Lachman, S. J. 1956. The Foundations of Science. Detroit, The Hamilton Press. *This is an outline of the main characteristics of science— what it is and what the perspective of the scientist is. There is a good account of the scientific method in this little monograph.*

Manville, R. H. 1952. The Principles of Taxonomy. Turtox News, vol. 30, No. 1 and No. 2. *A concise account of classification procedures.*

Mayr, E., E. G. Linsley, and R. C. Usinger. 1953. Methods and Principles of Systematic Zoology. New York, McGraw-Hill Book Co., Inc. *The present status of the rules and regulations of taxonomy is well discussed.*

Mayr, E. (editor). 1957. The Species Problem. Washington, American Association for the Advancement of Science. *This is a symposium by many authorities on the problems of species.*

Newman, J. R. (editor). 1955. What Is Science? New York, Simon & Schuster.

Pearse, A. S. (editor). 1948. Zoological Names: A List of Phyla, Classes, and Orders, ed. 3. Durham, N. C., American Association for Advancement of Science, Section F. *Helpful for those who wish to keep up with the constantly changing classification.*

Schenk, E. T., and J. H. McMasters. 1948. Procedures in Taxonomy, Including a Reprint of the International Rules of Zoological Nomenclature With Summaries of Opinions Rendered, ed. 2. Stanford, Stanford University Press.

Simpson, G. G. 1945. The Principles of Classification and a Classification of Mammals. Bull. Am. Mus. Nat. Hist., vol. 85. *A well-presented account of the bases of taxonomic procedures.*

Simpson, G. G., C. S. Pittendrigh, and L. H. Tiffany. 1957. Life. An Introduction to Biology. New York, Harcourt, Brace & Co.

Suner, A. P. 1955. Classics of Biology. New York, Philosophical Library. *This is an anthology of the classical publications in biology and introduces the reader to the high points of biolog- account of the bases of taxonomic procedures.*

chapter 2

Energy relations and the nature of protoplasm

GENERAL PROPERTIES OF MATTER

Inasmuch as the basic substance of life, protoplasm, is composed of the same elements found in the inorganic or nonliving world and probably obeys the same laws of physics and chemistry, it is well to point out a few of these relations. While there are certain distinctions between the living and nonliving, the fundamental characteristics of each are matter and energy.

Matter is something that occupies space and has mass or weight. In addition, matter has certain other characteristic properties, such as elasticity, inertia, and impenetrability. Two quantities of matter cannot occupy the same space at the same time. Neither can matter be created or destroyed. According to the kinetic theory of matter, a material body is not continuous but is made up of molecules in constant motion. The three states or forms of matter (solid, liquid, gas) are determined by the relative distance of the molecules and their velocities. In a solid the molecules are relatively close together and their velocity is slow; in a liquid they are farther apart, with a faster rate, but are still held together within a definite volume; and in a gas they are still faster and farther apart and are more or less free to stray from each other unless restrained by a vessel. Matter is made up of **chemical elements** which ordinarily cannot be resolved into other substances of different chemical properties. They differ from one another in the structure of their atoms, upon which depend their chemical and physical properties. At the present time, 102 elements are known to chemists, but some of these have been made artificially with the cyclotron and the nuclear reactor and may not occur in nature. Common elements familiar to all are carbon, nitrogen, oxygen (the most abundant element), and hydrogen. Some elements are uncombined in nature, such as gold, iron, and copper, but most of them are found only in compounds.

A **compound** is made up of two or more elements united in a definite proportion. Familiar examples of compounds are water (H_2O) and carbon dioxide (CO_2). Both elements and compounds are made up of **molecules** which are the smallest particles of a substance maintaining the characteristic chemical properties of that substance. Every molecule is like every other molecule in that substance. They can be separated from each other, and in solutions, such as sugar in water, they can exist apart from each other.

Most molecules can be broken down into small units known as **atoms**. These are considered the smallest divisions of matter and are ordinarily indivisible. Some molecules have only one atom (helium, for example), and in such a case the molecule

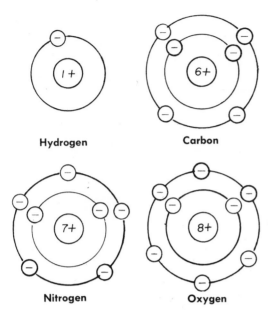

Hydrogen   Carbon

Nitrogen   Oxygen

Figure 2. Diagram of atomic structure of chief elements of body. Number in inner circle (nucleus) refers to protons and neutrons; orbits made up of electrons.

has the same meaning as the atom. A few molecules have only one kind of atom, such as oxygen (O_2), where each of the two atoms is the same. Most molecules, however, have more than one kind of atom. Glucose ($C_6H_{12}O_6$), for example, has three kinds. Still others, like the molecules of proteins, contain many different atoms.

Atoms themselves are made up of entities known as protons, neutrons, and electrons. These units are the same in all kinds of matter. Thus the protons, neutrons, and electrons in a molecule of carbon are like those in lead and so on. These three kinds of particles are organized around a central core, very much like the solar system around the sun. **Protons** have a positive electric charge and mass; **electrons** carry a negative charge with little mass; and **neutrons** have about the same mass as protons but carry no electric charges. Most of the atom is empty space with a center nucleus containing protons and neutrons. The sum of them make up the weight of the atom. The electrons

revolve around the nucleus in definite orbits. Different types of atoms have different numbers of electrons in their orbits and different numbers of protons and neutrons in their nuclei. In all atoms, however, the number of protons in the nucleus is the same as the number of electrons revolving around the nucleus, and since the nucleus is positively charged (protons) and the circling electrons are negative, the atom is in a state of electrical neutrality.

What accounts then for the different types of matter? The answer to this lies in the differences in the number and arrangement of the protons, neutrons, and electrons. An element is a substance whose atoms have the same number of associated electrons. Hydrogen (H), for instance, has only one proton in its nucleus and one electron in its orbit around the nucleus. On the other hand, the carbon (C) atom has 6 protons and 6 neutrons in its nucleus and 6 electrons in the surrounding shell (Figure 2). In similar manner every element has a different number of protons and electrons from every other element. On this basis the **periodic table** of the elements is formed according to the number of electrons and protons they contain. In this table the elements having like properties are placed in related position and their grouping is in accordance with the atomic number of each element.

The chemical properties of elements, or the way they react with other elements, depend mainly upon the number and arrangement of the electrons around the nucleus. Whenever the electrons are numerous, they are found in different orbits, some near and some farther away from the nucleus. The chemical reaction of an element is determined by the electrons in the outer orbit. This outermost orbit has from 0 to 8 electrons in the different atoms. Elements with the same number of electrons in this orbit have similar properties. If there are 0 or 8 electrons in this orbit, the element will not react chemically; if there are fewer than 8, the atom may gain or lose some electrons to make up an outer orbit of 8. Valence or the combining power of an atom depends mainly upon the number of electrons in this outer orbit. Carbon has only 4 such electrons which can be shared in a wide variety of ways, and this accounts for the many carbon compounds that can be formed. Whenever an atom gains or loses electrons, it becomes charged electrically, since the number of protons of the nucleus always remains the same. This component of an atom is called an **ion** and may be either negative (excess electrons) or positive (excess protons). In an aqueous solution, sodium chloride, for example, dissociates into the positive sodium ion (**cation**), which has a deficiency of one electron, and the negative chlorine ion (**anion**), with an excess of one electron. Thus by sharing or transferring electrons, atoms can combine to form compounds. In the case of sodium chloride, the sodium atom gives up one electron to the chlorine atom, so that the former is positively charged and the latter negatively charged. The two ions are held together by electrostatic attraction of unlike charges. A compound that will form ions in solutions is called an **electrolyte,** because the ions will conduct an electric current. Chemical unions also may be formed by mutually sharing electrons, such as the union of two oxygen atoms to form a molecule of O_2, each atom contributing two electrons to the outer orbit of the other. No part of this molecule is positively or negatively charged. Many organic compounds, such as the sugars, are of this nature and do not dissociate into ions in solutions; they are called **nonelectrolytes.**

SIGNIFICANCE OF TAGGED ATOMS IN BIOLOGY

Chemistry teaches us that most elements have two or more kinds of atoms according to the number of neutrons in their nuclei. These different kinds of atoms in an element are called **isotopes.** All the isotopes of an element have the same **chemical** properties, but they have certain **physical** differences. For example, the normal carbon atom has an atomic weight of 12 (C^{12}) but among its isotopes are C^{13} and C^{14}. All these atoms have the same chemical properties for they have the same number and the same arrangement of electrons outside the nucleus. Some isotopes are stable and do not disintegrate; others are unstable and tend to decay (radioactive), mainly because there is a disparity between the number of protons and neutrons in the nucleus. Radioactive atoms give off certain rays, such as alpha, beta, and gamma rays, which represent the emission of some part of the atom. Some radioactive substances disintegrate rapidly (radioactive iodine), others very slowly (radium). By means of the cyclotron and other devices, it is possible to make artificially many new isotopes. Those that are radiocative can be detected with the Geiger counter. By substituting or tagging a substance with a radioactive isotope and then feeding it to an animal, it is possible to trace it in the body tissues and fluids and determine its final fate. Thus radioactive iron can be traced in the body metabolism throughout its course—its absorption, its utilization, and its excretion. Thus many aspects of metabolism may be studied, so that the guesswork about what becomes of this or that substance has been eliminated and our knowledge about such matters has become more exact and definite.

MATTER AND THE LAWS OF ENERGY

Energy may be defined as the capacity to do work or produce a change in matter. The work performed is the product of the force and the distance. Lifting a pound weight one foot against gravity involves a certain amount of work; lifting it two feet requires twice as much work. Forms of energy include heat, light, electricity, and mechanical and chemical energy. There are also various forms of energy or work units, such as foot-pounds, calories, and photons, which are ways of expressing energy. In most cases, these forms can be converted from one form to another. Under certain conditions matter and energy are interconvertible as expressed in the famous Einstein equation: $E = mc^2$, where E is energy, m is mass,

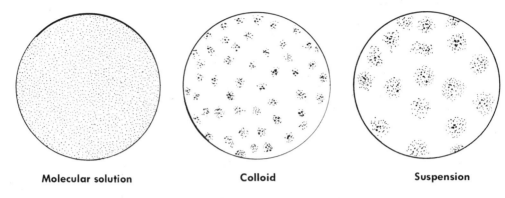

| Molecular solution | Colloid | Suspension |

Figure 3. Diagrams of three types of solutions or mixtures.

and *c* is the velocity of light (a constant). Thus it is possible by nuclear fission to get **atomic energy,** as shown by the development of the atomic bomb.

Mechanical energy, into which most of the others can be converted, exists in two categories: **potential,** or the capacity to do work because of the position of the body, and **kinetic,** which involves the energy of motion. Water at the top of a dam has potential energy; when it is actually falling over the dam this same water has kinetic energy. Light is kinetic energy for it is in motion. Two laws govern energy relations: **conservation of energy,** which states that energy can be changed in form but cannot be created or destroyed; and the law of **degradation of energy** (Second Law of Thermodynamics), which states that all the useful energy is slowly being converted into an unavailable form (entropy), or that all forms of energy are eventually transformed into heat, but that heat is never entirely converted into other forms. These laws of energy apply to both living as well as to nonliving systems. Living organisms make use of energy in all their bodily activities. To live is to make use of energy in some form. All biological systems are constantly changing potential energy into kinetic energy or the reverse.* In terms of electrons and protons, energy changes are produced whenever their arrangement is changed. One of the most common chemical reactions in

the body involves the union of oxygen with other substances. These reactions are called **oxidations,** and when they occur they release energy. By these means food is utilized in the body to produce energy for the living process. This energy may be in the form of either heat or movement.

MIXTURES AND THEIR PROPERTIES

Whenever masses of different kinds are thrown together, we have what is called a mixture. All the different states of matter, solids, liquids, gases, may be involved in these mixtures. The mixtures we are mainly interested in here are those in which water or other fluid is one of the states of matter. When something is mixed with a liquid, any one of three kinds of mixtures is formed.

Molecular solutions. If crystals of salts or sugar are added to water, the molecules or ions (in the case of salts) are uniformly dispersed through the water, forming a **true solution** (Figure 3). Such solutions are transparent. In such a case the water is the **solvent** and the dissolved salt or sugar the **solute.** Other solutions may be formed by adding acids and bases to water. Their freezing point is lower and their boiling point is higher than pure water.

Suspensions. If solids which are added to water remain in masses larger than molecules, the mixture is a suspension. Muddy water is a good example. When allowed to stand, the particles in suspension will settle out to the bottom. Suspensions

---

*Refer to Chapter 5, Principle 14.

38

have a turbid appearance and have the same boiling and freezing points as pure water.

Colloids. Whenever the dispersed particles are intermediate in size between the molecular state and the suspension, a third mixture is the result, the colloidal solution. Colloidal particles are rather arbitrarily considered to be between 1 and 100 millimicrons in size. If the particles are smaller, the solution is classified as a true solution; if larger, they are suspensions or emulsions. Colloids consist of two phases, an internal or discontinuous phase and an external or continuous phase. These phases may be represented by the same states of matter or different ones. Some familiar examples are as follows:

INTERNAL PHASE	EXTERNAL PHASE	EXAMPLE
Solid	Liquid	Ink
Liquid	Liquid	Emulsion
Liquid	Solid	Gel
Solid	Solid	Stained glass
Gas	Liquid	Foam, carbonated water
Liquid	Gas	Fog
Solid	Gas	Smoke

A true colloidal solution is stable (that is, will not settle out), has about the same boiling point and freezing point as pure water, and is either transparent or somewhat cloudy.

Proteins, which are important constituents of protoplasm, form colloidal solutions because their large molecules are well within the size range of colloidal particles and behave like colloids. Since protein molecules also dissolve as molecules in solution, such solutions may also be called molecular.

One special form of colloidal solution is the **emulsion** in which both phases are immiscible liquids (Figure 4). Cream is a good example. Here, droplets of oil or fat are dispersed in water. This type of colloidal solution has considerable significance in the make-up of protoplasm.

Colloidal emulsions also well illustrate the property of some colloids (but not all) to reverse their phases. When gelatin is poured into hot water, the gelatin particles (internal phase) are dispersed through the water (external phase) in a thin consistency which is freely shakable (Figure 5). Such a condition is called a **sol.** When the solution cools, gelatin now becomes the external or continuous phase and the water is in the discontinuous phase. Moreover, the solution has stiffened and become semisolid and is called a **gel.** Heating the solution will cause it to become a sol again, and the phases are reversed. Some colloidal emulsions are not reversible. Heating egg white, for example, will change the egg albumin from a sol into an irreversible gel. In such cases the coagulated particles may collect into larger particles and settle out.

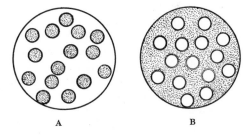

Figure 4. Diagram of colloidal solution in which each phase is a liquid. **A,** Oil-in-water emulsion, water being the continuous or external phase, oil the discontinuous or internal phase. **B,** Water-in-oil emulsion, water being the discontinuous or internal phase, oil the continuous or external phase. Certain agents can bring about this phase reversal.

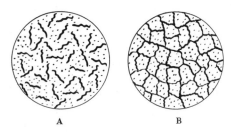

Figure 5. Diagram of a sol and a gel. **A,** Sol condition in which gelatin particles are the internal phase, water the external phase. **B,** Gel condition in which gelatin particles form external phase (network), enclosing water as internal phase.

Within a given colloidal system, the particles usually bear the same electric charge and thus repel each other. This, together with a phenomenon known as **Brownian movement** (the movement induced by the bombardment of the particles by water molecules), is mainly responsible for keeping colloidal solutions stable.

Behavior of colloidal solutions as contrasted with molecular solutions. In solid forms, substances such as salts and sugars are indefinite shapes known as crystals; hence they are called **crystalloids**. In solution, as we have seen, they form molecular solutions. There are two classes of crystalloids: **nonelectrolytes**, which do not ionize or carry electric charges (sugars and starches are examples), and **electrolytes**, which do ionize and carry positive or negative charges. Salts, acids, and bases are example of this class. As a group, crystalloids diffuse easily through membranes, have low freezing points, and have relatively high osmotic pressures.

In contrast to these properties of the crystalloids, colloids do not go through membranes readily, do not crystallize readily, have little effect on freezing point, and have relatively low osmotic pressures. Many of the properties of colloids depend upon the surface area between the dissolved particles and the surrounding medium.

Why do colloids play such an important role in the structure of protoplasm? There are several reasons, among which may be mentioned the following:

1. Great surface exposure which allows for many chemical reactions

2. The property of phase reversal which helps explain how protoplasm can carry on diverse functions and change its appearance during metabolic activities

3. The property of undergoing gelation or solation which enables the protoplasm to contract, thus explaining movements such as ameboid movement

4. The inability of colloids to pass through membranes which promotes the stability and organization of the cellular system, such as cell and nuclear membranes and cytoplasmic inclusions

5. The selective absorption or permeability of the cell membrane which is largely dependent upon the phase reversal of its colloidal structure

HYDROGEN ION CONCENTRATION (pH)

Solutions are classified as acid, base, or neutral according to the proportion of hydrogen (H^+) and hydroxyl (OH^-) ions they possess. In acid solutions there is an excess of hydrogen ions; in alkaline or basic solutions the hydroxyl ion is more common; whereas in neutral solutions, both hydrogen and hydroxyl ions are present in equal numbers.

To express the acidity or alkalinity (or pH concentration) of a substance, a logarithmic scale, a sort of mathematical shorthand, is employed. In this scale the numbers 1 to 7 indicate an acid range; from 7 to 14, an alkaline range. The number 7 indicates neutrality; that is, the presence of equal numbers of H^+ and OH^- ions. The smaller the number within the acid range, the greater the acidity; the larger the number on the alkaline range, the greater the alkalinity. According to this logarithmic scale, a pH of 3 is ten times as acid as one of 4; a pH of 9 is ten times as alkaline as one of 8.

In protoplasmic systems pH plays an important role, for, in general, slight deviations from the normal usually result in severe damage. Most substances and fluids in the body hover closely around the point of neutrality; that is, a pH of around 7. Blood, for instance, has a pH of 7.35, or just slightly on the alkaline side. Lymph is slightly more akaline than blood. Saliva has a pH of 6.8, on the acid side. A twenty-four-hour sample of urine gives an acid reaction of pH 6. Gastric juice is the most acid substance in the body, about pH 1.6. The regulation of the pH of the body tissue fluids involves many important physiological mechanisms, one of the most important of which is the buffer action of certain salts.

PROTOPLASM AS MATERIAL BASIS OF LIFE

Definition and historical background

The term **protoplasm** (*Gr. protos,* first, + *plasma,* anything formed) was first coined in 1840 by Purkinje, who used the word to designate the living substance in the embryo of animals. Earlier (1835) the French zoologist Dujardin had recognized its significance and called it "sarcode." Later, von Mohl applied this term to embryonic cells of plants. Gradually, protoplasm came to mean all living matter out of which plants and animals are formed. Huxley, in 1868, referred to protoplasm as the "physical basis of life," and we often see this phrase in descriptions of protoplasm. It was first thought that protoplasm was a definite chemical substance; but investigation has shown that it is not a single chemical substance but is made up of different compounds and that it differs in every species of plant and animal life and probably in every different kind of cell. Owing to the uniformity of the life process within all animals and plants, we speak of the properties of protoplasm as though it were one single kind of substance.

Physical characteristics*

The easiest place to study protoplasm is in the ameba, where its physical properties can be seen without great difficulty. The white of an egg also shows some of its physical properties. In the living condition protoplasm appears viscid, slimy, colorless, and more or less transparent. In general its viscosity is greater than water, in some cases being several times that of water. Protoplasm cannot be referred to as either liquid or solid, nor can it be called amorphous or crystalline. It is really an aggregation of crystalloids and colloids held in suspension in an aqueous solution. Some of its substances are dissolved in water and some are not. It often shows a granular, fibrillar, or even an emulsoid-like appearance. The denser

---

*Refer to Chapter 5, Principle 1.

portion of fixed protoplasm is sometimes referred to as **spongioplasm** and the more liquid part as **hyaloplasm,** although this difference may be due to artefactual fixation.

Because protoplasm may assume different forms under different conditions, several theories regarding its nature have been proposed. According to these theories protoplasm was variously described as (1) reticular or spongelike, (2) granular, with the granules embedded in fluid, (3) alveolar or foamlike, similar to an emulsion, and (4) fibrillar, with fibrils intertwining in the fluid.

These theories are mainly of historical interest now, for protoplasm in many instances can change from one condition to the other. Acid fixatives may cause protoplasm to show granules and fibrils, whereas neutral fixatives tend to produce a homogenous appearance. Also, a certain type may predominate in one kind of cell and another in a different kind of cell.

Protoplasm is nearly always organized into small units known as **cells.** Slime molds (botanical phylum Myxomycetes) may be an exception, for they form a relatively undifferentiated mass of granular protoplasm commonly called a plasmodium. Such an indefinite mass contains so many nuclei and may cover so much surface that it must be regarded as a kind of primordial ooze. The protoplasmic unit of a cell, however, usually shows an organization into a surface film (**plasma membrane**), a centrally located **nucleus** with specific nuclear structures (chromatin, nucleoplasm), and the **cytoplasm,** which includes the remainder of the unit. In some cells, such as some eggs and unicellular organisms that occur singly, the protoplasm zone just inside the plasma membrane may be specialized as a gel-like **ectoplasm.** In contrast to the more fluid internal endoplasm, this ectoplasm appears as a clear, nongranular region with many fine fibers, as revealed with the electron microscope. In body cells, however, which are found close together, the ectoplasm cannot be distinguished, and the entire cytoplasm consists of the fluid and granular **endoplasm.** Under certain conditions the endoplasm is seen to consist of a network of delicate fibers, forming the **endoplasmic reticulum.** With refined technique these fibers appear as a system of channels or canals. The fibers may appear or disappear at times, depending upon the reversible sol-gel behavior of protoplasm. Also, the endoplasm contains living components (organelles) and nonliving ones (cytoplasmic inclusions).

Chemical properties

Organic and inorganic substances. Organic and inorganic substances are both found in protoplasm. What is the distinction between the two? In a chemical sense the term **organic** refers to compounds that contain carbon. At one time it was thought that organic compounds could be produced only by living matter; but in 1828, Wöhler, a German chemist, produced urea (a waste in urine) synthetically from an inorganic substance, ammonium cyanate. Since that time many organic substances have been produced synthetically in the laboratory. With the exception of these artificially produced products, organic compounds are confined to the living body or its products. In contrast, **inorganic** substances are found in both the body and the nonliving world. While we often stress the importance of the organic components of the living body, the inorganic parts are even more numerous here than the organic parts.

Importance of water. Water makes up more than 60% of protoplasm. It varies in different tissues of the same animal and also in the same tissues of different animals. The enamel of teeth has about 2% water; muscle and nerve tissue, about 80%. In the jellyfish, protoplasm contains 95% water. Why is water important in protoplasm?

SOLVENT POWER. No other fluid is as important in this respect. Not only is water an effective solvent for inorganic matter but many organic materials are also dissolved in it. It serves as the dispersing phase of the colloidal system so characteristic of protoplasm. Moreover, dissolved substances react more rapidly than dry mixtures, and this property of water makes for richness in the variety of chemical reactions.

CAPACITY FOR HEAT. Water absorbs heat without markedly altering its own temperature. It thus protects protoplasm against sudden changes in temperature, for when environmental temperatures undergo sudden shifts up or down, the large water content of protoplasm prevents corresponding shifts in its own temperature.

Whenever a quart of perspiration is vaporized, nearly one-half of a kilocalorie of heat is lost from the body. This is important in keeping body temperatures within limits when environmental temperatures are excessive.

Water also has a fairly high heat conductivity, which promotes an equable distribution of heat over the body.

WATER AND ION FORMATION. Molecules in solution may form ions carrying electric charges. Water itself has the power to dissociate into H^+ and OH^- ions to a small extent. Although these ions may be relatively few in number, they are very active and engage in many metabolic processes.

DENSITY. Water's greatest density is at $4°C.$, so that ice floats upon it and allows life to continue in the deeper water.

Relation of protoplasm to sea water

Many inorganic salts are found in protoplasm. All of these are dissociated into ions, some of which are positively charged and some negatively charged. Sodium, potassium, calcium, and magnesium salts are the more common ones found. Most of the salts in protoplasm and their relative concentration show a remarkable similarity to sea water. One exception is magnesium which is common in sea water but rare in blood serum. It is suggested that protoplasm originated in sea water and incorporated within itself the salts thereof. Although the concentration of salts in many land forms, such as mammals, is less than 1% and sea water is much higher, when land forms left the sea in the Cambrian period the concentration of salt in the sea was about the same as that of body fluids now. Since that early geological period, the salt content of the sea has increased.

Mineral salts are important in maintaining the osmotic pressure and the fluid balance, in ionic regulation of heartbeat, and in structural patterns, such as bone.

Organic parts

The characteristic structure of protoplasm is made up of the three organic compounds, **carbohydrates, proteins,** and **fats.** The carbon element is present in all organic compounds, and the unique qualities of this element account for many of the properties of these compounds. Carbon can form a greater variety of compounds than any other element, because it can gain or lose four electrons in its outer orbit. It can combine with either electric-positive atoms or electric-negative atoms, and it also has a great capacity to unite with other carbon atoms to form long chains and ringlike molecules. The carbon compounds in protoplasm are continually reacting with one another and changing their form, but the three—carbohydrates, proteins, and fats—are the most abundant.

Carbohydrates. Carbohydrates are compounds made up of carbon, hydrogen, and oxygen, usually present in the ratio of $1 C : 2 H : 1 O$. This ratio between hydrogen and oxygen gives carbohydrates their name (hydrates of carbon) because this ratio is the same as that of water. Some carbohydrates, however, are exceptions to the rule. Familiar examples of carbohydrates are sugars, starches, and cellulose. They comprise about 1% of protoplasm. Carbohydrates are made synthetically from water and the carbon dioxide of the air by green plants and leaves with the aid of the sun's energy. This process is called **photosynthesis** and has never been duplicated by man. It is a reaction on which all life depends, for it is the starting point in the formation of food. Some bacteria, such as *Nitrosomonas,* have the power to synthesize complex organic substances from carbon dioxide and water (chemosynthesis) with the energy supplied by the oxidation of ammonium and other compounds.

Carbohydrates are usually divided into three classes: (1) **monosaccharides** or simple sugars, (2) **disaccharides** or double sugars, and (3) **polysaccharides** or complex sugars. Simple sugars, such as glucose, galactose, and fructose, have the formula $C_6H_{12}O_6$ (hexoses). The atoms in these molecules differ in arrangement which confers on them different chemical properties. Another simple sugar is the rare pentose ($C_5H_{10}O_5$) which has only five carbon atoms. A disaccharide is formed from two molecules of simple sugar by the loss of a molecule of water in this way:

$$C_6H_{12}O_6 + C_6H_{12}O_6 \longrightarrow H_2O + C_{12}H_{22}O_{11}$$
$$\text{(Glucose)} \quad \text{(Fructose)} \qquad \qquad \text{(Sucrose)}$$

Besides sucrose or cane sugar two other common disaccharides are maltose or malt sugar formed by the linkage of two molecules of glucose and lactose or milk sugar which is composed of one molecule of glucose and one of galactose.

Polysaccharides are made up of many molecules of a simple sugar (usually glucose). It is not known exactly how many molecules are found in these complex sugars, and since they are made up of a multiple number of molecules of the same substance they are referred to by the chemist as polymers. The formula for them is usually written ($C_6H_{10}O_5$)^n where n stands for the unknown number of simple sugar molecules of which they are composed. Starch is very common in most plants and is an important food constituent. *Glycogen* or animal starch is found mainly in the liver and muscle cells. When needed, glycogen is converted into glucose and is delivered by the blood to the tissues. A more complex polymer is *cellulose* which is an important part of the cell walls of plants. Cellulose cannot be digested by man, but some animals, such as the herbivora with the aid of bacteria and termites with the aid of flagellates, can do so. Sugars are soluble in water, but the polysaccharides are far less so and thus are ideal for storage since their large molecules will not pass through plasma membranes.

The main role of carbohydrates in protoplasm is to serve as a source of chemical energy. Protoplasm requires energy for its activities, and the oxidation of carbohydrates furnishes much of this energy. Glucose is the most important of these energy carbohydrates, and other carbohydrates are transformed into glucose before they are utilized as a source of energy. Some carbohydrates become basic components of protoplasmic structure, such as the pentoses which form constituent groups of nucleic acids and of nucleotides. The lipid compounds of nervous tissue known as cerebrosides also contain a simple sugar component, and certain sugars are found in the coenzymes of enzymatic systems.

Proteins. Proteins are organic compounds that contain carbon, hydrogen, oxygen, nitrogen, and sometimes sulfur, iodine, and phosphorus. The unique properties of proteins center mainly around nitrogen. Since proteins bear such an intimate relationship to protoplasm, they are often referred to as its foundation substance.

They are collodial by nature and form large and complex molecules. The molecular weight of certain representative proteins are as follows: insulin (a pancreatic hormone), 12,000; egg albumin, 40,000; and hemoglobin, 68,000. Others are far more complex, with molecular weights reckoned in millions. There are many different forms of proteins in animal tissues, and different species of animals have different kinds of proteins. The protein molecule is made up of many thousand atoms, but when broken down it always yields simpler components known as **amino acids.** At least twenty-five of these amino acids are recognized by biochemistry, and a dozen others of doubtful status are known to occur in nature. Few proteins contain all the different kinds of amino acids, but considering all the possible combinations of amino acids in protein molecules, it is easy to see that an almost in-

finite variety can be produced, just as by combining the twenty-six different letters of the alphabet we can get thousands of different words.

The structural formulas of all the amino acids are known to scientists. The distinctive formula for any amino acid is as follows:

$$R-CH-COOH$$
$$|$$
$$NH_2$$

In this formula the symbol R may represent any one of about twenty different atomic groupings. One of the simplest amino acids is glycine:

$$H-CH-NH_2$$
$$|$$
$$COOH$$

R here represents the single hydrogen atom, but in other amino acids R could stand for a methyl group $(-CH_3)$ or a variety of carbon radicals. Another amino acid, alanine, is represented thus:

$$CH_3-CH-COOH$$
$$|$$
$$NH_2$$

The various amino acids are chiefly distinguished from each other by what constitutes the R.

It will be seen, therefore, that amino acids contain an amino group (NH_2) and an acid group $(COOH)$. In solution, amino acids can dissociate into ions which can act both as base and as acid. The NH_2 group is basic and will combine with acids; the $COOH$ group is acid and will combine with bases. Proteins can thus serve as buffers against excess acids or bases which might harm the protoplasm. Also, by having both groups, proteins are very active chemically and can form large molecules. In forming a simple protein the amino acids are linked together by a bond between the NH_2 group of one and the $COOH$ group of the other; such is called a peptide linkage. A combination of two amino acids is called a dipeptide; of three amino acids, a tripeptide, etc. If many amino acids are combined a polypeptide is formed. Proteins are built up of polypeptide chains of the amino acids of great diversity in sequence. A simple

44

protein, such as albumin or egg white, contains at least 300 amino acids. The exact arrangement of the amino acids in a protein molecule is known in only a few proteins; insulin is one of these.

Proteins are usually classified into three major groups: (1) **simple,** such as the albumins and globulins which are represented in all cells, in blood plasma, in enzymes, and in muscle; (2) **compound** or **conjugated,** which are made up of a nonprotein group attached to a protein molecule and represented by the nucleoproteins (see below) and the chromoproteins (hemoglobin, visual purple); and (3) **derived,** which are obtained from the breakdown of natural proteins by digestion or otherwise are represented by proteoses, peptones, etc. There are many other subdivisions under each of these classes.

Since the amino acid molecules are relatively small, all of them can diffuse through the cellular membrane, and in the amino acid form they are transported in the blood.

Proteins have a great variety of functions to perform in the body. Not only do they serve as the chief structural pattern of protoplasm, but they also form enzymes, hormones, chromosomes, and other cell components and may release energy when utilized as food. Moreover, the uniqueness of different cells is mainly due to the unique proteins they possess, and different species of organisms have certain proteins different from those of other species. The more closely two organisms are related the more their proteins are alike, and, conversely, the more they are unlike the more their proteins differ. Proteins thus serve as evidence for evolutionary relationship (species specificity). This generalization has practical application in grafting tissues from one animal to another, because grafts are more likely to succeed in closely related animals which have similar protein patterns; in distantly related species these grafts will not "take" and degenerate.

Some amino acids can be made in the body from other amino acids, but others must always be supplied in the food. These latter are called essential amino acids and include tryptophan, phenylalanine, and five or six others. Therefore, a diet composed of these essential amino acids in pure form would supply the protein needs of the body. Most tissues have a 15% content of protein, and next to water, proteins are the most abundant constituent of protoplasm.

Nucleic acids and nucleoproteins. These complex substances of high molecular weight are universal in living systems and are considered to represent life at the most fundamental level. They contain the elements carbon, hydrogen, oxygen, nitrogen, and phosphorus. They can be broken down into structural units (nucleotides) of which there are nine known at present. Each nucleotide is composed of a nitrogeneous base, a pentose sugar, and phosphoric acid. When nucleic acids are conjugated with simple proteins, nucleoproteins are formed. According to the kind of pentose sugar present in the molecule, nucleic acids are divided into two classes (there may be more). One kind contains the sugar desoxyribose and is called desoxyribonucleic acid (DNA). This one is found chiefly in the nucleus and is supposed to make up the chief part of the hereditary genes. Some believe that each gene is a single molecule of nucleoprotein. The other kind contains the sugar ribose and is called ribose nucleic acid (RNA). It is found mainly in the cytoplasm and nucleoli and is directly concerned in the cellular synthesis of proteins. The reaction of substances in the cell to dyes depends upon the relative amount of nucleic acid in nucleoproteins. Chromatin, for instance, is highly basophilic because of its high content of nucleic acid. Viruses also consist of nucleoproteins, some of which contain DNA and others RNA, and have the power of reproduction in the cells of a living host. On this account viruses are often referred to as "naked genes." The quantity of DNA in a cell is very constant under nearly all conditions; that of RNA fluctuates with nutritional states, type of tissue, etc.

Lipids. Fats and fatlike substances are

known as lipids. They include the true fats, oils, compound lipids, and steroids. As a group they make up about 3% of protoplasm. The true fats or simple lipids are sometimes called the neutral fats. They consist of oxygen, carbon, and hydrogen and are formed by the combination of three fatty acid molecules and one glycerol molecule. True fats are therefore esters, that is, a combination of an alcohol (glycerol) and an acid. They also bear the term triglyceride because the glycerol radical is combined with three radicals from fatty acid groups. A chemically pure fat such as stearin is an ester of glycerol and three molecules of a single fatty acid (stearic acid). Most natural fats, however, such as lard and butter, are mixtures of chemically pure fats, for they usually have two or three different fatty acids attached to the three hydroxyl groups of glycerol. The production of a typical fat by the union of glycerol and stearic acid is shown by the following formula:

$$
\begin{array}{l}
C_{17}H_{35}CO|OH \quad\; H|O-CH_2 \qquad\quad C_{17}H_{35}OCO-CH_2 \\
C_{17}H_{35}CO|OH + H|O-CH \longrightarrow C_{17}H_{35}OCO-CH + 3H_2O \\
C_{17}H_{35}CO|OH \quad\; H|O-CH_2 \qquad\quad C_{17}H_{35}OCO-CH_2
\end{array}
$$

Stearic acid	Glycerol	Stearin
(3 mols.)	(1 mol.)	(1 mol.)

In this formula it will be seen that the three fatty acid molecules have united with the OH groups of the glycerol to form stearin (a neutral fat) with the production of three molecules of water. Other common fatty acids in nature are palmitic and oleic acids.

Most true fats are solid at room temperatures, but plant oils (linseed, cottonseed, etc.) and animals oils (fish and whale) are liquid because of the nature of their fatty acids. Waxes, such as beeswax, are secreted by certain glands and differ from true fats in having an alcohol other than glycerol in their molecular structure. Some waxes may also have hydrocarbons.

Compound lipids are fatlike substances which, when broken down, will yield glycerol (or some other alcohol), fatty acids, and some other substances such as a nitrogenous base (e.g., choline), phosphoric acid, or a simple sugar. Among these lipids are the phospholipids (lecithin) found in egg yolk and probably every living cell, and the cerebrosides (glycolipid) which are common in nervous tissue. The steroids or solid alcohols are not chemically related to fats but are included among the lipids because they have fatlike properties. Cholesterol ($C_{27}H_{45}OH$) is a common example of a steroid. Ergosterol, a plant steroid, becomes vitamin D (calciferol) when activated by ultraviolet rays. Male and female sex hormones and the adrenal gland hormones are other examples of steroids. Some of these steroids are derived from cholesterol by oxidation or reduction.

Lipids have many functions in protoplasm. The true fats furnish a concentrated fuel of high energy value and represent an economical form of storage reserves in the body. Excess carbohydrates can be transformed into fat, and to a limited extent fatty acids can be changed into glucose. Some phospholipids form part of the basic protoplasmic structure, such as lecithin which gives a constant characteristic pattern to all cells. Phospholipids also share with proteins the basic structure of the plasma membrane and of the myelin sheaths of nerve fibers. Cholesterol is a component of bile and of gallstone, which are bile precipitates.

Role of enzymes in the living process

The whole life process involves many chemical reactions within the cells. It is the chemical breakdown of large molecules that releases energy for the activities of any organism. Food to furnish potential energy must be taken into the body, for all organisms literally use themselves up as their molecules are oxidized in these energy-yielding reactions. **Enzymes** make these chemical activities possible. An enzyme is a biological catalyst produced by living protoplasm and regulating the speed and specificity at which these numerous reactions occur. A catalyst is any organic or inorganic substance that accelerates a chemical reaction without affecting the end products of the reaction and without being destroyed as a result of the reaction. Inorganic catalysts are common in the chemical industry, such as manganese dioxide in the liberation of oxygen from peroxide and the use of finely divided metals (iron, platinum, nickel, etc.) in surface catalysis. Water may be considered a catalyst, for many substances that are inert when mixed together in a dry condition will quickly react when a little water is added. Catalysts furnish no energy, and the reactions they promote would probably occur slowly without the presence of the catalysts.

There must be thousands of enzymes in the animal body, for physiological processes are mainly enzymatic. Enzymes are involved in every aspect of life phenomena. They control the reactions by which food is digested, absorbed, and metabolized. They promote the synthesis of structural materials to replace the wear and tear on the body. They determine the release of energy used in respiration, growth, muscle contraction, physical and mental activities, and a host of others. A few protoplasmic activities may involve no enzymes, such as the secretion of milk by the mammary glands. Much of our knowledge about enzymes may be summarized as follows.

Historical background. In 1896 Buchner, a German chemist, succeeded in extracting from yeast cells, by the use of a hydraulic press, a substance that was as active in fermentation (the production of alcohol and carbon dioxide from simple sugars) as the original yeast. This substance was later called zymase (1903) and represents a part of the enzyme system involved in fermentation. In 1926 Prof. Sumner of Cornell University isolated from jack beans, by means of acetone, the enzyme **urease** in crystalline form. Altogether in this field investigators have isolated more than forty enzymes. Some of the enzymes so obtained may not be chemically pure, for crystallization does not necessarily mean chemical purity.

Chemical nature of enzymes. All the enzymes so far isolated and crystallized are proteins. They are complex with large molecular weights, that of urease being 483,000. No enzyme has been artificially created in the laboratory. Most of them are colorless, but some are brown, red, green, etc. Many of them, such as pepsin, are pure proteins made up of chains of amino acids. Others, such as certain vitamins, are made up of proteins joined to chemical groups. Still others (cytochrome) contain a metal such as iron. Most of them are soluble in water, but those with lipoprotein are insoluble in water. All are insoluble in absolute alcohol. Most are destroyed or made inactive by temperatures over 65° C., some at lower temperatures.

Where enzymes are found in the cell. All enzymes are made in cells. Some are found dissolved in cytoplasm. Extracts made from ground-up liver cells have the team of enzymes necessary to convert glucose to lactic acid. Some enzymes may be found in small differentiated parts of the cells such as microsomes and mitochondria. Enzymes may be precipitated or thrown down from their natural sources by dilute alcoholic solutions, mercuric chloride solutions, acetone solutions, and others. Enzymes are colloidal in nature and behave like colloids with a precipitation agent. All cells do not necessarily produce the same enzymes. Certain cells only in the stomach wall manufacture pepsin; other cells in the pancreas make trypsin. What product a cell makes is determined mainly by the kind of enzymes the cell has. Some enzymes normally act only within the cell (intracellular) and are represented by such an enzyme as cytochrome oxidase; others (extracellular) perform their work in secretions, such as the digestive enzymes.

How enzymes are named. The most common method of naming enzymes is to add the suffix -ase to the root word of the substance or substrate on which the enzyme works. A substrate is the substance which is altered by the influence of the enzyme. Thus sucrase (an enzyme) acts upon sucrose, lipase upon lipids, protease upon proteins, etc. Some enzymes have special names, such as pepsin, ptyalin, and trypsin. Sometimes the suffix **-lytic** is used in naming enzymes. Proteolytic (protein-splitting) is a general term for an enzyme that digests protein and amylolytic (starch-splitting) for an enzyme that digests starch.

How enzymes are activated. Some enzymes are first produced in inactive forms without enzymatic properties (zymogens) in cells. Thus the zymogen of pepsin is pepsinogen, that of trypsin is trypsinogen, etc. Zymogens have entirely different properties from the enzymes they produce, for they are less sensitive to acids and alkalies. Zymogens can be demonstrated in gland cells as granules by proper techniques of fixation and staining. They are activated by various agents, such as by hydrogen ions, which change pepsinogen to pepsin, or by a special enzyme, enterokinase, which is supposed to convert trypsinogen into trypsin, although there is some doubt on this point. Other enzymes are activated by their coenzymes (usually vitamins). When separated by filtration or other means, neither enzymes nor coenzymes will produce enzymatic effect but will do so when brought together.

How enzymes act. Enzymes perform their action by combining with some particular part of the substrate molecule. This may be due to the unique shape of an enzyme molecule which can fit only a certain niche in the molecule of the substrate (the lock-and-key theory). When the enzyme-substrate combination has been formed, what happens depends upon the nature of the enzyme, substrate, and other factors. In some cases there is a transfer of electrons from the substrate to the enzyme (enzyme-substrate complex), or in other cases the enzyme simply brings a substrate molecule and a water molecule into closer association so that hydrolysis can be facilitated. Where the substrate molecule is changed, the enzyme is freed and is ready to combine with another substrate molecule. Enzymes rarely work singly but in teams. Whenever the end products of one enzyme-catalyzed reaction are produced, they become involved in other enzyme-controlled reactions. One enzyme carries out one step, and other enzymes carry on from there in succession. In this way the metabolism of cells becomes a continuous sequence of reactions, each of which is controlled by specific enzymes. One important aspect of enzymatic action is the so-called **coupled reaction.** This occurs whenever certain chemical reactions require the expenditure of energy and others release energy at the same time, to furnish this energy. This is well illustrated in muscular physiology when certain energy-yielding reactions produce the synthesis of high-energy substances, such as adenose triphosphate (ATP), which are used to contract the muscle.

Apoenzymes and coenzymes. Digestive enzymes such as pepsin and trypsin are made up entirely of protein, but many others have two parts, a protein and a nonprotein component. It is customary in such cases to call the protein part **apoenzyme** and the nonprotein, **coenzyme.** The combination of the two can be referred to as an enzyme system. Since the smaller molecules of the coenzymes may be able to pass through a dialyzing membrane, it has been possible to separate the two components from each other in many cases. Others have been separated by hydrolysis. When analyzed, coenzymes are found to consist of vitamins, such as niacin in coenzymes I and II, riboflavin in the yellow vitamin, thiamin in many enzyme systems, and so forth. It is as coenzymes that so many microconstituents or "trace" substances, such as the ions of magnesium, chloride, phosphate, iron, copper, etc., are absolute requirements for complete nutrition. Only when both components, apoenzyme and coenzyme, are combined can there be enzymatic activity; neither can produce catalytic action by itself.

Specificity of enzymes. Enzymes are usually highly specific among the molecules of protoplasm. Some will cause reaction only in certain substrates, even to the point of making subtle distinctions between isomers, that is, molecules of the

48

same atoms but different structural arrangements. Specificity is demonstrated by the different enzymes which split the double sugars, sucrose, lactose, and maltose. Other enzymes are not so specific. Proteases, for example, will influence the hydrolysis of nearly all proteins. The lock-and-key theory already mentioned may explain the specificity of many enzymes. Enzymes that can act on a number of different substrates possess a sort of "master" key.

Reversibility of enzyme action. A particular enzyme is effective in accelerating a reaction in either direction, for it does not determine the direction of a reaction. All enzymes simply accelerate the rate at which reactions reach that equilibrium which would be attained in the absence of the enzymes. The same enzymes that convert glucose to starch are equally effective in breaking down starch to glucose in the body. However, reversion may be prevented by removing the products of enzymatic action as fast as they are formed and also by other factors.

Catalytic power of enzymes. Enzymes are very effective in small amounts. For instance, a single molecule of catalase, the enzyme that splits hydrogen peroxide into hydrogen and water, can effectively transform more than 5 million hydrogen peroxide molecules a minute at certain temperatures. Other enzymes are not as effective, but many of them can split up to 500,000 molecules of the substrate per minute.

How enzyme activity is influenced. Besides the higher temperatures already referred to, enzymatic action can be affected by a number of factors. Freezing will slow or stop their action, but their activity is resumed when the temperature rises. As a general rule, enzymes accelerate chemical reactions with rise of temperature but will do so only within certain limits. Moreover, this increase in velocity is not proportional to the rise in temperature. Usually the rate is doubled with each 10° C. rise, but a change from 20° to 30° C. is greater than one from 30° to 40° C. The optimum temperature for animal enzymes is about body temperature. Above 40° C. most enzymes are slowed down or inactivated altogether.

Enzymes are also sensitive to hydrogen ion (pH) activity. Each enzyme usually works best within a certain range of acidity or alkalinity. Pepsin of the acid gastric juice is most active at about pH 1.8; trypsin of the alkaline pancreatic juice is most active at about pH 8.2. Many work best when the pH is around neutrality. In strong acid or alkaline solutions, enzymes lose irreversibly their catalytic power.

An enzyme will do its maximal work when there is enough substrate to combine with all of the enzyme present. In such a case no further increase in the substrate can increase the amount of reaction, for all of the enzyme is being used. Conversely, the initial rate of reaction (within the limits just stated) is proportional to the amount of enzyme present (at constant pH and temperature) if there is an excess of substrate.

Enzymes can be destroyed or their action can be inhibited by a number of agents besides those already mentioned. Enzymes placed in water without a substrate lose their catalytic power rapidly, because they themselves are hydrolyzed. Some of them are very sensitive to poisons, such as cyanide and iodoacetic acid, which tend to inactivate the enzymes. Cyanide poisoning is caused by the destruction of the respiratory cytochrome enzymes by the cyanide. On the other hand, enzymes are little affected by antiseptics (chloroform, alcohol, etc.) in concentrations strong enough to kill protoplasm.

Relation of hormones to enzyme systems

Considerable progress has been made in determining the part hormones play in enzyme activity. It has been found, for instance, that the balance between the sugar of the blood and the liver glycogen is influenced by the action of the diabetogenic hormone secreted by the pituitary gland. This hormone tends to inhibit the action of the enzyme hexokinase which promotes the storage of sugar as glycogen.

If the diabetogenic hormone is secreted in excess, sugar will not be stored in the liver as glycogen but will remain in the blood and thus cause the sugar level of the blood to be elevated. The diabetogenic hormone is itself controlled by the hormone of the pancreatic islets, insulin. But if insulin is deficient, the pituitary hormone is free to inhibit the action of hexokinase. From this standpoint sweet diabetes may be caused in either of two ways —by an underproduction of the hormone insulin or an overproduction of the diabetogenic hormone. When the two hormones are well balanced, such a diabetic condition does not occur. Other relationships of this kind between enzymes and hormones are probably common, but much additional work will be necessary to confirm this. It appears that hormones work hand in hand with vitamins in enzymatic systems. Indeed, some biochemists refer to all three substances as members of one family.

ANNOTATED REFERENCES

Avery, G. S., Jr. 1952. Survey of Biological Progress, vol. 2. New York, Academic Press, Inc. *The section on the structure of protoplasm includes the latest concepts on the finer structure of protoplasm. Only the advanced student will derive profit from reading it.*

Baldwin, E. 1957. Dynamic Aspects of Biochemistry, ed. 3. Cambridge, Cambridge University Press. *One of the best texts for the general zoology student. The most recent work on the highly important subject of enzymes is dealt with in a clear, well-balanced manner.*

Bourne, G. H. 1951. Cytology and Cell Physiology, ed. 2. New York, Oxford University Press. *Many parts of this work deal with the basic structure of protoplasm. Much attention is given to the cytoplasmic inclusions and their role in cytological functions.*

Downes, H. R. 1955. The Chemistry of Living Cells. New York, Harper & Brothers. *This is an interesting text in biochemistry which gives a good up-to-date account of the advances in this field.*

Edsall, J. T. (editor). 1951. Enzymes and Enzyme Systems: Their State in Nature. Cambridge, Harvard University Press. *This work is made up of a series of papers by eminent specialists in this field. Various enzyme systems are described, and the attempt is made to explain their complicated reactions. Primarily of interest to the advanced student.*

Frey-Wyssling, A. 1953. Submicroscopic Morphology of Protoplasm. New York, Elsevier Publishing Co. *An advanced work on the minute structure of protoplasm.*

Heilbrunn, L. V. 1952. An Outline of General Physiology, ed. 3. Philadelphia, W. B. Saunders Co. *Those who have had good training in physics and chemistry can derive much profit from the sections devoted to the basic structure of protoplasm.*

Heilbrunn, L. V. 1956. The Dynamics of Living Protoplasm. New York, Academic Press, Inc. *The author believes that an understanding of the mechanism of vital activity depends mainly upon the colloidal behavior of protoplasm and not merely upon a chemical analysis of the organism. He regards protoplasm as being in a state of equilibrium between factors that promote clotting and those that inhibit clotting. This clotting process is similar to blood clotting and requires the presence of a calcium ion. The author has long stressed the importance of the behavior of the calcium ion in many physiological phenomena, such as cell viscosity, mitosis, and muscular contraction.*

Laidler, K. J. 1954. Introduction to the Chemistry of Enzymes. New York, McGraw-Hill Book Co., Inc. *One of the best accounts for the beginning student of the mechanism of enzymatic action and of the more important enzyme groups.*

Mitchell, P. H. 1956. A Textbook of General Physiology. New York, McGraw-Hill Book Co., Inc. *The chapter on Catalysis and Enzymes is an excellent and up-to-date account of the nature and action of enzymes.*

Prosser, C. L. (editor). 1950. Comparative Animal Physiology. Philadelphia, W. B. Saunders Co. *Certain topics in this comprehensive comparative physiology deal with the structure of protoplasm in a manner which can be comprehended by the beginning student in zoology.*

Zirkle, R. E. (editor). 1959. A Symposium on Molecular Biology. Chicago, University of Chicago Press. *Molecular biology is the most active branch of biological investigation at the present time, and the papers in this symposium summarize many of the studies made in this field. There is an interesting chapter on the widely used electron microscope and its possibilities in molecular biology.*

chapter 3

The cell as unit of protoplasmic organization

CELL THEORY

Cells were first seen and described by Robert Hooke, the English scientist, in 1665. The cells he saw were the boxlike cavities he found in cork. In the next hundred years or so many other scientists made observations on the cell and some of its components. Among these were Lamarck (1809), Detrochet (1824), and Turpin (1826). Brown in 1831 noticed that the nucleus was a regular constituent in all plant cells. The time was ripe in 1838 for the formulation of the cell theory of Schleiden and Schwann. According to the generalization of these men, all plants and animals are made up of cells as units. At the time these men formulated their theory, very little was known about the details of cell structure. The term cell itself, as a chamber, applied with some logic to the cork cells, where they were first described, and probably to most plant cells, but so far as animals are concerned, the term is somewhat of a misnomer.

Since the time the cell theory was first proposed, the cell has been extensively studied. As first formulated, the doctrine had certain erroneous ideas. It is now known, for instance, that there are many parts of animals and plants which are not composed of cells. Some of these products may be derived from cells and others from environmental sources. Many of these substances are nonliving but are of functional importance nonetheless. Bone is one strik-

ing example of a structure that contains a large amount of nonliving matter. Bone histologically consists of three types of structures: (1) Cells are scattered through the main bony substance. (2) Connective tissue fibers are found in the spaces between the cells. These are derived from the cells and are cellular products. (3) The minerals which give bone its peculiar properties are carried by the blood and are laid down in the fibrous material. These minerals are not alive and are not products of the cells.

The cell theory, then, as known today, states that the organism is composed of **cells, cell products,** and **noncell products.**

STRUCTURE OF THE CELL

The **cell** is the structural and functional unit of the body and is usually a small mass of protoplasm definitely circumscribed by a **plasma membrane,** a thin film of lipid, and protein layers about 0.02 microns in thickness (Figure 6). Certain organoids are almost universally present in cells. Cellulose **cell walls** outside the plasma membrane give support to plant cells, but in most animal cells this cell wall is absent. Within the cell is a small spherical **nucleus** enclosed in a **nuclear membrane** which is thicker than the plasma membrane. The nucleus in some cells lies near the center and in others it is near the surface; in some it shifts its position. The protoplasm outside the nu-

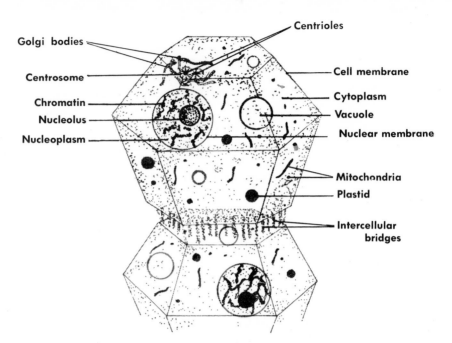

Figure 6. Scheme of generalized cell, showing principal constituents commonly found in most cells. Shape of cells is correlated with function and with mechanical pressure of adjacent cells. Pressure often produces fourteen-faceted surface which appears hexagonal in cross-section. Constituents vary with types of cells and phases of activity. Protoplasmic processes (intercellular bridges) may connect cells in some tissues such as epithelia. Smallest cells, probably bacteria, are less than 1 μ in diameter; ostrich eggs may be several inches around.

cleus is called **cytoplasm;** within the nucleus it is called **nucleoplasm.** Within the nucleoplasm is the **chromatin,** which may vary in appearance with different fixatives but usually contains angular knots (karyosomes) connected by pale threads (linin fibers). The nucleus also contains the **nucleolus,**[*] a spherical body of unknown function and variable form. Some nuclei contain several nucleoli.

Although most cells contain a single nucleus there are some protoplasmic units of living matter which contain many nuclei and are not divided into cells. Such a formation is called a **syncytium.** Syncytia may be formed by fusion of mononucleate cells (as in chorionic villi of the placenta)

or they may be produced by the repeated division of the nucleus (multinucleated cell) without cleavage of cytoplasm (as in striated muscle fibers). When an acellular organism has many nuclei it is called a **plasmodium** (slime molds and malaria parasites are examples).

The cytoplasm contains many structures, some of which are seen by ordinary techniques and others by special ones. Among these are the **centriole** which stains darkly, lies near the nucleus, and is concerned with cell division; **cytoplasmic inclusions** such as **Golgi bodies** and the granular or rod-shaped **mitochondria**[*];

---

[*]The nucleolus is a round body of smooth contour and appears to be made up of a mass of granules not bounded by a membrane. Its chief constituents, ribonucleic acid and proteins, may vary in relative proportion to produce variations in its staining.

---

[*]Recent investigations with the electron microscope and centrifugal separation reveal that each mitochondrion is made up of two compartments bounded by membranes, the inner of which has little folds which extend into the interior matrix of the mitochondrion. It has been definitely established that the mitochondria bear teams of enzymes which are important in cellular metabolism.

and various kinds of other inclusions such as fat and metaplasmic inclusions.

SOME COMMON EXAMPLES OF CELLS

To see a living cell, scrape the inside of your cheek with a blunt instrument, put the scrapings on a slide in a drop of salt solution, and examine, unstained, with a microscope. The flat circular cells with small nuclei that you see are the squamous epithelial cells that line the mouth region.

Cells vary greatly in size and form (Figure 7). Some of the smallest animal cells are certain parasites which may be 1 micron (1/25,000 of an inch) or less in diameter. At the other extreme we have the fertilized eggs of birds, some of which, including the extracellular material, are several inches in diameter. The hen's egg, a single cell, is more than an inch in diameter. A red blood corpuscle in man has a diameter of about 7.5 microns. We often use this corpuscle as a measurement of comparison when sizes of structures are given in microns. The longest cells are the nerve cells, for the fibers, which are parts of the cells, may be several feet long. Some striped muscle cells or fibers are several inches long. Most cells, although they appear flat under the microscope, have depth or the third dimension also.

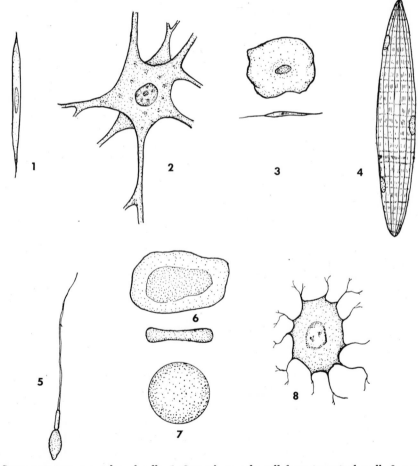

Figure 7. Some common examples of cells. **1,** Smooth muscle cell from intestinal wall; **2,** nerve cell from spinal cord; **3,** epithelial cell from lining of mouth, with side view underneath; **4,** striated muscle cell or fiber; **5,** human spermatozoan; **6,** white blood corpuscle; **7,** red blood corpuscle with side view above it; **8,** bone cell.

HOW CELLS ARE STUDIED

Our knowledge of cells and their structures has been acquired in a number of ways. The following methods have been found useful.

Microscopic examination of prepared tissues. By rather complicated processes of fixing tissues with certain chemicals and staining them with dyes, it is possible to see most of the cellular components mentioned in a previous section. This is one of the oldest and most valuable methods of cell study. There is always the danger of artefacts being formed in the preparations, so it is necessary to check by other methods. However, the findings of wholly different and more recent techniques have in general substantiated the old classical methods.

Besides the light microscope other types of microscopes are applied to the study of cells.

The electron microscope has been a powerful tool for biological research. Refined techniques in its use have enabled cellular biologists to see structures as small as one ten-millionth of an inch. The limitations of the microscope require that very thin sections of dead cells be used and that the electron beam be operated in a vacuum. Living cells cannot be studied under these conditions.

Other types of microscopes are useful for revealing certain aspects of cells, such as the phase-contrast microscope for enhancing the contrast of living cells, the polarizing microscope for understanding the orientation of molecules, and the interference microscope for determining mass and density.

Tissue culture. Many kinds of living cells can be removed from the animal body, such as embryonic chick hearts, white blood corpuscles, etc., and if kept in suitable media under proper temperature conditions, they will stay alive for long periods of time. Growth, transformation, and various other functions can thus be studied.

Micromanipulation. This is a method of studying living tissue by delicate manipulation of fine glass needles. In this way it is possible to find out many physical properties of cells and tissues, such as their consistency, effect of removing the nucleus, effect of dyes and other organic substances, and dissection procedures.

Isolation of living tissue. Many elements of the blood can be studied by simply removing them from the animal's body to isotonic salt solutions and observing their behavior under special conditions. Ameboid movement and phagocytosis can be studied in this way.

Chemical analyses. Much can be found out about cells by chemically analyzing them during various phases of their activity. Many things have been learned about cell permeability by analyzing the contents of tissues before and after exposure to various substances. Chemical analysis of muscle before and after exercise may show what products are being used up during exercise.

Microincineration. Microincineration is a method of burning all parts of the cell except the minerals, which are left in their natural position in the cell. With the use of a special furnace in which prepared slides of tissues are heated to high temperatures, the process reveals what minerals make up the ash of the body and where they are located in the various cells and tissues. The ash of the body, which is the part left after cremation, usually makes up about 5% of the total body weight.

WHAT DETERMINES THE FORM OF CELLS?

Cells exist in such a variety of shapes and sizes that it is impossible to describe a completely typical form. A single cell, not influenced by function or by location of neighboring cells, would probably be spherical, but this shape is actually found only in eggs and some protozoans. Most cells are in groups, where their shape is determined by the pressures of adjacent cells, resulting in polyhedral, cuboidal, flat, and other shapes. Factors such as unequal growth, inequality of surface tension, and restriction of space may affect their form. When pressed upon equally from all sides, cells typically have fourteen sides (which represents a minimal surface area). A cut through a fourteen-sided body (cell) usually shows six sides. Cells specialized for certain functions, such as the nerve cells, may differ greatly from this pattern.

Some of the contrasting cell forms are biconcave discs as in mammalian red blood corpuscles, cylindrical as in striped muscle, spindle shaped as in smooth muscle, many branched as in nerve cells, irregular as in bone cells, whiplike as in sperm cells, and thin and flat as in squamous epithelial cells.

THE ENORMOUS NUMBER OF CELLS IN TISSUES AND ANIMALS

It is difficult to visualize the great number of cells even in small masses of animal tissues. There are many trillions of cells in the human body, and some animals have more. In some low forms there may be a marked constancy in cell numbers. Certain rotifers always have 959 cells in their make-up and do not seem to vary from this number. However, it is doubtful whether there is such constancy in most animals. In the biceps muscle of the human being, for instance, there are around 260,000 muscle cells. The gastrocnemius muscle of the cat has 43,000 fibers or cells. Nerve cells are probably more numerous than those of any other tissue. The human brain is estimated to have 12 billion cells. With some tissues, the cells cease to increase in number early in the development of the animal and long before it reaches maturity. The child at birth has its full complement of muscular and nervous cells. Other tissues continue their cell divisions throughout life, although this may not indicate an actual increase in cell number, since replacement of cells may be involved.

PHYSIOLOGY OF THE CELL

In a protozoan all functions are carried on within its one cell membrane. Organelles are specialized to perform functions that are taken care of by groups of cells in metazoans. In many-celled animals where there is division of labor, the cells do not all have the same physiology, but there are certain structures and functions which are almost universal among all cells. The **nucleus** represents the controlling center of the cell, the center of dynamic metabolic processes. Through its enzymes and other agencies it is able to transform food material brought into the surrounding cytoplasm. The nucleus carries the important **chromatin,** the bearer of heredity. If the nucleus is removed from the cytoplasm, the latter dies. The cytoplasm, on the other hand, is concerned with such other cell activities as taking in food, formation of secretions, and the elimination of waste. In these activities the cytoplasm is aided by the cytoplasmic inclusions, mitochondria and Golgi bodies, and enzymes. The **centrioles** in the cytoplasm are concerned with cell division. The **plasma membrane** is one of the most important features of the cell. It is a complex film (about 0.02 micron in thickness) made up of lipid and protein layers sandwiched together. Its structure can be determined to some extent by the electron microscope. It is elastic, and when broken, the cytoplasm may run out, but the membrane may repair itself. The exchange between the cell and its environment must take place through this membrane.

Passage of materials through membranes: exchange between cell and environment*

The general metabolism of living cells requires a continuous supply of food materials and oxygen for the energy of the life process; it gives off, in turn, byproducts to the medium surrounding the cell. These substances must all pass through the plasma membrane of the cell, whether they are entering or leaving the cell. Most cells are surrounded by an aqueous solution of some kind. The ameba is surrounded by the fresh water in which it lives. In many-celled animals the cell lives in a medium composed of blood, lymph, or tissue fluid. Before a

---

*Refer to Chapter 5, Principle 5.

substance can enter a cell it must be soluble to some degree in the surrounding medium. The plasma membrane, then, acts as a doorkeeper for the entrance and exit of the substances which are involved in cell metabolism. Some things can pass through with ease; others enter slowly and with difficulty; and still others cannot enter at all.

To understand the passage of things in and out of cells is one of the great problems in biology. Much experimentation has been done and many important facts have been discovered, but the problem is far from being solved.

Diffusion. All molecules are in a state of motion because of the energy within them. In solids the molecules are so much restricted that they merely vibrate; within a liquid the molecules have more freedom of movement; but in gases the molecules have such freedom to move that they are restricted only by containing vessels. When molecules are free to do so, they will move in a straight line until they meet another; then they bounce off and take a different direction, producing a zigzag path (Brownian movement).

The total molecular activity of a substance in a particular region results in a **diffusion pressure.** This activity depends upon the concentration of molecules, the velocity of the molecules (faster at high temperatures), and any pressure on the molecules from the outside. **Diffusion** may therefore be defined as the movement of molecules or ions (brought about by their kinetic energy) from a region of greater to a region of lesser diffusion pressure (even against gravity), because there is less collision with other particles in the region of lesser concentration. Diffusion ceases when an equilibrium is established and the molecules are uniformly distributed, but molecular movement still continues.

If some salt is dropped in a beaker of water, salt molecules and ions will spread through the water until the concentration of salt is uniform throughout. What is happening, of course, is that the salt particles, as well as the water molecules, are in

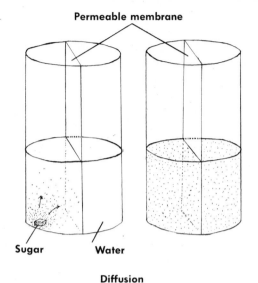

Permeable membrane

Sugar   **Water**

Diffusion

Figure 8. Diagram of diffusion and osmosis with permeable membrane. When lump of sugar is placed in left compartment of beaker, its molecules will diffuse through water of that compartment and through permeable membrane into right compartment until, as shown in right beaker, molecules are evenly dispersed.

a continuous state of movement, and through mass movement every component in the solution will diffuse until it reaches equal concentration everywhere in the solution (Figure 8).

Diffusion will occur in all states of matter but is much faster in gases, slower in liquids, and slowest of all in solids. The rate of diffusion depends upon a number of factors. The greater the concentration differences of the substance diffusing and the higher the temperature of the solution, the faster the particles diffuse. Also, small particles diffuse much faster than larger particles, and solutions with low viscosity faster than those with high. Agitation also hastens it.

Osmosis. Osmosis is essentially a diffusion process. Whenever a semipermeable membrane is placed between two unequal concentrations of dissolved substances, that is, two different diffusion pressures, water will pass from the higher to the lower diffusion pressure until equilibrium is established. Thus we may define **osmo-**

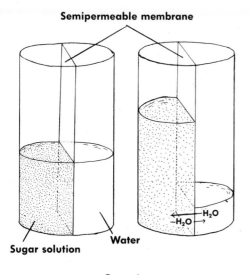

Semipermeable membrane

Sugar solution

Water

—H₂O ←→ H₂O

Osmosis

Figure 9. Diagram of diffusion and osmosis with semipermeable membrane. When sugar is placed in left compartment of beaker, only water is free to pass through semipermeable membrane and column of water in left compartment will rise, as shown by beaker on right.

sis as the diffusion of water (or gas) through a differentially permeable membrane. A **semipermeable** or **differentially permeable membrane** refers to a membrane that allows some molecules to pass through and prevents others. A membrane is **permeable** when it permits any molecule to get through and **impermeable** if it allows none to pass. In an osmotic system each substance will pass from the solution where its concentration is greater to the one where its concentration is lesser. This is the same law as that of diffusion except in this case a membrane has been introduced through which molecules must pass to bring about equilibrium (Figure 9).

A familiar example of osmosis is shown by the following experiment. A collodion membrane is formed in a large test tube, removed, and filled with a strong sugar solution such as thick molasses. A glass tube is tied in the open end of the bag, paraffined to waterproof it, and the bag is placed in a beaker of pure water so that the water levels inside and outside the bag are identical. In a short time the water level in the glass tube will be seen to rise, indicating that water is passing through the collodion bag into the sugar solution. The explanation lies in the difference between the water concentrations inside and outside the bag. Inside the bag are sugar molecules as well as water. In the beaker outside there are only water molecules. Thus the concentration of water is greater on the outside, because some of the space inside is taken up with sugar molecules. The water, therefore, will go from the greater concentration (outside) to the lesser (inside).

Actually, water molecules go in both directions, but the conditions favor the inflow rather than the outgo. Two forces may operate here. On the inside of the membrane sac there is less surface or fewer pores for the passage of the water molecules since part of the surface is occupied with sugar molecules. In addition, many water molecules are loosely bound or adsorbed to sugar molecules, so that there are fewer diffusible water molecules. On the outside there are no such handicaps and the water molecules freely enter.

Eventually the water in the glass tube will go so high and no higher. This indicates that the hydrostatic pressure of the column of water in the glass tube is sufficient to drive the water molecules back through the membrane as fast as they come in. This force is called **osmotic pressure.** It is caused by the influx of water molecules through a semipermeable membrane to equalize the concentration of water molecules on both sides of the membrane. However, this collodion membrane allows sugar molecules to pass through as well as water, but they do so slowly; hence the total osmotic pressure or **osmotic value** of this sugar solution is never realized, for the osmotic pressure of a solution is proportional to its number of solute particles which will not pass through the membrane. It is not the size of the particles but their number that matters. The osmotic pressure of a particular solution depends upon the concentration of the solute particles, temperature, electric charges (if any) on the particles, and other factors.

Dialysis is another form of osmosis and applies to the diffusion of solutes through a differentially permeable membrane. This process is often useful in separating salts from colloids or proteins, for the membrane allows salt molecules to pass through into a low concentration, but the membrane pores are too small to allow the colloid particles to pass, and they are left behind.

Substances of biological importance vary greatly in their power to pass through cell membranes which are selective in their action. Gases, such as oxygen and carbon dioxide, go through freely. Glucose, amino acids, and fatty acids pass through at a fairly slow rate. Strong electrolytes and most inorganic salts penetrate membranes very slowly, whereas polysaccharides, fats, and proteins will not pass through at all. Cell membranes can also alter their permeability and thus influence the substances which enter and leave cells. In any case only substances in solution can pass through cell membranes.

Filtration. Filtration is a mechanical process by which molecules under an external pressure are forced or filtered through a membrane. Blood pressure created by heart action is an outstanding example in the body. Not only is the blood propelled around the vascular system but also the force of blood pressure tends to drive water and solutes through capillary walls and membranes.

Application to zoology. In biological processes, osmosis, osmotic pressure, and filtration play an important role. The cells of the body are made up mainly of proteins, inorganic salts, and lipids, which do not pass through the plasma membrane readily, if at all. Water, however, which is abundant, can pass through the plasma membrane easily. When water molecules enter the cell more rapidly than they leave it, it is called **endosmosis;** the reverse process is **exosmosis.** Water is, therefore, the important component in establishing

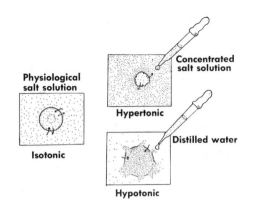

Figure 10. Diagram showing effect of osmosis and osmotic pressure on red blood corpuscle. In isotonic solution there is no change in volume of cell; in hypertonic solution cell shrinks, and in hypotonic solution cell swells and bursts.

osmotic equilibria between the cell and its surrounding medium. The ideal surrounding for the cells would be a fluid of the same osmotic pressure as that of the protoplasm in the cell. In such a condition the amount of water entering the cell would be balanced by an equivalent amount leaving the cell. Such a surrounding fluid is called **isotonic.** Blood and lymph are usually isotonic to the cells they carry or bathe. **Hypotonic** solutions contain less dissolved material than the protoplasm of the cell. In this case more water will enter the cell than leaves it because the greater concentration of water is on the outside. **Hypertonic** solutions contain a higher proportion of nonpenetrating solute than does the protoplasm of the cell, and more water leaves the cell than enters it. A physiological saline solution (0.9% sodium chloride) is isotonic to blood cells of mammals and is employed when blood is studied on the slide (Figure 10). Lower concentrations of salt (0.5%) will cause the blood corpuscles to rupture (**hemolysis**); higher concentrations will shrink the cell (**crenation**).

Osmosis naturally plays a part in the diffusion of food and oxygen into the tissue cells and, in return, the giving off of waste products. From the standpoint of osmotic behavior plasma membranes are

58

of three types: permeable, semipermeable, and impermeable.

An illustration of osmosis and osmotic pressures is seen in the use of Epsom salts (magnesium sulfate) as a laxative. When a solution of this salt is taken into the intestine, water is drawn into the intestine from the surrounding blood and body fluids because the Epsom salt solution has a higher osmotic pressure. Magnesium salts are largely nondiffusible and will not leave the intestine to enter the blood.

Filtration is employed in the kidneys when urinary constituents are separated from the blood, for this process is largely a filtering device.

Freezing point as expression of osmotic pressure. Physiologists often use the freezing point of a solution as a convenient way to determine its osmotic pressure. Compared with pure water, which freezes at $0°C.$, a watery solution, that is, containing particles in solution, will freeze at a lower temperature, depending upon its osmotic pressure or concentration. The greater the number of solutes the further the lowering of the freezing point. All solutions having the same freezing point have the same osmotic pressure. The freezing point is represented by the Greek letter Δ (delta) and is determined by a method called cryoscopy. For example, human blood will freeze at about $-0.56°$ C., or, in other words, its Δ is equal to $-0.56°$ C. The blood of other mammals has a similar Δ which tends to remain remarkably constant. Other body fluids, such as urine, often show a great variation in their freezing points over a period of time.

How aquatic animals meet problems of osmosis. Terrestrial animals, such as reptiles, birds, and mammals, have a skin that is largely impermeable to water and are adapted to their air environment. Such problems of water balance and composition of body fluids as they may have are regulated by their kidneys. It is different with aquatic animals, which are surrounded all the time by a watery medium. Even though their skins may be more or less water-impermeable, parts of their body, such as the gills, represent semipermeable membranes which can and do form osmotic systems. Water is thus free to pass into or out of the body in accordance with the laws of diffusion and osmosis. If the water outside has a higher concentration of solutes, the body fluids will lose water; the reverse will happen if the surrounding osmotic pressure is lower than that of the body fluids. In lower forms of fish, such as the cartilaginous ones (Chondrichthyes), the Δ of the body fluids is about the same as that of sea water (about $-2.25°$ C.). They are thus in osmotic equilibrium with their environment and any slight variations can be regulated quickly.

On the other hand, most marine bony fish have body fluids of a lower osmotic pressure than that of the surrounding sea water and tend to lose water through the gills. Their Δ is around $-1°$ C. How do they keep themselves from drying out in a watery environment? To prevent desiccation such fish drink much water and excrete little through the kidneys. The excess salt they take in with the sea water is excreted through the gills by an active secretory process requiring energy. Anadromous fish (marine fish that return to fresh water to breed) are able to retain about the same osmotic pressure of their body fluids in both fresh water and sea water. Marine mammals, such as whales and porpoises, have body fluids of the same osmotic pressure as terrestrial mammals.

The osmotic pressure of the body fluids of fresh-water fish is higher than that of fresh water. Their problem, then, is to get rid of excess water which tends to enter them all the time. To compensate, they drink little water, excrete freely through the kidneys, absorb salts through the gills, and carefully salvage most of the salt that enters the body, leaving free water available for urine formation.

CELL CYCLE

The cell cycle varies with different animals and with different tissues. This is to be expected, for the life cycle of some animals is relatively short as compared with others, and the life span of an animal is a composite of its component cells. Some cells in the body, red corpuscles, for example, have a life span of only a few weeks or months; others, such as muscle and nerve, live as long as the individual. Hair cells may live only a few hours, although these, as well as some other cells, may be of use to the animal for a long time after they are dead. The outer layers of our skin are composed of dead cells, and as they are shed they are renewed by newer layers pushing up from underneath.

The activities of cells slow down with age. Cells characteristically have one or more of the following movements: **ameboid, ciliary, flowing** or streaming of protoplasm, and **muscular.** All these decline with age. Cell division is much slower in the aged animal, and regeneration of lost parts slows down considerably. As a cell grows older, it accumulates more solids, and the percentage of water is cut down. The human organism may have as much as 90% of water at birth; in old age it has only about 60%. Experiments show that the environmental fluid media around cells bear an important relationship to the aging of cells. Young cells, or those formed by recent cell division, grow more slowly in an old animal than young cells in a young animal. However, the aging process involves the organism as a whole, and it is difficult to discover all the causes.

At some time in their life cycle cells must either stop growing beyond a certain size or divide into two daughter cells. Some cells, such as muscle and nerve in higher forms, cease cell division at the time of birth, and growth in these tissues is concerned with increase in size of the cells. Others keep on dividing throughout most of life, but at a steadily decreasing tempo. In the embryo, cell division is rapid. The initiation of cell division is perhaps due to the ratio between the nucleus and the cytoplasm more than to any other factor. A cell has three dimensions, and a surface membrane (nuclear and plasma) increases as the square of the

radius, whereas the cytoplasmic and nuclear masses increase as the cube of the radius. Inasmuch as diffusion of foods, wastes, and other substances takes place through the membranes, these membranes are unable to take care of the increased load of diffusion when the nucleoplasmic ratio gets out of line. It has been suggested that hormones are involved in starting off cell division.

CELL DIVISION (MITOSIS)

All cells of the body arise from the division of pre-existing cells. Indeed, all the cells found in a multicellular organism have originated from the division of a single cell, the **zygote**, formed from the union of an **egg** and **sperm** (fertilization). This is one of the basic principles of biology. This division provides the basis for one form of growth, for both sexual and asexual reproduction, and for the transmission of hereditary qualities from one cell generation to another cell generation.

In the formation of **body cells** (somatic cells) the process of cell division is referred to as **mitosis** and is the method of cell division to be described in this section. However, **germ cells** (egg and sperm) have a somewhat different type of cell division all their own, known as **meiosis**. Meiosis will be described in a later chapter.

There are two distinct phases of mitosis, the division of the nucleus and the division of the cytoplasm. These two phases ordinarily occur at the same time, but there are occasions when the nucleus may divide a number of times without a corresponding division of the cytoplasm. In such a case the resulting mass of protoplasm containing many nuclei is referred to as a multinucleate cell. Skeletal muscle is an example. A many-celled mass formed by fusion of cells which have lost their cell membranes is called a syncytium, such as cardiac muscle.

Amitosis or direct cell division. On rare occasions a type of direct cell division, **amitosis**, occurs which involves a constriction of the cytoplasm and of the nu-

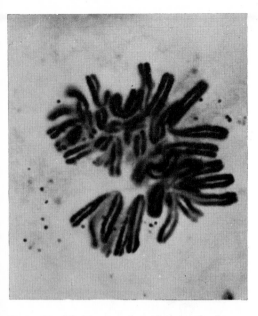

Figure 11. Mitosis in tail epidermis of salamander, *Ambystoma,* showing metaphase stage with chromosomes arranged on equatorial plate in process of separation. (Courtesy General Biological Supply House, Chicago.)

cleus into two parts or cells with approximately equal amounts of nuclear and cytoplasmic materials. In this process chromosomes are not formed, and the chromatin material is not divided in a strict quantitative way. Amitosis may occur in pathological and senescent tissues, and the daughter cells so formed have lost the power to continue as normal cells. Also, some so-called amitotic divisions may simply represent artefacts produced by poor preparations.

Mitosis or indirect cell division. The whole process of mitosis has been followed through all stages in living cells. As long ago as 1878 Flemming observed it in the skin cells of young salamanders. However, the usual study is made from specially prepared tissues that have been fixed, stained, and mounted on slides. The sequence is observed by finding cells caught in the various stages by the fixatives and arranging them in the proper order. Naturally, on stained slides one cannot follow all stages in one cell.

CHROMOSOMES. The nucleus bears **chromatin** material which in turn carries the **genes** responsible for hereditary qualities. During cell division this chromatin becomes arranged into definite **chromosomes** of varied shapes. These shapes are constant within a species. It is customary to consider the metaphase or anaphase chromosomes as most typical of their morphology, for at this time they have reached their maximum contraction. Each animal within a species has the same number of chromosomes in each body cell. Man has 46 in each of his body cells (but not in his germ cells).* The number of chromosomes a species possesses has no basic significance nor is there necessarily any relationship between two different species that have the same number. The guinea pig and the onion each have 16 chromosomes. Since there are thousands of different species of animals, many species must of necessity have the same number. The range is usually between 8 and 50 chromosomes although numbers in the hundreds are known (crayfish, for example). Some worms have as few as 2, the least number an organism can have.

Chromosomes are always arranged in pairs, or two of each kind. Of each pair, one has come from one parent and the other from the other parent. Thus in man there are twenty-three pairs. Each pair usually has certain characteristics of shape and form which aid in identification.

The purpose of mitosis is to ensure an equal distribution of each kind of chromosome to each daughter cell. A cell becomes highly abnormal in its reactions if it fails to receive its proper share of chromosomes, as the great German cytologist Boveri showed many years ago.

Structure of chromosome. The present concept of the finer structure of the chromosome is that it is made up of a

*Improved techniques have shown that man has only 46 diploid chromosomes instead of 48. (Tjio, J. H., and A. Levan. 1956. The Chromosome Number of Man. Hereditas, vol. 42, pp. 1-6.)

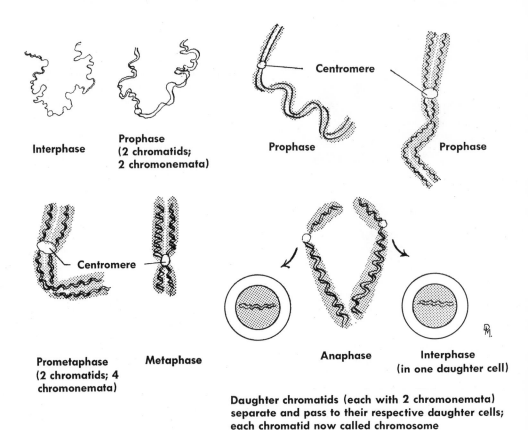

Interphase

Prophase
(2 chromatids;
2 chromonemata)

Prophase

Centromere

Prophase

Centromere

Prometaphase
(2 chromatids; 4
chromonemata)

Metaphase

Anaphase

Interphase
(in one daughter cell)

Daughter chromatids (each with 2 chromonemata)
separate and pass to their respective daughter cells;
each chromatid now called chromosome

Figure 12. Life cycle of chromosome in mitotic division. History of chromosome is based primarily on life cycle of coiled filaments called chromonemata whch are basic units of chromosome. In interphase, chromosome has reached its maximum length and consists of two chromatids (chromonemata). In prophase, two chromatids shorten by coiling. During prometaphase, chromonemata become duplicated, so that each chromatid contains two chromonemata. At anaphase, each daughter chromosome still has two chromonemata and remains so during telophase and interphase. Structure of chromosome still in process of analysis and not all details are fully known. (Modified from DeRobertis, Nowinski, and Saez: General Cytology, Philadelphia, 1954, W. B. Saunders Co.)

surrounding sheath, or **pellicle**, enclosing a complex of components. Of these components, the **matrix** forms the bulk of the chromosome and is the part that stains deeply with chromatin dyes at certain phases of the chromosome cycle. Within the matrix are the threadlike **chromonemata** (singular, **chromonema**), which are arranged like the coils of a spring and which bear the **chromomeres**. The chromonemata are probably arranged in pairs but give the appearance of a single thread. The chromomeres appear as gran-

ules and may be produced by tight coils in the chromonemata. Each chromomere may be made up of aggregations of genes, or they may represent the genes themselves, according to some authorities. Thus each chromonema is a continuous nucleoprotein bundle of fibers which bear the genes in a linear arrangement. The chromosome also shows somewhere along its length a constriction where the **centromere (kinetochore)** is located. This is an oval and often faintly staining body which has an important role in the formation of the spindle and in the behavior of the chromosomes during cell division.

INTERPHASE. Mitosis is a fairly regular process, but it is not precisely the same in all cases. The process is usually described in a regular sequence of stages called **prophase, metaphase, anaphase, and telophase** (Figures 12 to 14). When a cell is not dividing, it is said to be in **interphase**. This is often called the "resting" period, but actually the cell is carrying on all of its processes except that of dividing. Living cells are at all times in an **unresting** condition. In the interphase stage the nucleus is separated from the cytoplasm by a definite nuclear membrane. Living chromatin is mostly invisible, but when stained it appears as an irregular network scattered through most of the nuclear mass. In most cases the future chromosomes cannot be detected as distinct entities in the interphase. Usually the **centriole,** a granular body, is visible lying in the cytoplasm alongside the nucleus. When the cell is ready to divide, the centriole divides and each centriole goes to opposite sides of the cell.

An interesting problem in the behavior of the chromosomes during mitosis is the way in which they subdivide, especially with reference to the chromonemata. Many aspects of this problem, such as the mechanism by which the chromonemata are duplicated, have not yet been resolved to the satisfaction of cytologists. The prevailing opinion is that they do not "split" to form a duplicate but that a synthesis of an exact duplicate occurs in some manner.

PROPHASE. In **early prophase,** when the centrioles have gone to opposite sides, **spindle fibers** appear to connect the centrioles in a spindle-shaped figure, and radiating lines, **astral rays,** are formed about each centriole in the form of a star or aster (in animal cells). The spindle with the two asters is the **achromatic figure** or **amphiaster.** At this time the chromosomes appear as slender double threads. The two threads of a chromosome are called **chromatids** (chro-

mosome-halves) and are connected by the **centromere.** This latter structure is very important, for it serves for an attachment of the spindle fibers and for a gelatinization center of spindle formation. At this time each chromatid may have two chromonemata.

As the centrioles move farther apart and the spindle is forming, the chromosomes have been contracting and getting shorter and thicker. By the **late prophase** the nucleolus and nuclear membrane have disappeared from view, and the chromosomes are more or less scattered about, with their centromeres on or near the equatorial plate of the spindle.

METAPHASE. In this brief period the chromosomes line up across the equatorial plate in a radial manner. Here each chromosome is attached to the spindle, or to some fiber of the spindle, by its centromere. Each sister chromatid may have two chromonemata in the metaphase if the splitting or duplication has occurred earlier; otherwise there would only be one chromonema in a chromatid. At this stage or a little later, the centromere which has held the sister chromatids of each chromosome together divides, and the two parts of each centromere begin to repel one another.

ANAPHASE. The two halves or sister chromatids of each chromosome now separate from each other, one chromatid going to one pole and the other to the other pole.*

Just how they are able to do this is not known. The separation starts at the centromere, which advances ahead of the rest of the chromatid as it progresses toward the pole. In this way the position of the centromere determines the shape of the chromatid during the anaphase stage, such as the V-shaped form when the centromere is located in the center of

---

*An important cytological generalization is that intact homologous chromosomes attract each other (see meiosis), whereas the two parts (chromatids) of a split chromosome actually repel each other.

3. Middle prophase

Each chromosome may be visibly double; coils of chromonemata increase and make chromosome shorter and thicker; matrix from nucleolus or other source deposited around double-coiled chromonemata

4. Late prophase

Double nature of short, thick chromosome more apparent; each chromosome made up of 2 half-chromosomes or sister chromatids; nucleolus usually disappears

5. Prometaphase

Nuclear membrane disintegrates or changes structure; chromonema of each chromatid doubled by duplication

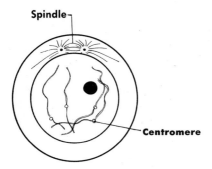

2. Early prophase

Each elongated chromosome now consists of 2 chromatids (chromonemata) attached to single centromere; double nature of chromosome not apparent; centrosome divides and spindle starts development

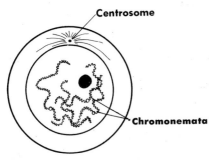

1. Interphase

Each chromosome reaches its maximum length and minimum thickness; each chromosome composed of coiled thread of genes (chromonema) and centromere; duplication of chromonemata may also occur at this stage

Figure 13. Diagrams of mitotic stages.

the chromatid or the J-shaped when it is located near the end of the chromatid.*

Several theories have been proposed to account for the mechanism of movement of the sister chromatids or half-chromosomes toward their respective poles. One theory suggests that special fibers run from each sister chromatid to the centriole nearest it and thus pull the chromosomes along. Another theory proposes that the protoplasm between the sister chromatids swells by the absorption of water and pushes them apart, the spindle fibers acting as guides along which the chromosomes move. Whatever the cause, one chromatid of each pair eventually reaches the end of the spindle and its sister mate goes to the other pole of the spindle. The end result of the process is that each pole of the spindle is going to be surrounded

---

*In the description of mitosis previously given the centromere is localized to a particular part of a chromosome. In *Ascaris* and some other forms the centromere is of the diffuse type in which each chromosome has a whole series of centromeres along its length attached to the spindle. This condition produces almost perfect alignment of the chromosome at right angles to the long axis of the spindle. The sister chromatids are thus parallel with each other as they move to opposite poles.

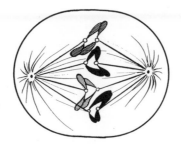

6. Metaphase

Chromosomes arranged on equatorial plate; centromeres (not yet divided) anchored to equator of spindle

7. Early anaphase

By splitting of centromere each chromatid has its own centromere which lies on equator and is attached to spindle fiber

8. Anaphase

Chromatids now called daughter chromosomes which are in 2 distinct groups; daughter centromeres, which may be attached at various points on different chromosomes, move apart and drag daughter chromosomes toward respective poles

Figure 13. (Cont'd)

by a group of chromatids which are going to be the chromosomes of the new cell when it is formed in the succeeding stage or telophase.

TELOPHASE. When the chromosomes are gathered around the poles, they begin a process which is the reverse of that at the beginning. The chromosomes are restored to a diffused network with only the chromatin granules visible. The chromonemata partly unwound are visible for some time after the matrix no longer stains. Nuclear membranes are formed around the new daughter nuclei, the spindle and astral rays gradually disappear, one or more nucleoli arise from a special region of a chromosome, and the centriole divides. In the equatorial plane during this time a constriction appears in the cytoplasm of the cell, deepens, and finally separates the cell into two daughter cells, each with a nucleus. It is not known with certainty that the cytoplasmic structures, such as mitochondria and the Golgi apparatus, are distributed equally to the two daughter cells. Each of the new cells now enters the interphase.

SIGNIFICANCE OF MITOSIS. There are many variations in the process of mitosis among different animals. In some the

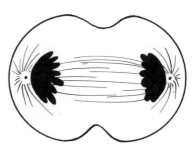

9. Early telophase

Chromosomes lie close together and form a clump; nuclear reorganization begins

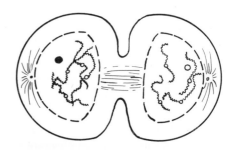

10. Late telophase

Chromonemata lose major coils and chromosomes become longer and thinner; matrix around chromosomes disappears and chromosomes may lose identity; nuclear membrane reappears and spindle-astral fibers fade away; cell body divides into 2 daughter cells, each of which now enters interphase

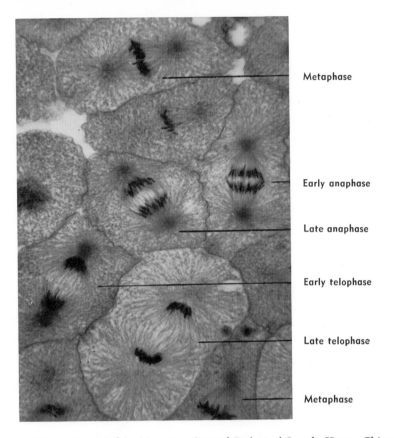

Metaphase

Early anaphase

Late anaphase

Early telophase

Late telophase

Metaphase

Figure 14. Stages of mitosis in whitefish. (Courtesy General Biological Supply House, Chicago.)

chromatin thread may be doubled or split in early prophase; in others the duplication is not found until the metaphase stage. However, the end result is the same. Each daughter cell has the same kind and the same number of chromosomes that the parent cell possessed. Each cell, therefore, has a complete set of the chromosomes. Inasmuch as the chromatin is the bearer of the hereditary qualities, the process of mitosis aims to divide the cell so that each daughter cell will have precisely identical chromosomes with identical chromatin material. This means that all the cells (except germ cells) in a multicellular animal have identical sets of chromosomes in them.

HOW LONG DOES IT TAKE FOR MITOSIS TO OCCUR? Several factors influence the duration of mitosis. Temperature is known to influence it as well as the type of tissue and the species of animal. In some observations on the length of time in the chick embryo it was found to vary between 120 and 180 minutes. Of this time the metaphase was only 2 minutes long. Other observations show a somewhat shorter time (30 to 60 minutes). Cell division is faster in the embryo, slowing down as the animal reaches maturity and thereafter.

CELLULAR METABOLISM

The cell is the seat of biological oxidations which furnish energy for the varied activities of the living process. This energy comes from the food materials, chiefly sugar, which all animals must consume in order to live. When this energy is released in respiration, it is used for growth, manufacture of new protoplasm, the syntheses of many compounds, secretion, the contraction of muscle, and numerous other processes. The following classical formula of respiration is an oversimplified picture of the respiratory process and tells nothing about the numerous intermediate steps which are involved.

$$6 O_2 + C_6H_{12}O_6 \longrightarrow 6 CO_2 + 6 H_2O + \text{Energy}$$
(Oxygen) (Sugar)   (Carbon (Water)
                  dioxide)

Respiration is not merely the gaseous exchange between the cell and its surroundings or the intake of oxygen and the giving off of carbon dioxide. Actually, the oxygen is utilized and carbon dioxide and water are released in the final stages of the process. The development of knowledge about the metabolic process during the past decade or so has been a great triumph of biochemists in many lands. It is now known (although many details are lacking) that there is a complicated sequence of enzymatic reactions in respiration, resulting in a step-by-step breakdown of the carbohydrate molecule and the incorporation of phosphate groups which are important in the energy relationship. Some of these groups are high-energy phosphate compounds, one of which is adenosine triphosphate (ATP), the chief carrier of chemical energy within the animal. These energy-rich compounds are mainly used up in the cell where they are produced, and the process is essentially the same for all animals. Several steps in the respiratory process produce these energy-rich phosphate bonds which are efficient means of transferring energy within the cell.

Carbohydrate metabolism in the cell is divided into two major groups of steps. One of these groups takes place without oxygen (anaerobic) and is called glycolysis; the other group requires oxygen (aerobic) and is called by various names, such as Krebs cycle, citric acid cycle, and tricarboxylic acid cycle. In the first of these groups, when glucose is carried by the blood to a body cell it combines with a phosphate group to form glucose-phosphate. This process is called phosphorylation and is controlled by a special enzyme.

Next, this glucose-phosphate in a series of several steps is converted into a number of compounds, each of which is catalyzed by a special enzyme, and finally ends up with pyruvic acid. The energy released during certain of these steps is trapped in the energy-rich bonds of ATP which is now available for the energy requirements of the cell. This process of converting glucose and its phosphate group to pyruvic acid yields about 5% of the potential energy of the glucose molecule. Pyruvic acid, one of the main sources of energy in the cell, may be metabolized to carbon dioxide and water if oxygen is present; if no oxygen is available, then to alcohol, acetic acid, or other products, depending upon the enzyme present. These so-called waste products, alcohol, acetic acid, etc., still contain a great deal of energy.

The next series of energy-yielding reactions is the aerobic phase (Krebs or citric acid cycle), and this involves the oxidation of pyruvic acid which is presided over by a series of enzymes mostly furnished by the mitochondria of the cell. It has been possible to separate mitochondria from other cell components and to study their chemical properties. The rat liver cell, a common object of study, contains about 1,000 mitochondria. They contain many enzymes and coenzymes which appear to be arranged on the infolded membranes that are found in the interior of each mitochondrion. In the Krebs cycle, which yields about 95% of the remaining energy of the glucose molecule, the pyruvic acid is first converted to acetic acid which reacts with coenzyme A (from the vitamin pantothenic acid) to form acetyl coenzyme A. The latter unites with oxaloacetic acid to form citric acid. Then in a cyclic series of steps, each controlled by a special enzyme, the citric acid is broken down through eight different organic acids back to oxaloacetic acid which then can continue the cycle again. In this cycle carbon dioxide and hydrogen are given off by specific enzymes, and the hydrogen atoms are transferred by the flavoprotein and cytochrome enzyme systems to

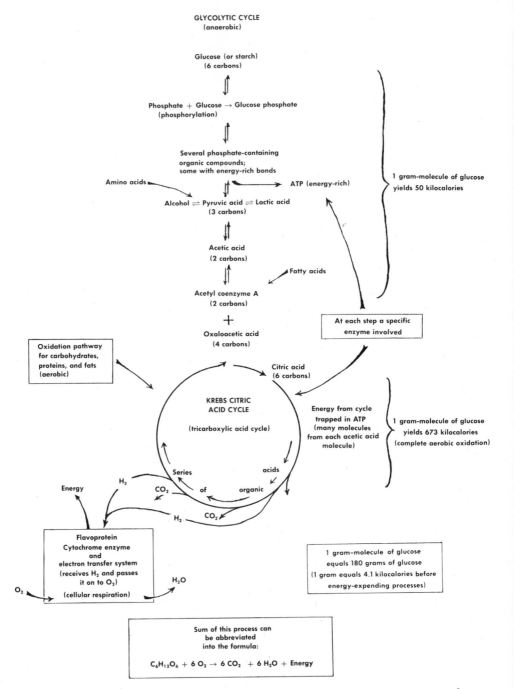

GLYCOLYTIC CYCLE
(anaerobic)

Glucose (or starch)
(6 carbons)

Phosphate + Glucose → Glucose phosphate
(phosphorylation)

Several phosphate-containing
organic compounds;
some with energy-rich bonds

Amino acids

Alcohol ⇌ Pyruvic acid ⇌ Lactic acid
(3 carbons)

ATP (energy-rich)

1 gram-molecule of glucose
yields 50 kilocalories

Acetic acid
(2 carbons)

Fatty acids

Acetyl coenzyme A
(2 carbons)

+

Oxaloacetic acid
(4 carbons)

At each step a specific
enzyme involved

Oxidation pathway
for carbohydrates,
proteins, and fats
(aerobic)

Citric acid
(6 carbons)

KREBS CITRIC
ACID CYCLE

(tricarboxylic acid cycle)

Energy from cycle
trapped in ATP
(many molecules
from each acetic acid
molecule)

1 gram-molecule of glucose
yields 673 kilocalories
(complete aerobic oxidation)

Series   acids

Energy   H₂   CO₂   of   organic

H₂   CO₂

Flavoprotein
Cytochrome enzyme
and
electron transfer system
(receives H₂ and passes
it on to O₂)

H₂O

O₂

(cellular respiration)

1 gram-molecule of glucose
equals 180 grams of glucose
(1 gram equals 4.1 kilocalories before
energy-expending processes)

Sum of this process can
be abbreviated
into the formula:

C₆H₁₂O₆ + 6 O₂ → 6 CO₂ + 6 H₂O + Energy

Figure 15. Scheme of some highlights of cellular metabolism. Within each cell glucose is first metabolized to pyruvic acid and then, if there is supply of O_2, to carbon dioxide and water. It is when hydrogen atoms are combined with oxygen that most of energy is released in cell. By storing energy in small packets (ATP), cell can utilize its energy for its various activities as needed. These reactions are universal in biological world. It will be seen that formula $C_6H_{12}O_6 + 6\ O_2 \rightarrow 6\ CO_2 + 6\ H_2O +$ energy gives little insight into actual oxidation of one molecule of glucose.

oxygen which unites with the hydrogen ions to form water (cellular respiration).

The result of this cycle is that the original pyruvic acid is oxidized to carbon dioxide and water and the energy released in the process is trapped in molecules of ATP, but far more of these energy-carrying compounds are formed in the Krebs cycle than in the glycolytic one. The Krebs cycle is also used in the oxidation of the fatty acids and amino acids of the other two classes of foodstuffs (fats and proteins) and is the chief source of chemical energy in the cell. The chief significance of these energy-rich phosphate bonds in the respiratory process is the efficient way they transfer energy within the cell to any site where energy is needed. There is also the importance of phosphorus in the life process. Whatever fuel is used, more ATP is gained than expended.

One of the most important activities of the cell is the synthesis of proteins. The main site of this protein synthesis is found in the microsomes which are tiny fragments of the endoplasmic reticulum, a system of membranes forming what appears to be a pattern of interconnecting canals. Microsomes have been separated from other cell constituents by the ultracentrifuge. By labelling amino acids (the building stones of proteins) with radioactive ions and introducing them into animal cells, it was found that only the protein of the microsomes had picked up the labelled ions, suggesting that protein synthesis was taking place here. Only a beginning has been made in solving the problem of how specific proteins are made.

ANNOTATED REFERENCES

Bonner, J. T. 1955. Cells and Societies. Princeton, Princeton University Press. *The author emphasizes the sameness of the basic biological requirements of all organisms, but the methods of meeting these requirements are highly varied. It is an excellent review of some of the chief functions of organisms.*

Bonner, J. T. 1959. The Cellular Slime Molds. Princeton, Princeton University Press. *In recent years interest has been focused on slime molds, which are saprophytes found growing on rocks and other places sufficiently moist. One group, Myxomycetes, forms a multinucleate mass of protoplasm called a plasmodium, but another unrelated group, called the simple slime molds (Acrasiales), form aggregations of multicellular individuals, not a concentration of protoplasm in one spot. The latter pose some interesting problems in development and differentiation.*

Brachet, J. 1957. Biochemical Cytology. New York, Academic Press, Inc. *An advanced work on the morphology and biochemistry of the cell. The author summarizes in admirable fashion the great strides made in this field during the past few decades but also warns that many of our concepts will no doubt be radically changed in the future.*

Brachet, J., and A. E. Mirsky. 1959. The Cell: Biochemistry, Physiology, Morphology. New York, Academic Press, Inc. *This is the first volume of a planned three-volume work on the various aspects of the cell and deals with the methods used in cytology and with some of the problems of cell biology. It is an ambitious work and should be a useful tool to many generations of biologists.*

Butler, J. A. V. 1959. Inside the Living Cell. Some Secrets of Life. New York, Basic Books, Inc. *This little volume will appeal to any ambitious zoology student who desires to know the scientist's present knowledge of the fundamental processes of life. "Multum in parvo" should be the subtitle of this revealing book.*

De Robertis, E. D. P., W. W. Nowinski, and F. A. Saez. 1948. General Cytology. Philadelphia, W. B. Saunders Co. *The third section in this excellent work deals with the morphological organization of the cell. A good description of mitosis is given in Chapter 8.*

Downes, H. R. 1955. The Chemistry of Living Cells. New York, Harper & Brothers. *This is an introductory text in biochemistry which gives an up-to-date account of the advances in this field.*

Giese, A. C. 1957. Cell Physiology. Philadelphia, W. B. Saunders Co. *An account of the latest concepts in cell physiology for students who have had good introductory courses in chemistry and physics.*

Gordon, M. (editor). 1959. Pigment Cell Biology. New York, Academic Press, Inc. *The pigment cell has been the focus of many investigations and this symposium attempts to resolve some of its many problems. A work for the specialist.*

Hall, T. S. 1951. A Source Book in Animal Biology. New York, McGraw-Hill Book Co., Inc. *Accounts of the development of the cell theory are included.*

Hughes, A. 1959. A History of Cytology. New York, Abelard-Schuman. *The development of cytology during the last half of the nineteenth century and the first part of the present century has formed a large part of biological history, and the present work is perhaps the most important account so far published of that development. An interesting series of plates from the works of the older cytologists adds much of interest to the book.*

Makino, S. 1951. An Atlas of the Chromosome Numbers in Animals. Ames, Iowa, The Iowa State College Press. *Brings up to date a summary of all chromosome counts.*

Mellors, R. C. (editor). 1959. Analytical Cytology, ed. 2. New York, McGraw-Hill Book Co., Inc. *An advanced treatise on the theory and practical application of the methods and techniques cytologists use in their investigations.*

Palay, S. L. (editor). 1958. Frontiers in Cytology. New Haven, Yale University Press. *This work is based on a series of lectures delivered at Yale University by many eminent specialists on current problems of cytology. It is a work for the serious student of zoology for it deals with the latest concepts of molecular biology.*

Rudnick, D. (editor). 1959. Developmental Cytology. New York, The Ronald Press Co. *This volume is based on a Symposium of the Society for the Study of Development and Growth which was held in 1957. It treats of surveys in the understanding of cellular structures and functions.*

Schrader, F. 1953. Mitosis. New York, Columbia University Press. *One of the best accounts of the latest concepts in the field of chromosome behavior and cell division.*

Sharp, L. W. 1943. Fundamentals of Cytology, rev. ed. New York, McGraw-Hill Book Co., Inc. *A good discussion of mitosis is given.*

Sussman, M. 1960. Animal Growth and Development, Englewood Cliffs, N. J., Prentice-Hall, Inc. *An excellent introduction to the problems of growth and development. Should be read by all zoology students in conjunction with the cell cycle.*

Swanson, C. P. 1957. Cytology and Cytogenetics. Englewood Cliffs, N. J., Prentice-Hall, Inc. *This is a lucid description of the present status of cytogenetics for the advance student. Students of genetics and evolution as well as cytologists will find this book a valuable tool. Such a work as this shows how far this science has advanced since Wilson's classical work on the cell.*

Swanson, C. P. 1960. The Cell. Englewood Cliffs, N. J., Prentice-Hall, Inc. *One of a series of biological monographs. An excellent account of the modern concept of the cell.*

Wyckoff, R. W. G. 1958. The World of the Electron Microscope. New Haven, Yale University Press. *This work explains the principles of this important tool of research and its practical application.*

chapter 4

Architectural
pattern of an animal

FUNDAMENTAL UNIFORMITY AMONG ANIMALS*

All animals have the same general plan, differing only in modification. There is a principle of uniformity throughout all biological organization. Of course there is a vast range of complexity between a protozoan and man, but the same life processes are found in each. The basic organization of all cells is much alike. Structural plans among animals vary but the organs are concerned with the same functions. Tracheal tubes, gills, and lungs, for instance, are all devices for breathing. Specialization or the division of labor of protoplasm has made possible the formation of tissues and organs. Changes in morphology and function have enabled animals to live in different kinds of habitats. The form of an animal determines how it meets its environment; a complex organization would be of no advantage in some situations; conversely, a simple organization could not survive in others. Nearly every structure in an animal has a functional or adaptational connotation. The student must not, however, think that structural adaptations are caused by the environment; rather the adaptations arose when, by natural selection, beneficial variations were preserved. This concept will be clearer when evolution is discussed.

*Refer to Chapter 5, Principles 4 and 15.

GRADES OF STRUCTURE AMONG ANIMALS

There are many grades of structure among animals. Through long geological periods of time, organic evolution has produced functional and structural adaptations which enable animals to fill a great variety of niches. The fossil record shows that some animals, such as lamp shells, have persisted unchanged for hundreds of millions of years because they were well adapted to an environmental niche which has changed little during that long time. The first grade of structure is that between the acellular (protozoa) and the cellular (metazoa). The **acellular** or single-celled forms are complete organisms and carry on all the functions of higher forms. Within the confines of their cell they often show complicated organization and division of labor, such as skeletal elements, locomotor devices, fibrils, beginnings of sense organs, and many others. On the other hand, the **metazoan** or multicellular animal has cells differentiated into tissues and organs which are specialized for different functions. The metazoan cell is not the equivalent of a protozoan cell; it is only a specialized part of the whole organism and usually cannot exist by itself.

How has complexity arisen in the animal kingdom? In general, it is a matter of difference in organization, but certain principles are involved. One of these is size, which will be discussed later in this chapter. Another is specialization and division of labor. An ameba can move without muscles, digest food without an alimentary canal, and can breathe without gills or lungs. But higher forms have specialized organs for these functions. The more complicated a device becomes, the more necessary it is to have accessory organs to help out. An alimentary canal is not a mere epithelial tube for secretion and absorption but has muscles to manipulate and nerves to control it. Specialization and division of labor have many advantages for adjustments to specific niches, but they require complicated machinery and more energy.

Does this mean that life is progressing toward higher and higher types, such as man? In the evolutionary picture the first animals were small and relatively simple, but there is no reason to believe that more recent animals are better adjusted to their environments than were their ancient ancestors. Nor is there any evidence that evolution has led in man's direction, for many lines definitely have not.

PRINCIPLE OF INDIVIDUALITY

All organisms, however simple, are composed of **units** with coordinated interreactions. The smallest units capable of independent existence are the **cells.** Among some biologists the **gene** is considered the chief biological unit. But many other units are recognized in both acellular and many-celled forms. Protozoans contain such units as the **contractile vacuole, nucleus,** and other organelles. In the metazoans units of different levels are **tissues, organs,** and **systems.** In some phyla **metamerism,** or the serially repeated division of the body into successive segments (as in the earthworm, for example), represents another grade of individuality. **Polymorphism,** in which there are more than one form of the same species, may consist of united individuals (Portuguese man-of-war) or they may be separate (certain ant colonies). Individuality is difficult to define because there are many gradations between separate organic entities and those of colonies whose members are attached together in some way. The organism is a historical entity which is made up of many stages in a life cycle, some of which may be very different, e.g., the tadpole and frog, the caterpillar and butterfly, etc. Is each stage a separate individual or should the combined stages of a life cycle be considered an individual?

Within the cell itself are found many other units. Whether there is an ultimate living unit, biologists do not know.

GRADES OF ORGANIZATION*

An animal is an organization of units differentiated and integrated for carrying on the life processes, but this organization goes from one level to another as we ascend the evolutionary path. The pattern of organization in a particular animal cannot be considered by itself but in conjunction with levels below and above it. While these levels are not always distinct but tend to merge, we may break down the animal kingdom into the following levels or grades of organization: protoplasmic, cellular, cell-tissue, tissue-organ, and organ system.

Protoplasmic grade of organization. This type is found in Protozoa or acellular forms. All activities of this level are confined to the one mass called the cell. Here the protoplasm is differentiated into specialized organelles which are capable of carrying on definite functions.

Cellular grade of organization. Here we have aggregations of cells where differentiation has occurred. This involves division of labor in which some cells are concerned with reproduction and others with nutrition. In its simplest form, the cells are scattered and have little tendency to become organized into definite layers (tissues). Sponges do not attain a higher level than this. In this sense, sponges may be considered the simplest of metazoan forms.

Cell-tissue grade of organization. A

---

*Refer to Chapter 5, Principle 6.

step beyond the preceding is the aggregation of similar cells into definite patterns of layers, thus becoming a tissue. The jellyfish are often referred to as the beginning of the tissue plan. This group is still largely of the cellular grade of organization, for most of the cells are scattered and not organized into tissues. An excellent example of a tissue in coelenterates is the **nerve net,** in which the nerve cells and their processes form a definite tissue structure with the function of coordination.

Tissue-organ grade of organization. The aggregation of tissues into organs is a further step in advancement. Organs are usually made up of more than one kind of tissue and have a more specialized function than tissues. The first appearance of this level is in the flatworms (Platyhelminthes), where there are a number of well-defined organs such as eyespots, proboscis, and reproductive organs.

Organ-system grade of organization. When organs work together to perform some function, we have the highest level of organization—the organ system. The systems are associated with the basic bodily functions—circulation, respiration, digestion, etc. Typical of all the higher forms, this type of organization is first seen in the nemertean worms in which a complete digestive system, separate and distinct from the circulatory system, is present.

PRELIMINARY SURVEY OF ANIMAL EMBRYOLOGY*

A brief summary of embryology is necessary for understanding the pattern of an animal and also for understanding some of the basic concepts used in describing animal groups and their classification. Broader problems in this field and those of experimental embryology will be discussed in Chapter 33, Principles of Development.

Embryology is the science that deals with the development of the organism from the zygote to the completion of its bodily structure. An embryo is the stage of an organism before birth or hatching.

All animals have a characteristic life history. This may be very simple but is often involved in the Metazoa. Many protozoa such as the ameba, are potentially immortal and come from an ancestral line that has never experienced natural death from old age, because their method of asexual binary reproduction is simply the dividing of the parent organism into two daughter cells, each essentially a continuation of the parent. Early in the life history of all metazoans, however, there occurs a differentiation of the germ cell from the body or soma cells. It is the uniting of the germ cells (male sperm and female ova) which gives rise to a new generation (sexual reproduction) while the body (soma) cells die. The real life history of a metazoan starts with the union of an ovum (egg) with a spermatozoan, a process called fertilization. **Sexual reproduction** may be of two types. If the egg develops without fertilization it is called **parthenogenesis;** if both egg and sperm are involved it is **biparental reproduction.** If only one kind of sex cell (egg or sperm) is produced in a single individual such a condition is called **dioecious;** if both kinds are in the same individual it is called **monoecious** or **hermaphroditic.** The fertilized egg, called a **zygote,** is really a one-celled organism, and from it develops a complete animal with all its structures and functions. The major process which makes this possible is **differentiation,** by which the various cells become unlike. How this occurs is only partly known. When a zygote divides into cells (**cleavage**), there is a distribution of different structures and functions to the cells. Both morphological differentiation and physiological division of labor thus take place. Some structures and functions are present in the zygote, but many new ones arise from new combinations, for embryology is synthetic. What determines the final animal pattern? Heredity stabilizes the pattern; variation makes evolutionary changes possible.

*Refer to Chapter 5, Principle 17.

Types of eggs and the zygote

Differences in embryonic development depend partly upon the type of egg involved. Some eggs have much food material (**yolk**) for the growing embryo; others have little yolk. It is an embryonic principle that the speed of cleavage (the cell division by which the embryo is formed) is inversely proportional to the amount of yolk.

Eggs may be classified as follows with respect to yolk distribution:

The **isolecithal egg** (also called alecithal or homolecithal) is small and the small amount of yolk (deutoplasm) and cytoplasm is uniformly distributed though the egg and the nucleus near the center. Cleavage is usually **holoblastic** (total) and the cells (blastomeres) are nearly equal in size. Such eggs are found in the protochordates (such as sea squirts and *Amphioxus*) and the echinoderms (sea stars and sea urchins).

In the **telolecithal egg** the large amount of yolk (50 to 90%) tends to be concentrated toward one pole (the vegetal pole) where metabolism is lower. The protoplasm and nucleus are found mainly at the opposite (animal) pole where metabolic activity is greater. There are two classes of this type: (1) Yolked eggs with **holoblastic** cleavage, in which the later cleavages produce unequal cells—small cells or micromeres at the animal pole and large cells or macromeres at the vegetal pole. Amphibians and bony fish have this kind of egg. (2) Yolked eggs (megalecithal) with **meroblastic** (partial or discoidal) cleavage, in which the small amount of protoplasm is concentrated at the animal pole in the germinal disc or blastoderm where cleavage occurs. These eggs are usually large, contain a great deal of albumin (egg white) derived from the oviducts, and have a hard or soft shell. Bird and reptile eggs are good examples.

In the **centrolecithal egg** the nucleus and the surrounding layer of protoplasm are at first in the center of the egg, but as cleavage occurs, most of the nucleated masses of cytoplasm migrate to the periphery and form a cellular layer (blastoderm), leaving the yolk in the center of the egg. From the blastoderm the embryo develops. These eggs are characteristic of the arthropods.

Eggs may also be classified with respect to their environment into **fresh-water eggs** with much salt and yolk (amphibians), **marine eggs** with little salt and yolk (fish), **terrestrial eggs** with much yolk and more or less free from environmental dependence (birds), and **intrauterine eggs** with little yolk and largely dependent on the maternal organism for nourishment (mammals).

In addition to the plasma membrane universally present in eggs, there are in the various animal groups many kinds of protective membranes or envelopes around the eggs. These include the **vitelline** or fertilization membrane secreted by the egg, the **zona pellucida** formed by the ovarian follicle cells of mammals, the **egg jelly** from the oviducts of bony fish and amphibians, and the **chitinous shell** (chorion) from the ovarian tubules of insects.

Formation of embryo

Cleavage. This is the mitotic division of the fertilized ovum (zygote) into cells (**blastomeres**) and is the first stage of embryonic development. There are a number of different types of cleavage, depending upon the amount of yolk in the

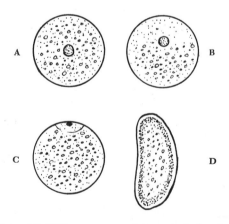

Figure 16. Different types of eggs. **A,** Isolecithal; **B** and **C,** telolecithal; **D,** centrolecithal.

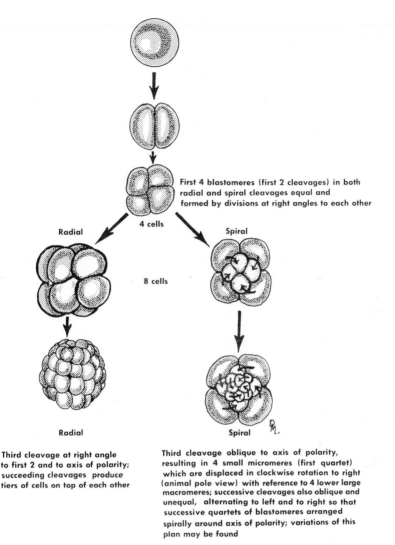

First 4 blastomeres (first 2 cleavages) in both
radial and spiral cleavages equal and
formed by divisions at right angles to each other

Radial

4 cells

Spiral

8 cells

Radial

Spiral

Third cleavage at right angle
to first 2 and to axis of polarity;
succeeding cleavages produce
tiers of cells on top of each other

Third cleavage oblique to axis of polarity,
resulting in 4 small micromeres (first quartet)
which are displaced in clockwise rotation to right
(animal pole view) with reference to 4 lower large
macromeres; successive cleavages also oblique and
unequal, alternating to left and to right so that
successive quartets of blastomeres arranged
spirally around axis of polarity; variations of this
plan may be found

Figure 17. Comparison of spiral and radial changes in holoblastic cleavage. Spiral cleavage (Annelida, Mollusca, Rhyncocoela, Platyhelminthes, and certain minor phyla) produces definite pattern of development, so that fate of early blastomeres can be foretold (determinate cleavage). In radial cleavage (Echinodermata, Chordata, and a few others) differentiation of early blastomeres is delayed and each one is equipotent, i.e., can give rise to a whole embryo (indeterminate cleavage). Nematodes have neither radial nor spiral cleavage.

egg. In **equal holoblastic cleavage** the egg and each succeeding cell splits so that the daughter cells are approximately equal (*Amphioxus,* sea star); in **unequal holoblastic cleavage** the daughter cells are unequal (most stages of the frog); in **meroblastic cleavage** division occurs only in the living matter on one side of the yolk mass (birds, reptiles); and in **superficial cleavage** division is restricted to a layer around the yolk (insects).

Cleavage can be divided into two types according to the potentialities of the blastomeres. In some all the blastomeres must be present to form a whole embryo (**determinate** or **mosaic** cleavage); in others, each separate early blastomere

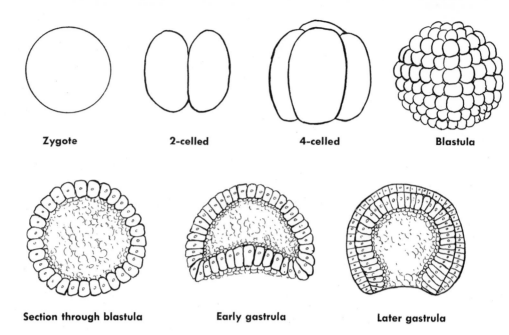

Zygote   2-celled   4-celled   Blastula

Section through blastula   Early gastrula   Later gastrula

Figure 18. Cleavage and gastrulation in isolecithal type of egg, such as *Amphioxus*.

may give rise to a complete embryo (**indeterminate** cleavage). (See Chapter 33.)

SPIRAL AND RADIAL CLEAVAGE. Holoblastic cleavage is also classified on the basis of radial and spiral types. In the **radial** type the cleavage planes are symmetrical to the polar axis and produce tiers or layers of cells on top of each other; in the **spiral** type the cleavage planes are diagonal to the polar axis and produce alternate clockwise and counterclockwise quartets of unequal cells around the axis of polarity. These types of cleavage have great significance in the two great groups of deuterostomes and protostomes. Radial cleavage is indeterminate and there is no definite relation between the position of any blastomere and the specific tissue it will form in the embryo; spiral cleavage is determinate and the fate of each blastomere can be foretold.

Blastula and gastrula formation. Further divisions of cleavage result in an embryo in the form of a hollow ball, with the wall usually consisting of a single layer of cells (**blastoderm**). This stage is the **blastula** and the cavity is called a **blastocoele** (segmentation cavity). An inpushing of one side of the blastula occurs next, partially obliterating the blastocoele and forming a two-layered cup-like stage, the **gastrula**. The new cavity so formed is the **archenteron** (primitive gut), with its opening to the outside, the **blastopore**. Modifications of this process of **gastrulation** are found in yolk-laden eggs.

Formation of germ layers and their fate.[*] The process of gastrulation gives rise at first to two germ layers, an outer (**ectoderm**) and an inner (**endoderm**) layer of cells. In certain simple metazoans, such as certain coelenterates, these are the only germ layers and the animal is called **diploblastic**. In higher forms a middle germ layer, **mesoderm**, develops either from pouches of the archenteron or from other cells, and such animals are called **triploblastic**. From these germ layers all the tissues and organs of an animal are derived.

---

[*]Refer to Chapter 5, Principle 30.

ECTODERM

Epidermis of skin
Lining of mouth, anus, nostrils
Sweat and sebaceous glands
Epidermal coverings, such as hair, nails, feathers, horns, epidermal scales, enamel of teeth
Nervous system, including sensory parts of eye, nose, ear

ENDODERM

Lining of alimentary canal
Lining of respiratory passages and lungs
Secretory parts of liver and pancreas
Thyroid, parathyroid, thymus
Urinary bladder
Lining of urethra

MESODERM

Skeleton and muscles
Dermis of skin
Dermal scales and dentine
Excretory and reproductive systems
Connective tissue
Blood and blood vessels
Mesenteries
Lining of coelomic cavity

The idea that each germ layer can give rise to certain tissues and organs only and to no others is no longer held. It is now known that the interactions of cells play a part in determining their differentiation in vertebrate animals. The precise position of a cell with relation to other cells and tissues during early development often controls the real fate of that cell. Under some conditions a certain germ layer may give rise to structures normally arising from a different germ layer. Experiments have demonstrated that a presumptive ectodermal structure when grafted into appropriate regions will form organs that normally come from a different germ layer. The topographical position, therefore, of cells in their development must play a significant role in their final fate and destiny. Embryological development must be considered quite flexible and indefinite. The biological system cannot be restricted to a definite pattern even though normally it appears to be. Are there any organs or structures which do not come from any germ layer? In a strict sense, the germ cells have not

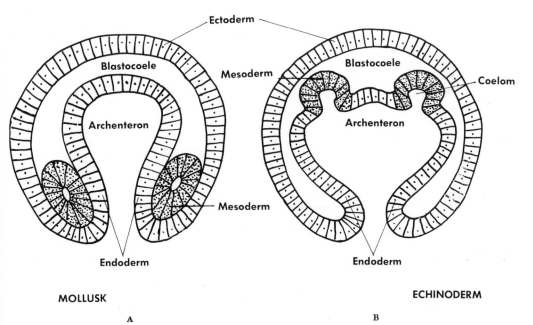

Figure 19. Two types of mesoderm and coelom formation. **A,** Mesoderm originates from wall of archenteron near lips of blastopore; coelom forms in splitting mesoderm. **B,** Mesoderm and coelom develop from endodermal pouches. **A** is schizocoelous and **B** is enterocoelous method of coelom formation.

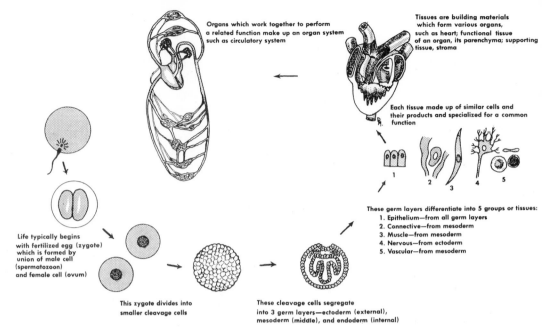

Organs which work together to perform a related function make up an organ system such as circulatory system

Tissues are building materials which form various organs, such as heart; functional tissue of an organ, its parenchyma; supporting tissue, stroma

Each tissue made up of similar cells and their products and specialized for a common function

These germ layers differentiate into 5 groups or tissues:
1. Epithelium—from all germ layers
2. Connective—from mesoderm
3. Muscle—from mesoderm
4. Nervous—from ectoderm
5. Vascular—from mesoderm

Life typically begins with fertilized egg (zygote) which is formed by union of male cell (spermatozoon) and female cell (ovum)

This zygote divides into smaller cleavage cells

These cleavage cells segregate into 3 germ layers—ectoderm (external), mesoderm (middle), and endoderm (internal)

Figure 20. How organism is formed.

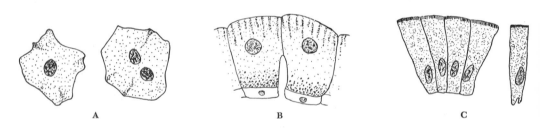

A   B   C

Figure 21. **A,** Simple squamous epithelial cells from lining of mouth. **B,** Simple cuboidal epithelium. **C,** Simple columnar epithelium.

originated from any of the three germ layers, for they have come directly from cells that were segregated in the early cleavage stages of the fertilized egg.

Differentiation of tissues, organs, and systems*

The processes by which germ layers give rise to tissues and organs vary. The germ layers by budding and folding first form a tubular embryo. Then by a process called **histogenesis** the five major tissues are differentiated: (1) epithelial

tissue, from all three germ layers; (2) connective or supporting tissue, from mesoderm; (3) muscular or contractile tissue, from mesoderm; (4) nervous tissue, from ectoderm; and (5) vascular tissue, from mesoderm. A tissue is a group of similar cells (together with associated cell products) specialized for the performance of a common function. The study of tissues is called **histology.** All cells in metazoan animals take part in the formation of tissues. Sometimes the cells of a tissue may be of several kinds, and some tissues have a great many intercellular materials.

Epithelial tissue. An epithelium is a

———

*Refer to Chapter 5, Principle 4.

78

tissue that covers an external or internal surface. It includes also hollow or solid derivatives from this tissue. Epithelial tissues (Figures 21 to 24) are made up of closely associated cells with some intercellular material between the cells. Some cells are bound together by **intercellular bridges** of cytoplasm. Most of them have one surface free and the other surface lying upon vascular connective tissue. A noncellular **basement membrane** is often attached to the basal cells. Epithelial cells are often modified to produce secretory glands which may be unicellular or multicellular. Some free surfaces (joint cavities, bursae, brain cavity) are not lined with typical epithelium. Epithelia are classified on the basis of cell form and number of cell layers. **Simple epithelium** is one layer thick, and its cells may be flat or **squamous** (endothelium of blood vessels), short prisms or **cuboidal** (glands and ducts), and tall or **columnar** (stomach and intestine). Any of these three forms of cells may occur in several layers as a **stratified epithelium** (skin, sweat glands, urethra). Some stratified epithelia can change the number of their cell layers by movement (**transitional,** bladder). Others have cells of different heights and give the appearance of stratified epithelia (**pseudostratified,** trachea). Many epithelia may be **ciliated** at their free surfaces (oviduct). Epithelia serve to protect, secrete, excrete, lubricate, etc.

Connective tissue (supporting). Connective tissues bind together and support other structures. They are so common that the removal of other bodily components would still leave the gross outlines of the body distinguishable. They are derived from the **mesenchyme,** a generalized embryonic tissue that can differentiate also into vascular tissue and smooth muscle. Mesenchyme may also be considered the most primitive connective tissue. When its cells are closely packed together it is called **parenchyma;** when loosely arranged with gelatinous material it is **collenchyma.** Connective tissue is made up of scattered cells and a great deal of formed materials such as **fibers** and

ground substance (**matrix**). Fibers probably originate from ground substances secreted by the cells. There are three types of fibers: white or collagenous, yellow or elastic, and branching or reticular. Connective tissue may be classified in various ways, but all the types fall under either **loose connective tissue** (reticular, areolar, adipose) or **dense connective tissue** (sheaths, ligaments, tendons, cartilage, bone). The distinction between these two groups is mainly one between fibers,

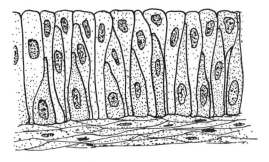

Figure 22. Pseudostratified epithelium.

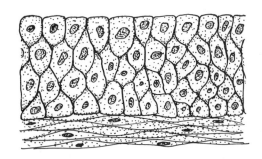

Figure 23. Stratified columnar epithelium.

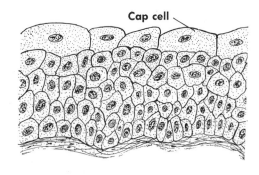

Cap cell

Figure 24. Transitional epithelium.

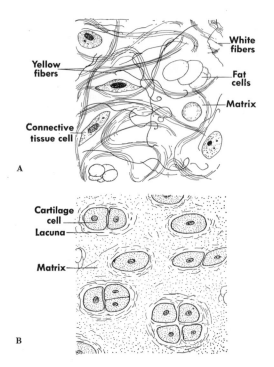

Figure 25. A, Areolar connective tissue. B, Hyaline cartilage, most common form of cartilage in body.

ground substance, and cells. For example, adipose stresses cells, ligaments stress fibers, and cartilage stresses ground substance (matrix).

MUSCULAR TISSUE. Muscle is the most common tissue in the body of most animals. It is made up of elongated cells or fibers specialized for contraction. It makes possible the movements of the body and its parts. It originated (with few exceptions) from the mesoderm and its unit is the cell or **muscle fiber.** The unspecialized cytoplasm of muscles is called **sarcoplasm,** and the contractile elements within the fiber (cell) are the **myofibrils.** Functionally, muscles are either **voluntary** (under control of will) or **involuntary.** Structurally, they are either **smooth** (fibers unstriped) or **striated** (fibers cross-striped). The three kinds of muscular tissue are **smooth involuntary** (walls of viscera, walls of blood vessels), **striated involuntary** or cardiac (heart), and **striated voluntary** or skeletal (limb and trunk).

NERVOUS TISSUE. This tissue is made up of cells specialized for irritability and conductivity (innate characteristics of protoplasm). The structural and functional unit of the nervous system is the neuron (Figure 27). This is a nerve cell made up of a body containing the nucleus and its processes or **fibers.** It originates from an embryonic ectodermal cell called a **neuroblast.** (Part of the nervous system of echinoderms may be mesodermal in origin.) In most animals the bodies of nerve cells are restricted to the central nervous system and ganglia, but the fibers may be very long and ramify through the body. Neurons are arranged in chains and the point of contact between neurons is a **synapse.** Some of the fibers bear a sheath (medullated or myelin); in others it is absent (nonmedullated).

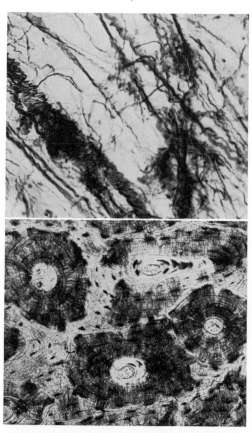

Figure 26. A, Photomicrograph of areolar connective tissue. B, Photomicrograph of section through bone, showing Haversian systems.

Sensory neurons are concerned with picking up impulses from sensory **receptors** in the skin or sense organs and transmitting them to nerve centers (brain or spinal cord). **Motor neurons** carry impulses from the nerve centers to muscles or glands (**effectors**) which are thus stimulated to act. **Association neurons** may form various connections between other neurons.

VASCULAR TISSUE. Vascular tissue is a fluid tissue composed of **white blood cells, red blood cells, platelets,** and a liquid, **plasma.** Through blood vessels it conveys to the tissue cells the materials necessary for their life process. **Lymph** and tissue fluids which arise from blood by filtration and serve in the exchange between cells and blood also belong to vascular tissue.

MOIST MEMBRANES

Important functional structures of the body are the moist mucous and serous membranes. These membranes are modified from epithelium and connective tissue and are kept moist by either thin watery secretions or thick mucous secretions. Both these membranes are found in the interior of the body; mucous membranes communicate with the outside of the body, whereas serous membranes are in closed body cavities. A **mucous membrane** is made up of a layer of epithelium (simple or stratified) resting upon a bed of connective tissue. Its surface is kept moist by goblet cells or multicellular glands. Mucous membranes have a wide distribution in the lining of hollow organs, such as the alimentary canal, urinary and genital tracts, sinuses, respiratory passageways, etc. A **serous membrane** consists of a flat mesothelium (sometimes cuboidal or columnar cells in lower vertebrates) which is supported by a thin layer of connective tissue. This membrane is kept moist by a scanty fluid and contains various free cells from the mesothelium and the blood. Serous membranes are usually divided into a parietal portion, which lines the external walls of the cavities, and a visceral portion, which is reflected over

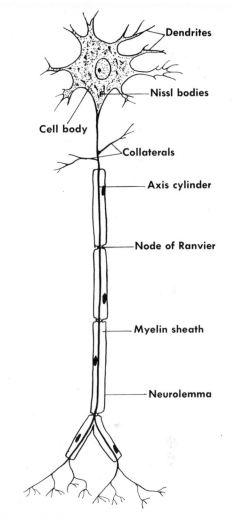

Figure 27. Diagram of neuron.

the exposed surfaces of organs. The pericardium, pleura, and peritoneum are all serous membranes. Both mucous and serous membranes perform important functions of lubrication, protection, support, and defense against bacterial infection.

ORGANS AND SYSTEMS*

Definitions. An **organ** is a group of tissues that performs a certain function. In higher forms many organs may have most of the various tissues in their make-up (Figure 28). If one looks at the heart

---

*Refer to Chapter 5, Principle 6.

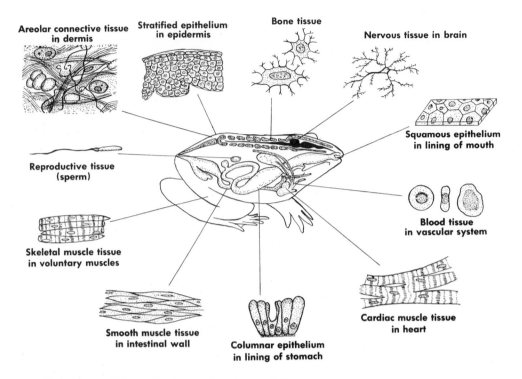

Areolar connective tissue in dermis

Stratified epithelium in epidermis

Bone tissue

Nervous tissue in brain

Squamous epithelium in lining of mouth

Reproductive tissue (sperm)

Blood tissue in vascular system

Skeletal muscle tissue in voluntary muscles

Cardiac muscle tissue in heart

Smooth muscle tissue in intestinal wall

Columnar epithelium in lining of stomach

Figure 28. Diagram of frog, showing various types of tissues.

(Figure 29) he finds epithelial tissue as covering and lining, connective tissue for framework, muscular walls for contraction, nervous elements for coordination, and vascular tissue for transportation.

The science of the arrangement of tissues to form organs is called **organology.** All organs have a characteristic structural plan. Usually one tissue carries the burden of the organ's chief function, such as the muscle does in the heart; the other tissues are of secondary importance. The chief functional cells of an organ are called its **parenchyma;** the supporting tissues are its **stroma.** For instance, in the pancreas the secreting cells (glandular epithelium) are the parenchyma; the capsule and connective tissue framework represent the stroma.

Organs, in turn, are associated and coordinated to form **systems,** each of which is concerned with performing some general function.

Eleven systems of animals. The eleven systems may be said to carry on the major life functions of the organism, and the sum total of these functions represents the life process as we commonly think of it.

INTEGUMENTARY. This system consists of the skin and its modifications—hair, scales, feathers, etc.

SKELETAL. This is made up of the bones and cartilages, serving as the framework of the body.

CIRCULATORY. The chief organs of this system are the heart, blood vessels, lymph nodes, and lymphatics. This is the transportation system of the body.

DIGESTIVE. Its organs are the mouth, pharynx, esophagus, stomach, intestines, together with the accessory salivary glands, the liver, and the pancreas. The chief function is the ingestion and digestion of food.

RESPIRATORY. Respiratory organs are the lungs, gills, air passageways, and others concerned with breathing.

EXCRETORY. The components of this system are the kidneys, nephridia, Malpighian tubules, urinary bladder, ureters, and other similar organs. These eliminate waste from the blood and from the body.

MUSCULAR. The various muscles and tendons represent its organs. Their purpose is to produce the movements of the organism.

NERVOUS. Its organs are the brain, various ganglia, spinal cord, and nerves. This is the great integrating and coordinating system of the body.

SENSORY. This system is made up of the various sense organs, including not only the complicated major organs of sense but also simpler receptors and sensory corpuscles. Its purpose is to receive stimuli from the animal's environment.

REPRODUCTIVE. The gonads, consisting of the testes in the male and the ovaries in the female, the reproductive ducts, and certain glands represent the organs of the reproductive system. They are concerned with the continuation of the species.

ENDOCRINE. This system is composed of various ductless glands, such as the thyroid, pituitary, adrenal, parathyroid, and others. Their secretory products, called hormones, are carried by the blood stream to target organs where characteristic responses are elicited. This system shares certain basic integrative functions with the nervous system.

INSTABILITY OF TISSUES AND ORGANS

Although in the popular concept tissues and organs are more or less fixed entities in their structure, the radioactive isotope technique has given a different picture. Instead of being fixed or static, most tissues, according to the new view, are continually undergoing change and remain constant only in their general pattern. There is a ceaseless ebb and flow of their constituents regardless of the nature of the tissue or organ. Molecules are being shifted from one region to another. There is a steady interchange of substances and a constant release and uptake from cellular tissues. Some substances are broken down; others are synthesized. Much of this dynamic state is influenced or controlled by hormones, vitamins, and enzymes. The evidence for this new view has been based primarily upon tagging suitable compounds by the isotope tracer method and introducing them into the biological system. Later, the location and fate of these labeled substances are de-

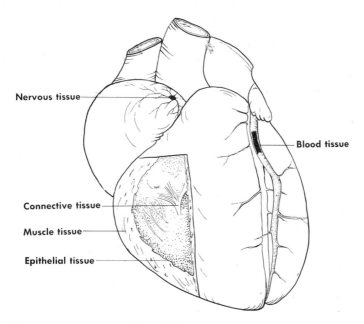

Figure 29. Heart, showing various types of tissue in its structure.

Nervous tissue

Blood tissue

Connective tissue

Muscle tissue

Epithelial tissue

termined. It is now possible to ascertain with great precision what goes on in metabolic reactions and how structural units are replaced.

PRINCIPLE OF ORGANIC SYMMETRY*

Symmetry is the arrangement of bodily parts in relation to planes and centralized axes in such a way that the parts exhibit geometrical designs. An object is symmetrical where there is a correspondence in form and arrangement of parts, so that a plane passing through the center will divide it into similar halves. When an object cannot be divided into like parts by a plane, it is **asymmetrical.** All animals are either asymmetrical or symmetrical. Examples of asymmetrical forms are most sponges, some Protozoa, and a few others. The most common types of symmetry are **radial** and **bilateral,** but two others, **spherical** and **biradial,** are recognized. In explaining organic symmetry, an **axis** is an imaginary line passing through the center of a body; a **pole** is either extremity of an axis; and a **plane** of symmetry is one that divides organisms into corresponding halves. The animal has three axes corresponding to the three dimensions of space, and each axis has two poles.

Spherical symmetry is found in organisms that have the form of a sphere. An infinite number of planes passed through the center of the body will cut it into similar halves. All the axes through the center have like ends (**homopolar**). Some protozoans, such as Heliozoa and Radiolaria, approach this type, and it is adapted only for floating or rolling movements.

In **radially symmetrical** animals the body has the form of a cylinder or similar shape, with the body parts arranged around a central **longitudinal axis** in a circular or radiating manner. Any plane through this longitudinal axis will divide the body into similar halves. The longitudinal axis has unlike ends (**heteropolar**). One of these ends is the **oral** (mouth) end and the other is the **aboral.**

---

*Refer to Chapter 5, Principle 9.

84

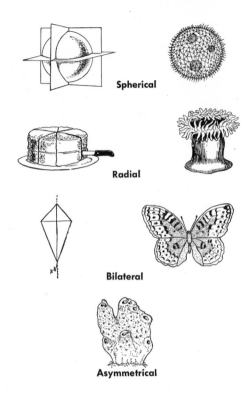

Figure 30. Types of symmetry.

A few sponges, many colenterates, and adult echinoderms are examples of radial symmetry, which is best suited for a sessile existence since the animal can react equally on all sides.

A variant form of radial symmetry is **biradial symmetry.** In this type there is a central longitudinal axis with two other axes (**sagittal** and **tranverse**) at right angles to it and to each other. A plane passing through the longitudinal and sagittal axes and also one through the longitudinal and transverse axes will divide the animal into halves. Such symmetry has two pairs of symmetrical sides. Only the longitudinal axis is heteropolar; the other two are homopolar. This symmetry is found in the Ctenophora and some of the Anthozoa and is best fitted for a floating life.

In **bilaterally symmetrical** animals the longitudinal axis runs from the anterior (head) end to the posterior (tail) end. There is only one plane that will divide the animal into two similar halves—the median longitudinal or **sagittal** plane dividing the animal into right and left halves. There are three axes of symmetry, of which the longitudinal axis is heteropolar, the sagittal axis is also heteropolar (dorsal or back side and ventral or belly side), and the transverse axis is homopolar (the lateral sides are alike). Most animals have bilateral symmetry, for this type stresses forward movement and the differentiation of a head end with high perception (brain, sense organs) so necessary in the search for food and protection. The upper (dorsal) and lower or belly (ventral) surfaces are unlike because they are exposed to different conditions.

PRINCIPLE OF CEPHALIZATION AND POLARITY*

The differentiation of the anterior or oral end of an animal into a definite head is called **cephalization** and is found chiefly in bilaterally symmetrical animals. Cephalization involves the concentration of nervous tissue (brain and sense organs) in the head. This arrangement in an actively moving animal makes possible the most efficient reaction with the environment. Cephalization is always accompanied by a differentiation along an anteroposterior axis or **polarity**. Polarity usually involves gradients which refers to ascending or descending activities between limits, such as between anterior and posterior ends (see axial gradient theory).

PRINCIPLE OF METAMERISM

Metamerism is a condition in animals in which the body is composed of a linear series of similar body segments Each segment is called a **metamere** or **somite**. There are some differences, however, among the various segments with respect to certain internal organs. In general, in forms such as the earthworm, where metamerism is best represented, the segmental arrangement includes both external and internal structures of several systems. There is repetition of muscles, blood vessels, nerves, and the setae of locomotion. Some other organs, such as those of sex, are repeated in only a few somites. In segmented animals higher than the earthworm, much of the segmental arrangement has become obscure through fusion and loss of metameres, disappearance of organs, and centralization and specialization of structural elements.

When the somites are similar, as in the earthworm, the condition is called **homonomous metamerism;** if they are dissimilar, as in the lobster and insect, it is called **heteronomous metamerism.**

Segmentation often shows up in embryonic stages, particularly in those forms in which metamerism is not so evident in the adult. Muscles of vertebrate animals show a marked metamerism in the embryo but little in the adult. In adult vertebrates the arrangement of the vertebrae shows a metameric condition.

Metamerism is found in three phyla: Annelida, Arthropoda, and Chordata.

PRINCIPLE OF HOMOLOGY AND ANALOGY*

The term **homology** is used in connection with body parts that correspond in type of structure or position and have a similar background, such as embryonic origin or evolutionary ancestry. It does not necessarily denote similarity of function. **Serial** or **general homology** refers to the relation in structures which are repeated on the same organism. The arms and legs of a man or the fingers of a hand are serially homologous. All of the appendages of a lobster, including antennae, mouth parts, legs, and swimmerets, are serially homologous, even though their functions differ, and so are the appendages of a centipede whose function is similar. **Special homology** refers to correspondence between parts of different animals. The arm of a man, the wing of a bird, the foreleg of a dog, and the pectoral fin of a fish are examples of this type. However different two structures may appear, if it can be shown through

---

*Refer to Chapter 5, Principle 24.

*Refer to Chapter 5, Principle 19.

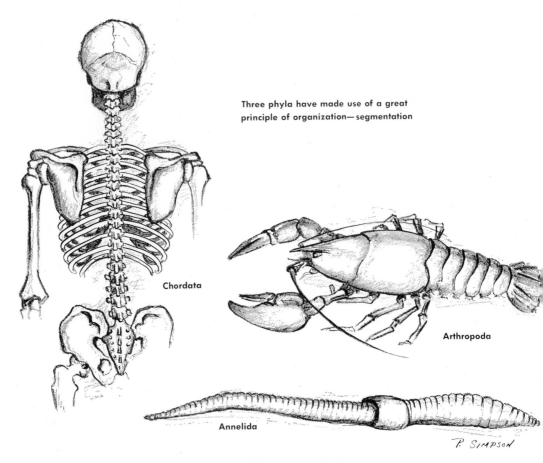

Three phyla have made use of a great principle of organization—segmentation

Chordata

Arthropoda

Annelida

P. SIMPSON

Figure. 31. Segmented phyla. These three phyla have all made use of an important principle in nature, polyisomerism, or repetition of structural units. Phyla Annelida and Arthropoda are definitely related, but chordates have derived their segmentation independently. Segmentation brings a more varied specialization, for segments, especially in arthropods, have become modified for different functions.

embryology, fossils, or other evidence that they have originated in the same way, they are considered homologous.

Analogy denotes similarity of function. The wing of a bird is analogous to the wing of a butterfly, for they have the same function, but they are not homologous because they are formed from different sources.

The principle of homology has a wide application in zoology. It is an argument for evolution because it is based upon the idea of inheritance from like ancestors. Homology is also an important consideration in classifying animals.

BODY CAVITY OR COELOM*

The coelom is the true body cavity. It is the space between the digestive tube and the outer wall; it contains the other visceral organs. Not all animals have a coelom, for example, the jellyfish and flatworms. Animals that have one may be compared to two tubes, one within the other. The outer tube is the body wall; the inner tube is the digestive tract and the space between is the coelom. This is called a "tube-within-a-tube" arrangement (Figure 32). A true coelom de-

———————

*Refer to Chapter 5, Principle 31.

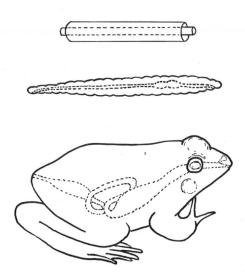

Figure 32. Tube-within-a-tube arrangement.

velops between two layers of mesoderm—an outer somatic layer and an inner visceral layer—and is lined with mesodermal epithelium called the peritoneum.

The coelom may be formed by one of two methods, schizocoelous or enterocoelous. In schizocoelous formation the coelom arises from the splitting of mesodermal bands which originate from the blastopore region and grow between the ectoderm and endoderm; in enterocoelous formation the coelom comes from the fusion and expansion of outfolding pouches of the archenteron or primitive gut. (See Figure 19.)

The coelom is of great significance in animal evolution, for it provides spaces for visceral organs, permits greater size and complexity by exposing more cells to surface exchange, and contributes directly to the development of certain systems, such as excretory, reproductive, and muscular.

There are modifications of the coelom in different animals. In some of the arthropods the coelom is made up of scattered spaces (hemocoel) in which blood circulates. In the earthworm and other annelids the coelom is divided by septa into chambers corresponding to the somites. In threadworms and some others the body cavities are not lined with mesoderm and

so are given the name of pseudocoel. Among certain vertebrates the coelom is divided by the diaphragm into the thoracic and abdominal cavities, with a separate pericardial cavity around the heart.

SIZE OF THE ORGANISM

Different species of animals show an enormous range in size from the tiny protozoan weighing a fraction of a milligram to the whale weighing more than one hundred tons. Many animals, such as birds and mammals, have definite age limits to growth, but in reptiles and fishes growth may continue throughout life, although at a reduced pace. Mammals vary from forms as small as shrews to those as large as whales. One may get the idea that the evolutionary trend has been from the small to the large, but this has not always been the case.

It is a general principle that every organism is distinguished by a characteristic size.* Of course, many factors may modify the dimensions of an individual animal, such as nutrition and hormone imbalance. When unicellular animals reach a certain size they divide, for beyond a certain size a definite limitation is imposed upon the animal. This is based upon the mechanical principle of surface-volume ratio. Every cell depends upon its surface membrane for the exchange of materials with the surrounding environment. This exchange rests upon the capacity of substances to diffuse through the membrane into or out of the cell. The volume increases as the cube of the radius; the surface as the square of the radius. Since the volume increases much faster than the surface, as the size of the cell increases the rate of exchange of food and waste decreases. Protozoans can solve the problem by simply dividing when they reach a certain size. Large animals are made up of cells. By keeping their cells small there is a morphological increase in surface. This is why large animals have digestive systems many times longer than their bodies, with various de-

---

*Refer to Chapter 5, Principle 9.

Architectural pattern of an animal 87

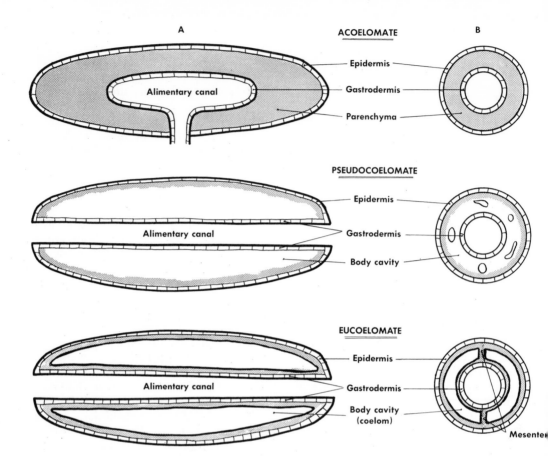

Figure 33. Schematic drawings of types of body cavity organizations. **A,** Longitudinal sections through organisms. **B,** Cross-sections through same. In acoelomate type, space between epidermis and gastrodermis is filled with mesenchymal parenchyma which may contain small spaces; in pseudocoelomate type space between body wall and digestive tract is remnant of blastocoele and is not lined with mesodermal peritoneum; and in eucoelomate, or true coelomate, type body cavity is lined with mesodermal peritoneum which also covers digestive tract. Mesenteries are made up of two peritoneal layers.

vices for greatly increasing the surface for absorption. Large animals have a relatively lower metabolism than small ones.

The ratio between the nucleus and cytoplasm may be a controlling factor in determining the size of cells, for these two units must be in a certain balance for the efficient functioning of the cell. The importance of cell size as a regulative force in metabolism is strikingly demonstrated by the fact that the volume is very much the same for any cell type and is independent of the animal's size. The cells found in a mouse are about the same size as those found in the largest mammals. Large organs contain a greater number of cells, not larger cells.

LARGER DIVISIONS OF ANIMAL KINGDOM

Although the phylum is often considered to be the largest and most distinctive taxonomic unit, zoologists often find it convenient to combine phyla under a few large groups because of certain common embryological and anatomical features. Such large divisions may have a logical basis, for the members of some of these arbitrary groups are not only united by common traits but also evidence indicates some relationship in phylogenetic descent.

Subkingdoms, branches, and grades. Hyman has proposed a scheme for some of these larger groupings which should give the student a more comprehensive view of animal classification.

Subkingdom Protozoa (acellular)—phylum Protozoa

Subkingdom Metazoa (cellular)—all other phyla
    Branch A (Mesozoa)—phylum Mesozoa
    Branch B (Parazoa)—phylum Porifera
    Branch C (Eumetazoa)—all other phyla
        Grade I (Radiata)—phyla Coelenterata (Cnidaria), Ctenophora
        Grade II (Bilateria)—all other phyla
            Acoelomata—phyla Platyhelminthes, Rhynchocoela
            Pseudocoelomata—phyla Acanthocephala, Aschelminthes, Entoprocta
            Eucoelomata—all other phyla

The protostome and deuterostome—divisions of bilateral animals. The greatest group of animals, the Bilateria, may be arranged into two major divisions—Protostomia and Deuterostomia. The characteristics and the phyla of each are as follows:

Protostomia—Mouth usually formed from blastopore; schizocoelous formation of body cavity (coelom); mostly spiral cleavage; determinate or mosaic pattern of egg cleavage; ciliated larva (when present) a trochophore or trochosphere. Examples: phyla Platyhelminthes, Aschelminthes, Rhynchocoela, Annelida, Mollusca, Arthropoda, and others.

Deuterostomia—Anus formed from blastopore; enterocoelous formation of coelom; mostly radial cleavage; indeterminate or equipotential pattern of egg cleavage; ciliated larva (when present) a pluteus type. Examples: phyla Echinodermata, Hemichordata, and Chordata.

These divisions form the two main lines of evolutionary ascent in the animal kingdom and are often referred to as the diphyletic theory of phylogeny.

ANNOTATED REFERENCES

Andrew, W. 1959. Textbook of Comparative Histology, New York, Oxford University Press. *The most up-to-date comparative histology in the English language. Unusually good treatment of the invertebrate groups.*

Arey, L. B. 1957. Human Histology. A Textbook in Outline Form. Philadelphia, W. B. Saunders Co. *An excellent summary of histology.*

Gillison, M. 1950. A Histology of the Body Tissues. Baltimore, Williams & Wilkins Co. *Gives concise descriptions of the various body tissues.*

Maximow, A. A., and W. Bloom. 1957. A Textbook of Histology, ed 7. Philadelphia, W. B. Saunders Co. *An authoritative text for medical students but of great value to all students of biology.*

Montagna, W. 1956. The Structure and Function of Skin. New York, Academic Press, Inc. *An up-to-date account of the most versatile organ in the body. Read especially the revealing chapters on the sweat glands, including the apocrine glands. Mainly for the advanced student, but others can profit from its reading.*

Montagna, W., and R. A. Ellis (editors). 1958. The Biology of Hair Growth. New York, Academic Press, Inc. *A book by many eminent scientists on the most modern research of the growth and development of hair. Read the excellent summary at the end of the book.*

Nonidez, J. F., and W. F. Windle. 1952. Textbook of Histology, ed. 2. New York, McGraw-Hill Book Co., Inc. *An excellent, well-written text on body tissues. Easily understood by the beginning zoology student.*

Page, I. H. (editor). 1959. Connective Tissue, Thrombosis, and Atherosclerosis. New York, Academic Press, Inc. *Aside from the clinical aspects of this work there is much general information about the properties of connective tissue found here.*

Romer, A. S. 1949. The Vertebrate Body. Philadelphia, W. B. Saunders Co. *Good descriptions of body tissues and organs. Will give the beginning student a good knowledge of body structures.*

Scott, G. G., and J. I. Kendall, 1935. The Microscopic Anatomy of Vertebrates. Philadelphia, Lea & Febiger. *Gives a general summary of comparative histology but is somewhat restricted in scope.*

chapter 5

Some important biological principles and concepts

A principle or generalization is a statement of fact that has a wide application and can be used to formulate other principles and concepts. The physical sciences such as physics and chemistry would be difficult to master without clear-cut formulas and rules. The biological sciences do not lend themselves to the mathematical exactness of the physical sciences, and few generalizations of universal application can be made. However, certain well-formulated principles are indispensable for clear thinking; they help the student see important relationships and form basic conclusions. Principles in biology as in other sciences are based upon observation and experimentation and have been tested by many workers over long periods of time. Biological principles are always subject to revision and new interpretation in the light of new knowledge.

The following list of basic concepts is not intended to be exhaustive. References to some of these principles have already been made. Further references will be made in later chapters where they will have significant application and will be better understood. These principles demonstrate the essential unity of the organism and the integration of all biological systems.

1. All organisms are composed of protoplasm which is the physical basis of life. Wherever there is life there is protoplasm. Not everything found in protoplasm, however, is alive, for many lifeless materials such as yolk granules, waste materials, and so on may be scattered through it. The elements in protoplasm are shared with nonliving matter, but protoplasm is highly selective and many of the elements in inanimate matter are not found in it. Protoplasm is always enclosed by a thin plasma membrane which is a specialized part of protoplasm. The mystery of protoplasm does not lie in its chemical elements but in the way they are linked together into compounds and organized into the complex substance to which we ascribe the phenomenon of the life process. (Chapters 2 and 3.)

2. Protoplasm has a unique physical and chemical organization which varies to produce the potentialities of each particular group of organisms. Superficially, protoplasm appears much the same in all organisms, but its submicroscopic organization and chemical characteristics vary widely with different species and with different cells in the same organism. This organization accounts for functional and morphological differences between organisms. That of man, for instance, is not the same as that of the ameba. Because of these facts and others, the real nature of protoplasm as seen under the microscope reveals little of its intrinsic makeup. Its real fundamental nature seems to be ultramicroscopic and hence a fruitful source of investigation in the relatively new and immature field of molecular biology. (Chapter 2.)

3. **In all protoplasmic systems the ground-substance is differentiated into a superficial region (ectoplasm) and an inner region (endoplasm).** Because of its position the ectoplasm serves as the boundary between the external environment and the inner part of the protoplasmic system. The ectoplasm is specialized to perform many roles, such as the exchange between the environment and the protoplasmic system, conduction, respiration, differentiation of development, fertilization, and the general integration of the system. Classification in protozoa is based upon ectoplasmic differentiation, such as pseudopodia, cilia, and flagella. This distinction between ectoplasm and endoplasm may be seen best in some eggs and ameboid cells; body cells in general do not show it clearly. (Chapters 3 and 6.)

4. **All protoplasm has certain general properties which are the basic expressions of life.** These characteristics distinguish the living from the nonliving and are the criteria by which we measure the dynamic aspects of the protoplasmic system. They also represent the adaptive nature of living systems as revealed in their mechanisms of survival. One fundamental property of protoplasm is its power to respond to its environment (irritability). Another is the ability to perform such essential physiological functions as ingestion and digestion of food, absorption, circulation, excretion, and reproduction. While all protoplasm has these properties, in multicellular organisms the protoplasm in cells or groups of cells (tissues) tends to be specialized to carry on these functions. Thus we have nerve cells for receiving and transmitting stimuli, muscle cells for contraction, and so on. (Chapters 2, 3, and 4.)

5. **Protoplasmic systems are differentiated and organized into compartment units.** This concept implies some sort of partition between the various units that go to make up living systems from the lowest to the highest. Integration of whatever kind takes place through membranes, films, ecto-endoplasmic differentiations, etc. Diffusion and osmosis of bodily fluids and what they carry are made along concentration gradients through membranes. A single cell is made up of many unitary compartments, such as the nucleus, food vacuoles, and cytoplasmic inclusions. A single chromosome is a compartment with its regulative sheath, the pellicle. Even nervous transmission occurs through membranes from one compartment to another (synaptic junctions). Some compartments (blood vessels and gut) are large and extensive to facilitate internal transport and to overcome the limitations of diffusion and osmosis. (Chapter 3.)

6. **Specialization and division of labor are correlated with the organization level of the organism.** The evolutionary trend is toward more specialized organs and division of labor. In Protozoa, specialized cytoplasmic structures (organelles) illustrate division of labor. Among Metazoa there is a progressive sequence of specialization ranging from the cell-tissue level of coelenterates to the organ-system level of the higher forms. Whenever structures become differentiated or specialized, they are always accompanied by physiological divisions of labor. (Chapters 3, 4, and 6.)

7. **All organisms come from pre-existing organisms.** This concept means that all protoplasmic units have come from similar units. This is the principle of **biogenesis** in contrast to the principle of **abiogenesis** (spontaneous generation), which has been discredited. The principle has been broadened to include the various units of protoplasmic systems, such as "all nuclei from previous nuclei," "all chromosomes from previous chromosomes," "all centrosomes from previous centrosomes," etc. Just how far this concept can be carried is a debatable point. It may be well to point out that **biogenesis** does not include the first beginning of life itself. If the animate has come from the inanimate, this fact would be difficult to reconcile with the principle. (Chapters 32 and 37.)

8. **Reproduction involves the division of parental material to form offspring.**

All new organisms are formed at the expense of the old. Whatever the nature of reproduction, whether of one-celled or many-celled animals, there is division of the parent or parents. This division may be equal or unequal and may or may not involve the destruction of the parental organism. In one-celled and some multicellular animals there is a simple division of the parent into two daughter cells or organisms. In sexual forms the eggs and sperm are the real offspring, and fertilization can be considered as a restorative process for the new parental body. (Chapters 6 and 32.)

9. All organisms develop within limits a characteristic form. Within variable limits all organisms develop a particular and predictable size and shape. This generalization emphasizes the science of **morphogenesis,** which is concerned with the developmental concepts of hormones, axial gradients, organizers, and specific patterns of embryological development. Many biologists have been interested in the interpretation of form in organisms on the basis of physical forces and causes. In some cases shapes and forms of animals can be explained by physical factors. For instance, the form of some of the low organisms, such as Protozoa, can be explained on the basis of surface tension forces according to the principle of maxima and minima of surface films. Closely allied to the principle of form is that of organic symmetry. (Chapters 4 and 6.)

10. The final form (morphology) of an animal is the result of the interactions between basic structural features and functions. In the early development of an animal, structural features precede function. A certain genetic pattern may be inherited, but what this pattern actually becomes depends to a great extent upon the functional experience of the animal. This functional modification is especially marked in the vertebrate body. The size of a muscle, the structure and nature of bone, tendons, and ligaments, the elaboration and distribution of blood vessels, and the detailed patterns of nervous systems are all dependent upon functional modifications. (Chapters 4 and 34.)

11. All organisms have the capacity for growth. Growth can be accomplished in two ways—by cell division and by cell expansion. In all true growth the increase in size is an actual increase in protoplasm and not merely a swelling induced by water or some other agent. This involves a distinction between volume (wet weight) increase and dry weight increase. In early cleavage stages of embryological development the cells become smaller with successive divisions, so there is no actual increase in the whole structure. For real growth to occur new material must be built up into protoplasm. Mere cell division is a preliminary to actual growth, however, for such division increases the total surface area of cell membranes, which facilitates diffusion of the minerals, proteins, etc. that go into the make-up of protoplasm. Growth within the protoplasmic structure (intussusception) must also be distinguished from accretionary growth, which involves the addition of materials externally. Examples of accretion are the growth of crystals, the shells of clams and snails, teeth, etc. These substances cause an increase in size but not necessarily in living matter. Patterns of growth are inherited so that certain proportions are usually constant from generation to generation. Other factors, such as vitamins and hormones, also play a part. (Chapter 33.)

12. All patterns of life are rhythmic in nature. The activities of the living organism fluctuate around some mean which best promotes physiochemical equilibrium. Cycles and rhythms are involved in practically every phase of the life process. This principle ranges from the ordinary physiological cyclic patterns of heartbeat, respiration, metabolism, reproduction, etc. to those larger cycles which include the external influences of light and temperature, such as the rhythms of day and night, sun and moon, and seasonal changes. The best-adapted organism is one that can adjust its own cycles of activity to those imposed by its surroundings. For such adjustments animals have evolved precise timing mechanisms (internal clocks) which enable them to synchronize their own activities with those of their external environment. (Chapters 16, 38, and 41.)

13. **All organisms tend to maintain a constancy of conditions within their internal media.** This is commonly known as the principle of **homeostasis**. It refers to the stabilization of internal conditions for which all organisms strive. External environmental factors tend to upset internal conditions in the organism; the organism is constantly trying to counteract these influences. There is an evolutionary progression in the development of this principle. Lower forms are more restricted in their activities because they have not evolved a control of stabilization to the same degree as higher ones. As an example, the temperature of warm-blooded animals is more easily regulated than that of cold-blooded animals, so they enjoy greater freedom of activity under more varied environmental temperatures. Organisms must also maintain stable fluid conditions of salt, acids, alkalines, foods, and oxygen within the body. (Chapter 38.)

14. **All organisms use energy in their living processes.** All aspects of life require energy in some form. Energy is the capacity to do work and can be measured in calories. The energy potentialities of most food substances can be measured, although some required substances are not energy-giving. The ultimate source of all energy is the sun. Plants utilize this energy directly by using the process of photosynthesis to form carbohydrates. Energy made and stored in plants is used by animals that eat plants. These animals may be eaten by other animals which get their energy this way. According to their type of nutrition, organisms may be divided into holophytic, or those which carry on photosynthesis; holozoic, or those which ingest and digest organic materials; and saprophytic, or those which absorb decayed organic matter through their body surface. Organisms that make

their own food are also called autotrophic; those that depend upon other organisms for their nutrition are called heterotrophic. (Chapters 2, 3, 30, and 38.)

15. **All organisms are fundamentally alike in their basic requirements.** Life processes are about the same everywhere in the animal kingdom. Animals carry on similar metabolic processes, such as nutrition, digestion, respiration, and excretion. They must adjust to their environment and develop adaptations for doing so. They must reproduce. This uniformity is to be expected, for all organisms are composed of protoplasm and the requirements of protoplasm are much the same wherever found. Organisms do show some differences in their basic requirements. Some can synthesize food elements which others cannot; some require different vitamins; some must even get along without oxygen and get their energy by anaerobic processes. (Chapters 1, 6, 30, and 38.)

16. **The parts of any one organism are so closely connected that the character of one part must receive its pattern from the character of all the rest.** This may be referred to as correlation of growth. A single tooth may indicate whether the animal was carnivorous or herbivorous, whether it was a mammal or other vertebrate, etc. Certain structural features always coexist. This principle is very helpful to paleontologists in the reconstruction of an organism from fossil parts. Thus if a fossil lower jaw is strengthened inside by a shelf of bone, it belonged to an ape; if strengthened outside, it belonged to a human being. (Chapters 4 and 36.)

17. **All organisms pass through a characteristic life history.** This principle is concerned with the life cycle, which is more or less characteristic for each species of organism. It involves the life span and the various phases of the cycle, such as the period of development, the reproductive span, and the postreproductive period. It also includes other factors such as litter size, frequency of litters, age differential of reproductive capacity, and

population relations. (Chapters 4, 6, 33, and 38.)

18. Existing organisms have developed by a process of gradual change from previously existing organisms. This is the **evolutionary concept,** better known as organic evolution. It is based upon the belief that present-day forms have descended with modifications from primitive forms which may have been radically different in structure and behavior. This principle is the key to our modern interpretation of animal origins and relationships. It gives us an explanation of phylogeny, or racial relationships, and helps in the taxonomic groupings of animals. Much fundamental evidence is still lacking, for more specific ancestral forms are needed for understanding the exact relationships of animal groups. The idea that there has been direct evolutionary progression from simple to complex forms is only partly true, for it is not always possible to suggest what ancestral forms may have been like. This does not, however, invalidate the concept of evolution. (Chapters 1 and 37.)

19. Animals that have many morphological characters in common have a common descent. The more characters organisms have in common, the more closely they are related. This phylogenetic scheme forms the basis for modern classification of animals. A few common characters shared by two groups may have limited significance because of the possibility of convergent evolution; in other words, the characters may have originated independently. When these common characters are homologous, or similar in origin, the evidence for relationships is considered fundamental. (Chapters 1, 33, and 37.)

20. Organisms of higher levels may repeat in their embryonic development some of the corresponding stages of their ancestors. This is better known as the **biogenetic law,** which was formerly interpreted to mean that the embryonic stages of an animal are similar to the adult stages of its phylogenetic ancestors. This was the principle of **recapitulation,** or the idea that ontogeny (the life history) repeats phylogeny (ancestral history). The modern interpretation is merely that some of the corresponding embryonic stages of the early ancestor are repeated. The earlier viewpoint would assume that all evolutionary advancements were added on to the terminal stages of the life histories of organisms, but early embryonic stages have also undergone evolution. Evolution has produced many ontogenies in the phylogeny of an animal. Some biologists have suggested that **paleogenesis** is a better term to express the tendency for early developmental patterns to become more or less stabilized in successive ontogenies of later descendants. In early stages this tendency is more marked than it is in later stages, because the developmental adjustments produced by the evolution of animals may involve embryonic adaptations (caenogenesis) and other changes which may appear in the terminal or adult stages. The principle must be considered very generalized and not absolute, for some animal ontogenies do not repeat ancestral ontogenies at all. (Chapters 33 and 37.)

21. All organisms inherit a certain pattern of structural and functional organization from their progenitors. This generalization involves the laws of **heredity** and applies to all living things. The highest and lowest types of animals have the capacity for reproducing their kind and transmitting their characteristics to their offspring. Hereditary transmission is much the same in all organisms. What is inherited by an offspring is not necessarily the exact traits as expressed by the parents, for heredity is not as simple as this. What is inherited is a certain type of organization which, under the influence of developmental and environmental forces, gives rise to a certain visible appearance. Many potentialities may be inherited, but only one of these may express itself visibly. (Chapter 34.)

22. Patterns of organization can be changed suddenly by mutation. Sudden changes in the appearance of an animal or plant different from anything inherited

94

from the parents do appear in nature. Some of these changes are not transitory but are transmitted to the offspring. Mutations that occur in somatic (body) cells disappear with that generation. Mutations in the germ cells can be inherited by future generations. The latter usually involve changes in the genes and may be induced by artificial means, such as x-rays, radium, and mustard gas. Their natural causes are largely obscure. Although most mutations are considered harmful, some may be useful under favorable environmental conditions. Mutations play an important role in the evolutionary process. (Chapters 34 and 37.)

23. All organisms are sensitive to changes in their environment. No organism could survive long without mechanisms for responding to the environment. This is a basic reaction of all protoplasmic units. Specialization and division of labor have resulted in sensory organs which are especially sensitive to changes in the environment. Most of an animal's activities are directed toward finding a favorable ecological environment and avoiding unpleasant stimuli. (Chapters 6 and 31.)

24. There is a definite gradient of physiological activities in the body, from the anterior region of high activity to the posterior region of low activity. This is the principle of **axial gradients.** Metabolic rates vary within an animal, being greater at the anterior end and progressively less toward the posterior end. This rate is correlated with the regeneration of lost parts. The anterior end of a fragment of an animal may regenerate a new head while the posterior end with a lower metabolism will form a tail. What a regenerating part becomes is determined mainly by its relation to the animal as a whole. Some forms, such as flatworms and coelenterates, seem to demonstrate the principle better than most groups. (Chapters 4, 10, and 33.)

25. All organisms are adapted in some way to their environment. To survive, an organism must adapt to the conditions imposed by its environment. Universal adaptations by which animals can adjust to all conditions are nonexistent. Adaptations are always special adjustments to particular conditions and are always relative. Some animals are better adjusted to their environment than others. Most animals have become specialized in their adaptive relations, so that the more perfectly they are adapted to one environment, the less they are fitted for adjustment to a different environment. Adaptations are either inherited or acquired. Inherited adaptations are present from birth, such as the sense organs; acquired adaptations originate in response to definite stimuli, such as the formation of antibodies against a particular disease. (Chapters 38, 40, and 41.)

26. All organisms have some capacity to adjust themselves to changes in their environment. This is the principle of **acclimatization** which refers to the process by which an organism within the limits of its life history is able to become inured to conditions that are normally harmful or injurious to it, such as extremes of heat, cold, salinity of water medium, oxygen pressure, toxins, and many others. The process must be distinguished from adjustments that are made over many generations, such as the accumulation of mutant genes which may favor the new adjustment in an organism over a long period of time. Acclimatization also does not refer to the routine and rapid adjustments that physiological organs are able to make in their normal functioning, such as the ability to adapt to dim and strong light or the ability to detect differential sensitivity. (Chapter 38.)

27. All organisms fit into a scheme of interrelationships between themselves and their environment. No animal can live apart from its environment. All animals are influenced by environmental forces, but the interrelationship is mutual, for each organism also influences its environment. The factors of the environment may be **biotic,** which includes interrelations between the animal and other animals within its range, or **physical,** which involves such forces as temperature, moisture, soil, air, light, and many others. Biotic factors may involve members of the same or different species. The interrelationships are often different in the two groups, for competition between members of the same species includes the search for the same food, shelters, and water; those of different species include such problems as food chains, population pressures, and other general community relations. Through the operation of these environmental factors a balance of nature is worked out. (Chapter 38.)

28. In all group organizations individuals profit mutually from an unconscious cooperation. No animal lives to itself throughout its life history, for it either comes in contact with other members of the same species or with other species of the animal community to which it belongs. In animals with definite social organizations, there are optimal population sizes which determine their success. Definite hazards appear when there are too few or too many organisms within a population. The rate of evolution appears to bear a definite relationship to an optimal-sized population. Many biological processes are dependent upon an optimum factor of numbers involved in any particular process. It is easy to see that overcompetition for mates, for food, and for shelter may result in a decrease rather than an increase. (Chapter 38.)

29. In metazoan forms the segregation of germ plasm and somaplasm represents the first specialization of cells. This principle stresses the separation of somatic cells, which take care of the general bodily functions of locomotion, nutrition, etc. from the germinal cells which are responsible for reproduction. In general, the principle holds true, but there are cases in which sex cells have come directly from soma cells in some animals. In colonial Protozoa, which are intermediate between the Protozoa and the Metazoa, the first differentiation is that between nutritive and reproductive cells. (Chapters 4 and 6.)

30. Embryonic germ layers are the forerunners of adult organs and structures. The differentiation of the early embryo into three germ layers is an important event in the embryology of most metazoans, for these germ layers give rise to the future body structures. Some lower metazoans are diploblastic, that is, they have only two germ layers, ectoderm and endoderm, so their capacity for developing complex organs is restricted. In higher metazoans (triploblastic animals) the third germ layer, mesoderm, is added which forms most of the body organs. The importance of germ layers in animal development gave rise to the germ layer theory which states that the layers have been formed in much the same way throughout all metazoans and that each layer is destined to form certain specific organs. For instance, the skin and nervous system are derived from ectoderm and muscle and skeleton from mesoderm. Modern embryologists, however, have found many exceptions to this theory. Muscle usually comes from mesoderm, but lower animals with only the two germ layers also have muscle, which must come from ectoderm or endoderm. (Chapters 4 and 33.)

31. A body cavity of some form is characteristic of most bilateral animals. Body cavities are varied in form. Coelenterates and other radially symmetrical forms have only a digestive cavity. In flatworms and some others the space between ectoderm and endoderm is filled with mesenchyme or its derivatives. The roundworms have a form of cavity known as the pseudocoel. The true coelom, a space that appears in the mesoderm, is characteristic of the higher phyla which have a "tube-within-a-tube" arrangement. The coelom encloses most of the internal organs, and its development has made possible the differentiation of many systems in the evolution of the animal. (Chapters 4, 12, and 15.)

32. An organism is a biological system whose parts are organized into a functional whole. An organism is not a mere summation of its constituent parts. It is a self-sufficient unit, and its parts, whether they be cells, tissues, or organs, cannot survive apart from the whole. The

96

organism as a whole has properties which cannot be explained merely by considering the sum of the properties of its individual parts. It is impossible to understand the whole organism by analyzing its parts, for such a procedure destroys the organization which is the basic part of life. This, then, refutes much of the mechanistic interpretation of life, for while physics and chemistry may be able to explain the parts, they cannot as yet explain the life process as a whole. (Chapters 1 and 4.)

Morphological and physiological principles of animal life as revealed by the various groups (phyla)

chapter 6

Phylum Protozoa*

BIOLOGICAL PRINCIPLES

Protoplasmic level of animal organization

1. The life activities are all carried on within the limits of a single plasma membrane.

2. The protozoan is thus a complete organism and functionally and structurally is not the same as a metazoan cell.

3. By tradition, Protozoa are considered as single cells, but by the concept of the organism they may be regarded as a protoplasmic mass that is not divisible into cells and is therefore **acellular**.

Biological contributions

1. Specialization in Protozoa is mainly confined to the cytoplasm, where certain areas are organized into **organelles**, but nuclear material may also undergo specialization (macronuclei and micronuclei).

2. Asexual reproduction involving the behavior of the nuclear elements of chromosomes and genes is first developed in Protozoa (and probably bacteria) and is the method of all division (mitosis) in all cell-bodies of Metazoa.

3. In certain Protozoa the behavior of conjugant mates may indicate the early **differentiation of sex**. True sexual reproduction with zygote formation is found in some.

4. The **taxes** or responses of Protozoa to stimuli represent the early beginnings of **reflexes** and **instincts** as we know them in Metazoa.

5. The first appearance of an **exoskeleton**, so well developed in the Metazoa, is indicated by certain shelled Protozoa.

---

*Prō'to-zō'a (Gr. *protos*, first, + *zoon*, animal).

6. In colonial Protozoa we have the first indication of **division of labor** among cells. These may be considered the transition links between the protozoan and the metazoan.

Position in animal kingdom

1. Metazoa may not have come directly from protozoans as we now know them but may have been derived from organisms similar to Protozoa. Protozoa are often placed close to the beginning of the genealogical tree.

2. The flagellates are considered to be nearest the ancestral stem of both the plant and animal kingdoms.

3. Protozoa may furnish types that fit into a logical sequence for the development of Metazoa.

Relation to man's welfare

1. Many are parasitic in man and in animals affecting man.

2. Some are responsible for the contamination of water.

3. Others are concerned in the formation of the earth's crust and the fertility of the soil.

HISTORICAL BACKGROUND

It was impossible to discover forms as small as protozoans before the invention of the microscope. By the latter half of the seventeenth century the use of lenses was fairly common, so there arose an enthusiastic group of observers often designated as the classical microscopists. The greatest of all these was Anton van Leeuwenhoek, a Dutch lens maker, who lived from 1632 to 1723. With the microscope he himself constructed he roamed through the world hidden to the unaided eye, finding wonders over which he raved with childlike enthusiasm. Most of his observations were sent to the newly formed Royal Society of London, for which he was a regular correspondent. Among his many discoveries were organisms he called **animalcula,** which we now know as Protozoa. He found these by examining stagnant rainwater, water scum, rotten vegetable infusions, etc. He described such common protozoan forms as *Vorticella, Volvox, Carchesium,* and many others. The term Protozoa was first used by Goldfuss (1809), who also included under this group many forms not protozoans. In 1845 von Siebold first used the term Protozoa in its present sense of an organism consisting of one cell.

POSITION IN ANIMAL KINGDOM

Sometimes it is difficult to tell whether noncellular organisms are plants or animals. Some have the characteristics of animals, some of plants, but between these categories are intermediate forms which possess both animal and plant characteristics. Some biologists propose the term Protista for all acellular organisms. This grouping of Protista would include such forms as bacteria, slime molds (Mycetozoa), and the Protozoa.

CHARACTERISTICS

1. **Acellular** (or one cell), some colonial
2. **Mostly microscopical,** although some large enough to be seen with the unaided eye
3. All symmetries represented in the group; shape variable or constant (oval, spherical, etc.)
4. **No germ layer present**
5. No organs or tissues, but **specialized organelles** found; nucleus single or multiple
6. Free-living, mutualism, commensalism, parasitism, all represented in the group.
7. Locomotion by **pseudopodia, flagella, cilia,** and direct cell movements; some sessile

8. Some provided with a **simple protective exoskeleton,** but mostly naked
9. Holozoic, holophytic, saprozoic, and saprophytic nutrition represented
10. Reproduction asexually by fission, budding, and cysts, and sexually by conjugation of gametes

HABITAT

Most Protozoa live in water or damp soil, although a number are parasitic in other forms. They are found in both fresh water and marine water. Pond scums and cesspools often yield large numbers of them. They prefer quiet pools in which aquatic plants are growing but usually are scarce if the water tends toward the acid side.

NUMBER OF SPECIES

The number of named species of Protozoa lies somewhere between 15,000 and 30,000, but this figure probably represents only a fraction of the total number of species. Some protozoologists think that there may be more protozoan species than all other species together, for each species of the higher phyla may have its own unique protozoan parasites, and many protozoans bear parasites themselves.

The body of a protozoan is made up of what is called a cell, and all division of labor must be carried on within that cell. In a strict meaning of the term, they should be called **acellular,** for the cells of Metazoa do not correspond to the unit which we call a protozoan, although some protozoans with single nucleus and chromosomal patterns similar to Metazoa may be called **unicellular.**

A protozoan, then, might be defined as an organism which is made up of a mass of protoplasm not divided into cells and which carries on all the life processes. Although it is not divided into cells, it has specialization and division of labor within its cytoplasmic mass. It is altogether erroneous to think of protozoans as simple animals, for many have complicated structures and are physiologically complex. Evolution has occurred among

Protozoa the same as among other groups. Their organelles have some resemblance to cell differentiations among the Metazoa and may be quite complex, such as skeletons, sensory systems, conducting mechanisms, contractile systems, organs of locomotion, defense mechanisms, and others.

Inasmuch as Protozoa are not made up of cells, they represent what is called the **protoplasmic level of organization.** From this standpoint and others, many biologists place them close to the common ancestor of the many-celled forms. Some Protozoa are quite close to the plants and may be considered as connecting links between animals and plants. (See section on Origin of Life, Chapter 37.) In the early evolution of animals, holophytic flagellates may have lost their chloroplasts and become colorless animals.

Most Protozoa are small or microscopic, usually from 3 to 300 microns long. The largest are among the Foraminifera, some of which have shells 4 to 5 inches in diameter. Certain amebae may be 4 to 5 mm. in diameter. Some of them are found in colonies, where each individual carries on its functions independent of the others, although in a few colonies there is a small amount of differentiation.

Arbitrary lines between colonial Protozoa and Metazoa cannot be drawn sharply. The distinction is mainly a matter of degree of division of labor. If the cells are dependent upon each other for such functions as nutrition, movement, excretion, and reproduction, the colony belongs properly to the Metazoa; if only certain cells are for reproduction and the rest can perform all other bodily functions, the grouping is a protozoan colony. *Volvox*, for instance, is difficult to appraise this way. Those protozoans with many nuclei may be considered analogous to the syncytial tissues of metazoans.

CLASSES

Protozoa are placed in classes based on the kind of locomotor organs they possess. Some authorities divide this group into four classes; others, into five classes. Many of the classes bear two names because some biologists refer to them by one name and some by another.

Subphylum Plasmodroma (plas′mo-dro″ma) (Gr. *plasma*, anything formed, + *dromos*, course). With pseudopodia, flagella, or no locomotor organs.

> **Class Sarcodina** (sar′ko-di″na) (Gr. *sarkos*, flesh) (**Rhizopoda**). Move and capture food by pseudopodia. Example: *Amoeba proteus.*
>
> **Class Mastigophora** (mas′ti-gof″o-ra) (Gr. *mastix*, whip, + *pherein*, to bear) (**Flagellata**). Move by flagella; some with pseudopodia. Example: *Euglena viridis.*
>
> **Class Sporozoa** (spor′o-zo″a) (Gr. *sporos*, spore, + *zoon*, animal). No special locomotor organs; may move by changing shape of body or gliding; spore formation common. Example: *Monocystis lumbrici.*

Subphylum Ciliophora (sil′i-of″ora) (L, *cilium*, eyelid, + *phoros*, bearing). Cilia throughout life or at certain stages.

> **Class Ciliata** (si′li-at″a) (L. *cilium*, eyelid) (**Infusoria**). Usually move by cilia throughout life. Example: *Paramecium caudatum.*
>
> **Class Suctoria** (suc-tor′i-a) (L. *sugere, suctum*, to suck). Move by cilia in the young and by tentacles in the adult. Example: *Podophrya.*

EVOLUTION

It is not known just what were the ancestors of Protozoa. With the exception of certain shell-bearing Sarcodina, such as Foraminifera and Radiolaria, Protozoa have left no fossil records. Mastigophora are considered to be the oldest of all Protozoa and may have arisen from bacteria and spirochetes. This group also includes members which are chlorophyll bearing and resemble the plant algae. This may indicate a common origin for both plants and animals. Sporozoa are somewhat degenerate in structure because of their parasitic habits and may have come from Sarcodina and Mastigophora. Evidence for the origin of Sarcodina from Mastigophora is shown by the fact that both flagellate and ameboid stages are found in some forms. However, the evidence strongly indicates that the different orders of Sarcodina may have arisen independently from different kinds of flagellates (Mastigophora). The orders of Sporozoa may also have had separate origins. The origin of the most highly specialized protozoan forms, ciliates, is somewhat obscure, but there is some evidence that they, too, have come from flagellates.

PROTOZOA IN THE ECONOMY OF NATURE

Protozoans have both a theoretical and a practical importance. In a theoretical sense these organisms afford a great deal of speculation on the problems of phylogeny and of evolution. Biologists do not agree on where the protozoans fit into the pattern of animal evolution. That some of them are ancient cannot be doubted, but many are certainly far from primitive.

Protozoa have been extensively studied with the hope that the basic problems of the life process may be determined. Many believe that generalizations which apply to these small forms also apply to higher animals. But the more we learn about Protozoa, the more complicated they appear to be. The extensive work now being done on mating types and extranuclear inheritance in *Paramecium* illustrates this. It is too optimistic to regard them as the key to the solution of all biological problems.

From the practical standpoint protozoans have played an important role in building up soil and forming earth deposits; they have formed important symbiotic relationships; they have been responsible for the contamination of water; they have important roles in food chains; and, above all, many of them as parasites have been responsible for serious diseases in man and other animals.

Role in building earth deposits

In the class Sarcodina (to which the common ameba belongs) there are two orders, Foraminifera and Radiolaria, which have existed since Pre-Cambrian time or the Proterozoic era. They have left excellent fossil records, for their hard shells have been preserved unaltered. Many of the extinct species are identical

to present ones. These ancient forms were especially abundant during the Cretaceous and Tertiary periods of geological history. Some of them are among the largest of protozoans, attaining a diameter of more than 18 cm. (7 inches), although most species are less than 1 mm. in diameter.

Both these orders are of practical interest because of the enormous accumulation of their tests and skeletons on the ocean floor and in the solidified limestone and chalk deposits of land formations. For untold millions of years the tests of dead Foraminifera have been sinking to the bottom, building up a characteristic ooze rich in lime and silica. Most of this ooze is made up of the shells of the genus *Globigerina*. About one-third of all sea bottom (50 million square miles) is covered with *Globigerina* ooze. This ooze is especially abundant in the Atlantic Ocean. The Radiolaria, with their less soluble silicious shells, are usually found at greater depths (15,000 to 20,000 feet),

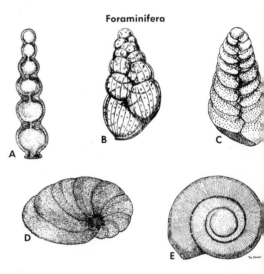

Foraminifera

A B C D E

Figure 34. Foraminifera shells. Millions of square miles of thick ocean ooze is made up of tests of forams. **A**, *Nodosaria vigula Brady* (fossil, Brunn, Moravia). **B**, *Textularia fucosa Reiss* (recent, Antillen Is.). **C**, *Bolivina punctata d'Orb* (fossil. Santa Monica, U.S.A.). **D**, *Monionina scapha Ficht* (recent, Samoa). **E**, *Spirillina vivipara Ehr.* (recent, Samoa). (Courtesy General Biological Supply House, Inc., Chicago.)

104

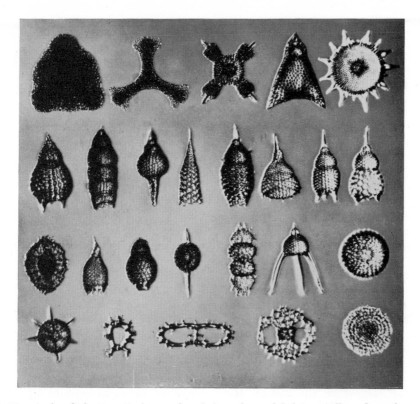

Figure 35. Types of radiolarians. In his study of these beautiful forms collected on famous *Challenger* expedition, Haeckel worked out our present concepts on symmetry. (Courtesy General Biological Supply House, Inc., Chicago.)

mainly in the Pacific and Indian Oceans. Radiolarian ooze probably covers about 2 to 3 million square miles. Under certain conditions, radiolarian ooze forms rocks (chert). Many fossil Radiolaria are found in the Tertiary rocks of California. In northern seas diatom (a plant) ooze is also abundant, covering around 12 million square miles of sea bottom. The thickness of these deep-sea sediments has been estimated to be from 2,000 to 12,000 feet. Although the average rate of sedimentation must vary greatly, it is always very slow. *Globigerina* ooze probably forms from 0.04 to 0.5 inch in a thousand years. When one considers that as many as 50,000 shells of Foraminifera may be found in a single gram of sediment, one can form some idea of the magnitude of numbers of these microorganisms and the length of time it has taken them to form the sediment carpet on the ocean floor.

Of equal interest and of greater practical importance are the limestone and chalk deposits on land which were laid down when a deep sea covered the continents. Later, through a rise in the ocean floor and other geological changes, this sedimentary rock emerged as dry land. Many years ago Professor Thomas H. Huxley wrote a classic essay, "On a Piece of Chalk," in which he described how the chalk deposits of many areas of England, including the White Cliffs of Dover, were laid down by the accumulation of these small microorganisms. The great pyramids of Egypt were made from limestone beds which were formed by a very large foraminiferan that flourished during the early Tertiary period. Since petroleum oil is of organic origin the presence of fossil Foraminifera (and also Radiolaria) in oil-bearing rock strata may be significant to oil geologists. For this reason, borings from test wells are carefully examined, rock strata compared, and contour plotting of the various layers done. From this and other knowledge it is possible to predict the location of oil with a fair degree of accuracy.

Protozoan fauna of plankton

Plankton is a general term for those organisms that passively float and drift with the wind, tides, and currents of both fresh water and marine water. It is mostly composed of microscopic animals and plants of which protozoans form an important part. Some Foraminifera and almost all Radiolaria are represented among the fauna of ocean plankton. Although members of the classes Sarcodina and Flagellata make up the most important protozoan members of plankton, the ciliates are also represented. Even members of the parasitic class Sporozoa are found in the bodies of certain plankton animals.

Plankton is important as food. Many fish, such as the herring and mackerel, and even the largest of all animals, the whalebone whales, feed directly upon plankton. As the animals of the surface plankton die, they sink to deeper layers of the ocean to serve as food for animals at lower levels.

Symbiotic relationships

The term **symbiosis** refers to the intimate interrelationships between two organisms of different species for the purpose of deriving energy or for some other benefit. This special relationship may be beneficial to both (mutualism) or beneficial to only one but not harmful to the other species (commensalism), or the relationship may be forced so that one receives benefit and the other furnishes all the energy and may actually be harmed (parasitism). These relationships are not always clear-cut, and there are intermediate grades which are difficult to distinguish. Protozoans are represented by all three major types of symbiosis.

Mutualism. There are some interesting examples of mutualism in which at least one of the members is a protozoan.

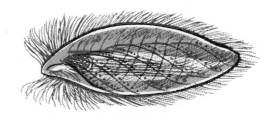

Figure 36. Intestinal flagellate, *Spirotrichonympha,* from gut of termite. Many individuals or species found in same host. Their relations to termite represent classical case of mutualism in animal kingdom. Note large number of flagella.

Paramecium bursaria harbors a green alga (zoochlorellae) which manufactures carbohydrates (by photosynthesis) for the benefit of the paramecium and receives a safe shelter in return. Zoochlorellae are also found in other protozoans, such as *Stentor,* certain amebae, and heliozoans. Zooxanthellae (a yellow or brown alga) is found in certain ectoparasitic ciliates, such as *Trichodina.*

Another example of mutualism is the relation between certain flagellates and termites and cockroaches. These flagellates (many belonging to the genus *Trichonympha*) live in the intestines of termites and wood-feeding roaches (*Cryptocercus*), where they secrete enzymes for digesting the cellulose which is thus made available to their hosts. The Protozoa cannot live outside the host; the termite or roach would starve without the flagellates. The protozoans ingest the wood after the insects have chewed it up into small bits. When termites lose their protozoan fauna (by high oxygen exposure, high temperatures, or prolonged starvation), they can survive only a short time even when fed an abundance of wood, unless they are reinfected with the flagellates.

Commensalism. Commensal protozoans may live on the outside (ectocommensals) or, more commonly, on the inside (endocommensals) of other organisms. Common ectocommensals are the ciliates *Kerona* and *Trichodina,* which are often seen on hydra. Some *Vorticella* and suctorians are also found attached to hydroids as ectocommensals. Endocommensals are

106

especially common in the digestive tubes of higher forms including man. Ruminants and other herbivorous mammals contain great numbers of ciliates and also a few flagellates and amebae. The commensal ciliates belong to the order Spirotricha (suborder Entodiniomorphina). Instead of body cilia they often have tufts or rows of cirri (fused cilia). In ruminants such as cattle and sheep they are found in the first two stomach compartments where they digest bacteria and foodstuffs in the host's food. Eventually they pass into the other compartments of the stomach and intestine where they are destroyed and digested, so that the host gets all the nutrition after all. Estimates show as many as 100,000 to 1,000,000 ciliates per cubic millimeter of gut contents and a total number in a mature cow of 10 to 50 billion. The number is influenced by the kind of food, acidity, starvation, and so on. Apparently Protozoa are not essential to the cattle, which can live and grow normally when the commensals are removed.

Parasitism. Parasitism is the most common form of symbiosis among Protozoa. Ectoparasites live on the outside of the body and endoparasites live within the host. Most animals, especially higher ones, have one or more kinds of protozoan parasites. Protozoa, even protozoan parasites, are often parasitized by other Protozoa. For instance, the opalinid ciliate which lives in the frog's intestine is parasitized by a certain ameba. Parasitic species are found among all classes of Protozoa, and one of them, Sporozoa, is entirely parasitic. Every vertebrate species probably harbors a parasitic or endocommensal ameba. Protozoan parasites have different ways of infecting the host. Some are transferred by cysts in water or food (*Entamoeba histolytica*); by arthropod or other vectors (*Trypanosoma, Plasmodium*); by placenta (blood parasites); and by invasion of ovary or egg (*Babesia*).

Protozoan parasites may differ little in structure from free-living forms, but they undoubtedly have physiological adaptations. Some protozoans have acquired structures adapted for parasitism, such as the organelles of attachment in *Gregarina*. Host-specificity varies. Some protozoan parasites such as *Trypanosoma, Entamoeba,* and *Eimeria* are adapted to a wide range of hosts and parasitize many species; others such as the Coccidia of mammals are restricted to a few species.

Many other examples of protozoan parasites will be mentioned later under the classes to which they belong.

Contamination of water

Many protozoan parasites are transmitted in water and may give rise to serious diseases, such as amebic dysentery. But protozoans also affect the taste and odor of water and often determine its drinking qualities. Water derived from surface sources and stored in large reservoirs is most likely to suffer this way. Other factors, such as algae and decomposing organic matter, also cause bad odors and taste. The chief cause of fishy, aromatic, or other odors is the production of aromatic oils by the disintegration of microscopic organisms. Some odors are characteristic of certain organisms. The worst protozoan offenders are certain flagellates, such as *Dinobryon* and *Uroglena*, which impart a pronounced fishy odor, not unlike cod-liver oil, to water. *Synura*, another flagellate, gives a bitter and spicy taste to water. Other flagellates also produce odors.

In recent years much attention has been given to certain dinoflagellates which are responsible for the so-called "red or poisonous tides" that have destroyed so many fish and other marine forms. In 1946 along the west coast of Florida the sea water was viscid and yellowish from the enormous swarms of these microorganisms. Dead fish piled up along the coast for many miles. Similar outbreaks have been reported in many other parts of the world. It is thought that the upwellings of nutrient-laden cold waters along coasts may explain the outbreaks of the dinoflagellates, and the consequent decay of dead fish may increase the nutrients of the protozoans. A toxic alkaloid, which acts

Figure 37. *Gonyaulax polyhedra,* a dinoflagellate responsible for red tides along coast of southern and lower California. This organism produces toxic alkaloidal substance which is very destructive to fish. Similar dinoflagellate, *Gymnodinium brevis,* causes frequent red tides along Florida coast. Shellfish that feed on these organisms may be source of food poisoning in man.

on the synaptic regions of the nervous systems of animals, is responsible for the harm the dinoflagellate does. Only a few species of naked dinoflagellates seem to be involved; *Gymnodinium* on the Florida coast and *Gonyaulax* on the Pacific coast have caused the American outbreaks (Figure 37).

REPRODUCTION AND LIFE CYCLES
Reproduction

Reproduction in most Protozoa is primarily by cell division (asexual). It is comparable in some respects to cell division in the multicellular animals. The Protozoa, however, has certain structural specializations (organelles), such as flagella, cilia, contractile vacuole, gullet, etc., which may be divided equally or unequally to the two daughter cells, so that a certain amount of differentiation or regeneration may be necessary to make the new animal complete. Some of these organelles are self-reproducing, but others are lost by resorption (dedifferentiation),

then differentiated anew in each of the daughter organisms. The method of reproduction varies. Some Protozoa simply undergo binary fission, budding, or sporulation. All of these are basically asexual processes. In others, however, asexual reproduction is often followed at certain periods by some form of sexual reproduction which may or may not be necessary for the continued existence of the organism.

Most Protozoa will fall under one or more of the following types, although there are many variations.

Binary fission. This process, the most common among Protozoa, involves the division of the organism, both nucleus and cytoplasm, into two essentially equal daughter organisms. Binary fission may be transverse (most ciliates) or longitudinal (Mastigophora). The nucleus divides by mitosis, and in many cases the chromosomes found in it are similar in structure and behave very much like metazoan chromosomes; in other cases the chromosomes are granular and highly atypical. Chromosome numbers appear to be constant for a species; for example, *Zelleriella intermedia* (Ciliata) has 24, *Entamoeba histolytica* (Sarcodina) 6, *Oxytricha fallax* (Ciliata) 24, and *Euglena viridis* (Mastigophora) 30.

Budding. Budding involves unequal cell division in which usually the parent organism retains its identity while forming one or more small cells, each of which assumes the parent form after it becomes free. In some cases the bud may be as large as the parent. Budding may be either external (certain suctorians and ciliates) or internal (suctorians and sporozoans). In internal budding the young cells are formed inside of the parent, from which they escape.

Multiple division (sporulation). In multiple division the nucleus divides a number of times, followed by the division of the cytoplasm of the organism into as many parts as there are nuclei. It is a method of rapid multiplication and is characteristic of such parasitic forms as the Sporozoa. It is often found in those

Protozoa with complicated life cycles including asexual and sexual phases.

Protozoan colonies. Colonies of Protozoa are formed when the daughter zooids remain associated together instead of moving apart and living a separate existence. Protozoan colonies vary from individuals embedded together in a gelatinous substance to those that have protoplasmic connections among them. The spatial relations of the individuals also serve as the basis for certain types of colonies, such as **linear** (daughter cells attached endwise), **spherical** (grouped in a ball shape), **discoid** (platelike arrangement), and **arboroid** (treelike branches). All the individuals of a colony are usually structurally and physiologically the same, although there may be a minor degree of division of labor among some of them, such as differentiation of reproductive and somatic zooids. Simple colonies may have only a few zooids (*Pandorina*) or they may have thousands of zooids (*Volvox*). Division of labor, however, may be carried so far that it is difficult to distinguish between a protozoan colony and a metazoan individual.

Sexual phenomena. Sex is found in certain Protozoa but is absent in others. When sex is found in Protozoa, it may involve the formation of male and female gametes (similar or unlike in appearance) which unite to form a zygote (synkaryon), or there may be variant forms of this, such as the complete union of two mature sexual individuals which merge their cytoplasm and nuclei together to form the zygote. By division the zygote may give rise to many individuals or to a new colony. Many other kinds of sexual phenomena have been described for Protozoa, such as **autogamy,** in which gametic nuclei arise and fuse to form a zygote in the same organism which produces the gametes; **endomixis,** which involves nuclear reorganization without fusion of micronuclei; **parthenogenesis,** or the development of an organism from a gamete without fertilization (syngamy); **conjugation,** in which there is an exchange of gametic nuclei of micronuclear origin between two paired organisms (conjugants).

Some of these processes are described under the discussion of the paramecium.

Life cycles

Many Protozoa have very complex life cycles; others have simple ones. A simple life cycle may consist of an active phase and a cyst. In some cases the cyst may be lacking. *Amoeba* has a relatively simple life cycle. The more complex life cycles include two or more stages in the active phase and a reproductive phase which may include sexual phenomena as well as asexual. Some protozoans, for example, have both a ciliated and a nonciliated stage in the same organism; others have ameboid and flagellate stages; and still others, free-swimming and sessile, etc. The most complex life cycles among the Protozoa are found in the parasitic class, Sporozoa, a good example of which is *Plasmodium,* the malarial parasite, described in a later section.

Encystment is common among protozoans, helping them withstand drought and extreme weather. There is usually a complex series of events when free-living forms encyst. The organism becomes quiescent and many organelles (cilia, flagella, contractile vacuole, etc.) may disappear. A cyst wall is secreted over the surface, so that the animal can withstand desiccation, temperature changes, and other harsh conditions. Reproductive cycles, such as budding, fission, and syngamy, may also occur in the encysted condition of some protozoans. The cysts of some protozoans may be viable for many years.

REPRESENTATIVE TYPES

In the following section descriptions are given of types from each class of Protozoa. The ones here presented are usually the ones the student studies in the laboratory and are, therefore, Protozoa with which he will become most familiar. Forms such as *Amoeba* and *Paramecium* offer some advantages for study, for they are large and easy to obtain, but they cannot be called truly representative, for their life histories are somewhat simplified compared with other members of their respective classes. More or less the same plan of presentation will be given in each case, so that the student may have some basis for comparison.

CLASS SARCODINA

Amoeba proteus

Habitat. Amoeba proteus is widely distributed. It lives in slow streams and ponds of clear fresh water, often in shallow water on the underside of aquatic vegetation. The underside of lily pads is a good place for them. On the sides of dams, in watering troughs, and in the sides of ledges where the water runs slowly from a brook or spring are other good places to collect them. They are rarely found in free water, for they require a substratum to glide on from place to place. In cultures they are somewhat

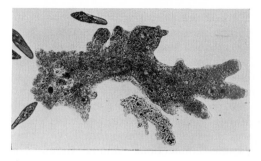

Figure 38. Comparison in size of *Pelomyxa* (larger) and *Amoeba*. The former may attain length of 5 mm. Several paramecia also shown. (Courtesy Carolina Biological Supply Co., Elon College, N. C.)

more difficult to grow than are other Protozoa.

Structure. The ameba is irregular in shape (Figure 38), because of its power to thrust out **pseudopodia** or false feet at any point on its body. It is a mass of clear, colorless jelly about 250 to 600 mi-

---

*Refer to Chapter 5, Principle 3.

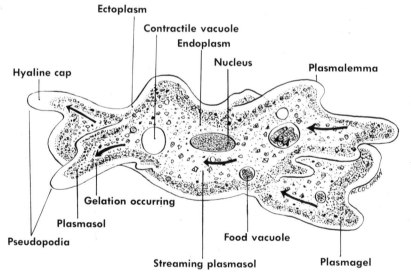

Figure 39. Structure of *Amoeba* in active locomotion. Arrows indicate direction of streaming plasmasol. There is no entirely satisfactory theory of ameboid movement. First sign of formation of new pseudopodium is thickening of ectoplasm to form clear hyaline cap. Into this hyaline region flow granules from the fluid endoplasm (plasmasol), forming a sort of tube with walls of plasmagel and core of plasmasol. As plasmasol flows forward it is converted into plasmagel which may involve contraction that squeezes the pseudopodium in a definite direction. A substratum is necessary for ameboid movement, but only tips of pseudopodia touch it.

110

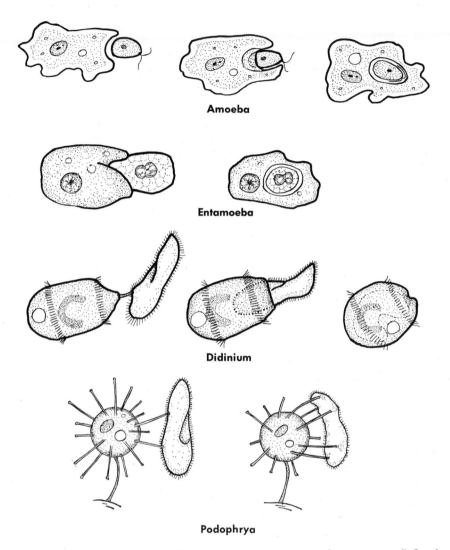

Amoeba

Entamoeba

Didinium

Podophrya

Figure 40. Some typical methods of ingestion among protozoans. *Amoeba* ingests small flagellate. *Entamoeba*, a parasite, engulfs leukocyte. *Didinium*, a holotrich, eats only paramecia. It pierces prey before swallowing it whole. Suctorians such as *Podophrya* have protoplasmic tentacles with funnel ends that suck protoplasm from prey.

crons in greatest diameter. The ameba is continually changing its shape by sending out and withdrawing its pseudopodia. Sometimes its shape is almost spherical when all its pseudopodia are withdrawn. Although it possesses no cell wall, it has a thin delicate outer membrane called the **plasmalemma** (Figure 39). Just beneath this is a nongranular layer, the **ectoplasm,** which encloses the granular **endoplasm.** The endoplasm is made up of an outer, relatively stiff **plasmagel** and a more fluid inner **plasmasol,** which exhibits flowing or streaming movements. In the gel layer the crystals and granules keep their distance (fixed) from each other; in the sol they bump and move over each other.

A number of **organelles** are found within the endoplasm. One of these is the disc-shaped **nucleus,** which is somewhat difficult to see. When the streaming movements are vigorous the nucleus can sometimes be seen carried along with the current. The nucleus is granular and refractive to light. Another organelle is the **contractile vacuole,** a bubblelike body that grows to a maximum size and then contracts to expel its fluid contents. Scattered through the endoplasm are **food vacuoles,** which are drops of water enclosing food particles. There are also other vacuoles, **crystals,** and **granules** of various shapes and forms. Foreign substances such as sand and bits of debris may also be in the protoplasm, where they have been picked up accidentally.

Metabolism. The ameba lives upon algae, protozoans, rotifers, and even other amebae. It shows some selection in its food, for it will not ingest everything that comes its way. Food may be taken in at any part of the body surface. When the ameba engulfs food, it thrusts out pseudopodia to enclose the food particle completely (Figure 40). Along with the food, some water in which the food is suspended is also taken in. These food vacuoles are carried around by the streaming movements of the endoplasm. Digestive juices and enzymes from the surrounding cytoplasm pour into the vacuoles, beginning the digestive process. At first the vacuoles give acid reaction because of a secretion which kills the prey, but later they become alkaline. As digestion proceeds, the vacuoles decrease

in size because of loss of water and the passage of the digested material into the surrounding cytoplasm. Finally, only indigestible material is left, which is eliminated simply by the animal flowing away from the mass as the latter passes out through the plasmalemma.

The ameba is able to live for many days without food but decreases in volume during this process. The actual time necessary for the completion of the digestion of a food vacuole varies with the kind of food, but the usual time is around 15 to 30 hours.

The ameba needs and utilizes energy like any other animal. It gets this energy by oxidation, which results in waste products such as carbon dioxide, water, and urea. Many of these waste substances are eliminated through the body surface, but some are discharged though the contractile vacuole. The contractile vacuole also has the important function of getting rid of excess water which the ameba is continually taking in. It is thus responsible for regulating the osmotic pressure of the body. The ameba has a certain amount of salt in its protoplasm which makes it hypertonic to the surrounding fresh water. Water will therefore enter the ameba by osmosis through its plasmalemma. It is interesting to note that marine amebae do not have contractile vacuoles because they are immersed in isotonic sea water

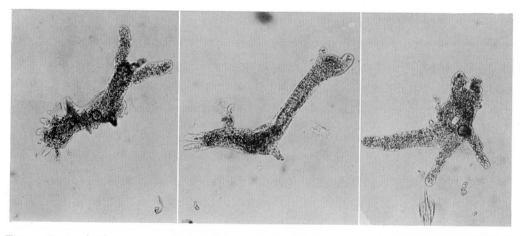

Figure 41. Ameboid movement. Series photographed at intervals of less than a minute. In view at right, pseudopodium is extending toward escaping rotifer.

(but placed in fresh water they will form them). Respiration occurs directly through the body surface by diffusion. Oxygen is dissolved in the water, which is everywhere in contact with the cell membrane, so that the gas is easily accessible and diffuses into the ameba.

Locomotion. Locomotion takes place by the formation of temporary locomotor structures, the pseudopodia, which are thrust out on any part of the body surface and into which the cytoplasm flows. This characteristic movement is called **ameboid movement.** When a pseudopodium is beginning to form, a blunt, fingerlike projection called the **hyaline cap,** composed only of ectoplasm, first appears. A little later the granular plasmasol flows into this projection as it extends forward. Usually the ameba forms several small pseudopodia at the start of the movement; one of these gradually becomes larger, while the others disappear.

Theories to account for ameboid movement are far from satisfactory. One theory stresses changes in surface tension which is lessened at the point where pseudopodia are formed. Mast's theory based upon the colloidal nature of protoplasm, states that the movement is caused by the reversible change from the fluid sol state to the gel condition. In this process the posterior part of the moving ameba is changing from plasmagel to plasmasol, while just the reverse is occurring in the pseudopodium. In the gel state protoplasm can contract to some extent, which exerts a squeezing action on the sol, pushing it along into the pseudopodium, the tip of which is not a gel. When the fluid protoplasm reaches the tip, or hyaline cap, it fountains to the sides and is converted into a gel. A necessary feature of ameboid movement is the attachment of the ameba (at the tips of pseudopodia) to a substratum during the act of moving.

Ameboid movement is also found elsewhere in the animal kingdom, notably in the white corpuscles of blood, in amebocytes of sponges, etc.

Reproduction. When the ameba reaches full size, it divides into two animals by the process of **binary fission.** A series of nuclear changes accompanies this process. Typical mitosis (Figure 42) occurs with all the phases: prophase, metaphase, anaphase, and telophase. It takes about 30 minutes. During the process of division the shape of the ameba is spherical, with a number of small pseudopodia. The nuclear membrane disappears during the metaphase and the body elongates and separates by fission into two daughter cells. Under ordinary conditions the ameba attains a size for division about every three days.

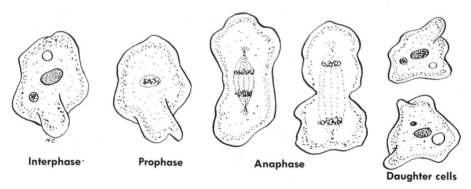

Interphase·   Prophase   Anaphase

Daughter cells

Figure 42. Mitosis in nucleus of *Amoeba.* There are many mitotic patterns among protozoa. In most cases nuclear membrane persists throughout mitosis, and division bodies of centrioles, centrosphere, and spindle are of nuclear rather than of cytoplasmic origin. Sometimes one of these division bodies may be absent. In many cases chromosomes behave as in metazoans. In others chromatin mass splits and passes to poles without forming chromosomes. Amitosis in protozoans restricted mainly to macronucleus of ciliates.

Sporulation and budding may occur in the ameba under favorable conditions. Binary fission seems to be the only regular method employed.

Behavior. The ameba reacts to stimuli just as any other animal does. Its behavior pattern naturally is simpler than those of most metazoans, yet fundamentally they are the same. Its reactions center around food getting, locomotion, changes in shape, avoidance of unfavorable environments, hunger, and so on. Its responses to different forms of stimuli vary. In a positive reaction the ameba goes toward the stimulus; in a negative reaction it moves away. If touched with a needle it will draw back and move away, but when floating it will respond in a positive way to a solid object. It moves away from a strong light and may change its direction a number of times to avoid it, but it may react positively to a weak light. The ameba's rate of locomotion is lessened by colder temperatures and may cease entirely near the freezing point. Its rate increases up to 30° C., but it ceases to move at temperatures higher than this.

Its response to chemicals varies with the nature of the chemical. While indifferent to most normal constituents in its medium, the ameba will react positively toward substances of a food character.

Other members of class Sarcodina

There are a number of other species of *Amoeba,* such as *A. verrucosa,* with short pseudopodia; *Chaos chaos (Pelomyxa carolinensis),* which is several times as large as *A. proteus;* and *A. radiosa,* with many slender pseudopodia.

Most of the parasites of Sarcodina are amebae (order Lobosa or Amoebina), which live in the intestine of man and other animals There are two common

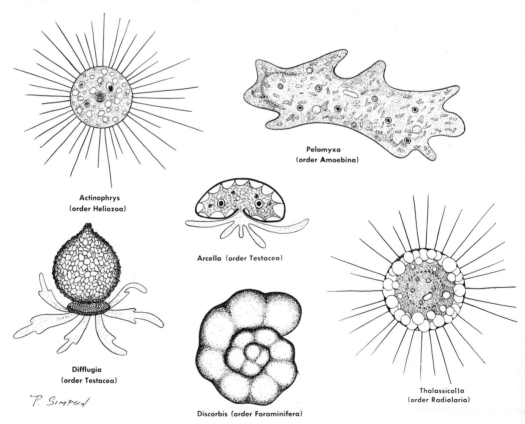

Actinophrys
(order Heliozoa)

Pelomyxa
(order Amoebina)

Arcella (order Testacea)

Difflugia
(order Testacea)

Discorbis (order Foraminifera)

Thalassicolla
(order Radiolaria)

P. SIMPSON

Figure 43. Some examples of Sarcodina, showing wide variety of forms.

genera, *Endamoeba* and *Entamoeba*. *En-lamoeba blattae* is common in the intestine of cockroaches. This form may be an endocommensal rather than a parasite. Related species are also found in the gut of termites. The only serious rhizopod parasite of man is *Entamoeba histolytica* which is responsible for amebic dysentery. This species lives in the connective tissues and muscular layers of the intestinal wall, which it enters by secreting a substance that dissolves away the intestinal lining. They often produce severe lesions and abscesses and may spread to the liver, lungs, brain, and other organs. Not all infected persons show severe symptoms, but they may become carriers. Contaminated water or food containing the cysts discharged through the feces are the chief methods of spreading the infection. *E. histolytica* or a closely related form is also found in monkeys, rats, and other animals. Among other species of *Entamoeba* found in man are *Entamoeba coli*, which is usually considered to be nonpathogenic but may cause intestinal disturbances, and *Entamoeba gingivalis*, found in the mouth and causing pyorrhea by dissolving away the cement that holds the teeth to the bone. Many species of *Entamoeba* are found in all classes of vertebrates.

The **Foraminifera** are found in all oceans and a few live in fresh and brackish water. They are mostly bottom-living but a few live in open water. Most forms are invested with shells or tests which are of many types and may be one or many chambered. The tests are made of calcium carbonate, chitin, or silica and sometimes of silt and other foreign materials. Slender pseudopodia extend through openings in the test, then branch and run together to form a protoplasmic net in which they ensnare their prey. Here the captured prey is digested and the digested products carried into the interior by the flowing protoplasm. Their life cycles are complex, for they have multiple division and alternation of generations.

The **Radiolaria** are the oldest known group of animals. They live in open water,

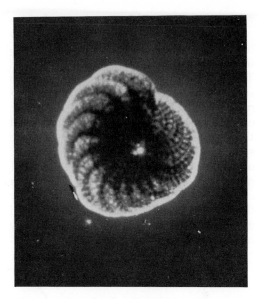

Figure 44. Foraminiferan shell.

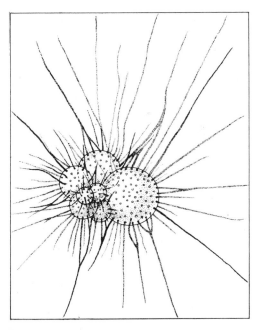

Figure 45. *Globigerina* alive, showing pseudopodia of streaming cytoplasm. Order Foraminifera. (Courtesy General Biological Supply House, Inc., Chicago.)

both surface and deep. Their highly specialized skeletons are intricate in form and of unimaginable beauty. The body is divided by a central capsule which separates inner and outer zones of cytoplasm. The central capsule, which may be spherical, ovoid, or branched, is perforated to allow cytoplasmic continuity. The skeleton is made of silica or strontium sulfate and usually has a radial arrangement of spines which extend through the capsule from the center of the body. At the surface a shell may be fused with the spines. Around the capsule is a frothy mass of cytoplasm from which stiff pseudopodia arise. These are sticky for catching the prey which are carried by the streaming protoplasm to the central capsule to be digested. Radiolaria may have one or many nuclei. Their life history is not completely known, but binary fission, budding, and sporulation have been observed in them (Figure 35).

Arcella and *Difflugia* (order Testacea) are two common members of Sarcodina that have shells for protection (Figure 43). Their shells may be secreted or built of sand. They move by pseudopodia which project from openings in the shell.

CLASS MASTIGOPHORA
Euglena viridis

Habitat. The normal habitat of *Euglena viridis* is in fresh-water streams and ponds, where there is considerable vegetation. Lily ponds in well-kept parks are often a

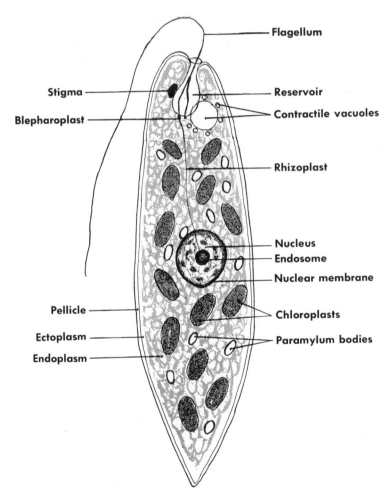

Figure 46. General structure of *Euglena.* Features shown are a combination of those visible in living and in stained preparations.

good source for them. They are sometimes so numerous as to give a distinct greenish color to the water. Although light is necessary for their metabolism, they are often found at various depths below the surface of water, for they are fairly active forms. In the laboratory they thrive best in a jar exposed to indirect sunlight.

Structure. The euglena's spindle-shaped body is about 60 microns (0.06 mm.) long, with a rather pointed posterior end. It is covered by a **pellicle** flexible enough to permit movement. Movement is effected by fine contractile fibers beneath the pellicle. Inside the pellicle is the clear **ectoplasm** which surrounds the mass of **endoplasm**. A flask-shaped **reservoir** or gullet dips into the anterior end and from it springs a **flagellum**. A typical flagellum is composed of a sheath and an inner axoneme which arises from the **blepharoplast**, a granule beneath the reservoir. The axoneme continues posteriorly as a **rhizoplast** to connect with the nucleus. The blepharoplast may function as a centriole in division. The electron microscope reveals that the flagellum contains two central and nine peripheral fibrils. This same pattern is true of cilia and of the tail or flagellum of the sperm of higher animals.

A large **contractile vacuole**, which is formed by fusion of smaller vacuoles, empties wastes and excess water into the reservoir, the anterior opening of which (called the mouth) is an exit.

Near the reservoir is a red **eyespot** or **stigma**. This is a shallow cup-shaped spot of pigment which allows light from only one direction to strike a light-sensitive receptor located as a swelling near the base of the flagellum. When the euglena is moving toward the light the receptor is illuminated; when it changes direction the shadow of the pigment falls on the receptor. Thus the animal, which depends upon sunlight for its photosynthesis, can orient itself toward the light.

The **nucleus,** a slightly oval body near the center of the cell, has a prominent center body, the **endosome**. Within the cytoplasm are the oval **chromatophores**

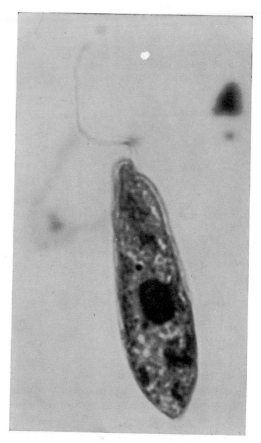

Figure 47. Photograph of *Euglena viridis,* showing flagellum. (Courtesy Ward's Natural Science Establishment, Inc., Rochester, N. Y.)

which bear chlorophyll and give the euglena its greenish color. They function as in plants in the manufacture of carbohydrates. **Paramylum bodies** of various shapes are masses of starch, a means of food storage.

Metabolism. The euglena derives its food mainly through **holophytic** nutrition, which makes use of photosynthesis, a process that takes place within the chromatophores through the action of chlorophyll. This form also makes use of **saprophytic nutrition,** which is the absorption of dissolved nutrients through the body surface. It is very doubtful whether the euglena ingests solid food particles through its mouth region, **holozoic nutrition,** although some flagellates such as *Paranema* ingest other organisms. Respira-

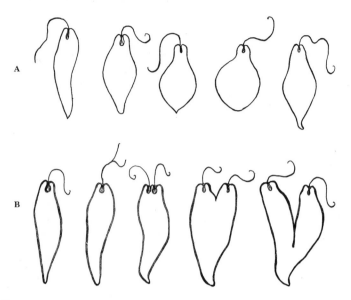

Figure 48. A, Shapes assumed by *Euglena* in its euglenoid movement. **B,** Longitudinal fission in *Euglena*.

tion and excretion are carried out by diffusion through the body wall.

Locomotion. The euglena swims freely by the movement of the flagellum, which carries the animal forward in a straight course while the body rotates spirally. It can also move by a squirming, worm-like action called "euglenoid" movement (Figure 48, *A*).

Reproduction. Euglena reproduces by **binary** longitudinal division. The nucleus undergoes mitotic division while the body, beginning at the anterior end, divides in two lengthwise (Figure 48, *B*). This division may involve a splitting of the flagellum, blepharoplast, reservoir, and eyespot, or else there is a duplication of these organelles. During inactive periods and for protection the euglena assumes a spherical shape surrounded with a gelatinous covering, thus becoming encysted. In this condition it can withstand drought and become active when it is again in water. Encysted euglenae usually divide so that each cyst may contain two or more euglenae.

Behavior. The euglena is sensitive to light and will swim toward light if it is not too bright. If given the choice, it will avoid shady areas and regions of bright light. The eyespot seems to be responsible for determining its reactions to light

Volvox globator

The group (order Phytomonadina) to which *Volvox* belongs includes many fresh-water flagellates that have a close resemblance to algae. Their cells or zooids are usually enclosed in a cellulose membrane through which two short flagella project. Most of them are provided with green chromatophores. Many of them are colonial forms. *Volvox* is a green hollow sphere which may reach a diameter of 0.5 to 1 mm. It is a colony of many thousands of zooids (up to 50,000) embedded in the gelatinous surface of a jelly ball. Each cell is much like a euglena with a nucleus, a pair of flagella, a large chloroplast (a type of chromatophore) and a red stigma. Adjacent cells are connected with each other by cytoplasmic strands. At one pole (usually in front as the animal moves) the stigmas are a little larger. Coordinated action of the flagella causes the colony to move by rolling over and over. Here we have the beginning of division of labor to the ex

118

ent that some of the zooids (somatic) are concerned with nutrition and locomotion and others (germ cells), located in the posterior half, are responsible for reproduction.

Reproduction is asexual or sexual. In either case only certain zooids located around the equator or posterior half take part. **Asexual reproduction** occurs by the repeated mitotic division of one of the germ cells, to form a hollow sphere of cells with the flagellate ends of the cells inside. It then invaginates, or turns itself wrong side out, to form a daughter colony like the parent colony. Several daughter colonies are formed inside the parent colony before they escape by rupture of the parent.

In **sexual reproduction** some of the zooids differentiate into **macrogametes** (ova) and **microgametes** (sperm). The macrogametes are fewer and larger and loaded with food for nourishment of the young colony. The microgametes, by repeated division, form bundles or balls of small flagellated sperm which, when mature, leave the mother colony and swim about to find a mature ovum. When a sperm enters or fertilizes an egg, the zygote so formed secretes a hard, spiny, protective shell around itself. When released by the breaking up of the parent colony, the zygote remains quiescent during the winter. Within the shell the zygote undergoes repeated division until a small colony is produced which is released in the spring. A number of asexual generations may follow before sexual reproduction occurs again.

Other members of class Mastigophora

The class is divided into two groups, those that have chlorophyll, such as the euglena, and those without chlorophyll. The second group may be holozoic, saprozoic, or **euzoic** (living within another animal). The class is a large one and there are many types (Figure 50). *Noctiluca,* a marine form, is luminescent and produces a striking greenish light at night. Another common form is *Chilomonas,* which has two flagella at the anterior end and is used as food by the ameba. There are also other species of *Euglena,* such as *E. spirogyra,* with marked spiral striations and often seen in mixed cultures; *E. oxyuris,* with sharp-pointed posterior ends; and *E. gracilis,* which is similar to *E. viridis.* Another flagellate, *Ceratium,* found in both fresh water and marine water, has a body of plates and horns.

Other colonial fresh-water flagellates, some of which show trends toward multicellular organization, are *Gonium* (4 cells), in which each zooid can become free and divide to form a colony; *Pandorina* (16 cells), with each cell capable of forming a colony; *Eudorina* (32 cells) and *Pleodorina* (32 cells), where reproduction is confined to certain flagellate zooids in the posterior part of the colony. The colorless flagellates (order Protomonadina) are represented by *Proterospongia* (Figure 51), a gelatinous mass of collar zooids at the surface and internal collarless ameboid zooids. *Proterospongia* may be a link between the choanoflagellates and the sponges.

Some of the worst of the protozoan parasites are flagellates. Many of these belong to the genus *Trypanosoma* and live in the blood of fishes, amphibians, reptiles, birds, and mammals. Some are nonpathogenic, but those that infect the mammals produce severe diseases. Im-

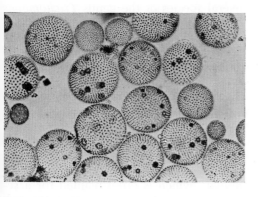

Figure 49. Colonies of *Volvox* in various stages of reproduction. Larger ones contain small daughter colonies. Class Mastigophora.

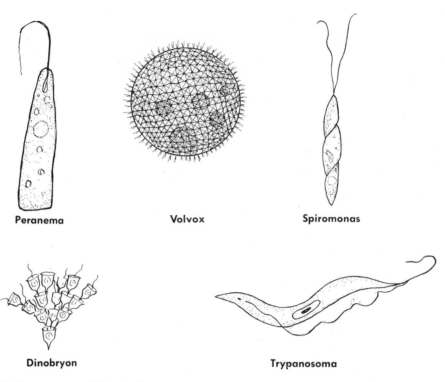

Peranema   Volvox   Spiromonas

Dinobryon   Trypanosoma

Figure 50. Various types of Mastigophora.

portant to man are *Trypanosoma gambiense,* which causes African sleeping sickness, and *Trypanosoma rhodesiense,* the cause of the similar but more virulent Rhodesian sleeping sickness. *Trypanosoma brucei* causes nagana in domestic cattle but does not infect man. The three are indistinguishable morphologically, and all are transmitted by the tsetse fly *(Glossina).* Their natural reservoirs, antelope and other wild mammals, are apparently not harmed by harboring these parasites. *Trypanosoma cruzi* causes Chagas' disease in man in Central and South America. It is transmitted by the bite of a "kissing bug" *(Triatoma). Trypanosoma lewisi,* a parasite of rats, is transmitted by the rat flea and is probably nonpathogenic. *Trypanosoma rotatorium,* which occurs in the blood of frogs, is transmitted by the bite of the leech. Three species of another flagellate *(Leishmania)* cause severe diseases in man. *Leishmania donovani* causes a disease of the spleen and liver, *Leishmania tropica* causes a peculiar type of skin lesion, and *Leishmania brasiliense* produces lesions in the mucous membranes of the nose and throat. These are transmitted by sandflies or by direct contact and are common in Africa, around the Mediterranean, in Asia, and in Central and South America. Several species of the genus *Trichomonas* (order Polymastigina) are commensals. *Trichomonas hominis* is found in the cecum and colon of man, transmitted by trophozoites; *Trichomonas vaginalis* is sometimes found in the vagina of women when secretions are acid and may cause vaginitis; and other species of *Trichomonas* are widely distributed through all classes of vertebrates and many invertebrates. A common flagellate of the small intestine of man is *Giardia intestinalis* (G. lamblia), which is often blamed for a severe diarrhea. It is transmitted through fecal contamination. Species are found in all classes of vertebrates.

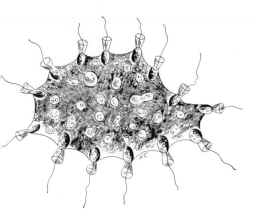

Figure 51. *Proterospongia*, colonial choanoflagellate supposed to be connecting link between protozoans and sponges. In gelatinous mass, collared zooids are embedded on the outside and collarless ameboid zooids on the inside. Collared cells resemble choanocytes of sponges. Only choanoflagellates and sponges have these peculiar cells.

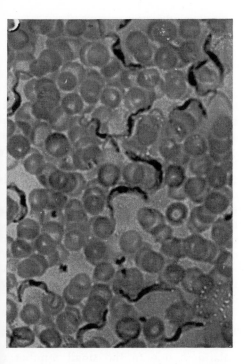

Figure 52. *Trypanosoma gambiense* scattered among red blood cells of a man. These blood parasites cause sleeping sickness (trypanosomiasis) in tropical Africa. One part of their life history is passed in tsetse flies which distribute the parasites to man and wild game animals. Class Mastigophora.

CLASS SPOROZOA
Plasmodium

Malaria is caused by a protozoan parasite, *Plasmodium,* which belongs to order Haemosporidia of class Sporozoa. All known members of this class are parasitic. They have rather simple bodies, no well-defined organelles for locomotion, and no contractile vacuoles. They reproduce by spore formation which may involve both asexual and sexual methods. Malaria is one of the most widespread diseases in the world. It is mainly a disease of tropical and subtropical countries but is also common in the temperate zones. The vectors of the parasites are female mosquitoes of genus *Anopheles.* Four species of *Plasmodium* are known to infect man: *P. vivax, P. malariae, P. falciparum,* and *P. ovale.* Each produces its own peculiar clinical picture, although all malarial parasites have similar cycles of development in the host (Figure 53).

Man acquires malaria from the bite of the mosquito, which introduces the parasites from its salivary glands into the blood in the form of **sporozoites.** It was once thought that these minute slender bodies at once entered the red blood corpuscles of the host, although no signs of malarial parasites could be found in human blood for a week or more after a mosquito had injected them. It was found in 1948 that the sporozoites first enter the cells of the liver. Here, as **cryptozoites,** they pass through a process of multiple division (**schizogony**). The products of this division, **merozoites,** then enter the red corpuscles. This period when the parasites are in the liver is called the incubation period. During this time antimalarial drugs may have little effect upon the parasites. When they enter the red blood corpuscles (usually only one to a cell), they become ameba-like **trophozoites.** These feeding forms then develop into **schizonts,** which have granules of black pigment. The schizonts, by multiple fission (schizogony), each divide into many daughter asexual **merozoites** (6 to 36 in number, according to the species of *Plasmodium*); these break out of the red cells to enter

Phylum Protozoa 121

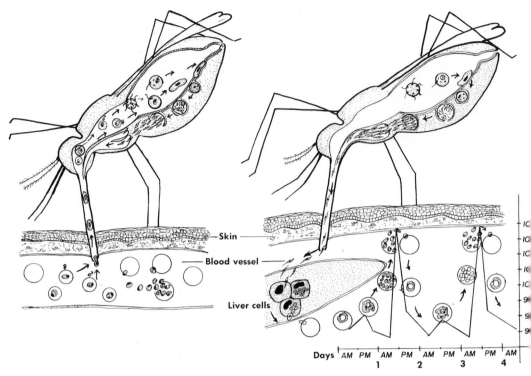

Figure 53. Life cycle of *Plasmodium vivax*, malarial parasite. At left, mosquito, *Anopheles*, ingests infected blood; at right, sporozoites injected into man by mosquito. Fever cycle of infected case is shown in lower right-hand corner.

other red corpuscles and continue the asexual cycle. In a few days the number of parasites is so great that the characteristic chills and fever occur; these symptoms are caused mainly by the toxins released by the parasites. The time elapsing between the fever-chill stages of the cycle depends upon the type of malaria. In *P. vivax* (benign tertian), the chills and fever occur every 48 hours; in *P. malariae* (quartan), every 72 hours; in *P. falciparum* (malignant tertian), usually every 24 to 48 hours, although it may be irregular; and in *P. ovale*, every 48 hours. After a period of this asexual reproduction, or schizogony, the merozoites become sexual forms, **gametocytes.** When these gametocytes are sucked up into the stomach of the mosquito, they become **microgametocytes** (male) and **macrogametocytes** (female). A zygote is formed by the union of two gametes from opposite sexes and develops into the mobile **oökinete.** The oökinetes penetrate

into the stomach walls of the mosquito to lie under the covering epithelium. Later the oökinetes enlarge to form oöcysts. Each oöcyst then divides in a few days into thousands of sporozoites which rupture the cyst and migrate to the salivary glands, whence they are transferred to man by the bite of the mosquito. The developmental cycle in the mosquito requires from seven to eighteen days but may be longer in cool weather. After being inoculated by the mosquito, man usually manifests the symptoms of the disease ten to fourteen days later.

Some forms of malaria may persist for some years without showing clinical symptoms. It is thought that this latent malaria is due to the small number of parasites in the blood. The body gradually acquires an immunity to the disease; this causes malaria to subside. However, this immunity does not prevent relapses. The time-honored treatment for malaria has been quinine, which was found effec-

122

ve three hundred years ago; but Atabrine nd Plasmochin are also employed. The limination of mosquitoes and their breed- ng places (by DDT, drainage, etc.) has een effective in controlling malaria.

Other species of *Plasmodium* parasitize irds, reptiles, and mammals. Those of irds are transmitted chiefly by the *Culex* nosquito.

regarinida

This order of Sporozoa consists of para- tes that live mainly in the digestive tract nd body cavity (sometimes in tissue ells) of certain invertebrates, such as ar-

thropods and annelids. A familiar example is *Monocystis lumbrici* (Figure 54) which lives in the seminal vesicles of earth- worms. They can be seen when pieces of seminal vesicles of living earthworms are examined in salt solution under the micro- scope. They may cause sterility in the parasitized worm, for the sperm are de- stroyed. Earthworms are infected by spores, each of which contains 8 sporozo- ites. Each sporozoite enters a bundle of immature sperm cells and becomes a tro- phozoite which lives on the sperm cells. Two trophozoites (gametocytes) come to- gether and are surrounded by a cyst wall.

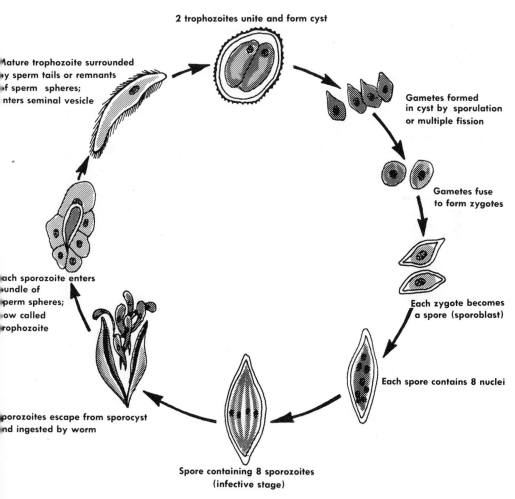

2 trophozoites unite and form cyst

Mature trophozoite surrounded by sperm tails or remnants of sperm spheres; enters seminal vesicle

Gametes formed in cyst by sporulation or multiple fission

Gametes fuse to form zygotes

Each sporozoite enters bundle of sperm spheres; now called trophozoite

Each zygote becomes a spore (sporoblast)

Each spore contains 8 nuclei

porozoites escape from sporocyst nd ingested by worm

Spore containing 8 sporozoites (infective stage)

Figure 54. Diagram of life cycle of *Monocystis*, sporozoan that lives in seminal vesicles of rthworms. They destroy some sperm cells of hosts but otherwise do little damage to rthworms.

Each divides a number of times to produce gametes. Two of these from different trophozoites unite to form the zygote, which forms a hard case around itself. This is the spore case or oöcyst. The zygote nucleus divides into 2, 4, then 8 daughter nuclei. Each of these nuclei with a small amount of cytoplasm becomes a sporozoite, and the cycle is ready to start over.

Coccidia

The order Coccidia are Sporozoa whose life cycle (which involves both schizogony and sporogony) is passed in a single host. They are parasites that infe epithelial tissues in both invertebrate (annelids, arthropods, mollusks) and ve tebrates. A few cases of infection ha been reported from man. They are foun chiefly in the epithelial lining of the co lom, alimentary canal, bile duct, bloo vessels, etc. The disease produced called coccidiosis and may be serious. Th symptoms are usually severe diarrhea dysentery. Infection is by the ingestio of oöcysts and sometimes by separat sporozoites. *Eimeria* (Figure 55) is common genus found in rabbits an chickens. *Eimeria magna* and *Eimer*

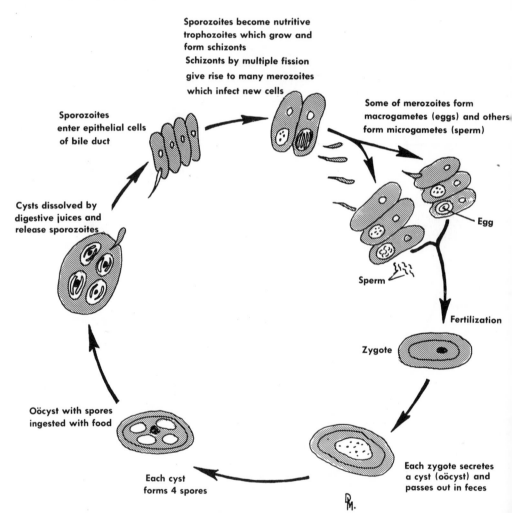

Sporozoites become nutritive trophozoites which grow and form schizonts
Schizonts by multiple fission give rise to many merozoites which infect new cells

Sporozoites enter epithelial cells of bile duct

Some of merozoites form macrogametes (eggs) and others form microgametes (sperm)

Cysts dissolved by digestive juices and release sporozoites

Egg

Sperm

Fertilization

Zygote

Oöcyst with spores ingested with food

Each zygote secretes a cyst (oöcyst) and passes out in feces

Each cyst forms 4 spores

Figure 55. Diagram of life cycle of *Eimeria stiedae,* sporozoan (Coccidia) parasite of rabbits. Severe infections may cause many deaths in young rabbits.

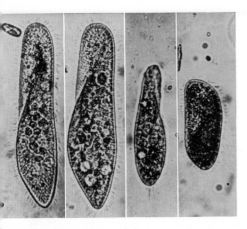

Figure 56. Comparison of four common species Paramecium photographed at same magnification. Left to right: *P. multimicronucleatum*, *P. caudatum*, *P. aurelia*, and *P. bursaria*. (Courtesy Carolina Biological Supply House, Elon College, N. C.)

iedae infect the intestine and liver of rabbits. Their life history is briefly as follows: after the oöcysts are ingested by the host, the sporozoites are released and enter epithelial cells where they develop into trophozoites. Each of the latter produces a number of merozoites asexually by schizogony. The merozoites also enter epithelial cells, become trophozoites, and repeat the cycle. Some of the merozoites develop through intermediate stages into macrogametes and microgametes which unite to form zygotes. A wall is secreted around the zygote which is now an oöcyst. Oöcysts usually pass in the feces of the rabbit. Later each zygote divides into four sporoblasts, each of which forms a sporocyst enclosing two sporozoites. When ingested, the life cycle is repeated.

CLASS CILIATA

Paramecium caudatum

Habitat. Paramecia are usually abundant in fresh water that contains a great deal of decaying organic matter. A good place for them is in ponds or sluggish streams containing aquatic plants, such as *Ceratophyllum* and *Elodea*. Reservoirs containing sewage, such as those found at sewage disposal plants, are excellent places for them. A jar of contaminated water allowed to stand for a day or so will yield them in abundance. They gather in scum near the surface but are active and free swimming and may be found throughout the water in which they live.

Structure. The paramecium is often described as slipper shaped. *Paramecium caudatum* is from 150 to 300 microns (0.15 to 0.3 mm.) in length.* It is blunt at the anterior end and somewhat pointed at the posterior end, with the greatest width behind the center of the body. The animal has an asymmetrical appearance because of the **oral groove,** a depression which runs obliquely backward, ending just behind the middle of the body. Viewed from in front, the groove usually runs clockwise, but in some individuals it runs in a counterclockwise direction. The **oral,** or **ventral,** side is the side containing the oral groove; the opposite side is called the **aboral,** or **dorsal,** side.

Over the entire surface is a clear, elastic membrane, the **pellicle,** or **cuticle.** This membrane is divided into small hexagonal areas by tiny elevated ridges (Figure 58). The pellicle is covered over its entire surface by fine cilia, which are characteristic of the class to which *Paramecium* belongs. The cilia are arranged in lengthwise rows, and in some species, *P. caudatum* among them, they are longer at the posterior end, producing a caudal tuft. Just below the pellicle is the thin clear **ectoplasm,** which surrounds the larger mass of grandular *endoplasm.* Embedded in the ectoplasm just below the surface are spindle-shaped cavities, known as

---

*Within each species of *Paramecium* the individuals exhibit morphological and physiological differences. Since these differences are usually more minor and more superficial than those which distinguish species, the groups within a species are referred to as strains, biotypes, or varieties. Most species of Protozoa can be divided into a number of these groups. Jennings was able to find in one species of *Paramecium* eight races differing in total length and size. The individuals of a group fluctuated around the same average generation after generation and were rigidly fixed by heredity. Other races or varieties may be due to diverse environmental factors and may disappear when the environment changes.

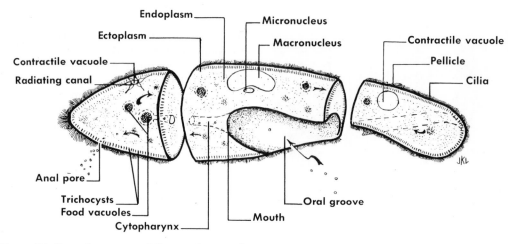

Figure 57. General structure of *Paramecium caudatum*.

trichocysts, filled with a semifluid substance which may be discharged as long threads for attachment and defense. The trichocysts alternate with the bases of the cilia.

At the posterior end of the oral groove is the **mouth** (**cytostome**), which leads into the tubular **gullet,** or **cytopharynx.** Along the gullet are two rows of fused cilia, the **undulating membrane.** When discharging fecal material, the **anal spot** can be seen posterior to the oral groove. The endoplasm contains **food vacuoles** with food in various stages of digestion. Toward each end of the cell body and near the surface is a **contractile vacuole.** Each contractile vacuole is made up of a central space surounded by several **radiating canals.** There are two **nuclei:** a large kidney-shaped **macronucleus** and a smaller **micronucleus** fitted into a depression of the former.

Paramecia are complex little animals. Special fixing and staining methods show that the cilia are connected to **basal granules,** which in turn are linked to each other by longitudinal fibers, the whole comprising the **neuromotor system** concerned with the coordination of ciliary action (Figure 58).

Metabolism. Paramecia do not have chlorophyll for forming their own food. They are holozoic, living upon other Protozoa, bacteria, algae, and other small or-

ganisms. They are selective in choosir their food, for some things are taken and others rejected. The cilia in the or groove sweep food particles in the wat into the cytostome, whence they a carried into the cytopharynx by the und lating membrane. At the posterior part the cytopharynx the food is collected in a food vacuole which is constricted c and dropped into the endoplasm. Th food vacuoles take a definite course their circulation, first posteriorly, the forward near the dorsal surface to the a terior end. During this course the food digested by enzymes from the endoplasr and the vacuoles become smaller. By th use of indicator dyes, it is possible demonstrate that the vacuoles are fir acid and later alkaline. The indigestib part of the food is ejected through th anal pore.

Respiration takes place through th body surface by diffusion, oxygen di solved in the surrounding water passir in and the waste, including carbon dio ide, passing out.

The two contractile vacuoles regula the water content of the body and ma also serve to get rid of the nitrogenou waste. The vacuoles lie close to the dors surface and drain fluid from the cyt plasm by means of radiating canals whic are easily seen when the vacuole is forr ing. When the vacuole reaches a certa

126

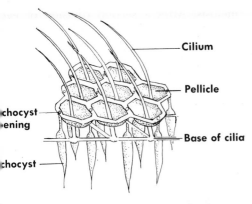

Cilium

Pellicle

.chocyst
.ening

.chocyst

Base of cilia

Figure 58. Diagram of section of pellicle of *Para-mecium*, showing arrangement of cilia, tricho-ysts, and neuromotor system. (Modified after ..und.)

ze it discharges to the outside through pore. The two vacuoles contract alter-ately at intervals of about 10 to 20 sec-nds. They contract more frequently at igher temperatures and in the mature ..imal. Since the contents of the para-ecium are hypertonic to the surround-ig fresh water, osmotic pressure would ause water to diffuse into the cell, and us one of the main functions of the ontractile vacuoles is to get rid of the xcess water.

Locomotion. The body of the parame-ium is elastic, for it can squeeze its way rough a narrow passage. Its cilia can eat either forward or backward, so that e animal can swim in either direction. he cilia beat obliquely, thus causing the ..imal to rotate on its long axis. In the al groove the cilia are longer and beat ore vigorously than the others so that e anterior end swerves aborally. As a esult of these factors, the animal follows spiral path in order to move directly orward (Figure 59). In swimming back-ard the beat and path of rotation are eversed.

When the paramecium comes in contact ith a disturbing chemical stimulus, it erforms the **avoiding reaction** (Figure 0). In this process it reverses its cila, acks up a short distance, and swerves e anterior end aborally as it pivots on s posterior end. While it is doing this,

samples of the surrounding medium are brought into the oral groove. When the sample no longer contains the unfavora-ble stimulus, the animal moves forward.

Reproduction. Paramecia reproduce only by **transverse binary fission** but have certain forms of nuclear reorganizations called **conjugation** and **autogamy.**

In **binary fission** the micronucleus di-vides mitotically into two daughter micro-nuclei, which move to opposite ends of the cell. The macronucleus elongates and divides amitotically. Another cytopharynx is budded off and two new contractile

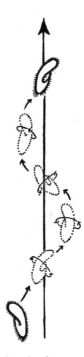

Figure 59. Spiral path of paramecium swimming.

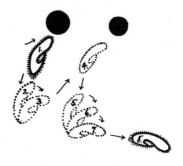

Fig. 60. Avoiding reaction of paramecium.

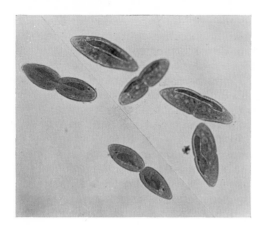

Figure 61. Binary fission in *Paramecium*.

vacuoles appear, one near the anterior end and another posteriorly. In the meantime, a constriction furrow appears near the middle of the body and deepens until the cytoplasm is completely divided. The process of binary fission requires from one-half to two hours. The division rate usually varies from one to four times each day. About 600 generations are produced in a year. Naturally, if all descendants were to live and reproduce, the number of paramecia produced would soon equal the volume of the earth. The term **clone** is used to refer to all the individuals that have been produced from one individual by binary fission. All the members of a clone are hereditarily alike.

The process known as **conjugation** (Figure 62) occurs in ciliates and a few other Protozoa. This phenomenon happens only at intervals. It is more frequent in *P. caudatum* than it is in *P. aurelia*. It is the temporary union of two individuals which mutually exchange micronuclear material. Conjugating individuals come together and attach by their oral surfaces, and a protoplasmic bridge forms between them. In thriving cultures one may see a number of these conjugating pairs swimming about. A series of nuclear changes now occurs. The micronucleus of each member moves from its recess in the macronucleus, while the latter starts to disintegrate and finally disappears. The micronucleus enlarges, forms a spindle, and divides by

meiosis. After a second division of eac micronucleus, 3 of the resulting micronu clei degenerate, leaving only 1. This re maining micronucleus divides unequall into 2 micronuclei, the smaller of whic in each animal moves across the prote plasmic bridge into the other anima Each of these exchanged micronucl fuses with the larger micronucleus of th other animal. The 2 paramecia now sep

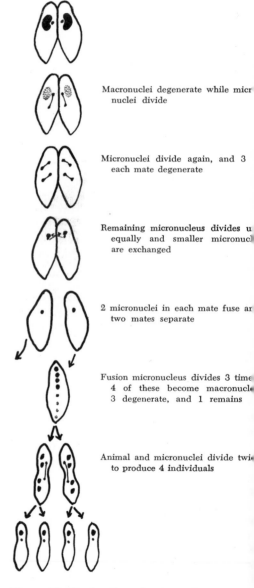

Macronuclei degenerate while micr nuclei divide

Micronuclei divide again, and 3 each mate degenerate

Remaining micronucleus divides u equally and smaller micronuc are exchanged

2 micronuclei in each mate fuse ar two mates separate

Fusion micronucleus divides 3 time 4 of these become macronucl 3 degenerate, and 1 remains

Animal and micronuclei divide twi to produce 4 individuals

Figure 62. Conjugation of paramecia.

128

arate, and in each the fused micronucleus, which is comparable to a zygote in higher forms, divides by mitosis into 2, 4, and 8 micronuclei. Four of these enlarge and become macronuclei, and 3 of the other 4 disappear. The paramecium now divides twice, resulting in 4 paramecia, each with 1 micronucleus and 1 macronucleus. After this complicated process, the animal continues its binary fission reproduction.

What is the meaning of this unique phenomenon? There is first of all an exchange of hereditary material so that each conjugant profits from a new hereditary constitution. It is not the same as the union of the gametes in higher forms (zygote formation), where direct progeny is the result, for in conjugation the animals still continue asexual division. However, about the same result is attained, for the nucleus of each exconjugant contains hereditary material from two individuals. The process does not seem necessary for rejuvenation, for experiments have been conducted which show that cultures can be maintained for many years without undergoing conjugation.

Autogamy refers to a process of self-fertilization and is a newer version of endomixis, which had long been described as a nuclear reorganization that had interrupted binary fission. Endomixis was first described in *Paramecium aurelia*, but this process has been utterly discredited. In autogamy, after the disintegration of the macronucleus and the division of the 2 micronuclei to form 8 micronuclei, 2 of the haploid gametic nuclei which result from this division enter a small bulge (paroral cone), fuse together, and restore the diploid number of chromosomes in the synkaryon or zygote. The other 6 micronuclei degenerate and the synkaryon divides twice to produce 2 macronuclei and 2 micronuclei. At the first binary fission each daughter cell will receive 1 of the macronuclei and by division of the micronuclei also 2 micronuclei. This process is similar to conjugation but does not involve two individuals.

A variant form of conjugation and autogamy is **cytogamy**, where two ciliates become fused along their oral surfaces and three pregametic divisions occur. Two of the gametic nuclei then form a synkaryon as in autogamy. However, there is no exchange of nuclear material between the two fused members.

In 1937 it was discovered that not every paramecium would conjugate with any other paramecium of the same species. Sonneborn found that there were physiological differences between individuals which set them off into mating types. Ordinarily, conjugation will not occur between individuals of the same mating type but only with an individual of another (complementary) mating type. It was also found that within a single species there are a number of varieties, each of which has mating types that conjugate among themselves but not with the mating types of other varieties. In *Paramecium aurelia*, for instance, each of six varieties has two mating types; conjugation, however, will occur only between members of opposite or complementary mating types within their own variety. Mating types are usually designated by Roman numerals. Thus, in variety 1 of *P. aurelia*, the mating types are called mating types I and II; in variety 2 they are called mating types III and IV, etc. New varieties of this species have been described from time to time until 16 were known in 1957. Their wide and sporadic distribution pose interesting evolutionary problems. With few exceptions, each variety has only two interbreeding mating types. There is no morphological basis for distinguishing mating types within a variety; such differences that exist must be physiological. Some varieties, however, can be distinguished from each other morphologically. Mating types are found in other species of paramecia as well as among other ciliates. *Paramecium bursaria* has six varieties, but only one variety has a system of two mating types; the others have multiple (four to eight) mating types. Each mating type can conjugate with all the others in the same variety but not with individuals of its own mating type. Genetically, each variety may be considered a separate species since they do not inter-breed, but this taxonomic scheme has not yet been adopted.

As an example of how conjugation occurs, the mating types of three varieties of *P. aurelia* are shown in Table 3.

Behavior. The avoiding reaction already described serves as a key in the interpretation of the various reactions of paramecia to stimuli. In its responses a paramecium makes use of the "trial-and-error" method to make its adjustments. In this method the animal attempts many directions until it finds one that is favorable and then makes its escape from the injurious environment.

Paramecia do not always respond in the same manner to the same stimuli. Their physiological states vary with conditions. A hungry animal will react in a different way from one that is well fed. In general,

Table 3. Examples of conjugations

Variety	Mating type	1		2		3	
		I	II	III	IV	V	VI
1	I	−	+	−	−	−	−
	II	+	−	−	−	−	−
2	III	−	−	−	+	−	−
	IV	−	−	+	−	−	−
3	V	−	−	−	−	−	+
	VI	−	−	−	−	+	−

+indicates conjugation will occur.
−indicates conjugation will not occur.

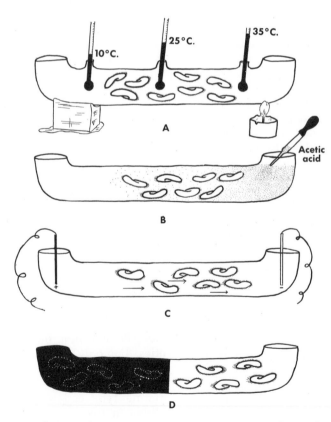

Figure 63. Certain typical taxes of paramecia. **A,** Temperature; **B,** acid; **C,** electric current; **D,** light.

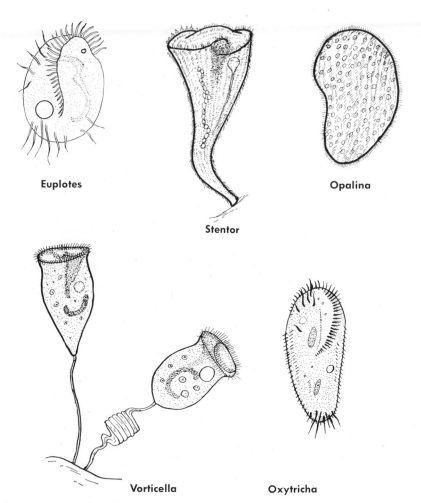

Euplotes

Stentor

Opalina

Vorticella

Oxytricha

Figure 64. Some representative ciliates.

its behavior is conditioned by factors that favor or hinder the normal life processes.

The responses of paramecia and other Protozoa are often called **taxes.** A taxis is an orientation of the body either toward or away from a stimulus (Figure 63). If the response is toward the stimulus, it is called a **positive response;** if the animal avoids the stimulus, it is termed a **negative response.**

With respect to the kind of stimuli, taxes are classified as follows:

thermotaxis Response to heat. For the paramecium the optimum temperature lies between 24° and 28° C.

phototaxis Response to light rays. The optimum for paramecia is subdued light; it will try to avoid total darkness or bright light.

thigmotaxis Response to contact. Response to this stimulus is varied. When the anterior end is touched lightly, the animal will usually back up, but if some other part is touched, it may be indifferent.

chemotaxis Response to chemical substances. Paramecia react negatively to most chemicals, yet to mild acid solutions they often respond in a positive way. They are partial to carbon dioxide solutions.

rheotaxis Response to currents of air or water. The paramecium will swim toward a current of water if it is not too swift, or it will head upstream.

galvanotaxis Response to constant electric current. Paramecia will move toward the negative (cathode) pole. This response is supposed to be due to the effect of the electrons upon the action of the cilia.

Phylum Protozoa 131

geotaxis Response to gravity. The response of paramecia is mostly negative; they tend to gather close to the surface film with their anterior ends uppermost.

Since no nervous system is found in Protozoa (except perhaps the neuromotor system in ciliates), these responses must be due to the inate irritability of protoplasm. The complex responses of higher forms are thought to have developed from these simple mechanical responses.

Other members of class Ciliata

This is an interesting class, with many forms in both fresh water and marine water. There is a great diversity of shape and size among them. Among the more striking forms of ciliates are *Stentor* (Figure 64), trumpet shaped and solitary; *Vorticella*, inverted bell form and solitary (Figures 64 and 65); and *Euplotes*, flattened body with groups of fused cilia (cirri) which function as legs (Figure 64).

Ciliates are represented by a number of parasitic forms, most of which are not very harmful. Some may even be commensals. *Balantidium coli* is the only important ciliate parasite in man. It is often found in hogs where it usually does no harm. Man becomes infected by water and food contaminated by cysts from the hog's feces. The parasite enters the intestinal submucosa and causes ulcers and severe and even fatal dysentery. It is not as common in America as it is in Europe, Asia, and Africa. Other similar species are found in cattle and horses; *Epidinium* (Figure 67) in cattle, for example. Interesting ciliate parasites in the colon of frogs and toads are *Nyctotherus* and *Opalina*. The latter is oval and flattened and is one of the easiest protozoan parasites to demonstrate. Frogs in captivity, however, tend to lose them rapidly. Tadpoles are infected when they eat the feces of frogs containing the cysts.

CLASS SUCTORIA

Suctorians are found in both fresh water and marine water. The young possess cilia and are free swimming. As

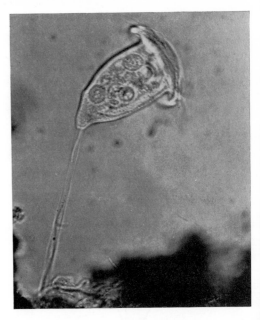

Figure 65. Living *Vorticella* attached by its stalk to debris in pond water culture. Class Ciliata.

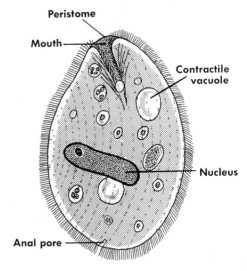

Figure 66. *Balantidium coli,* ciliate parasitic in man. Ciliate is common in hogs in which it does little damage; man becomes infected by food or water contaminated by cysts in hog feces or by handling intestines. In man it lives in cecum or colon, in which it produces ulcers and severe chronic dysentery. Cysts formed by ciliate are protective; no multiplication occurs within them. Infections common in parts of Europe, rare in United States.

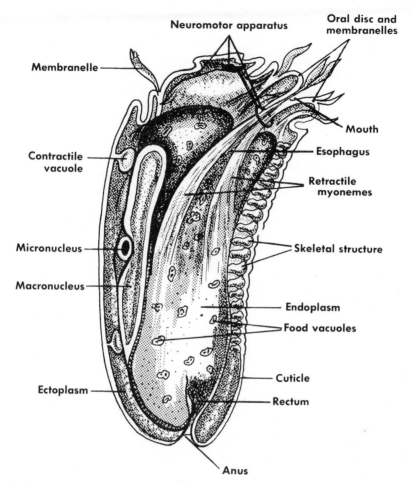

Neuromotor apparatus

Oral disc and membranelles

Membranelle

Mouth

Esophagus

Contractile vacuole

Retractile myonemes

Skeletal structure

Micronucleus

Macronucleus

Endoplasm

Food vacuoles

Cuticle

Ectoplasm

Rectum

Anus

Figure 67. *Epidinium.* This ciliate, which lives in stomach of ruminants, shows how complex a protozoan can be. It was with this ciliate that Sharp made his classical demonstration of neuromotor apparatus. He showed how organelles are controlled by neurofibrils connected anteriorly with motor mass (brain). Note that this so-called single cell has organelles specialized for coordination, ingestion and digestion, support, contraction, food storage, egestion, and hereditary continuity. (After Sharp.)

adults they grow a stalk for attachment to animal or nonliving matter and lose their cilia. As young they are often mistaken for ciliates, and some authorities consider them as a subdivision of the class Ciliata. The body, covered with a pellicle, may be spherical, branched, or other form. Nutrition is holozoic. They have no cytostome but have protoplasmic processes which serve as tentacles. Some of these have rounded knobs for capturing their prey—usually ciliates; some are sharp or piercing and for sucking up the protoplasm. The tentacles in some are scattered over the body; in others, arranged in clusters. Reproduction, mostly asexual, includes both fission and budding. In sexual reproduction two individuals undergo a complete fusion, which is a type of conjugation.

One of the best places to find suctorians is in the algae that grows on the carapace of turtles, such as the snapping turtle (*Chelydra serpentina*) and the western painted turtle (*Chrysemys picta belli*). Common genera of suctorians found there are *Anarma* (without stalk or lorica) and *Squalorophrya* (with stalk and lorica).

Suctorian parasites include the *Trichophrya*, which are parasitic on the gills of the small-mouthed black bass and may cause serious damage to the fish; *Allantosoma*, which occurs in the intestine of certain mammals; and *Sphaerophrya*, which is found in *Stentor*.

Among fresh-water representatives are *Podophrya* (Figure 40) and *Dendrosoma*. Some salt-water forms are *Acinetopsis* and *Ephelota*.

VALUE IN BIOLOGICAL INVESTIGATION

Protozoa are widely studied by biologists everywhere. Geneticists have long given consideration to the problem of heredity and variation in Protozoa. The rapid multiplication of protozoans and the many generations one can produce in a short time make these animals ideal for this study. The more some of these are studied, the more complex they turn out to be. The discovery of mating types in paramecia gives a hint or suggestion of sex. Although individual paramecia cannot be labeled male or female, there is definitely a physiological difference between individuals just as there is in well-established sexual forms. In recent years much interest has centered upon the role *Paramecium aurelia* plays in explaining the phenomena of cellular transformations, that is, the changing of one type of cell into another type. Sonneborn made use of two hereditary strains of paramecia which he called killers and sensitives. The killer strain contained in its cytoplasm certain visible particles (kappa particles) which liberated into the culture fluid a chemical substance (paramecin) that had the effect of destroying the other strain, the sensitive. Kappa particles, or killer substances, are transmitted directly by cytoplasmic genes (plasmagenes) from the cytoplasm of the parent cell to the daughter cells and not by nuclear genes as in ordinary heredity. This is often used as an example of cytoplasmic inheritance. Sonneborn was also able to change, ex-perimentally, killers into sensitives and the reverse, thus producing a form of cellular transformation. There are many problems in this interesting phenomenon still unsolved.

Many other studies of Protozoa of current interest involve their nutritional needs, population crowding, permeability, and problems of serology and immunity.

Derivation and meaning of basic terminology

Amoeba (Gr. *amoibe,* change) Genus (Sarcodina).

Arcella (L. *area,* box) Genus (Sarcodina); with a boxlike test.

aurelia (L. *aurum,* gold) Species of *Paramecium.*

autogamy (Gr. *autos,* self, + *gamos,* marriage) Conjugation without exchange of micronuclei.

axopodia (L. *axis,* an axis, + Gr. *podos,* foot) Long, thin projections of cytoplasm, but not for locomotion.

blepharoplast (Gr. *blepharon,* eyelid, + *plastos,* formed) Granule connected with a flagellum.

caudatum (L. *caudata,* tail) Species of *Paramecium.*

cilium (L. *cilium,* eyelash) Threadlike organ of locomotion.

Coccidia (Gr. *kokkos,* kernel, berry) Order (Sporozoa).

conjugation (L. *congure,* to yoke together) Temporary union of two Protozoa while they are exchanging chromatin material; may be a complete fusion in Suctoria.

cytopharynx (Gr. *kytos,* cell, + *pharynx,* throat). Short tubular gullet in protozoans.

cytostome (Gr. *kytos,* cell, + *stoma,* mouth) Mouth of a unicellular animal.

Difflugia (L. *diffluo,* to flow apart) Genus (Sarcodina); refers to the flowing out of the pseudopodia.

Eimeria (after Eimer, German zoologist) Genus (order Coccidia of Sporozoa).

endomixis (Gr. *endon,* within, + *mixis,* mixing) Reorganization of the nuclear material in the protozoan.

Entamoeba (Gr. *endon,* within, + *amoibe,* change) *histolytica* (Gr. *histo,* tissue, + *lysis,* dissolve) Genus and species (Sarcodina).

Euglena (Gr. *eu,* true, + *glene,* eye pupils) Refers to the stigma or eyespot.

Euplotes (Gr. *eu,* good, + *ploter,* swimmer) Genus (Ciliata).

flagellum (L. *a whip*) Whiplike organ of locomotion.

Foraminifera (L. *foramen,* hole, + *fero,* bear)
The tests are frequently perforated.

holozoic (Gr. *holos,* whole, + *zoikos,* of animals) That type of nutrition which involves ingestion of solid organic food.

Infusoria (L. *infusus,* crowded) So-called because of their abundance in a culture.

Leishmania (Leishman, who discovered it).

macronucleus (Gr. *makros,* large, + L. *nucleus,* kernel) Larger of the 2 nuclei in a ciliate.

Mastigophora (Gr. *mastix,* whip, + *phero,* bear).

micronucleus (Gr. *mikros,* small, + L. *nucleus,* kernel) Smaller of the 2 nuclei in a ciliate.

Monocystis (Gr. *monos,* single, + *kystis,* bladder) Parasitic genus (Sporozoa).

Noctiluca (L. *nox,* night, + *luceo,* shine) Genus (Mastigophora). Their luminescence is most apparent at night.

Opalina (L. *opalus,* opal) Genus (Ciliata).

organelle (Gr. *organon,* an organ) Specialized part of a cell; literally, a small organ.

Paramecium (Gr. *paramekes,* oblong) Genus (Ciliata).

paramylum (Gr. *para,* beside, + *mylos,* mill) Starch inclusions in certain protozoa.

Pelomyxa (Gr. *pelos,* mud, + *myzo,* suck in) Refers to the black and brown inclusions in body. Genus (Sarcodina).

proteus (Gr. *Proteus,* sea god who could change shape) Species (*Amoeba*).

Protozoa (Gr. *protos,* first, + *zoon,* animal).

pseudopodium (Gr. *pseudes,* false, + *podos,* foot) Protrusion of part of cytoplasm of an ameba.

Radiolaria (L. *radius,* ray) Order (Sarcodina). The axopodia radiate in all directions.

Rhizopoda (Gr. *rhiza,* root, + *podos,* foot) Many pseudopodia may be extended at one time.

saprophytic (Gr. *sapros,* rotten, + *phyton,* plant) Type of nutrition where the organism lives on decayed organic matter.

Sarcodina (Gr. *sarx,* flesh).

schizogony (Gr. *schizo,* to split, + *gonos,* seed) Asexual reproduction by multiple fission.

Sporozoa (Gr. *spora,* seed, + *zoon,* animal) Refers to their spore-forming characteristics.

Stentor (Gr. Grecian herald with loud voice) Genus (Ciliata). Shaped like a megaphone.

stigma (Gr. *stigma,* a point) Eye spot in certain Protozoa.

Suctoria (L. *suctus,* sucking) Food is sucked in by the tentacles.

symbiosis (Gr. *symbios,* a living together) Includes mutualism, commensalism, and parasitism.

taxis (Gr. arrangement) Response of animal organisms to sources of stimuli.

trichocyst (Gr. *thrix,* hair, + *kystis,* bladder) Saclike organelle in the ectoplasm of ciliates, which discharges a threadlike weapon of defense.

Trichomonas (Gr. *thrix,* hair, + *monas,* single) Genus (Mastigophora).

Trypanosoma (Gr. *trypanon,* auger, + *soma,* body) Genus (Mastigophora). The body with undulating membrane is twisted.

viridis (L. *viridis,* green) This species bears chloroplasts.

Volvox (L. *volvo,* to roll) Genus (Mastigophora). Refers to their characteristic movement.

Vorticella (L. *vortex,* a whirlpool) Genus (Ciliata). Movement of their cilia creates a spiral movement of water.

ANNOTATED REFERENCES

Borradaile, L. A., and F. A. Potts. 1932. The Invertebrate. New York, The Macmillan Co. *The first section of this work is devoted to protozoans and contains many excellent descriptions and illustrations of the various types.*

Brown, F. A., Jr. (editor). 1950. Selected Invertebrate Types. New York, John Wiley & Sons, Inc. *The section on Protozoa contains short descriptions of the morphology and life histories of various types. The excellent illustrations are line drawings; no microphotographs are included.*

Buchsbaum, R. 1948. Animals Without Backbones. Chicago, The University of Chicago Press. *Excellent illustrations, mostly photographs, are included. Descriptions are clearly written, but technical terms are kept at a minimum, and little attention is given to taxonomy.*

Bütschli, O. 1889. Protozoa (Bronn's Klassen und Ordnungen des Tier-Reichs). *This great monograph has been of the utmost importance to students of Protozoa. No other work on a like scale has ever been produced in this field of study.*

Calkins, G. N. 1933. The Biology of the Protozoa. Philadelphia, Lea & Febiger. *Excellent descriptions of the morphology and physiology of protozoan types. This work is recognized as authoritative in the field.*

Calkins, G. N., and F. M. Summers (editors). 1941. Protozoa in Biological Research. New York, Columbia University Press. *This pretentious work by the leading American protozoologists covers nearly every aspect of protozoan research. Although some of its concepts have been greatly expanded and some have been outdated, it is a stimulating work for all students of Protozoa.*

Chandler, A. C. 1949. Introduction to Parasitology, ed. 8. New York, John Wiley & Sons, Inc. *The first part of this standard work is devoted to protozoan parasites of animals, including man.*

Cushman, J. A. 1948. Foraminifera, Their Classification and Economic Use, ed. 4. Cambridge, Harvard University Press. *A definitive treatise on this important group of Protozoa. The student will appreciate how important these animals, small in size but abundant in numbers, are in the building of geological formations.*

Davis, C. C. 1955. The Marine and Fresh-Water Plankton. East Lansing, Michigan State University Press. *This treatise gives a good introductory account of plankton and contains good definitions of ecological concepts. Much of the work is devoted to keys and figures of plankton forms. An excellent account (with keys) of the protozoan part of plankton is given on pages 169 to 199.*

Doflein, F., and E. Reichenow. 1929. Lehrbuch der Protozoenkunde, ed. 5. Jena, Gustav Fischer. *A classical work on Protozoa. Authoritative and technical.*

Edmondson, W. T. (editor). 1959. Ward and Whipple's Fresh-Water Biology, ed. 2. New York, John Wiley & Sons, Inc. *In this handbook there are useful and up-to-date keys of the major groups of Protozoa.*

Gojdics, Mary. 1953. The Genus Euglena. Madison, The University of Wisconsin Press. *A comprehensive and technical account of this group. Much attention is given to taxonomy, but there are also good descriptions of morphology.*

Grant, M. P. 1953. Microbiology and Human Progress. New York, Rinehart & Co., Inc. *An excellent account of the influence of the minute forms of life as they affect the human being.*

Hall, R. P. 1953. Protozoology. Englewood Cliffs, N. J., Prentice-Hall, Inc. *A standard text on Protozoa. Good accounts of the morphology and physiology as well as taxonomy. There is an excellent chapter on reproduction and life cycles.*

Hardy, A. C. 1956. The Open Sea. Its Natural History: the World of Plankton. Boston, Houghton Mifflin Co. *This fine work shows the role Protozoa and other forms play in the natural history of plankton. Good descriptions are given of the Radiolaria and other protozoans in Chapter 6. Beautiful color illustrations add much to the book.*

Hyman, L. H. 1940. The Invertebrates: Protozoa Through Ctenophora, vol. 1. New York, McGraw-Hill Book Co., Inc. *In this first volume of a highly technical project on invertebrates, an extensive and exhaustive section is devoted to the morphology and physiology of protozoans. Some attention is given to classification, but this ambitious work summarizes in an admirable way many concepts in this field.*

Jahn, T. L., and F. F. Jahn. 1949. How to Know the Protozoa. Dubuque, Iowa, Wm. C. Brown Co. *A valuable manual on the identification and description of protozoan forms. There is an excellent introductory account of the general features of Protozoa. All students of Protozoa will find this little book useful.*

Jennings, H. S. 1906. Behavior of the Lower Organisms. New York, Columbia University Press. *A classical work on the tropisms (taxes) of Protozoa forms. This treatise has had a profound influence on all subsequent investigations along this line.*

Kirby, H. 1950. Materials and Methods in the Study of Protozoa. Berkeley, University of California Press. *This is a very useful manual on the ways of collecting, cultivating, and preparing Protozoa for study. This work is equally useful to the beginning student in protozoan study as well as to the specialist who has had extensive experience in the techniques of handling these organisms. Adequate bibliographies included.*

Kudo, R. R. 1947. Protozoology, ed. 3. Springfield, Ill., Charles C Thomas, Publisher. *An up-to-date and authoritative account of protozoan taxonomy. An introductory part gives consideration to the morphology and physiology of the group.*

Mayr, E. (editor). 1957. The Species Problem. Washington, American Association for the Advancement of Science. *This is a symposium by many authorities on the problems of species. The paper entitled "Breeding Systems, Reproductive Methods, and Species Problems in Protozoa" by Professor T. M. Sonneborn is a masterly analysis of the present status of mating types and the new concept of syngen as applied to the varieties found within the traditional species of Protozoa.*

Pennak, R. W. 1953. Fresh-Water Invertebrates of the United States. New York, The Ronald Press Co. *A very complete and up-to-date reference work with considerable attention devoted to Protozoa.*

Pettersson, H. 1954. The Ocean Floor, New Haven, Yale University Press. *The role the Foraminifera and Radiolaria have played in building up the sediment carpet of the ocean floor is vividly described in this little book. The author thinks the time of accumulation* of deep-sea deposits to be 2 billion years and the rate of sedimentation of *Globigerina* ooze to be 0.4 inch in a thousand years.

Pratt, H. S. 1935. A Manual of the Common Invertebrate Animals. Philadelphia, P. Blakiston's Son & Co. *A useful and widely used reference work on the classification of Protozoa as well as other invertebrates.*

Schechter, V. 1959. Invertebrate Zoology. Englewood Cliffs, N. J., Prentice-Hall, Inc. *An up-to-date book on this important and extensive group of animals. The illustrations are very attractive and clear, and the text material is presented in an interesting manner. The taxonomic presentation includes some of the old* as well as the new and differs somewhat from that of other invertebrate studies.

Wichterman, R. 1953. The Biology of Paramecium. New York, Blakiston Division, McGraw-Hill Book Co., Inc. *Those who think Protozoa are "simple animals" will be disillusioned by this well-written treatise on one genus of protozoans. A bibliography of more than 2,000 references gives an idea of the impressive amount of work performed on an animal that must meet all the basic physiological functions of animal life (with all of its variations and complications) within the confines of a single-cell membrane.*

chapter 7

Phylum Porifera*

BIOLOGICAL PRINCIPLES

Cellular level of animal organization

1. The cells in sponges have division of labor with certain cells specialized for special functions.

2. Although these cells are often collected into groups, their relationship is so loose that they do not form definite layers. Therefore, the cells in sponges are not coordinated to form tissues.

3. The organization in sponges has gone a step farther than it has in Protozoa, for the life activities are now distributed among a number of specialized cells instead of being carried on by one.

Biological contributions

1. The highly aberrant organization of sponges is copied little, if at all, by higher forms.

2. The division of labor among the cells suggests the development of this tendency in the evolutionary blueprint. In them there is some division of labor among somatic cells, leading to such differentiations as the primitive neuromuscular cells (**myocytes**) and some others.

3. The sponges show us, for the first time, **cell differentiation** without cell coordination.

4. A striking difference from other Metazoa is that their principal opening is an exit, the **osculum.**

5. Their basic structure is a gelatinous mesenchyme in which are free cells of several kinds, and skeletal elements of spicules and spongin.

6. Their life history has a pattern of a metazoan.

---

*Po-rif'e-ra (L. *porus,* pore, + *ferre,* to bear).

7. A primitive type of nervous system made up of a diffuse network of neurons is found in some sponges.

Position in animal kingdom

1. This aberrant group is near the bottom of the animal series and represents a step beyond Protozoa in having a cellular level of organization. If the sponge possesses individuality, it is of the lowest order.

2. Sponges have evolved from different Protozoa than those that gave rise to higher forms, for there is no evidence that higher animals have come from Porifera. Early stages of the sessile form have some resemblance to the colonial protozoan *Proterospongia.*

3. Therefore, sponges represent an evolutionary side line which is not duplicated in other many-celled animals, but they also represent an interesting and effective adaptive organization, such as the unique canal and skeletal systems.

Relation to man's welfare

Sponges are used by man for commercial purposes and some are destructive to man's food supplies, since they injure oysters and other mollusks.

POSITION IN ANIMAL KINGDOM

Sponges belong to phylum Porifera, which means to bear pores, because all the members of this group have bodies that contain tiny pores that are basic structures in their functional activity. Most biologists consider the group to be aberrant, that is, deviating widely from standard patterns. Sponges are not in direct line of evolution of other animals and are placed as an offshoot from the main line of animal descent. They may have come from the flagellate or similar Protozoa because of the flagella-bearing **choanocytes** which line their cavities. One family (Craspedomonadidae) of colorless flagellate protozoans is made up of choanoflagellates or forms provided with transparent collars that enclose the single flagellum. The collar (which may have come from the fused axopods of Heliozoa) catches food which is passed down the outside of the collar to the cytosome. The colonial choanoflagellate *(Proterospongia),* which consists of a gelatinous mass of collared zooids at the surface and collarless ones in the center, may be an ancestor of the sponges. Less than a hundred years ago they were placed among the plants, for they cannot move about in the adult stage, and there is a considerable diversity of form and size in some of the species. Because they do vary so much from other Metazoa they are often called **Parazoa,** which means *beside the animals.**

Organization in sponges does not go farther than the cellular level. There is little indication in sponges to show grouping and coordination of cells to form tissues. Sponges therefore are said to have **cellular level of organization.** This particular type of organization would logically follow the protoplasmic level of organization characteristic of Protozoa. It

---

*In the last decade some evidence, both pro and con, has been advanced with respect to this point. Biochemical investigations show that sponges have about the same nucleic acids and amino acids as metazoans. They have both phosphoarginine (an invertebrate phosphagen) and phosphocreatine (a chordate phosphagen). Embryologically, they have two types of larvae, the amphiblastula in calcareous sponges and the parenchymula in Demospongiae. In the amphiblastula the flagellated half invaginates into the inside to become the collar cell lining; in the parenchymula the flagellate cells on the outside may move in by ameboid movement and transform into choanocytes, or new choanocytes may be provided by transformation of cells already present there. In either case, the embryological development is different from that of metazoans.

has recently been shown that sponges have a primitive nervous system with only slight coordination, although physiological evidence is lacking on this point.

There is no evidence to indicate that any of the higher Metazoa arose from sponges. They may be considered as "dead ends" so far as evolutionary descent is concerned. Within the group, however, there has been considerable variation which has resulted in about 3,000 distinct species, although classification of sponges within the group is difficult.

The fossil record of sponges is very incomplete. Sponges with exclusively spongin skeletons are not preserved as fossils. Class Calcispongiae are poorly preserved because their spicules are soluble in deep waters. The best sponge fossils are those of class Hyalospongiae which occur from the Cambrian period to the present.

Sponges have many unique features. One of these oddities is their complicated system of canals and chambers. Another is their lack of a metazoan type of digestive system, for they rely entirely on **intracellular** digestion, as do Protozoa.

CHARACTERISTICS

1. Mostly marine, although a few fresh-water forms; all aquatic
2. All sponges **attached** and with a variety of body forms, such as **vaselike, globular, many branched,** etc.
3. Radial symmetry or none
4. **Multicellular;** body a loose aggregation of cells of mesenchymal origin; body surface or dermal cortex of spongin, spicules, or simply a colloid with freely movable cells or a syncytium
5. Body with many **pores** or **ostia, canals,** and **chambers** which serve for the passage of water
6. Most of the inner chambers and interior surfaces lined with **choanocytes** or **flagellate collar cells**
7. No organs or definite tissues
8. Digestion intracellular and no excretory or respiratory organs; contractile vacuoles in some fresh-water sponges

9. A primitive nervous system of neurons arranged in a diffuse network of bipolar or multipolar cells found in some

10. **Skeleton usually of calcareous** or **siliceous crystalline spicules** or of **protein spongin**

11. Asexual reproduction by **buds** or **gemmules** and sexual reproduction by eggs and sperm; free-swimming, ciliated larva

HABITAT

Sponges are found in both fresh water and sea water, although the greater number are found in the latter. They are abundant everywhere in the sea, from the shallow water of the shore to the abysmal depths. The common bath sponge is found in warm, tropical, fairly shallow waters. All adult sponges are sessile and are attached to rocks and other solid objects.

The glass sponges (class Hyalospongiae) are mostly deep-sea inhabitants and have rarely been seen alive, for most specimens have been dredged from great depths. They are especially abundant in the waters off the coasts of Japan and the Philippines.

Most sponges form colonies which often attain great size (1 to 2 meters in diameter); other are quite small (1 to 2 mm.). They vary greatly in color, ranging from dull gray and brown to brilliant scarlet and orange.

CLASSES

There are three classes of sponges, depending mainly upon the kinds of skeletons they possess.

Class **Calcispongiae** (cal'ci-spon″gi-ae) (L. *calcis*, lime, + *spongia*, sponge) (**Calcarea**). Have spicules of carbonate of lime which often form a fringe around the osculum. Spicules are single or three- or four-branched. All three types of canal systems represented. All marine. Examples: *Scypha, Leucosolenia*.

Class **Hyalospongiae** (hy'a-lo-spon″gi-ae) (Gr. *hyaleos*, glassy, + *spongos*, sponge) (**Hexactinellida**). Have six-rayed siliceous spicules in three dimensions; often cylindrical or funnel shaped. Choanocytes limited to certain chambers. Habitat mostly in deep water; all marine. Examples: Venus's flower basket (*Euplectella*), *Hyalonema*.

Class **Demospongiae** (de'mo-spon″gi-ae) (Gr. *demas*, frame, + *spongos*, sponge). Have siliceous spicules, spongin, or both. One family found in fresh water; all others marine. Examples: *Thenea, Cliona, Spongilla, Meyenia*, and all bath sponges.

STRUCTURE

Sponges vary enormously in their structure and other features. Most sponges we see consist only of the skeletal framework. In the living condition many of them appear as slimy gelatinous masses resembling masses of liver. The common bath sponge is of this appearance, and only when the protoplasmic mass is removed in the method of preparing them do we see the commercial sponge with its skeleton of fibers.

The surface of sponges possesses many small pores (**ostia**) for the inflow of water. The ostia open into **canals**, simple or complex, which run into a central cavity, the **spongocoel** (cloaca). The opening of the spongocoel to the outside is known as the **osculum**. Colonial sponges have many oscula. The sponge has no mouth and no organs. The outer surface and the incurrent canals are covered with a thin layer of dermal epithelium composed of flat, highly contractile **pinacocyte** cells. The term layer of cells must be used with certain reservations, for there are no true layers of cells in sponges but simply masses of cells clustered in a gelatinous **mesenchyme**; in some cases even cells may be lacking and only a spongin sheet or syncytium is present.

In simple sponges the spongocoel is lined with a characteristic flagellate-bearing cell, the **choanocyte**, commonly called "collar cell" because each has a little collar around the base of the flagellum. In more complex sponges the collar cells are confined to the radial canals and chambers and are not present in the spongocoel. In these sponges the spongocoel is lined with a thin epithelium derived from the epidermis. Another type of cell is the **amebocyte**, many kinds of which wander around in the mesenchyme.

140

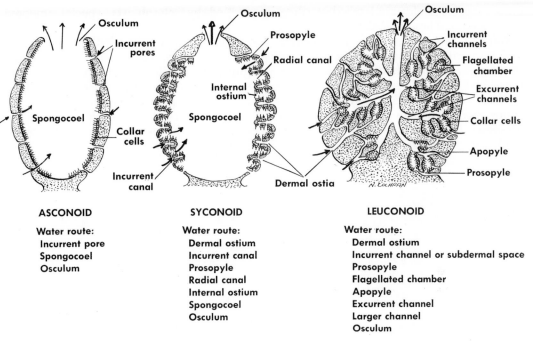

ASCONOID	SYCONOID	LEUCONOID
Water route:	Water route:	Water route:
Incurrent pore	Dermal ostium	Dermal ostium
Spongocoel	Incurrent canal	Incurrent channel or subdermal space
Osculum	Prosopyle	Prosopyle
	Radial canal	Flagellated chamber
	Internal ostium	Apopyle
	Spongocoel	Excurrent channel
	Osculum	Larger channel
		Osculum

Figure 68. Diagrams of three types of sponge structure. Degree of complexity from simple asconoid type to complex leuconoid type has involved mainly the water and skeletal systems, accompanied by outfolding and branching of collar cell layer. Leuconoid type considered major plan for sponges, for it permits greater size and more efficient water circulation.

Among the different sponges are a great variety of canals (Figure 68). Most sponges fall into one or the other of three principal types.

Asconoid type. The canals pass directly from the ostia to the spongocoel, which is lined with collar cells. *Leucosolenia* has this type of canal.

Syconoid type. The incurrent canals (from the outside) lie alongside of the radial canals which empty into the spongocoel. Both types of canals end blindly in the body wall but are connected by minute pores. Only the radial canals are lined with collar cells. *Scypha* is an example of this type.

Leuconoid or rhagon type. The canals of this type are much branched and complex, with numerous chambers lined with collar cells. The spongocoel lacks collar cells. The larger sponges, including the bath sponge, are all this type.

These three types of canals are correlated with the evolution of sponges from the simple to the complex forms. It has been mainly a matter of increasing the surface in proportion to the volume, so that there may be enough collar cells to meet the food demands. This problem has been met by the outpushing of the spongocoel of a simple sponge, such as the asconoid type, to form the radial canals (lined with choanocytes) of the syconoid type. The formation of incurrent canals between the blind outer ends of the radial canals completes this type. Further increase in the body wall foldings produces the complex canals and chambers (with collar cells) of the leuconoid type. Along with this evolution of canals and chambers there has been a more efficient flow of water.

SKELETONS

The skeleton serves as the basis of classification of sponges (Figure 69). In sponges, such as *Scypha,* the skeleton consists of spicules of calcium carbonate;

glass sponge spicules are formed of siliceous material. These spicules are of many different forms and shapes. The straight ones are called the **monaxons;** those of three rays in one plane are **triradiates;** those of four rays in four planes are **tetraxons;** and those of many rays are **polyaxons.** Some sponges have the spicules arranged in regular order, others in a haphazard arrangement. Spicules are formed by **scleroblasts,** special ameboid cells.

Sponges, such as the bath sponge, freshwater sponges, and others, contain **spongin** (Figure 70, A), a proteinlike substance. This type of skeleton is a branching, fibrous network which supports the soft, living cells of the sponge. Special cells from the mesenchyme, called **spongioblasts,** form this type of skeleton.

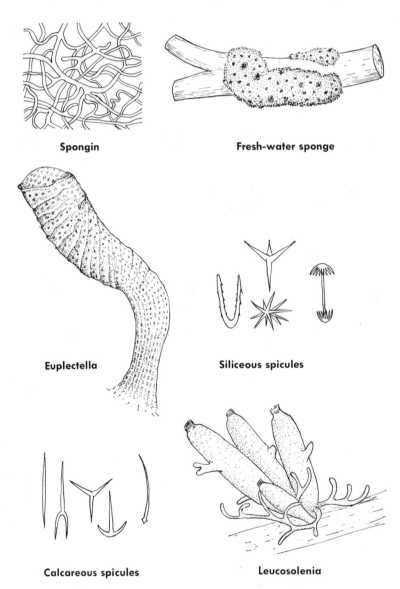

Spongin

Fresh-water sponge

Euplectella

Siliceous spicules

Calcareous spicules

Leucosolenia

Figure 69. Types of skeletal structure found in sponges, with example of each. There is amazing diversity, complexity, and beauty of form among the many types of spicules.

142

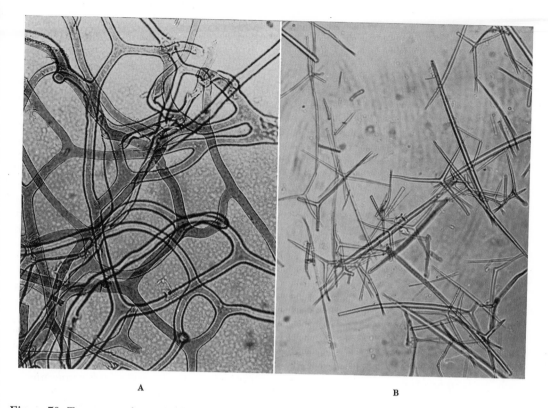

A   B

Figure 70. Two types of sponge skeleton. A, Spongin. B, Calcareous spicules.

TYPES OF CELLS

Although there are many types of cells in sponges, none of them are actually arranged with the regularity of tissues. Perhaps the nearest approach to tissues in the sponges are the flat protective cells (**pinacocytes**) of the dermal and gastral epithelium and the collar cells (**choanocytes**) wherever these are found. The pinacocytes are contractile and help regulate the surface area of the sponge. Choanocytes create water currents and engulf and digest food. **Gland cells** provide a means of attachment for the animal; tubular **porocytes** form the ostia in asconoid sponges; and **myocytes** or muscle cells form sphincters around the pores and oscula.

The middle layer or mesenchyme contains ameboid cells known as **scleroblasts**, which form the spicules; **spongioblasts**, which form spongin; and **archeocytes**, which have a variety of functions,

such as the digestion of food and the formation of eggs and sperm.

Sponges have great power of regeneration. H. V. Wilson discovered many years ago that when sponge cells were sifted through bolting cloth into small groups upon a surface under water each group of cells would grow into a separate sponge.

METABOLISM

Metabolism in sponges is mainly a matter of individual cellular function. Their food consists of small organic substances, both plant and animal, which are drawn into the ostia and through the canal system by currents of water induced by the waving of the flagella on the choanocytes. As the flagella undulate spirally from base to tip, water currents are set up which bring particles of food to the outer surface of the collars where the food adheres. Later the food reaches the base of the cells and passes into the cytoplasm where food vacuoles are formed. Digestion is therefore **intracellular** in sponges. Digestive enzymes aid in digestion just as we have seen in the Protozoa. Amebocytes in the mesenchyme layer may aid in digestion and distribution of food from the choanocytes to other parts of the body. Absorption of food substances from cell to cell may also occur.

Excretion and respiration are taken care of by each individual cell by simple diffusion processes. Contractile vacuoles have been found in the amebocytes and choanocytes of fresh-water sponges (*Spongilla* and *Ephydatia*). Undigested food is ejected by the amebocytes into outgoing currents.

Since water currents are of such a primary importance to sponges, many studies have been made to determine the mechanics, rate of flow, amount of water discharged, and other aspects of these currents. In the syconoid type of sponge, such as *Scypha*, the route of the water current is through the dermal pores, incurrent canals or spaces, prosopyles, radial canals, internal ostia, spongocoel, and osculum. As the result of the movement of the many flagella of the collar cells the water is sucked through the route mentioned, but the rate of flow is different in the various parts of the passageway. One investigator found in a certain sponge that the velocity of discharge through the osculum was 8 cm. per second but in the flagellate chambers it was only 2 to 4 cm. per hour, because only one osculum (or relatively few oscula) must carry away the water which enters many chambers or canals of a sponge. The hydraulic pressure of the water current in the flagellate chambers of some sponges studied was equivalent to a column of water 4 mm. in height. The amount of water passing through a sponge depends upon its size; a large sponge with many oscula was found by Parker to filter more than 1,500 liters of water a day. It is to the advantage of the sponge to discharge the current of water from its oscula as far away as possible to prevent reusing water that

must be loaded with waste and carbonic acid. The water flow is regulated by the contractions and expansions of the pores and oscula.

Adult sponges have very limited motion, although the ciliated larval forms move freely about. In the adult condition, **myocytes** around the ostia can contract or relax, thus regulating the size of the openings. Several factors may influence these contractile cells. Still water tends to close them; moving water, to open them. The drug atropine in weak solutions also will cause them to open, whereas injurious agencies will cause the pores to close.

REPRODUCTION

Sponges reproduce both asexually and sexually. **Asexual** reproduction is mainly a matter of bud formation. After reaching a certain size, these buds may become detached or they may remain to form colonies. Internal buds, or **gemmules,** are formed in fresh-water and some marine sponges (Figure 71). Here, archeocytes are collected together in the mesenchyme and become surrounded by a siliceous shell or sometimes by a cluster of spicules. When the animal dies, the gemmules survive and preserve the life of the animal during periods of severe drought or freezing. Later, the cells in the gemmules escape through a special opening and develop into new sponges.

In **sexual** reproduction ova and sperm develop from archeocytes or from choanocytes. The ova are fertilized in the mesenchyme, develop there, and finally break out into the spongocoel and then out the osculum. Some sponges are monoecious (having both male and female sex organs in one individual) and others are dioecious (having separate sexes).

During development the zygote undergoes cleavage and differentiation of cells in the mesenchyme of the sponge, and finally a flagellated larva, **amphiblastula** (calcareous sponges), emerges. This larval form is made up of flagellate cells at one end and nonflagellate at the other. In time the flagellate cells are invaginated

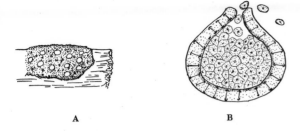
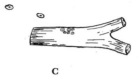

A   **B**   **C**

Figure 71. Gemmule and colony formation in *Spongilla*, fresh-water sponge. **A**, Sponge in winter, showing cluster of gemmules. **B**, Greatly enlarged cross-section of gemmule, showing cells, some emerging from pore. **C**, Cells from gemmule which will develop into new colony.

into or overgrown by the nonflagellate group and become the choanocytes. The larval form after swimming around soon settles down and becomes attached to some solid object, where it grows into an adult.

REPRESENTATIVE TYPES
CLASS CALCISPONGIAE
Scypha

Scypha is a marine form, living in shallow water where it is usually attached to rocks. It may be free living or it may form a cluster or colony by budding.

The animal is vase shaped and is from ½ to 1 inch in length (Figure 72). At the unattached end is the opening, or **osculum**, with a fringe of straight spicules which discourage small animals from entering. Spicules also project from other parts of the body, so that the animal has a hairy appearance. There is no outer covering or cortex in *Scypha*, the common form studied in America; a European genus called *Grantia*, often confused with *Scypha*, does have such a cortex. The entire outside of the body is full of tiny pores, or **ostia**. These ostia are the openings into the so-called **incurrent canals** (actually spaces), which end blindly near the central cavity, or **spongocoel**. This central cavity is sometimes called the cloaca or gastral cavity. From the spongocoel **radial canals,** or flagellate chambers, run toward the outer surface and end blindly and nakedly. Their openings into the spongocoel are called **apopyles,** or **internal ostia.** The incurrent and the radial

canals are connected by small pores called **prosopyles** which are intercellular spaces and not canals through tubular porocytes as in the asconoid type.

The incurrent canals are lined with spicules and a few pinacocytes, whereas radial canals are lined mainly with **choanocytes**, or flagellate collar cells. The spongocoel is lined by a thin epithelium from the epidermis.

The body wall contains a large number of interlacing spicules of carbonate of lime which support and protect the soft parts of the body. About four types of spicules are recognized: **short monaxons, long monaxons, triradiates,** and **polyaxons.** All spicules originate from **scleroblasts.** The body substance between the

Figure 72. Cluster of sponges, *Scypha*. About natural size.

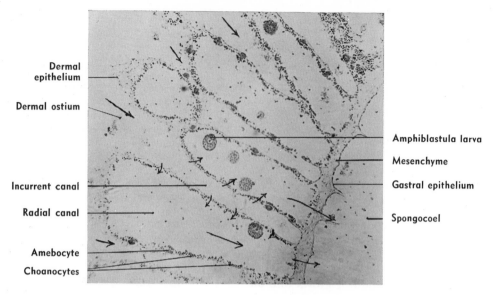

Dermal epithelium

Dermal ostium

Incurrent canal

Radial canal

Amebocyte

Choanocytes

Amphiblastula larva

Mesenchyme

Gastral epithelium

Spongocoel

Figure 73. Cross-section through wall of a sponge, *Scypha,* showing canal system. Photomicrograph of stained slide.

epithelium and the choanocytes is an indefinite gelatinous mass called the **mesenchyme.** It contains skeletal spicules and the **ameboid** wandering cells which have a great variety of functions to perform, such as the digestion of food, the formation of skeleton, and the origin of the reproductive cells.

Scypha lives upon minute organisms and bits of organic matter in the water. Water containing these is drawn into the incurrent canals by the beating of the flagella of the collar cells and thence is passed through the prosopyles into the radial canals, which carry it to the spongocoel and finally discharge it through the osculum. The rate of water flow is determined by the diameter of the osculum and the dermal ostia which are regulated by myocyte sphincters and by the action of the encircling pinacocytes. This action is more pronounced in the Demospongia. Digestion is **intracellular** by the choanocytes, which engulf the food and form food vacuoles. Distribution of the digested food from cell to cell takes place by diffusion and by the wandering ameboid cells of the mesenchyme layer. Respiration occurs by direct absorption of oxygen from the water and the giving off of carbon

dioxide to the water as it flows throug the canal system. Excretory products an other waste substances are also carried b the water out through the osculum.

Reproduction in *Scypha* is by two meth ods, asexual and sexual. The **asexua** method involves **budding;** that is, a sma bud appears at the base of an adul sponge and grows into full size. It ma adhere to the parent and thus help forr a colony, or it may break free and forr a new attachment.

Sexual reproduction occurs by the for mation of eggs and sperm which develo from **archeocytes,** special ameboid cell Both types of sex cells are formed in th same individual and thus *Scypha* is **mon ecious.** The zygote, or fertilized egg, de velops into an embryo while in positio in the mesenchyme and later in the radia canals. The flagellated larval form finall escapes from the parent, swims aroun a while, settles down, becomes attached and grows into an adult.

CLASS HYALOSPONGIAE
Glass sponges

The glass sponges are nearly all deep sea forms which are collected by dredg ing. Most of them are radially sym

146

etrical with vase- or funnel-shaped
bodies which are usually attached by
stalks of root spicules to a substratum. In
size they range from 3 or 4 inches to more
than 4 feet in length. Their distinguishing
features are the skeleton of six-rayed
siliceous spicules, which are commonly
bound together into a network forming a
glasslike structure, and the **trabecular net**
— living tissue produced by the fusion of
the pseudopodia of many types of amebocytes. Within the trabecular net are
elongated finger-shaped chambers lined
with choanocytes and opening into the
spongocoel. The osculum is unusually
large and may be covered over by a
sievelike plate of silica. There is no epidermis or gelatinous mesenchyme, and
both the external surface and spongocoel
are lined with the trabecular net. Because
of the rigid skeleton and lack of contractility, muscular elements (myocytes)
appear to be absent. The general arrangement of their chambers fits glass
sponges into both syconoid and leuconoid
types. Their structure is adapted to the
slow constant currents of sea bottoms, for
the channels and pores of the sponge wall
are relatively large and uncomplicated
and permit an easy flow of water. Little,

however, is known about their physiology.

Glass sponges can reproduce asexually
by buds and sexually by germ cells which
are developed from archeocytes. The fertilized egg develops into a flagellated larva
which swims around and finally settles
down into a sessile existence.

The framework or latticelike network of
spicules found in many glass sponges is
of exquisite beauty, such as that of *Euplectella*, or Venus's flower basket, a classical example of the Hyalospongiae. Many
fossil sponges, especially of the Cretaceous and Jurassic periods, are members
of this class.

CLASS DEMOSPONGIAE
Fresh-water sponges

Fresh-water sponges are of special interest, because they are about the only
living sponges students ever see. They
have a wide distribution and are not uncommon if one knows where to look.
Most of them live in clear, well-oxygen-
ated water of ponds, lakes, and slow
streams where they may be found encrust-
ing twigs, plant stems, old pieces of submerged wood, sluiceways, etc. In standing water they are usually found where
there is some wave action. Their appear-

Figure 74. A bit of fresh-water sponge, *Spongilla*, greatly enlarged.

ance is a sort of wrinkled, irregular scum, pitted with some pores. They are yellowish or brownish, although some have a greenish tinge from the presence of the symbiotic algae (zoochlorellae). In certain cases they may grow several inches in diameter (Figures 69 and 74.)

They all belong to the family Spongillidae (class Demospongiae) of which the most common genera are *Spongilla* and *Myenia*. *Spongilla lacustris*, the commonest fresh-water sponge, develops fingerlike branches and is usually green. Another common species is *Spongilla fragilis*, which is unbranched. *Myenia* may be found either in still or running water. Fresh-water sponges are most common in midsummer, although some are more easily found in the fall. They die and disintegrate in late autumn, leaving the gemmules (already described) which are able to survive drying and freezing for many months.

When examined closely, fresh-water sponges reveal a thin dermis underneath which are large subdermal spaces (separated by columns of spicules) with many water channels. There are usually several oscula, each of which (at least in *Myenia*) is mounted on a small chimneylike tube. Their spiculation also includes a spongin network. Their cells include a variety of amebocytes.

Although the gemmule method of asexual reproduction is common among fresh-water sponges, sexual reproduction also occurs.

ECONOMIC IMPORTANCE

The skeletons of sponges have long been used by man, mostly for washing, bathing, and mopping. Although many artificial sponges are made out of rubber or other materials, natural sponges are still in demand, and sponge fisheries are a profitable industry in many parts of the world. The best commercial sponges are found in the warm shallow waters of the Mediterranean Sea, the Gulf of Mexico, the West Indies, and off the coast of Florida. In the latter place more than a million dollars worth of sponges have been collected in a single year. The bath sponges belong to the family Spongiidae and the genera *Spongia* and *Hippospongia*. These are members of the group known as horny sponges which have only spongin skeletons. Sponges are collected by hooks, by dredging or trawling, or by divers. After their collection they are exposed out of water to kill them and then placed in shallow water, where they are squeezed or treaded upon to remove the softened animal matter until only the horny, spongin skeleton remains. After being cleaned and bleached, they are trimmed and sorted for the market. In recent years a fungus disease has greatly depleted the sponge industry in the West Indies.

Sponges are often cultured by cutting out pieces of individuals, fastening them to concrete or rocks, and dropping them into the proper water conditions. It takes many years for sponges to grow to market size.

Since sponges have great capacity for absorbing water, they are used in surgical operations for picking up excess fluid, blood, etc. They are also used for sound absorption and for packing material, as well as for cleaning in glass manufacturing.

The taste of sponges is so unpleasant that few animals eat them. However, many small animals, such as shrimp, fish, and crab, take advantage of the canals and cavities in sponges to make their homes. This relationship is probably commensal, for these tenants do the sponges no harm in return for a safe hiding place from enemies. One sponge, *Cliona*, bores into mollusk shells by employing a dissolving secretion and destroys the animal within the shell.

PROBLEMS STILL TO BE SOLVED

The fact that sponges have been a blind branch in the evolutionary blueprint and have not led to other forms may be responsible for a certain lack of interest in their study by zoologists. There are many aspects of their morphology and physiology that have not been satisfactorily

148

lved. One of these problems is how the flagellate chambers are formed during development. There is still much to learn about the integration of the various cells, their primitive nervous system, and how cells aggregate again after being dissociated. Little is known about the relationships of the three sponge classes. Experimental modifications of sponge morphology is still in its infancy. Not least among the many unsolved problems is their complicated taxonomy.

Derivation and meaning of basic terminology

amebocyte (Gr. *amoibe*, change, + *kytos*, cell) Free cells in the mesenchyme.

amphiblastula (Gr. *amphi*, double, + *blastos*, a germ) Larval stage in sponges, so called because one-half bears flagella cells and the other half does not.

apopyle (Gr. *apo*, away from, + *pyle*, gate) Opening of the radial canal into the spongocoel.

archeocyte (Gr. *archos*, chief, + *kytos*, cell) Ameboid cells of varied function in sponges.

ascon (Gr. *askos*, bladder) Simplest form of canal in sponges leading directly from the outside to the interior.

Calcarea (L. *calcarius*, limy) A class of sponges.

Calcispongiae (L. *calcis*, lime, + *spongia*, sponge) Synonym for class Calcarea (Blainville, 1830).

choanocyte (Gr. *choane*, funnel, + *kytos*, cell) Flagellate collar cells which line cavities and canals.

Demospongiae (Gr. *demas*, frame, + *spongos*, sponge) A class of sponges (Sollas, 1875).

gemmule (L. *gemma*, bud) Asexual reproductive unit in certain sponges.

Hexactinellida (Gr. *hex*, six, + *actin*, ray, + *-ell*, diminutive, + *ida*, terminal suffix).

Hyalospongiae (Gr. *hyalos*, glass, + *spongos* sponge) Synonym for class Hexactinellida (Vosmaer, 1886).

Leucosolenia (Gr. *leukos*, white, + *solen*, pipe).

mesenchyme (Gr. *mesos*, middle, + *enchyme*, infusion) Gelatinous middle layer in sponges.

myocyte (Gr. *myos*, mouse [muscle], + *kytos*, cell) A contractile cell.

ostium (L. a door) Opening to the incurrent canal in sponges.

Parazoa (Gr. *para*, beside, + *zoon*, animal) Sponges are so called because they do not appear to be closely related to any group of the Metazoa.

pinacocyte (Gr. *pinac*, plank, + *kytos*, cell) Flat cell found on surface and lining of sponge cavities.

Porifera (L. *porus*, pore, + *ferre*, to bear).

prosopyle (Gr. *pros*, near, + *pyle*, gate) Connection between the incurrent and radial canal.

rhagon (Gr. *rhagos*, a berry) Same as the leucon type of canals; contains small chambers lined with collar cells.

scleroblast (Gr. *skleros*, hard, + *blastos*, germ) Mesenchyme cell which secretes spicules.

Scypha (Gr. *skyphos*, cup) This genus is often incorrectly called *Grantia* or *Sycon*.

spicule (L. *spica*, a point) Skeletal element found in certain sponges.

spongocoel (Gr. *spongos*, sponge, + *koilos*, hollow) Cloaca or central cavity in sponges.

sycon (Gr. *sykon*, a fig) Sometimes called Syconoid. A type of canal system.

ANNOTATED REFERENCES

deLaubenfels, M. W. 1936. Sponge Fauna of the Dry Tortugas With Material for a Revision of the Families and Orders of the Porifera. Carnegie Institute, Washington, Tortugas Laboratories, Pub. 30. *An important work in resolving many of the difficulties of sponge classification.*

deLaubenfels, M. W. 1945. Sponge Names. Science, n.s. vol. 101, pp. 354-355. *The author points out the confusion resulting from the incorrect usage of the genus name Grantia, a European sponge, for Scypha, the form commonly used in American laboratories.*

Hyman, L. H. 1940. The Invertebrates: Protozoa Through Ctenophora. New York, McGraw-Hill Book Co., Inc. *The section on Porifera represents one of the most up-to-date accounts of sponges. The different types are well illustrated.*

Minchin, E. A. 1900. "Porifera," in Lankester's Treatise on Zoology, part II. *A detailed account of the general morphology of sponges, invaluable to the student who wishes to know the basic structure of sponges.*

Wilson, H. V. 1907. On Some Phenomena of Coalescence and Regeneration in Sponges. J. Exper. Zool., vol. 5, pp. 245-258. *This classical experimental work on siliceous sponges first showed the phenomenon of regeneration after dissociation by which a new sponge is formed by aggregation and fusion out of the cells of an old sponge which have been separated by squeezing through a piece of gauze. This phenomenon also occurs in forms other than the Porifera.*

chapter 8

Phylum Coelenterata (Cnidaria)*

BIOLOGICAL PRINCIPLES

Tissue level of animal organization

1. The cells of coelenterates are not only specialized for different functions but there also is a tendency for similar cells to be gathered together to form a **tissue**.

2. The best example of a tissue in coelenterates is the **nervous**, where the **protoneurons** (nerve cells) are bound together to form a **nerve net**.

3. The ectoderm and endoderm in these forms are made up of a variety of cells too scattered to be called tissues.

Biological contributions

1. Two germ layers, **ectoderm** and **endoderm**, are well established. In two classes (Scyphozoa and Anthozoa) an intermediate layer, **mesoglea**, contains some free cellular elements or connective tissue and may be considered the beginning of a third layer (**ectomesoderm**). With the exception of class Hydrozoa this phylum is therefore **triploblastic**. There is an advancement in **division of labor**. The ectoderm is specialized for protection and sensation; the endoderm for secretion and digestion.

2. The saclike body plan suggests what is going to be emphasized in higher forms, for it resembles an early embryonic stage (gastrula) through which all advanced forms pass. Its gastrovascular cavity (coelentron) has but one orifice (mouth) and no anus. In class Anthozoa the ectoderm forms a stomodaeum which is charac-

teristic of the embryo and becomes the phary and gullet of the adult in advanced phyla.

3. Coelenterates give us the first true ner cells (**protoneurons**) in the animal kingdom. Their arrangement to form a **nerve net** coord nated with muscle, gland, and sensory cells re resents an advancement. This diffused nerve n is largely supplanted by a more concentrate nervous system, but not entirely discarded, higher forms.

4. Also introduced by the coelenterates a **polymorphism** and **nematocysts**.

5. There is radial symmetry with one ma oral-aboral axis. All bodily structures are a ranged around this axis. A specialized head er begins to emerge.

Position in animal kingdom

1. With a tissue grade of organization an most of the specialized cells of higher form coelenterates are considered near the direct lir of evolution of other metazoans.

2. The coelenterates probably originate from a ciliated, free-swimming gastrula-type an mal similar to the **planula** larva found through out the group.

POSITION IN ANIMAL KINGDOM

This large and interesting group of an mals takes its name from the large cavit in the body which serves as an intestine The name "coelenteron" means "hollo intestine." Of the more than 9,000 specie some are found in fresh water but th greater number are marine. There are n terrestrial forms. Because of the aberran

---

*Se-len′te-ra′ta (Gr. *koîlos*, hollow, + *enteron*, gut). Ni-da′ri-a (Gr. *knide*, nettle).

ture of the sponges, coelenterates may be considered the first phylum of Metazoa. They include the jellyfish, sea anemones, corals, and some other forms.

Evidence indicates that the coelenterates arose from Protozoa, probably by way of a free-swimming ciliated planula larva. Such a form, pushed inward to form a double-layered gastrula form, would correspond roughly to a coelenterate with an outer ectoderm with sensory and protective functions and an inner endoderm specialized for digestion and absorption. Between these two layers the mesoglea would provide an elastic framework of support. The addition of tentacles and other modifications would transform this ancestor into a coelenterate. This theory is supported by the fact that most forms of this group have such a larva somewhere in their life cycle.

Of the two types of individuals, polyps and medusae, one view holds that polyps are the ancestral type. By attachment to its aboral pole the ancestral form developed into a polyp similar to hydra. By asexual budding hydroid colonies emerged with specialization among the polyps, some of which were modified into medusae. An alternative view is that the ancestral coelenterate was a medusa and that the polyp arose as a larval stage, later becoming established in its own right as an important phase of the life cycle and, in some groups, becoming sexually mature, so that the medusa—the original adult—was no longer necessary.

In coelenterates the main central cavity (gastrovascular) opens to the outside by a mouth. Sponges use their main opening (osculum) for an exit. Here coelenterates show that they have come from the same ancestors as higher forms.

Coelenterates are a step ahead of the sponges in organization. Instead of a mere cellular differentiation there is a tendency for cells to be arranged into **tissues.** This is not carried very far. The epidermis, for instance, includes many types of cells and cannot be called a tissue in the strictest sense. However, the nerve net is a well-defined tissue, for its nervous elements are similar and are in intimate contact with each other.

Coelenterata is the best example of the radiate phyla, animals that have primary radial symmetry or some modification of it. They consist of a solid body wall enclosing a gastrovascular cavity. The body wall consists of two well-defined epithelial layers, **epidermis** (ectodermal) and **gastrodermis** (endodermal) and an intermediate layer, **mesoglea,** which is somewhat gelatinous in structure and contains cellular elements or connective tissue (in Scyphozoa and Anthozoa). Because of the nature of its origin, the mesoglea is sometimes called **ectomesoderm** (Hyman). It is not an epithelium and is the only mesoderm present in coelenterates. In higher phyla most mesoderm is endodermal (endomesoderm) in origin and may be in the form of mesenchyme or epithelium.

CHARACTERISTICS

1. Entirely aquatic, some in fresh water, but mostly marine
2. **Radial symmetry,** or biradial symmetry, around a longitudinal axis with **oral** and **aboral ends;** no definite head
3. Two types of individuals, **attached polyps** or **free medusae**
4. Exoskeleton (perisarc) of chitin or lime in some
5. Body with two layers, epidermis and gastrodermis, with mesoglea between; mesoglea with cells and connective tissue (ectomesoderm) in some
6. A **gastrovascular cavity** (often branched or divided with septa) with a single opening which serves as both mouth and anus; extensible tentacles often encircling the mouth or oral region
7. Special stinging cell organoids called **nematocysts** in either or both epidermis and gastrodermis; nematocysts very abundant on tentacles where they may form batteries
8. **Nerve net** of synaptic and nonsynaptic patterns; with some sensory organs; diffuse conduction
9. Muscular system (epitheliomuscular type) of an outer layer of longitudinal fibers at base of epidermis and an inner

one of circular fibers at base of gastrodermis; modifications of this plan in
higher coelenterates, such as separate
bundles of independent fibers in the
mesoglea

10. Reproduction by asexual budding
(in polyps) or sexual reproduction by
gametes (in all medusae and some polyps). Sexual forms monoecious or dioecious; **planula larva;** holoblastic cleavage;
mouth from blastopore

11. No excretory or respiratory system
12. No coelomic cavity

TWO TYPES OF INDIVIDUALS

Coelenterates may be single or in colonies. Two morphological types of individuals are recognized in the group:

1. **Polyps** with tubular bodies having
a mouth surrounded by tentacles at one
end. The other end is blind, and usually
attached by a pedal disc or other device
to substratum.

2. **Medusae,** or free-swimming jellyfish,
with umbrella-shaped bodies having a
mouth centrally located on a projection of
the concave side. Around the margin of
the umbrella are the tentacles provided
with stinging cells.

Some species have both types of individuals in their life history *(Obelia);* others
have only the polyp stage (hydra, Anthozoa); and still others have only the
jellyfish or medusa stage (certain Scyphozoa).

Though polyps and medusae seem su
perficially to be different from each othe
actually this difference is not marked. I
a polyp form such as that of the hydr
were inverted, broadened out laterally t
shorten the oral-aboral axis, the hypostom
lengthened to form a manubrium, an
mesoglea greatly increased, the resu
would be a structure similar to a medus
or jellyfish (Figure 75). The great amou
of mesoglea in the medusa makes it mor
buoyant so it can float easily. It also nece
sitates a system of circular and radi
canals in the jellyfish to carry nourishmer
from the gastrovascular cavity to othe
parts of the body.

In the evolution of the two types, poly
and medusae, it is thought that the jelly
fish represents the complete and typica
coelenterate, whereas the polyp is mere
a persistent larval stage.

The view formerly held that coelen
terates which had both polyp and medus
stages in their life histories represente
metagenesis or alternation of asexual an
sexual generations is no longer considere
valid by many authorities. The polyp ma
be considered as an asexual juvenile stag
in the development of a complete coelen
terate and merely fits into the plan of
general life cycle.

CLASSES

Class Hydrozoa (hy'dro-zo"a) (Gr. *hydra,* ·
zoon, animal). Solitary or colonial; asexu
polyps and sexual medusae, although on
type may be suppressed; hydranths with n
mesenteries; medusae (when present) wit
a velum; both fresh water and marine. E>
amples: hydra, *Obelia, Physalia.*

Class Scyphozoa (si'pho-zo"a) (Gr. *skypho*
cup, + *zoon,* animal). Solitary; polyp stag
reduced or absent; bell-shaped medusae witl
out velum; gelatinous mesoglea much e>
larged; margin of bell or umbrella typicall
with eight notches which are provided wit
sense organs; all marine. Examples: *Aureli*
Cassiopeia.

Class Anthozoa (an'tho-zo"a) (Gr. *antho*
flower, + *zoon,* animal). All polyps; no med
usae; solitary or colonial; enteron subdivide
by at least eight mesenteries or septa wit
nematocysts; gonads endodermal; all marin
Examples: sea anemone *(Metridium),* coral
sea pens.

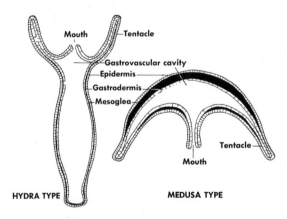

Mouth ──Tentacle

──Gastrovascular cavity
─Epidermis ──
─Gastrodermis─
─Mesoglea─

Tentacle─
Mouth

HYDRA TYPE   **MEDUSA TYPE**

Figure 75. Comparison of polyp and medusa
types of individuals.

152

Figure 76. Representative coelenterates. Class Hydrozoa: **1**, *Physalia;* **2**, *Gonionemus;* **3**, *Obelia.* Class Scyphozoa: **4**, *Aurelia;* **5**, *Chrysaora.* Class Anthozoa: **6**, *Metridium;* **7**, *Astrangia;* **8**, *Gorgonia;* **9**, staghorn coral.

HABITAT

Most coelenterates are marine, although there are a few interesting fresh-water forms. The fresh-water forms, such as the hydra, are found in quiet streams, lakes, and ponds attached to the underside of aquatic plants. Colonial polyp coelenterates are found along the coast, usually in shallow water, where they may be attached to mollusk shells, rocks, and wharves. Corals are found in reefs along the shallow waters of the southern seas.

The free-swimming medusae are found in the open sea and lakes, often a long distance from the shore. Floating colonies, such as Portuguese man-of-war and *Velella,* have floats or sails (pneumatophores) by which they are carried in the wind.

REPRESENTATIVE TYPES
CLASS HYDROZOA
Hydra

The common fresh-water hydra is a solitary polyp and one of the few coelenterates found in fresh water. Its normal habitat is the underside of aquatic leaves and lily pads in cool, clean fresh water of pools and streams. The hydra family is found throughout the world, with ten species occurring in the United States. Two common species are the green hydra (*Chlorohydra viridissima*), which owes its color to symbiotic algae (Zoochlorella) in its cells, and the brown hydra (*Pelmatohydra oligactis*). With the exception of a few minor details, a description of one of the species will apply to all.

Structure. The body of the hydra can extend to a length of 25 to 30 mm. or contract to a tiny mass of jelly. It is a cylindrical tube with the lower (aboral) end drawn out into a slender stalk (*Pelmatohydra*) on the end of which is the basal or pedal disc for attachment. This pedal disc is provided with gland cells to enable the hydra to adhere to a substratum and also to secrete a gas bubble for floating. In the center of the disc there may be an excretory pore. The opposite, or oral, end contains a **mouth** located on a conical elevation, the **hypostome,** which is encircled by six to ten hollow tentacles. Like the body, the tentacles can be greatly extended and may stretch out for several millimeters when the animal is hungry. In some of the larger species the extension is much more; in fact as much as 8.5 cm. has been reported in one species. The

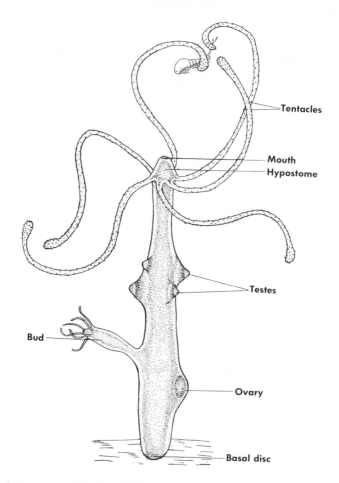

Figure 77. General structure of hydra. Although specimen shown is hemaphroditic, most species are dioecious.

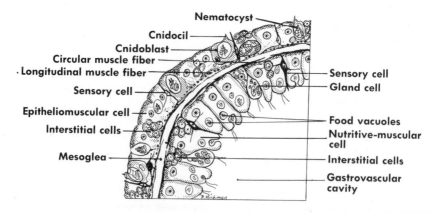

Figure 78. Portion of cross-section through body of hydra to show cellular detail. Diagrammatic.

154

mouth opens into the **gastrovascular cavity**, or **enteron**, which communicates with the cavities in the tentacles. In some individuals **buds** may project from the sides, each with a mouth and tentacles like the parent. Testes or ovaries, when present, appear as rounded projections on the surface of the body.

Cross-sections of the body and tentacles reveal a body wall surrounding the gastrovascular cavity. The wall consists of an outer **epidermis** (ectodermal) and an inner **gastrodermis** (endodermal) with **mesoglea** between them.

EPIDERMIS. The epidermis is made up of small cubical cells and is covered with a delicate cuticle. This layer contains several types of cells—epithelomuscular, interstitial, gland, cnidoblast, and sensory and nerve cells.

1. Epitheliomuscular cells. These cells make up most of the epidermis and serve both for epithelial covering and for muscular contraction. Each cell has an outer portion extending to the body surface and a basal part made up of one or more stalks which are drawn out into longitudinal muscle fibers (**myonemes**), fastened to the surface folds of the mesoglea. Contraction of the fibers shortens the body or tentacles. Each fiber is made up of minute fibrils.

2. Interstitial cells. These are small, oval, undifferentiated cells that lie among the bases of the epitheliomuscular cells. Really a form of mesenchyme, they can transform into cnidoblasts, sex cells, or buds.

3. Gland cells. These are tall cells found chiefly on the pedal disc and around the mouth region. They produce a secretion by which the animal can attach itself and sometimes a gas bubble by which the animal can rise and fasten on to the surface of the water to float.

4. Cnidoblasts. Cnidoblasts are found throughout the epidermis but especially on the tentacles. These somewhat oval-shaped cells contain the cell organoid, the **nematocyst** or stinging cell. The nematocyst is made up of a rounded capsule which encloses a coiled tube or thread

that is continuous with the capsular wall to which it is attached.

5. Sensory and nerve cells. Sensory cells are long, slender cells scattered among the other epidermal cells, especially around the mouth, on the tentacles, and on the pedal disc. Each sensory cell terminates near the body surface in a flagellated point or bulb. The other end of the cell branches into fine fibrils attached to the nerve plexus found in the epidermis next to the mesoglea. They serve as receptors for touch, temperature, and other stimuli.

The many nerve cells of the epidermis are either bipolar with two processes or multipolar with many processes. These processes or neurites are not polarized and will conduct impulses in either direction. They lie in the epidermis near the level of the nuclei of the epidermal cells, although they may occupy a position adjacent to the mesoglea. There is no evidence that they lie in the mesoglea. Their processes connect with sensory cells, with the longitudinal fibers of the epitheliomuscular cells and with other nerve cells. The latter connections are usually continuous in the hydra but synaptic junctions may be present.

GASTRODERMIS. The inner gastrodermis, a layer of cells lining the coelenteron, has a plan similar to the epidermis. It is made up chiefly of large columnar epithelial cells with irregular flat bases. The free ends of the cells give a jagged and uneven contour to the coelenteron in cross section. The cells of the gastrodermis include nutritive-muscular, interstitial, and gland cells.

1. Nutritive-muscular cells. These are similar to the epitheliomuscular cells and have their bases drawn out into muscles or myonemes which run circularly around the body or tentacles. When the myonemes contract they lengthen the body by decreasing its diameter. Some of them serve as sphincters to close the mouth. Myonemes may be lacking in some cells. The cell is highly vacuolated and often filled with food vacuoles. The free end of the cell usually bears two flagella. Gas-

trodermal cells in the green hydra (*Chloro-hydra*) bear green algae (Zoochlorella) which give the hydrae their color. This is probably a case of symbiotic mutualism, for the algae utilize the carbon dioxide and waste to form organic compounds useful to the host and receive shelter and other advantages in return. Nutritive-muscular cells may also secrete digestive enzymes into the coelenteron for the digestion of foods.

2. Interstitial cells. There are a few of these small cells scattered among the bases of the nutritive cells. They may transform into other types of cells when the need arises.

3. Gland cells. Gland cells both in the hypostome and in the column secrete digestive enzymes. Mucous glands about the mouth apparently aid in ingestion. Gland cells are often club shaped, with the larger end facing the coelenteron.

Cnidoblasts are not found in the gastrodermis, for nematocysts are lacking in this layer.

MESOGLEA. The mesoglea lies between the epidermis and gastrodermis and is attached to both layers. It is gelatinous or jellylike and has no fibers or cellular elements. It is a continuous layer which extends over both body and tentacles, thickest in the stalk portion and thinnest on the tentacles. This arrangement allows the pedal region to withstand great mechanical strain and gives the tentacles more flexibility. The mesoglea supports and gives rigidity to the body, acting as a sort of elastic skeleton.

The nematocyst as a characteristic structure of Coelenterata. One of the most characteristic structures in the entire coelenterate group is the stinging organoid called the **nematocyst.** Seventeen different types of nematocysts have been described in the coelenterates so far; they are important in taxonomic determinations. The nematocyst is a tiny capsule composed of material similar to chitin and containing a coiled tubular "thread" or filament which is a continuation of the narrowed end of the capsule. This end of the capsule is covered by a little lid, or **operculum.** The inside of the undischarged thread may bear little barbs or spines. The nematocyst is found in a modified interstitial cell called a **cnidoblast.**

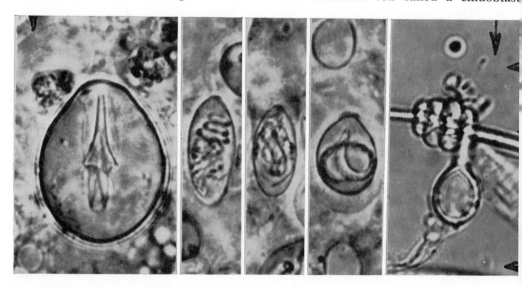

Figure 79. Nematocysts of *Hydra littoralis*, swift-water hydra. Left to right: penetrant, streptoline glutinant, stereoline glutinant, volvent, and discharged volvent attached to copepod bristle. Largest and most familiar type is the penetrant, provided with barbed spines and long threadlike tube. Nematocysts used to immobilize prey and to aid in locomotion. (Courtesy Carolina Biological Supply Co., Elon College, N. C.)

hich is provided with a projecting iggerlike **cnidocil.** When the cnidocil is imulated by food, prey, or enemies, the piled thread turns inside out with explosive force, the spines unfolding to the utside as the tube everts. Many chemicals (e.g., weak acetic acid or methyl reen) will cause discharge of nematocysts. Neither touch alone nor the presence of animal fluids (food) alone causes ischarge, but touch, combined with the resence of food, does. The exploding orce is probably pressure caused by the increase of water in the capsule, a result of osmotic changes, plus contraction of the cnidoblast which forces the operculum pen. The nematocysts may occur singly or in batteries, each consisting of one arge and many small ones. They are pund everywhere except on the basal isc but are especially abundant on the entacles. Four kinds of nematocysts are pund in the hydra:

1. The **penetrant** is long and thread-ke with spines and thorns. When discharged it is capable of entering the odies of small animals that happen to puch the tentacles, paralyzing them with the druglike hypnotoxin that it secretes. The hydra may then seize its prey with s tentacles and draw it into the mouth.

2. The **streptoline glutinant** is a long arbed thread which usually coils when ischarged. It produces an adhesive secretion used in locomotion and attachment.

3. The **volvent** is a short thread which oils in loops around the prey.

4. The **stereoline glutinant** is a straight nbarbed thread also used for attachment.

Nervous connections play no direct part n the discharge of nematocysts for they re indirect effectors. However, nerves ould affect the threshold of discharge; a ull hydra ceases to discharge nematocysts at prey; so does an overstimulated ne.

When a nematocyst is discharged the nidoblast is digested and replaced from the interstitial cells. Cnidoblasts do not riginate on the tentacles. There is a zone f growth near the base of the tentacles.

From here the maturing cnidoblasts are carried out along the tentacles by normal growth of the whole epidermis.

The nematocysts of most coelenterates are not harmful to man, but the stings of the Portuguese man-of-war and certain large jellyfish such as the *Cyanea* are quite painful and may even be dangerous to life. Some small fresh-water worms that feed on hydrae digest all the body except the nematocysts which migrate to the surface of the predator, where they serve for defense.

The nerve net and sensory mechanisms. The nerve net of the coelenterates is one of the best examples of a diffused nervous system in the animal kingdom. This plexus of nerve cells (protoneurons) connected with nerve fibers is found at the base of the epidermis near the mesoglea. In the hydra the net appears to be continuous. However, there is evidence[*] that in some coelenterates there are two nervous systems, one continuous and one discontinuous or synaptic. Impulses can pass in all directions over the net. Although the nerve net of coelenterates is generally unpolarized and characterized by diffuse transmission, unrestricted spreading of excitation is found only in those parts specialized for through conduction. The nerve cells of the net are connected to slender sensory cells which receive external stimuli and to epitheliomuscular cells which react by contracting. The only localization of nervous function in the hydra is found around the hypostome and on the pedal disc where sensory and other nerve cells are more numerous. Separated bodily parts when stimulated often react just as they do in an intact animal.

Together with the contractile fibers of the epitheliomuscular cells, the sensory-nerve cell net combination is often re-

---

[*]Mackie (1960) reports that in *Velella* there is evidence of two nervous systems, one continuous and one discontinuous. The continuous one would seem comparable to the syncytial giant nervous system in squids, annelids, and some arthropods, being specialized for rapid conduction to all parts for, say, an escape response.

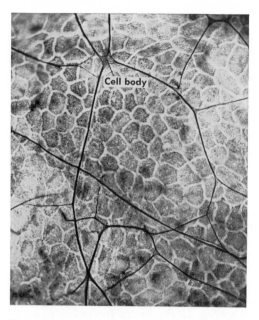

Figure 80. Portion of syncytial giant fiber nervous system of *Velella*. *Velella* is provided with two nervous systems—one of syncytial (continuous) giant fibers and one of nonsyncytial (discontinuous) neurons. (Courtesy G. O. Mackie, University of Alberta.)

ferred to as a **neuromuscular system,** the first important landmark in the evolution of the nervous system. The nerve net is never completely lost from higher forms. Annelids have it in their digestive systems. In the human digestive system it is represented by the plexus of Auerbach and the plexus of Meissner. The rhythmic peristaltic movements of the stomach and intestine are coordinated by this counterpart of the coelenterate nerve ring.

Metabolism. The hydra feeds upon a variety of small crustaceans, insect larvae, and annelid worms. It is especially fond of *Cyclops* and *Daphnia,* which are small crustaceans. A hungry hydra waits for its food to come to it. It may, if necessary, shift to a more favorable location, but once attached to its chosen substratum it waits motionless, its tentacles fully extended. Any small organism that brushes against one of its tentacles is immediately stopped, harpooned by dozens of tiny nematocyst threads, some of which penetrate the prey's tissues to inject a poison-

ous paralyzing fluid, while some coil themselves about bristles, hairs, or spines for holding. The hapless prey may be many times as large as its captor. Now the tentacles begin to move; some of them become attached to the prey and then move slowly toward the hydra's mouth. The mouth slowly opens and the prey slides slowly in. It is not pushed in or swallowed by muscular action; the mouth simply extends and widens and, well moistened with mucus, glides over and around the prey (Figure 81).

The stimulus which actually causes the mouth to open is now known to be chemical (glutathione) which is found in all living cells. Glutathione is released from the prey through the wounds made by the nematocysts, but only those animals that release enough of the chemical are eaten by the hydra. This explains how a hydra distinguishes between *Daphnia* that it relishes and some other forms that it refuses. When commercial glutathione is placed in water containing hydrae, the hydra will go through all the motions of feeding even though no prey is present.

Inside the gastrovascular cavity contraction of the body wall forces the food downward. Gland cells in the gastrodermis discharge extracellular enzymes and digestive juices on the food. The digestion started in the gastrovascular cavity is called **extracellular digestion,** but many of the food particles are drawn by pseudopodia into the nutritive-muscular cells of the gastrodermis where **intracellular digestion** occurs. Indigestible particles are forced back out of the mouth, for there is no anus. Digested food products may be stored in the gastrodermis or distributed by diffusion to other cells, including the epidermis.

Respiration and **excretion** are carried on individually by each cell. There are no special organs for these processes, although it is thought that the endoderm of the pedal disc does accumulate some excretory matter, which may be discharged through a pore.

Locomotion. A hydra has several ways

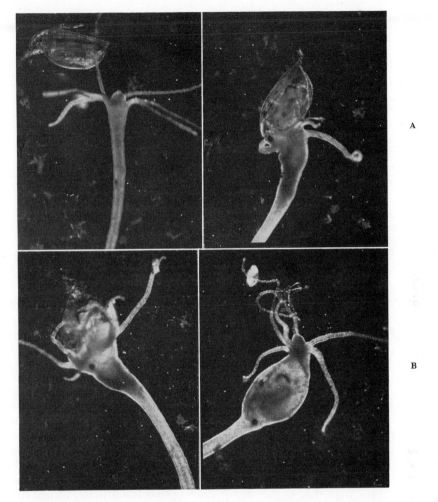

Figure 81. Lunch for hungry hydra. **A,** Unwary daphnia gets too close to waiting tentacle. Still kicking, he is drawn into widening mouth of captor. **B,** Swallowing process is slow but odds are against daphnia. Mission accomplished, hydra settles down to digest lunch.

of moving from one region to another. One is a gliding movement with the basal disc sliding slowly over the substratum, aided by secretions from mucous glands. A second method is a "measuring-worm" type of movement, where the hydra bends over and attaches its tentacles, slides its basal disc up close to the tentacles, and then releases its tentacles and straightens up. Another method is like a handspring, where the animal suddenly releases its basal disc, carries it completely over, and attaches it to a new position. The hydra may move from one place to another in an inverted position by using its tentacles as legs. To rise to the surface of the water it often forms a gas bubble on its basal disc and floats up.

Reproduction. The hydra uses both asexual and sexual methods of reproduction. Asexual reproduction is by **budding,** where projections grow out from the body wall by a proliferation of cells (Figures 77 and 83). Several buds may be found on the same animal, and these may bear secondary buds of their own. Buds represent outpocketings of the entire body wall with the gastrovascular cavity of the bud in communication with the cavity of the parent. The bud acquires a hypostome

Figure 82. Methods of locomotion in hydra. **1,** Contracted; **2,** extended; **3,** rising to surface by bubble; **4** to **8,** steps in "somersaulting"; **9** to **11,** steps in measuring-worm movements; **12,** ingesting food by aid of tentacles; **13,** floating while suspended.

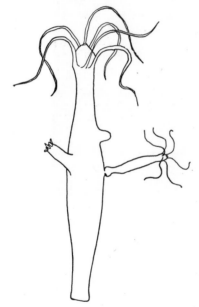

Figure 83. Asexual reproduction in hydra, showing buds in three stages.

with mouth and a ring of tentacles. Eventually it constricts at its base and detaches to lead a separate existence. Buds are formed at the junction of the gastric region and stalk (budding zone).

In sexual reproduction some species are **dioecious** and others are **monoecious** or hermaphroditic. Most hydra species are dioecious. Sexual reproduction involves the formation of gonads which are more

common in the autumn. Reduction of water temperature will promote their formation but recent work (Loomis) has shown that high pressures of free carbon dioxide and reduced aeration in stagnant water may be the responsible factor for sexuality in the hydra. Gonads are temporary structures that are formed from interstitial cells which have accumulated at certain points, multiply, and undergo all the stages of gametogenesis. In monoecious species the several **testes** form rounded outgrowths near the oral end whereas the **ovaries,** nearer the basal end, are larger and more conical. In dioecious species the testes or ovaries may be spread throughout the gastric region. Gonads are never found in the stalk region. Many sperm are produced and set free in the water, although only one egg is found in an ovary. In the development of the egg one centrally located egg cell enlarges by the union of other interstitial cells and eventually occupies most of the space in the ovary. In some species the eggs ripen one at a time, in succession; in others, several may ripen at once. The egg undergoes two maturation divisions, produces two polar bodies, and reduces its chromosome number from 30 to 15 (*Pelmatohydra*). The sperm also has 15 chromosomes, and thus the zygote will have 30 chromosomes.

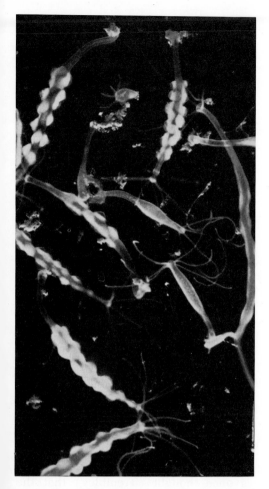

Figure 84. Living hydrae, mostly males with testes. (Courtesy General Biological Supply House, Chicago.)

Figure 85. Living hydrae, mostly females with ovaries and eggs. (Courtesy General Biological Supply House, Chicago.)

While the fertilized egg or zygote is still in the ovary, it undergoes holoblastic **cleavage** and forms a hollow **blastula**. The outer part of the blastula becomes the **ectoderm** which later forms the epidermis; the inner part of the blastula delaminates to form an inner solid mass, the **endoderm** (gastrodermis in the adult). The **coelenteron** is later formed in this mass, and the mesoglea is laid down between the ectoderm and endoderm (Figure 86.) About this time a shell or cyst is secreted about the embryo which breaks loose from the parent. In the encysted condition the embryo may pass the winter and complete its development when weather con-

ditions are more favorable. After a resting period, which varies according to weather conditions, the shell ruptures and a young hydra with tentacles hatches out and soon grows into the adult condition without a larval stage.

When testes and ovaries appear together, self-fertilization may occur, but when the gonads are produced at different times, cross-fertilization is the procedure.

Regeneration. The power of the hydra to restore lost parts is pronounced, as Trembley long ago discovered (about 1745). When the hydra is cut into several pieces, each fragment will give rise to an

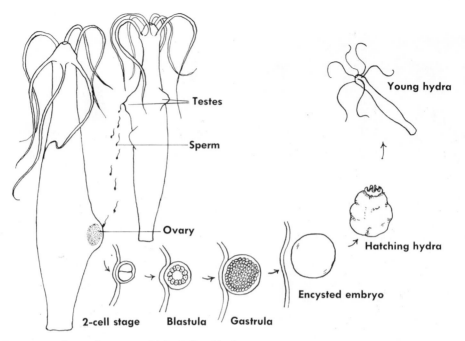

Figure 86. Sexual reproduction and life cycle of hydra.

entire animal (Figure 87). If the hypostome and the tentacles are cut off, they also will give rise to a new individual. It is also possible to produce a two-headed hydra by splitting it through the mouth. Parts of individuals of the same species (and sometimes of different species) may be grafted together, even though these fragments are too small to grow independently. The endodermal layer appears to be responsible for fusion, for cells of this layer project out ameboid processes that produce an interlacing effect.

Investigations by Brien and others on the growth patterns of the hydra indicate that the hydra may be considered immortal. When a stained graft is inserted at the growth zone just below the tentacles, colored cells are seen to move gradually toward the base where dead or worn out cells are shed. In this way the various cells that arise at the growth zone occupy successively different levels of the hydra as they make their way toward the base (or toward the tip of the tentacles where a similar renewing is taking place). This active renewing of all the cells in the hydra is supposed to take about 45 days

and appears to continue indefinitely. If the interstitial cells (which transform into the various types of cells) are destroyed by x-rays the hydra will live for only a few days.

When a hydra is turned inside out, either by natural or artificial means, it was once thought (Trembley) that the epidermal cells became gastrodermal cells and the gastrodermal cells became epidermal cells in their new positions. Many investigations, however, have shown that in some cases they turn themselves right side out, and in other cases they switch their layers by the migration of the inside cells to the outside and of the outside cells to the inside, thus restoring the original arrangement of the cells.

Behavior. The hydra will respond to various stimuli, both internal and external. Spontaneous movements of body and tentacles occur while the animal is attached. If the individual is well fed, its movements are slow, but they step up whenever it becomes hungry. These movements are produced by the contractile fibers in the wall when they are stimulated through the nerve net.

162

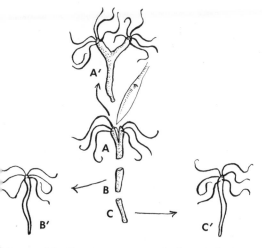

Figure 87. Regeneration in hydra. Splitting hydra part way through mouth and hypostome, **A**, will give rise to two-headed polyp, **A'**. When pieces cut off below head, **B** and **C**, each will give rise to whole individual, **B'** and **C'**.

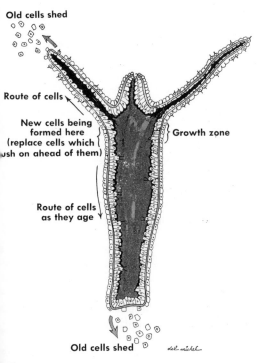

Old cells shed

Route of cells

New cells being formed here (replace cells which push on ahead of them)

Growth zone

Route of cells as they age

Old cells shed

Figure 88. Why hydra is considered immortal. New cells, continually being formed in a growth zone below tentacles, force older cells basally and distally. Eventually old cells shed at base or tip of tentacles as they are replaced by newer cells.

How the hydra reacts to stimuli depends upon the kind and intensity of the stimuli. If the stimulus is strong, the animal usually responds negatively. A slight jar will cause the whole animal to contract rapidly. The same effect may be produced by a localized stimulus, such as touching one of the tentacles with a sharp needle, in which case all the tentacles and body may contract. The explanation for this probably lies in the widespread transmission of the nerve impulse over all the nerve net. If such a localized stimulus is mild, there may a more or less localized response, such as the contraction of a single tentacle or the pulling away of that part of the body touched.

To light stimuli hydras respond in an optimum way, tending to avoid very strong light but seeking lighted regions of moderate intensity. By trial and error they find that situation which best suits them. When subjected to a weak **constant electric current,** they become oriented so that the oral end is toward the anode and the basal end toward the cathode. Water currents produce little or no response in them. They are partial to cold water and quickly disappear from surface water when it reaches 20° to 25° C. They will avoid strong and injurious chemicals.

The **physiological** state of the hydra determines to a great extent the nature of its responses to stimuli. When the hydra is not hungry, it is sluggish to most stimuli, but the hungry hydra will react to the same stimuli in a more vigorous manner.

The student will frequently note small protozoans crawling over the body surface of a live hydra, particularly on the tentacles. Most of these are ciliates, *Kerona* and *Trichodina*. They are probably commensals and do the hydra no harm.

Obelia and Gonionemus as examples of hydroid and medusa stages

Both *Obelia* and *Gonionemus* are strictly marine and have polyp and medusa stages in their life histories. *Obelia*

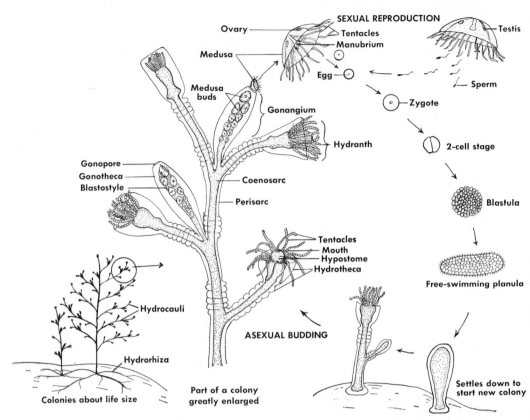

Figure 89. Life cycle of *Obelia,* showing alternation of polyp (asexual) and medusa (sexual) stages.

has a prominent hydroid (juvenile) stage but an inconspicuous medusa (adult) stage. The reverse conditions are found in *Gonionemus* where the medusa is large and the hydroid small.

Obelia may be considered as a typical colonial hydroid. Its habitat is both the Atlantic and Pacific coasts, where it is found attached to stones and other objects by a rootlike base called **hydrorhiza,** from which arise branching stems (**hydrocauli**). On these stems are large numbers of polyps which are of two types: **hydranths,** which are nutritive, and **gonangia,** which are reproductive. The hydranths furnish nutrition for the colony; the gonangia produce young medusae by budding. The medusae are sexual, giving rise to sperm and eggs. When zygotes are formed they develop through a series of stages, terminating in a polyp form, thus completing the life cycle. In this way the

polyps represent the asexual phase and the medusae the sexual phase.

The **hydrocaulus,** or stem that bears the polyps, is a hollow tube composed of a cellular **coenosarc** surrounding the **gastrovascular cavity** and covered by a transparent, chitinous **perisarc.** The coenosarc, like the body of the hydra, has an outer epidermis, an inner gastrodermis, and mesoglea between them. The gastrovascular cavity is continuous throughout the colony so that nourishment can be distributed from polyps to hydrorhiza. The perisarc is also continuous, being modified to cover the polyps.

The nutritive polyp, or **hydranth,** is very much like a miniature hydra, with a **hypostome** and **mouth** surrounded by many **tentacles.** By means of the tentacles and **nematocysts,** these feeding polyps capture their prey. They are strictly carnivorous, eating any small crustaceans,

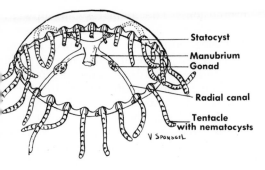

Figure 90. Medusa of *Obelia* is only 1 to 2 mm. in diameter. Note that velum is rudimentary, although *Obelia* belongs to Hydrozoa. Compare with *Gonionemus*, Figure 91.

worms, or insect larvae that come their way. Within the gastrovascular cavity food is reduced by digestive enzymes to a broth containing small particles. This is driven throughout the colony by convulsive peristaltic contractions of the hydranth. Cells of the gastrodermis pick up the food and complete digestion in food vacuoles. So far as is known, starches, cellulose, and chitin are not digested by hydroids. The hydranth is protected by a cuplike **hydrotheca,** a continuation of

the perisarc, into which the tentacles can contract.

The reproductive **gonangium** is club shaped. In it the coenosarc continues as a **blastostyle** on which the **medusae** develop as lateral buds, **gonophores.** The gonangium is surrounded by the transparent **gonotheca,** a protective sheath with an opening, the **gonopore,** through which the medusae escape.

The cellular structure of the colony is much like that of the individual hydra. Myonemes from the epitheliomuscular and nutritive-muscular layers provide movement, stimulated through a **nerve net.** **Sensory cells** are most abundant around the mouth and tentacles. Digestion, as in the hydra, is both extracellular and intracellular, with distribution being effected by both bodily contractions and ciliary movement within the digestive cavity.

Gonionemus is frequently studied as a type of jellyfish, since the medusa is much larger than that of *Obelia*. It is fairly typical of the medusae of this class. The polyp of this form is extremely small. *Gonionemus* is bell shaped and about ½ inch in diameter. The convex, or aboral,

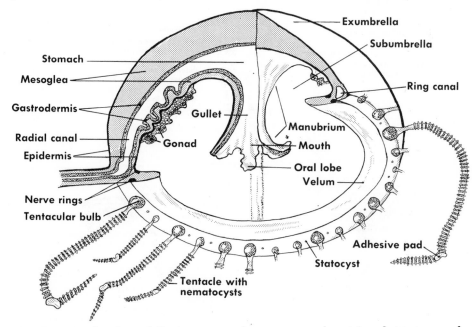

Figure 91. Diagram of medusa of *Gonionemus*, partly cut away to show internal structures and relations of parts.

side is called the **exumbrella,** whereas the concave, or oral, side is the **subumbrella.** Around the margin of the bell are a score or more of **tentacles** with nematocysts, each tentacle with a bend near the tip bearing an **adhesive pad.** Inside the margin is a thin muscular membrane, the **velum,** which partly closes the open side of the bell. The velum distinguishes the hydrozoan from the scyphozoan jellyfish. It is used in swimming movements. Contractions in the velum and body wall bring about a pulsating movement which alternately fills and empties the subumbrellar cavity. As the animal contracts, forcing water out of the cavity, it is propelled forward, aboral side first, with a sort of "jet propulsion." The animal swims upward, turns over, and floats lazily downward, tentacles outspread to capture unwary prey. It rests while attached to vegetation by its adhesive pads. Hanging down inside the bell is the **manubrium,** at the tip of which is the **mouth** surrounded by four **oral lobes.** From the mouth a **gullet** leads to the **stomach** at the base of the manubrium. Four **radial canals** lead out from the stomach to a **ring canal** around the margin, which connects with all the tentacles. The entire continuous cavity from the gullet to the tips of the tentacles makes up the **gastrovascular cavity,** in which food is partly digested by enzymes and distributed to all parts of the body.

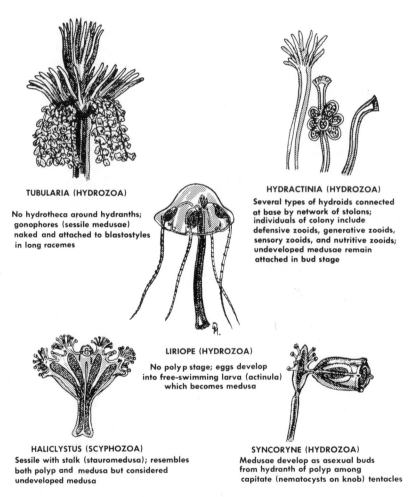

TUBULARIA (HYDROZOA)

No hydrotheca around hydranths; gonophores (sessile medusae) naked and attached to blastostyles in long racemes

HYDRACTINIA (HYDROZOA)

Several types of hydroids connected at base by network of stolons; individuals of colony include defensive zooids, generative zooids, sensory zooids, and nutritive zooids; undeveloped medusae remain attached in bud stage

LIRIOPE (HYDROZOA)

No polyp stage; eggs develop into free-swimming larva (actinula) which becomes medusa

HALICLYSTUS (SCYPHOZOA)
Sessile with stalk (stauromedusa); resembles both polyp and medusa but considered undeveloped medusa

SYNCORYNE (HYDROZOA)
Medusae develop as asexual buds from hydranth of polyp among capitate (nematocysts on knob) tentacles

Figure 92. Types of coelenterates, showing diversity of life histories and structures.

Digestion is completed in the cells of the gastrodermis. Worms, crustaceans, and small fish are favorite foods.

Medusae are dioecious. In *Gonionemus* the **gonads** are suspended under each of the radial canals. The eggs, or sperm, break through the epidermis into the water outside. The fertilized egg develops into a ciliated **planula** larva which swims about for a time, then settles down, attaches to some object, loses its cilia, and develops into a minute polyp. The cycle begins again with the young polyp budding off additional polyps which finally produce tiny medusae by asexual budding.

Since free-swimming medusae are more active than the polyps, they need a little more elaborate nervous system. The **nerve net** is concentrated into two **nerve rings** at the base of the velum, one in the exumbrellar and one in the subumbrellar epithelium. **Statocysts** around the margin provide a sense of balance. Each statocyst is a small sac with a hard mass inside which moves about as the animal moves, acting as a stimulus to direct the movements. **Tentacular bulbs** are enlargements located at the base of the tentacles. Within the bulbs nematocysts are formed which migrate out to the batteries on the tentacles. The bulbs may also help in intracellular digestion. The entire animal seems to be photosensitive.

A life cycle composed of both sexual and asexual generations is typical of this group, although there are interesting exceptions. The fresh-water hydra, which has no medusoid stage, is, of course, an exception, as is also the marine *Hydractinia.* Other forms such as the marine jellyfish *Liriope* have no hydroid stage. The larvae of *Liriope* develop directly into medusae (Figure 92). Other forms *(Sarsia),* besides reproducing sexually, also **bud off medusae** from the manubrium or from the base of the tentacles.

Polymorphism

Coelenterates such as *Obelia,* which have in the hydroid colony only two types of zooids (individuals), are called **dimor-** **phic.** Some coelentrates have more than two kinds of individuals and are called **polymorphic.** Polymorphism is, then, a condition in which the hydroid colony of a species has a variety of forms so that individuals have different functions. It is a division of labor involving several zooids instead of several organs in the same individual.

Order Siphonophora of Hydrozoa are polymorphic swimming or floating colonies made up of a number of modified medusa and polyp types. The gonophores do not develop into complete and freed medusae as in the dimorphic forms such as *Obelia. Velella,* the "sailor," and *Physalia,* the Portuguese man-of-war, are well-known forms (Figures 93 and 94). Siphonophora is a very ancient group as revealed by fossils and other evidence.

Physalia is a colony of incredible beauty with a rainbow-hued float of bright blues and pinks which carries it along on the surface waters of the southern seas. Many of them are carried northward by the Gulf Stream and blown to shore on our eastern coast. Bathers frequently find that the long graceful tentacles (sometimes as much as 60 feet long) are laden with nematocysts and capable of painful and sometimes dangerous stings.

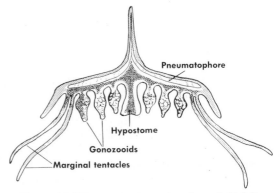

Figure 93. Diagrammatic section through *Velella,* thought to be essentially an expanded hydranth. Gonozooids are reproductive polyp-individuals. The hypostome considered by some to be a gastrozooid and the tentacles, dactylozooids. Vertical extension forms "sail" by which colony is carried about by wind.

Phylum Coelenterata (Cnidaria) 167

Figure 94. Portuguese man-of-war, *Physalia physalis* (order Siphonophora, class Hydrozoa) eating fish. This colony of medusa and polyp types is integrated to act as one individual. As many as a thousand zooids may be found in one colony. They often drift upon southern ocean beaches, where they are hazard to bathers. Although a drifter, the colony has restricted directional movement. Their stinging organelles secrete a powerful neurotoxin. (Courtesy New York Zoological Society.)

The **pneumatophore,** or float, of *Physalia* (Figure 94) is considered to be the vastly expanded body of the original larval polyp, hatched from a fertilized egg (Totton). It contains an air sac which is an invagination of the aboral body wall and is filled with a gas similar to air. This larval body acts as a sort of nurse-carrier (paedophore) for future generations of individuals which bud from it and hang suspended in the water. There are several types of polyp-individuals that include the **gastrozooids** (also called siphons). These are the only members that can ingest food; they have the usual

polyp form, but instead of the hypostomal tentacles they have one long tentacle arising from the base. Some of them are separated from their tentacles. The separated stinging tentacles are often called dactylozooids or fishing tentacles. There are three types of medusoid individuals: the **gonophores,** which are little more than sacs containing either ovaries or testes; the **nectophores,** or swimming bells, which cannot feed or reproduce but merely serve to propel the colony; and the so-called **jelly polyps,** which are probably reduced nectophores.

An interesting symbiotic relationship is found between *Physalia* and a small minnowlike fish called *Nomeus.* This fish swims in and out among the tentacles with perfect safety. Other larger fish however, are caught by the deadly tentacles when they try to catch *Nomeus.* The latter lives upon pieces of the prey which is broken up in the process of digestion. However, according to another theory, the immunity *Nomeus* enjoys is due to its habit of eating the zooids and the nematocysts of the tentacles, thus becoming immune to the poison of the stinging organoids.

Fresh-water medusae

The fresh-water medusa, *Craspedacuste sowerbyi* (class Hydrozoa, order Trachylina), was first discovered many years ago in London, where it was introduced from Brazil. Since that time this interesting form has been found in many parts of Europe and the United States. At one time it was considered extremely rare, and its discovery in a particular region was published usually without delay. It is still not a common animal but has been found all over the United States and in parts of Canada, usually in artificial ponds. (Figures 95 to 97.)

This animal has a hydroid phase, but for a long time its relation to the medusa was not recognized, and thus the hydroid was given a name of its own, *Microhydra ryderi.* This hydroid is tiny (2 mm.) and hard to find and appears to be more or less degenerate, for it has no perisarc

nd no tentacles. It occurs in colonies of
 few polyps. On the basis of its relation-
hip to the jellyfish and the law of priority,
 oth the hydroid (polyp) and the medusa
 hould be called *Craspedacusta*. This hyd-
 oid gives rise to the tiny medusae by
 udding.

This polp has three methods of asexual
 eproduction: (1) by budding off new
 ndividuals which may remain attached
 o the parent (colony formation); (2) by
 onstricting off nonciliated planula-like
 arvae which can move around and give
 ise to new polyps; and (3) by producing
 medusa buds which develop into sexual
 ellyfish. Monosexual populations (i.e.,
 nale or female) are characteristic of this
 pecies; both sexes are rarely found together. This may be due to environmental
 auses (temperature of water), or the
 olyps in a particular habitat may be
 ither male-producing or female-produc-
 ng individuals (Payne).

The jellyfish, which may attain a diameter of 20 mm. when mature, has some
 odd features. The tentacles are very numerous and are arranged in three or more
 ets. Unlike *Gonionemus* and many other
 ellyfish, the tentacles of this fresh-water
 ellyfish are unequal in length and are not
 provided with adhesive pads. Only one
 kind of nematocyst is found. The gonads

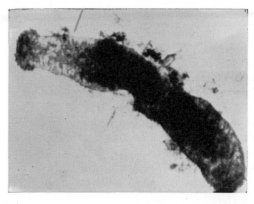

Figure 96. Polyp of fresh-water jellyfish,
Craspedacusta. Only 2 mm. long, this polyp has
no tentacles and its nematocysts are restricted
to mouth region. Polyp can creep around on
a substrate and feed on small organisms. (Photomicrograph courtesy Charles F. Lytle.)

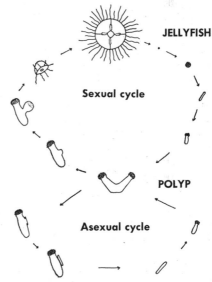

Figure 97. Life history of the fresh-water jellyfish, *Craspedacusta,* showing both sexual and
asexual cycles. Polyp may bud off planula-like
larvae (frustules) which grow into polyps, or
it may produce medusa buds that develop into
sexual jellyfish whose zygotes develop into polyps.
(Courtesy Charles F. Lytle.)

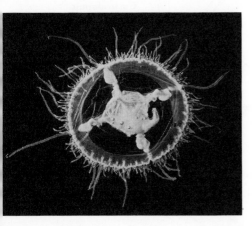

Figure 95. Fresh-water jellyfish, *Craspedacusta
sowerbyi.* Although closely resembling *Gonionemus,* tentacles are more varied in length and
have no adhesive pads. (Courtesy Carolina
Biological Supply Co., Elon College, N. C.)

are enlarged sacs which hang down inside the subumbrella, and the manubrium
extends down almost to the level of the
velum. Although the medusae are dioecious, usually all the jellyfish of a habitat
are of the same sex.

Phylum Coelenterata (Cnidaria) 169

CLASS SCYPHOZOA (SCYPHOMEDUSAE)

This class contains most of the large jellyfish and can be distinguished from the jellyfish of class Hydrozoa by the absence of a velum and the presence of a notched margin of the umbrella. Most of them have polyps and medusa stages, but the polyp stage is insignificant. Some of these jellyfish are several feet in diameter, with tentacles more than 75 feet long (*Cyanea*). Others, however, are quite small. Most are found floating in the open sea, although others are attached. Although constructed on the coelenterate plan, this class shows some advancements over class Hydrozoa. It has in its middle layer (mesoglea) ameboid cells and fibers embedded in jelly, so that this stratum is called now a **collenchyme.** Other differences from the Hydrozoa are the location of the gonads in the gastrodermis, the more complicated sense organs, the presence of gastrodermic tentacles, and the division of the gastrovascular cavity by septa.

Aurelia

Aurelia is 3 or 4 inches in diameter and is found in the coastal waters from Maine

Figure 98. Large jellyfish, *Cyanea*. Some may attain diameter of more than 6 feet in Arctic waters but are smaller in warmer waters. Its many hundred tentacles may reach length of 100 feet or more. It is one of the most striking of all jellyfish. (Courtesy Vancouver Public Aquarium, British Columbia.)

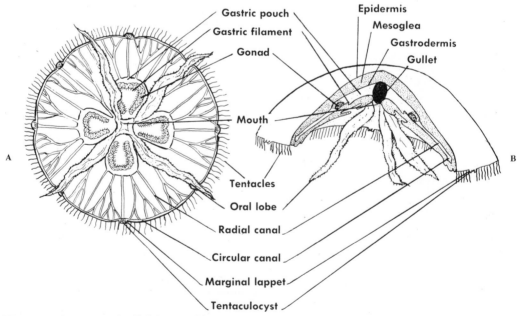

Figure 99. Structure of jellyfish, *Aurelia*. **A,** Oral view. **B,** Side view with part of body cut away to show internal structure.

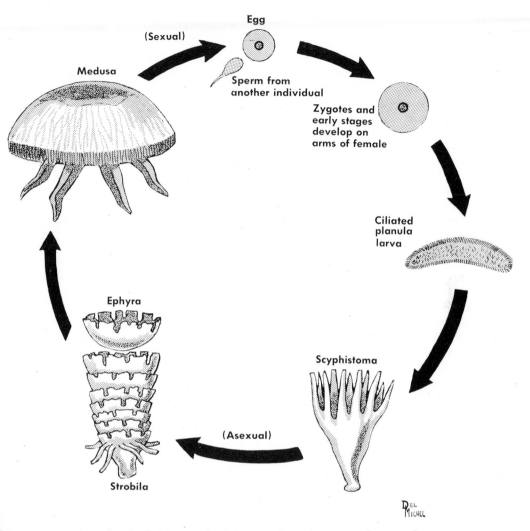

Egg

(Sexual)

Medusa

Sperm from
another individual

Zygotes and
early stages
develop on
arms of female

Ciliated
planula
larva

Ephyra

Scyphistoma

Strobila

(Asexual)

DEL
MICHEL

Figure 100. Life cycle of jellyfish, *Aurelia* (class Scyphozoa). Eggs and sperm from separate sexes form zygotes which develop on oral arms of female. After early stages of development (not shown on diagram), ciliated planula larva swims away and becomes attached to form a scyphistoma. The latter by transverse fission or strobilation develops into strobila stage, made up of saucerlike ephyrae. Ephyrae separate and float off as small jellyfish. Life cycle is thus made up of sexual and asexual phases.

to Florida. Its general form is similar to *Gonionemus,* for it has **exumbrella** (aboral) and **subumbrella** (oral) surfaces. In the margin of the umbrella there are eight indentations and many small tentacles. In each of the marginal notches there is a sense organ, **tentaculocyst,** which is flanked by marginal lappets. Each sense organ consists of a pigmented eyespot sensitive to light and a hollow statocyst for equilibrium. Mineral parti-

cles enclosed in cells near the tip of the tentaculocyst act as weights, causing the structure to bend up and down at its base when the animal tilts to one side or the other. This bending is recorded by sensory cells near the base of the organ and provides a sense of equilibrium. Two olfactory pits are near the tentaculocyst. In the oral surface is the **mouth** at the end of a short **manubrium**. From each corner of the square mouth an **oral**

Phylum Coelenterata (Cnidaria) 171

lobe or arm hangs down. Nematocysts in the lobes paralyze small prey which are then carried up ciliated grooves in the lobes and through the mouth into the digestive cavity. Flagella in the gastrodermis keep a current of water moving to bring in food and oxygen and to carry away wastes. Extending out from the central digestive cavity are four **gastric pouches** in which the gastrodermis extends down in little tentacle-like projections called **gastric filaments**. These are covered with nematocysts for further quieting any prey that are still struggling. Gastric filaments are not found in hydrozoan medusae. **Radial canals** branch out from the pouches to a **ring canal** in the margin. In each gastric pouch there is a C-shaped **gonad.** As in many of the syphomedusae and anthozoans, *Aurelia* has two nerve nets—a giant fiber system for controlling the swimming contraction and a diffuse one for local reactions, such as feeding. The two systems, however, communicate with each other.

The jellyfish is covered with epidermis, and the mesoglea (collenchyme) is unusually thick. The bulk of the jellyfish is water. Movement is by rhythmic pulsations of the umbrella.

The sexes are separate, and fertilization is internal, the sperm of the male being carried into the gastric cavity where the eggs are. The zygotes then lodge on the oral lobes, where they develop into ciliated planula larvae. After swimming about, the larva becomes fixed and develops into a **scyphistoma,** a hydralike form. By a process of **strobilation** the scyphistoma forms a series of saucerlike buds, **ephyrae,** and is now called a **strobila.** When the ephyrae break loose, they become inverted and grow into mature jellyfish.

CLASS ANTHOZOA (ACTINOZOA)

This class includes the sea anemones, the stony corals, the horny, black, and soft corals, the sea pens, sea pansies, sea feathers, and others. Some of them are provided with an external or internal skeleton, and they may be solitary or colonial. They have a flowerlike appearance and are strictly polyps, for no medusa stages are found. They are found in deep as well as in shallow marine water and in polar seas as well as in the tropics. They vary greatly in size and are firmer in texture than are the polyps of other coelenterates.

The class Anthozoa differs from the other classes of Coelenterata in a number of particulars (some of which may be considered advancements), such as an exclusively polypoid form, a tendency toward biradial and even bilateral symmetry, the presence of a mesoglea made up of a mesenchyme of ameboid cells, the formation of a true stomodaeum (lined with invaginated ectoderm), and the presence of a disc-shaped oral end.

Metridium

Metridium, a sea anemone, which is one of the types of the class, is 2 to 3 inches long and is commonly found on wharves, piers, and rocky bottoms along the North Atlantic coast. It is cylindrical in form, with a crown of hollow tentacles arranged in circlets around the **mouth** on the flat **oral disc.** The base, or **pedal disc,** serves for attachment. The mouth leads into a **gullet,** or stomodaeum, on either side of which is a **ciliated groove** called the **siphonoglyph** (single in some species). These grooves create water currents to carry in oxygen, while the cilia on the rest of the gullet carry water and waste products out. The gullet leads into the **gastrovascular** cavity which is divided into six **radial** chambers by six pairs of **septa,** or **mesenteries,** that extend vertically from the body wall to the gullet. These chambers communicate with each other by means of **ostia** in the mesenteries and are open below the gullet. Smaller mesenteries partially subdivide the larger chambers but do not reach the gullet. Attached to the base of the mesenteries are the threadlike **acontia** which bear nematocysts and gland cells. The acontia can be protruded through the mouth or pores in the body wall and help overcome prey. The pores (cinclides) in the

Figure 101. Cluster of sea anemones, *Metridium*.

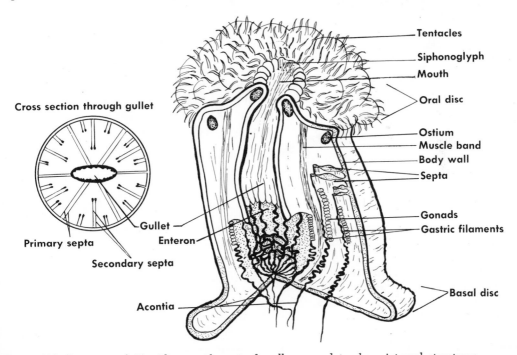

Figure 102. Structure of *Metridium*, with part of wall removed to show internal structures.

body wall also aid in the rapid discharge of water from the body when the endangered animal contracts to a very small size.

The sexes are separate, and the gonads are arranged on the margins of the mesenteries. The zygote develops into a ciliated larva. Asexual reproduction sometimes occurs by budding and fragmentation.

Sea anemones are muscular, having muscle fibers not only in the epidermis and gastrodermis but in the collenchyme

Phylum Coelenterata (Cnidaria)   173

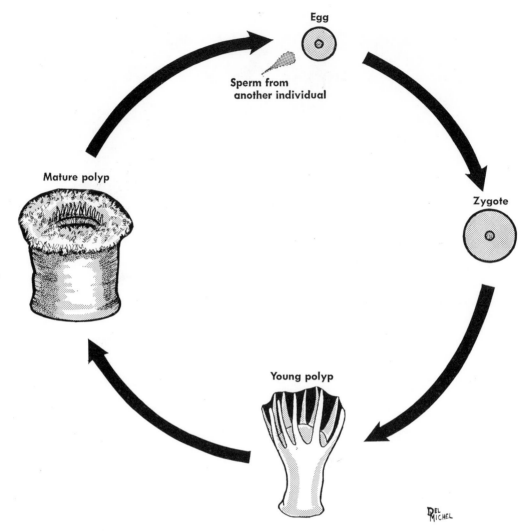

Figure 103. Life history of sea anemone, Anthozoa. This class has only the polyp type.

as well. There are definite muscle bands in the mesenteries. Anemones can glide along slowly on their pedal discs. They can expand and stretch out their tentacles in search of small vertebrates and invertebrates which they overpower with tentacles and nematocysts and carry to the mouth. When disturbed they contract and draw in their tentacles and oral discs. Respiration and excretion are by diffusion through the body walls and cells. Some of these animals are very colorful when open and look like incredibly beautiful aquatic flowers.

Corals

Most corals belong to class Anthozoa, although one or two are from Hydrozoa. Many species, both living and fossil, are recognized. The coral organism is a small polyp (about ½ inch long) which looks like a miniature sea anemone living in a stony cup with radial ridges. The cup is a limy exoskeleton secreted by the epidermis around the polyp and between its mesenteries. Living polyps can withdraw into these cavities when not feeding. While some are solitary, most are in colonies which assume a great variety of

Figure 104. Group of coral polyps, *Astrangia danae,* protruding from their shallow cups. This is a common coral of Atlantic coast. (Courtesy General Biological Supply House, Chicago.)

forms, such as multiple branching and rounded masses. Living polyps are found only on the surface layers of coral masses. Thus there is deposited over long periods of time large amounts of calcareous coral.

Reef-building corals are mainly restricted to shallow water of tropic seas. They are rarely found in water below 100 to 150 feet in depth and flourish best in temperatures between 22° and 28° C. They are most common in the coastal waters of Florida and the West Indies, the east coast of Africa and Madagascar, the East Indies, Australia and the islands of the Coral Sea, and a few other places. Three kinds of coral reefs are commonly recognized, depending on how they are formed. One of these is the **fringing reef,** which may extend out to a distance of a quarter mile from the shore with the most active zone of coral growth facing the sea. A **barrier reef** differs from a fringing reef in being separated from the shore land by a lagoon of varying width and depth. The Great Barrier Reef off the northeast coast of Australia is more than 1,200 miles long and up to 90 miles from the shore. A third type of reef is the **atoll,** which is a reef that encircles a lagoon but not an island. Of the many theories advanced to explain coral reef formation, none are entirely satisfactory. Darwin's theory assumed that fringing reefs were first formed on a

Figure 105. Organ-pipe coral, *Tubipora.* These often build extensive reefs.

Figure 106. Stony coral, *Oculina,* showing cups in which polyps once lived.

Phylum Coelenterata (Cnidaria) 175

sloping shore, and by subsidence of the sea floor in the regions of the reefs and the simultaneous upward and outward growth of the coral, these fringing reefs became barrier reefs. In places an entire volcanic island may have become submerged, leaving only the coral atoll which in time acquired a growth of vegetation. Another theory (Daly) stresses the lowering of the ocean level by the withdrawal of water for glacial formation. Wave action then produced flat areas. When the glaciers melted and the temperature became favorable, the corals began to grow on these surfaces, building higher as the ocean level rose. Recent borings to great depths on certain atolls confirm a belief that atolls developed on volcanic tops or mountains as they became submerged. Most reefs grow at the rate of 10 to 200 mm. each year. Most of the existing reefs could have been formed in 15,000 to 30,000 years.

Some solitary sea corals that do not form reefs have been found at depths of 4 or 5 miles, and a few have been collected from the waters of northern latitudes.

Coral reefs have great economic importance, for they serve as habitats for a great variety of organisms, such as sponges, worms, echinoderms, mollusks, and many kinds of fish. Nearly every phylum of marine life is found among their crevices and chasms.

ECONOMIC IMPORTANCE

As a group, coelenterates have little economic importance. Some animals use them as food, although this is rarely done by man. Precious coral serves for jewelry and ornaments. Corals also are important in building the coral reefs and islands, some of which are used as habitations by man and other animals. In places where it is available, coral rock serves for building purposes. Some mollusks and flatworms eat hydroids bearing nematocysts and utilize these stinging cells for their own defense. Planktonic medusae may be of some importance as food for fish that are of commercial value; on the other

hand, the reverse is true—the young of the fish fall prey to coelenterates.

Derivation and meaning of basic terminology

acontia (Gr. *akontion*, a dart). Threads with nematocysts on mesenteries of sea anemone.

Anthozoa (Gr. *anthos*, flower, + *zoon*, animal).

Aurelia (L. *aurelia*, gold colored) Genus (Scyphozoa).

Chlorohydra (Gr. *chloros*, green, + hydra) Genus (Hydrozoa).

cinclide (Gr. *kinklis*, an opening or lattice) Small pores in the external body wall of sea anemones.

cnidoblast (Gr. *knide*, nettle, + *blast*, germ) Modified interstitial cell that holds the nematocyst.

cnidocil (Gr. *knide*, nettle, + *cilium*, hair) Triggerlike spine on nematocyst.

collenchyme (Gr. *kolla*, glue, + *enchyma*, an infusion) A gelatinous mesenchyme that forms the third layer in the wall of coelenterates.

Craspedacusta (Gr. *kraspedon*, border, + *acusta*, pointed) Genus (Hydrozoa).

ephyra (Gr. *Ephyra*, Greek city) Refers to castlelike appearance. Stage in development of Scyphozoa.

gonangium (Gr. *gon*, seed, + *angeion*, vessel) Reproductive zooid of hydroid colony.

Gonionemus (Gr. *gonia*, angle, + *nema*, thread) Genus (Hydrozoa).

Hydra (Greek mythology, water serpent).

hydranth (Gr. *hydra* + *anthos*, flower) Nutritive zooid of hydroid colony.

Hydrozoa (Gr. *hydra* + *zoon*, animal).

interstitial (L. *inter*, among, + *sistere*, to stand) Refers to one of the totipotent cells in the body wall of coelenterates.

medusa (Greek mythology) Jellyfish stage in coelenterates.

mesoglea (Gr. *mesos*, middle, + *glea*, glue) Jellylike noncellular layer between epidermis and gastrodermis.

Metridium (L. *metricus*, rhythm) This animal has symmetrical parts.

nematocyst (Gr. *nema*, thread, + *kystis*, bladder) Stinging cell of coelenterates.

Nomeus (Gr. herdsman) Refers to the habits of this commensal fish in inducing larger fish to chase it into the grasping tentacles of the Portuguese man-of-war.

Obelia (Gr. *obelias*, a round cake) Genus (Hydrozoa).

Pelmatohydra (Gr. *pelma*, stalk, + *hydra*) These hydrae have a stalk at the basal disc end of body. Genus (Hydrozoa).

perisarc (Gr. *peri*, around, + *sarx*, flesh) Sheath covering the stalk and branches of a hydroid.

Physalia (Gr. *physallis*, bladder) *Genus* (Hydroza).

polymorphism (Gr. *poly*, many, + *morpha*, form) A condition where there are more than two types of individuals within a single species.

polyp (L. *polypus*, many-footed) Sedentary form of coelenterates.

scyphistoma (Gr. *skyphos*, a cup, + *stoma*, mouth) A stage in the development of scyphozoan jellyfish just after the larva becomes attached.

Scyphozoa (Gr. *skyphos*, cup, + *zoon*, animal).

siphonoglyph (Gr. *siphon*, a siphon, + *glyphe*, a carving) Ciliated furrow in the gullet of sea anemones.

Siphonophora (Gr. *siphon*, siphon, + *phoros*, bearing) An order of Hydrozoa. Refers to the gastrozooid polyp with a single hollow tentacle in these polymorphic hydrozoan colonies.

strobila (Gr. *strobilos*, anything twisted) A stage in the development of the scyphozoan jellyfish.

tentacle (L. *tentare*, to feel) Flexible processes about the mouth and margin of the umbrella in coelenterates.

tentaculocyst (L. *tentaculum*, a feeler, + *kystis*, a bladder) A sense organ on the margin of the jellyfish umbrella.

Trachylina (Gr. *trachys*, rough) An order of Hydrozoa. Refers to the appearance produced by the long-haired sensory cells and lithostyles or sense clubs.

velum (L. a veil) A membrane on the subumbrella surface of jellyfish of class Hydrozoa.

ANNOTATED REFERENCES

Berrill, N. J. 1957. The Indestructible Hydra. Scientific American, vol. 197, p. 48 (Dec.). *Summarizes in a clearly written manner the many facets of the hydra's structure and regenerative behavior.*

Brown, F. A., Jr. 1950. Selected Invertebrate Types. New York, John Wiley & Sons, Inc. *Good for certain representative marine forms.*

Buchsbaum, R. 1948. Animals Without Backbones, Chicago, University of Chicago Press. *Many excellent illustrations of coelenterates.*

Bullough, W. S. 1950. Practical Invertebrate Anatomy. London, The Macmillan Co. *An excellent practical manual of certain selected types.*

Burnett, A. L. 1959. Hydra: An Immortal's Nature. Natural History, p. 498 (Nov.). *Describes among other aspects of the hydra's nature the experiments of P. Brien on the renewal of cells.*

Fraser, C. M. 1937. Hydroids of the Pacific Coast of Canada and the United States. Toronto, University of Toronto Press. *This monograph and a similar one on the hydroids of the Atlantic coast are the most comprehensive taxonomic studies yet made on the American group.*

Hardy, A. C. 1956. The Open Sea. Boston, Houghton Mifflin Co. *Many beautiful plates of medusae and other coelenterates in this outstanding treatise on sea life.*

Hyman, L. H. 1940. The Invertebrates: Protozoa Through Ctenophora. New York, McGraw-Hill Book Co., Inc. *Extensive accounts are given of the coelenterates (Cnidaria) and the ctenophores in the last two chapters of this authoritative work.*

Lane, C. E. 1960. The Portuguese Man-of-War. Scientific American, vol. 202, p. 158 (March). *The author considers this jellyfish to be made up of a colony of four kinds of polyps—the float, the fishing tentacles, the gastrozoids, and the reproductive polyps. A revealing article on the morphology and physiology of this remarkable form.*

Loomis, W. F. 1959. The Sex Gas of Hydra. Scientific American, vol. 200, p. 145 (April). *Describes the factors that induce sexual reproduction in the hydra.*

Mackie, G. O. 1960. The Structure of the Nervous System in Velella. Quarterly Journal of Microscopical Science, vol. 101, pp. 119-131 (June).

Mayer, A. G. 1910. Medusae of the World. Washington, Carnegie Institution of Washington. *A comprehensive and authoritative monograph on jellyfish.*

Miner, R. W. 1950. Field Book of Sea Shore Life. New York, G. P. Putnam's Sons. *An excellent taxonomic description of many coelenterates, as well as revealing plates of medusae and polyps.*

Monkman, N. 1958. From Queensland to the Great Barrier Reef. Garden City, Doubleday & Co., Inc. *A popular but interesting account of the great coral reef by the well-known underwater cameraman.*

Pennak, R. W. 1953. Fresh-Water Invertebrates of the United States. New York, The Ronald Press Co. *A very complete and up-to-date reference work on this group. Chapter 4 is devoted to the fresh-water coelenterates, including a good description of the rare fresh-water jellyfish.*

Pratt, H. S. 1935. A Manual of the Common Invertebrate Animals. Philadelphia, P. Blakiston's Son & Co. *A useful reference work on* the taxonomy of invertebrates, including coelenterates.

Roughley, T. C. 1947. Wonders of the Great Barrier Reef. New York, Charles Scribner's Sons. *Many fine natural-colored photographs of the reef and its varied life.*

Russell, F. S. 1953. The Medusae of the British Isles. Cambridge, Cambridge University Press. *In this magnificent monograph the many species of British medusae are described fully in text and by beautiful plates, many in color. An excellent account of the structural characters of medusae as well as methods for rearing and preserving them is included.*

Smith, F. G. W. 1948. Atlantic Reef Corals. Miami, University of Miami Press. *Describes with diagrams the manner of formation of* coral reefs and an account of the weste Atlantic reefs.

Totton, A. K., and G. O. Mackie. 1960. Studi on *Physalia physalis* (L.). Discovery Report vol. 30, pp. 301-407. Cambridge, Cambridge University Press. *This excellent up-to-da monograph is an exhaustive treatment of t natural history and morphology (Totton) an the behavior and histology (Mackie) of t Portuguese man-of-war. It is a superb wo of interest to both the specialist and all ser ous students of zoology.*

Yonge, C. M. 1949. The Sea Shore. Londo Collins, *Many descriptions of coelenterat are scattered throughout this fascinating wor Some very revealing colored photographs sea anemones.*

chapter 9

Phylum Ctenophora*

BIOLOGICAL PRINCIPLES

Tissue level of animal organization

1. Although ctenophores have not advanced beyond the tissue grade of organization, they show here and there a greater development of tissue patterns than do the coelenterates.

2. Some examples of this advancement are shown by a more complicated branched gastrovascular cavity, the tendency of muscle fibers to be gathered into bundles, and the presence of an aboral sensory organ.

Biological contributions

1. Ctenophores have advanced further than coelenterates with the mesoglea. Ctenophores have connective tissue and muscle cells differentiated from mesenchymal cells instead of the contractile fibers which are part of the epithelial cells of ectoderm and endoderm (some coelenterates). Ctenophores thus have a better-developed ectomesoderm than coelenterates.

2. The arrangement of the tentacle sheaths and the gastrovascular canals has given ctenophores **biradial symmetry**, although some parts, such as the comb plates, have a radial distribution.

3. The presence of an **aboral sense** organ for equilibrium and coordination represents a distinct advancement.

4. The **mosaic type of development** first introduced by the ctenophores is also found in the development of many higher forms.

5. Unique characters of ctenophores are **comb plates** and **colloblasts**.

Position in animal kingdom

1. Evidence indicates that ctenophores had a coelenterate-like ancestor.

2. The ancestral form of this phylum was probably a more or less spherical animal with a concentration of cilia along eight meridional rows which later developed into the comb plates.

3. Ctenophora are not in direct line of evolutionary development but represent an offshoot which gave rise to no higher form.

GENERAL RELATIONS

Many zoologists have placed ctenophores in phylum Coelenterata. The tendency at present is to consider them as a separate phylum. They comprise a small group of fewer than 100 species, and they are strictly marine forms. They take their name from the eight comblike plates they bear for locomotion. Common names for them are "sea walnuts" and "comb jellies." They are widely distributed, especially in warm waters, and are extensively used in biological investigations.

Although they have some common characteristics there is no convincing evidence that ctenophores were derived from coelenterates, although there may be some kinship. The ancestral ctenophore seems to have been a spherical form with eight radially arranged nerves which represented a concentrated form of advancement over the nerve net of the coelenterates. In time the eight meridional rows of comb plates developed over the regions of these nerves. In contrast to coelenterates, nematocysts are lacking in ctenophores, except in one species (*Euchlora rubra*) which is provided with nematocysts on certain regions of its tentacles. These nematocysts are a part of

*Te-nof'o-ra (Gr. *ktenos*, comb, + *phoros*, bearing).

this ctenophore and are not obtained by eating hydroids.

The ctenophores must be considered as a blind offshoot which gives rise to no higher form. They are thus not in direct evolutionary line with the pattern of animal life. They, with coelenterates, represent the only two phyla with basic radial symmetry in contrast to the other Metazoa, which have developed bilateral symmetry. Ctenophores have some resemblance to the Trachylina and may have diverged very early from that coelenterate stem. The flat creeping ctenophores, *Ctenoplana* and *Coeloplana,* formerly thought to show affinities between the flatworms and the Radiata, are now considered to be highly modified ctenophores which have acquired a creeping mode of life.

In common with the coelenterates, ctenophores have not advanced beyond the tissue grade of organization. There are no definite organ systems in the strict meaning of the term.

CHARACTERISTICS

1. Symmetry **biradial;** arrangement of internal canals and the opposite position of the tentacles changing the radial symmetry into a combination of the two (**radial + bilateral**)

2. Usually ellipsoidal or spherical in shape **with eight rows of comb plates on the external surface**

3. Ectoderm, endoderm, and a mesoglea (ectomesoderm) with scattered cells and muscle fibers; ctenophores may be considered **triploblastic**

4. Nematocysts absent (except in one species) but **adhesive cells (colloblasts)** present

5. Digestive system consisting of a mouth, stomodaeum, stomach, and a series of canals

6. Nervous system consisting of an aboral sense organ (**statocyst**) with a subepidermal plexus arranged into eight strands beneath the eight comb plate rows

7. No polymorphism or attached stages

8. Reproduction monoecious; gonad (endodermal origin) on the walls of the digestive canals which are under the row of paddle plates; cydippid larva

COMPARISON WITH COELENTERATA

Ctenophores resemble the coelenterate in the following ways:

1. A form of radial symmetry; with the coelenterates they form the group Radiata

2. An aboral-oral axis around which the parts are arranged

3. A well-developed gelatinous ecto mesoderm (collenchyme)

4. No coelomic cavity

5. Diffuse nerve plexus

6. Lack of organ systems

They differ from the coelenterates in the following ways:

1. No nematocysts except in *Euchlor*

2. Development of muscle cells from mesenchyme

3. Presence of comb plates and collo blasts

4. Mosaic or determinate type of development

5. Presence of stomodaeum general

HABITAT

The ctenophores are strictly marine and all are free swimming. They are feeble swimmers and are carried by tides and currents. Storms may drive them in concentrated numbers onto beaches and sea bays and inlets. Although they are more common in surface waters they also occur at great depths in the sea.

CLASSES

Class Tentaculata (ten-tac′u-la″ta) (L. *tentaculum,* feeler). With tentacles. Tentacles may or may not have sheaths into which they retract. Some types of this class flattened for creeping; others compressed to a bandlike form. In some the comb plates may be confined to the larval form. Examples: *Pleurobrachia, Cestum.*

Class Nuda (nu′da) (L. *nudus,* naked). Without tentacles; conical form; wide mouth and pharynx; gastrovascular canals much branched. Example: *Beroë.*

REPRESENTATIVE TYPE
CLASS TENTACULATA
Pleurobrachia

Structure. Pleurobrachia is a ctenophore commonly studied in zoological laboratories. Its transparent, whitish body is a little less than 1 inch in diameter and is ovoid in shape (Figure 107). The oral pole bears the mouth opening, and the aboral pole has a sensory organ, the statocyst.

On the surface there are eight equally spaced **comb plates** (paddle plates) which extend as meridians from the aboral pole and end before reaching the oral pole (Figure 108). Each plate is made up of a transverse row of long fused cilia. On opposite sides, near the aboral end, are the two **tentacle sheaths,** blind sacs which contain the bases of the tentacles. The two tentacles are long and solid and very extensible and are provided with muscle fibers and lateral branches. They can be fully retracted into the sheaths, and, when completely extended, they may be 6 inches long. The surface of the tentacles bear **colloblasts,** or glue cells, which secrete a sticky substance for catching small animals.

The **gastrovascular** system consists of a **mouth** which opens into a **pharynx,** or **stomodaeum,** whose much folded wall

Figure 107. *Pleurobrachia,* common ctenophore, about ¾ inch in diameter. Note rows of ciliated comb plates, also tentacle sheaths near upper (aboral) end. Tentacles are retracted.

carries on most of the digestive process. The pharynx extends more than half the distance to the aboral pole and enters the **stomach,** which gives rise to the **gastrovascular canals.** These canals branch and form a definite pattern in their course through the jelly to the underside of the

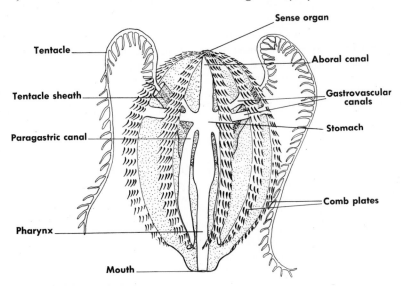

Figure 108. Structure of *Pleurobrachia.*

comb plates, to the tentacular sheath, and elsewhere. From the oral side of the stomach there are also two blind sacs, **paragastric canals,** which pass orally and terminate near the mouth. From the aboral side of the stomach an **aboral** canal passes to near the statocyst, where it gives rise to four small canals; two of these canals are blind and the other two open on opposite sides of the sense organ. Some indigestible material may be ejected through the openings of these two canals.

The **sense organ** at the aboral pole consists of four tufts of cilia which support a calcareous **statolith,** the whole being enclosed in a bell-like container. This is an organ of equilibrium, for alterations in the position of the animal would change the pressure on the tufts of cilia so that a differential discrimination would be possible. It is also concerned in the coordination of the beating of the comb rows.

Pleurobrachia has a nervous system similar to that of the coelenterates. It is made up of a subepidermal plexus of multipolar ganglion cells and neurites which may or may not anastomose. There is a concentration of the nerve plexus under each comb plate, but there is no central control such as is found in higher forms.

The cellular layers of ctenophores are similar to those of the coelenterates. On the exterior of the body there is a ciliated **epidermis** of **ectodermal** origin. Most of the gastrovascular cavity is lined with **gastrodermis.** Between the two layers is the jellylike **collenchyme** which makes up most of the interior of the body and contains muscle fibers of mesenchymal origin and ameboid cells.

Metabolism. Ctenophores live on small organisms, such as marine eggs, crustaceans, and mollusks. In catching their prey they make use of the two tentacles which hold onto the prey with the glue cells and bring it to the mouth. Digestion is extracellular in the gastrovascular cavity and its numerous branches, but some intracellular digestion also occurs in the gastrodermis. Most indigestible material is voided through the mouth and through the anal pores on each side of the sense organ. Respiration and excretion occur through body surface.

Locomotion. They are propelled by the beating of the cilia on the comb or paddle plates. The beat in each row starts at the aboral end and proceeds successively along the combs to the oral end. The animal is thus driven forward with the mouth in advance. The animal can swim backward by reversing the direction of the wave. The beat of the comb plates is under nervous control of the diffuse nervous system but is not initiated by the aboral sense organ. However, the sense organ is concerned with coordination between the comb rows.

Reproduction. Pleurobrachia, in common with other ctenophores, is monoecious. The gonads are arranged on the endodermal lining of the gastrovascular canals under the comb plates. Fertilized eggs are discharged through the epidermis into the water. Cleavage in ctenophores is determinate (mosaic), for the various parts of the animal are mapped out in the cleavage cells. If one of the cells is removed in the early stages, the resulting embryo will be deficient. This type of development is just the opposite of that of coelenterates. The free-swimming larval form of ctenophores, which is different from that of coelenterates, develops directly into an adult. The larval form is called cydippid and is characteristic of most ctenophores.

Behavior. Not much is known about the reactions of ctenophores to various types of stimuli. They seem to avoid bright light, which causes them to seek a lower level in water. Whenever the surface of the sea is agitated by a storm they will also swim rapidly downward. Much of their activity has been studied with reference to their locomotion, and experiments on their comb plates have been carried out.

The epidermis is abundantly supplied with sensory cells, so that they are sensitive to chemical and other forms of stimuli. When a ctenophore comes in contact with an unfavorable stimulus, it often reverses the beat of its comb plates and backs up. The comb plates themselves are very sensitive to touch which often causes them to be withdrawn into the jelly.

Other ctenophores

Ctenophores are among the most beautiful of all creatures. Their transparent bodies glisten like fine glass, brilliantly iridescent during the day and luminescent at night.

One of the most striking ctenophores is *Beroë* which may be more than 100 mm. in length and 50 mm. in breadth. Its shape is conical or ovoid, and it is provided with a large mouth but no tentacles. It is pink-colored, and the body wall is covered with an extensive network of canals formed by the union of the paragastric and meridional canals. Venus's girdle (*Cestum*) is compressed and bandlike, may be more than a yard long, and presents a graceful appearance as it swims. The highly modified *Ctenoplana* and *Coeloplana* are very rare but are interesting because they have flattened disc-shaped bodies and are adapted for creeping rather than swimming. Both have unusually long tentacles. A common ctenophore along the Atlantic coast is *Mnemiopsis*, which has a laterally compressed body with two large oral lobes and unsheathed tentacles.

Nearly all ctenophores give off flashes of luminescence at night, especially such forms as *Mnemiopsis*. The vivid flashes of light seen at night in southern seas are often due to members of this phylum.

ECONOMIC IMPORTANCE

Ctenophores have little economic importance. They are used as a food by many marine forms, but their main interest to man is their position in the phylogeny of animals and their divergence from the coelenterates, the other great phylum of the division Radiata.

Derivation and meaning of basic terminology

Cestum (Gr. *kestos*, girdle) Genus (Tentaculata).

colloblasts (Gr. *kolla*, glue, + *blastos*, germ) Glue-secreting cells on the tentacles.

comb plate One of the plates of fused cilia which are arranged in rows for ctenophore locomotion.

Ctenophora (Gr. *ktenos*, comb, + *phoros*, bearing).

Nuda (L. *nudus*, naked).

Pleurobrachia (Gr. *pleuron*, side, + *brachia*, arms). Genus (Tentaculata).

statocyst (Gr. *statos*, standing, + *kystis*, bladder) Aboral sense organ which is concerned with orientation and coordination of the comb plates.

statolith (Gr. *statos*, standing, + *lithos*, stone) Small calcareous body resting on the tufts of cilia in the aboral sense organ.

Tentaculata (L. *tentaculum*, feeler).

ANNOTATED REFERENCES

Bourne, G. C. 1900. Ctenophora. In E. R. Lankester: A Treatise on Zoology. London, A. & C. Black, Ltd. *Good, detailed descriptions of the morphology of ctenophores; taxonomy only briefly considered.*

Hickson, S. J. 1906. Ctenophora. In S. F. Harmer and A. E. Shipley: The Cambridge Natural History, London, Macmillan & Co., Ltd. *A brief account of the more common ctenophores.*

Hyman, L. H. 1940. Phylum Ctenophora. In the Invertebrates: Protozoa Through Ctenophora, vol. 1. New York, McGraw-Hill Book Co., Inc. *The best general account of ctenophores yet published. Their classification, morphology, and physiology are all treated with considerable detail. An interesting account of their phylogenetic relations is also given.*

Mayer, A. G. 1912. Ctenophores of the Atlantic Coast of North America. Washington, Carnegie Institution of Washington, Publication No. 162. *Many useful plates and figures are included in this technical account.*

chapter 10

Phylum Platyhelminthes*

BIOLOGICAL PRINCIPLES

Tissue-organ level of organization

1. The Platyhelminthes are acoelomate vermiform Bilateria without an anus and belong to the Protostomia.

2. Flatworms show an advancement over previous phyla in having their tissue organized into definite organs.

3. Three embryonic germ layers are present: ectoderm, mesoderm, and endoderm. Mesoderm forms many organ-systems, such as those of excretion and reproduction.

4. The flatworms are found at the bottom of the bilateral animals.

5. There is more specialization in this group and more division of labor, resulting in more definite tissue layers and the arrangement of these layers to form organs.

6. The general structure of flatworms points the way to the complexity of higher forms.

7. Behavior organization through learning is first found in the flatworms.

Biological contributions

1. The third germ layer, true **mesoderm**, is definitely established by endomesodermal inwandering of embryonic endoderm.

2. **Bilateral symmetry** is definitely established.

3. Head specialization (cephalization) has made some advancements, such as a brain, eyespots, and a few other structures.

4. A subepidermal system of circular, longitudinal, and oblique muscle fibers and a mesenchymal system of fibers within the body tissues allows great variability of movement.

5. In contrast to the nerve net of coelenterates there is a tendency toward centralization of

the nervous system by the formation of longitudinal cords provided with **ganglia** (the ladder type).

6. Sensory organs are now better developed and indicate something of what is found in more complex animals.

7. In connection with their bilateral symmetry a definite **head** and **tail** are established.

8. The development of the flame cell (**protonephridium**) suggests a pattern for the excretory systems of higher organisms.

9. This phylum emphasizes parasitic living more than most phyla and has developed special adhesive organs, such as suckers and hooks.

Position in animal kingdom

1. Free-living forms, such as Planaria (Turbellaria), probably represent the basic type of the phylum. The parasitic habits among the group may account for some specialized structures, such as the degenerate digestive and neurosensory systems, the suckers and hooks for attachment to the hosts, and the overdeveloped reproductive system.

2. The relation of flatworms to coelenterate or ctenophore ancestors which acquired a creeping habit and bilateral symmetry is indicated. This ancestor may have resembled a planula larval form.

3. Within the phylum the evidence indicates that all of the orders of Turbellaria were derived from the primitive order Acoela. The strictly parasitic classes—Trematoda and Cestoda—are thought to have arisen from parasitic forms of the order Rhabdocoela.

GENERAL RELATIONS

The term "worm" has been loosely applied to elongated invertebrate animals without appendages and with bilateral symmetry. At one time zoologists con-

---

*Plat′y-hel-min″thes (Gr. *platys*, flat, + *helmins*, worm).

sidered worms (Vermes) to be a group in their own right. Such a group included a highly diverse assortment of forms. Modern classification has broken up this group into phyla and reclassified them. By tradition, however, zoologists still refer to these animals as "flatworms," "roundworms," "segmented worms," etc.

The term Platyhelminthes, "flat worms," was first proposed by Gegenbaur (1859) and applied to the animals now included under that heading. At first nemertines and some others were included but later were removed to other groups. The phylum is now restricted to three classes, Turbellaria, Trematoda, and Cestoda. Although these classes have many structural and functional differences, they all show enough similarity in body pattern to indicate a common origin.

The appearance of flatworms in the evolution of the animal kingdom brought many characteristics that were essential for the complexity of structure found in higher phyla. According to Hyman's classification the phyla of the animal kingdom may be placed in three great divisions: **Acellular** (Protozoa), **Radiata** (Porifera, Coelenterata or Cnidaria, Ctenophora), and **Bilateria** (other phyla). The emphasis placed upon bilateral symmetry by Hyman is indicated by the name she has given to the higher division. The bilateral condition may be considered a basic morphological plan for all animals which have advanced far in complexity of organization.

Most zoologists believe the flatworms came from a coelenterate-like ancestor which had acquired a creeping habit and a transformation of radial into bilateral symmetry, a differentiation of circular and longitudinal muscles, sensory emphasis of the anterior end (cephalization), and the formation of mesoderm. The transformation of a radially symmetrical animal into a bilateral one involves many modifications in body form. There would be a dorsoventral flattening of the animal, with the oral end becoming the ventral surface and the aboral the dorsal surface. The ventral surface would become specialized for locomotion with the aid of cilia and muscles. Directional movement would result in an elongated body and the development of anterior and posterior ends. No doubt the advantages of cephalization put a premium on the natural selection of the best type of head development. The change to a bilateral form would also involve the appearance of the three axes, dorsoventral, anteroposterior, and mediolateral. The small flatworms (order Acoela) seem to meet many of the requirements of an early ancestor of Platyhelminthes. They have many characteristics of the planula larva (coelenterate), such as no epidermal basement membrane, no digestive cavity, a centroventrally located mouth, no excretory system, a nerve plexus under the epidermis, and no distinct gonads.

True mesoderm (endomesoderm) originating from endoderm laid the basis for a higher type of organization with well-defined tissues and the beginnings of organs and organ systems. Structures already present in coelenterates have become more specialized in flatworms. The gastrovascular cavity is more efficient and complex; the nervous system with its anterior ganglia (brain), together with the sensory eyespots, indicates cephalization. An entirely new system, the excretory, with its characteristic network of tubes and the flame cells provides for the efficient removal of waste.

CHARACTERISTICS

1. Three germ layers (**triploblastic**)
2. **Bilateral symmetry;** definite polarity of anterior and posterior ends
3. **Body flattened dorsoventrally;** oral and genital apertures mostly on ventral surface
4. Body segmented in one class (Cestoda)
5. No definite coelom (acoelomate)
6. Epidermis may be cellular, syncytial, or absent (ciliated in some); **rhabdites in epidermis or mesenchyme** of some Turbellaria; thick cuticle with suckers or hooks in parasitic forms

7. Digestive system incomplete (gastrovascular type); absent in some

8. Muscular system of a sheath form and of mesenchymal origin; layers of circular, longitudinal, and oblique fibers beneath the epidermis

9. Spaces between organs filled with **parenchyma,** a form of connective tissue or mesenchyme

10. **Nervous system consisting of a pair of anterior ganglia with longitudinal nerve cords connected by transverse nerves and located in the mesenchyme** in most forms; similar to coelenterates in primitive forms

11. Simple sense organs; eyespots in some

12. Excretory system of two lateral canals with branches bearing **flame cells (protonephridia);** lacking in some primitive forms

13. Respiratory, circulatory, and skeletal systems lacking; lymph channels with free cells in some trematodes

14. Most forms monoecious; reproductive system complex with well-developed gonads, ducts, and accessory organs; internal fertilization; development direct; usually indirect in internal parasites in which there may be a complicated life cycle often involving several hosts

15. One class (Turbellaria) mostly free-living; others (Trematoda and Cestoda) parasitic

CLASSES

Class Turbellaria (tur'bel-la"ri-a) (L. *turbella,* a stirring). Usually free-living forms with soft flattened bodies; covered with ciliated epidermis containing secreting cells and rodlike bodies (rhabdites); mouth usually on ventral surface, sometimes near center of body; no body cavity except intercellular lacunae in parenchyma; mostly hermaphroditic, but some have asexual fission. Examples: *Dugesia* (Planaria), *Microstomum, Planocera.*

Class Trematoda (trem'a-tod"a) (Gr. *trematodes,* with holes). Body covered with thick cuticle without cilia; leaflike or cylindrical in shape; presence of suckers and sometimes hooks; alimentary canal usually with two main branches; nervous system similar to turbellarians; mostly monoecious; development direct in external parasites but usually indirect in case of in-

ternal parasites with alternation of hosts; all parasitic. Examples: *Fasciola, Opisthorch* *Schistosoma.*

Class Cestoda (ses-tod'a) (Gr. *kestos,* girdl + *eidos,* form). Body covered with thick, non ciliated cuticle; scolex with suckers or hook and sometimes both for attachment; body divided into series of proglottids; no digestiv or sense organs; general form of body tap like; usually monoecious and self-fertilizin many organs reduced; all parasitic, usual with alternate hosts. Examples: *Diphyllobotrium, Taenia, Echinococcus.*

REPRESENTATIVE TYPES
CLASS TURBELLARIA

Class Turbellaria is made up of a number of orders. *Dugesia* belongs to orde Tricladida, which has for its chief characteristic a three-prong enteron. Some members of this order are marine, such a *Bdelloura,* an ectoparasite on the gills c *Limulus,* the horseshoe crab. Anothe member of this order is a terrestrial form *Bipalium,* which is common in gree houses.

Closely related to order Tricladida the order Alloeocoela with irregular sac like intestine.

Another order is Acoela, comprised c animals that are small and have a mout but no gastrovascular cavity or excretor system. Food is merely passed throug the mouth or pharynx into temporar spaces which are surrounded by a syncytial mesenchyme where gastroderm phagocytic cells digest the food intracellularly. This order has many other primtive characteristics, such as syncytial epdermis and a diffuse nervous system. I is thought that this group has change little from the ancestral form from whic all flatworms have come. Some member of this order, such as *Otocelis,* live a commensals in the digestive system c echinoderms (sea urchins and sea cucumbers).

Order Rhabdocoela is characterized b a straight, unbranched gastrovascular cavity. One representative *(Microstomum)* c this order has the interesting habit of feeding on hydrae and taking over the nemato cysts for its own defense.

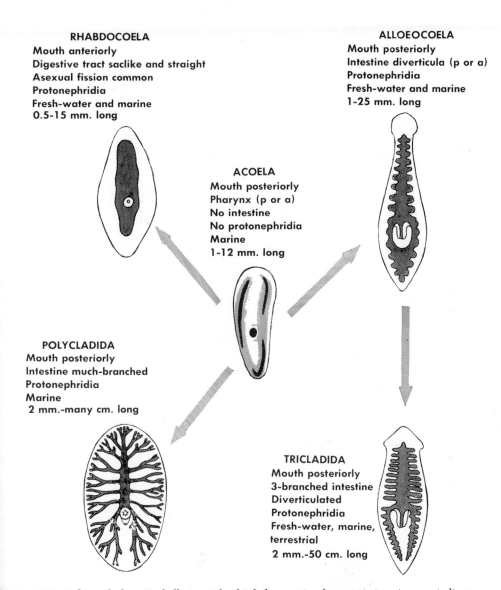

RHABDOCOELA
Mouth anteriorly
Digestive tract saclike and straight
Asexual fission common
Protonephridia
Fresh-water and marine
0.5-15 mm. long

ALLOEOCOELA
Mouth posteriorly
Intestine diverticula (p or a)
Protonephridia
Fresh-water and marine
1-25 mm. long

ACOELA
Mouth posteriorly
Pharynx (p or a)
No intestine
No protonephridia
Marine
1-12 mm. long

POLYCLADIDA
Mouth posteriorly
Intestine much-branched
Protonephridia
Marine
2 mm.-many cm. long

TRICLADIDA
Mouth posteriorly
3-branched intestine
Diverticulated
Protonephridia
Fresh-water, marine,
terrestrial
2 mm.-50 cm. long

Figure 109. Orders of class Turbellaria with chief diagnostic characteristics. Arrows indicate possible phylogenetic relationships. Structures marked "p or a" may be present or absent.

Another order, Polycladida, is comprised of animals that have many intestinal branches from the central digestive cavity and are leaflike marine forms. Some are ectoparasites, such as *Planocera*, which lives in the mouth of certain marine snails. One interesting feature of some polyclads is the presence of a ciliated free-swimming larval form. One of these, called Müller's larva, is provided with ciliated projecting lobes and eyespots.

Dugesia tigrina—common planaria

Habitat. A well-known representative of the triclad turbellarians is the common fresh-water planarian (*Dugesia tigrina*) (Figure 110). This species is found on the underside of rocks and debris in brooks or ponds of cold running water—but not in springs or in water immediately fed by springs. They are not easy to see unless they are moving, for they are small and flat and their dark mottled color blends perfectly with the rocks or plants to which they cling. Three other species of *Dugesia* are known to occur in the United States. One of these, *Dugesia dorotocephala*, a dark, almost black, form is found in springs or spring-fed water. This species has sharp-pointed auricles in contrast to the more rounded lobes of *D. tigrina*. Two other species, *D. agilis* and *D. microbursalis*, are more restricted in their distribution and have been found in spring-fed swamps and under stones in streams.

Structure. *Dugesia* is flat and slender and about ¾ inch or less in length. The head region is triangular with two lateral lobes known as **auricles.** These are not ears but olfactory organs. Two **eyespots** on the dorsal side of the head near the mid-ventral line give the animal a cross-eyed appearance. Dark pigment in the body gives it a mottled or streaked look that accounts for the species name. Its background color may range from a dark yellow to olive, brown, or blackish brown. The ventral side is lighter or white, with no pigment pattern. Near the center of the ventral side is the **mouth** through which the muscular **pharynx (proboscis)** can be extended for the capture of prey.

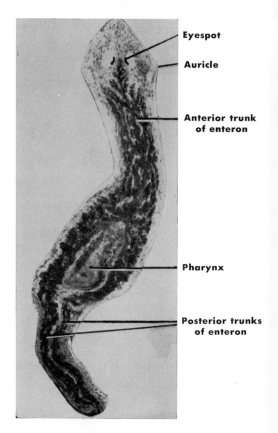

Figure 110. Photograph of living planarian.

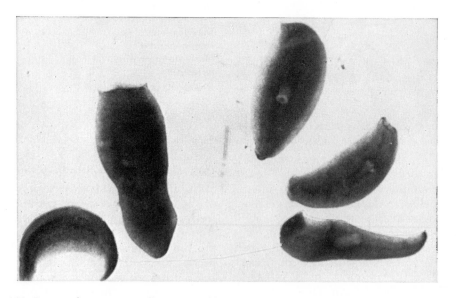

Figure 111. Living planarians. Small amount of chloroform in culture water has caused them to contract and thrust out tubular pharynxes.

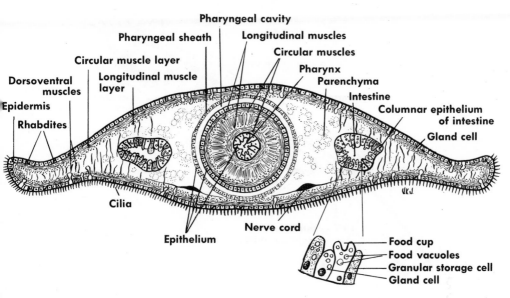

Figure 112. Cross-section of planarian through pharyngeal region, showing relations of body structures.

Posterior to the mouth on the ventral surface is the **genital pore**, the external opening of the reproductive system.

The **skin** is ciliated epidermis resting on basement membrane. It contains rod-shaped **rhabdites** which, when discharged into water, swell and form a protective gelatinous sheath around the body. Single-cell mucous glands open on the surface of the epidermis. In the body wall below the basement membrane are layers of **muscle** fibers which run circularly, longitudinally, and diagonally. A meshwork of **parenchyma** cells, developed from mesoderm, fills the spaces between muscles and visceral organs.

Digestion. The digestive system includes a mouth, pharynx, and **intestine** (enteron). The pharynx lies in a **pharyngeal sheath**, to which it is attached at the anterior end. The pharynx opens posteriorly just inside the mouth, through which it can extend. The intestine has three main trunks, one anterior and two posterior, each with many lateral **diverticula**. The whole forms a **gastrovascular cavity** lined with columnar epithelium (Figure 113).

Planarians are mainly carnivorous, feeding upon injured, intact, or dead prey, such as small crustaceans, nematodes, rotifers, and insects. In the laboratory they are often fed liver or chopped up animals. By their chemoreceptors they can detect food from some distance. They capture their prey by entangling them in mucous secretions from the mucous glands and rhabdites. The planarian grips its prey with its anterior end, wraps its body around the prey, extends its proboscis, and sucks up minute bits of the food. When one animal feeds, others are soon attracted by the juices from the food. Neither the pharyngeal nor intestinal secretions apparently have any enzymes or digestive action. Bits of food are sucked up into the intestine, where the phagocytic cells of the gastrodermis engulf and digest the food. Digestion is therefore **intracellular**. The gastrovascular cavity, which ramifies to most parts of the body, distributes the food that is absorbed through its walls into the cells. Since these forms have no anus, undigested food is egested through the pharynx. Planarians can go a long time without feeding, for they can draw food from the parenchyma cells back into the intestinal

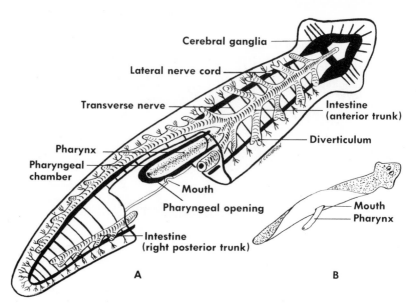

Figure 113. **A,** Diagrammatic view of digestive system and ladder-type nervous system of planaria. Cut section shows relation of pharynx, in resting position, to digestive system and mouth on ventral surface. **B,** Pharynx extended through ventral mouth.

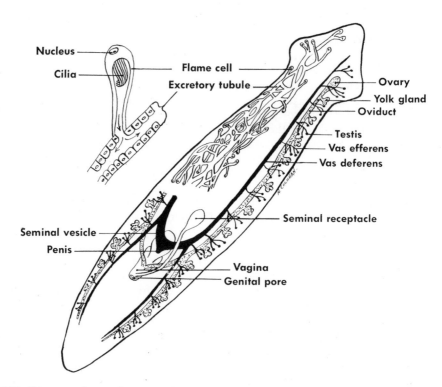

Figure 114. Diagram of reproductive and excretory systems in planaria. Portions of male and female organs omitted to show part of excretory system. Insert at left is enlargement of a flame cell.

190

lls where it is digested. During starva-
on they literally eat themselves, sacrific-
g first the reproductive organs, then the
arenchyma, muscles, and so on as they
ow smaller in size. When they feed
gain they regenerate the missing parts.

Excretion. The excretory system con-
sts of two longitudinal canals with a
omplex network of tubules which branch
 all parts of the body and end in **flame
lls** (protonephridia). The flame cell is
ollow and contains a tuft of cilia which
v beating carries water and metabolic
astes into the tubules. The two main
nals open on the dorsal body surface by
xcretory pores. The excretory system is
oncerned largely with water regulation
; well as excretion of organic wastes.
xcretion of metabolic wastes takes place
ot only through these tubes but also
rough the epidermis and probably
rough the gastrodermis (Figures 114
d 115, *A*).

Respiration. There are no respiratory
organs. Exchange of gases takes place
through the body surface.

Nervous system. Two **cerebral ganglia**
beneath the eyespots serve as the "**brain.**"
Two ventral and lateral longitudinal
nerve cords extend from the brain to the
posterior end of the body. Transverse
nerves connect the nerve cords, and short
nerves extend from the brain to the anterior end and to the eyespots. This arrangement is often called a "ladder-type"
nervous system (Figures 113 and 116).

The **eyespots** (Figure 117) are made
up of pigment cups located in a nonpig-
mented area in such a manner as to look
cross-eyed. Retinal cells extend from the
brain to dip into the pigment cups, with
the photosensitive ends of the cells inside
of the cup. They are sensitive to light intensities and can distinguish the direction of a light source, but they can form
no images. The pigment cups serve as

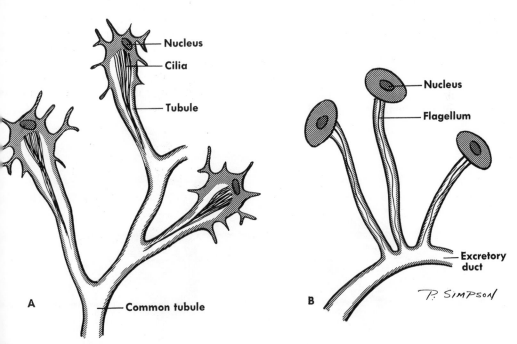

igure 115. Two types of protonephridia. **A,** Flame cells, typical of flatworms. Each flame cell
as one or more nuclei and tuft of cilia projecting into bulb cavity. Beating of cilia (flame)
roduces water diffusion currents into blind tubule, forcing fluid to larger tubules that empty
 outside by excretory pores. **B,** Solenocytes, found in polychaetes and protochordates
mphioxus). Single, long flagellum produces current. Solenocytes often found in clusters, have
in walls, and are well supplied with blood vessels. Thought to have evolved from flame bulbs.

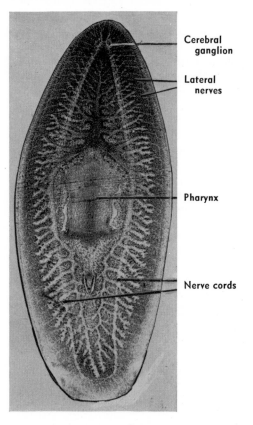

Cerebral
ganglion

Lateral
nerves

Pharynx

Nerve cords

Figure 116. Ladder-type nervous system shows up clearly in this photomicrograph of stained preparation of *Bdelloura,* marine triclad.

shields which allow light to reach th
light-sensitive ends of the cells throug
the openings of the cups only, thus per
mitting the animal to ascertain the exac
direction of the light source. Planaria ar
negatively phototactic and are most ac
tive at night. The auricular sense organ
on the side of the head are concerned witl
taste, smell, and touch. If the auricles ar
removed the animal cannot locate food

Reproduction. Triclad turbellarians re
produce both sexually and asexually
Asexually the animal merely constrict
behind the pharyngeal region and sep
arates into two animals. Each new anima
regenerates its missing parts—the anterio
piece growing a new tail end, the pos
terior piece a new head. Sexually th
worm is monoecious; each individual i
provided with both male and femal
organs (Figure 114).

In the **male** system two rows of **teste**
produce sperm. Each of the testes in a
row empties its sperm by a tiny tube (**va**
efferens) into a common duct (**va**
deferens), which enlarges posteriorly t
form a **seminal vesicle** where the spern
are stored until discharged through th
muscular **penis**. The penis opens into a
genital atrium, a cavity that terminates i

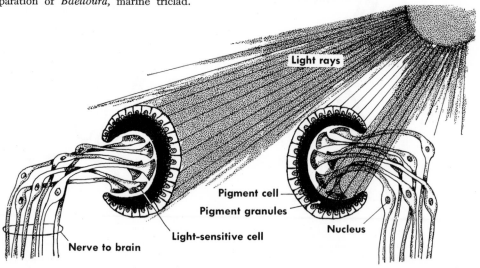

Light rays

Pigment cell

Pigment granules

Nucleus

Light-sensitive cell

Nerve to brain

Figure 117. Ocelli, or eyes, of planarian. Pigment cup lets light enter open side, parallel to long axis of retinal (light-sensitive) cells. Planarian determines light direction from stimulation of light-sensitive cells.

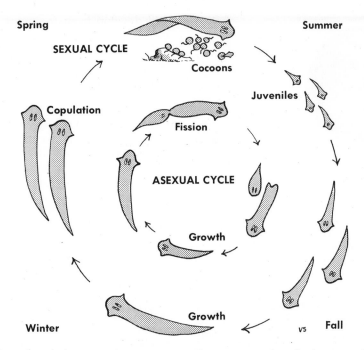

Spring   Summer

SEXUAL CYCLE

Cocoons

Juveniles

Copulation

Fission

ASEXUAL CYCLE

Growth

Growth

Winter   vs   **Fall**

Figure 118. Life cycles of planarian, *Dugesia tigrina*, showing asexual cycle (inner circle) and sexual cycle (outer circle).

the **genital pore** through which the penis extends during **copulation** (the mating act).

The **female** system contains two ovaries near the anterior end of the body which discharge eggs into two tubular **oviducts,** one along each side. **Yolk glands** empty into the oviducts which join to form a median **vagina.** The vagina opens into the genital atrium which also receives the penis. Connected to the vagina is a rounded **seminal receptacle** which receives and stores the sperm from the mating partner. Each spermatozoan is long and filamentous and is provided with a flagellum. Planarians have a reproductive system only during the breeding season, from early spring to late summer; at other times the system disappears and the worms reproduce by fission (Figure 118).

Although turbellarians are hermaphroditic they practice cross-fertilization. Two animals in copulation bring their posterior ventral surfaces together and each inserts its penis into the genital pore of the other. Sperm from the male seminal vesicle passes through the penis to the female seminal receptacle of the other so that sperm are mutually exchanged between the two partners. Self-fertilization does not occur, probably because the sperm are not activated until they are injected by the penis into another animal or because the dilated penis blocks the oviducts and prevents its own sperm from entering and fertilizing the eggs. After the worms separate, the sperm pass up the oviducts to fertilize the eggs as they are discharged from the ovaries. As the zygotes move down the oviducts, the yolk cells are added from the yolk glands. Several eggs (from two to a dozen), together with their yolk cells, become enclosed in a proteinaceous capsule, or cocoon. After a short development in the atrium the cocoons pass to the outside and in many species become attached by little stalks, usually to the underside of stones. The embryos finally emerge as little planarians (**juveniles**).

Locomotion. Fresh-water planarians move in two ways. The usual way is by

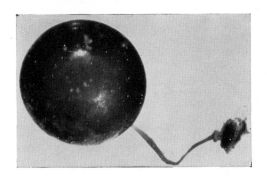

Figure 119. Egg capsule, or cocoon, of planarian with stalk for attachment to rock. Capsule containing many eggs and yolk cells is formed in male atrium. In two or three weeks eggs hatch into small, fully formed worms. (Courtesy Carolina Biological Supply Co., Elon College, N. C.)

gliding, head slightly raised, over a slime tract secreted by its marginal adhesive glands. The beating of the epidermal cilia in the slime tract drives the animal along. Rhythmic waves of movement can be seen passing backward from the head as it glides. A less common method is crawling. The worm lengthens, anchors its anterior end with mucus or by its special adhesive organ, and by contracting its longitudinal muscles pulls up the rest of its body. By means of its oblique muscles it can change its direction.

*Regeneration.** Planarians have great power to regenerate lost parts (Figure 120). When an individual is cut in two, the anterior end will grow a new tail and the posterior end a new head. Regeneration in these organisms is used as evidence for the **axial gradient theory.** According to this theory there are different metabolic rates in different regions of the body. The rate is greatest at the anterior end of the gradient and decreases gradually to the posterior end. The metabolic activity of any fragment will depend upon its position with respect to this axial gradient. Metabolic activity is measured by the amount of oxygen consumed and the amount of carbon dioxide given off. In any fragment a head will develop where metabolic activity is greatest, while a tail

will develop from that part in which the rate is lowest.

In addition to regenerating lost parts planarians may be grafted or cut in such ways as to produce freakish designs, such as two heads or two tails.

Recent work on regeneration reveal that when a planarian is cut across, free cells (neoblasts) from the mesenchym migrate to the cut surface and aggregate there to form a blastema, which develops into the new part. X-radiation of a worm will destroy these neoblasts and no regeneration will occur. It has been suggested that the neoblasts are attracted the cut region by chemical emanations which cease when the blastema is formed.

Behavior. Planarians respond to the same kinds of stimuli mentioned in the discussion of other animals. Their ventral surfaces are positively thigmotactic whereas their dorsal surfaces are negatively thigmotactic. Flowing-water planarians are positively rheotactic; pond-dwelling forms usually do not react water currents. Weak mechanical chemical stimuli applied to the head will cause the animal to react positively by turning toward the stimulus. When strong stimulus is applied to the posterior parts of the body, it moves rapidly forward. Planarians also respond in a positive way to the juices of foods, especially those of meat or liver. They avoid strong light and will seek out dark or dim lighted regions. With their eyespots they can detect light and the direction it comes from. They are more active at night than during the day. The auricular lobes appear to be sensitive to both water currents and chemical stimuli. In general their reactions to water currents (rheotaxis) depends upon their normal habitat. Those from flowing water are usually positively rheotactic; those from still water will not react or else are positively rheotactic to weak currents only.

The behavior patterns of flatworms have been the subject of numerous investigations all over the world, for animal behaviorists have considered them to be the lowest group that show any capacity for

_____
*Refer to Chapter 5, Principle 24.

194

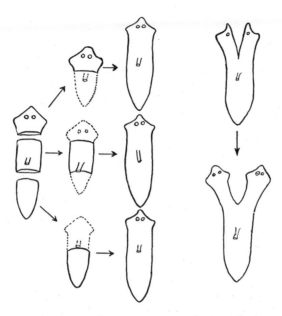

Figure 120. Regeneration in planarian. When cut transversely into three separate pieces as shown at left, each piece develops into little planarian. If head is split (shown at right), a double-headed animal results.

...arning in response to simple conditioned ...anges.

CLASS TREMATODA

The flukes or trematodes are all para-...tic (usually in vertebrates), are chiefly ...aflike in form, and do not have cilia in ...e adult condition. Although parasitic, ...ey are not, as a rule, much different ...ructurally from the nonparasitic turbel-...rians. Some of their parasitic adapta-...ons are the lack of an epidermis, the ...resence of a noncellular cuticle resting ...irectly on mesenchyme, and the develop-...ent of special adhesive organs for cling-...g to their host, such as glandular or ...uscular discs, hooks, and true suckers. ...hey retain also some of the turbellarian ...aracteristics, such as a well-developed ...imentary canal (but with the mouth at ...e anterior or cephalic end) and similar ...productive, excretory, and nervous sys-...ms, as well as a musculature and mesen-...yme which are only slightly modified ...om those of the Turbellaria. Sense or-...ns are poorly developed in flukes and ...ccur only in larval stages and in a few ...ults (eyespots in order Monogenea).

Just as in Turbellaria, the body shows many variations among the different groups. Although basically they all have the flattened form of flatworms, some are round, some are elongated and oval, and others are slender.

According to their parasitic habits class Trematoda is divided into two main orders or subclasses, the Monogenea and the Digenea. The monogenetic flukes require only one host for their life history, whereas the digenetic ones require two to four hosts.

The members of the order Monogenea are mostly ectoparasites. They live on the gills or skin or in cavities that open to the exterior (nose, mouth, urinary bladder) of vertebrates, such as fish, amphibians, reptiles, and rarely mammals. Some are found on invertebrates, such as crusta-ceans and cephalopods. Only one or two species are endoparasites. All of them de-velop directly on one host. Adhesive structures are found at both ends of the worm, but the posterior adhesive organ is usually a complex of hooks and suckers. Unlike the order Digenea, the mouth is rarely encircled by a sucker. Their repro-

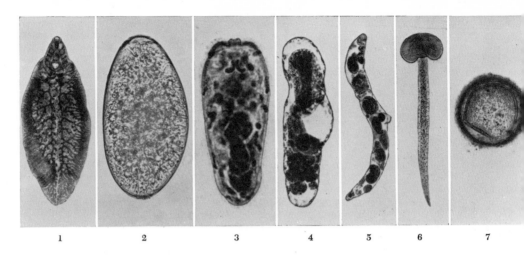

Figure 121. Stages in life cycle of sheep liver fluke, *Fasciola hepatica* (class Trematoda, order Digenea). **1**, Adult; **2**, egg; **3**, miracidium; **4**, sporocyst; **5**, redia; **6**, cercaria; **7**, metacercaria. (Courtesy Carolina Biological Supply Co., Elon College, N. C.)

ductive system is similar to the turbellarians, especially that of rhabdocoeles. Their eggs are few in number and frequently only one egg is present in the uterus. The egg hatches a ciliated larva which attaches itself to the host to develop, or the larva may in some cases swim around in the water before its attachment. The best-known monogenetic genera are *Polystoma,* which is found in the urinary bladder of frogs, and *Gyrodactylus,* which lives on the skin and gills of fresh-water fish. Monogenetic flukes damage fish by feeding on epithelial cells and blood, often producing fatal injury to the gills. They move by leechlike or measuring-worm methods, alternately attaching their anterior and posterior adhesive organs.

The order Digenea is almost exclusively endoparasitic, having two or more hosts in the life cycle. They rarely have more than two suckers and are without hooks. The anterior or oral sucker surrounds the mouth; the ventroposterior sucker is commonly called the **acetabulum.** The latter is quite large in some flukes and may be important in taxonomic determinations. Internal structures are similar to the turbellarians with certain modifications. The pharynx is an-

terior with two long branches of the intestine which end blindly. Digenetic trematode development involves a succession of forms which live in certain organs of different hosts. Their life cycle may be described as the alternation of a bisexual generation (chiefly in vertebrates) with parthenogenetic generations (in invertebrates). The adults are found mainly in terrestrial, fresh-water, and marine vertebrates. Various species are found only in certain organs, such as the intestine, lungs, bile passages, kidneys, urinary bladder, coelom, head cavities, etc. It is an extensive group, and new species are described frequently. They have the most complicated life histories in the animal kingdom. They usually have four larval stages: miracidium, sporocyst, redia, and cercaria. Another stage, the metacercaria (or adolescaria), is considered a juvenile fluke with the general structural features of the adult. Of the larval stages the miracidium nearly always enters a mollusk (bivalve or snail) as the first intermediate host. However, in 1944 the American investigator, Martin, found the rare exception—the sporocysts and cercaria of a certain fluke developed in a polychaete annelid *(Eupomatus)* instead of a mollusk. The larval stages may also

196

be abbreviated, as when cercariae arise directly from sporocysts without the intervention of the redia stage.

Examples of Digenea are often studied because of their complicated life histories and their economic importance. Some of our most serious parasites belong to this group. One of the first digenetic forms to be worked out was the sheep liver fluke, *Fasciola hepatica,* which is often used as a type for study. However, other flukes that attack man are of more practical importance and are more easily studied than the sheep liver fluke.

Opisthorchis (Figure 122) is the most important liver fluke of man and is very common in many regions of the Orient, especially in China, Indo-China, and Japan. In addition to man, cats, dogs, and pigs are often infected. This fluke has two intermediate hosts for the larval stages and a final host for the adult.

Opisthorchis (Clonorchis) sinensis— liver fluke of man

Structure. The worms vary from 10 to 20 mm. in length and from 2 to 4 mm. in width (Figure 122). They have two small suckers, an anterior oral sucker and a ventral **acetabulum** about one-third of the distance from the anterior end. They are covered externally by a rough cuticle (cuticula). The **digestive system** consists of a globular pharynx and a muscular esophagus followed by two long, unbranched intestinal ceca which extend almost to the posterior end of the body. The **excretory** system consists of two protonephridial tubules with branches provided with flame cells or bulbs. The two tubules unite to form a single median one which opens to the outside. The **nervous system,** like that of turbellarians, is made up of two cerebral ganglia connected to longitudinal cords which have transverse

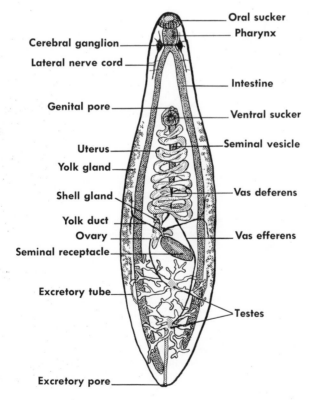

Figure 122. Human liver fluke, *Opisthorchis (Clornorchis) sinensis.* General structure of adult (dorsal view).

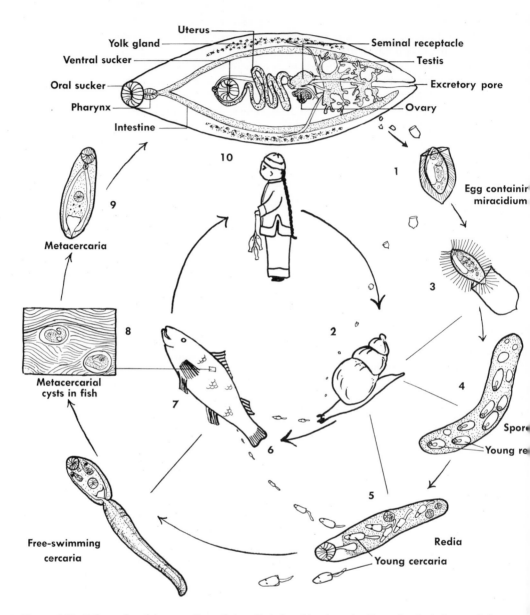

Adult Opisthorchis sinensis

Figure 123. Life cycle of human liver fluke, *Opisthorchis sinensis*. Egg, **1**, shed from adult trematode, **10**, in bile ducts of man is carried out of the body in feces, is ingested by snail (*Bythinia*), **2**, in which the miracidium, **3**, hatches and becomes mother sporocyst, **4**. Young rediae are produced in sporocyst, grow, **5**, and in turn produce young cercariae. Cercariae now leave snail, **6**, find a fish host, **7**, and burrow under scales to encyst in muscle, **8**. When raw or improperly cooked fish containing cysts is eaten by man, metacercaria is released, **9**, enters bile duct where it matures, **10**, to shed eggs into feces, **1**, thus completing cycle.

198

onnectives. The **muscular system** also is ke the planarian type—an outer circular, middle longitudinal, and an inner diagnal layer. The **reproductive system** is ermaphroditic and complicated. The ale system is made up of two muchranched testes, from each of which runs vas efferens. The two vasa efferentia nite to form a single vas deferens which idens into a seminal vesicle. To the eminal vesicle a protrusible penis or a irrus sac is attached within the genital pening. The **female system** contains a ightly branched ovary from which the hort oviduct runs to the centrally placed hell gland which also receives the yolk ucts from the yolk glands. Connected to e oviduct is a seminal receptacle. From e shell gland the much-convoluted terus runs to the genital pore. Cross-ferlization is the usual method of fertilizg the eggs. Two flukes in copulation ring their genital pores in opposition and rtilize each other's ova. After the ova ave received yolk and a shell, they pass hrough the genital pore.

Life cycle. The normal habitat of the dults is in the bile passageways of man Figure 123). The eggs, each containing complete **miracidium,** are shed into the ater with the feces but do not hatch ntil they are ingested by the snail, *ythinia* or related genera. The eggs, howver, may live for some weeks in the ater. In the snail the miracidium enters e tissues and is transformed into the **porocyst** (a baglike structure with emryonic germ cells) which produces one eneration of **rediae.** The redia is elonated, with an alimentary canal, a nervus system, an excretory system, and many erm cells in the process of development. he rediae pass into the liver of the snail here, by a process of internal budding, hey give rise to the tadpolelike **cercariae.** he cercariae escape into the water, wim about until they meet with fish of he family Cyprinidae, and then bore nto the muscles or under the scales. Here he cercariae lose their tails and encyst as etacercariae. If man eats raw infected sh, the metacercarial cyst dissolves par-

tially in the stomach and completely in the intestine, and the metacercariae are free to migrate up the bile duct, where they become adults. Here the flukes may live for fifteen to thirty years. The effect of the flukes on man depends mainly upon the extent of the infection. A heavy infection may cause a marked cirrhosis of the liver and result in death. Cases are diagnosed through fecal examinations. One interesting diagnostic aspect is the high eosinophil (white corpuscle of the blood) count in those infected. To avoid infection, all fish used as food should be thoroughly cooked. Destruction of the snails which carry larval stages would be a method of control.

Schistosoma—blood flukes

Three important species of blood flukes belong to genus *Schistosoma.* Infection by these flukes is called **schistosomiasis,** a disorder very common in Africa, China, and parts of South America. The old generic name was *Bilharzia,* and the infection was called **bilharziasis.** The blood flukes differ from most other flukes in being dioecious and having the two branches of the digestive tube united into a single tube in the posterior part of the body. The male is usually broader and encloses the very slender female (Figure 124) in his gynecophoric canal, a ventral fold on the body.

The plan of the life history of blood flukes is similar in all species. Eggs are discharged in human feces or urine; if they get into water they hatch out as ciliated **miracidia** which must contact a certain kind of snail within twenty-four hours to survive. When they find the right snail they burrow into the soft flesh and transform into **sporocysts,** which develop **cercariae** directly without the formation of rediae. These cercariae have two suckers, a forked enteron, an excretory system with flame cells, and a forked tail. They escape from the snail and swim about in the water until they come in contact with the bare skin of a human being bathing or wading. They penetrate through the skin into a blood vessel, which they follow to

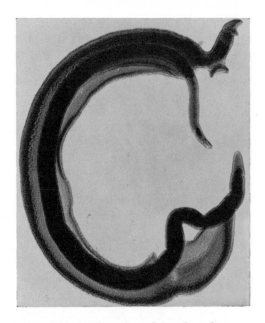

Figure 124. Adult male and female *Schistosoma mansoni* in copulation. Male has long sex canal which holds female during insemination and oviposition. In photograph, female is darker individual. Man usually host of adult parasites, found mainly in Africa but also in South America and elsewhere. Man becomes infected by wading or bathing in cercaria-infested waters. (AFIP No. 56-3334.)

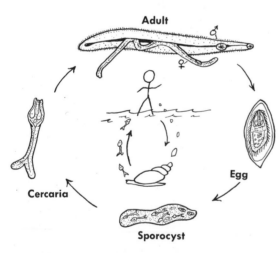

Figure 125. Life history of blood fluke. An egg discharged in human feces passes into water and hatches into miracidium (shown enclosed in egg) which enters a snail and transforms into a sporocyst. Cercariae escape from snail and penetrate exposed skin of man to enter blood stream.

200

the blood vessels of certain regions, depending upon the kind of fluke. When they enter with drinking water they may bore through the mucous membrane of the mouth or throat, but they do not survive in the stomach.

No encysted metacercarial stage is found, for the cercariae lose their tail as they enter the host, and by the time they settle down they have transformed into the adult condition. When the eggs are fertilized, the female leaves the male gynecophoric canal and goes into small blood vessels where she lays the eggs. The ova may be provided with spines (Figure 126) which facilitate their penetration into the intestine or urinary bladder. By the time these ova reach the exterior, they have within them fully formed miracidia.

Following is a comparison of the three species— S. *haematobium,* S. *mansoni,* and S. *japonicum.*

Schistosoma haematobium. This species is found chiefly in Africa and is one of the most dangerous of the blood flukes. The adults (the male being about 10 to 15 mm. long) live in the blood vessels of the bladder and urinary tract. The eggs have sharp spines which enable them to pass through the walls of the blood vessels into the urine. Lacerations of the mucous membrane of the bladder are caused by the passage of these eggs, and bloody urine results. Inflammation of the bladder also frequently occurs, and the ova may also serve as nuclei for kidney stones. The eggs escape in the urine and, if snails of genus *Bulinus* are available, the miracidia will enter them and start the life cycle. Infections with these flukes are very common, for in the regions where they are found the poor hygienic conditions of the people promote the spread of *Schistosoma.*

Schistosoma mansoni. This species is common in the West Indies, parts of South America, and Egypt. The adults live chiefly in branches of the portal and mesenteric veins. The ova have sharp lateral spines and escape into the intestine, from which they are discharged with the feces. A number of different kinds of snails, in

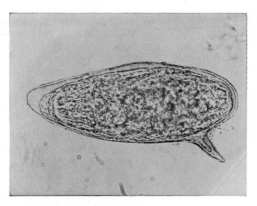

Figure 126. Egg of *Schistosoma mansoni*. (Courtesy Ward's Natural Science Establishment, Inc., Rochester, N. Y.)

cluding the common genus *Planorbis*, seem to be the intermediate host. Symptoms of this form of **schistosomiasis** are severe dysentery and anemia.

Schistosoma japonicum. These flukes often cause a lot of trouble in Japan, China, and the Philippines. The life history is similar to that of the other blood flukes. The adults live in the small veins of the superior and inferior mesenteric vessels. Infection with these causes liver enlargement, formation of ulcers, and disturbances in the spleen. The chief intermediate host is the snail *Oncomelania*.

Schistosoma dermatitis (swimmer's itch). Bathers in northern lakes, such as those of Michigan, Wisconsin, and Canada, often suffer from a skin irritation that is now known to be caused by cercariae of *Schistosoma*. It is detected soon after the bather leaves the water and is felt as a prickling sensation. After an hour or so the irritation subsides, to return as severe itching with edema and pustules. The reaction reaches its climax by the second or third day, but the infection may last longer. Infection is most common in July and August. Summer resorts in some regions have had to close because of these infections.

Several species of cercariae are known to cause these infections. Infections of man are purely accidental attempts of the flukes to penetrate man's skin and use him as a host, but it is a "dead end" for the cercariae, for none are known to survive. Many species of snails serve as intermediate hosts and aquatic birds are the final hosts. Destroying the snails near beaches by copper sulfate helps control infections. Soothing applications are helpful in treating this type of dermatitis. Wiping the body thoroughly and quickly after leaving the water has been recommended, for some think the cercariae enter the skin as the water evaporates, but the efficacy of this preventive treatment has been disputed by some parasitologists.

Paragonimus westermani—lung flukes

Lung flukes are found in many parts of the Orient and to some extent in America. One of the most common is *Paragonimus westermani* (Figure 127) which uses the

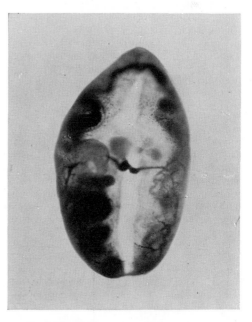

Figure 127. Pulmonary fluke, *Paragonimus westermani*, infects human lung, producing paragonimiasis. Adults are up to ½ inch long. Eggs discharged in sputum or feces hatch into free-swimming miracidia. Miracidia enter snails in which sporocyst and redia stages are passed. Cercariae emerge from snail, eventually enter viscera and muscles of fresh-water crabs. Here they encyst in soft tissues. Man infected by eating raw crabs or by drinking water containing larvae freed from dead crabs. Infection common in parts of Orient. (AFIP No. 52-1862.)

carnivorous mammals, such as mink, cats, dogs, etc., as the definitive host. It is also the only species of lung fluke known to infect man. In China, Korea, and Japan human infection may reach 40 to 50% in some regions. In the United States it appears to be most common in the Great Lakes area. The life history involves snails, fresh-water crabs, and crayfish as intermediate hosts and man and mammals as the final hosts. Ova are coughed up in the sputum, and under moist conditions the miracidia develop in three weeks. After entering certain species of snails they develop a sporocyst and two generations of rediae. The cercariae, after leaving the snail, crawl about and encyst in fresh-water crabs and crayfish. Whenever man eats poorly cooked crustaceans, the ingested flukes pass through the intestinal walls into the abdominal cavity, then through the diaphragm into the lungs. Here they exist as adults, which may be about 20 mm. long.

Other trematodes

Fasciola hepatica (liver fluke of sheep). This fluke (Figure 121) is responsible for "liver rot" in sheep and other ruminants. It lives in the liver and bile passageways and may attain a length of 30 mm. Although often used as a type for studying the Digenea, it must be considered somewhat atypical because of the much-branched intestine and other structural differences. The undeveloped eggs are shed in the feces in damp surroundings and in the course of some weeks develop into ciliated miracidia. If the miracidia find a certain snail *(Lymnaea)* within eight

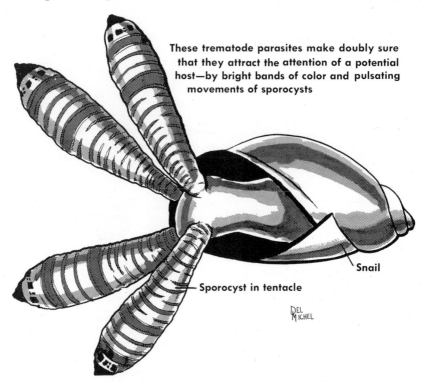

These trematode parasites make doubly sure that they attract the attention of a potential host—by bright bands of color and pulsating movements of sporocysts

Sporocyst in tentacle

Snail

DEL MICHEL

Figure 128. *Leucochloridium,* trematode found in birds and snails. Snails, *Succinea,* eat vegetation infected with capsules from bird droppings. Capsules hatch into miracidia followed by generations of sporocysts. Sporocysts branch and enter snail's head and tentacles, where they enlarge, become brightly colored with orange and green bands, and pulsate at frequent intervals. This attracts attention of birds, which eat them. Thus color and movement combine to ensure complete life history.

hours, they penetrate into the soft tissues. The miracidium is transformed into a sporocyst which produces two generations of rediae. The rediae give rise to cercariae which burrow out of the snail and swim in the water. In a short time the cercariae encyst on aquatic vegetation as metacercariae. When the infested vegetation is eaten by the definitive host (sheep or other ruminant) the cysts hatch into young flukes which burrow through the intestinal wall and body cavity to the liver. There have been some cases of human infection.

Fasciolopis buski (intestinal fluke of man). This fluke is a common parasite of man and pigs in India and China. The leaflike adult may be 70 mm. long. Larval stages occur in snails of the genera *Planorbis* and *Segmentina*. The cercariae encyst on certain nutlike fruits of aquatic vegetation (water chestnut) which are eaten raw by man.

CLASS CESTODA

The third class of Platyhelminthes is Cestoda, the tapeworms. The members of this class differ in many respects from those of the preceding classes: their long flat bodies are usually made up of many sections, or **proglottids,** and there is a complete lack of epidermis and digestive system. They have no cilia, are covered with a thick cuticle, and possess well-developed muscles. They have an excretory system and a nervous system somewhat similar to those of other flatworms. They are all monoecious with the exception of the genus *Dioecocestus*. They have no special sense organs but do have free sensory nerve endings. One of their most specialized structures is the **scolex,** or holdfast, which is the organ of attachment. It is provided with a varying number of suckers, and, in some cases, also with hooks. All members of this class are endoparasites, and all, with a few exceptions, involve at least two hosts of different species. The adults are always found in vertebrates; other stages may be found in either vertebrates or invertebrates.

Class Cestoda is divided into two subclasses, Cestodaria and Eucestoda. Subclass Cestodaria is made up of forms that have undivided bodies and no scolices but are provided with some organ of attachment, such as a rosette or proboscis. They have only one set of reproductive organs and give rise to ten-hooked larvae. Most of them are found as parasites in lower fish. *Amphilina foliacea* is a common type. Subclass Eucestoda is composed of members that have the body divided (rarely undivided) into proglottids and are provided with a scolex. Their

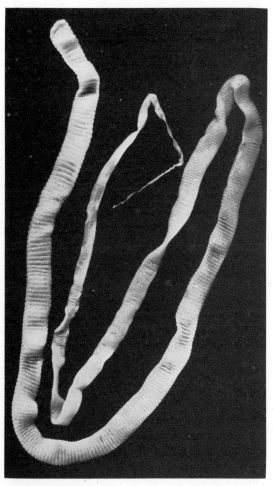

Figure 129. Section of sheep tapeworm, *Moniezia expansa*. Note progressive increase in size. Young proglottids are budded from scolex and neck (center); oldest (gravid) proglottids shown at upper left.

larval forms have only six hooks. This subclass contains the typical tapeworms, of which the beef tapeworm (*Taenia saginata*) is an example (Figure 131).

Is the tapeworm a single animal with subdivided parts (proglottids), or is it a series of separate individuals loosely held together like a colony? Is it a true segmented animal like the annelids or arthropods? Zoologists differ in their interpretation of these points. Although the tapeworm forms its segments from the proliferation of the scolex and the true segmented animals from the proliferation of the region just in front of the anal segment, this difference is considered unimportant by some. From this viewpoint cestodes would be considered segmented rather than colonial.

The scolex may be regarded as the an-

cestral individual which gives rise by strobilation to daughter individuals, the proglottids. The scolex, or holdfast organ, is not a head specialized for perceiving or food handling, and some zoologists think it is really the original posterior end which has been modified for attachment, but embryology does not support this view. As long as the scolex is present, it is impossible to get rid of a tapeworm, for new proglottids will be formed as the old ones are shed. A proglottid is a sexually complete unit, for it is hermaphroditic. Its chief function is the production of ova, and its structure is specialized toward this end.

Taenia saginata—beef tapeworm

Structure. The beef tapeworm lives as an adult in the alimentary canal of man

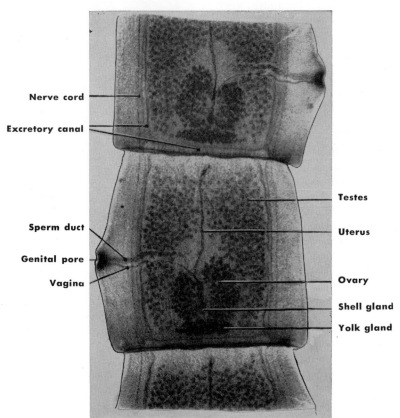

Nerve cord

Excretory canal

Sperm duct

Genital pore

Vagina

Testes

Uterus

Ovary

Shell gland

Yolk gland

Figure 130. Photomicrograph of mature proglottid of *Taenia pisiformis,* dog tapeworm. Portions of two other proglottids also shown. (Courtesy General Biological Supply House, Chicago).

204

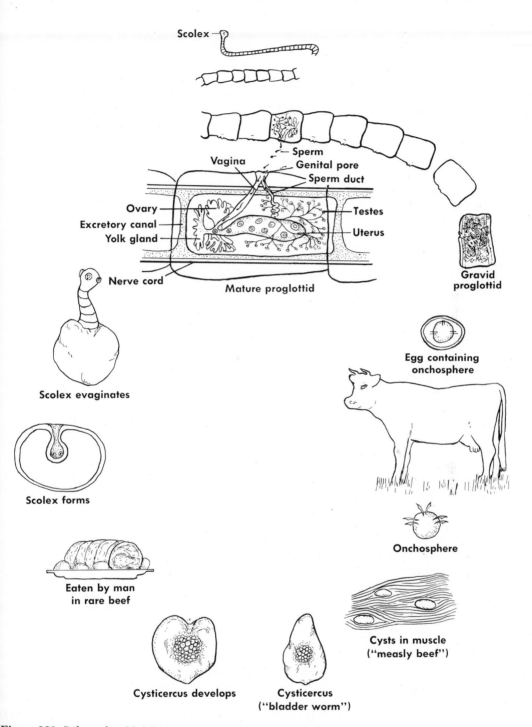

Figure 131. Life cycle of beef tapeworm, *Taenia saginata*. Ripe proglottids break off in man's intestine, pass out in feces, and are ingested by cows. Eggs hatch in cow's intestine, freeing onchospheres which penetrate into muscles and encyst, developing into "bladder worms." Man eats infected rare beef and cysticercus is freed in intestine where it develops, forms a scolex, attaches to intestine wall, and matures.

whereas the larval form is found primarily in the intermuscular tissue of cattle. The mature adult may reach a length of 30 feet or more. Its **scolex** has four **suckers** but no hooks. Back of the suckers is a short neck which connects the scolex to the body, or **strobila,** which may be made up of as many as 2,000 **proglottids.** The scolex is the attachment organ and by means of the suckers is firmly fastened to the intestinal wall. New proglottids are formed by **transverse budding** of the neck region. As they move backward, the proglottids increase in size, so that the proglottids are narrow near the scolex and broader and larger toward the posterior end, where they are finally detached and shed in the feces. The youngest and smallest proglottid is therefore nearest the scolex and the oldest one at the posterior end.

The tapeworm shows some unity in its organization (Figure 130), for **excretory canals** in the scolex are also connected to the canals, two on each side, in the proglottids, and two **longitudinal nerve cords** from a **nerve ring** in the scolex run back into the proglottids also. Attached to the excretory ducts are the **flame cells.** Each proglottid also contains **muscles** and **parenchyma** as well as a complete set of **male and female organs** similar to those of a trematode. Ova may be fertilized by the sperm of the same proglottid, from other proglottids of the same individual, or from other tapeworms if more than one should be present. As the terminal proglottids with their eggs break off and pass with the feces, the proglottids disintegrate and the eggs with the embryos may be scattered on the soil, grass, dust, etc., where they may be picked up by grazing cattle.

Life cycle. When cattle swallow the eggs or proglottids, the egg shells are dissolved off in the intestine, and the six-hooked larvae (**oncospheres**) burrow through the intestinal wall into the blood or lymph vessels and finally reach voluntary muscle, where they encyst to become **bladder worms** (**cysticerci**). Here in a period of ten to twenty weeks the larvae

develop an invaginated scolex with suckers and remain quiescent until the uncooked muscle is eaten by man or other suitable host. Such infected meat is known as "measly" meat (Figure 132). When the cyst wall is dissolved off by the digestive juices of the host, the bladder disappears, the scolex evaginates and becomes attached to the intestinal mucosa, and new proglottids begin to develop. It takes two or three weeks for a mature worm to form. When man is infected with one of these tapeworms, many single proglottids are expelled daily from his intestine. Usually only one tapeworm infects a host; an immunity against others is apparently established. Man usually becomes infected by eating rare steaks and hamburgers. In the southwest (Arizona and New Mexico), where barbecued meat is popular, a considerable percentage of the people may be infected. About 1% of American cattle are infected, and since a great deal of meat is consumed without government inspection, a certain amount of tapeworm infection must be expected.

Other tapeworms

More than a thousand species of tapeworms are known to parasitologists. Almost all vertebrates are infected. Nearly all tapeworms have an intermediate host and a final host which is infected by preying upon the former. Some of these tapeworms do considerable harm to the host by absorbing nourishment and by secreting toxic substances, but unless present in large numbers, they are rarely fatal.

Some of the more common ones are *Taenia solium, Diphyllobothrium latum, Dipylidium caninum, Hymenolepis nana, Echinococcus granulosus, Moniezia expansa,* and *Taenia pisiformis.*

Taenia solium (pork tapeworm). The adult lives in the small intestine of man, whereas the larvae live in the muscles of the pig. Adults may be 20 feet or longer. The scolex (Figure 133) of *T. solium* differs from that of *T. saginata* in having both suckers and hooks arranged on its tip, the **rostellum.** More than 1,000 proglottids may be in a single tapeworm. The

206

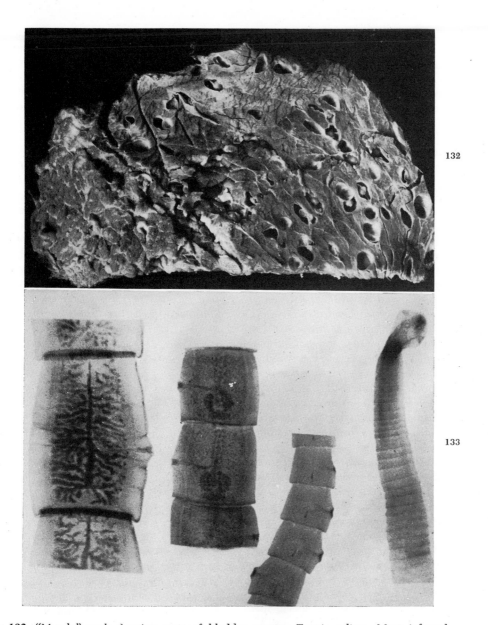

132

133

Figure 132. "Measly" pork showing cysts of bladder worms, *Taenia solium*. Meat infected with beef tapeworm has similar appearance.

Figure 133. Pork tapeworm, *Taenia solium*. Scolex shown at right. Note genital pores on larger segments, and, in gravid segment on left, note uterus distended with eggs. (Photograph of stained preparation.)

life history of this tapeworm is similar to that of the beef tapeworm. Man becomes infected by eating improperly cooked pork. The incidence of infection is much lower than that of the beef tapeworm.

It is also possible for the larvae or bladder worms to develop in man, although this is not the normal procedure. If eggs or proglottids are ingested by man or broken-up proglottids from an adult tapeworm are carried back by reverse peristalsis to the stomach, the liberated embryos may migrate into any of several organs, including the brain. Disorders from these causes are called **cysticercosis.** One form of this may cause epilepsy.

Diphyllobothrium latum (fish tapeworm). The adult tapeworm is found in the intestine of man, dog, and cat; the immature stages are in crustaceans, such as *Cyclops,* and fish. This tapeworm, often called the broad tapeworm of man, is the largest and most destructive of the cestodes that infect man. It sometimes reaches a length of 60 feet and may have more than 3,000 proglottids. After the eggs are discharged in water by the human host, they hatch into a ciliated **coracidium** which is swallowed by the first intermediate host, a crustacean *(Cyclops).* The coracidium loses its cilia in this host and undergoes other changes. When the crustacean is eaten by the second intermediate host, a fish, the larva penetrates the stomach walls and migrates to the muscles, where it develops into a **plerocercoid** larva about 1 inch long. Usually the larva encysts in the muscle. When raw or poorly cooked fish is eaten by man or other suitable host, the larva is liberated and grows into adult form. It has been known to live in man for many years. Broad tapeworm infections are found all over the world; in the United States infections are most common in the Great Lakes region.

Dipylidium caninum (dog tapeworm). This is a very common tapeworm in pet dogs and cats and sometimes in children. It may be 1 foot or more in length and has about 200 proglottids. The larval form is found in the louse and flea of dogs. The dog or cat becomes infected by licking or biting these ectoparasites. It takes about two weeks for the worm to mature.

Hymenolepis nana (dwarf tapeworm). This is the smallest of human tapeworms and is very common in the United States. In some parts of the country the incidence runs as high as 5%. No intermediate host is necessary. The adults are ½ to 2 inches long and have 100 to 200 proglottids. After the eggs have been ingested, the larval forms (**oncospheres**) are liberated and penetrate the intestinal mucosa, where they are transformed into cysticercoid larvae. After a few days they re-enter the lumen of the intestine, evaginate their heads, become attached, and mature. Unsanitary toilet habits will cause superinfection. The tapeworm is also found in rats and other rodents.

Echinococcus granulosus (hydatid worm) (Figure 134). The adult is found in the dog, wolf, and a few other animals; the larvae, in more than forty species of mammals, including man, monkeys, cat, sheep, and cattle. Man thus serves as an intermediate host in the case of this tapeworm. The adults are only 5 or 6 mm. long and are composed of a scolex and four proglottids. The larval stages do most of the harm in the life cycle, for the cysticer-

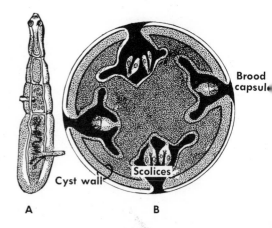

Figure 134. *Echinococcus granulosus,* dog tapeworm which may be dangerous to man. **A,** Adult tapeworm. **B,** Early cyst. Small adult (5 to 10 mm.) lives in intestine of dogs and some other carnivores. Bladder worm stage found in cattle, sheep, hogs, sometimes man, producing hydatid disease. Man acquires disease by unsanitary habits in association with dogs. Human cases reported from central Europe, Australia, South Africa, and Argentina and some 500 cases in the United States. When eggs are ingested by intermediate host, liberated larvae usually encyst in liver. Brood capsules containing scolices are formed from inner layer of each cyst. Cyst enlarges, developing other cysts with brood pouches. May grow for years, to size of orange, necessitating surgery.

208

us forms what is known as a **hydatid cyst.** These cysts are usually formed in the liver but may be found in other organs. Some of them are 2 or 3 inches in diameter in man and may produce death by their pressure and other effects. Wherever a cyst is formed it slowly enlarges by the continuous formation of brood capsules, each of which buds off many scolices internally. Many cases of hydatid cysts are reported each year in the United States. Man probably gets his infections from ingesting the eggs of a tapeworm eliminated by a dog.

Moniezia expansa (sheep tapeworm). The adult is found in sheep and goats (Figure 129); the larva in a small mite (*Galumna*).

Taenia pisiformis (dog tapeworm). This is widely used as a type for study in the laboratory (Figure 130).

Derivation and meaning of basic terminology

Acoela (Gr. *a*, without, + *koilos*, hollow) These worms have no enteron.

Alloeocoela (Gr. *alloios*, different, + *koilos*, hollow) Order of turbellarians.

cercaria (Gr. *kerkos*, tail) Tadpolelike larva of trematodes.

Cestoda (Gr. *kestos*, girdle) The tapeworm looks like a ribbon.

Digenea (Gr. *dis*, double, + *genos*, race) Subclass (Trematoda). These flukes require two or more hosts for their complete development.

Diphyllobothrium (Gr. *dis*, double, + *phyllon*, leaf, + *bothrion*, hole) Genus (Cestoda). The scolex of these tapeworms has only two suckers instead of four, which is the number commonly found.

Dugesia (formerly called *Euplanaria* but changed by priority to *Dugesia* after Dugès who first described the form in 1830). Genus (Trematoda).

Echinococcus (Gr. *echinos*, spiny, + *coccus*, berry) Genus (Cestoda). The multiple scolices give a spiny and berrylike appearance to the dangerous tapeworm larval cysts.

fluke (AS. *floc*, flat) A member of class Trematoda.

Monogenea (Gr. *monas*, single, + *genos*, race) Subclass (Trematoda). Only one host required for development.

Opisthorchis (Gr. *opistho*, behind, + *orchis*, testis) Genus (Trematoda). Testes are located in the posterior part of the body.

Paragonimus (Gr. *para*, beside, + *gonimos*, generative) Genus (Trematoda). Refers to the position of the reproductive organs. Testes lie side by side and the ovary lies opposite the uterus.

Platyhelminthes (Gr. *platys*, flat, + *helmins*, worm).

Polycladida (Gr. *poly*, many, + *klados*, branch) Order of turbellarians which have intestines of many branches.

proglottid (Gr. *pro*, before, + *glotta*, tongue) A section of a tapeworm. Dujardin (1843) gave this derivation because of its resemblance to the tip of the tongue.

protonephridium (Gr. *protos*, first, + *nephros*, kidney) Primitive excretory organ of tubule with terminating flame tube or solenocyte.

Rhabdocoela (Gr. *rhabdos*, rod, + *koilos*, cavity) Order of turbellarians that have a straight intestine of smooth contour.

redia (after Francesco Redi, Italian microscopist) Larva stage in the development of trematodes.

rhabdite (Gr. *rhabdos*, rod) Ectodermal rodlike structures in certain turbellarians. May function in slime formation.

rosette (F. little rose) An organ for attachment in the subclass Cestodaria.

rostellum (L. a little beak) Hook-bearing tip of the tapeworm scolex.

Saginata (L. *saginare*, to fatten) Species name of the beef tapeworm. The proglottids have a plump appearance.

Schistosoma (Gr. *schistos*, divided, + *soma*, body) Genus (Trematoda) Male canal in which the female is held gives a split appearance to the body.

scolex (Gr. *skolex*, worm) Term restricted to the so-called head of the tapeworm.

sporocyst (Gr. *spora*, seed, + *kystis*, bladder) One of the larval stages of trematodes.

Taenia (Gr. *tainia*, band, ribbon). Genus (Cestoda).

Trematoda (Gr. *trematodes*, with holes) The suckers give the appearance of holes.

Tricladida (Gr. *treis*, three, + *klados*, branch) Order of turbellarians with three-branched intestines.

Turbellaria (L. *turbella*, a stirring) These worms agitate the mucus in which they swim.

ANNOTATED REFERENCES

Chandler, A. C. 1949. Introduction to Parasitology. New York, John Wiley & Sons, Inc. *Emphasizes many flatworms which infect man. A good and authoritative presentation by one of America's foremost parasitologists.*

Craig, C. F., and E. C. Faust. 1945. Clinical Parasitology, ed. 4. Philadelphia, Lea & Febiger. *A good account of those flatworms that are most often seen in clinical examinations.*

Dawes, B. 1946. The Trematoda With Special Reference to British and Other European Forms. Cambridge, Cambridge University Press. *A rather comprehensive review of the group. An excellent bibliography is included.*

Hyman, L. H. 1951. The Invertebrates: Platyhelminthes and Rhynchocoela. The Acoelomate Bilateria. New York, McGraw-Hill Book Co., Inc. *This is volume two of a projected masterly work. It represents the best-up-to-date account available at present. While it is technical and planned for the advanced student, the beginning student can glean much of profit from certain sections.*

Thomas, A. P. 1883. The Life History of the Liver Fluke (*Fasciola hepatica*). Quart. J Micro. Sc., series 2, vol. 23, pp. 99-133. *This classical work is justly famous, for it represent the first life history of a digenetic trematode to be worked out. The work is also noteworthy because there are simpler trematode life histories than that of Fasciola. It gave a great impetus to work in the field of parisitology.*

Wardle, R. A., and J. A. McLeod. 1952. The Zoology of Tapeworms. Minneapolis, University of Minnesota Press. *A comprehensive account of these highly specialized parasites. It is an indispensable work for investigators in this field.*

chapter 11

Phylum Rhynchocoela
(Nemertina)*

BIOLOGICAL PRINCIPLES

Organ-system level of organization

1. In this group there is a tendency for organs with related functions to be collected into **organ systems.**

2. Division of labor and specialization have developed to the point of breaking up composite systems into separate systems. For instance, the gastrovascular system of Platyhelminthes and Coelenterata is now separated into the distinct blood vascular and digestive systems.

3. Most of the primary features contributed by previous groups are retained, such as bilateral symmetry, three primary germ layers, and cephalization.

4. This phylum belongs to the acoelomate Bilateria and to the Protostomia.

Biological contributions

1. Two important advancements are made beyond the flatworm plan, the closed **blood vascular** and the **digestive systems.**

2. The blood vascular or circulatory system now separates the circulatory function of the gastrovascular cavity and embodies this function within itself.

3. The digestive system is now complete with mouth, enteron, and anus. This produces a one-way traffic of food products, prevents the mixing of freshly ingested food with partly digested food, and provides for the elimination of the indigestible products through an opening of its own, the **anus.**

---

*Ring'ko-se"la, Gr., *rhynchos*, beak, + *koílos*, hollow (nem'er-tin"na, Gr. *nemertes*, unerring one).

4. These two advantages are found in all higher forms and are associated with the progressive complexity of the animal plan.

5. A unique and distinctive character is the **proboscis**, a long hollow organ which protrudes and retracts for food catching or defense.

6. In connection with the circulatory system, some of the nemertines have hemoglobin and red blood.

7. The brain is larger than that of Platyhelminthes and forms a ring around the rhynchodaeum.

8. In contrast to Platyhelminthes, few nemertines are parasites.

Position in animal kingdom

1. The general body plan of the nemertines, with few exceptions, is similar to that of the turbellarians of the flatworm group. Among these similarities are the ciliated epithelium, the lack of a coelom, the excretory system with flame cells, the muscular layers, and the parenchyma layer, enteron, body wall, and rhabdites.

2. The **pilidium larva** of marine nemertines is ciliated with ventral mouth but no anus, which is also a flatworm characteristic.

3. Many zoologists are inclined to place this group as a class under Platyhelminthes, which indicates the close affinity of the two phyla.

4. All the evidence indicates that nemertines arose from an ancestor closely related to the turbellarians and ctenophores.

5. Although there are no external features of metamerism or segmentation in these forms, there is some internal segmentation, such as the repetitive arrangement of the gonads, the intestinal ceca, and secondary blood vessels. This may indicate that the nemertines have followed the annelid plan of evolution.

Phylum Rhynchocoela (Nemertina) 211

6. The group as a whole represents the climax of those animals without a coelom (acoelomate). Animals higher in the scale have a body cavity of some form.

GENERAL RELATIONS

The nemertinean worms are commonly known as ribbon worms. They derive their name from a long, muscular tube known as the **proboscis**, which can be thrust out to grasp the prey and which is supposed to be unerring in its aim (Nemertina, Gr. *nemertes,* unerring one). They were formerly classed under Platyhelminthes, but most zoologists now consider them a separate phylum. They are mostly marine forms, and there are about 500 species in the group. Some are less than an inch long, and others are several feet in length. Their colors are often bright, and almost all hues are represented among the various species.

With few exceptions, the general body plan of the nemertines is similar to that of Turbellaria. Like the latter, their epidermis is covered with numerous short cilia with many gland cells. Another striking line of evidence in favor of their flatworm affinities is the presence of flame cells in the excretory system. Recently, rhabdites have been found in several nemertines, including *Lineus.* However, they differ from Platyhelminthes with respect to their reproductive system. In the marine forms there is a ciliated larva, the **pilidium larva.** This larva has a ventral mouth but no anus—another flatworm characteristic. It also has some resemblance to the trochophore larva which is found in several higher phyla, such as annelids and mollusks. Other flatworm characteristics are the presence of bilateral symmetry, mesoderm, and lack of coelom. All in all, the present evidence seems to indicate that the nemertines came from an ancestral form closely related to Platyhelminthes and Ctenophora.

The nemertines show some advances over the flatworms. One of these is the retractile **proboscis** and its sheath, for which there are no counterparts among Platyhelminthes. Another difference is the presence of an **anus.** Thus these form have a complete digestive system, the first to be found in the animal kingdom. They are also the simplest animals to have a **blood vascular** system, which usually consists of a median dorsal and two lateral trunks. The complete digestive system and the vascular system are also found in higher forms and indicate the early appearance of part of the future basic pattern of animal structure. Most of them are dioecious, and their reproductive systems are much simpler than that of Platyhelminthes.

CHARACTERISTICS

1. Bilateral symmetry; highly contractile body
2. Three germ layers
3. Epidermis with cilia and gland cells; rhabdites in some
4. Body spaces with parenchyma which is partly connective tissue and partly gelatinous
5. An **eversible proboscis** which lies free in a cavity (rhynchocoel) above the alimentary canal
6. **Complete digestive system**
7. Body-wall musculature of outer circular and inner longitudinal layers with diagonal fibers between the two; sometimes another circular layer inside the longitudinal
8. **Blood vascular system with three longitudinal trunks**
9. No regular coelom; rhynchocoel may be considered true coelom
10. Nervous system usually a four-lobed brain connected to paired longitudinal nerve trunks or, in some, mid-dorsal and mid-ventral trunks
11. Excretory system of two coiled canals which are branched with flame cells
12. Sexes separate with simple gonads; asexual reproduction by fragmentation; few hermaphrodites; pilidium larva in some
13. No respiratory system
14. Sensory **ciliated pits or head slits on each side of head,** which communicate between the outside and the

brain; tactile organs and ocelli (in some)

Figure 135. *Amphiporus*, with proboscis extended to catch prey.

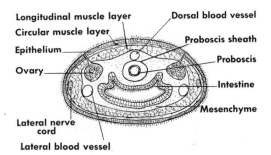

Figure 136. Diagrammatic cross-section of female nemertine worm.

HABITAT

A few of the nemertines are found in moist soil and fresh water, but by far the larger number are marine. At low tide they are often coiled up under stones. It seems probable that they are active at high tide and quiescent at low tide. Some nemertines such as *Cerebratulus* frequent empty mollusk shells. The small species live among seaweed, or they may be found swimming near the surface of the water. Nemertines are often secured by dredging at depths of 15 to 25 feet or deeper. In a few instances they are commensals or parasitic.

CLASSES

Class Enopla (en'o-pla) (Gr. *enoplos,* armed). Proboscis armed with stylets; muscular layer of outer circular and inner longitudinal muscles; no nerve plexus; intestinal ceca; mouth opens in front of brain. Example: *Amphiporus.*

Class Anopla (an'o-pla) (Gr. *anoplos,* unarmed). Proboscis lacks stylets; muscular layer of inner and outer longitudinal and middle circular muscles; nerve plexus present; mouth opens behind brain; intestinal pouches absent or rudimentary. Example: *Cerebratulus.*

REPRESENTATIVE TYPE
CLASS ENOPLA

Most nemertines have a very close resemblance to each other, and almost any one of them, with few exceptions, can be taken as a type. Some are very long and difficult to study in the laboratory because their internal organs are not easily seen. They are slender worms, and when handled they are likely to break into pieces. No group of worms shows a greater diversity in size than do nemertines. *Amphiporus* (Figure 135), which is here taken as the type for description, is one of the smaller ones.

Amphiporus ochraceus— ribbon or band worm

Structure. This worm is from 1 to 3 inches long, with a width of about 1/10 inch. It is dorsoventrally flattened (Fig-

ure 136), with both anterior and posterior ends rounded. The body is composed first of an epidermis of ciliated columnar cells with some of the cells specialized for sensory and mucous functions and all resting on a basement membrane of connective tissue. Just underneath the basement membrane is the **muscle** layer composed of an **inner longitudinal** and an **outer circular** layer. Some nemertines have both an outer and inner circular layer of muscle. Eyes, or **ocelli,** are found on each side of the anterior end. Beneath the body wall and surrounding the visceral organs is the **parenchyma,** which consists partly of connective tissue and partly of a gelatinous substance. On the ventral surface near the front end of the body is the **mouth** with thick tumid lips. Just above the mouth is a small terminal pore, the external opening of the **proboscis.** The proboscis pore opens into a short cavity, the rhynchodaeum, to the inner end of which is attached the anterior end of the proboscis. The latter structure is an eversible organ which can be protruded and retracted through the above-mentioned pore. The proboscis is made up of three

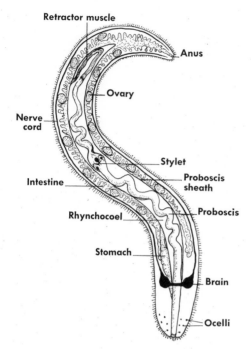

Retractor muscle

Anus

Ovary

Nerve cord

Stylet

Intestine

Proboscis sheath

Rhynchocoel

Proboscis

Stomach

Brain

Ocelli

Figure 137. Structure of nemertine worm, *Amphiporus* (diagrammatic). Dorsal view to show proboscis.

parts—a thick-walled tube, a middle bulbous sac with stylets, and a blind tube. It is contained within a sheath to which it is attached at its anterior end by strong muscles inside the sheath. The proboscis sheath is made up of a muscular wall and a cavity (rhynchocoel) which encloses the proboscis. This rhynchocoel is filled with fluid, and by muscular pressure on this fluid the anterior part of the tubular proboscis is everted or turned inside out. The proboscis apparatus is an invagination of the anterior body wall and its structure therefore duplicates that of the body wall. The retractor muscles attached at the end are used to retract the everted proboscis, very much like everting the tip of a finger of a glove by a string attached to its tip. The proboscis is armed with a sharp-pointed stylet. A frontal gland also opens at the anterior end by a pore.

The **digestive system** is complete and extends straight through the length of the body to the terminal **anus.** The **esophagus**

is straight and opens into a dilated part of the tract, the **stomach.** The blind anterior end of the intestine, as well as the main intestine, is provided with paired **lateral ceca.** Throughout its course the alimentary tract is lined with ciliated epithelium, and in the wall of the esophagus there are cells which are glandular in function. The digestive system lies ventral to the proboscis sheath.

The **blood vascular system** is simple and enclosed, with a single dorsal vessel and two lateral vessels. Both dorsal and lateral vessels are connected together by regularly arranged transverse vessels. All three longitudinal vessels join together anteriorly to form a sort of collar. The blood is colorless, containing nucleated corpuscles, although in some nemertines the blood is red because of the presence of hemoglobin. There is no heart, and the blood is propelled by the muscular walls of the blood vessels and bodily movements.

The **excretory system** contains a pair of lateral tubes with many branches and flame cells. Each lateral tube opens to the outside by one or more pores.

The **nervous system** is composed of four fused ganglia, one pair lying dorsal and one pair ventral to the rhynchodaeum, and united by commissures which pass around it. Five longitudinal nerves extend from the brain posteriorly—a large lateral trunk on each side of the body, paired dorsolateral trunks, and one mid-dorsal trunk. These are connected by a network of nerve fibers. From the brain, anterior nerves run to the proboscis; and peripheral nerves, both sensory and motor, run to the ocelli and other sense organs and to the mouth and esophagus. In addition to the eyes, or ocelli, already mentioned, there are other sense organs, such as tactile papillae, sensory pits and grooves, and probably auditory organs.

In common with most nemertines, *Amphiporus* is dioecious. The gonads in either sex are sacs which lie between the intestinal ceca where they have developed from lateral mesenchyme. From each gonad a short duct (gonopore) runs o the dorsolateral body surface to discharge the sex products to the outside.

Metabolism. The nemertines are carnivorous and very voracious, eating either dead or living prey. In seizing their prey, they thrust out the slime-covered proboscis which quickly ensnares the prey by wrapping around it (Figure 135). The stylet also pierces and holds the prey. Then by retracting the proboscis, the prey is drawn near the mouth and is engulfed by the esophagus which is thrust out to meet it. They do not hesitate to eat each other when they are confined together. Digestion is largely extracellular in the intestinal tube, and when the food is ready for absorption, it passes through the cellular lining of the intestinal tract into the blood vascular system. The indigestible material passes out the anus in contrast to Platyhelminthes, where it leaves by the mouth. Waste is picked up from the mesenchyme spaces and blood by the flame cells and carried by the excretory ducts to the outside. Respiration occurs through the body surface.

Locomotion. Amphiporus can move with considerable rapidity by the combined action of its well-developed musculature and its cilia. It glides mainly against a substratum; some make use of muscular waves in crawling. Some nemertines have the interesting method of protruding the proboscis, attaching themselves by means of the stylet and then drawing the body up to the attached position.

Reproduction. Eggs and sperm are discharged into the water where fertilization occurs. Egg production in the females is usually accompanied by degeneration of the other visceral organs. From the zygote there develops a pilidium larva which is helmet shaped and bears a dorsal spike of fused cilia and a pair of lateral lobes. The entire larva is covered with cilia and has a mouth and alimentary canal but no anus. In some nemertines the zygote develops directly without undergoing metamorphosis. The fresh-water species, *Prostoma rubrum,* is hermaphroditic. A few nemertines are viviparous. Nemertines have great powers of re-

generation. At certain seasons some of them fragment by autotomy, and from each fragment a new individual develops. This is especially noteworthy in the genus *Lineus.* Fragments from the anterior region will produce a new individual more quickly than one from the posterior part, in accordance with the principle of the axial gradient. Sometimes the proboscis is shot out with such force that it is broken off from the body. In such a case a new proboscis is developed within a short time. The severed proboscis behaves very much like an individual worm for some time before it dies. The abundant nerve plexus it possesses may account for this behavior.

Derivation and meaning of basic terminology

Amphiporus (Gr. *amphi,* double, + *porus,* pore) Genus (Enopla). Refers to the mouth and proboscis pores at the anterior end.

Anopla (Gr. *anoplos,* unarmed) These do not have stylets.

Cerebratulus (L. *cerebrum,* the brain) Genus Anopla). Refers to the relatively prominent cerebral ganglia.

Enopla (Gr. *enoplos,* armed) These are provided with stylets on the proboscis.

Nemertina (Gr. *Nemertes,* unerring one) Refers to the proboscis which is thrust out to seize prey.

pilidium (Gr. *pileos,* a cap) Refers to the shape of the larva.

proboscis (Gr. *pro,* before, + *bosko,* to feed).

rhynchodaeum (Gr. *rhynchos,* beak, + *daio,* to divide) Short tubular cavity to which the proboscis is attached in Rhynchocoela. It opens anteriorly by a small pore. It must not be confused with the rhynchocoel in which the proboscis lies.

Rhynchocoela (Gr. *rhynchos,* beak, + *koilos,* hollow) Refers to the proboscis cavity.

stylet (Gr. *stylos,* a stake) Sharp-pointed defense organ on the proboscis.

ANNOTATED REFERENCES

Böhmig, L. 1929. Art. Nemertini. In Kükenthal and Krumbach: Handbuch der Zoologie, vol. 2, part 1, section 3. Berlin, Walter de Gruyter & Co. *One of the best detailed accounts in German.*

Coe, W. R. 1943. Biology of the Nemerteans of the Atlantic Coast of North America. Hartford, Transactions of Connecticut Academy of Arts and Science. *This is only one of many valuable papers on Rhynchocoela by this author.*

Hyman, L. H. 1951. The Invertebrates: Platyhelminthes and Rhynchocoela. The Acoelomate Bilateria. New York, McGraw-Hill Book Co., Inc. *The latest and most comprehensive account of this group yet published.*

Pennak, R. W. 1953. Fresh-Water Invertebrates of the United States. New York, The Ronald Press Co. *An excellent description of the structure and life history of the fresh-water nemertine, Prostoma rubrum.*

chapter 12

Phylum Aschelminthes*

BIOLOGICAL PRINCIPLES

Organ-system level of organization

1. Like the members of Rhynchocoela, this phylum has reached the organ-system level.

2. Since the phylum contains many different groups, there are several diverse structural features within it.

3. The phylum shows an advancement over Rhynchocoela in having a **pseudocoel**, but it does not have a circulatory system.

4. The **tube-within-a-tube** arrangement is now established as a definite pattern of animal organization.

Biological contributions

1. The **pseudocoel** represents one of the earliest appearances of a body cavity, although it is not a true coelom, for it is not lined with mesodermal epithelium.

2. In number of species this phylum may exceed the arthropods, although only a relatively few have been described and named to date.

3. A complete digestive system—mouth, enteron, and anus—is characteristic of most members of this phylum. Modifications of this plan may be found in parasitic forms. The digestive tract consists mostly of endoderm, thus differing from that of higher forms where mesoderm is also present. A complete digestive system provides for a specialized line of separate metabolic functions, so that digestive products and waste food products are not mixed. This plan is necessary for rapidity of growth and size increase found in higher forms.

4. The group as a whole has become adapted to a wide range of ecological niches.

---

*As'kel-min"thes (Gr. *askos,* cavity, + *helmins,* worm).

Position in animal kingdom

With relation to other phyla, the phylogenetic position of this phylum is obscure, for it seems to have few affinities with other major groups. The classes Rotifera and Gastrotricha show some resemblances to the Turbellaria and may have come from a type similar to a primitive flatworm. Within the phylum itself the relationships between the various classes are clearer and form one of the main reasons for grouping them together into the one phylum.

GENERAL RELATIONS

This phylum has been classified in different ways by many authorities. Until recently some of the classes under Aschelminthes were considered as separate phyla. For instance, the rotifers were once included in a phylum of their own, Trochelminthes, and the horsehair worms (Nematomorpha) were placed as a class under phylum Nemathelminthes. The recent tendency is to drop the names of phyla Nemathelminthes and Trochelminthes altogether and to combine them under one phylum, Aschelminthes. This is not altogether arbitrary, for there are evidences of relationship among the varied forms which make up this new phylum.

The proposed name, Aschelminthes, is derived from the Gr. *askos,* cavity, + *helmins,* worm. The animals that make up the group all have some form of pseudocoel, bilateral symmetry, and a wormlike form or a modification of it. Most of them are small, even microscopic, although some of the parasitic nematodes may reach a length of more than a meter. The body is often round or cylindroid, although it is distinctly flattened in some. One of their striking characteristics is the almost universal presence of a thick, tough cuticle which is often molted in some. With few exceptions, the muscles are not arranged in the circular and longitudinal layers found in Platyhelminthes; often only the longitudinal layer is present. They occupy a wide range of habitat distribution. Many are aquatic in both fresh water and marine water; others occupy terrestrial habitats. Although most are free living, some are among the most common of all parasites. Probably all vertebrates and most of the invertebrates are parasitized by one or more kinds of aschelminths. The number of species in this phylum must be very great, although only a relatively few have been named to date in some of its classes, such as the nematodes.

The relations of the Aschelminthes to other major phyla are very obscure. Rotifers and gastrotrichs have often been grouped together because of the similarity between their muscular and excretory systems, but Gastrotricha seems to be more closely related to nematodes in other particulars. Hyman suggests that all three groups may stem from a turbellarian-like ancestor. Within the phylum certain relationships from structural similarities are more revealing. Radial symmetry of the anterior end is pronounced in nematodes, kinorhynchs, and priapulids. Superficial segmentation, especially of the cuticle, is common among most classes. The epidermal cords, one of the characteristic features of nematodes, are also found in modified form in the kinorhynchs, nematomorphs, and priapulids. Nearly all members of Aschelminthes have emphasized longitudinal muscles in their muscular systems. Among all the members of this heterogeneous grouping, perhaps only Priapulida should be considered as a separate phylum.

CHARACTERISTICS

1. Symmetry bilateral; unsegmented; and triploblastic (three germ layers)

2. Size mostly small; some microscopic; a few a meter or more in length

3. Body usually vermiform, cylindroid, or flattened; body wall a **syncytial** or cellular **epidermis** with thickened cuticle; cuticle often ringed with spines and bristles, sometimes molted; **cilia mostly** absent

4. Muscular layers of the body mostly of **longitudinal fibers,** with few exceptions; only Priapulida has definite muscle layers

5. Body cavity an unlined **pseudocoel** (except Priapulida)

6. Digestive system complete with mouth, enteron, and anus; pharynx muscular and well developed; **tube-within-a-tube arrangement;** digestive tract usually only an epithelial tube with **no definite muscle layer**

7. Circulatory and respiratory organs lacking

8. Excretory system of canals and protonephridia (in some); cloaca which receives excretory, reproductive, and digestive products present in some

9. Nervous system of cerebral ganglia or of a circumenteric nerve ring connected to anterior and posterior nerves; sense organs of **ciliated pits,** papillae, bristles, and eyespots (few)

10. Reproductive system of gonads and ducts which may be single or double; sexes nearly always separate, with the male usually smaller than the female; eggs microscopic with chitinous shell

11. Development may be direct or with a complicated life history; cleavage mostly determinate; **cell or nuclear constancy common**

CLASSES

Class **Rotifera** (ro-tif'er-a) (L. *rota*, wheel, + *ferre*, to bear). Aquatic and microscopic; shell-like cuticle (lorica); anterior end with ciliary organ (corona); forked foot with cement gland; digestive system usually complete with grinding organ (mastax); body cavity without lining; excretory system of protonephridia and two canals which empty into a bladder; nervous system of a ganglion with nerves; eyespots; separate sexes, males much smaller than females; parthenogenesis and sexual reproduction; no larval stages; about 1,500 species. Examples: *Asplanchna, Epiphanes (Hydatina), Philodina.*

Class Gastrotricha (gas-trot'ri-cha) (L. *gaster*, stomach, + *trichos*, hair). Aquatic microscopic animals of about the same size as rotifers; no corona; cilia present; cuticle often covered with short, curved, dorsal spines; body usually posteriorly forked with adhesive tubes and glands for attachment; excretory system (when present) of a pair of protonephridia; digestive system complete with mouth surrounded with bristles; nervous system of a ganglion with two main longitudinal nerves; females found only in some species, eggs develop parthenogenetically; some species hermaphroditic; about 100 species. Examples: *Chaetonotus, Macrodasys.*

Class Kinorhyncha (kin'o-rhyn"ca) (Gr. *kineo*, to move, + *rhynchos*, beak) (**Echinodera**). Marine, microscopic animals; body of 13 or 14 rings (zonites); spiny cuticle but no cilia; retractile head with circlet of spines; digestive system complete with distinct lining epithelium in pharynx; pseudocoel with fluid containing amebocytes; excretory system of a pair of tubes and protonephridia; nervous system of a dorsal ganglion in epidermis with a ventral ganglionated nerve cord; eyespots in some; sexes separate with gonads in the form of tubular sacs; penial spicules in males; metamorphosis of several larval stages; about 100 species. Examples: *Centroderes, Echinoderella.*

Class Priapulida (pri'a-pu"li-da) (Gr. *priap*, phallus). Marine forms up to 80 mm. in length; body cylindrical and warty; retractible proboscis with spines and papillae; trunk of body superficially segmented; body wall of cuticle, cellular epidermis, and both circular and longitudinal muscles; digestive system complete and straight; body cavity lined with a nonnucleated membrane; excretory system of a pair of protonephridia made up of solenocytes and opening into the sex ducts; nervous system of a circumenteric ring with ventral nerve cord; ganglionic enlargements lacking; sexes separate; gonads of numerous tubules; urogenital ducts open separately at posterior end of body; development chiefly direct; three species. Example: *Priapulus.*

Class Nematoda (nem'a-to"da) (Gr. *nema*, thread, + *eidos*, form). Aquatic, terrestrial, or parasitic worms; body cylindrical, unsegmented, and elongated; body wall of thick cuticle, syncytial epithelium, longitudinal muscles which are divided into four sections by four longitudinal epidermal cords; no cilia; body cavity an unlined pseudocoel; circulatory and respiratory systems absent; digestive system complete without muscles and glands; excretory system of one or two glandular organs or of canals or of both; nervous system of a circumenteric ring with anterior and posterior nerves; sense organs simple; sexes usually separate with female generally larger than male; gonads single or double; male duct enters cloaca, female duct with separate opening (vulva); penial spicules in male; fertilization internal; development usually direct but life history may be intricate; a few thousand species named, but their number has been estimated to be at least 500,000. Examples: *Ascaris* (intestinal roundworm), *Necator* (hookworm), *Wuchereria* (filarial worm). *Dioctophyma* (giant kidney worm), *Trichinella* (Trichina worm), *Enterobius* (pinworm).

Class Nematomorpha (nem'a-to-mor"pha) (Gr. *nema*, thread, + *morphe*, shape) (**Gordiacea**). Long, slender worms with cylindrical bodies; size from a few millimeters to a meter in length; larval forms parasitic, adults free living; body wall of cuticle bearing small papillae, one-layered epithelium, and longitudinal muscles; no lateral cords; digestive system complete in larvae but degenerate in adults; pseudocoel mostly filled with parenchyma; no circulatory, respiratory, or excretory system; nervous system of a circumenteric ring with a single mid-ventral nerve cord; separate sexes with paired gonads; paired ducts; cloaca in both sexes; development mostly direct. Example: *Paragordius.*

REPRESENTATIVE TYPES
CLASS ROTIFERA

Rotifers are microscopic animals about 0.5 mm. to 1.5 mm. in length. They are found mostly in fresh water, although a few are marine, and some are even parasitic. Their common habitats are sluggish waters, such as that found in ponds, ditches, and gutters, and wet mosses and similar places. They derive their name from the beating of the cilia on the anterior end (corona) of the body, which gives one the impression of rotating wheels. The more than 1,500 species have a world-wide distribution. Some of the rotifers have beautiful colors and odd,

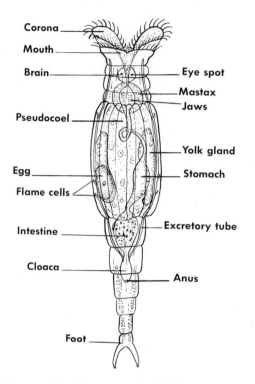

Figure 138. Structure of *Philodina*, common rotifer.

glands which enable the rotifer to cling to objects. The **cuticle** is ringed to simulate segmentation, but there is no lorica in this form. It is fairly easy to see the internal structures of the animal, for it is transparent. Underneath the cuticle is the syncytial **epidermis** with scattered nuclei which secretes the cuticle. Adjacent to the epidermis are the **subepidermal muscles**. These muscles are arranged in a variety of muscle bands which run in different directions, some of them through the pseudocoel. There are no definite muscle layers. Muscles serve to contract the body and to move the foot. The **pseudocoel** is large and occupies the space between the body wall and the viscera. It is filled with a fluid, some of the longitudinal muscle bands, and a network of ameboid or mesenchymal cells. The **digestive** system is made up of the **mouth**, just below the corona; a **buccal tube**; a **pharynx** or **mastax**, a complex muscular, elongated organ which bears the hard **jaws** (trophi) with **teeth** for grinding the food (mainly algae and microscopic forms); a short **esophagus**; an enlarged **stomach** made up of a syncytial wall and provided with circular and longitudinal muscles and a pair of gastric glands; a short **intestine**; the **cloaca**, which receives the intestine and the **oviducts**; and the **anus**, which is the external opening of the cloaca at the dorsal side of the posterior end of the trunk. Most of the digestive tract is ciliated and is of endodermal origin. Enzymes from the gastric glands help in extracellular digestion. The **excretory** system is made up of a pair of protonephridial tubules, each provided with flame bulbs and opening into a common ventral **urinary bladder** which, by pulsating, discharges its contents into the cloaca. The **nervous system** consists of the bilobed **brain**, dorsal to the mastax, which sends nerves to the sensory organs, to the muscles, and to the wall of the mastax. **Sensory** organs are well represented by the paired **eyespots**, by various ciliated pits and papillae, and the fingerlike **dorsal antennae**. Although they are dioecious, no males are known in *Philodina* and the females are partheno-

bizarre shapes. They may be free swimming, colonial, or sessile. Because of their structure and interesting behavior, they have been extensively studied.

Among the many species, *Philodina roseola* and *Epiphanes (Hydatina) senta* are among the best known and have been most studied. As a type description of a rotifer, *Philodina* (Figure 138) may be selected (although there are many variable types), and the following account is based largely on this form.

Philodina

Structure. The body of the rotifer is elongated and cylindrical and is divided into three regions: the broad anterior head provided with two retractile trochal discs (**corona**) with cilia; an elongated and enlarged trunk; and the slender posterior tail, or **foot**, which bears four toes. The body and foot are superficially segmented, the joints of the foot being telescopically retractile. The toes have **cement**

220

genetic. The female **reproductive** system consists of paired **ovaries**, yolk glands or vitellaria, and paired **oviducts** which open into the cloaca. When the eggs are laid they are fastened to some object and hatch in about two days. At hatching, the female has the adult form and reaches sexual maturity in a few days.

In some rotifers, but not in *Philodina*, three kinds of eggs are produced: thin-shelled amictic eggs (diploid number of chromosomes), which always develop parthenogenetically into females; smaller thin-shelled mictic eggs (haploid), which can develop parthenogenetically into males; and thick-shelled dormant eggs, which are fertilized mictic eggs (diploid), which hatch into amictic females. Amictic eggs are produced only by one kind of female and mictic eggs only by another kind of female. However, both kinds of females look alike and are diploid. The fertilized dormant egg is often called the winter egg, for it does not hatch until after the winter season. Winter eggs can also be dispersed by wind or on the feet of wading birds, a fact that may account for the peculiar distribution of some species of rotifers.

Most rotifers can withstand extreme desiccation and freezing. Some have even been found in hot springs where nothing else can live.

Cell or nuclear constancy in rotifers

Most structures in rotifers are syncytial, but the nuclei in the various organs show a remarkable constancy in number in any given species. One German investigator reports that one species, *Hydatina sp.*, always recorded 959 nuclei. Another investigator (Martini) has reported on the number of nuclei in the different organs in a certain species of rotifer. He found 183 nuclei in the brain, 172 in the corona epidermis, 108 in trunk and foot epidermis, 91 in the mastax epithelium, 39 in the stomach, etc. Other zoologists, however, are not convinced that cell constancy is as absolute as these investigations appear to show.

Figure 139. Gastrotrich.

CLASS GASTROTRICHA

The organisms of this class (Figure 139) are found in both fresh water and salt water, and their habitats are about the same as those of rotifers. They are common in protozoan cultures, where they are found creeping along on a substratum and feeding on microscopic organisms. They are ventrally flattened with dorsal spines and can glide by means of bands of cilia on the ventral side. The body of some species is forked posteriorly. The head is in the form of a lobe and bears cilia and, in some species, long bristles. The body structures have some resemblance to the rotifers, especially with reference to the body wall. A syncytial epidermis is found beneath the cuticle. Longitudinal muscles are better developed than circular ones, and in most cases they are unstriped. Adhesive tubes, which secrete a substance for attachment, are also found. The pseudocoel is somewhat reduced and contains no amebocytes. The digestive system is complete and is made up of an anterior mouth surrounded by bristles; a long muscular pharynx, which is lined with a cuticle; a stomach-intestine, which lacks a cuticular lining; and an anus, which may be located dorsally or ventrally. Protonephridia are restricted to certain species. The nervous system contains a brain near the pharynx and a pair of lateral nerve trunks through the body. Sensory structures are similar to those in rotifers, except the eyespots are generally lacking. Only females occur in fresh-water species, and the eggs all develop parthenogenetically. The female reproductive system consists of one or two ovaries, a uterus, an oviduct, and an opening (gonopore), which may open anteriorly to, or in common with, the anus. Eggs are laid on some substratum, such as weeds, and hatch in a few days. Development is direct and the larvae have the same form as the adults. Species of *Chaetonotus* are common fresh-water gastrotrichs.

Gastrotrichs are supposed to be closely related to rotifers. They resemble the rotifers in having cilia, protonephridia, and a similar pattern of muscles. They differ from rotifers in their digestive system, cuticular spines, and the presence of adhesive tubes. Some of their structures are similar to those of nematodes.

CLASS KINORHYNCHA

The class Kinorhyncha (Echinodera) gets its name from the Greek words *kineo,* to move, + *rhynchos,* beak, and refers to the retractile proboscis which these animals possess. They are marine worms about 1 to 5 mm. long and are found in the bottom muck of shallow or deep water. Their cylindrical body is divided into thirteen or fourteen rings (zonites) which bear spines that may be quite long in the tail region, but they have no cilia. The retractile head has a circlet of spines and is provided with a small retractile proboscis. The body is flat underneath and arched above, with the posterior end more or less tapering. In common with other members of this phylum, their body wall is made up of a cuticle, a syncytial epidermis, and longitudinal epidermal cords much like those of nematodes. The arrangement of the muscles is correlated with the zonites, and circular, longitudinal, and diagonal muscle bands are all represented. By means of these muscles the animal can contract and extend its body and head. The digestive system is complete with a mouth at the tip of the proboscis, a pharynx, an esophagus, a stomach-intestine, and an anus in the terminal zonite. The pseudocoel is filled with fluid-bearing amebocytes. The excretory system contains a pair of flame cells, each provided with an excretory canal that opens on the eleventh zonite. In close contact with the epidermis is the nervous system, with a brain encircling the pharynx, from which extends a ventral ganglionated cord throughout the body. Sense organs are represented by eyespots in some and by the sensory bristles. Sexes are separate, with the gonads in the form of elongated sacs. From each ovary an oviduct extends to the genital pore in the female; in the male a vas deferens runs from each testis to the genital pore, which has penial spicules.

The members of this strange group are not easy to find, although some 100 species have been reported. They cannot swim and probably have little need to in their slimy and mucky surroundings, but they move by squirming and by wormlike contraction and relaxation of their longitudinal muscles.

Among the most widely known of the genera of the Kinorhyncha are *Echinoderes, Echinoderella, Pycnophyes,* and *Trachydemus.*

Class Kinorhyncha shares anatomical features with a number of other groups without being closely related to any. The segmental arrangement of kinorhynchs makes them somewhat intermediate between annelids and arthropods, but the development of their segmentation is not as basically tied in with the mesoderm formation as it is in the case of annelids and arthropods. In other words, segmentation in kinorhynchs is more superficial and secondary to the body plan. They have, in common with such forms as rotifers and gastrotrichs, spines, flame cells, and retractile head ends; with the nematodes they share a similar pattern of the nervous system, longitudinal cords, and copulatory spicules. Authorities, such as Hyman, for instance, think Kinorhyncha represents an offshoot from a common stem which also gave rise to the nematodes and the gastrotrichs.

CLASS PRIAPULIDA

Only three species have been found in this class to date, although the group has been known to zoologists for a long time. These animals are wormlike forms which may reach a length of 3 to 4 inches. They live in the soft muck in the littoral regions of the sea (where they prey on annelids and other forms) and have a wide distribution. The body is cylindrical in shape, more or less superficially segmented, and provided with an anterior retractile proboscis (presoma). The presoma region may actually be greater in diameter than the trunk. The body has a warty appearance because of the spines and papillae it bears. In addition, some of them have caudal appendages in the form of hollow gill-like outgrowths of unknown function. The body wall consists of a cuticle, an epidermis of tall cells, outer circular and inner longitudinal muscles, and a lining membrane without nuclei. The digestive system is made up of the mouth at the terminal part of the proboscis and is surrounded with spines; a muscular pharynx, also lined with spines; an intestine, with muscular walls and folds, lined with columnar cells; a short rectum lined with cuticle; and an anus at the posterior end of the trunk. The nature of the body space is not well known, but some consider it a coelom. It contains a fluid with circular cells. The excretory system is closely connected with the reproductive system, and the two are referred to as the urogenital system. The sexes are separate and fertilization is external. The excretory part is made up of clusters of protonephridia (solenocytes) on each side of the body opening into a urogenital canal, which also carries sex cells from a gonad on that side. Both urogenital canals open separately by pores at the posterior end of the trunk. The nervous system is found in the epidermis and consists of a nerve ring around the pharynx, with scattered nerve cells and nerves, and a ventral nerve cord which extends posteriorly. Peripheral nerves run to various parts of the body.

Students of the group place them close to Kinorhyncha because of their retractile proboscis, their superficial segmentation, their nervous system, and their excretory system. However, it is impossible to assign this class's derivation to any particular group, and many zoologists think it should be considered a separate phylum.

CLASS NEMATODA

The members of class Nematoda are among the most numerous of any phylum. There are thousands of them in every fistful of soil, and water, whether fresh or salt, contains them in great numbers. Some of them are parasitic, but more of them are free living. Many also live in the tissue fluids of plants, where they do considerable damage. It has been estimated that when all the species of nematodes are properly classified they will outnumber the arthropods.

The distinctive characteristics of this extensive group of animals (which now number more than 12,000 named species) are their cylindrical wormlike shape, their flexible, but inelastic cuticle which prevents them from changing length and thickness, and their unique manner of thrashing around, forming patterns of C's and S's. Other more or less unique features are (1) the pharynx, which is three-angled, lined with cuticle and a syncytial epithelium, highly muscular, and often bearing differentiated parts, such as glands, swellings (bulbs), and ceca; and (2) the excretory system, consisting either of one or more large gland cells (the renette) opening by an excretory pore in the mid-ventral line, or a canal system (without protonephridia) formed by outgrowth from the renette cells, or both renette and canals together.

Nematodes are now commonly divided by some authorities into two subclasses, Phasmidia and Aphasmidia. Subclass Phasmidia bears a pair of unicellular pouches (**phasmids**) near the posterior tip, a pair of porelike sense organs (**amphids**) at the anterior end, and an excretory system of lateral canals. Most of the common parasitic forms as well as many free-living ones, such as *Rhabditis*,

Ascaris, Enterobius, belong to this group. Subclass Aphasmidia lacks phasmids and lateral excretory canals and has spiral or disc-shaped amphids and special caudal glands. Most members of this subclass are free living, but a few parasitic ones include the trichina worm and the giant kidney worm.

The various members of the nematodes are very much alike in their general appearance, although there are some structural differences here and there as well as striking diversities in their life histories. Because of the simplicity of their structure and life history as well as their availability, some member of genus *Ascaris* is usually selected as a type for study in zoology. There are many species of this genus or closely related ones. One of the most common species *(Ascaris megalocephala)* is found in the intestines of horses. *Neoascaris vitulorum* is another species found in cattle. The common roundworm of the cat is *Toxocara cati;* that of the dog, *Toxocara canis.* Infection with *Toxocara* is rare in man. The roundworm *Ascaris lumbricoides suilla* found in pigs is morphologically similar to *Ascaris lumbricoides* found in man, but the two species or subspecies seem to be physiologically distinct, for it is rare for the larval form of the one found in man to grow to maturity in the pig and vice versa.

Ascaris lumbricoides— intestinal roundworm

Ascaris lumbricoides is found in man and, according to some authorities, in the pig. It is one of the most common parasites found in man. In some communities of the southern states its incidence may run as high as 5 to 10%, sometimes higher in children. Infection normally occurs by swallowing embryonated ova. Unsanitary habits in which contaminated food and vegetables containing the ova are conveyed to the mouth represent one of the most frequent methods of infection.

Structure. The females of this species are about 20 to 33 cm. long; the males, about 15 to 30 cm. *Ascaris lumbricoides* is

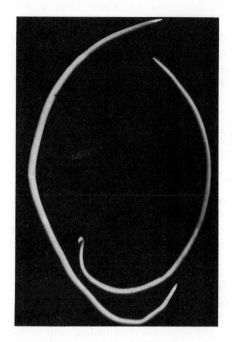

Figure 140. Intestinal roundworm, *Ascaris lumbricoides,* male and female. Male has sharp kink in end of tail.

pointed at both ends and whitish yellow in color (Figure 140). The body is covered with a tough elastic **cuticle,** and four brownish or whitish lines (dorsal, ventral, and two lateral), thickenings of the subcuticular region, extend length of the body. The head end bears three lips, a dorsal and two lateroventral, provided with papillae. Between these lips is the mouth. The male can be distinguished from the female by the smaller size and by the sharply curved posterior end which bears two **penial spicules** in the genital pore. In the female the posterior end is straight, and the **vulva,** or genital pore, is found on the ventral surface about one third of the distance from the head end. The **anus** is a ventral slit near the posterior end.

The body wall (Figure 141) is made up of the noncellular cuticle of many layers, formed from the epidermis, a syncytial **epidermis** or hypodermis with many nuclei, and a layer of **longitudinal muscles.** There are no circular muscles. The longitudinal muscles are divided into four

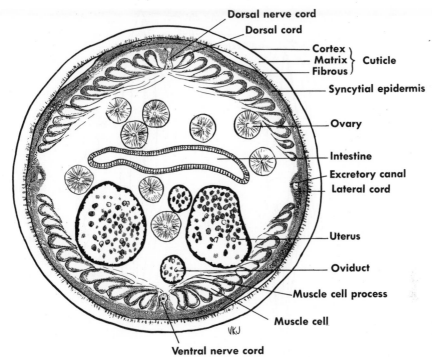

Dorsal nerve cord
Dorsal cord
Cortex
Matrix } Cuticle
Fibrous
Syncytial epidermis
Ovary
Intestine
Excretory canal
Lateral cord
Uterus
Oviduct
Muscle cell process
Muscle cell
Ventral nerve cord

Figure 141. Cross-section of *Ascaris*.

andlike parts by the four longitudinal cords which represent epidermal bulges into the pseudocoel. Two of them are lateral, one mid-dorsal, and one mid-ventral in position. These cords are usually better developed in the anterior regions of the body, and they divide the muscular coat into four quadrants. Each muscle is large and spindle-shaped. In cross section it shows two portions or zones, an outer U-shaped contractile or fibrillar zone which partly surrounds an inner or protoplasmic zone containing a nucleus. The protoplasmic zone also gives off a process which bends inward and runs to a nerve trunk in either the dorsal or ventral longitudinal cord. In this way the muscle receives its nerve supply. Each muscle quadrant is supposed to have about 150 muscle cells. The **body cavity**, in which the visceral organs lie, is called a **pseudocoel** and is not lined with mesoderm. It is filled with fluid and contains fibers and giant cells (a nematode characteristic).

The alimentary canal consists of a **mouth** (Figure 142), a short muscular sucking **pharynx**, a long nonmuscular **intestine** lined with endodermal cells for absorption, and a short **rectum** with **anus**.

The excretory system consists of a lateral **excretory canal** in each lateral cord, with a transverse network connecting the two lateral canals anteriorly, and a common tube from the transverse network to the ventral excretory pore just behind the mouth. There are no flame cells.

There are no special organs for respiration and circulation.

A ring of nerve tissue and ganglia around the pharynx gives rise to several small nerves to the anterior end and two main nerve cords, dorsal and ventral, and several small ones to the tail end. Sense organs are poorly developed. The chief ones are the papillae of the lips. Amphids, lateral chemoreceptors characteristic of free-living nematodes, are greatly reduced in *Ascaris*.

The **reproductive organs** are tubular, with many coils in the body cavity, and are attached only at the genital pore (female) or cloaca (male) (Figure 142).

Phylum Aschelminthes 225

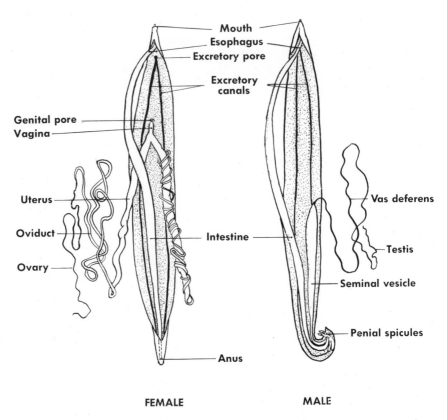

Figure 142. Internal structure of *Ascaris,* showing digestive and reproductory systems.

The male system is single and consists of a coiled **testis** for producing sperm, a **vas deferens** for conducting sperm, a **seminal vesicle** for storing sperm, an **ejaculatory tube** for discharging sperm into the **rectum** or cloaca, and the two **penial spicules** for attachment into the female genital pore during copulation. The whole reproductive system is a single, continuous, much-coiled tubule and is unattached except where it connects with the digestive tract. The various divisions show certain structural differences, such as a gradually increased diameter from the testes to the ejaculatory duct.

Instead of a single reproductive system the female has a partly paired one. It contains two **ovaries** for producing eggs, two **oviducts** for carrying eggs, and two **uteri** which unite into a common **vagina** that opens to the outside at the genital pore.

Metabolism. Since the ascaris is parasitic in the intestine of man, its food is the partly digested and semifluid material found there. Food is sucked into the worm's digestive tract by its muscular esophagus, and after digestion is completed, the soluble food is absorbed through the walls of the intestine and the indigestible part eliminated through the anus. A thick cuticle protects against the digestive juices of the host. Such oxygen as it needs is obtained mainly from the breakdown of glycogen within its own body. Waste is picked up by the excretory canals and discharged to the outside.

Locomotion. Because of its lack of circular muscles, the ascaris is restricted to dorsoventral bending of its body produced by the alternate contractions of the dorsal and ventral longitudinal muscles. Nevertheless, it can thrash about and, by taking advantage of the friction afforded by the

226

itestinal contents of the host, manages rogressive locomotion.

Life cycle. A female ascaris may produce millions of eggs which she lays at ne daily rate of about 200,000. The eggs ass with the feces, are deposited on the round, and develop into small worms inide their shells. If taken into the body n this form they will grow into mature vorms, but they have many hazards. In ne first place, a too dry or too cold environment may be fatal to the young vorm in the shell. Second, the sanitary abits of man may prevent the ingestion f the embryonated eggs. Also, if eggs re ingested before they develop embryo vorms, they will not be infective. This development within the egg usually requires wo to three weeks. When such eggs are wallowed, they pass to the intestine and atch into tiny larvae (0.2 mm.) which urrow through the intestinal wall into ne veins or lymph vessels. In the blood ney pass through the heart to the pulnonary capillaries of the lungs, break nrough into the air passageways, move p the trachea, cross over into the esophaus, and then go down the alimentary anal to the intestine, where they grow) maturity in about two months. Here ne two sexes copulate and the female beins her egg laying.

Thus only one host is involved in the fe cycle. They do their greatest damage) the host while the juvenile worms are nigrating, especially through the lung acs, where they may cause inflammation.)rdinarily the adult worms live in the pper small intestine, but, when numrous, they will wander to other parts of ne body, such as the appendix, bile ducts, ose, and sinuses. In very large numbers ney are known to cause intestinal obtructions. In its life history the ascaris ndergoes four molts before becoming exually mature. One of these molts occurs n the egg, two in the lungs, and the last ne in the intestine of the host.

)ther nematodes

In addition to the parasitic nematodes lready described, there are many others, some of which resemble *Ascaris lumbricoides* and others that differ in minor details. Most of these differences are found in the mouth regions and in the reproductive system. Nearly all vertebrates, as well as many invertebrates, are parasitized by nematodes.

Not all nematodes are parasites; most are actually free living. Many feed on plant juices, algae, and bacteria; others feed on small live forms; or some may be scavengers which feed upon dead animals and plants. Those parasitic in plants often cause galls or nodular growths on roots and leaves. The vinegar eel, *Turbatrix*, often found in cider, is a good example of a free-living nematode.

Hookworm. There are three common forms of hookworms which infect man. *Ancylostoma duodenale* is common in Europe, Asia, and Africa and in a few places in North and South America. A closely

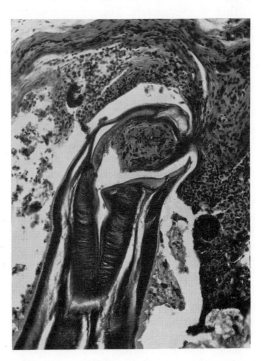

Figure 143. Hookworm attached to human intestine. Note cutting plates of mouth pinching off bit of mucosa from which thick muscular pharynx will suck blood. Mouth secretes anticoagulant to prevent blood clotting. (AFIP No. 33810.)

Phylum Aschelminthes 227

related species, *Ancylostoma braziliense,* is restricted to certain regions in Brazil. *Necator americanus* is the common American form, although it was introduced from Africa. These worms are called hookworms because the male has a hook-shaped body; they actually have no hooks. The adult worms are 10 to 15 mm. long, the females being longer than the males. They have cutting plates or teeth in their mouths by which the worms cut holes into the intestinal mucosa (Figure 143). By means of the sucking pharynx they draw blood, fluids, etc. into their intestines. To facilitate their feeding they have an anticoagulant in their mouth secretions to prevent blood clotting. They often take more blood into their bodies than they can digest, and they leave a bleeding wound after feeding.

The life cycle is similar in some ways to that of the ascaris. The sexes copulate in the intestine, after which the female lays several thousand eggs daily. The eggs pass out with the host's feces and hatch in about a day on warm moist soil. The larvae feed on bacteria or organic matter and undergo two molts.

They are now about 0.5 mm. long and are infective. If opportunity does not present itself, they may live (without feeding) in warm, moist soil four to eight weeks; in a cool, moist environment they have been known to live six months. If infected soil touches the skin, the larvae burrow through the skin into the blood. In warm countries the bare foot is the most common point of entry. That entrance causes a mild irritation known as "ground itch." One can also become infected by swallowing larvae. After entering, their subsequent journey is the same as described for the ascaris. In their journey to the intestine they undergo a third molting and then after reaching the intestine, a fourth molting. They may live for several years in the host, and an infection of 25 to 50 worms may cause pronounced anemia. Infection with 1,500 worms is known. The results of infection are, in addition to anemia, retarded mental and physical growth and general loss of energy.

In the United States hookworm disease is common in the rural areas of the southern states. In certain countries, such as China and India, the incidence of infection is much higher. Sanitary disposal of feces and the wearing of shoes are excellent preventives. Worms can be gotten rid of in infected cases by the use of drugs.

Trichinia worm. *Trichinella spiralis* is a nematode worm 1.5 to 4 mm. long and is responsible for the serious disease trichinosis. The adults live in the small intestine, where the female burrows into the intestinal mucosa and for several weeks produces living larvae about 0.1 mm. long. These larvae penetrate into the lymphatics or veins and are carried to the skeletal muscles, especially those of the diaphragm, tongue, eye, and neck. Here they coil up and form a cyst which be-

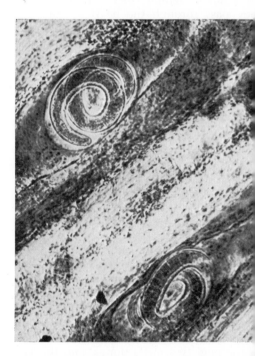

Figure 144. Muscle infected with trichina worm, *Trichinella spiralis.* Larvae may live 10 to 2 years in these cysts. If eaten in poorly cooked meat, larvae are liberated in intestine. They quickly mature and release many larvae into blood of host.

omes calcified (Figure 144). Each cyst measures 0.25 to 0.5 mm. in diameter. In the cyst the worm may live for ten to twenty years if undisturbed, but eventually the worms die. When the cysts are swallowed in the ingestion of infected meat, the larvae are liberated in the intestine and develop in a few days into mature worms and die within a few months, after releasing many living larvae into the blood of the host.

Besides man, the worms infect many mammals, such as hogs, rats, cats, and dogs. Man becomes infected by eating raw or improperly cooked pork. Hogs usually get their infection by eating garbage containing pork scraps infected with the cysts. Hogs may also get infected from eating rats. Rats can get the worms from infected pork scraps or from eating each other. Nearly 75% of all rats are infected. So far as man is concerned, the infection of man is a "dead-end alley" for the worms, unless human flesh should be eaten, which is rare.

In the United States 18 to 20% of the people are infected, but this infection is usually mild and gives rise to no pronounced symptoms. Heavy infections, however, cause trichinosis, the symptoms of which vary greatly. Some of these symptoms are intestinal disturbances, muscular pains, fever, mental conditions, and edema. The disease often terminates fatally. There is no effective treatment for trichinosis.

The simplest preventive measure is the thorough cooking of all pork; a pink color indicates insufficient cooking. Cooking garbage before it is fed to hogs is required in many communities, a practice which keeps down the incidence of infected pork.

Pinworms. The pinworm *Enterobius* or *Oxyuris vermicularis* is also very common, especially in warm countries. In some communities, nearly 40% of the children are infected. The adult worms live in the cecum and adjacent parts of the large intestine with their heads attached to the mucosa. The female is the larger, being about 12 mm. long and about the thick-

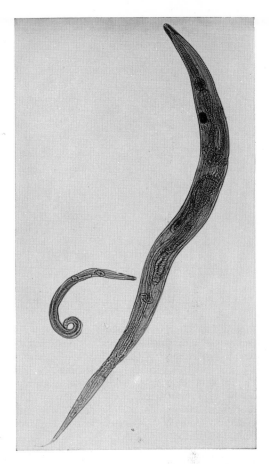

Figure 145. Male and female (larger) pinworms, *Enterobius vermicularis*. Infestation in up to 40% of school children has been found in some communities; this worm may be most common and most widely distributed of human helminth parasites. (Courtesy Indiana University School of Medicine, Indianapolis.)

ness of a thread. Females with eggs often migrate to the anal region at night and deposit their eggs. Since they cause irritation, scratching often contaminates fingers, as well as bedclothing, with the ova, and reinfection can occur if the person is unsanitary. Each generation lasts about three to four weeks, and, if reinfection does not occur, the infection will die out. When the ova are swallowed, they are carried to the duodenum, where they hatch. They then pass through the small intestine, molt, and become adults in the upper part of the large intestine.

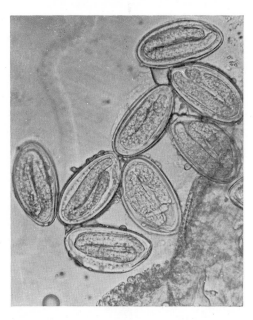

Figure 146. Group of pinworm eggs containing embryos. These eggs are usually discharged by female just outside of anus of infected persons. By scratching, fingernails and clothing are contaminated with eggs, which serve as immediate source of future reinfections. No intermediate host required and life cycle is about a month. (Courtesy Indiana University School of Medicine, Indianapolis.)

No intermediate host is necessary. Infection through inhalation of dust containing the ova is known to occur.

The widespread distribution of pinworm infection has been revealed by the better development of diagnostic techniques. The older fecal examinations have been found to be unreliable in giving a true picture of the state of this infection. Present-day methods of diagnosis emphasize perianal and perineal scrapings and show a much higher incidence of pinworm infection than was shown by the older methods. These newer diagnoses reveal that in some communities there may be 100% infection. Infection is naturally higher among people of low social level because of poorer sanitary methods of living, but it is also too common in those of higher social levels. Authorities are agreed that there may be ways by which infection is disseminated that are not

fully known. An interesting fact is tha incidence is higher among white perso than among Negroes. Children also have higher incidence than do adults. Surgical removed appendices reveal, in ma cases, the presence of pinworms. Pi worms in small numbers show few sym toms, but heavy infections are nearly a ways marked by intestinal disturbance an intense pruritus. Injuries are caused in th intestinal wall where the worms are a tached, and these sites may be invade by bacteria. In some cases they a thought to cause appendicitis. Extrem nervousness and irritability may be man fested in those who are heavily infecte Infection of the nasal mucosa sometim occurs in those who are constantly pic ing their noses. The worms may also gi off toxic substances, which add to th clinical picture.

Filarial worms. Filarial worms *(W chereria bancrofti)* are found in tropic and subtropical countries. The adu worms (2 to 4 inches long) live in th lymphatic glands where they often of struct the flow of lymph, producing, i severe infections, **elephantiasis,** which i volves an excessive growth of connecti tissue and enormous swelling of th affected parts, such as the scrotum, leg arms (Figure 147). The females give birt to microscopic larvae known as **micr filariae,** which are discharged into th lymph and are carried to the blood. He they undergo no further development u less sucked up by a mosquito of the rig kind (usually some species of *Culex* Aëdes). During the night the larvae a found in the surface blood vessels but a in the deeper vessels during the day. I places where there are diurnal mosquito they reverse this periodicity. In the mo quito they pass from the stomach to th thoracic muscles, where they metamo phose, and then migrate to the probosci When a mosquito bites a person, the la vae crawl out on the skin, enter it, an pass to the lymph vessel. In the lymp glands they coil up and mature.

In a large percentage of cases filarial i fection is not injurious to man. Wher

230

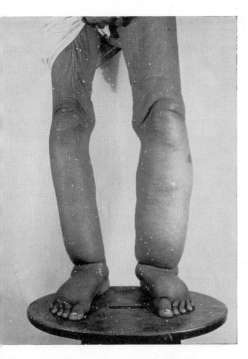

Figure 147. Elephantiasis of leg. Condition produced by adult filarial worms of *Wuchereria bancrofti*, which live in lymph passages and block flow of lymph. Females give birth to microfilariae which circulate in blood, are picked up by a biting mosquito (female of several genera of mosquitoes), and are transmitted to another individual bitten by infected mosquito. Larvae are not infective until they have passed through this part of their life cycle in mosquito. (AFIP No. A-44430-1.)

there are repeated reinfections there is built up in time the condition of elephantiasis.

Guinea worms. Guinea worms (*Dracunculus medinensis*) are long worms, the females being from 2 to 4 feet long and 1/25 inch in diameter. They are found in Africa, Arabia, India, and other places in the East. They are also found in South America, the West Indies, and in dogs and mink in the United States. The female adult worm (the males are small and rarely found) lies near the surface of the skin, where it has the appearance of an elongated and much-coiled varicose vein. The anterior end of the worm protrudes through an ulcer in the

skin, and the living young are discharged to the outside when the ulcer comes in contact with water. If the larvae are ejected into water and come in contact with *Cyclops,* a crustacean, they enter its body and undergo development. When a human being swallows *Cyclops* in drinking water, the worms pass to the intestine and then migrate to the subcutaneous tissue where they develop into mature worms in about a year.

The time-honored method of removing the worm is by winding it out on a stick, a little each day. If the worm is ruptured by winding too rapidly, serious consequences may result. It is interesting to note that the "fiery serpent" of Biblical times was this worm.

Ecology and economic relations of nematodes

A great student of nematodes once said that if the earth were to disappear, leaving only the nematode worms, the general contour of the earth's surface would be outlined by the worms, for their presence is indicated in nearly every conceivable kind of ecological niche. They are the most highly adaptable of all metazoans, for the same species may be found in arctic as well as tropical habitats. They are not common in extremes of dry and wet soils, but many can live either in freshwater or in terrestrial habitats if the latter have water films. They have been found in the soil to a depth of 25 feet. Rich agricultural lands may have as many as five billion nematodes per acre in the few inches of topsoil.

Although many nematode species are cosmopolitan, some are restricted to special habitats, such as *Turbatrix* in the felt mats of beer mugs in Germany. Many nematodes, especially the microscopic ones, live in or around the roots of plants. Larval forms feed extensively on root tissues which react by forming galls. Excessive gall formation causes the death of the plant, and plant parasitic nematodes do extensive damage to many crops, for several generations of worms each year are possible in warm soil. Recently the golden potato nematode (*Heterodera rostochiensis*) has damaged potato crops to an alarming extent in many parts of the country. Nematodes occur wherever decaying animal or plant food is found. Many species can withstand great extremes of temperature and desiccation. Nematode eggs are especially resistant and are easily transported long distances by animals and winds.

CLASS NEMATOMORPHA

The popular name for this group is "horsehair worms," based on the superstition that they arise from horsehairs that happen to fall into the water. They have a wide distribution and are found in aquatic habitats in both the temperate and tropical zones. These animals are interesting in that in the adult condition they never feed, for their digestive system is degenerate, and they are free living. The larval stages, however, are parasitic in some arthropod host. The different species vary in length from a few millimeters to about a meter, and many of them have the habit of coiling themselves into a knot, often around an aquatic plant or other object.

Structure. The worms are long and slender, with a cylindrical body. With one or two exceptions, the females are longer than the males, in which the posterior ends are slightly curved as in nematodes. The diameter of the body rarely exceeds 1 or 2 mm. and is usually uniform throughout except at the ends, which are rounded or slightly tapered. The coloration is usually a dirty brown, although brighter hues are occasionally found. The surface of the body may bear small papillae (areoles) which give a rough appearance to the cuticle. Small bristles or pores may also be found on these areoles. The body wall consists of a cuticle of a fibrous nature, an epidermis, and a musculature of longitudinal fibers only. Dorsal and ventral longitudinal cords (thickenings) of the epidermis may also be present. A pseudocoel of some form is found which in some is filled with parenchyma.

The digestive system appears to be more or less incomplete in both the adult and larval forms, although the latter absorb food from their hosts through the body wall. When present, the mouth is located at the anterior end, followed by a pharynx, an elongated intestine, a cloaca, and an anus at the terminal end. Circulatory, respiratory, and excretory systems are lacking. The nervous system contains a nerve ring around the pharynx and a single mid-ventral cord. Sensory structures are represented by various sensory cells located on the epidermis and eyespots in some.

Each sex has a pair of gonads which run through much of the body in some species. The female system on each side contains an ovary and an oviduct which enters into the cloaca. In the male system each testis discharges its sperm through a short sperm duct into the cloaca which may bear some spines but no copulatory spicules. The female lays strings of eggs which develop into the larvae. These swim around and may enter the body of an aquatic host, although they must find the right host before they can complete their development. This is usually a grasshopper, beetle, or cricket that may happen to come to aquatic habitats. Only one host is involved in the parasitic existence of horsehair worms. The larval worm remains in the body cavity of the host for several months, grows in size until it reaches adult condition, leaves its host, and molts. As an adult it leads a free existence in the water until it dies.

Common species of Nematomorpha are represented by *Gordius robustus, Gordius aquaticus, Paragordius varius,* and *Nectonema agile*. Of these, only the last-named one is marine.

The nematomorphs were long included with the nematodes, with which they have many common characters, such as the structure of the cuticle, the presence of epidermal cords, longitudinal muscles only, and pattern of nervous system. However, the early larval form of some species has a striking resemblance to the priapulid, so that it is impossible to state to ust what group in the Aschelminthes they are most closely related.

Derivation and meaning of basic terminology

amictic (Gr. *a*, without, + *miktos*, mixed or blended) Pertains to diploid egg of rotifers, or the females which produce such eggs.

amphid (Gr. *amphi*, double) One of a pair of anterior sense organs in certain nematodes.

Ascaris (Gr. *askaris*, intestinal worm).

Aschelminthes (Gr. *askos*, cavity, + *helmins*, worm)

Dioctophyma (Gr. *di*, double, + *okto*, eight, + *phyma*, swelling) Refers to the papillae around the mouth, six to eighteen in number.

Dracunculus (L. *draco*, dragon, + *unculus*, small).

elephantiasis (Gr. *elephas*, elephant, + *osis*, state of) A condition of enormous swelling and connective tissue growth induced by filarial worms.

Enterobius (Gr. *enteron*, intestine, + *bios*, life).

Gastrotricha (Gr. *gaster*, stomach, + *trichos*, hair) Refers to the bands of ventral cilia.

Gordius (Gr. mythological king who tied an intricate knot).

mictic (Gr. *miktos*, mixed or blended) Pertains to haploid egg of rotifers or the females that lay such eggs.

Necator (Gr. *necator*, killer).

Nemathelminthes (Gr. *nema*, thread, + *helmins*, worm).

Nematomorpha (Gr. *nema*, thread, + *morphe*, shape).

Oxyuris (Gr. *oxys*, sharp, + *oura*, tail).

phasmid (Gr. *phaskolos*, pouch) One of a pair of glands found in the posterior end of certain nematodes.

Priapulida (Gr. *priapos*, phallus) Refers to the large retractile proboscis or presoma which has a resemblance to the male organ.

pseudocoel (Gr. *pseudes*, false, + *koilos*, hollow) Body cavity in the roundworms is so called because it is not a true coelom.

Rotifera (L. *rota*, wheel, + *ferre*, to bear).

solenocyte (Gr. *solen*, pipe, + *kytos*, cell) Special type of protonephridium in which the end bulb bears a flagellum instead of a tuft of cilia as in Platyhelminthes.

Trichinella (Gr. *trichos*, hair).

trichinosis (Gr. *trichos*, hair, + *osis*, state of) Parasitized condition produced by heavy infection of the trichina worm.

ANNOTATED REFERENCES

Baer, J. G. 1952. Ecology of Animal Parasites. Urbana, The University of Illinois Press. *Excellent and up-to-date account of the ways parasites have adapted themselves.*

Borradaile, L. A., and F. A. Potts. 1958. The Invertebrata, ed. 3. (revised by G. A. Kerkut). Cambridge, Cambridge University Press. *A new up-to-date revision of a standard work on this group. Some of the newer taxonomic concepts have been incorporated, as well as the latest factual material relating to the morphology and physiology of the various invertebrate phyla. It is a book in the finest tradition of English textbooks.*

Chandler, A. C. 1949. Introduction to Parasitology. New York, John Wiley & Sons, Inc. *A standard work on parasitology with good treatment of the nematodes.*

Hyman, L. H. 1951. The Invertebrates: Acanthocephala, Aschelminthes, and Entoprocta, vol. 3. New York, McGraw-Hill Book Co., Inc. *The newest classification of the invertebrates is presented in this series, of which this volume is one. Aside from the logical taxonomy Miss Hyman has also described with great accuracy the many types in these phyla.*

Lapage, G. 1951. Parasitic Animals. Cambridge, Cambridge University Press. *Good descriptions of the life histories of many nematodes, including Ascaris and Trichina.*

Pennak, R. W. 1953. Fresh-Water Invertebrates of the United States. New York, The Ronald Press Co. *This excellent work deals with the free-living, fresh-water invertebrates, and omits the parasitic forms. Many of the sections describe various types of Aschelminthes under the old classification. The treatment of Gastrotricha among the rarer types is especially noteworthy.*

Sasser, J. N., and W. R. Jenkins (editors). 1960. Nematology. Chapel Hill, University of North Carolina Press. *An important work by more than a score of eminent authorities in this relatively new and difficult field.*

chapter 13

Phylum Acanthocephala*

BIOLOGICAL PRINCIPLES

Organ-system level of organization

1. The Acanthocephala are pseudocoelomate vermiform Bilateria without a digestive system and belong to the Protostomia.

2. In accordance with their parasitic habits, the group shows a degeneration of certain structures and a specialization of others.

3. The presence of a **pseudocoel** marks an advancement over an acoelomate form such as Platyhelminthes. This cavity lacks a lining membrane and thus cannot be called a true coelom.

4. The absence of a **digestive system** makes it difficult to place the acanthocephs in the tube-within-a-tube arrangement. The **ligament strand** to which the gonads are attached is supposed to represent a degenerate digestive tract.

Biological contributions

1. The **pseudocoel** represents one of the earliest appearances of a body cavity, although it is not a true body cavity.

2. The presence of **separate sexes** represents a marked distinction from the monoecious flatworms.

3. The epidermis (hypodermis) is of the syncytial nucleated pattern and is unique in having in its inner radial layer a **lacunar** system. This system is made up of a number of channels or canals which are arranged either in the form of a network or of a few main longitudinal channels. It is a blind system which does not open to the outside and appears to be concerned with distributing food absorbed from the host.

4. In the male there is a peculiar eversible copulatory **bursa** which is used to hold the penis when it is inserted into the vagina of the female.

---

*A-can'tho-ceph"a-la (Gr. *akantha,* spine or thorn, + *kephale,* head).

5. A unique device (the **selective apparatus**) for separating mature from immature embryo and eggs is found in the female genital tract.

6. In common with nematodes, rotifers, an tunicates, this phylum displays a remarkable ce or nuclear constancy among its various organ. This may indicate a uniformity and stability o bodily characteristics which may have evolu tionary significance.

Position in animal kingdom

1. The highly specialized parasitic habits o the group with the consequent alteration of struc tures make it difficult to appraise their affinities

2. They have some resemblances to both th platyhelminths and aschelminths and difference from either of these two groups. In structure acanthocephs seem to be more closely allied t aschelminths, and, in development, to platyhel minths.

GENERAL RELATIONS

This group of parasitic worms was for merly included as a class under Nemathel minthes but is now considered as a sep arate phylum in its own right. Thes worms are endoparasitic and live as adult in the intestines of vertebrates and a larval forms in arthropods. The worm de rives its name from one of its most dis tinctive characters, a cylindrical invagin able proboscis bearing rows of recurve spines, by which it attaches itself to th intestine of its host. The origin of th term is thus derived from the Gr. *akan tha,* spine or thorn, + *kephale,* head. Th group is commonly known as the spiny headed worms. They possess several pe culiar features which make it difficult t determine their relations to other animal groups. Their totally parasitic habits have no doubt been responsible for many of their distinctive characters. None of them has a free-living stage, and neither the larvae nor adults have a digestive system at any stage of their existence. In their affinities they resemble in some ways platyhelminths and in other ways aschelminths, in which group they were once included. They differ from most aschelminths in having no digestive system, in having circular muscles, and in having certain peculiarities of the reproductive system. On the other hand, they show some resemblances to aschelminths in possessing a pseudocoel and a syncytial nucleated epidermis. They resemble platyhelminths in their reproductive system and their method of development.

About 300 species of acanthocephs have been named, most of which parasitize fish, birds, and mammals. They are worldwide in their distribution. In size the various species show a wide range from less than 2 mm. to 650 mm. in length. Sexual dimorphism is usually quite marked, the females being much larger than the males of the same species. The shape of the body also shows considerable difference among the various species. In some the body is long, slender, and cylindrical; in others it may be laterally flattened or short and plump. The body surface may be smooth, but often it is wrinkled. In most cases the body is capable of considerable extension and contraction because of the muscular arrangement. The color of the worms is often determined by the kind of food they absorb from their hosts, ranging all the way from a dirty brown to brighter colors.

Acanthocephs share with rotifers, nematodes, and tunicates the condition of cell or nuclear constancy. Van Cleve found in five different species of *Eorhynchus* the same number of nuclei in each of several organs, such as the lemnisci (3 nuclei), the cement glands (8 nuclei), the uterus (2 nuclei), the retractor muscles of hooks (4 nuclei), the selective apparatus (2 nuclei), etc. On this account, increase in size of the worm is correlated with a definite increase in cell size rather than in cell number. Some theories consider such a constancy a barrier to evolutionary development and progress.

CHARACTERISTICS

1. Anterior end with **spiny retractile proboscis** and **sheath**
2. Body cylindrical in form, in three sections: proboscis, neck, and trunk
3. **Epidermis syncytial in structure** and covered with cuticle and containing **fluid-filled lacunae;** cell constancy pronounced
4. Body wall with circular and longitudinal muscle layers
5. Body cavity fluid-filled, without epithelial lining
6. **No digestive tract**
7. Excretory system (when present) with two branched ciliated protonephridia which are connected to a common excretory duct
8. No circulatory or respiratory organs
9. Nervous system with a central ganglion on the proboscis sheath and nerves to the proboscis and posterior parts of the body
10. Sensory papillae near male genital orifice and on the proboscis
11. Separate sexes; male organs of paired testes formed in cordlike ligament, vas deferens, cement glands, and penis; female organs of paired ovaries formed in a ligament and breaking down into ova; young develop in body cavity of female; special selector apparatus in female system
12. **Parasitic in the intestine of vertebrates**

CLASSIFICATION

The acanthocephs have been classified in various ways by different authorities who have worked with this group. The most recent classification is that of Hyman, who has divided the phylum into three orders but into no classes. The classification is based upon the arrangement of the proboscis spines and a few other characteristics.

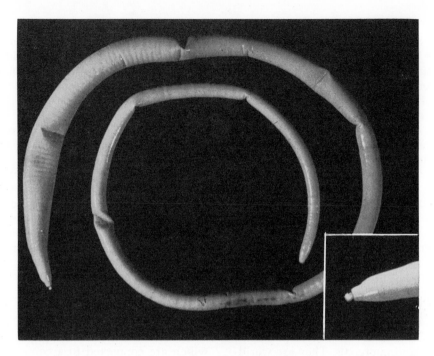

Figure 148. Spiny-headed worm of pigs, *Macracanthorhynchus hirudinaceus* (female), shown about life size. Inset is enlarged view of head, showing proboscis.

Order 1. Archiacanthocephala (ar"ki-a-can'tho-ceph"a-la) (Gr. *arch*, chief, + acanthocephala). Acanthocephs with an excretory system of protonephridia; median lacunar channels; proboscis spines in a concentric arrangement. Example: *Macracanthorhynchus hirudinaceus* (intestinal worm of pigs).

Order 2. Palaeacanthocephala (pa"le-a-can'tho-ceph"a-la) (Gr. *palaios*, old, + acanthocephala). Acanthocephs without excretory system; with lateral lacunar channels; with the proboscis spines in alternating radial rows. Example: *Leptorhynchoides thecatus* (a common fish parasite).

Order 3. Eocanthocephala (e"o-can'tho-ceph"-a-la) (Gr. *eos*, dawn, + acanthocephala). Acanthocephs without an excretory system; with median lacunar channels; with proboscis spines radially arranged. Example: *Neoechinorhynchus emydis* (a common parasite of turtles).

REPRESENTATIVE TYPE

The acanthoceph that is used as a type description of the phylum is *Macracanthorhynchus hirudinaceus*, which occurs in the small intestine of the pig through-out the world. It has also been found occasionally in other mammals. Its common occurrence and large size have caused it to be extensively studied from every aspect, and its life cycle has been known for a long time.

Macracanthorhynchus hirudinaceus— intestinal spiny-headed worm of pigs

Structure. The cylindrical body of *Macracanthorhynchus* is widest near the anterior end and tapers to the posterior end. At the anterior end is the **proboscis** and at the posterior end is the **genital pore.** The **body** is covered by a thin **cuticle,** beneath which is the syncytial **epidermis.** The epidermis or hypodermis contains the lacunar system of ramifying fluid-filled canals which do not communicate with anything outside the epidermis. This system, unique in the Acanthocephala, absorbs and distributes food from the host. The proboscis bears six rows of recurved hooks for clinging to the intestine and is attached to the neck region. In size the female is from 10 to 65 cm. in length and

236

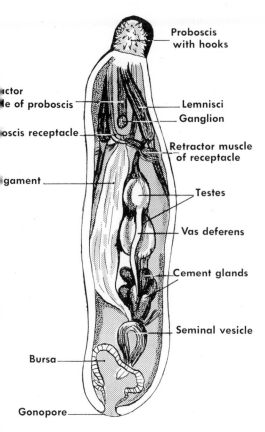

- Proboscis with hooks
- ctor
- le of proboscis
- Lemnisci
- Ganglion
- oscis receptacle
- Retractor muscle of receptacle
- igament
- Testes
- Vas deferens
- Cement glands
- Seminal vesicle
- Bursa
- Gonopore

Figure 149. Internal structure of male acanthoceph.

usually less than 1 cm. in thickness. The male is only about a quarter the size of the female and is provided with a **genital bursa** which is partly everted through the terminal genital pore.

The **body cavity** (which is not a true coelom) is lined with **longitudinal muscles; circular muscles** are found outside of the longitudinal fibers. At the anterior end is the **proboscis sheath** which receives the proboscis when the latter is retracted by the **invertor** and **retractor** muscles. Attached to the posterior end of the sheath are two elongated **lemnisci,** which may act as reservoirs for the fluid of the invaginated proboscis, and tubular **genital ligaments** or ligament sacs which run back to the posterior end of the worm. The **excretory** system, which is difficult to distinguish, consists of paired protonephridia

lying dorsal to the reproductive ducts and ligament. Each protonephridium is much branched with flame cells, and the two unite to form a common tube which opens into either the sperm duct or the uterus.

In the **female** the genital ligament bears a whitish ovarian tissue with masses of eggs scattered over it as well as in the body cavity. A single funnel-shaped oviduct is modified at its posterior end into a **uterus** and **vagina.** A special selective apparatus (Figure 150) forms the anterior part of the genital tract or oviduct and is provided with a rejection pore through which eggs and immature embryos are returned to the pseudocoel or to one of the

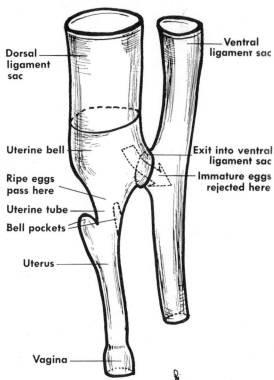

- Dorsal ligament sac
- Ventral ligament sac
- Uterine bell
- Ripe eggs pass here
- Exit into ventral ligament sac
- Immature eggs rejected here
- Uterine tube
- Bell pockets
- Uterus
- Vagina

Figure 150. Genital selective apparatus of female Acanthocephala (diagrammatic). This is unique device for separating immature from mature fertilized eggs. Uterine bell draws in developing eggs through dorsal ligament sac and passes them toward uterine tube. Immature eggs are shunted by special aperture into ventral ligament sac or pseudocoel; mature ones continue into uterus and vagina to outside.

ligament sacs; the mature embryos pass on into the uterus and vagina. The latter opens through the genital pore which also receives the male penis during copulation. The **male** organs consist of paired **testes** on the genital ligament and a **vas deferens** from the anterior end of each testis, running side by side to the common **ejaculatory duct** which ends in a small penis or cirrus at the posterior end of the body. The penis projects into a copulatory bursa which grips the posterior end of the female during copulation. **Cement** glands pour their secretions into the vasa deferentia and the copulatory bursa for binding the bodies of the two sexes together during copulation.

The **nervous system,** also difficult to distinguish, consists of an oval, flat ganglion on the proboscis and a number of nerves running anteriorly to the proboscis and posteriorly to other parts of the body. The few tactile sense organs are found on the proboscis and the male bursa.

Life cycle. This worm, which is common in pigs, has for its intermediate host the larva or grub of the June beetle *(Lachnosterna).* The eggs which are discharged from the female worm contain embryos provided with hooks and are eliminated in the feces of the primary host. The eggs have several coats or shells and do not hatch until eaten by the intermediate host. In this host the first larva (acanthor) burrows through the intestine and encysts as a juvenile. Pigs become infected by eating the grubs. Man rarely becomes infected, although cases have been reported from south Russia where the natives sometimes eat raw beetles.

Members of this phylum are the most harmful of all parasites, for great damage is done mechanically by the spiny head. Multiple infection may do considerable damage to the pig's intestine and perforation may occur.

Metabolism. Acanthocephala with their parasitic habits derive their nourishment from the host by absorption through the thin, delicate cuticle. The actual digestion of their food is done for them by their host. This power of absorption is strikingly shown when they are placed in water, for their bodies become swollen in a short time. After absorption into the body of the worms, the food products are distributed by the fluid-filled lacunar canal system and the body cavity.

Derivation and meaning of basic terminology

acanthor (Gr. *akantha,* thorn) First larval form of acanthocephalans in the intermediate host

cement gland One of a cluster of unicellular glands near the testes in acanthocephalan which furnishes secretions for binding the sexes together during copulation.

lacunar system (L. *lacuna,* channel) Epidermal canal system peculiar to acanthocephalans.

lemniscus (L. a ribbon) One of a pair of internal projections of the epidermis from the neck region of Acanthocephala which functions in fluid control in the protrusion and invagination of the proboscis.

Leptorhynchoides (Gr. *leptos,* slender, + *rhynchos,* beak, + *oideos,* form of).

Macracanthorhynchus (Gr. *makros,* long, + *akantha,* thorn + *rhynchos,* beak).

Neoechinorhynchus (Gr. *neos,* new, + *echinos* hedge-hog, + *rhynchos,* beak).

ANNOTATED REFERENCES

Brown, F. A., Jr. (editor). 1950. Selected Invertebrate Types. New York, John Wiley & Sons, Inc. *An account is given of Neoechinorhynchus emydis, the common parasite of freshwater turtles.*

Hyman, L. H. 1951. The Invertebrates, vol. 3. New York, McGraw-Hill Book Co., Inc. *The best up-to-date description of Acanthocephala.*

Meyer, A. 1933. Acanthocephala. In H. G. Bronn (editor): Klassen und Ordnungen des Tierreichs, vol. 4, part 2, sec. 2. *The definitive German account.*

Van Cleve, H. J. 1941. Relationships of Acanthocephala. American Naturalist, vol. 75. *In this and many other articles the most active American investigator of this group has attempted to appraise the position of the Acanthocephala in the animal kingdom. Read also his revealing article, "Expanding Horizons in the Recognition of a Phylum," Journal of Parasitology, vol. 34, 1948.*

chapter 14

Phyla of uncertain relationships (miscellaneous phyla)

GENERAL RELATIONS

In the animal kingdom there are many forms whose classification is obscure. Usually their species are few as compared with those in the major phyla, but just where they fit into the phylogenetic tree is difficult to state. Many of them share some of the characteristics of the more common groups. Yet they have enough differences to prevent their inclusion in the major phyla. Some authorities consider them as separate subdivisions under this or that phylum; others simply place them as separate phyla and thus avoid any entangling alliances which they cannot support with satisfactory evidence. This latter view is followed in the present work because of the present-day tendency to do so and because there is less likelihood of confusing the student of zoology.

These groups of uncertain relations are often lumped together and called the **miscellaneous phyla.** Nemertina, or Rhynchocoela, are often included in these miscellaneous groups, but we think these worms, because of their level of organization and their biological contributions, should be accorded a more important place in the evolution of the animal kingdom. Most of these minor phyla belong to the Protostomia division of the Bilateria in which the blastopore usually becomes the mouth, the cleavage is determinate, and the body cavity is formed from a split in the mesoderm. A trochophore larva is also common in this group.

Only the principal ones will be briefly discussed here. Those who are interested in these particular forms will find extensive descriptions of them in the larger zoological treatises.

SOME BIOLOGICAL CONTRIBUTIONS OF MINOR PHYLA

Although they are assigned a subordinate position in the animal kingdom, these phyla exhibit many interesting structural features. Some of their characters show advancement over the forms already considered; other characters are probably quite primitive. Many members are specialized for unique habits of living, and others are more generalized. A few of their outstanding contributions to the evolutionary blueprint are listed:

1. A true coelomic cavity lined with peritoneum is found in the phyla Phoronida, Echiuroidea, Sipunculoidea, Bryozoa, Brachiopoda, and Chaetognatha.
2. Hormonal differentiation of sex is represented in the phylum Echiuroidea.
3. The phylum Phoronida is probably the lowest group of animals in which a respiratory pigment (hemoglobin) is carried within blood corpuscles.
4. A contractile heart in phylum Brachiopoda is an advancement over contractile blood vessels.

5. Phylum Chaetognatha is the only invertebrate with more than one layer of cells in the epidermis, the beginning of stratified epithelium characteristic of vertebrates.

6. A postanal tail (Chaetognatha) is shared only with the chordates.

7. A cellular epidermis in place of a syncytial one marks an advancement over the Aschelminthes.

TROCHOPHORE LARVA AND ITS SIGNIFICANCE

The larval form of many aquatic invertebrates is a pear- or top-shaped organism (**trochophore**) (Figure 151) with two rings of cilia and an apical eyespot. It has a complete digestive system and bilateral symmetry. There are also excretory organs and muscles in its make-up. The larva of certain annelids is supposed to represent many of the characteristics of such an ancestral larval form and therefore is often considered the typical trochophore larva. With certain modifications the early larval forms of bryozoans, mollusks, brachiopods, and nemertines have a close resemblance to it. This has given rise to the theory of some zoologists that these phyla should be considered together as an annelid superphylum on the basis that their ancestors arose from forms that had trochophore-like features. This superphylum may also include other phyla (Arthropoda, Platyhelminthes) which may have lost the trochophore somewhere in their evolution.

This common larval form suggests a common ancestral relationship between all these phyla, even though the adults may show great differences. The common ancestor from which these groups have descended is called the **trochozoon** and is supposed to have resembled the rotifers. The trochophore larval theory accounts satisfactorily in many ways for a common ancestor of the coelomate Protostomia but not for the acoelomate groups. Many authorities, however, are very cautious about evaluating larval forms. There is always the possibility that they may be the result of coincidental evolution, thus signifying no actual relationship.

PHYLUM MESOZOA*

The members of this group probably have the simplest structure of any metazoan form. They are minute wormlike forms composed of an outer layer of somatic cells (somatoderm) often ciliated, and a syncytium enclosing one or more reproductive cells (axial cells). This two-layered pattern does not correspond to the ectoderm and endoderm of other Metazoa, for the inner layer (often of one cell) is concerned with reproduction and not digestion. They are endoparasites with a life cycle involving both asexual and sexual generations. The body is composed of a small head region and a long trunk. The head consists of eight or nine polar cells and the trunk of a greater number which is constant for each species. The germ cells, called **agametes,** are formed by the repeated division of the axial reproductive cells without maturation. These agametes develop into new individuals (**nematogens**) which break out of the parent as asexual individuals (Figure

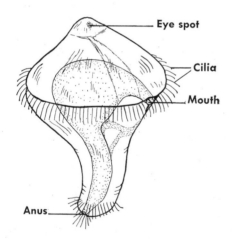

Figure 151. Generalized trochophore larva (trochosphere). This larva in modified form is found in many invertebrates, such as polychaetes, rotifers, mollusks, and others. It is supposed to signify common ancestry of the coelomate Protostomia.

*Mes'o-zo"a (Gr. *mesos,* middle, + *zoion,* animal).

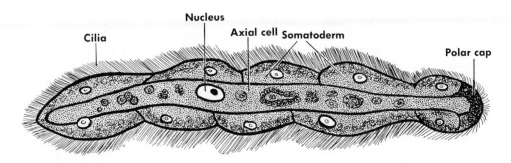

Cilia   Nucleus   Axial cell   Somatoderm   Polar cap

Figure 152. Primary nematogen stage of *Dicyema* (phylum Mesozoa), common endoparasite of squids and octopuses. Mesozoans are considered simplest of multicellular animals (about 25 cells). Their complicated life history involves asexual and sexual generations. In nematogen stage, agametes (germ cells without maturation) are formed by division of axial cell nucleus, and each agamete forms a nematogen. After leaving mother and giving rise to other generations, each nematogen is transformed into sexual rhombogen stage. Phylogenetic status of phylum is obscure. Some think they are degenerate flatworms; others consider them primitive and related to protozoans.

152). In some mesozoans the sexual generation (rhombogen) is represented by separate sexes which give rise to sperm and eggs; others are hermaphroditic. Fertilization may be internal, and the zygote develops into a ciliated larva before escaping from the mother.

Mesozoa are found as parasites in the spaces and tissues of many invertebrates, including annelids, squids, flatworms, echinoderms, and mollusks. Common forms are represented by *Dicyema, Pseudicyema, Microcyema,* and *Rhopalura*.

Some authorities consider Mesozoa to be degenerate flatworms or coelenterates, with the evidence perhaps stronger in favor of the flatworms. This affinity to Platyhelminthes is based largely upon the resemblance between life cycles of the two groups, both of which produce ciliated larvae. Another view emphasizes the primitive nature of their organization as intermediate between Protozoa and Metazoa.

PHYLUM ENTOPROCTA*

The members of Entoprocta were once included with Bryozoa, but a number of zoologists consider them sufficiently different to be placed in a phylum of their

*En'to-prok"ta (Gr. *entos,* inside, + *proktos,* anus).

own. They are stalked sessile animals, solitary or colonial, which are found in both fresh water and sea water. They are small forms which do not exceed 5 mm. in length and have some superficial resemblances to the hydroids of the coelenterates. The body is made up of the **calyx,** which bears a circlet of tentacles and contains the visceral organs, a slender **stalk,** and an **attachment disk** with adhesive glands. The crown of the calyx bearing the tentacles is retractile and can be contracted inward when the animal is disturbed. The tentacles may vary in the same species, although the number is usually between eight and thirty. They are ciliated on their inner surfaces, and each can move individually.

The digestive system is complete and U shaped. Unlike Bryozoa, in which only the mouth is found within the circle of tentacles, members of Entoprocta have both mouth and anus opening inside the tentacles. The system consists of mouth, esophagus, stomach, and rectum and is ciliated throughout. The body wall contains a cuticle, a cellular epidermis, and a longitudinal musculature. Between the body wall and the digestive system, and also in the interior of the tentacles and stalk, is the pseudocoel. A gelatinous parenchyma fills most of it. The excretory system consists of a pair of protonephridia,

Phyla of uncertain relationships   241

each of which is provided with a canal. These canals unite and open to the outside by a single pore near the mouth. Circulatory and respiratory organs are absent. The nervous system contains a mass of ganglia on the ventral side of the stomach, from which nerves pass to various parts of the body. Sense organs are represented by surface bristles and sensory pits and are chiefly tactile in function. Some members of this phylum are monoecious and others are dioecious. Some also appear to be protandric—that is, the gonad at first produces sperm and later eggs. The paired gonads are found near the ventral side of the stomach. Each gonad is provided with a duct which unites with the other duct to open by the common gonopore on the ventral surface of the calyx.

Urnatella gracilis is a common fresh-

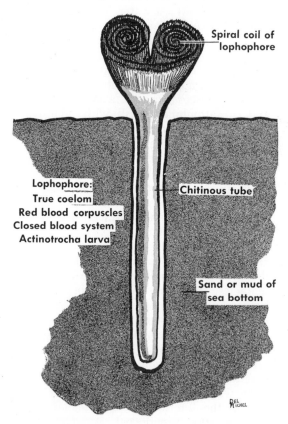

Lophophore:
True coelom
Red blood corpuscles
Closed blood system
Actinotrocha larva

Spiral coil of lophophore

Chitinous tube

Sand or mud of sea bottom

Figure 153. Diagram of phoronid, *Phoronis*, in its habitat.

water species in North America, where it is found growing under stones in running water; *Loxosoma* is one of the more familiar marine forms and has a wide distribution along the coast lines of America, Europe, Asia, and Africa. Many marine species are found attached to other animals, such as sponges and various worms.

Although Entoprocta were long included with Ectoprocta and placed in phylum Bryozoa, it is the opinion of some, including Hyman (1951), that these organisms have little in common and that there is very little evidence to support the view that these two groups are closely related. For one thing, Entoprocta belong to those animals that have some form of a pseudocoel, whereas Ectoprocta are higher in organization in having a true coelom and in other features. It is thought that the closest affinity of Entoprocta is to certain types of rotifers because of the similarity between the two groups of the digestive system, the excretory system of protonephridia, the body stalk, and the oral region.

PHYLUM PHORONIDA*

This phylum is made up of wormlike animals that live in tubes on the bottom of shallow seas. Most are small (1 mm. or less), but some are more than 1 foot long. They have some resemblance to Bryozoa and in the past have been included in that group. Some species are more or less solitary, but other species are found in associations of many individuals. Each worm is enclosed in a leathery or chitinous tube which it has secreted and from which its tentacles are extended. As in the bryozoans, the ciliated tentacles are borne on a lophophore which may be spirally coiled. When disturbed, the animal draws back into its tube with its tentacles completely hidden. The body is well advanced, for it has a body wall of cuticle, epidermis, and both longitudinal and circular muscles. The coelomic cavity is a true coelom, being lined with peri-

*Pho-ron'id-a (Gr. *phoros*, bearing, + *nid*, nest).

242

toneal epithelium. It is subdivided by mesenteric partitions into compartments.

The alimentary canal is U shaped, as in Bryozoa, is made up of esophagus, stomach, and intestine, and is ciliated most of its length. Although there is no respiratory system, the circulatory system is a closed system of blood vessels which have contractile walls, but a heart is absent. Red blood corpuscles are found also. The nervous system just below the epidermis consists of a nerve ring around the mouth with nerves running to various parts of the body. The members of this phylum are monoecious; a testis and ovary are found in each individual near one of the large blood vessels. When the sex cells are released, they pass through the paired nephridia to the space enclosed by the tentacles, where fertilization occurs. The larva which is characterized by a large hoodlike lobe over the mouth is called an actinotrocha and is commonly considered a type of the trochophore larva.

Two of the common species of the phylum are *Phoronopsis californica*, a large form found along the Pacific coast, and *Phoronis kowalevskii*, which has a wide distribution.

PHYLUM ECHIUROIDEA*

The members of this group have often been a taxonomic puzzle, and many zoologists have included them as a class under the annelids. It seems best, however, to assign them phylum rank, for they logically do not belong to any other group. They are unsegmented worms which are found in the mud and sand in shallow coast waters of warm and temperate seas. Many of them dwell in burrows, from which they feed by means of a proboscis. Their general body shape is cylindrical or ovoid, and most of them have a long nonretractile proboscis with ciliated groove. The body wall consists of a thin cuticle; an epidermis with glandular cells and papillae, arranged in rings; and a muscular layer of both longitudinal and circular

muscles. A pair of ventral anterior setae is characteristic of most species, and some have a row of chitinous bristles around the posterior end of the body near the anus.

The coelom is well developed and crossed by muscular strands which help support the alimentary canal. The latter contains a mouth at the base of the proboscis; a muscular pharynx; a coiled intestine; a slightly enlarged rectum, with a pair of long anal vesicles; and the terminal anus. The anal vesicles have ciliated openings into the body cavity and may help control the amount of fluid in the body cavity and the excretory process. The closed circulatory system consists of a contractile dorsal vessel on the alimentary canal and proboscis and a ventral vessel which is found on the dorsal surface of the nerve cord. The two vessels unite at the tip of the proboscis. There may be two or three pairs of nephridia which serve mainly to carry the sex products. The nervous system is made up of a nerve ring around the pharynx and an unsegmented ventral nerve cord which gives off paired lateral nerves to the skin. There are no special sense organs. The sexes are separate with a single gonad in each sex. The mature sex cells break loose from the gonads and leave the body cavity by way of the nephridia, and fertilization is usually outside. In some species sexual dimorphism is marked, the female being much the larger of the two.

Bonellia (Figure 154) is noteworthy for the way sex is differentiated in this genus. At first most of the larvae are sexually indifferent and can develop either into males or females. Those larvae that come into contact with the female proboscis become males in the larval stages and spend most of their lives in the nephridium of the female as a parasite. Those larvae that do not come into contact with the female undergo a metamorphosis into females. The stimulus for the male development appears to be a chemical one from the proboscis of the female. Baltzer was able to get various degrees of intersexuality by removing

---

*Ech'i-u-roi"de-a (Gr. *echis*, an adder, + *oura*, tail, + oidea).

larvae at various stages of male transformation.

Besides *Bonellia*, other common echiuroids are *Echiurus, Urechis, Hamingia,*

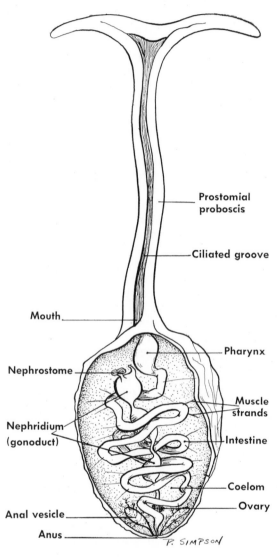

Figure 154. Chief internal organs of *Bonellia* (phylum Echiuroidea). This form is famed for extreme sexual dimorphism and peculiar sex determination. Larva has potentialities of both sexes. If larva attaches to body of female it metamorphoses into minute male with a gonad but with other organs degenerated. It migrates to female nephridium to fertilize eggs for a season. If larva develops in sea water it becomes a female.

and *Saccosoma*. Altogether there are more than sixty species.

PHYLUM SIPUNCULOIDEA*

Sipunculoids are marine worms which live in the sand or among the rocks of the seashore. Some are small, slender worms but generally they are more robust and may reach a length of 1 foot or more. They have no segmentation or setae. The anterior part of the body is called the **introvert** and is retractile. The body wall is made up of a cuticle, an epidermis of a single layer of cells, a dermis of connective tissue which contains several kinds of glands and sense papillae, and a musculature of three layers—circular, oblique and longitudinal. The ciliated **coelom** is large and contains connective tissue, muscle fibers, and coelomic fluid. The mouth region is surrounded by tentacles, and the alimentary canal is a uniform tube which turns to the posterior end and then doubles back on itself to end in the anus near the base of the introvert. Two groups of rectal glands open into the rectum near the anus. Usually there is a single pair of nephridia, which are brown tubes that open into the coelom and to the outside anterior to the anus.

There are no circulatory or respiratory systems, but the coelomic fluid contains red corpuscles which bear a pigment haemerythrin, containing iron. This pigment is used in the transportation of oxygen. The coelomic fluid also contains other formed elements, such as amebocytes. The nervous system has a bilobed cerebral ganglion just behind and dorsal to the tentacles, which sends connectives to a ventral nerve cord extending the length of the body. Although it has no ganglionic enlargements, the cord gives off many lateral nerves. The sexes are separate, but definite gonads are lacking, for the ovaries or testes develop seasonally in the connective tissue covering of the retractor muscles. When released, the sexual elements are carried from the

*Si-pun′cu-loi″de-a (L. *sipunculus*, a little siphon).

244

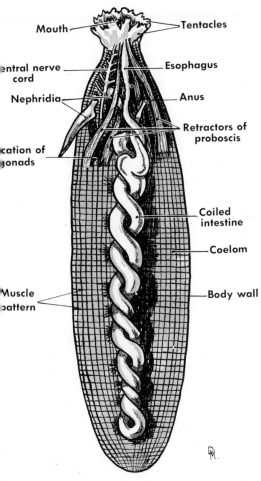

Mouth—
—Tentacles
entral nerve—
cord
—Esophagus
Nephridia—
—Anus
—Retractors of
proboscis
cation of
gonads
—Coiled
intestine
—Coelom
Muscle
pattern
—Body wall

Figure 155. Internal structure of *Sipunculus*. Although not segmented, phylum Sipunculoidea shows many close affinities to annelid worms, for two groups have same type of cleavage, same method of coelom formation, same type of nervous system, and other similarities.

coelomic fluid to the outside through the nephridia. The larval form is usually a trochophore, and no trace of segmentation is found in it. Of the 200 or 300 species, the best known genera are *Sipunculus* (Figure 155), *Dendrostoma*, and *Phascolion*.

Many authorities have placed the sipunculoids and echiuroids together under the group Gephyrea as a class of the Annelida, but aside from some similarities, the two groups differ in many important respects, such as the anterior end, the position of the anus, and the presence or absence of the setae.

PHYLUM BRYOZOA (ECTOPROCTA)*

Bryozoa take their name from the Greek word *bryon*, moss, and are commonly called the moss animals. They have a more advanced structure than hydroids, which they resemble. Most of them live in marine waters, although a few are found in fresh water. They are forms which one is likely to overlook, for they are microscopic and form colonies that resemble thin, matlike debris on rocks, shells, or stems of plants. Some of the colonies, however, may attain considerable size. Although most colonies are attached, there are some that float around free. Since these have plantlike characteristics, they are often confused with seaweeds.

Characteristics. Bilateral symmetry; unsegmented; form colonies by budding; each individual in a cup-shaped shell (zoecium); coelom; U-shaped alimentary canal; ciliated lophophore around mouth; anus outside lophophore; no excretory or vascular systems; nerve ganglion between mouth and anus; monoecious or dioecious reproduction; brood pouch (ooecium); form of trochophore larva.

Structure and behavior. Bryozoa are ordinarily found in shallow water. Their food consists of small plants and animals caught by the lophophore, which is also used for respiration. This ridge, the lophophore, bears a circle of ciliated tentacles and tends to be circular in marine forms and U shaped in fresh-water Bryozoa. The entire crown can be drawn into the protective shell or zoecium by retractor muscles. The digestive system is U shaped, consisting of a mouth within the ring of tentacles, an enlarged pharynx, a slender esophagus, a V-shaped stomach, and an intestine which terminates in the anus outside of the lophophore. Digestion is extracellular. The true coelom is filled with

---

*Bri′o-zo″a (Gr. *bryon*, moss, + *zoion*, animal). Ek′to-prok″ta (Gr. *ektos*, outside, + *proktos*, anus).

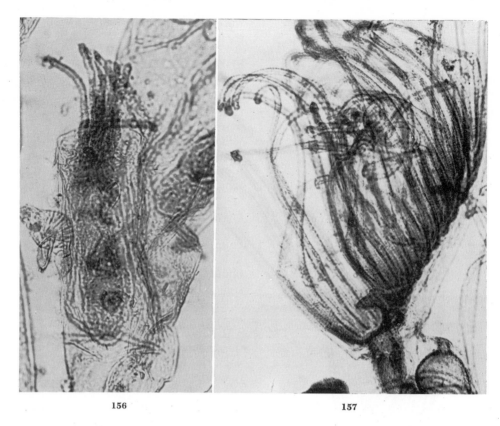

Figure 156. Part of a colony of *Bugula*. Zooid is seen with tentacles above, an avicularium, looking like a bird's beak, on left. See Figure 158 for detailed structure.

Figure 157. Zooid of *Plumatella,* colonial fresh-water bryozoan.

a coelomic fluid which distributes the food in the absence of a circulatory system. Most members of the phylum go through a periodical renewal process, when the tentacles and internal organs degenerate into a compact mass called the "brown body." When new organs are regenerated from the body wall, the brown body is discharged through the anus. Since there is no excretory system, the brown body may have some relation to excretion. The muscular system consists mainly of the body wall muscles and the retractor muscles referred to earlier. The nervous system is composed of a single ganglion between the lophophore and anus and many nerves to the tentacles, digestive system, muscles, and a few other places. No sense organs can be detected.

The colonies grow by asexual reproduction. Some of the individuals (zooids) (Figure 158) are provided with an interesting structure, the **avicularium,** which resembles the beak of a bird and is used to keep other animals away as well as to remove debris which might settle on the colonies. When living zooids are observed, these avicularia are seen constantly opening and snapping closed. In sexual reproduction the eggs are fertilized in the coelom and develop in the ooecium, which is a modified portion of the body cavity. The testis is formed on a special mesentery (funiculus) which extends from the stomach to the posterior body wall; the ovary, on the peritoneum of the coelom.

Fresh-water bryozoans form interesting mosslike colonies on the stems of plants or on sticks. They are usually found in shallow water of ponds or pools; the colonies as a whole may have the power of gliding along the object on which they are supported. Fresh-water bryozoans also have a peculiar type of asexual reproduction by which internal buds known as statoblasts (Figure 159) are formed. When the members of a colony die in late autumn these statoblasts are released and in the spring can produce new colonies.

The most common marine form of the bryozoans is *Bugula* (Figures 156 and 158); the most common fresh-water ones

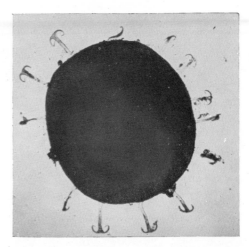

Figure 159. Statoblast of *Pectinatella*. (Photomicrograph, greatly enlarged.)

are *Plumatella* and *Pectinatella*. Altogether, there are more than 2,000 species recognized in this phylum.

PHYLUM BRACHIOPODA*

The animals of phylum Brachiopoda resemble the mollusks in having two valves (shells), but in this phylum the valves are dorsal and ventral instead of lateral, as in the mollusks. The name is derived from the Greek words *brachion*, arm, and *podos*, foot. Formerly these animals were classified with the Mollusca, but they differ from that phylum not only in the arrangement of the valves but also in internal details. Because brachiopods resemble the lamps of the ancients, they are often referred to as lamp shells. The ventral valve is larger than the dorsal one and is provided with a fleshy peduncle which is used for attaching the animal to the sea bottom or to some object. All members of the phylum are marine and solitary. They represent a very ancient group, and in the past they were far more abundant than they are now. Some have undergone few changes since early geological periods. They have left an excellent fossil record. About 200 living species are found in the group.

—————
*Bra'chi-op"o-da (Gr. *brachion*, arm, + *podos*, foot).

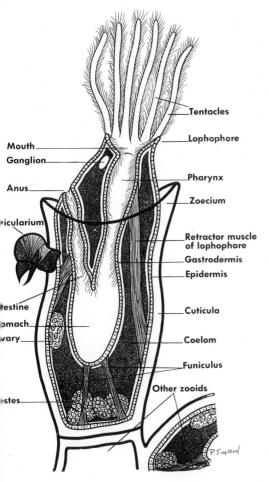

Tentacles
Lophophore
Mouth
Ganglion
Pharynx
Anus
Zoecium
icularium
Retractor muscle of lophophore
Gastrodermis
Epidermis
testine
Cuticula
omach
vary
Coelom
Funiculus
Other zooids
stes

P. Simpson

Figure 158. Semidiagrammatic structure of zooid of *Bugula* (phylum Ectoprocta.) This phylum has external fossil record dating back to Ordovician period. Its nearest relatives seem to be members of phylum Phoronida.

Phyla of uncertain relationships 247

Figure 160. *Terebratulina*, common brachiopod, or lamp shell. Anterior end is gape of shell. Note how shell is covered with skeletons of other invertebrates, including another brachiopod.

Characteristics. Bilateral symmetry; no segmentation; dorsal and ventral calcareous shells; peduncle as an attachment organ; true coelom; lophophore of two coiled ridges; heart and blood vessels; one or two pairs of nephridia; nerve ring; separate sexes; digestive system complete or incomplete; a form of trochophore larva.

Structure and behavior. The body is enclosed between the two valves, but most of it is in the posterior region. Two flaps, the dorsal and ventral mantle lobes, are formed from the body wall. The horseshoe-shaped lophophore bears long ciliated tentacles which are used for food getting and respiration. The mouth is in the middle of the lophophore and leads into a gullet which opens into the stomach provided with digestive glands. The intestine usually ends blindly in most lamp shells. There are well-developed muscles for opening and closing the valves. The nephridia have one opening in the coelom and the other in the mantle cavity. A contractile heart, blood vessels, and nerve ring are also present. The paired gonads in each sex discharge their

products through the nephridia. Development is by metamorphosis, and the free-swimming larval form has a resemblance to the trochophore larva before it becomes attached.

The most common species are *Terebratulina transversa* (Figure 160) and *Megellania leticularis.*

PHYLUM CHAETOGNATHA*

Another name for these organisms is arrowworms. They are marine animals and are considered by some to be related to the nematodes and by others, to the annelids. However, they really show no distinct relations to other groups and are aberrant. The name Chaetognatha is derived from the Greek words *chaeton,* bristle, and *gnathos,* jaw. These forms bear sickle-shaped bristles on each side of the mouth, hence their name. This is not a large group, for there are fewer than fifty known species. Their small, straight bodies, which resemble miniature torpedoes, are from 1 to 3 inches long and are transparent and difficult to see. They are the only invertebrates with more than one layer of cells in the epidermis.

Characteristics. Bilateral symmetry; unsegmented; body divided into head, trunk, and tail; body with lateral fins and caudal fins; coelom present; digestive system complete; vascular, excretory, and respiratory organs absent; dorsal and ventral ganglia; head with eyes, hermaphroditic with self- or cross-fertilization; no metamorphosis; belong to the Deuterostomia.

Structure and behavior. Arrowworms are fairly advanced worms, as attested by their complete digestive system, their well-developed coelomic cavity, their distinct regions of the body, and their prominent nervous system. However, their lack of vascular and excretory systems indicates a rather primitive structure. Their postanal tail is found in no other group except the chordates. An unique hood

---

*Ke-tog′na-tha (Gr. *chaeton,* bristle, + *gnathos,* jaw).

Figure 161. The arrowworm, *Sagitta*. Head (top) is largely covered with hood formed from epidermis. When worm is engaged in catching its prey, hood is retracted to neck region.

(fold of body wall) can be drawn over the head.

Most of these forms swim near the surface, although sometimes they may be found at a depth of several hundred feet. They have the habit of coming to the surface at night and descending to lower depths during the day. They are rapid swimmers. Arrowworms are predaceous and feed on small plants and animals. Each specimen has two ovaries and two testes; these are provided with oviducts and vas deferens. The sperm of one animal enter the oviducts of another, fertilizing the eggs internally, although self-fertilization may also occur. When the eggs are laid they develop directly into worms without metamorphosis.

The most common representative is *Sagitta*, the common arrowworm (Figures 161 and 162).

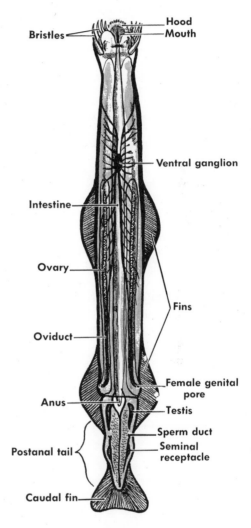

Figure 162. Arrowworm, *Sagitta*, from ventral side. These worms, rarely more than 2 or 3 inches long, form important part of marine plankton in both littoral and open sea waters. They have many resemblances to certain pseudocoelomates, and some authorities hesitate to call them coelomate animals, although they are enterocoelous and are placed in Deuterostomia. Among their features are postanal tail, hood, fins, and stratified epidermis.

Phyla of uncertain relationships 249

Derivations and meaning of basic terminology

avicularium (L. *avis*, bird, + *aria*, like) Modified zooid which is attached to the surface of the major zooid in Bryozoa and resembles a bird's beak.

Bugula (L. *bugulus*, bunch of flowers).

Ectoprocta (Gr. *ektos*, outside, + *proktos*, anus) Another name for the phylum Bryozoa.

Entoprocta (Gr. *entos* inside, + *proktos*, anus) Anus is located inside of the lophophore in this phylum.

lophophore (Gr. *lophos*, crest, + *phoros*, bearing) A ridge about the mouth region bearing tentacles.

ooecium (Gr. *oion*, egg, + *oikos*, house) Brood pouch.

Phoronida (Gr. *phoros*, bearing, + *nidus*, nest).

Sagitta (L. *sagitta*, arrow).

Sipunculoidea (L. *sipunculus*, a little siphon) Refers to the long slender worm and the U-shaped alimentary canal.

trochophore (Gr. *trochos*, wheel, + *phoros*, bearing).

trochozoon (Gr. *trochos*, wheel, + *zoon*, animal).

zoecium (Gr. *zoon*, animal, + *oikos*, house) Cuticular sheath or shell of Bryozoa.

ANNOTATED REFERENCES

Borradaile, L. A., and F. A. Potts. 1958. The Invertebrata, ed. 3 (revised by G. A. Kerkut). Cambridge, Cambridge University Press. *Descriptions of the various minor phyla are given. The most complete account is the one on Bryozoa (Ectoprocta).*

Hyman, L. H. 1951. The Invertebrates. Vol. 3 Acanthocephala, Aschelminthes, and Entoprocta. New York, McGraw-Hill Book Co. Inc. *An excellent account is given of the phylum Entoprocta in the last chapter of this volume.*

Hyman, L. H. 1959. The Invertebrates: Smaller Coelomate Groups, vol. 5. New York, McGraw-Hill Book Co., Inc. *Up-to-date accounts of Chaetognatha, Phoronida, Ectoprocta, Brachiopoda, and Sipunculida. This volume maintains the high traditions of the others in this outstanding modern treatise of zoology.*

Rogick, M. D. 1935. Studies on Fresh-Water Bryozoa. II. The Bryozoa of Lake Erie. Tr. Am. Micro. Soc., vol. 54, pp. 245-263. *This and other papers on Bryozoa by the same author represent the best available accounts of American fresh-water species.*

Stunkard, H. A. 1954. The Life History and Systematic Relations of the Mesozoa. Quart. Rev. Biol., vol. 29, pp. 230-244. *The author presents evidence that the primitive characters of this group are secondarily acquired and that the Mesozoa should be assigned the status of a class in the phylum Platyhelminthes.*

chapter 15

Phylum Annelida*

BIOLOGICAL PRINCIPLES

Organ-system level of organization

1. The organs having related functions are now grouped into definite **systems.**

2. The appearance of **metamerism** for the first time lays the groundwork for a more highly organized type of animal.

3. Annelids as a group show a primitive metamerism with few differences between different somites but some do show the beginning of such differentiation.

4. Annelids belong to the protostome branch, or schizocoelous coelomates, of the animal kingdom and have spiral and determinate cleavage.

Biological contributions

1. The introduction of **metamerism** by the group represents the greatest advancement.

2. A true coelomic cavity reaches a high stage of development, necessitating development of various systems to carry out its functions, such as a separation of the circulatory from the digestive system.

3. Specialization of the head region into differentiated organs, such as the tentacles, palps, and eyespots of the polychaetes, is carried further in some annelids than in other invertebrates so far considered.

4. The tendency toward **centralization of the nervous system** is more developed, with cerebral ganglia (brain), two closely fused ventral nerve cords running the length of the body with unique giant fibers, and various ganglia with their lateral branches.

5. The well-developed **nephridia** in most of the somites have reached a differentiation which involves a removal of waste from the blood as well as from the coelom.

6. The circulatory system is much more complex than any we have so far considered. It is a closed system with muscular blood vessels and **aortic arches (hearts)** for propelling the blood.

7. The appearance of the fleshy **parapodia** with their respiratory function introduces the possibility of the specialized gills in higher forms.

8. Annelids are the most highly organized animals capable of complete regeneration.

Position in animal kingdom

1. The segmented worms share with the flatworms similar larval forms, such as the trochophore larva which is used as a basis of relationship between the two.

2. Subphylum Onychophora of the arthropods has both annelid and arthropod characteristics and is often considered as a transitional link between the two phyla.

3. In their embryonic patterns, annelids have much in common with the mollusks.

4. In the genealogical tree, Annelida are usually placed between Mollusca and Arthropoda, all three coming from the same common stem.

GENERAL RELATIONS

The Annelida are worms whose bodies are divided into similar rings or segments. The origin of the name of the phylum describes this basic characteristic, for it comes from the Latin, *annellus,* meaning little ring. This biological principle of body segmentation is commonly called **metamerism,** and the divisions are known as **segments, somites,** or **metameres.** Worms previously considered do not possess this property of body segmentation, although a hint here and there in the form of transverse grooves may be found.

---

*An-nel'i-da (L. *annellus,* ring).

This metamerism in Annelida is manifested not only in external body features but also in the internal arrangement of organs and systems. Circulatory, excretory, nervous, muscular, and reproductive organs all show a segmental arrangement, and there are internal partitions between the somites.

The phylum is an extensive one and is divided into several classes. Annelids are found in the soil, in fresh water, and in the sea. Many are free living, but some are parasitic in whole or in part of their life cycles.

The annelids show some striking relations to certain other phyla. Their larval stages are similar to those of Platyhelminthes, and their marine representatives have trochophore larvae. One view holds that the adult forms of segmented worms and of flatworms have come from a common ancestor. The gap between the annelids and flatworms is the metamerism. However, the annelids also have many arthropod characteristics such as a hypodermis-secreted cuticle and a nervous system which is fundamentally similar to that of arthropods.

One subphylum (Onychophora) of Arthropoda is a classic example of an intermediate or transition form, for it has both annelid and arthropod characters. Also, there is some similarity of the parapodia in the annelid class Polychaeta to the foliaceous appendages of certain arthropods. In embryonic development, Annelida have a pattern not much different from Mollusca and thus have some features in common with that group. Within the phylum, it is supposed that Polychaeta gave rise to Oligochaeta and Archiannelida, and Oligochaeta gave rise to Hirudinea.

SIGNIFICANCE OF METAMERISM

No satisfactory reason can be given for the origin of metamerism. A number of theories have been proposed, but they lack convincing evidence. One is that chains of subzooids formed by asexual fission in flatworms, instead of separating into distinct individuals, may have held together and developed structural and functional unity with the passage of time. This theory would take into account the axial gradient idea that the anterior individuals would become the dominant part of the chain in determining the coordination of the whole. It is well known that in some platyhelminths the daughter individuals formed by asexual division cling together for some time before separating. Another theory stresses the secondary origin of metamerism by the repetition of body parts, such as muscles, nerves, nephridia, coelom, blood vessels, etc., in a single individual. Later, partitions were interposed to form definite segments. It is also possible that segmentation may have started in the musculature of an elongated, swimming animal, for the breaking up of the body into segments would facilitate swimming movement.

Three phyla—Annelida, Arthropoda, and Chordata—and at least one group (Monoplacophora) of the mollusks exhibit metamerism. Specialization of body parts has rendered it somewhat obscure in the adults of arthropods and chordates, but the larval and embryonic stages, as well as some adult features of these two phyla, reveal it clearly. The fact that these groups have metamerism does not necessarily indicate a close relationship between them, for the condition may have arisen independently by convergent evolution.

It is not clear just why segmentation evolved or how animals were benefited by it in their primitive form. Authorities often mention this character as an advancement, pointing out that each metamere acts as a subunit, specialized for particular functions. This viewpoint would indicate that metamerism is not unlike the formation of cells in a metazoan body in which each cell or group of cells is differentiated for some definite purpose. The possibility of having metameres specialized in various directions for various functions, not marked in the Annelida but well developed in the arthropods, has made possible a rapid evolution of high organization in animals.

252

CHARACTERISTICS

1. Body **metamerically segmented;** symmetry bilateral; three germ layers
2. Body wall with outer circular and inner longitudinal muscle layers; transparent moist cuticle, secreted by columnar epithelium (hypodermis), covers body
3. **Chitinous setae,** which may or may not be on fleshy parapodia for appendages; absent in some
4. Coelom (schizocoele) well developed in most and usually divided by septa; coelomic fluid for turgidity
5. **Blood system closed** and segmentally arranged; respiratory pigments (erythrocruorin and chlorocruorin) with amebocytes in blood plasma
6. Digestive system complete and not metamerically arranged
7. Respiration by skin or **gills**
8. Excretory system typically a **pair of nephridia for each metamere**
9. Nervous system with a double ventral nerve cord and a pair of ganglia with lateral nerves in each metamere; brain a pair of dorsally located cerebral ganglia
10. Sensory system of tactile organs, taste buds, statocysts (in some), photoreceptor cells, and eyes with lenses (in some)
11. Hermaphroditic or separate sexes; larvae, if present, trochophore; asexual by budding in some; spiral and determinate cleavage

CLASSES

The annelids are divided into classes primarily on the basis of the presence or absence of parapodia, setae, metameres, and other morphological features.

Class Oligochaeta (ol'i-go-chae"ta) (Gr. *oligos,* few, + *chaite,* hair). Segmented inside and out; no parapodia, relatively few setae present; head small; clitellum present; hermaphroditic, testes anterior to ovaries; no larval stages. Examples: *Lumbricus, Allolobophora, Aeolosoma, Tubifex.*

Class Polychaeta (pol'y-chae"ta) (Gr. *polys,* many, + *chaite,* hair). Parapodia with numerous setae; distinct head with eyes, palps, tentacles; segmentation inside and out; no clitellum; sexes usually separate; gonads in many segments but not permanent; trocho-

phore larva. Examples: *Neanthes, Chaetopterus, Amphitrite, Arenicola, Aphrodite.*

Class Hirudinea (hir'u-din"e-a) (L. *hirudo,* leech). Body with fixed number (thirty-four) of segments subdivided into many annuli; no parapodia or setae; anterior and posterior suckers; coelom reduced by connective tissue and muscles; hermaphroditic; eggs in cocoons; no larval stages; many ectoparasites. Examples: *Hirudo, Placobdella, Macrobdella.*

Class Archiannelida (ar'ki-a-nel"i-da) (Gr. *arch,* first, + annelida). Segmentation chiefly internal; no parapodia or setae; sexes usually separate; trochophore larva usually. Examples: *Polygordius, Dinophilus.*

Since classes Oligochaeta and Polychaeta are both provided with setae, both these classes are sometimes assigned to a group called Chaetopoda (ke-top'o-da) (Gr. *chaite,* hair, + *pous,* foot).

REPRESENTATIVE TYPES
CLASS OLIGOCHAETA
Lumbricus terrestris—earthworm

Habitat. Nearly everyone is familiar with the common earthworm, for it is almost world wide in distribution. One cannot spade the soil without coming in contact with these worms. Moreover, they crawl out on the sidewalks after a heavy rain and are easily seen there. The German name for them is Regenwürmer (rain worms). Who has not observed the robins running over our lawns, stopping now and then to pull a "fishing worm" out of its burrow? Earthworms like moist, rich soil for their burrows. Golf courses are excellent places to see these holes, for there the same burrow may be used for a long period of time and the castings of the worms are very much in evidence. *Eisenia foetida,* the brandling, a smaller worm and often studied in zoology, is found in manure piles. Sandy, clay, and acid soils and soil deficient in humus are unfavorable for earthworms. Earthworms are chiefly nocturnal. At night they emerge from their burrows to explore their surroundings, often keeping their tails in their burrows into which they rapidly withdraw when disturbed. During very dry weather the earthworm may coil up in a slime-lined chamber several feet under-

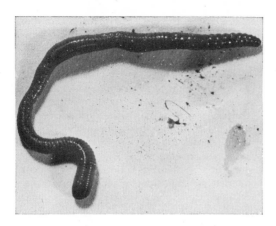

Figure 163. Common earthworm, *Lumbricus terrestris*. Head at upper right. Swollen region about one-third of distance from anterior end is clitellum.

ground and pass into a state of dormancy.

External features. The body of the earthworm is elongated, cylindrical in form, and tapering at each end. The body is divided into 100 to 175 **metameres** or somites (500 to 600 in giant earthworms) which are separated from each other by grooves. Few metameres are added after hatching. The usual length of the common earthworm is from 5 to 12 inches. On the anterior side of the first metamere is the **mouth** overhung by the fleshy **prostomium** (regarded by some as the first segment). The **anus** is located on the last segment. Straddled over the back like a saddle (in somites 31 to 37) is the swollen, whitish, glandular **clitellum,** which is important in the reproductive process. Both prostomium and clitellum are useful in taxonomic determinations.

The external surface of the worm is covered by a thin, transparent **cuticle** (cuticula) bearing cross-striations which give it an iridescent appearance. The cuticle is secreted by the epidermal cells which lie just beneath it. The **epidermis** contains **unicellular glands** whose secretions reach the surface through pores in the cuticle. There are also sensory and small basal cells in the epidermis. Beneath the epidermis is the **basement membrane** which rests upon the muscle layers that make up most of the body wall. Certain pigments, such as protoporphyrin, are also found in the body wall.

OPENINGS. Many external openings are found for taking in food, for discharging feces and waste products, and for the exit and entrance of the reproductive cells. They may be enumerated as follows: (1) **mouth;** (2) **anus;** (3) openings of the paired **vasa deferentia** on somite 15; easily recognized on the ventral surface of this somite by their swollen lips; serve for the exit of the sperm; (4) openings of the paired **oviducts** on the ventral side of somite 14; are small and serve for the exit of the eggs; (5) openings of the two pairs of **seminal receptacles** in the grooves between somites 9 and 10 and 10 and 11; serve to pick up sperm from a mate during copulation; (6) paired excretory openings (**nephridiopores**) on the lateroventral side of each segment except the first three and the last; (7) **dorsal pores,** one of which is located in the mid-dorsal line at the anterior edge of each somite from 8 or 9 to the last one; are openings into the coelomic cavity. Coelomic fluid of a malodorous nature may be ejected through these pores for defense.

LOCOMOTION. With the exception of the first and last somites, each segment bears four pairs of chitinous **setae** which are located on the ventral and lateral surfaces. Each seta (Figure 164) is a bristlelike rod which is set in a sac within the body wall. It is moved by retractor and protractor muscles attached to the sac. The setae project through small pores in the cuticle to the outside. When an earthworm is moving forward, the setae anchor the somites of a part of the body and prevent backward slipping. The contraction of the circular muscles in the anterior end pushes the body forward and is followed by the contraction of the longitudinal muscles which pulls the posterior part of the body anteriorly. By the repetition of this process the worm is able to advance with speed. Rarely do worms use the setae as levers while moving, for this is usually too slow for them. Setae are also used by the worm to hold fast in the burrow, as

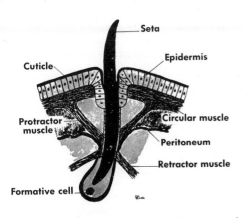

Figure 164. Diagram of a seta with its muscle attachments, showing relation to adjacent structures. Setae lost by wear and tear are replaced by new ones which develop from formative cell. (Modified from Stephenson and others.)

all robins well know. When a seta is lost, a new one is formed in a reserve follicle to replace it.

Body plan. The earthworms have a tube-within-a-tube arrangement. There is a body wall of external **circular** muscles and a thicker internal layer of **longitudinal** muscles lying just underneath the epidermis and its basement membrane. This body wall surrounds the **coelomic cavity. Coelomic fluid** within the cavity gives rigidity to the body by maintaining turgor. The fluid contains two main types of coelomic cells: **leukocytes** (phagocytic ameboid cells), and **eleocytes** which come from the chlorogogue cells of the digestive tract and carry nutritive granules to all parts of the body. The coelomic cavity is divided by **septa** which mark the boundaries of the somites. These septa are not always complete and may be absent between certain somites. The inner surface of the coelom, as well as the outer surface of its organs, is lined with **peritoneum.** Through the center of the coelom runs the alimentary canal from the first to the last segment. The septa help hold it in place. The metameric arrangement is noticeable in the distribution of certain visceral organs; for instance, a pair of nephrida and a pair of nervous ganglia are located in each of the somites. Other

visceral organs—reproductive apparatus and the main circulatory vessels—are closely located around the alimentary canal, which serves as a sort of body axis.

Internal features. When an earthworm is placed in water and cut open through the mid-dorsal region and the walls are pinned out, the internal organs are revealed to the view of the student. The visceral organs and systems that are easily seen in such a dissection are as follows: (1) the alimentary canal, running straight through the worm, (2) the dorsal blood vessel just dorsal to the digestive tract, and the paired aortic arches in segments 7 to 11, (3) the white, glandlike seminal vesicles folded over on the digestive system in segments 9 to 12, (4) the thin partitions of septa (with pores for passage of coelomic fluid) which divide the coelom into compartments, (5) the little fluffy nephridia in each somite, (6) the cerebral ganglia (brain) on the dorsal side of the anterior pharynx, and (7) the ventral nerve cord and its ganglia running along the floor of the coelomic cavity when the alimentary canal is pushed aside.

DIGESTIVE SYSTEM. The alimentary canal of the earthworm is divided into a large number of compartments, each with certain special functions to perform. The parts of the system are (1) the **mouth** and **buccal cavity** in somites 1 to 3, (2) the muscular **pharynx** in somites 4 to 5, (3) the straight **esophagus** with three pairs of **calciferous** glands in somites 6 to 14, (4) the thin-walled, enlarged **crop** in somites 15 to 16, (5) the thick, muscular **gizzard** in somites 17 to 18, and (6) the long **intestine,** with slight bulges in each somite, from somite 19 to the last somite, where it ends in the **anus.** When seen in section, the intestine reveals on its dorsal wall a peculiar infolded **typhlosole** (Figure 166), which greatly increases the absorptive and digestive surface. The lining of the digestive system is made up of simple columnar epithelium which is ciliated. Longitudinal and circular muscles are found in the wall of the system, and curious yellow **chloragogue cells** from the

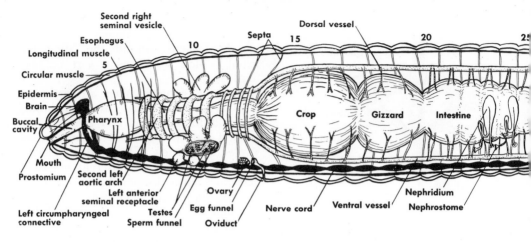

Figure 165. Chief internal features of anterior portion of earthworm as shown by removal of left body wall.

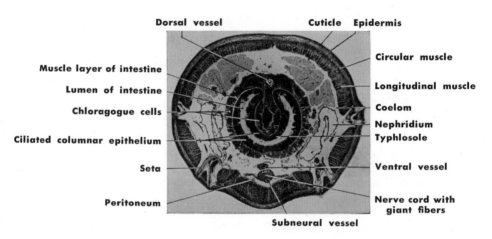

Figure 166. Cross-section of earthworm back of clitellum, showing arrangement of setae and general internal structures. Section made between septa to reveal muscular bands. (Courtesy General Biological Supply House, Chicago.)

peritoneum surround the digestive tract and fill much of the typhlosole. The chloragogue cells store foodstuffs and may convert protein into fat. When a cell is ripe (full of fat) its nucleus divides mitotically and the fat-containing portion of the cell constricts off as an eleocyte. The eleocytes, or wandering cells, apparently contribute their fat to other body cells. The chloragogue cells also function in excretion.

The food is mainly decayed organic matter, bits of leaves and vegetation, refuse, and animal matter. After being moistened by secretions from the mouth food is drawn in by the sucking action of the pharynx when it is enlarged by the numerous muscles extending from it to the body wall. The liplike prostomium aids in manipulating the food into position. The calciferous glands, by secreting calcium carbonate, may neutralize the acidity of the food, or they may simply excrete calcium as a metabolic product. Food is stored temporarily in the crop before being passed on into the gizzard which grinds the food into small pieces. Digestion and absorption take place in the intestine. The digestive system secretes various enzymes which break down the food—pepsin, which acts upon protein; amylase, which acts upon carbohydrates; cellulase, which acts upon cellulose; and lipase, which acts upon fats. The indigestible residue is discharged through the anus. Naturally, earthworms take in a great deal of soil, sand, and other indigestible matter along with their food. In hard, firm soil, worms literally eat their way through the soil in their burrowing; this accounts for their numerous castings. The food products are absorbed into the blood which carries them to the various parts of the body for assimilation. Some of the food is absorbed into the coelomic

fluid which also aids in food distribution.

CIRCULATORY SYSTEM. The circulatory system of the earthworm (Figure 167) is a "closed system" consisting of a complicated pattern of blood vessels and capillaries which ramify to all parts of the body. There are five main blood trunks, all running lengthwise of the body. These may be described as follows:

1. The **dorsal vessel** (single), which runs above the alimentary canal from the pharynx to the anus. It is provided with valves and is the true heart. This vessel receives blood from the **parietal vessels,** the **dorsointestinal vessels,** and the **lateral esophageal vessels** and pumps the blood by peristalsis anteriorly into the five pairs of **aortic arches** ("hearts"), pharyngeal wall, and **afferent typhlosolar**

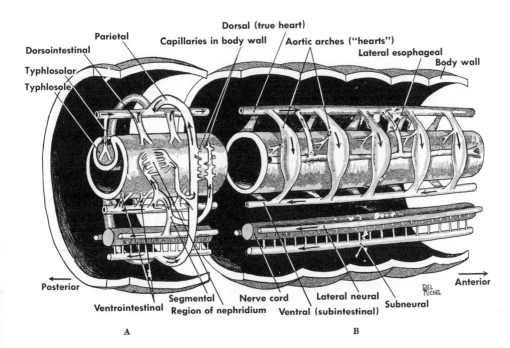

Figure 167. Scheme of circulatory system in the earthworm, *Lumbricus terrestris,* showing direction (by arrows) of blood flow in principal blood vessels (semilateral view). **A,** Region of body behind somite 12. **B,** Region of somites 7 to 11, showing aortic arches or hearts. Septa relations not shown. Blood is distributed to dorsal vessel (true pumping organ) by parietals, dorsointestinals, and lateral esophageals; dorsal vessel sends blood to dorsal wall of gut by typhlosolars and to subintestinal by aortic arches; subintestinal gives off ventrointestinals to ventral part of intestine and segmentals to lateral neurals, body wall, and nephridia; parietals pick up vessels from nephridia and subneural (from nerve cord) and dermal vessels (from body wall) before entering dorsal vessel. (Modified from many sources.)

vessel. The chief function of the aortic arches is to maintain a steady pressure of blood into the subintestinal vessel.

2. The **ventral vessel (subintestinal)** (single), which lies between the alimentary canal and the nerve cord. This vessel may be considered the real aorta of the earthworm. It receives blood from the aortic arches and delivers it anteriorly to the brain and other regions and posteriorly to the tail region. As the subintestinal vessel passes backward it gives off (a) a pair of **segmental vessels** in each segment, which sends branches to the body wall musculature, nephridia, and lateral neural vessels, and (b) a pair of **ventrointestinal vessels** in each segment to the alimentary canal.

3. The **lateral neural vessels** (double), which lie one on each side of the nerve cord. These receive the blood from the segmental vessels and carry it posteriorly with many branches to the nerve cord.

4. The **subneural vessel** (single), which is found under the nerve cord. This blood vessel is the main vein. It receives blood from the nerve cord and passes it backward toward the tail and upward through the paired **parietal vessels** in each segment (from somite 12 posteriorly). The parietal vessels also drain the blood from the nephridia and from the body wall and return it to the dorsal vessel.

In this scheme it will be seen that the circulation of the alimentary tract is the most involved, for its ventral half is supplied by the ventral intestinal vessels

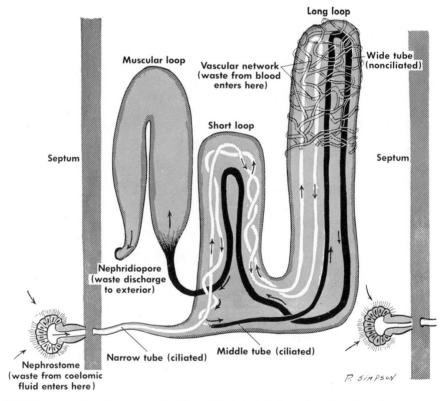

Figure 168. Diagram of earthworm nephridium. Wastes picked up by ciliated nephrostome in one somite, carried through tube enclosed in loops of connective tissue, and expelled through nephridiopore in next somite. Only part of extensive network of blood vessels shown. Note that tube is differentiated into characteristic regions. (Redrawn with modifications from Moment: General Zoology, Houghton Mifflin Co.)

258

rom the subintestinal vessel and its dorsal half by paired typhlosolar vessels (two per somite) from the dorsal vessel. Nearly all the blood from the alimentary anal returns to the dorsal vessel by the dorsointestinal vessels (two pairs per somite). Since the parietal vessels do not extend anteriorly to somite 12, the anterior end is drained by the lateral esophageal vessels, which empty into the dorsal vessel at somite 10 and into the parietal vessels at somite 12.

The propulsion necessary to force the blood along is provided by the peristaltic or milking action of the muscular walls of the blood vessels, particularly the dorsal vessel. Valves in the vessels prevent backflow.

The blood of the earthworm is made up of a **liquid plasma** in which are colorless ameboid cells, **corpuscles**. Dissolved in the blood plasma is the pigment **erythrocruorin** which is similar to hemoglobin and of enormous molecular weight. This gives a red color to the blood and aids in the transportation of oxygen for respiration.

EXCRETORY SYSTEM. The organs of excretion are the **nephridia**, a pair of which is found in each somite except the first three and the last one. These nephrida are all of the same plan, and each one is found in parts of two successive somites (Figure 168). A ciliated funnel known as the **nephrostome** is found just anterior to an intersegmental septum and leads by a small ciliated tubule through the septum into the somite behind, where it connects with the main part of the nephridium. This part of the nephridium is made up of several complex loops of increasing size, which finally terminate in a bladder-like structure leading to an aperture, the **nephridiopore**; this opens to the outside near the ventral row of setae. By means of cilia, wastes from the coelom are drawn into the nephrostome and tubule, where they are joined by organic wastes from the blood capillaries in the glandular part of the nephridium. All the waste is discharged to the outside through the nephridiopore. Chloragogue cells may store

waste temporarily before releasing it into the coelomic fluid.

RESPIRATORY SYSTEM. The earthworm has no special respiratory organs, but the gaseous exchange is made in the moist skin, where oxygen is picked up and carbon dioxide given off. Blood capillaries are fairly numerous just below the cuticle, and the oxygen combines with the erythrocruorin of the plasma and is carried to the various tissues.

NERVOUS SYSTEM AND SENSE ORGANS. The nervous system in earthworms (Figure 169) consists of a **central system** and **peripheral nerves.** The central system is made up of a pair of **suprapharyngeal ganglia** (brain) just above the anterior part of the pharynx; a pair of **circumpharyngeal connectives,** which run from the brain around the pharynx to the **subpharyngeal ganglia,** located in somite 4; a **ventral nerve cord** (really double), which runs along the floor of the coelom to the last somite; and a pair of fused **ganglia** on the ventral cord in each somite. Each pair of fused ganglia gives off six lateral nerves to the body structures, such as muscles, epidermis, nephridia, and setae, in each somite. Both sensory and motor fibers are found in these lateral nerves. The sensory fibers come from special cells in the epidermis and carry impulses originating there to the ventral nerve cord. Motor nerves run from cells in the ganglia to muscles or glands. The unit of nervous structure here, as in all higher forms, is the **neuron,** which is a nerve cell with its branches. Thus the sensory fibers belong to sensory neurons and motor fibers to motor neurons. The brain of an earthworm contains neurosecretory cells, and the segmental ganglia have chromaffin cells; each of these types of cells may have an endocrine function.

For rapid escape movements, the nerve cord of earthworms is provided with three giant fibers (neurochords) which run the length of the cord (Figure 170). Each neurochord is made up of fibers (axons) contributed by nerve cells in each segment. These axons are fused end to end at the intersegmental synapses which al-

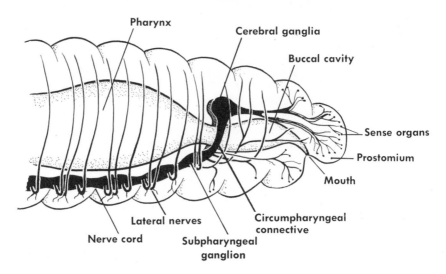

Figure 169. Anterior portion of earthworm, showing relations of nervous system to that part of body. Note concentration of sense organs in this region. (Modified from Hess and others.)

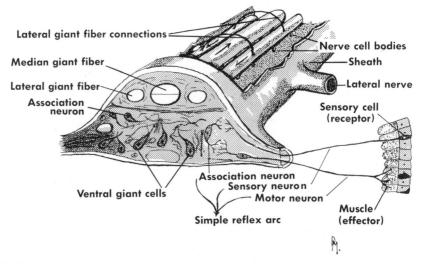

Figure 170. How an earthworm jerks back into its burrow. Nerve cord of earthworm has five giant fibers—three dorsal and two ventral—running lengthwise in it. Dorsal fibers are adapted for fast movement. Ordinary crawling involves succession of reflex acts from anterior to posterior somites; stretching of one somite stimulates next one to stretch, producing waves of muscle contraction in response to sequence of reflex acts. When danger threatens, the three dorsal giant fibers allow rapid transmission. Median fiber conducts toward tail; lateral fibers toward head, with rate of nervous conduction in giant fibers five times as fast as in regular nerves, so that every segment can contract simultaneously and jerk worm into its burrow. Arrangement of a simple reflex arc is shown in right foreground.

low rapid transmission of impulses because of the direct one-to-one relation. The giant fibers carry impulses at a rate of 100 feet per second; in other nerves the speed is only 20 feet per second. The median neurochord is concerned with sensory stimulation in the anterior part of the animal and transmits impulses to posterior

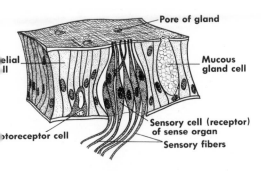

Pore of gland

...elial ...ll

Mucous gland cell

...toreceptor cell

Sensory cell (receptor) of sense organ

Sensory fibers

...igure 171. Diagram of a portion of epidermis ...f earthworm, showing its various specializations. ...vidence indicates that earthworms are sensitive ...) many kinds of stimuli, such as mechanical ...ibration, light, temperature, taste, and touch. ...Vhether or not earthworms have differentiated ...ense organs for each of these senses is not ...nown, but several different morphological types ...f sense organs have been demonstrated.

...ffectors (muscles or glands). The lateral ...eurochords (which are connected) are ...timulated behind that level and send ...nessages to anterior effectors. This mech ...nism explains the speed with which ...vorms can withdraw into their burrows.

Sense organs are distributed all over ...he body and are particularly abundant ...t the anterior and posterior ends. Each ...ense organ consists of sensory cells sur ...ounded by supporting epidermal cells ...Figure 171). The sensory cells are pro ...ided with small, hairlike tips which pro ...ect through pores in the cuticle; the bases ...f these projections are attached to sen ...ory nerve fibers which run to the cen ...ral system. There are also light-sensitive ...ells (photoreceptors) which are in the ...pidermis and which pick up different de ...rees of light intensity. In addition to ...hese sensory organs there are also free ...erve endings between the cells of the ...pidermis which are concerned with sense ...erception.

Earthworm behavior is largely, if not ...ntirely, a matter of reflex acts. These ...nay be considered the unit of physiolog ...cal activity. In the simplest reflex arc a ...ensory neuron makes direct contact with ...1 motor neuron, and such arcs may occur ...n the nervous system of the earthworm.

However, earthworms apparently have a more complicated kind of arc which in volves not only sensory and motor but also **association** neurons (Figure 170). Stimuli are picked up by the **receptor,** or sensory neuron, and the impulse is carried into the central system; here, motor neurons may immediately receive it or it first may be sent to the association neurons which relay it along to the motor. The motor neuron then carries the impulse to the **ef fector** (muscle or gland), and a reflex act is consummated. Reflex acts are usually more involved than this simple one, for many receptors are stimulated and many effectors act at the same time. The asso ciation neurons and fibers are mainly localized in the three **giant fibers** that are found in the dorsal side of the ventral nerve cord and connect the nerve cells in the ganglia with each other, thus facilitat ing widespread contractions of the worm's body.

REPRODUCTIVE SYSTEM. Earthworms are monoecious or hermaphroditic; that is, both male and female organs are found in the same animal (Figure 172). The male organs consist of (1) two pairs of small, hand-shaped **testes** in somites 10 and 11, (2) a **sperm funnel** behind each testis, (3) a small tube, the **vas efferens,** connected

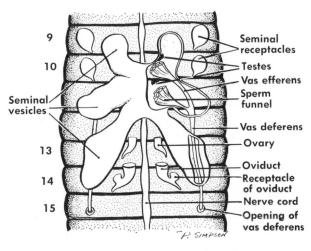

9

10

Seminal vesicles

13

14

15

Seminal receptacles

Testes

Vas efferens

Sperm funnel

Vas deferens

Ovary

Oviduct

Receptacle of oviduct

Nerve cord

Opening of vas deferens

R. SIMPSON

Figure 172. Reproductive organs of earthworm. Dorsal view, with seminal vesicles partly removed on right side.

to each sperm funnel, (4) a pair of **vasa deferentia,** each of which is made up of two vasa efferentia on a side, (5) the openings of the two vasa deferentia on the ventral side of somite 15, and (6) three pairs of large white **seminal vesicles,** two pairs of which surround the testes. Undifferentiated sperm cells from the testes mature in the seminal vesicles before they are discharged during copulation through the sperm funnels and duct systems to the outside. The female system contains (1) a pair of small **ovaries** in somite 13, (2) a pair of **oviducts,** which open internally by ciliated funnels into the coelom on somite 13 and lead to the exterior on somite 14, and (3) two pairs of **seminal receptacles** in somites 9 and 10, which store sperm received from another worm during copulation. The ovaries discharge mature eggs into the coelomic cavity, whence they are passed into the oviducts.

Reproductive process. Reproduction in earthworms may occur at any season, but it is most common in warm moist weather, such as the spring of the year. The earthworm does not self-fertilize its eggs but receives sperm from another worm during **copulation,** which usually occurs at night. When two worms mate they extend their anterior ends from their burrows and bring their ventral surfaces together with their anterior ends pointed in opposite directions (Figure 173). This arrangement of the bodies places the seminal receptacle openings of one worm in opposition to the clitellum of the other worm, somite 26 of each making contact with somite 15 of the other. They are held together by mucous bands and by special ventral setae which penetrate each other's bodies in the regions of contact. Each worm secretes a slime tube about itself from somites 9 to 36. Sperm passes out of the vasa deferentia of each worm and travels by seminal canals or grooves on the ventral surface to the openings of the seminal receptacles of the other. Thus a reciprocal exchange of sperm is made, and the worms separate. This process of copulation requires about

Figure 173. Two earthworms in copulation. Anterior ends point in opposite directions as their ventral surfaces are held together by mucus band secreted by clitellum. (Courtesy General Biological Supply House, Chicago.)

two hours. Later, each worm secretes a barrel-shaped cocoon about its clitellum within the posterior end of the slime tube. Eggs from the oviducts on somite 14 and albumin from the skin glands are passed to the cocoon while it still encircles the clitellum. The worm then backs out, allowing the slime tube and cocoon to be slipped forward over the head. As the cocoon passes the openings of the seminal receptacles between somites 9 and 10 and 10 and 11, sperm stored from the opposing animal are poured into it. Fertilization of the eggs now takes place within the cocoon. When the cocoon leaves the worm, its ends close, producing a lemon-shaped body. (Figures 174 and 175.) The size of the cocoon varies with different species of earthworms; those in *Lumbricus terrestris* are about 7 by 5 mm. In this form only one of several fertilized eggs develops into a worm, the others acting as nurse cells. Cocoons are commonly deposited in the earth, although they may be found at the surface near the entrance of burrows. Between copulations the earthworm continues to form many cocoons so long as sperm are in the seminal receptacles.

In their development, the eggs are holoblastic, but the cleavage is unequal and spiral. The embryo passes through the blastula and gastrula stages and forms the three germ layers typical of the development of higher forms. The young worm is similar to the adult and escapes from the cocoon in two to three weeks. It does not develop a clitellum until it is sexually mature.

General behavior. Earthworms are admirably adapted for their mode of life. They are part and parcel of the soil, and no form is more earthy than they. They are among the most defenseless of all living creatures, yet their abundance and wide distribution indicate their ability to survive. Although they have no specialized sense organs, they are sensitive to

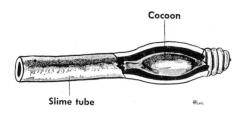

Cocoon

Slime tube

Figure 174. Slime tube and cocoon of earthworm after being cast from body. Each copulating earthworm secretes a slime tube around its segments 9 to 39. Sperm from seminal vesicles on segment 15 of each worm pass along seminal grooves into seminal receptacles of other worm. Cocoons are secreted over clitellum within slime tube, either at time of copulation or after the worms have separated. Eggs and albumin deposited in cocoon while still on clitellum. As worm backs out of slime tube and cocoon, sperm from seminal receptacles enter to fertilize eggs. When cocoon is freed from body its ends close up by constriction of slime tubes (Foote and Strobell). In some species, many eggs develop in each cocoon; in *Lumbricus*, only one.

Figure 175. Earthworm cocoon.

many stimuli, which plays a part in their survival. Among the stimuli to which they are sensitive are **mechanical,** to which they are positive when it is moderate, **vibratory,** such as a footfall near them which causes them to retire quickly into their burrows, and **light,** which they avoid unless it is very weak. They also have chemical responses which undoubtedly aid them in the choice of food. These reactions to chemicals occur not only when the substances are in contact with their bodies but also when substances that produce strong stimuli are some distance away. When irritated they eject coelomic fluid through the dorsal pores.

Experiments show that earthworms have some learning ability. They can be taught to avoid an electric shock, and thus an association reflex can be built up in them. Darwin credited earthworms with a great deal of intelligence in pulling leaves into their burrows, for they apparently seized the leaves by the apex or narrow end, which is the easiest way for drawing such a shaped object into a small hole. Darwin assumed that the seizure of the leaves by the worms was not due to random handling or to chance but was purposeful in its mechanism. Careful investigations by others since Darwin's time have showed that the process is mainly one of trial and error and is accomplished as a chance effect, for earthworms would often seize a leaf several times before the right position was attained.

Annelid worms are perhaps the most highly organized animals that have the power of complete regeneration. Not all of them have this capacity, and in most of them there are certain limitations in the regeneration of lost parts. Leeches have little or no regenerative abilities. Earthworms vary; some species can form two complete worms when cut in two, but other species cannot. In the common earthworm (*Lumbricus*), a posterior piece may regenerate a new head of three to five segments, and an anterior piece (from segment 35 posteriorly) may form a new tail. In the latter case the level of the cut will determine the number of segments regenerated. A cut at segment 50 will regenerate ten fewer segments than one made at the level of segment 40. Earthworms can also be grafted, and pieces of several worms may be grafted end to end to form long worms. The axial gradient theory of the physiological dominance of the anterior end seems to apply to earthworm regeneration the same as to planarians.

Earthworm farming. The value of earthworms in increasing the fertility of the soil has been recognized for centuries. Aristotle called earthworms the "intestines of the soil." Gilbert White, in his well-known *Natural History of Selborne,* spoke of their value in promoting the growth of vegetation by perforating and loosening the soil. He pointed out that a monograph on the economic value of earthworms to agriculture should be written some day. About a century later, Charles Darwin fulfilled this need by writing his classical work, *The Formation of Vegetable Mould Through the Action of Worms.* This work records the observations of the great naturalist on the habits of earthworms over a period of many years. He showed how worms brought the subsoil to the surface and mixed it with the top soil. He estimated that from ten to eighteen tons of dry earth per acre pass through their bodies annually and are brought to the surface. All vegetable mold, he states, passes through the intestines of worms many times. They expose the mold to the air and sift it so that only small particles are left in it. They drag leaves, twigs, and organic substances into their burrows and bring them closer to the roots of plants. The earthworm is known to ingest its own weight in soil every twenty-four hours. Not the least of the worms' value in enriching the soil is the great amount of food elements, such as potassium and phosphorus, which they bring to the surface from the subsoil; the latter is often richer in these elements than the top soil itself. Moreover, the soil that passes through the earthworm's digestive systems may have valuable nitrogenous products from the worms' metabolism. From these benefits and others, Darwin came to the conclusion that it may be doubted whether there are many other animals that have played so important a part in the world's history as have the lowly earthworms.

In recent years many individuals have stressed the importance of culturing earthworms to build up the soil. These enthusiasts maintain that by utilizing the earthworm and promoting its living conditions it is possible to build up any soil to a high degree of fertility. They think that the 25,000 to 50,000 earthworms per acre which Darwin estimated could be multiplied with a consequent improvement of the soil. A great deal of work has been done by selective feeding and breeding to determine what kinds of earthworms are best suited for certain types of soil and food. It is found that certain kinds will thrive only within a range of certain soil acidity, whereas others live in much wider ranges of acidity and alkalinity. This has led to an extensive earthworm culture. Worms are propagated under favorable conditions; then the worms and their egg capsules are planted on soils with the idea of improving them. So far the reports of such experiments have been conflicting, and many scientists are not convinced that such methods of soil improvement are as effective as has been claimed.

Other common oligochaetes

The more than 2,000 species of oligochaetes are found in a great variety of sizes and habitats. Most are terrestrial or fresh-water forms, but some are parasitic. They also vary a great deal in bodily structures and organization. Some of the more common oligochaetes other than earthworms (chiefly small fresh-water forms) are *Aeolosoma* (1 mm. long), which contain red or green pigments, have bundles of setae, and are often found in bay cultures; *Nais* (2 to 4 mm. long), which is brownish in color, with two or three bundles of setae on each segment; *Stylaria* (10 to 25 mm. long), which has two bunches of setae on each segment and

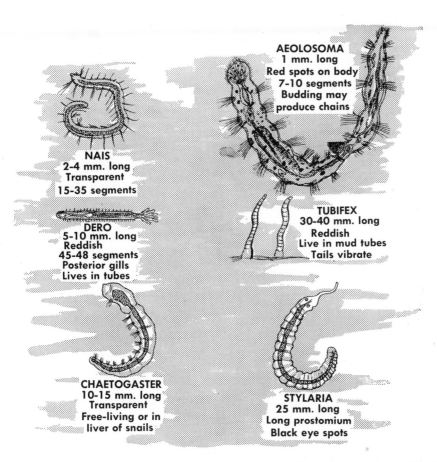

NAIS
2-4 mm. long
Transparent
15-35 segments

AEOLOSOMA
1 mm. long
Red spots on body
7-10 segments
Budding may
produce chains

DERO
5-10 mm. long
Reddish
45-48 segments
Posterior gills
Lives in tubes

TUBIFEX
30-40 mm. long
Reddish
Live in mud tubes
Tails vibrate

CHAETOGASTER
10-15 mm. long
Transparent
Free-living or in
liver of snails

STYLARIA
25 mm. long
Long prostomium
Black eye spots

Figure 176. Some aquatic annelids (Oligochaeta). These are small forms found in mud and debris of stagnant pools and ponds. Their body walls are thin and their internal organs easily seen. Likely to be found in any pond culture, especially one containing blanket algae.

he prostomium extended into a long process; *Dero* (5 to 10 mm. long), which is reddish in color, lives in tubes, and has three tail gills; *Tubifex* (30 to 40 mm. long), which is reddish in color and lives with its head in mud at the bottom of ponds and its tail waving in the water; *Chaetogaster* (10 to 15 mm. long), which has only ventral bundles of setae; and the Enchytraeidae, small whitish worms, which live in both moist soil and water. Some oligochaetes such as *Aeolosoma*, may form chains of zooids asexually by transverse fission.

Giant earthworms (*Megascolides*), some as long as 11 feet and one inch in diameter and weighing more than a pound, are found in Australia. Some in South America are more than 6 feet long. Cocoons of these giant earthworms may be more than 2 inches long and ½ inch in diameter. Naturally the burrows of these giants are large and extensive.

CLASS POLYCHAETA

Comparison of Polychaeta with Oligochaeta. The name Polychaeta comes from a Greek word meaning "many setae," and herein lies one of the main differences between this class and the oligochaetes which have few setae. There are other differences; some concern advancements and some the structures that are less complex than those of the earthworm group. Polychaetes have a well-differentiated head with sensory appendages, lateral parapodia with many setae, and usually separate sexes. Their development is indirect, for they undergo a form of metamorphosis which involves a type of trochophore larva. In contrast to the oligochaetes, members of Polychaeta have no permanent sex organs, and they possess no permanent ducts for their sex cells such as we have seen in the earthworm. However, the polychaetes show a marked differentiation of some body somites and a marked specialization of sensory organs practically unknown among the oligochaetes.

Neanthes (Nereis) virens—clamworm

Habitat. The clamworm (sandworm) (Figure 177) lives in or near the low tide line of the seacoast. These animals often live in burrows which are lined with mucus from their bodies, and sometimes they are found in temporary hiding places such as under stones, where they stay, bodies covered and heads protruding. They are most active at night, when they

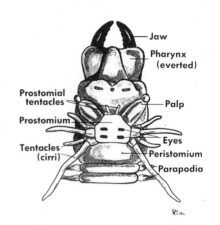

Figure 178. Dorsal view of head region of *Neanthes,* clamworm, with pharynx protruded

wiggle out of their hiding places and swim about or crawl over the sand in search of food.

Structural characteristics. The body is made up of about 200 somites and may be longer than 15 inches. The anterior somites are distinct from the others and form a definite **head** which is divided into the **prostomium** and **peristomium.** The prostomium has a pair of stubby **palps** (for touch and chemical sense), a pair of short **prostomial tentacles,** and two pairs of small dorsal **eyes.** The peristomium is made up of the ventral **mouth,** a pair of chitinous **jaws,** and four pairs of **peristomial tentacles** on the dorsal side. The tentacles and eyes represent specialized organs for sensory perception; the tentacles are for touch, the palps are for taste and smell, and the eyes, for sight. Along the sides of the body are the fleshy **parapodia,** a pair to each somite except those forming the head. Each parapodium is formed of two lobes, a dorsal **notopodium** and a ventral **neuropodium.** The parapodia bear numerous setae and are abundantly supplied with blood vessels. Covering the body of the animal is a cuticle and epidermis, underneath which are circular and longitudinal muscles (Figure 179).

The **coelomic cavity** is lined with peritoneum and is divided by septa between the somites. Holding the digestive system in place and dividing the coelomic cavity of each somite into right and left

Figure 177. Clamworm, *Neanthes virens.* Head with specialized structures at top.

266

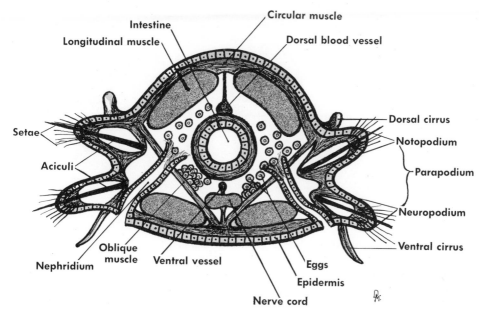

Figure 179. Diagram of transverse section through polychaete, *Neanthes*. Note sharp-pointed, chitinous aciculi, one in each lobe of parapodium. Aciculi, which are really enlarged setae, help support and move parapodium. Contrast this cross-section with that of earthworm.

halves are the dorsal and ventral mesenteries. The **digestive system** contains a mouth, a protrusible pharynx with chitinous jaws, a short esophagus, a stomach-intestine, and an anus. Digestive glands open into the esophagus. The main blood vessels of the **circulatory system** are two longitudinal ones, one ventral and the other dorsal, from which transverse vessels run to the body wall and various visceral organs. Like the earthworm, the clamworm has red blood. There are no special respiratory organs; this function is taken care of by the body wall and by the parapodia. Paired **nephridia** in most of the somites take care of **excretion.** Each nephridium opens into the coelomic cavity by a ciliated funnel, passes posteriorly in coils, and opens to the exterior near the base of a parapodium by the nephridiopore. The whole nephridium is enclosed in a mass of connective tissue.

The **nervous system** is made up of a pair of cerebral ganglia, circumpharyngeal connectives to the ventral nerve cord, and a pair of ganglia with lateral nerves in each somite. Sexes are separate, but the reproductive organs are not permanent, for the sex cells are budded off from the coelomic lining and are carried to the outside by the excretory ducts and by bursting through the body wall. Fertilization is external, and the zygote develops into a free-swimming trochophore larva, which later transforms into a worm.

Locomotion. The worm moves by means of its circular and longitudinal muscles and by its parapodia. The latter are manipulated by oblique muscles which run from the mid-ventral line to the parapodia in each somite. Parapodia are used both for creeping over the sand and for swimming. The animal swims by a lateral wriggling of the body and can dart through the water with considerable speed.

Physiological aspects. The clamworm lives upon small animals, other worms, larval forms, etc., which it seizes with its chitinous jaws that are protruded through the mouth when the pharynx is everted. By withdrawing the pharynx, the food is swallowed. Movement of the food through the alimentary canal is by peristalsis.

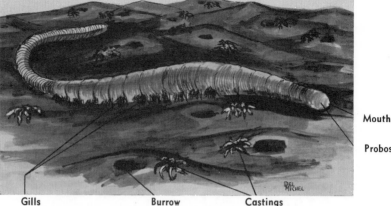

Mouth

Proboscis

Gills   Burrow   Castings

Figure 180. Lugworm, *Arenicola*. A burrowing polychaete which lives in intertidal mud flats. When worm is in burrow mound of castings indicates position of hind end; the crater, head end. Worm may reach length of 8 to 10 inches and diameter of ¾ inch in thickest part. Its narrow posterior end lacks parapodia and chaetae. Feeding habits are similar to those of earthworm, for its swallows great amounts of indigestible material which it discards in castings from its burrow. In burrowing it makes use of eversible proboscis and stiffening of anterior part of body by forcing coelomic fluid forward when it contracts its muscles. Its well-developed circulatory system contains red blood, and there is a row of tufted gills along each side of middle back region.

The worm will usually seek some kind of burrow if it can find one. When a worm is placed near a glass tube, it will wiggle in without hesitation. In its burrow it is able to suck or pump water in by dorsoventral undulatory movements which pass in waves from the anterior to the posterior end of the body.

Other common polychaetes

There are many species of polychaetes, some with structures and habits similar to *Neanthes* and others that are quite different. Most are found in fairly shallow water, but some live in deep seas. *Arenicola,* the lugworm (Figure 180), has the interesting habit of burrowing through the sand and forming castings. On certain of its somites are paired gills. *Aphrodite,* the sea mouse, has an oval body which bears large plates and very long setae. *Amphitrite* (Figure 181) has a head with long, extensible tentacles.

One of the most interesting of class Polychaeta from the standpoint of its

Figure 181. *Amphitrite,* polychaete worm with long tentacles.

268

natural history is the palolo worm, *Eunice viridis,* whose habitat is the South Pacific. These animals live in burrows among the coral reefs at the bottom of the sea. Just before swarming, their posterior somites become filled with enormous numbers of eggs or sperm. These somites are cast off as one unit at the time of swarming and float to the surface, where they burst, releasing the sex cells. This swarming always occurs on the first day of the last quarter of the October-November moon and lasts for a few days. Usually, just before sunrise on that day, the surface of the sea is covered with these posterior units of the worms, which burst just as the sun rises. Fertilization of the eggs occurs at this time. The anterior part of the worm regenerates a new posterior part. A related form *(Leodice)* found in the

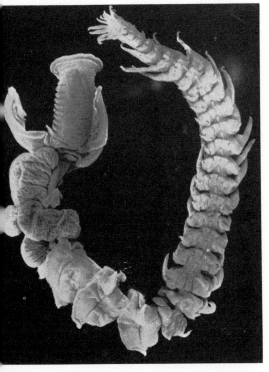

Figure 182. *Chaetopterus,* highly specialized polychaete worm. Worm lives permanently in U-shaped tube near surface of mud flats. It uses its fan-shaped parapodia to propel currents of water past its body in the tube.

Atlantic waters swarms in the third quarter of the June-July moon.

Chaetopterus (Figure 182) is an interesting polychaete which lives in a U-shaped burrow along the seashore. This form has flaplike structures formed by the union and modification of certain segments and appendages. By means of these it can draw water into its tube like a suction pump. This worm also has powers of luminescence.

CLASS HIRUDINEA

When one thinks of leeches he invariably thinks of blood-sucking creatures, and that is precisely what they are. Leeches are well adapted for this mode of life, for they have anterior and posterior suckers for locomotion and attachment and chitinous jaws for making incisions in the skin to promote the flow of blood from their victims. They have definite annelid characteristics, such as a ventral nerve cord with segmental ganglia, serial nephridia, and gonads in the coelom. The body is divided into somites (usually thirty-four). However, these animals lack setae, which most other annelids possess, and they have copulatory organs and genital openings on the midventral line, which other annelids do not have.

Hirudo medicinalis—medicinal leech

Structural characteristics. Leeches appear to have more metameres than they really have, for their somites are marked by transverse grooves (annuli). In this species and many others, the anterior sucker surrounds the mouth. The body is covered with a cuticle which is secreted by an epidermis beneath, and there are many mucous glands which open on the surface. Pigment and blood vessels are in the dermis. The muscular system is well developed with circular, longitudinal, and oblique bands. Internally, the coelom is reduced by mesenchyme and visceral organs to a system of sinuses. The alimentary canal is made up of a mouth with three jaws and chitinous teeth, a strong muscular pharynx with salivary glands, an esophagus, a crop with eleven pairs of lateral ceca, a slender intestine, a rectum, and an anus; the latter opens anterior to the posterior sucker. The circulatory system has the typical annelid plan of dorsal, ventral, and lateral longitudinal vessels with many cross-connections. Respiration takes place through the skin, and the excretory system has about seventeen pairs of nephridia. The nervous system is not greatly different from the typical annelid plan, and there are sensory organs of taste, touch, and sight. Leeches are hermaphroditic, but they have cross-fertilization. The male organs are the paired testes beneath the crop, a pair of vasa deferentia with some glands, and a median penis which opens into the male pore. Female organs include a pair of ovaries with oviducts, an albumin gland,

and a vagina which opens near the male pore. The sperm is transferred in little packets (spermatophores) by the filiform penis which penetrates the vagina of the mate in mutual copulation. The fertilized eggs are deposited in cocoons formed by glandular secretions. These cocoons may be attached to stones or other objects or even to the leech itself.

Behavior. Leeches are found both on land and in water. They move in a manner similar to a measuring worm, that is, by looping movements of the body. When the medicinal leech fastens itself to another animal by means of its suckers, the sharp chitinous teeth make an incision in the skin, and at the same time an anticoagulant substance (hirudin) from the salivary glands is introduced into the wound to make the blood flow freely. Then the blood is sucked up by the muscular pharynx and stored in the large crop. A leech is said to suck up three times its own weight in blood, which may take several months to digest. This is a useful adaptation, for leeches may not often have the chance to eat.

There are many different species of leeches, and many kinds of behavior are found among them. Some of them are jawless but have an eversible proboscis with which they can pierce the body of another animal. Fish and turtles are parasitized by them (Figure 183). Others live mainly on dead animals and some are predaceous. Tropical countries are plagued by more leeches than are temperate ones. Many of these attack human beings and are quite a nuisance. In Egypt and elsewhere in that region, a small aquatic leech is often swallowed in drinking water, and, by fastening on the pharynx and epiglottis, becomes a serious pest.

The leech in medical practice. For centuries the medicinal leech was employed in medical practice for bloodletting under the mistaken idea that bodily disorders and fevers were caused by a plethora of blood. Since the leech is 4 or 5 inches long and can extend to a much greater length when distended with blood, the amount

183   184

Figure 183. *Placobdella,* common leech found on turtles. A living specimen, about 1 inch long. Figure 184. *Hirudo medicinalis,* medicinal leech. This form was once widely used in bloodletting. This one is contracted, but it can stretch itself out to much greater length. (About life size.)

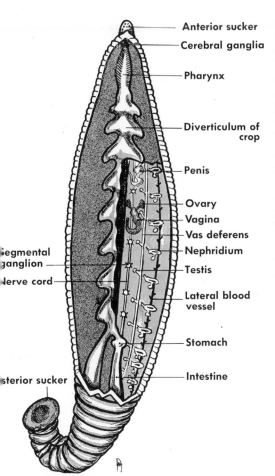

Anterior sucker
Cerebral ganglia
Pharynx
Diverticulum of crop
Penis
Ovary
Vagina
Vas deferens
Nephridium
Testis
Lateral blood vessel
Stomach
Intestine
Segmental ganglion
Nerve cord
Posterior sucker

Figure 185. Internal structure of leech, *Hirudo medicinalis*. Dorsal view. Part of long crop with its many diverticula cut away to show underlying structures.

of blood it can suck out of a patient is considerable. Leech collecting and leech culture in ponds were practiced in Europe on a commercial scale during the nineteenth century. Wordsworth's interesting poem, "The Leech-Gatherer," was based on this use of the leech. In some of our museums containing the relics of old pharmacies there still can be seen bottles labeled "Leeches" in which the animals were kept for the use of doctors of that period.

CLASS ARCHIANNELIDA

This is a group of worms of simple organization that live in the sea and have annelid characteristics only to a minor extent. There are fewer than fifty species of them, and they are highly aberrant. *Polygordius*, which is found on our eastern seashore, is one of the most familiar examples of the class. It has a body length of 1 to 4 inches, with indistinct segmentation. There is a small prostomium which bears a pair of fleshy tentacles, sensory and respiratory in function. On each side of the prostomium are ciliated pits which are often referred to as eyes. Within the coelom, each somite bears a pair of nephridia. There are no parapodia or setae. The nervous system, more primitive than that of most annelids, is found in the epidermis. The sexes are separate in *Polygordius*, with the ovaries or testes being confined to the posterior somites. Its larval form is a typical trochophore, and its subsequent metamorphosis is quite similar to Polychaeta. Archiannelids are not now considered degenerate or primitive but have undergone retrogression because of their small size.

Some authorities place the archiannelids and the peculiar order Myzostomata under Polychaeta. The Myzostomata, or sucker-mouthed worms, live mainly as parasites on echinoderms, especially crinoids. They are disc shaped or oblong, with cirri around the edge of the body, and the paired parapodia are provided with hooks. They also have suckers. In reproduction they function first as males, then as hermaphrodites, and finally as females. *Myzostomum* is the most common genus.

Derivation and meaning of basic terminology

Amphitrite (Gr. *amphitrite*, sea nymph).
Annelida (L. *annellus*, little ring).
Archiannelida (Gr. *arch*, first, + annelida).
Arenicola (L. *arena*, sand, + *colo*, to inhabit).
Chaetopoda (Gr. *chaite*, hair, + *pous*, foot).
chloragogue (Gr. *chloros*, green, + *gogue*, a leading).
clitellum (L. *clitella*, packsaddle).
Enchytraeidae (NL. *enchytrae*, to live in an earthen pot) These small, white or reddish worms were often encountered by florists in potting their plants.

Hirudinea (L. *hirudo,* leech).

Lumbricus (L. *lumbricus,* intestinal worm).

metamere (Gr. *meta,* after, + *meros,* part) Other names are somite and segment.

Myzostomata (Gr. *myzo,* to suck in, + *stoma,* mouth).

Neanthes (Gr. *neanthes,* new bud).

Oligochaeta (Gr. *oligos,* few, + *chaite,* hair).

parapodium (Gr. *para,* beside, + *pous,* foot).

peristomium (Gr. *peri,* around, + *stoma,* mouth).

Polychaeta (Gr. *polys,* many, + *chaite,* hair).

Polygordius (Gr. *polys,* many, + *gordius,* knot.)

prostomium (Gr. *pro,* before, + *stoma,* mouth).

seta (L. *seta,* bristle).

typhlosole (Gr. *typhlos,* blind, + *solen,* channel).

ANNOTATED REFERENCES

Barrett, T. J. 1947. Harnessing the Earthworm. Boston, Bruce Humphries, Inc. *An explanation of earthworm farming and the possibilities it has. A popular account.*

Beddard, F. E. 1901. Earthworms and Their Allies. Cambridge, Cambridge University Press. *A technical treatise and one of the best published. Comprehensive and authoritative.*

Bell, A. W. 1947. The Earthworm Circulatory System. Turtox News, vol. 25, pp. 89-94.

Borradaile, L. A., and F. A. Potts. 1958. The Invertebrata, ed. 3 (revised by G. A. Kerkut). New York, Cambridge University Press. *Chapter 8 of this well-known work is devoted to the Annelida. Short descriptions with diagrammatic illustrations mostly employed.*

Buchsbaum, R. 1948. Animals Without Backbones, rev. ed. Chicago, University of Chicago Press. *Good illustrations of many annelid forms.*

Buchsbaum, R., and L. J. Milne. 1960. The Lower Animals. Garden City, Doubleday & Co., Inc. *A superb work on invertebrates with unsurpassed photographs (many in color) by two famous field naturalists.*

Cambridge Natural History. 1896. Annelida. London, Macmillan Co., Ltd. *Good authoritative account.*

Darwin, C. R. 1911. The Formation of Vegetable Mould Through the Action of Worms. *A classical account of the way in which earthworms improve and transform the surface of the soil.*

Hess, W. N. 1925. Nervous System of the Earthworm, Lumbricus terrestris L. Journal of Morphology and Physiology, vol. 40, pp. 235-259. *A widely known investigation of great value to all students of the annelids.*

Krivanek, J. O. 1956. Habit Formation in the Earthworm Lumbricus terrestris. Physiol. Zool. vol. 29, pp. 241-250. *An interesting study in animal behavior.*

Moment, G. B. 1953. On the Way a Common Earthworm, *Eisenia foetida,* grows in length. J. Morphol., vol. 93, pp. 489-503.

Moore, J. P. 1956. Annelida. Encyclopaedia Britannica, Chicago, Encyclopaedia Britannica, Inc. *A comprehensive description of the group with many revealing illustrations.*

Parker, T. J., and W. A. Haswell. 1940. A Textbook of Zoology, 2 vols., ed. 6. New York, The Macmillan Co. *A comprehensive treatment of the phylum with emphasis upon morphology.*

Pratt, H. S. 1935. A Manual of the Common Invertebrate Animals, ed. 2. Philadelphia, P. Blakiston's Sons & Co. *Includes brief descriptions and classifications of the various groups of annelids.*

Schechter, V. 1959. Invertebrate Zoology. Englewood Cliffs, N. J., Prentice-Hall, Inc. *Simple descriptions with schematic drawings. Good introduction to the segmented worms.*

Zappler, G. 1958. Darwin's Worms. Natural History, vol. 67, pp. 488-495. *An account of an experiment on the annelid intelligence by the great naturalist. Should be read by all beginning zoology students.*

chapter 16

Phylum Arthropoda*

Subphylum Chelicerata and minor groups

BIOLOGICAL PRINCIPLES

Organ-system level of organization

1. Arthropods have the characteristic structure of higher forms, bilateral symmetry, triploblastic, coelomic cavity, and organ systems, and have reached the peak of invertebrate evolution.

2. They share with annelids the property of conspicuous segmentation, which is manifested especially in the body, muscles, and nervous elements.

3. The arthropod plan has emphasized a greater variety and grouping of somites for specialized purposes and has added on to the somites the jointed appendages with pronounced division of labor, thus making for greater variety of action.

4. Arthropods have furthermore stressed the importance of the chitinous exoskeleton, modifying it into a great variety of specialized structures.

5. Arthropods by their locomotory mechanism and other adaptations were the first great group to make the transition from water to land where they have undergone amazing adaptive radiation. The animal can now walk without dragging the body.

Biological contributions

1. Although **chitin** is found in a few other forms below arthropods, the latter have developed its uses.

2. **Cephalization** makes additional advancements by stressing control in the head region, by

fusion of ganglia, and by locating important sensory and other organs in the head.

3. The presence of paired **jointed appendages** diversified for numerous uses makes for greater adaptability.

4. Locomotion is by extrinsic limb muscles in contrast to the body musculature of annelids.

5. The **somites** have gone beyond the sameness of the annelid type and are now **specialized** for a variety of purposes.

6. The gills, and especially the **tracheae**, represent an efficient breathing mechanism.

7. **Striated muscles** are emphasized, thus ensuring rapidity of movement.

8. The alimentary canal shows greater specialization by chitinous teeth, compartments, and gastric ossicles.

9. Behavior patterns have advanced far beyond most invertebrates with the development of primitive intelligence and **social instincts** in some of the groups.

10. **Metamorphosis** is common in development.

Position in animal kingdom

1. The evidence indicates that arthropods are more closely related to annelids than to any other group.

2. Although they cannot be said to come directly from annelids, they probably came from the same ancestors as segmented worms such as polychaetes.

3. Subphylum Onychophora, with both annelid and arthropod characters, represents a connecting link. This form can be considered as a descendant from a line close to the primitive ancestor of annelids and arthropods. *Aysheaia*, a fossil form of the middle Cambrian period shares many common characteristics with *Peripatus*.

---

*Ar-throp'o-da (Gr. *arthron*, joint, + *pous*, foot).

GENERAL RELATIONS

This is the most extensive group of animals in the animal kingdom, containing more than three-fourths of all known forms. The total number of species recorded to date is between 700,000 and 800,000, and probably as many more remain to be classified. Among the living forms the phylum includes crustaceans, spiders, ticks, millipedes, centipedes, and insects. In addition, many fossil forms belong to the arthropods, for this phylum goes back to pre-Cambrian times in geological history.

Arthropoda (Gr. *arthros*, joint, + *pous* foot) means joint footed. Arthropods are characterized by having a **chitinous exoskeleton** and a **linear series of somites,** each with a pair of **jointed appendages.** Body organs and systems are usually well developed, for they represent, on the whole, a very active and energetic type of life. They share with the nematodes an almost complete absence of **cilia.**

Arthropods live in a greater variety of habitats than the members of any other phylum. They are adapted for life in and on the land, in water, and in the air. They are found on the highest mountains (spiders were found on Mount Everest at 22,000 feet) and at great depths in the sea. They are often found in places where no other forms could survive. The brine shrimp *(Artemia salina)* and the brine flies *(Ephydra)* of Great Salt Lake are about the only living animals in the highly concentrated salt water of that lake. Some arthropods are parasitic on plants and animals, although parasitism is not dominant in this group. In no other group of invertebrates has social organization been carried as far. The gregarious termites, ants, and bees have worked out marvelous systems of division of labor of great ingenuity and complexity.

They are man's greatest competitors, contending for food supplies and spreading serious diseases. No sooner do we suppress a destructive insect than another springs up to do mischief. However, not all arthropods are harmful; some, such as lobsters, shrimp, and crabs, serve as food, the silkworms furnish clothing, insects are necessary for cross-pollination of plants, bees furnish honey and beeswax, and other insects yield useful drugs and dyes.

The arthropods have the pattern of organization characteristic of higher invertebrates. They have the organ-system level of organization, bilateral symmetry, coelomic cavity, a centralized nervous system, separate sexes, and paired reproductive organs and ducts. In some respects they are more specialized than lower forms, such as having a chitinous exoskeleton, a variety of modified appendages, metamorphosis of development, high metabolism, etc. Distinct advancements over most invertebrates are a greater cephalization, better sense organs, greater specialization and modifications of somites, more efficient breathing (gills and tracheae), higher development of social organization and instinct, and better development of protective coloration and protective resemblance.

Since there are so many common points between the organization of segmented worms and arthropods, zoologists nearly all agree that they must have evolved from the same ancestors. Both have striking metamerism, but arthropods show advancement in the reduced number of somites and in their differentiation and grouping. The striking similarity between the parapodia of the polychaete annelids and the limbs of the living Branchiopoda (Crustacea) and of the fossil Trilobita is often cited as evidence of close affinity between the two phyla. Subphylum Onychophora, with characteristics of both arthropods and annelids, appears to be closest to the ancestral form. The generalized structure of Branchiopoda places it close to the bottom of the arthropod series. The relationship of the various arthropod classes seems to indicate that the groups Onychophora, Crustacea, Myriapoda, and Insecta have evolved along one line and the radically different Arachnida and related forms along another. The Insecta appear to have been derived from primitive pre-Cambrian annelids and are more closely related to centipedes and millipedes than to other arthropods.

WHY HAVE ARTHROPODA BEEN SO SUCCESSFUL?

Some of the criteria for the success of an animal group are the number and variety of species, the variety of habitats, widespread distribution, ability to defend themselves, variety of food habits, and the power to adapt themselves to changing conditions. The fact that Arthropoda are so common and so diversified indicates that they have met most of these requirements. Some structural and physiological patterns which have been helpful to them stand out in bold relief. We may briefly summarize some of these.

Chitin. Chitin is nonliving and noncellular and is secreted by the underlying epidermis. It is a protein-carbohydrate compound and is composed of several different substances. It is really made up of an outer waxy layer, a middle horny layer, and an inner flexible layer. These layers are modified among the various arthropods and also among the different parts of the body. In some the chitin is soft and permeable; in others it forms a veritable coat of armor. Between joints and between segments it is flexible and thin to permit free movements. It is harder in crustaceans, where it is infiltrated with calcium salts. In general its structure is admirably adapted for protection of delicate internal organs, for attachment of muscles, for serving as levers and centers of movement, for preventing the entrance and loss of water, and, because of its arrangement, for affording the maximum amount of protection without sacrificing mobility.

Although hard protective structures are common among other groups of animals, none have used them so effectively as have the arthropods. Chitin in arthropods is used for biting jaws, for grinders in the stomach, for lenses of the eye, for sound production, for sensory organs, for copulatory organs, for organs of defense, and for ornamental purposes; some arthropods even have a chitinous lining in the digestive tract. Chitin is also found in certain sponges, annelids, and a few other phyla.

A chitinous exoskeleton limits the size of the animal, which, in order to grow, must shed its outer shell at intervals and grow a larger one—a process called **ecdysis,** or molting. While waiting for the new shell to harden, the animal is vulnerable to enemies. Arthropods must undergo from four to seven moltings before reaching adult size. This chitinous exoskeleton limits the size and weight of the members, for aside from a few crabs and lobsters with long slender legs, few arthropods exceed 2 feet in length and most are far below this limit. The largest is the Japanese crab *(Macrocheira)* which is about 11 feet in span; the smallest is the parasitic mite *(Demodex)* which is less than 1/10 mm. long.

The presence of chitin helps arthropods adapt themselves to a wide variety of land habitats, including deserts and dry places that would mean fatal desiccation to forms not provided with such a cuticle.

Segmentation and appendages. Arthropods share with annelids and vertebrates the characteristic of having the body divided into similar segments. Each somite typically is provided with a pair of jointed appendages, but this arrangement is often modified, with both segments and the appendages specialized for adaptable functions. This has made for great efficiency and wider capacity for adjustment to different habitats.

Respiratory devices. Aquatic arthropods breathe mainly by some form of gill which is quite efficient; most land arthropods have the unique and highly efficient **tracheal** system of air tubes which delivers the oxygen directly to the tissue cells. This makes possible the high metabolism so characteristic of active insects.

Sensory organs. No other group of invertebrate animals has the diversity of specialized and delicate organs that arthropods have. These are found in great variety from the mosaic eye to those simpler senses which have to do with touch, smell, hearing, balancing, chemical, and others. They are keenly alert to what goes on in their environment.

Locomotion. Their jointed appendages have been modified and adapted into swift and efficient locomotor organs, such as walking legs, swimming appendages, and wings.

Reproduction and metamorphosis. They lay large numbers of eggs, and many of them pass through metamorphic changes in reaching maturity—the larva, pupa, and adult stages. Some have a series of nymphal stages preceding the adult stage. This results in less competition within a species, for the larval form is often adapted for eating a kind of food different from that of the adult. The caterpillar, for instance, lives on vegetation, whereas the adult butterfly sucks the nectar of flowers.

Behavior patterns. Arthropods exceed most other invertebrates in the complexity and organization of their activities. Most of their behavior patterns fall under the so-called instinctive action which is supposed here to reach its peak. Whether or not learning is involved to any great extent in their reactions to environmental stimuli is open to question (see Chapter 41, Animal Behavior Patterns), but no one can deny the complex adaptability of the group. As an example of arthropod adaptability the time-measuring mechanism of fiddler crabs has been investigated by Brown and his associates in recent years. This work showed how these crustaceans with great precision regulated their rhythmic color patterns of dark by day and light by night by means of an internal time clock which can work independently of external influences, can be set for different cycles, and is definitely inherited.

CHARACTERISTICS

1. Symmetry bilateral; triploblastic; body metameric
2. **Appendages jointed,** with one or two pairs to a somite and more or less modified for specialized functions
3. **Exoskeleton of chitin,** secreted by the underlying epidermis, and shed at intervals

4. Body often divided into **three regions:** the **head,** usually of six somites, the **thorax,** and the **abdomen,** the latter two divisions having a variable number of somites; head and thorax often united into a cephalothorax
5. Muscles mostly **striated** and rapid in action; unstriated muscle in visceral organs
6. True coelom small in adult; most of body cavity a **hemocoele filled with blood**
7. Digestive system complete with mouth, enteron, and anus; **mouth parts modified from somites and adapted for different methods of feeding**
8. Circulatory system open, with dorsal heart, arteries, and mesenchymal blood cavities (sinuses)
9. **Cilia practically absent throughout group**
10. Respiration by body surface, gills, **air tubes (tracheae),** or **book lungs**
11. Excretory system by green glands or by a variable number of **Malpighian tubules** opening into the digestive system; Onychophora with segmental nephridia
12. Nervous system of dorsal brain connected with a ring around the gullet to a double nerve chain of ventral ganglia
13. Sensory organs well developed and include eyes, antennae (tactile and chemical), balancing organs, auditory organs, and sensory bristles
14. Sexes nearly always separate with paired reproductive organs and ducts; fertilization internal; oviparous or ovoviviparous; metamorphosis direct or indirect; parthenogenesis in a few forms

CLASSIFICATION

The Arthropoda is such an extensive phylum with so many different groups that authorities have subdivided it in various ways. A strict phylogenetic grouping is impossible with the knowledge available at present. Some merely assign class rank to all the definite groups, but the arrangement given here recognizes higher taxonomic divisions on the basis of common morphological characteristics and phylogenetic relationships.

Subphylum Onychophora (on'y-koph"o-ra) (Gr. onyx, claw, + pherein, to bear). Wormlike and soft skinned with papillae; anterior end with pair of eyes; antennae and slime-secreting papillae; body externally unsegmented with imperfectly jointed legs, each with two claws; pair of anal papillae; respiration with unbranched tracheae; pair of nephridia in each internal segment; separate sexes and viviparous. Example: Peripatus.

Subphylum Trilobita (tri'lo-bi"ta) (Gr. trias, three, + lobos, lobe). All fossil forms; Cambrian to Carboniferous; body divided by two longitudinal furrows into three lobes; head, thorax, abdomen distinct; somites except last with biramous appendages. Example: Triarthrus.

Subphylum Chelicerata (ke-lis'e-ra"ta) (Gr. chele, claw, + keraos, horny). First pair of appendages modified to form chelicerae with claws; pair of pedipalps and four pairs of legs; no antennae; cephalothorax and abdomen usually unsegmented.

Class Merostomata (mer'o-sto"ma-ta) (Gr. meros, thigh, + stoma, mouth). Cephalothorax; compound lateral eyes; appendages with gills; sharp telson.

Subclass Eurypterida (u'rip-ter"i-da) (Gr. eurys, broad, + pteryx, wing). Extinct, largest of fossil arthropods, some to 6 feet; exoskeleton of chitin with cephalothorax (prosoma) completely covered by dorsal carapace; abdomen (opisthosoma) with twelve segments and postanal telson; six pairs of appendages, first pair of which are chelicerae; ventral mouth; pair of simple ocelli and pair of compound eyes; separate sexes. Example: Eurypterus.

Subclass Xiphosurida (zif'o-su"ri-da) (Gr. xiphos, sword, + oura, tail). Body composed of cephalothorax in form of convex, horseshoe-shaped carapace; abdomen unsegmented and terminated by long spine; three-jointed chelicerae and six-jointed walking legs; pair of simple eyes and pair of compound eyes; book gills; paired genital openings. Example: Limulus (king crab).

Class Pycnogonida (pik'no-gon"i-da) (Gr. pyknos, compact, + gonos, gonad) (Pantopoda). Size usually small (3 to 4 mm.), but some reach 500 mm; body chiefly cephalothorax; abdomen tiny; usually eight pairs of long walking legs, but some with ten to twelve pairs; pair of subsidiary legs (ovigers) for egg bearing; mouth on long proboscis; four simple eyes; no respiratory or excretory system. Example: Pycnogonum (sea spiders).

Class Arachnida (a-rack'nid-a) (Gr. arachne, spider). Body with anterior somites fused into a cephalothorax with two chelicerae with claws, two pedipalpi, and four pairs of legs; no antennae or true jaws; abdomen segmented or unsegmented with or without appendages and generally distinct from cephalothorax; respiration by gills, tracheae, or book lungs; excretion by Malpighian tubules or coxal glands; dorsal bilobed brain connected to ventral ganglionic mass with nerves; simple eyes; sexes separate; chiefly oviparous; no true metamorphosis. Examples: scorpions, spiders, mites, ticks, harvestmen.

Subphylum Pentastomida (pen'ta-stom"i-da) (Gr. penta, five, + stoma, mouth) (Linguatulida). Wormlike and unsegmented; body divided externally into annuli; legless; no antennae; mouth surrounded by two pairs of retractile hooks; no respiratory or excretory system; some with complex life histories, parasitic in respiratory passages of vertebrates (reptiles, mammals). Example: Linguatula (tongueworms).

Subphylum Tardigrada (tar'di-gra"da) (L. tardus, slow, + gradior, walk). Size about 1 mm. or smaller; body cylindrical with weakly chitinized integument; four pairs of stumpy, unjointed legs with claws; last pair of legs at posterior end of body; tubular mouth parts provided with a stylet; antennae absent; eyes (in some); no respiratory or circulatory system; development usually direct. Example: Macrobiotus (water bears).

Subphylum Mandibulata (man-dib'u-la"ta) (L. mandibula, mandible). One or two pairs of antennae form first two pairs of appendages, and functional jaws (mandibles) form third pair of cephalic appendages.

Class Crustacea (crus-ta'she-a) (L. crusta, shell). Aquatic with gills; body with dorsal carapace; telson at posterior end; hard exoskeleton, of chitin reinforced with limy salts; appendages biramous and modified for capturing food, walking, swimming, respiration, and reproduction; coelom reduced and hemocoel present; head of five segments with two pairs of antennae, a pair of jaws, and two pairs of maxillae; sexes usually separate; development with nauplius stage; paired sex openings. Examples: Homarus, Cambarus, Asellus, Eubranchipus, Cyclops, Daphnia.

Class Diplopoda (di-plop'o-da) (Gr. diploos, double, + pous, foot). Body subcylindrical;

head with short antennae and simple eyes; body with variable number of somites; short legs, usually two pairs to a somite; maxillae and jaws; separate sexes; oviparous; Malpighian tubules for excretion; dorsal brain with double ventral nerve cord. Examples: *Julus, Spirobolus* (millipedes).

Class **Chilopoda** (ki-lop′o-da) (Gr. *cheilos*, lip, + *pous*, foot). Form elongated and dorsoventrally flattened; pair of jointed maxillae and jaws with variable number of somites, each with a pair of legs; Malpighian tubules for excretion; respiration with tracheae; separate sexes; oviparous; dorsal brain and double ventral nerve cord; pair of long antennae. Examples: *Cermatia, Lithobius, Geophilus* (centipedes).

Class **Pauropoda** (pau-rop′o-da) (Gr. *pauros*, small, + *pous*, foot). Minute (1 to 1.5 mm.); body cylindrical of double segments and bearing nine or ten pairs of legs; no eyes; genital openings near head end. Example: *Pauropus*.

Class **Symphyla** (sym′phy-la) (Gr. *syn*, together, + *phylon*, tribe). Slender (1 to 8 mm.) with long, filiform antennae; body of fifteen to twenty-two segments with ten to twelve pairs of legs; no eyes; genital openings near head end. Example: *Scutigerella* (garden centipede).

Class **Insecta** (in-sec′ta) (L. *insectus*, divided). Body with head, thorax, and abdomen distinct; pair of antennae; mouth parts modified for different food habits; head with six somites, thorax with three somites, and abdomen with variable number, usually eleven somites; thorax with two pairs of wings (sometimes one pair or none) and three pairs of jointed legs; respiration by branched tracheae; brain of fused ganglia and double ventral nerve cord; eyes both simple and compound; separate sexes; usually oviparous; metamorphosis gradual or abrupt. Examples: various orders to be described.

ECONOMIC IMPORTANCE

A group as common and widely distributed as the arthropods must necessarily have great economic importance. Their relations to other members in the animal kingdom are both harmful and beneficial. We may group the economic importance under three headings—arthropods as food, harmful arthropods, and beneficial arthropods.

Arthropods as food. Lobsters, crabs, shrimp, and, in some localities, crayfish are widely used as food all over the world. Honey from bees has been a delicacy since primitive times. Plankton, made up of small organisms found at the surface of waters, contains large numbers of crustaceans and is an important source of food for fish. Insects furnish many birds and animals with food.

Harmful arthropods. Harmful arthropods are numerous. Only a few of these will be pointed out here. Insects rank first destroying millions of dollars worth of food each year. Insects as well as other arthropods carry devastating diseases. The most widespread is malaria, carried by the mosquito. Other arthropods important in restricted regions are the copepods, which carry larval stages of the guinea worm and fish tapeworm; mites and ticks, which carry diseases and cause irritation and debility by living as ectoparasites; and spiders and scorpions, which do harm by poison bites. Barnacles foul the bottom of ships, and crayfish through their burrowing habits, do much harm to levees and also to crops in lowlands. Crustaceans such as sow bugs do much harm in greenhouses.

Beneficial arthropods. Insect predators which live upon other insects aid in checking the ravages of the harmful ones. Cross-pollination, so essential to fruit growing, is effected by insects. Arthropod products include shellac produced by certain scale insects, cochineal (a histological dye) obtained from another type of tropical scale insect, silk spun by the larvae of silkworm moths, beeswax from bees, and a drug from the Spanish fly.

COMPARISON OF ARTHROPODA WITH ANNELIDA

Similarities between the two phyla are (1) external segmentation, (2) segmental arrangement of muscles, and (3) metamerically arranged nervous system with dorsal cerebral ganglia.

The most striking differences between the two phyla are as follows. Arthropods have (1) fixed number of segments, (2)

278

usually a lack of intersegmental septa, (3) open (lacunar) circulatory system, (4) body segments usually grouped into three regions—head, thorax, and abdomen, (5) coelomic cavity reduced, (6) special mechanisms (gills, tracheae, book lungs) for respiration, (7) chitin or exoskeleton, (8) jointed appendages, (9) compound eye and other well-developed sense organs, (10) absence of cilia, and (11) metamorphosis in many cases.

REPRESENTATIVE TYPES
SUBPHYLUM ONYCHOPHORA
Peripatus

From the standpoint of phylogenetic relationship between two groups as different as two phyla, few animals are more interesting than a small wormlike form called *Peripatus* (Figures 186 and 187). This animal is a type of a small subphylum of arthropods, Onychophora. There are about seventy species in this class widely distributed over the world—Africa, Australia, New Zealand, Central America, Mexico, and other localities. Their wide distribution in local habitats, an example

Figure 187. Ventral view of anterior end of *Peripatus*, which combines annelid-like and arthropod-like structures. Note antennae, ventral mouth surrounded by a fleshy fold and two small horny jaws, and a short oral papilla on each side of mouth. Small skin papillae found all over body. Seventy species (2 to 3 inches long) have wide tropical discontinuous distribution. Annelid characteristics are the nephridia (paired and segmental in distribution), ciliated reproductive organs, structure of eyes, and arrangement of organs. Arthropod characteristics are jaws (derived from appendages), hemocoele body cavity, dorsal heart with ostia, tracheae for breathing, and paired appendages of short stumpy legs, each with pair of claws. Segmentation apparent only by number of legs. This strange animal may be a link between annelids and arthropods, or it may be an independent branch from a form common to all segmented groups. (Courtesy Ward's Natural Science Establishment, Inc., Rochester, N. Y.)

Figure 186. *Peripatus* in its natural habitat, usually moist places under logs, bark, or other rubbish. Subphylum Onychophora. (Courtesy Ward's Natural Science Establishment, Inc., Rochester, N. Y.)

of discontinuous distribution, may indicate that once they were common and widespread over the world but are now disappearing. This subphylum shows characteristics of two phyla, Annelida and Arthropoda, and its members are often referred to as "missing links." If this subphylum is primitive, which is denied by some zoologists, then its members must be considered similar to the ancestors of Arthropoda.

The various species of Onychophora live in moist places in crevices of rock, under logs and bark, and other dark places. They are nocturnal in their habits and avoid light at all times. When annoyed, they eject slime from their peculiar oral papillae.

External structure. Peripatus is about 2 to 3 inches long and resembles a caterpillar. It is cylindrical in body form but shows no external segmentation. The integument is soft and velvety and thrown into fine transverse wrinkles with many conical papillae which bear chitinous spines. The head, which is not well marked off from the rest of the body, bears two short antennae, a pair of dorsal eyes, a pair of short, fleshy oral papillae, and a midventral mouth with a pair of chitinous jaws. On the oral papillae are the openings of the slime glands. Both the jaws and oral papillae represent modified limbs. The legs, which are not jointed, are ringed with ridges bearing rows of papillae. Each leg is short and stocky and bears a pair of claws. In some species there are seventeen pairs of legs, but other species contain more. At the posterior end of the body are the anus and a ventral genital opening.

Internal structure. The **body wall** consists of a cuticle, epidermis, dermis, and layers of unstriped circular and longitudinal muscles. Special muscles are used to manipulate the jaws. The **body cavity** (hemocoel) is lined with epithelium, which also invests the organs within the body cavity. The body cavity is imperfectly divided by muscular partitions into a few compartments. The slime glands which open on the oral papillae are found on either side of the body cavity. Secretions from these glands are ejected a considerable distance and adhere to the objects they hit. In this way the animal can capture its prey. The slime glands are modified from the paired coxal glands of the legs.

The **digestive system** is made up of the mouth, the tongue with rows of small spines, a muscular pharynx into which open two large salivary glands, short esophagus, long intestine, and rectum. The **excretory system** consists of a pair of nephridia in each segment. Each nephridium has a vesicle, ciliated funnel, and duct which has an opening at the base of the leg. A dorsal blood vessel forms a contractile heart lying within the pericardial space and receives blood from each segment by a pair of ostia. Respiration is carried on by a **tracheal system** which ramifies to all parts of the body and communicates to the outside by openings, or stigmata. These tracheae, however, are not homologous with those of insects. The **nervous system** contains a pair of cerebral ganglia connected to two widely separated ventral nerve cords by two circumpharyngeal connectives. The two nerve cords are connected by transverse commissures. Slight enlargements of the nerve cords opposite each pair of legs represent the only signs of ganglia. The nerve cords, however, are made up of continuous layers of ganglionic cells. Nerves are given off from the nerve cords to the legs and from the dorsal brain to anterior regions. Sensory organs are represented by the two simple eyes on top of the head and by the conical papillae (tactile) of the integument.

The sexes are distinct in *Peripatus*. Female organs are two tubular ovaries, a pair of oviducts, and paired uteri which join to form a vaginal opening. The **male** system has paired testes, seminal vesicles, vasa deferentia, and genital opening to the outside. The male in some species deposits its spermatophores or bundles of sperm on the body of the female, from whence the sperm penetrate the thin skin to fertilize the eggs in the oviducts. Thirty or more young, each about ½ inch long, are produced each year by the female, but all are not born at the same time. In some there is a definite placenta by which the young are attached to the uterus where nutrition and other exchanges between mother and young are carried on. The young resemble the adults.

Evolutionary status of Peripatus. The subphylum Onychophora seems to have a structure intermediate between a generalized annelid type and the common ancestor of such arthropods as centipedes and insects. According to Gregory, *Peripatus* is more primitive than insects and agrees somewhat with centipedes in the arrangement of its internal metamerism. Its morphological pattern has not changed in 400 million years and represents a stage in the long evolutionary road between annelids and insects. It has remained the same because it has been restricted to narrow ecological niches where selective mutations did not have a chance to operate. A fossil form, *Aysheaia,* discovered in the mid-Cambrian shale of British Columbia, is so much like *Peripatus* that it is considered a direct ancestor.

Comparison of Onychophora with Annelida

Although Onychophora are placed as a class under the arthropods, they have many annelid features. They show a resemblance to the annelids as follows: (1) segmentally arranged nephridia, (2) ciliated reproductive ducts, (3) muscular body wall, and (4) structure of the eyes.

They resemble the arthropods as follows: (1) tubular heart with ostia, (2) presence of tracheae, (3) mouth parts modified from appendages, (4) hemocoele for body cavity, and (5) large size of brain.

Their own unique characters are (1) scanty metamerism, (2) structure of the jaws, and (3) the separate arrangement of the nerve cords with no well-defined ganglia.

SUBPHYLUM TRILOBITA

Trilobites flourished during the Cambrian period and became extinct by the Permian period (200 million years ago). Their great variety and complexity (more than 1,200 species) indicate that their beginning was millions of years before the Cambrian period. They are more primitive than true crustaceans and probably descended from a pre-Cambrian ancestor which also gave rise to all the arthropods. As marine forms, their fossils were laid down when seas covered what is now land. Since they are so abundant, they are useful to geologists in the indexing of rock layers.

Their body was covered by a hard chitinous-calcareous shell which was divided into three longitudinal lobes by two dorsal furrows. They had three transverse lobes: head, thorax, and pygidium. The head was one piece but showed signs of former segmentation; the thorax had a variable number of somites; and the pygidium had also a variable number of somites fused together in a plate. Most of them could roll up like a pill bug. They were from 2 to 27 inches long. The head contained a pair of jointed antennae, usually a pair of large compound eyes (sometimes on stalks), and four pairs of biramous (two-branched), jointed appendages on the ventral side. On the ventral

Figure 188. Trilobite (dorsal view) from plaster cast impression. All members of this class now extinct.

side of the thorax and pygidium each somite (except the last, or telson) bore a pair of two-branched, jointed appendages with a fringe of bristles. They lived on other invertebrates and some were scavengers. Fossilized trilobite eggs have been found.

SUBPHYLUM CHELICERATA

The chelicerate arthropods are characterized by a lack of mandibles and antennae and the presence of six pairs of appendages which include one pair of pedipalps, one pair of chelicerae, and four pairs of legs. They suck up liquid food from their prey. The group is a very ancient one and includes the eurypterids (extinct), horseshoe crabs, spiders, ticks, and some others.

CLASS MEROSTOMATA
SUBCLASS EURYPTERIDA

The members of this extinct class were the largest of all fossil arthropods, some of them reaching a length of 9 feet. They have been found in rocks from the Ordovician period to the Carboniferous period. Eurypterids resembled king crabs. The prosoma (head) had six fused segments and bore two simple and two compound eyes. Six pairs of appendages were found beneath the prosoma. The body of eurypterids was incased in a chitinous covering. The twelve segments of the abdomen (opisthosoma) were divided into the mesosoma (anterior six segments) and the metasoma (last six segments plus the spikelike telson). They also had many structural features in common with existing scorpions, which may be considered their land representatives, for both have the same number of segments in the three regions of the body and the same arrangement of appendages in the presoma. However, the last pair of legs in eurypterids were much more developed than they are in scorpions. There are conflicting theories regarding their early habitats. Some maintain that eurypterids evolved mainly in fresh water along with ostracoderms; others hold that they arose in brackish lagoons.

SUBCLASS XIPHOSURIDA
Xiphosura polyphemus— king or horseshoe crab

This is often referred to as a "living fossil," for it represents a very ancient group of animals (Figure 189). Although the genus *Xiphosura* goes back only to the Triassic period, other xiphosurans can be traced back to the Cambrian period. There are five living species divided among three genera as follows: *Xiphosura* along the Atlantic coast of North America, *Carcinoscorpius* along the southern shore of Japan, and *Tachypleus* in the East Indies and along the coast of southern Asia.

Xiphosurans live in shallow water and are often left stranded at low tide. They are characterized by an unsegmented horseshoe-shaped carapace (hard dorsal shield) and a broad hexagonal abdomen which has a long telson, or tail piece. The cephalothorax bears on the ventral side five pairs of walking legs and a pair of chelicerae, while the abdomen has six pairs of broad thin appendages which are fused in the median line. On some of the

Figure 189. Ventral view of horseshoe crab *Xiphosura* (class Merostomata). They grow up to 15 to 18 inches long.

282

abdominal appendages gill books (leaflike gills) are exposed. There are two compound and two simple eyes on the carapace. The horseshoe crab swims by means of its abdominal plates and can walk with its walking legs. It feeds at night on worms and small mollusks which it seizes with its chelicerae. Fertilization is external, and the larvae are segmented like the trilobites. The latter are often considered the ancestors of the king crabs.

Xiphosurans were formerly classified with the Arachnida, but they differ in having a venous system, aquatic gill books, paired genital openings, a "trilobite larval stage," a pair of compound eyes, a heart which is blind behind, and other distinctions.

CLASS PYCNOGONIDA (PANTOPODA)

A common name for these odd animals is **sea spiders.** Some are only a few millimeters long but others are much larger. They have small bodies and usually four pairs of legs, but twelve-legged forms are known. Some species are provided with chelicerae and palpi. One unique feature is the subsidiary pair of egg-bearing legs (ovigers) in the males (and a few females). Their body consists principally of a cephalothorax, for the abdomen is rudimentary. The mouth is located at the tip of a suctorial proboscis which may be longer than the body. Most of them have four simple eyes. They have a heart but no blood vessels. Excretory and respiratory systems are absent. The males carry the eggs on their ovigers during most of the development. Because of the small size of the body, the digestive system sends branches into the legs, and most of the gonads are also found there. Sea spiders are exclusively marine and are found in all oceans from the littoral zone to depths of 2,000 fathoms, but they are most abundant in polar waters. They feed on coelenterates and soft-bodied animals, from which they suck out the juices by means of their long proboscis. The group is probably more closely related to the Crustacea than to any other arthropods, although they do not have a nauplius larva. *Pycnogonum* is a common intertidal genus found on both the Atlantic and Pacific coasts.

CLASS ARACHNIDA

This class is considered an isolated group of Arthropoda. It is not as closely knit a group as the insects, for it has considerable variety of bodily organization. The name comes from the Greek word *arachne*, spider. Besides spiders, the group includes scorpions, ticks, mites, harvestmen, and others. There are many differences among these with respect to form and appendages. Their most distinguishing characteristics are the fusion of the head and thorax into a cephalothorax, the presence of four pairs of walking legs instead of three pairs as in insects, and the lack of antennae and mandibles. Most of them are free living and are far more common in warm, dry regions than elsewhere. They are provided, as a rule, with claws, poison glands, fangs, and stingers. Most are highly predaceous and suck the fluids and soft tissues from the bodies of their prey. Some have interesting adaptations, such as the spinning glands of the spiders.

Economic importance

Most arachnids are quite harmless and actually do much good by destroying injurious insects. A few, such as the black widow spider, can harm man by their bites. The sting of the scorpion may be quite painful. Some ticks and mites are vectors for diseases as well as causes of annoyance and painful irritations. Certain mites damage plants by sucking their juices or by damaging valuable fruits.

Phylogenetic relations

Arachnids represent a very old group of invertebrates. It is thought that Arthropoda split into two main branches probably as early as the Cambrian period. One of these branches became Arachnida and the other developed into the other classes of arthropods. Some of the earliest arachnids were the large Paleozoic eurypterids. It is generally agreed that spiders are closely related to scorpions, but the stem ancestor of spiders is unknown. Some fossil spiders have a segmented cephalothorax—a primitive condition. Some authorities think spiders have come from some scorpion stock, and by pedogenesis they have developed and stressed their web-weaving habits. Their web-making may have originated from their habit of making silky cocoons.

Although the earliest arachnids were aquatic, the great majority of the present-day ones are terrestrial.

Characteristics

Body of unsegmented cephalothorax and abdomen usually; antennae and mandibles lacking; six pairs of appendages usually, of which two pairs are the chelicerae and pedipalpi and the others are walking legs; sucking mouth parts mainly; poison glands in some; respiration by gill books or by lung books or tracheae; excretion by Malpighian tubules and coxal glands; circulatory system typically of heart, arteries, veins, sinuses; nervous system of arthropod plan, or more concentrated anteriorly; eyes simple usually; separate sexes; development direct.

Miranda aurantia (Argiope)—spider

The spiders are a very large group of more than 20,000 species distributed all over the world. They are found in most kinds of habitats, in forests, on mountains, in deserts, on plains, in swamps, etc. All are predaceous, but they have different

Figure 190. Garden spider, *Miranda* (class Arachnida). Good example of protective marking.

ways of catching their prey. Some chase and others simply ambush their food, but most of them spin a net in which to trap the forms they live upon. Many of them have poison glands in connection with their fangs, but while this poison is effective in overcoming small invertebrates, very few have poison bites that are dangerous to man. In their habits they are mostly nocturnal. Outside of a relatively few species, they lie concealed more or less during the day. The large garden spider, *Miranda aurantia*, is often studied in the laboratory.

External structure. The body is compact and consists of distinct **cephalothorax** and **abdomen,** both divisions without segmentation, and joined by a slender **peduncle.** Eight simple eyes are on the dorsal side of the cephalothorax, and six pairs of appendages are on its ventral side. The first pair of appendages is the **chelicerae** which have basal segments and terminal fangs (claws). Each fang may be provided with a duct which leads to a poison gland. The **pedipalpi** (second pair of appendages) have basal parts (maxillae) with which they chew and squeeze their food; they also have sensory functions and are used by the males to transfer their sperm. The four pairs of **walking legs** each have seven joints and terminate in two or three claws. In addition, some spiders have hairy pads between their claws for holding onto steep surfaces.

The openings found in the spider are the **mouth** between the maxillae; the opening on either side to the **book lungs;** the **genital opening** on the ventral surface, covered by the epigynum plate; a single **spiracle** just anterior to the anus and connected to the tracheal system; two or three pairs of **spinnerets** posterior to the spiracle, used for spinning threads; and the **anus.**

Internal structure (Figure 191). The **digestive system** is made up of the mouth, a slender esophagus, a stomach provided with strong muscles for sucking, a digestive stomach with five pairs of ceca, a long intestine with two enlargements (one where the ducts of the digestive gland

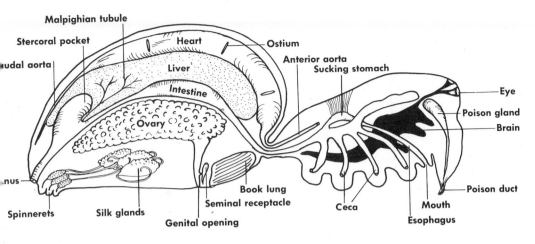

Malpighian tubule
Stercoral pocket
Heart
Ostium
Caudal aorta
Liver
Anterior aorta
Sucking stomach
Intestine
Eye
Poison gland
Ovary
Brain
Anus
Book lung
Poison duct
Seminal receptacle
Ceca
Mouth
Spinnerets
Silk glands
Esophagus
Genital opening

Figure 191. Internal structures of female spider (diagrammatic).

join it and the other at the stercoral pocket), and the anus. The digestive gland, or liver, is large and surrounds a great part of the intestine. It secretes a fluid which is emptied into the intestine.

The **circulatory system** is made up of a dorsal heart, arteries, veins, and sinuses. The heart is located in a pericardial space and has three pairs of ostia. There are an anterior aorta with branches that run to the stomach, legs, eyes, and other organs and a caudal artery that runs to the posterior region of the body. The blood is colorless with ameboid corpuscles. In its course it is carried to the book lungs where it is aerated.

Respiration is carried on by both book lungs and tracheae. The latter, however, play a minor part. The book lungs are peculiar to the arachnids and they are usually paired. Each consists of many parallel invaginated air pockets from a posterior chamber into a blood-filled anterior chamber. Air enters the posterior chamber by a slit in the body wall. Because these air pockets are flattened and leaflike, the whole structure is called a **book lung.** The blood carries the oxygen, for such tracheae as are present do not go everywhere as they do in insects.

The **excretory system** consists of the Malpighian tubules, which empty into the intestine, and a pair of **coxal glands** in the

cephalothorax, which discharge through ducts between the legs.

The **nervous system** is of the arthropod plan, although a little more concentrated than some. It comprises a dorsal brain, a subpharyngeal ganglionic mass of many fused ganglia from which nerves run to the various organs. This type of system will be described more fully in the crayfish later. The **sense organs** are centered mainly in the sensory hairs, and there are usually eight **simple eyes.** The eyes are chiefly for the perception of moving objects, but some may form distinct images. Each eye is provided with a lens, optic rods, and a retina. Just what senses spiders have is not known completely, but they are sensitive to touch and smell and probably to some other stimuli.

The **sexes** are separate, and the reproductive organs of each sex are located in the ventral part of the abdomen. The **male** organs are the paired testes below the intestine, the coiled vasa efferentia, and a single seminal vesicle which leads to the genital opening. The paired ovaries of the **female** system are hollow, each being connected to an oviduct which opens into the common vagina. Two seminal receptacles are joined to the vagina. In the transfer of sperm the male spins a small web, deposits his sperm on it, and stores the whole in cavities of the pedipalpi. When he mates he inserts his pedipalpi into the female genital opening and the sperm are stored in her seminal receptacles. Sometimes the male then serves as a meal for the much larger female. Before the mating act, spiders (usually the male) perform various courtship rituals, such as waving the appendages, assuming peculiar attitudes, touching the tip of the female's legs, and even offering her insect prey.

When the eggs are laid they are fertilized by the sperm as they pass through the vagina. The eggs are usually laid in a silk cocoon; this may be carried around by the female or it may be attached to a web or plant. A single cocoon may contain hundreds of eggs. About two weeks are necessary for hatching, but the young remain in the sac for a few weeks longer and molt once before leaving the sac. Several molts are necessary before they become mature.

Web-spinning habits of spiders. No aspect of spider life is more interesting than the spinning of webs. Not all spiders spin webs, for some, such as the hunting spider (*Lycosa*), simply chase and catch their prey, although they may spin an anchor thread so that they can return to a certain spot. The majority of spiders, however, spin some kind of web in which to ensnare and wrap up their food. Here, entrapped forms are killed by the poison fangs. The

Figure 192. Hunting spider strikes defensive pose that shows his appendages and chelicerae and eyes to good advantage.

spider punctures the body of its prey with its fangs, then alternately injects digestive fluid through the puncture and sucks up the dissolved tissues until the prey has been sucked dry. Tarantulas, wolf spiders, and others may crush the prey with very strong jaws to facilitate the digestive process. Usually only small invertebrate forms are caught in these webs, but instances are known where mice have actually been caught. *Dolomedes*, a species common east of the Rocky Mountains, is known to kill and eat small fish.

The spinning organs of spiders consist of two or three pairs of **spinnerets**, fingerlike appendages, which contain many hundred microscopic tubes that run to special abdominal glands. A protein secretion of these glands passes through these tubes to the outside, where it hardens into the silk thread on contact with the air.

Spiders use these threads for many purposes, such as lining their nests, forming cocoons, for balloons, and for spinning their webs. Two kinds of silk threads are used by spiders in making their nets, elastic and inelastic. The inelastic threads are usually used to make the framework of the net, which consists of threads radiating out from a center to an extensive periphery. The elastic type forms the spirals that run in concentric rows from the center outward and are supported by the radiating fibers. These spiral threads have viscid masses of sticky material for holding the prey when it becomes entangled in the web.

Different species of spiders make different kinds of nets. Some are quite simple and primitive and consist merely of a few strands radiating out from a spider's burrow or place of retreat. On the other hand the webs of the orb-weaving spiders are beautiful geometrical patterns (Figure 193). Cobwebs, which are usually irregular strands of silk, are formed by certain species of spiders. These untidy masses are often rendered more so by the dust that collects on them. The silk threads of spiders are stronger than steel threads of the same diameter.

P. SIMPSON

Figure 193. Web of orb-weaving spider. Most spiders bear three pairs of spinnerets on posterior ventral surface of abdomen. From silk glands inside abdomen liquid is forced out of spigots of spinnerets under pressure and hardens on contact with air. Each of four or five different kinds of glands secrete a different kind of silk. Orb weaver follows definite pattern in constructing web, but finished web may show many variations in given species. Starting with a "bridge thread," framework is made of boundary threads of dry silk glued in place and is usually an irregular four- or five-sided figure. Spokes, or radii, of dry silk are next spun and held in place at "hub" or center by platform of spiral dry silk thread. Functional spiral of sticky threads is next spun by spider working inward from rim to hub, being careful to walk on nonsticky radii while doing so.

Students who are interested in the many types of spider webs and the habits of spiders should consult that fascinating work on spiders by McCook. Although out of date with regard to classification and some other particulars, it is still one of the most interesting accounts of this group ever written.

Our most interesting spider—trap-door spider. Although spiders as a group have many interesting examples of habits and adaptations, perhaps none is more fascinating than the trap-door spider. There are several species of trap-door spiders, which are related to the well-known tarantulas. They are found in the southern and western parts of our country, although they have been most extensively studied in southern California. The common species found there is known as *Bothriocyrtum californica.* This spider exercises great ingenuity and architectural ability in the construction of her nest, which is a burrow in the ground that she excavates with her fangs, palps, and front legs. The burrow she makes is about 6 to 10 inches deep and a little more than 1 inch in diameter. Its walls are firm and smooth and are lined with a silken web. The walls are ashy gray in color, and the burrow is waterproof. The trap door, which is semicircular in outline, is hinged at the straight edge by means of the web which lines the inner surfaces of both the door and the burrow (Figure 194). When closed, the door fits snugly into the beveled entrance of the burrow flush with the surface of the surrounding ground. The door is carefully camouflaged with moss, lichen, and other vegetation, so it is very difficult to detect. On the inside surface of the door are little "arm holds" of silken web by which the spider with her fangs can keep the door closed against intruders. When watching for food she holds the lid partly ajar,

Figure 194. Burrow of trap-door spider with lid thrown open and its owner just retreating within.

seizes her prey, and drags it into her burrow. Her food consists mainly of insects and small crustaceans. She spends her entire life in the burrow, where she raises her young, and the length of time she has been in it can be estimated by the number of web layers on the underside of the door, one layer for each year of occupation. Some have been known to live more than seven years. The small males have rarely been found.

Trap-door spiders have their enemies, as do most animals. The one that does them the most harm is a wasp, *Pedinaspis planatus,* which is able either to slip in while the door is ajar or to force it open with her jaws. Inside she overcomes the spider and paralyzes her by stinging. On the abdomen of the spider the wasp lays an egg which hatches in a few days into a larva that lives on the paralyzed spider. Authorities state that more than a third of all burrows reveal dead spiders that have been destroyed in this way.

It is interesting to note that a spider in Africa has a similar habit of making a trap-door burrow except that this particular species makes its home in the soft bark of trees. The burrow in this case is also lined with a silken web but is much smaller and more shallow than that found in America.

Our most dangerous spider—black widow. Spiders have a bad reputation the world over and some can give painful bites, but most of them are quite harmless. Neither are they as aggressive as one commonly supposes when he sees one running toward him, for they will fight and bite only when they are tormented or when they are defending their young or egg cases. There is one, however, in the United States which deserves some of the bad reputation spiders have. This is the black widow (*Latrodectus mactans*) (Figure 195), which can give severe, even fatal, bites. This spider is not a large one. It is coal black with a prominent orange or reddish colored "hourglass" beneath the abdomen, which usually serves to identify it. The name widow has been

Figure 195. This black widow spider, *Latrodectu* suspended on her web, has just eaten large cock roach. Note "hourglass" marking (orange co! ored) on ventral side of abdomen.

given to it because she was reputed t eat her mate immediately after mating Those who have observed her habit closely conclude that the male is seldom sacrificed this way, although such prac tices are known to occur among othe spiders.

The distribution of the black widow seems to be a very wide one, for her pres ence has been reported from most of ou states. However, she seems to be far mor abundant in the warm regions, such a our southern states and southern Cali fornia. Her habitat may be almost any where around rubbish, in dark cellars and under stones and objects in gardens Dark outbuildings are favorite places, an it is said that 90% of the people bitter by them were in outdoor toilets at th time.

Several hundred authentic cases of bite from the black widow have been re ported. These cases cover thirty-tw states, and deaths from the bites hav been reported from seventeen states. O the more than fifty deaths reported, thirty two of them have been in California. Th mortality rate is about 5%.

A considerable number of the bites occurred on or around the groins or genital
organs. Many of the male victims were
bitten on the penis. The symptoms have
varied somewhat with individual cases.
In general, there is acute pain, often
sharp and stinging. There are often great
burning sensations which may be local or
general. Severe muscle spasms also occur,
as well as vomiting, general restlessness,
and cyanosis. Most of the symptoms are
characteristic of a neurotoxic venom, that
is, venom which acts upon the nervous
system. Most of the patients are incapaci-
ated for several days.

In the treatment of the black widow
bite various procedures are followed by
doctors, such as those commonly used
with neurotoxic poisons. Partial success
has been achieved with antivenom and
serums.

Scorpions

Although scorpions are more common
in tropical and subtropical countries, they
have been reported from at least thirty
of our states. More than 600 species are
known. Their habitat is in trash piles,
under boards and other objects, around
dwellings, and in burrows of desert regions. Most of them will burrow but a
few will not. They are most active at night
when they seek their prey (insects, spiders, etc.). The elongated body is divided
into two major regions: (1) the cephalothorax (prosoma) and (2) the abdomen
(preabdomen and postabdomen). The
postabdomen, or metasoma, is often called
the tail. The cephalothorax is made up of
six segments and is enclosed by a dorsal
chitinous plate, the carapace, and by
various ventral plates. The carapace bears
from two to twelve eyes (depending on
the species) which are grouped into median and sometimes lateral eyes. From
the cephalothorax, six pairs of appendages arise: (1) the small paired chelicerae, each of three joints, (2) the paired
pedipalps, each of six joints and a pincer,
and (3) the four pairs of walking legs,
each of eight joints. The chelicerae and
pedipalps, which are provided with jaws

Figure 196. Tropical blue scorpion, *Centrurus*,
which is common in Cuba. Note terminal poison
claw. (Preserved specimen.)

Figure 197. Pseudoscorpion, or false scorpion.
Order Chelonethida (Pseudoscorpionida). Most
members of this group do not exceed 1/5 inch
in length. They live under stones, bark of trees,
and sometimes between pages of books. Their
food is chiefly small insects and mites. In winter
they construct cocoons from silk glands, which
open on the chelicerae. Note large pedipalps
which resemble those of true scorpions. (Courtesy Robert Weber and Bill Vesey, Fort Wayne,
Ind.)

and teeth, are used for seizing and tearing their prey.

The abdomen consists of twelve segments (seven in the preabdomen and five in the postabdomen, or "tail"). At the end of the postabdomen is the postanal telson which bears the terminal poison claw or stinger. Scorpions may or may not use the stinger in overcoming their prey. On the ventral side of the abdomen are the curious comblike pectines which are tactile organs used for exploring the ground and for sex recognition. Of the more than forty American species, only two are said to be dangerous to man. These two belong to the genus *Centruroides* found mainly in Arizona and nearby states. Their venom affects the nervous system, whereas the bite of most scorpions produces only a painful swelling. Scorpions bring forth living young which are carried on the back of the mother, but they do not feed upon her tissues (a popular superstition).

In mating, scorpions have an interesting courtship ceremony in which the two mates seize each other's claws and perform a dance.

Mites and ticks

These arachnids have the cephalothorax and abdomen fused and there is no external sign of segmentation. They are found almost everywhere, but their small size causes them to be overlooked even when they are abundant. Some live in water, both fresh and marine, others live on vegetation and on the ground, and still others are parasitic on animals. The itch mite burrows into the skin where the female lays her eggs. Another species is responsible for mange in dogs and other domestic animals.

Among the worst pests to contend with are the **chiggers,** or red bugs (*Eutrombicula*). These are the larval forms of red mites; they have only six legs, which is the number the larval forms of other mites and ticks have. When a chigger attaches itself to the skin, it forms, with the aid of a digestive secretion, a sort of burrow at the site where it is eating. Many persons are irritated by this fluid, and a large

Figure 198. The wood tick, *Dermacentor*, one species of which transmits Rocky Mountain spotted fever and tularemia, as well as producing tick paralysis.

reddish blotch and intense itching result. Chiggers do not suck blood. They are especially abundant in raspberry patches and often on lawns. The precaution of dusting sulfur on the hose around the ankles is fairly effective in discouraging their attacks. After feeding for a time the chigger will drop off to the ground, although some are known to be carried in clothing of infested persons. Chiggers attack nearly all land vertebrates.

Ticks are usually larger than mites and feed upon the blood of various vertebrate animals. With their mouth parts they pierce the skin and draw up blood with their sucking pharynx until their bodies are enormously distended. They can survive long periods of time without feeding. The female lays her eggs on the ground; these eggs hatch into larvae, which climb on bushes and fasten themselves to the host which happens to pass that way. After filling themselves, the ticks will drop off, digest their meal, undergo molting, climb up another bush, and patiently wait for another meal.

Ticks are among the greatest arthropod vectors of disease. Among the diseases for which they are responsible are relapsing fever, Rocky Mountain spotted fever (Figure 198), and Texas cattle fever (Figure 199). The wood tick *(Dermacentor)* which infests various mammals, including man, is the vector for Rocky Mountain spotted fever which is caused by a rickettsia organism carried in the salivary secretions of the tick.

SUBPHYLUM PENTASTOMIDA (LINGUATULIDA)

The tongue worms are vermiform, somewhat flattened, ringed externally, and legless. They have no oral appendages, but two pairs of movable hooks or claws are found in shallow pits near the mouth. Immature forms have four or six legs. They have no respiratory or excretory organs. They are provided with a chitinous exoskeleton and striated muscles. The genital openings are either at the base or apex of the abdomen. All tongue worms are parasitic; the immature forms are usually found in the internal tissues of mammals

and the adults in the mouth, nasal cavity, or respiratory tract of a carnivorous vertebrate (reptile, wolf). *Porocephalus* is a common form in snakes; *Linguatula,* in mammals.

SUBPHYLUM TARDIGRADA

Water bears (Figure 200) are minute forms, usually less than 1 mm. in length, and are found in both fresh water and salt

Figure 200. Dorsal view of water bear (subphylum Tardigrada). The taxonomic position of these little animals is uncertain. Some consider them as separate phylum. About forty species (0.5 to 1 mm. long) have been reported from North America (many more in Europe). They live in terrestrial mosses, lichens, aquatic plants, debris of ponds, blanket algae of ponds and lakes, and other places. Although dioecious, most specimens collected are females that produce two kinds of eggs similar to the summer and winter eggs of rotifers. Their most unique characteristics are their four pairs of short, unjointed, claw-bearing legs and their complicated buccal apparatus for sucking liquid food.

water, moss, sand, and damp soils. The body is elongated, cylindrical, or a long oval, and it is unsegmented. It bears four pairs of short, stubby, unjointed legs armed with claws. The last pair of these appendages lies at the posterior end of · the body. The body is covered with a thin cuticle which is shed from time to time by ecdysis. The digestive system is straight with the mouth at the anterior end and the anus at the posterior end. They have no special respiratory or circulatory systems, but Malpighian tubules are present. The separate sexes have unpaired genital glands which open into the cloaca. The nervous system is similar to that of other arthropods, but the ventral cords lie far apart from each other (ladderlike). Two eyespots are found on the head. Many of them can withstand desiccation for years and can be revived when wetted.

The systematic position of Tardigrada is uncertain, for they lack segmentation and their unjointed legs resemble those of *Peripatus*, but some zoologists consider them a side branch of the arthropods.

ANNOTATED REFERENCES

Arachnida

Baerg, W. J. 1958. The Tarantula. Lawrence, University of Kansas Press. *A monograph on the habits and natural history of a greatly misunderstood member of an animal group, which is one of the most fascinating in the animal kingdom.*

Comstock, J. H., and W. J. Gertsch. 1940. The Spider Book, ed. 2. New York, Doubleday Doran & Co., Inc. *A well-written account of spiders. Much emphasis is given to their habits and behavior.*

Fabre, J. H. 1919. The Life of the Spider. New York, Dodd, Mead & Co. *An interesting description of the adaptations of the spider. Especially good for the beginner in zoology.*

Herms, W. B. 1950. Medical Entomology, ed. 4. New York, The Macmillan Co. *A section of this book is devoted to Arachnida. The role arachnoids play in disease transmission is emphasized.*

Kaston, B. J., and E. Kaston. 1953. How to Know the Spiders. Dubuque, Iowa, Wm. C. Brown Co. *This is an excellent taxonomic manual of the common spiders.· It is fully illustrated with line drawings and the keys are exceptional. Aside from the valuable taxonomic part, the book contains much information about spiders in general. If you are interested in spiders, study this book.*

McCook, H. C. 1889-1893. American Spiders and Their Spinningwork. Philadelphia, Academy of Natural Science. *A great classical work which in many ways has never been surpassed in this field.*

Pratt, H. S. 1935. A Manual of the Common Invertebrate Animals, ed. 2. Philadelphia, The Blakistan Co. *A section of the book deals with descriptions and classifications of Arachnoidea.*

Savory, T. H. 1952. The Spider's Web. New York, Frederick Warne & Co., Ltd. *An interesting account of the way spiders spin and make use of their webs. There are a number of plates, some in color. The viewpoint of the author that only spiders and the larvae of caddis flies build traps to catch their prey may well be questioned. How about the pit of the ant lion?*

chapter 17

Phylum Arthropoda

Subphylum Mandibulata—except insects

CLASS CRUSTACEA

The members of class Crustacea get their name from the hard shells they bear (L. *crusta,* a shell). The class includes lobsters, crayfish, shrimp, crabs, water fleas, copepods, barnacles, and some others. There are about 30,000 species in the class. Many of them are marine, some live in fresh water, and others are found in moist soil. Most of them are free living, but a few are sessile, commensal, or parasitic. They differ from other arthropods chiefly by having gills for breathing, by having two pairs of antennae, one pair of mandibles, and two pairs of maxillae, by having the appendages modified for various functions, and by lacking Malpighian tubules.

Crayfish

The crayfish is found in fresh-water streams, ponds, and swamps over most of the world. There are a number of genera and more than 130 species have been described in the United States. Common genera in North America are *Or-conectes* and *Cambarus,* which are found east of the Rocky Mountains, and *Astacus,* which occurs mainly on the western slopes of the Rockies; the latter is also common in Europe. The various species resemble each other very closely, except for minor details, and any one of them can well serve as a representa-

tive type for study. Even the large lobster *(Homarus)* has about the same plan of structure.

Habitat. Most students are familiar with the natural history of this form, for it is one of the most common animals in fresh water. Some are found in slow-moving water, others prefer swift streams, and some blind ones dwell in caves. They are primarily bottom dwellers and spend the day under rocks and vegetation, coming out at night in search of food. Some are terrestrial in their habits and make characteristic chimneylike burrows in the soil if the water level is not too far under the surface. When hiding in its retreat the crayfish keeps its head end at the entrance with its antennae and pincers extended out. One way of catching them is to drag a piece of meat on a hook over the bottom of a pool, for they will grasp any food they can reach.

Behavior. Crayfish endangered can dart off to a hiding place with considerable speed. In their burrows they face outward so they can dart out for food. While stationary they keep currents of water moving by waving the bailer and swimmerets back and forth. They can walk in any direction with most of the weight supported chiefly by the fourth pair of legs. When escaping from danger they move rapidly backward by extending and flexing the abdomen, uropods, and telson, thus producing a series of backward darts.

With reference to orientation, crayfish are positively thigmotactic and try to get most of the body in contact with a surface. Many chemical substances, unless concentrated, will attract them. Most light sources will cause them to retreat, although they do have a liking for red. They are mainly nocturnal animals.

The behavior of the crayfish is mostly instinctive, although they can be taught simple habits through experience.

Regeneration and autotomy. Crayfish have the power to regenerate lost parts. In general, any of the appendages and the eyes will be renewed when removed, although regeneration is faster in young animals. A lost part is partially renewed at the next molting, and after several moltings it is completely restored. The new structure is not always the same as the one lost. If only part of the eye stalk is cut off, normal regeneration will occur, but if the entire eye stalk is removed, a structure similar to an antenna replaces it. Whenever the part regenerated is different from the lost part, such a regeneration is called **heteromorphosis.**

The power of self-amputation is called **autotomy.** It refers to the breaking off of the legs and chelae at a definite point whenever they are injured. The definite breaking point is near the base of the legs and is marked by an encircling line on the basal segment of the chelae and at

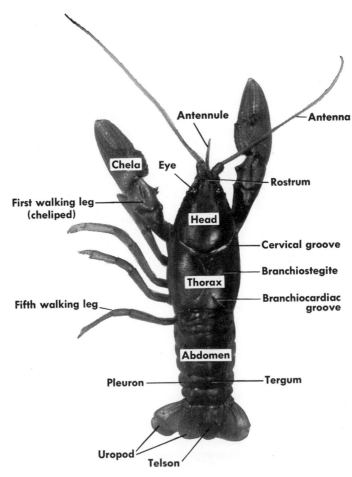

Figure 201. Dorsal view of crayfish.

the third joint on the walking legs. If one of these appendages is injured, all parts terminal to the breaking point are cast off. The process is effected by a special muscle. Autotomy has the advantage of preventing excess loss of blood, for the wound closes more quickly when the legs are broken off at the breaking point. After a part is cast off in this manner, a replacement regenerates in the regular way.

External features. The body, about 3 to 4 inches long, is covered with an exoskeleton composed of chitin and lime. This hard protective covering is soft and thin at the joints between the somites, allowing flexibility of movement. The somites are grouped into two main regions,

the **cephalothorax** (head and thorax) and the **abdomen.** There are nineteen somites in the body: five in the head, eight in the thorax, and six in the abdomen. Each somite has a pair of jointed appendages. The cephalothorax is enclosed dorsally and laterally by the continuous skeletal shell, the **carapace,** where the joints between somites are obliterated, except for the cervical groove which marks the division between the head and thorax. The anterior tip of the carapace is called the **rostrum.** The compound eye which is stalked and movable lies beneath and on either side of the rostrum. A typical somite in the abdomen consists of a dorsal plate, or **tergum,** and a ventral transverse bar, or **sternum,** joined together by a lateral

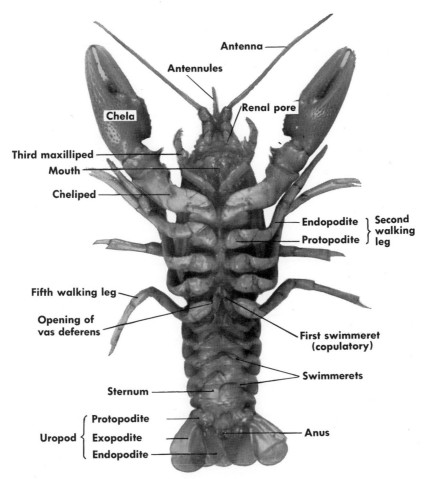

Figure 202. Ventral view of male crayfish.

Phylum Arthropoda—subphylum Mandibulata—except insects 295

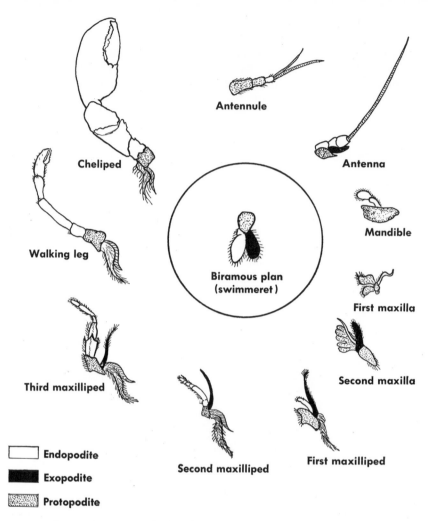

Figure 203. Appendages of crayfish, showing how they have become modified from basic biramous plan, such as found in swimmeret.

pleuron on each side. The segmented abdomen terminates in the broad, flaplike **telson,** which is not considered a somite. On the ventral side of the telson is the **anus.** The openings of the paired **vasa deferentia** are on the median side at the base of the fifth pair of walking legs, and those of the paired **oviducts** are at the base of the third pair. In the female the opening to the seminal receptacle is located in the mid-ventral line between the fourth and fifth pairs of walking legs.

APPENDAGES. The crayfish has typically one pair of jointed appendages on each somite. These appendages differ from each other, depending upon their functions. All, however, are variations of a common plan. This common plan, best illustrated by the swimmerets of the abdominal region, is a two-branched, or **biramous,** appendage. It consists of a basal **protopodite** that bears a lateral **exopodite** and a median **endopodite.** The protopodite is made up of two joints, **coxopodite** and **basipodite,** whereas the exopodite and endopodite have from one to several segments each. From this common biramous type of appendage have come all the different kinds of ap-

Table 4 Crayfish appendages

Appendage	Protopodite	Endopodite	Exopodite	Function
Antennule	3 segments, statocyst in base	Many-jointed feeler	Many-jointed feeler	Touch, taste, equilibrium
Antenna	2 segments, excretory pore in base	Long, many-jointed feeler	Broad, thin, pointed squama	Touch, taste
Mandible	2 segments, heavy jaw and base of palp	2 distal segments of palp	Absent	Crushing food
First maxilla	2 thin medial lamellae	Small unjointed lamella	Absent	Food handling
Second maxilla	2 bilobed lamellae, an extra plate, epipodite	1 small pointed segment	Dorsal plate, the scaphognathite (bailer)	Draws currents of water into gills
First maxilliped	2 medial plates and epipodite	2 small segments	1 basal segment plus many-jointed filament	Touch, taste, food handling
Second maxilliped	2 segments plus gill	5 short segments	2 slender segments	Touch, taste, food handling
Third maxilliped	2 segments plus gill	5 larger segments	2 slender segments	Touch, taste, food handling
First walking leg (cheliped)	2 segments plus gill	5 segments with heavy pincer	Absent	Offense and defense
Second walking leg	2 segments plus gill	5 segments plus small pincer	Absent	Walking and prehension
Third walking leg	2 segments plus gill; genital pore in female	5 segments plus small pincer	Absent	Walking and prehension
Fourth walking leg	2 segments plus gill	5 segments, no pincer	Absent	Walking
Fifth walking leg	2 segments; genital pore in male; no gill	5 segments, no pincer	Absent	Walking
First swimmeret	In female reduced or absent; in male fused with endopodite to form tube			Transfers sperm to female
Second swimmeret Male	Structure modified for transfer of sperm to female			
Female	2 segments	Jointed filament	Jointed filament	Creates water currents; carries eggs and young
Third, fourth, and fifth swimmerets	2 short segments	Jointed filament	Jointed filament	Create current of water; in female carry eggs and young
Uropod	1 short, broad segment	Flat, oval plate	Flat, oval plate; divided into 2 parts with hinge	Swimming; egg protection in female

pendages in the crayfish. Three kinds are recognized in the adult: (1) **foliaceous,** such as the second maxillae, (2) **biramous,** such as the swimmerets, and (3) **uniramous,** such as the walking legs. All these appendages have been derived from the biramous type, as shown in the embryonic crayfish in which all the appendages arise as two-branched structures. Structures that have a similar basic plan and have descended from a common form are said to be **homologous,** whether they have the same function or not. Since the specialized walking legs, mouth parts, chelipeds, and swimmerets have all developed from a common type and have become modified to perform different functions, they are all homologous to each other (serially homologous). In this structural modification some branches have been reduced, some lost, some greatly altered, and some new parts added. The crayfish and its allies are one of the best examples of **serial homology** in the animal kingdom.

Table 4 shows how the various appendages have become modified from the biramous plan to fit specific functions.

Internal features. The crayfish has all the organs and systems found in the higher forms (Figure 204). A few of the systems, such as the muscular and nervous, show segmentation, but most of them are modified from this plan. Most of the changes involve concentration of parts in a particular region or else reduction or complete loss, for example, the intersepta. In contrast to annelids, arthropods have a much reduced **coelomic cavity** which is divided into a number of separate spaces. One of these cavities encloses the excretory green glands and another the reproductive organs. The larger cavities around the alimentary canal are not true coelomic cavities; they contain blood and are known as **hemocoeles.**

MUSCULAR SYSTEM. Striated muscles make up a considerable part of the body of a crayfish. It uses them for body movements and for manipulation of the appendages. The muscles are often arranged in opposite pairs. **Flexors** draw a part toward the body; **extensors** straighten it out. The abdomen has very powerful flexors which are used when the animal swims backward—his best means of escape. Strong muscles on either side of the stomach manipulate the mandibles.

RESPIRATORY SYSTEM (Figure 205). Crayfish breathe by means of gills, which are delicate featherlike projections of the body wall and are located on either side of the thorax in the **gill chambers.** The gill chamber is covered by the **branchiostegite,** or lateral wall of the carapace, and opens ventrally and at both ends. The bailer of the second maxilla draws water over the gill filaments by moving back and forth. In *Cambarus* the gills are arranged in two rows (in some others there is a third row); those in the outermost row are called the **podobranchiae** and are attached

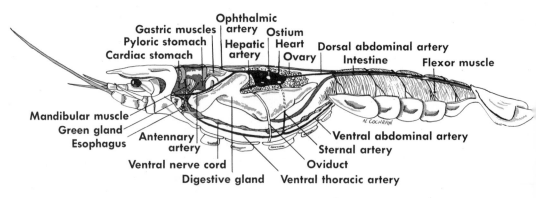

Figure 204. Semidiagram of internal structure of large female crustacean such as crayfish.

298

to the coxopodites of appendages VII to XII; those in the inner double row are the **arthrobranchiae** and are attached to the membranes that join these appendages to the thorax. Altogether there are seventeen gills on each side.

DIGESTIVE SYSTEM. The alimentary canal is made up of the following: (1) The **mouth** opens on the ventral surface between the mandibles (jaws). (2) A short tubular **esophagus**. (3) The **stomach** is a large, thin-walled cavity divided into an anterior **cardiac** chamber and a smaller **pyloric** chamber. In the cardiac portion is the **gastric mill** consisting of one median and two lateral chitinous ossicles manipulated by powerful muscles for grinding the food. Between the cardiac and pyloric chambers is a strainer of hairlike setae, which permits only fine particles to pass through. Small calcareous bodies, **gastroliths**, may also be present in the cardiac walls. These gastroliths enlarge during molting, for they serve as storage for calcium withdrawn from the exoskeleton. (4) A short midgut. (5) The long, slender **intestine** extends dorsally along the abdomen and opens through the **anus** on the ventral side of the telson. (6) Two large digestive glands lie beneath and posterior to the stomach and open by separate ducts into the midgut. Each digestive gland consists of three lobes composed of many tubules lined with glandular epithelium which produce the digestive secretion. With the exception of the midgut, the entire digestive system is lined with delicate chitin. At each molt this lining is shed and when renewed is hardened by the calcareous gastroliths.

METABOLISM. Crayfish will eat almost anything that is edible—insects, worms, snails, flesh of dead animals, and even plants. Before reaching the mouth, the food is broken into small pieces by the maxillipeds, maxillae, and mandibles. The latter are especially adapted for crushing the food. When the food reaches the cardiac stomach it is further subjected to the grinding action of the gastric mill. Only the finer particles pass the strainer between the cardiac and pyloric stomachs;

coarser particles are further acted upon by the grinding mechanism. When the food is fine enough it passes in a fluid stream to the tubules of the digestive glands, where digestion is completed by enzymes and the food is absorbed. The indigestible part of the food is passed on into the intestine to be eliminated by the anus. Because of the thorough treatment the food gets before reaching the intestine, the latter is less important in digestion than is the case with many other animals.

After the digested food is absorbed into the blood it is carried to the tissue cells to be utilized. The metabolic waste is removed by the green glands. Oxygen which is picked up by the circulating blood of the gills is transported in the blood plasma by the pigment **hemocyanin**; CO_2 is given off from the gills in the exchange.

CIRCULATORY SYSTEM. The crayfish has an **open**, or **lacunar**, blood system in which veins are absent. It will be recalled that Annelida have a closed system, as do the highest group of all, Vertebrata.

The circulatory system (Figures 204 and 205) is made up of a muscular **heart**, seven **arteries** which carry blood to the body, and certain **sinuses** which return the blood to the large mid-dorsal **pericardial sinus** surrounding the heart. The heart is held in place by six ligaments attached to the walls of the pericardial sinus. Blood from the pericardial sinus enters the heart through three pairs of valves known as **ostia**. The arteries are (1) **ophthalmic**, which runs in a median dorsal direction over the stomach and supplies the cardiac stomach, the esophagus, and head; (2) two **antennary**, which arise on each side of the ophthalmic and run forward and downward and supply branches to the cardiac stomach, to the antennae, to the green glands, and to the muscles of the head; (3) two **hepatic**, which arise from the heart below the antennary arteries and supply the digestive glands; (4) **dorsal abdominal**, which passes backward from the ventral part of the heart and supplies the dorsal region of the abdomen and the appendages; (5) **sternal**, which leaves the

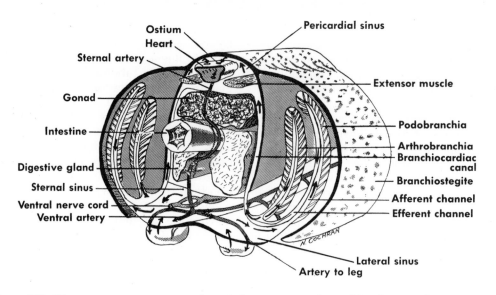

Figure 205. Diagrammatic cross-section through heart region of crayfish, showing direction of blood flow in this "open" type blood system. Blood is pumped from heart to body tissues through arteries which empty into tissue sinuses. Returning blood enters sternal sinus, is carried to gills for gas exchange, then back to pericardial sinus by the branchiocardiac canals. Note absence of veins.

heart near the origin of the dorsal abdominal and extends straight down to the nerve cord. It passes through the cord, then divides into the **ventral thoracic,** which runs anteriorly to supply the thoracic appendages, mouth, and esophagus, and the **ventral abdominal,** which runs posteriorly to feed the abdominal appendages and muscles.

Valves in the arteries prevent a backflow of blood. The large arteries give rise to smaller arteries which empty into the tissue sinuses which in turn discharge into the large **sternal sinus.** From the sternal sinus afferent channels carry blood to the gills, where O_2 and CO_2 are exchanged. The blood now is returned to the pericardial sinus by the efferent **branchiocardiac canals.**

Blood in arthropods is largely colorless. It contains a number of ameboid cells and hemocyanin, a copper-containing respiratory pigment. This blood has the property of forming a clot, which prevents loss of blood in minor injuries.

REPRODUCTION. The crayfish is dioecious, and there is some sexual dimorphism, for the female has a broader abdomen than the male and lacks the modified swimmerets which serve as copulatory organs in the male. The **male organs** consist of two whitish, three-lobed **testes** lying just beneath the pericardial sinus and two long, coiled **vasa deferentia** which pass from the testes out over the digestive glands and down to **genital pores** located at the base of the fifth walking legs. The **female organs** are paired **ovaries,** resembling the testes and located in a similar place, and short **oviducts,** which pass down to the genital pores at the base of the third walking legs.

Crayfish mate in the spring or early fall. If they copulate in the fall the eggs are usually not laid till spring. In the process of copulation the male inverts the female, holds her with his body, chela and telson, and tranfers his sperm from the openings of his vasa deferentia to her seminal receptacle by means of the first two pairs of his swimmerets (Figure 202). The seminal receptacle is a shallow cavity in the midline between the fourth and fifth pairs of walking legs. Here the sperm cells are retained until the mature eggs pass out of the oviducts. Two to three hundred eggs are discharged at one time, and as they pass by in slimy strings, they are fertilized by the sperm from the seminal receptacle. After fertilization, the masses of eggs are attached to the swimmerets like bunches of grapes and remain there during development (Figure 206). It takes five to six weeks for hatching, and each embryo resembles the adult except for size. The young remain attached to the mother for several weeks, during which time they begin their molting. After leaving the mother they undergo several more molts during the first season, reaching a length up to 2 inches by fall. Crayfish have a life span of three to five years.

Ecdysis, or molting, is absolutely necessary for the body to increase in size. Molting occurs less frequently as the animal grows older. In the adult, molting occurs in the spring and fall. Just before each molt inorganic salts are withdrawn from the exoskeleton and a new, softer exoskeleton is formed underneath; the old splits open dorsally between the carapace and abdomen. The animal then backs out of the old exoskeleton, shedding even the lining of the digestive system and the cornea of the eyes, as well as the gross external structures. During the period of molting the animal is quite defenseless and remains hidden away.

EXCRETORY SYSTEM. The excretory organs are a pair of **green glands** (Figure 204) found in the ventral part of the head anterior to the esophagus. Each green gland consists of a glandular portion, a thin-walled bladder, and a duct opening to the exterior by a pore (Figure 202) on the basal segment. The small cavities around the green glands and the genital organs represent what remains of the coelom.

NERVOUS SYSTEM. The nervous systems of the crayfish and earthworm have much in common, although that of the crayfish is somewhat larger and has more fusion of ganglia (Figure 207). The **central nervous** system consists of (1) a **brain,** or supraesophageal ganglia, which supplies nerves to the eyes, antennules, and antennae; this is connected by (2) a pair of **circumesophageal connectives** to the **subesophageal ganglion,** which lies at the anterior end of the ventral nerve cord and represents a fusion of at least five pairs of ganglia that supply nerves to the mouth, appendages, esophagus, and green glands; and (3) a double **ventral nerve cord.** The

Figure 206. Female crayfish with eggs hanging like grapes from swimmerets. Crayfish with eggs are said to be "in berry." The young, when hatched, also cling to swimmerets, protected by tail fan.

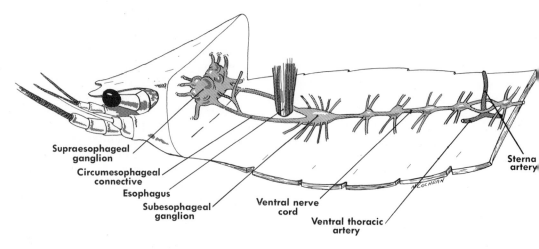

Figure 207. Anterior part of nervous system of crayfish. Primitive nervous system of crustaceans is constructed on same plan as that of the annelids, that is, a dorsal brain, two longitudinal ventral cords, and pair of ganglia for each somite. This primitive plan has been altered in adult crayfish in accordance with transformation brought about by fusion of somites and other changes, so that double ganglia and nerve cords of each somite are fused into one. Many ganglia are displaced and fused together, and some ganglia may be lost. The brain is a complex of many ganglia and gives off nerves to the eyes, antennules, and antennae. Fused subesophageal ganglion is made up of five or six pairs of ganglia which send nerves to mandibles, maxillae, maxillipeds, and excretory organs. Along ventral nerve cord, fused ganglia give off paired nerves to appendages, muscles, and other parts of body.

cord has typically a fused pair of ganglia for each somite from VIII to XIX. These ganglia give off nerves to the appendages, muscles, etc. In addition to this central system, there is also a visceral system, which arises partly from the brain and partly from the circumesophageal connectives and passes to the pyloric stomach. In the primitive Branchiopoda, the ventral nerve cord has the ladder arrangement characteristic of flatworms and some annelids, for the two parts are separated and are connected by transverse commissures.

SENSORY SYSTEM. The crayfish has better developed sense organs than the annelids. The largest sense organs are the two **eyes** and the two **statocysts. Tactile** organs are widely distributed over the body in the form of tactile hairs, delicate projections of the cuticle, which are especially abundant on the chelae, mouth parts, and telson. The chemical senses of **taste** and **smell** are found in hairs on the antennules, antennae, mouth parts, and other places.

A saclike **statocyst** is found on the basal segment of each antennule and opens to the surface by a dorsal pore. The statocyst contains a ridge which bears sensory hairs formed from the chitinous lining and grains of sand that serve as **statoliths.** Whenever the animal changes its position, there are corresponding changes in the presence of the grains on the sensory hairs which are relayed as stimuli to the brain, and the animal can adjust itself accordingly. The chitinous lining of the statocyst is shed at each molting (ecdysis), and with it the sand grains are also lost, but new grains are picked up through the dorsal pore when the animal renews its statocyst lining.

The eyes in crayfish are **compound** and are made up of many units called **ommatidia.** Covering the rounded surface of each eye is the transparent **cornea,** which is divided into some 2,500 small squares known as **facets,** representing the outer ends of the ommatidia. Each ommatidium, starting at the surface, consists of a corneal facet, two **corneagen cells** which form the cornea, a **crystalline cone** of four **cone cells** (vitrellae), a pair of **retinular cells** around the crystalline cone, several retinular cells which form a central **rhabdome,** and black **pigment cells** which separate the retinulae of adjacent ommatidia. The inner ends of the retinular cells connect with sensory nerve fibers which pass through optic ganglia to form the optic nerve to the brain. The movement of the pigment in the arthropod compound eye makes possible two kinds of vision. In each ommatidium there are three sets of pigment (distal retinal pigment cells, proximal retinal pigment cells, and reflecting pigment cells) and these are so arranged that they can form a more or less complete collar or sleeve around each ommatidium. For strong light or day adaptation the distal retinal pigment moves inward and meets the outward moving proximal retinal pigment so that a complete pigment sleeve is formed around the ommatidium. In this condition only those rays that strike the cornea directly will reach the retinular cells, for each ommatidium is shielded from the others. Thus each ommatidium will see only a limited area of the field of vision (a mosaic or apposition image). In dim light the distal and proximal pigments separate, so that the light rays with the aid of the reflecting pigment cells have a chance to spread to adjacent ommatidia and form a continuous or superposition image. This second type of vision is less precise but takes advantage of the amount of light received. Compound eyes also have the power to analyze polarized light, as shown by the honeybee.

Endocrine functions. The **sinus gland** at the base of the eyestalk is known to have a number of hormones. They are supposed to control the spread of pigment in the chromatophores of the epidermis and

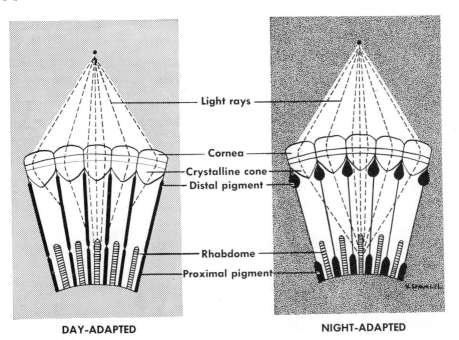

Light rays

Cornea

Crystalline cone

Distal pigment

Rhabdome

Proximal pigment

DAY-ADAPTED   **NIGHT-ADAPTED**

Figure 208. Diagram of compound eye of arthropod, showing migration of pigment in ommatidia for day and night vision. Five ommatidia represented in each diagram. In daytime each ommatidium is surrounded by a dark pigment collar, so that each ommatidium is stimulated only by light rays which enter its own cornea (mosaic vision); in nighttime pigment forms incomplete collars and light rays can spread to adjacent ommatidia (continuous or superposition image). (Redrawn from Moment: General Zoology, Houghton Mifflin Co.)

in the compound eyes. They also seem to have some regulatory power over molting and affect the deposition of limy salts in the exoskeleton. The blood probably distributes the hormone just as in higher forms.

The exact mechanism by which these physiological processes are carried out is still very obscure. Extensive research indicates that there is an X organ in the eyestalk along with the sinus gland. Neurosecretory cells in the X organ and in the brain produce a molt-preventing hormone which is stored in the sinus gland. When eyestalks are removed experimentally from a nonmolting specimen, molting will occur in a few days because the inhibiting effect of the hormone is removed; when eyestalks from nonmolting crayfish are implanted into the body of an eyestalkless specimen, molting is delayed. A Y organ, which produces a molt-accelerating hormone, has been described in some crustaceans. The interaction of the molt-preventing and the molt-accelerating hormones may be the regulatory device in the molting process.

The pigments of crustaceans are of a great variety, such as yellow, red, orange, green, brown, black, etc. Some of these are lipochromes and others are melanins. Most of the pigments are found in special branched cells (chromatophores), but some are found in the tissues. For the expansion and contraction of these pigments into and out of the chromatophore processes, certain chromatophorotropic hor-mones in the sinus gland appear to be responsible, as revealed by the removal of the eyestalk (darkening effect) or by the injection of eyestalk extracts (paling effect).

A specific hormone from the sinus gland is known to control the retinal pigment movements also.

Other Crustacea

The crustaceans are an extensive group with many subdivisions. There are many patterns of structure, habitat, and mode of living among them. Some are quite a bit larger than the crayfish; others are smaller. Some are highly developed and specialized; others have simpler organizations. The older classification divided the crustaceans into two subclasses—Entomostraca and Malacostraca. The Entomostraca are simpler in structure and usually smaller than the Malacostraca and do not have abdominal appendages. The Malacostraca form a natural division, for its members have an eight-segmented thorax, a six- or seven-segmented abdomen, a gastric mill, and abdominal appendages. The term Entomostraca is largely being discontinued, for its members lack morphological unity.

The principal subclasses of class Crustacea are as follows:

Subclass Branchiopoda. (bran'chi-op"o-da) (NL. *branchio*, gill, + *podos*, foot). The members of this group are among the most primitive of all the crustaceans. One common example is the transparent fairy shrimp (*Eubranchipus*)

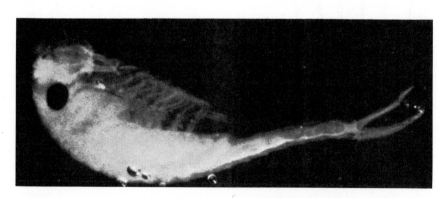

Figure 209. Fairy shrimp, *Eubranchipus*. Often swims with ventral side up.

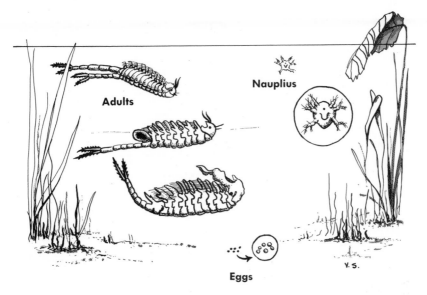

Figure 210. Seasonal cycle in *Eubranchipus,* fairy shrimp. Order Anostraca. These beautiful crustaceans found chiefly in vernal pools and ponds which dry up during summer. Their appearance is sporadic and their distribution irregular. Females lay eggs in clutches of 10 to 250 which can withstand drying during the summer. Eggs in temperate climates usually hatch in winter and early spring, and after passing through a nauplius stage develop quickly into adults. In certain latitudes adults may be found during the summer if ponds do not dry up. Drying promotes hatching of eggs but is not always necessary. Twenty-seven species have been recorded for North America. Most species are around 1 inch in length, but some are smaller or larger than this. (Redrawn from Moment: General Zoology, Houghton Mifflin Co.)

(Figures 209 and 210) which is found in temporary pools in pasture fields and elsewhere early in spring when melting snows have left little pools of water. They have eleven pairs of broad, leaflike trunk appendages which are all basically alike. These appendages are used for locomotion, respiration, and egg bearing, and bear chromatophores which add to their beauty. Males are not common in some species and parthenogenesis frequently occurs in the brine shrimp. The males of fairy shrimp are provided with penes for the transfer of sperm to the female. The developing eggs are carried by the female in a ventral brood sac, where they are released in clutches at intervals of a few days. Released eggs are resistant to freezing and desiccation and remain viable after the ponds dry up. Both freezing and drying stimulate hatching but are not always necessary. The following spring, usually between January and May in our northern states, these eggs hatch into free-swimming nauplius larvae with three pairs of appendages and a single eye. Their distribution is very sporadic, both geographically and in annual occurrence. The eggs may be distributed by the wind and on the feet of birds.

The subclass Branchiopoda is divided into four orders: (1) Anostraca (fairy shrimps and brine shrimps); Notostraca (tadpole shrimps, such as *Triops*); Conchostraca (clam shrimps, such as *Lynceus*); and Cladocera (water fleas, such as *Daphnia*) (Figure 211).

Subclass Cephalocarida (sef′a-lo-kar″i-da) (Gr. *kephale,* head, + *karis,* shrimp). This is a small group of one or two species which have been found along both the Atlantic and Pacific coasts. They are strictly marine (sometimes found in brackish water). They are provided with five pairs of biramous thoracic appendages but have no abdominal appendages.

Subclass Ostracoda (os-trak′o-da) (Gr. *ostrakodes,* testaceous). These are enclosed in a bivalve shell and resemble a small clam. When they move, they thrust out their two pairs of appendages through the open shell. Ostracods make up a part of the crustacean population of plankton.

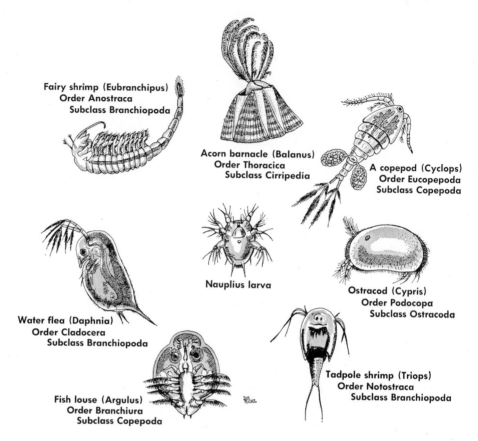

Figure 211. Group of smaller crustaceans. Orders Anostraca and Notostraca are exclusively fresh water; order Thoracica is exclusively marine; and orders Branchiura, Cladocera, Eucopepoda, and Podocopa are found in both fresh water and marine water. Nauplius larva is common to group.

Subclass Copepoda (co-pep'o-da) (Gr. *kope,* an oar, + *-poda*). These are small crustaceans with elongated bodies and forked tails. One of the common representatives is *Cyclops,* which has a single median eye in the head region. Some copepods serve as intermediate hosts for certain parasites, such as the broad tapeworm of fish, *Diphyllobothrium. Argulus* is a common parasite on fresh-water fish.

Subclass Cirripedia (cir'ri-pe"di-a) (L. *cirrus,* curl, + *pes,* foot) (Figures 212 and 213). These include the barnacles *(Balanus),* which are enclosed in a calcareous shell. At one time they were mistaken for mollusks, but they have jointed appendages which they use for creating currents of water. In the larval stage they are free swimming but soon attach themselves to a firm surface where they remain throughout their lives. Barnacles frequently foul ships' bottoms. So great may their num-

ber be that the speed of ships may be re duced 30 to 40%. This necessitates drydock ing the ship and removing them. An importan parasite belonging to this group is *Sacculin* (Figure 214), which parasitizes crayfish an crabs.

Subclass Malacostraca (mal'a-cos"tra-ca) (Gr *malakos,* soft, + *ostrakon,* shell). These in clude the larger crustaceans and also som not so large, such as lobsters, crayfish, crabs shrimp, sow bugs, and amphipods. Thre common orders are Isopoda, Amphipoda, an Decapoda.

Order Isopoda (i-sop'o-da) (Gr. *iso,* equal, + *pous,* foot). These are found both in wate and on land. They are flattened dorsoven trally, lack a carapace, and have simila legs except the anterior and posterior pair The thorax and abdomen are usually fused A common land form is the sow bu

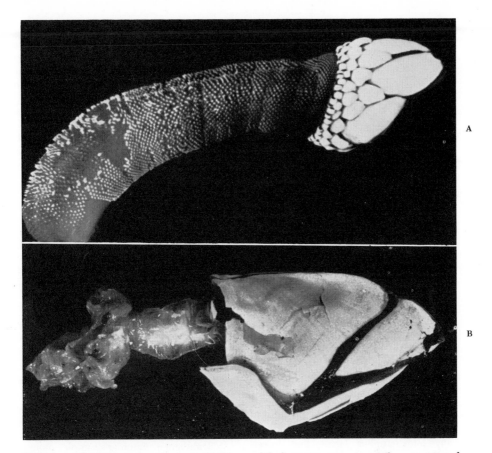

Figure 212. Two stalked barnacles; these are highly modified crustaceans. Appendages retracted within crown of calcareous plates. **A,** *Mitella.* **B,** *Lepas.* Subclass Cirripedia.

Figure 213. **A,** Group of acorn barnacles, *Balanus,* and sea mussels, *Mytilus,* along the Pacific coast line (Vancouver, Canada). **B,** Large cluster of goose barnacles, *Lepas,* which have hitch-hiked ride on fishing net float. *Balanus* and *Lepas* from subclass Cirripedia. (Collected off coast of British Columbia in August, 1958, by Vancouver Public Aquarium.)

Phylum Arthropoda—subphylum Mandibulata—except insects 307

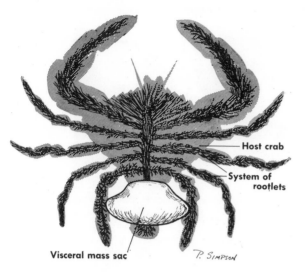

Host crab

System of rootlets

Visceral mass sac

P. SIMPSON

Figure 214. *Sacculina*, unusual crustacean (subclass Cirripedia) that parasitizes a crustacean—the crab. *Sacculina* larva enters host through a hollow bristle on crab's body and discharges cells into crab's blood. At junction of crab's stomach and intestine these cells become attached and form a mass which sends a system of branching rootlets to all parts of crab's body to supply parasite with nourishment. Eventually *Sacculina* forms opening on ventral side of crab and extrudes a soft sac filled with eggs. Eggs develop parthenogenetically into nauplius larvae that infect other hosts. Parasite destroys crab's reproductive organs and so alters its sex hormones that host always assumes female form at next molt.

Figure 215. Hermit crab, *Pagurus*, lives in empty shells of marine gastropods. As it increases in size, it moves into larger shell, and wherever it goes it carries its shell with it.

(*Porcellio*) which lives under stones and objects. Although a land form, it breathes by gills, which is possible only under moist conditions. *Asellus* is a common fresh-water form. The marine isopod (*Bathynomus*) grows to be 14 inches long. Some isopods are parasites on fish and crustaceans.

Order Amphipoda (am-phip'o-da) (Gr. *amphis*, double, + *pous*, foot). These forms are laterally compressed and have no carapace. Thorax and abdomen are not sharply marked off from each other. Of the eight pairs of thoracic appendages, the first five are used in feeding and the others in crawling. The six pairs of abdominal appendages are employed in swimming and jumping. These include beach fleas (*Orchestia*) and the aquatic forms *Hyalella* and *Gammarus*.

Order Decapoda (de-cap'o-da) (Gr. *deka*, ten, + *pous*, foot). These all have five pairs of walking legs, of which the first pair is modified to form pincers (chelae). The larger crustaceans belong to this group and include lobsters, crayfish, and shrimp (Figure 217). This is an extensive group of many thousand species. The crabs, especially, exist in a great variety of forms. Although resembling the pattern of crayfish they differ from the latter in having a broader cephalothorax and a much-reduced abdomen. Familiar examples along the seashore are the hermit crabs (*Pagurus*) (Figure 215), which live in snail shells, the fiddler crabs (*Uca*) (Figure 216), and the spider crabs (*Libinia*).

Biogenetic laws as illustrated by Crustacea

Although the young of crayfish resemble the adult, this is not true of all members of this class. In some, the larval stages are unlike the adult. Some of these larvae have a strong resemblance to types which are lower in the scale of life. One common larval form, called **nauplius** (Figures 217 and 218), is found in the life cycle of the shrimp, *Penaeus*, and some other species. The nauplius larva has an unsegmented body, frontal eye, and three pairs of biramous appendages. With successive molts the nauplius is transformed into a **metanauplius**, with six pairs of appendages; a **protozoea**, with seven pairs of appendages and developing somites; the **zoea**, with

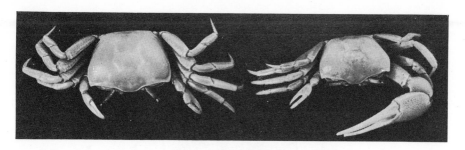

Figure 216. Fiddler crab, *Uca*. Male (right) waves its large claw back and forth in presence of female; hence the name "fiddler." Subclass Malacostraca.

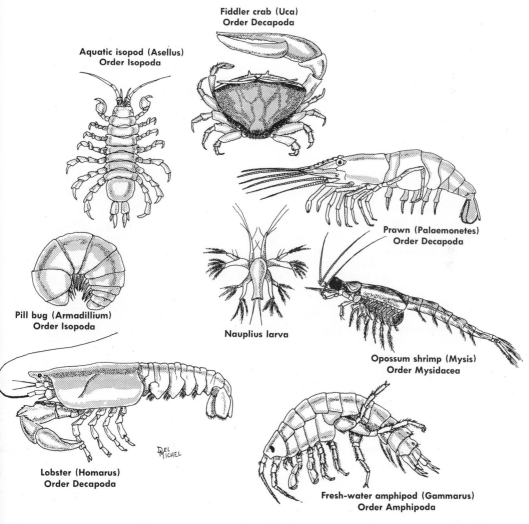

Fiddler crab (Uca)
Order Decapoda

Aquatic isopod (Asellus)
Order Isopoda

Prawn (Palaemonetes)
Order Decapoda

Pill bug (Armadillium)
Order Isopoda

Nauplius larva

Opossum shrimp (Mysis)
Order Mysidacea

Lobster (Homarus)
Order Decapoda

Fresh-water amphipod (Gammarus)
Order Amphipoda

Figure 217. Larger crustaceans (subclass Malacostraca). All members of this subclass have abdominal appendages, gastric mill, eight-segmented thorax, and typical body of nineteen segments.

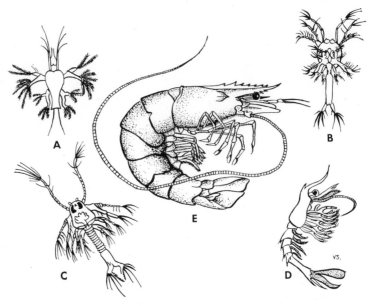

Figure 218. Life history of shrimp. **A**, Nauplius; **B**, protozoea; **C**, zoea; **D**, mysis (note exopods on thoracic legs); **E**, adult. (Redrawn from Moment: General Zoology, Houghton Mifflin Co.)

Figure 219. Centipede, *Scolopendra*. Most segments have one pair of appendages each. First segment bears pair of poison claws which in some species can inflict serious wounds to man. Some tropical forms are nearly 1 foot long. Centipedes are carnivorous and prey upon earthworms, insect larvae, and even larger prey.

eight pairs of appendages and six more appendages in early stages of development, as well as a distinct cephalothorax and abdomen. From the zoea stage develops the **mysis** larva, bearing thirteen pairs of biramous appendages on the cephalothorax. Then the adult shrimp with nineteen pairs of appendages comes from the mysis larva. One or two of these larval stages resemble the adults of lower crustaceans, especially the mysis stage, which closely resembles the still living adult *Mysis*.

This correspondence between larval stages and the adults of types lower in the animal scale is called the **biogenetic law of recapitulation.** According to this principle, animals in their individual development pass through stages in the evolution of the race. Thus ontogeny repeats

hylogeny. Although the biogenetic law
n its original sense has been criticized, the
escription of the crustacean stages may
t least give an insight into the course
f evolutionary development of this group.

CLASS CHILOPODA

Centipedes

Classes Chilopoda and Diplopoda are
ften referred to as Myriapoda, but the
vo groups are sufficiently different from
ach other to justify placing them in sep-
rate classes.

The members of class Chilopoda are
and forms whose bodies are somewhat
attened dorsoventrally and may contain
om a few up to 177 somites (Figure
19). Each somite, with the exception of
ne one behind the distinct head and the
st two posterior ones, bears a pair of
jinted appendages. The appendages of
ne first body segment are modified to
orm poison claws.

The head is made up of six somites,
ne appendages of which are modified
miliarly to those of an insect. There is
single pair of antennae of few or many
egments, a pair of mandibles with no
alps, and one or two pairs of maxillae,
f which the second pair are usually
ised together. A pair of **eyes** are on the
orsal surface of the head and consist of
roups of ocelli.

The body wall is covered with a chiti-
ous cuticle, and in some there are odorif-
cous glands opening on the body surface.
he digestive system is a straight tube
nto which salivary glands empty at the
nterior end; two pairs of Malpighian
abules empty into the hind part of the
ntestine and take care of the **excretory**
rstem. The circulatory system contains
n elongated heart with a pair of arteries
o each somite. Respiration is by means
f a tracheal system of branched air tubes
rhich come from a pair of openings
piracles) in each somite. The nervous
rstem consists of a pair of cerebral gan-
lia (brain), a pair of esophageal connec-
ves, and a double nerve cord with gan-
lia in each somite. There is also a visceral
ervous system. Sexes are separate. The

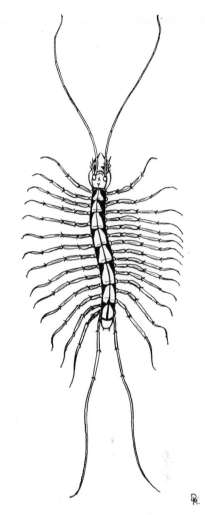

Figure 220. Common house centipede, *Cermatia
(Scutigera) forceps*. Often seen scurrying around
house, where it eats roaches, bedbugs, and other
insects. Its bite was once supposed to be poisonous but is now known to be harmless to man.

reproductive system in each sex contains
an unpaired gonad with paired ducts
which open by a single aperture at the
posterior end of the body. Some lay eggs
and others are viviparous. The young
are similar to the adults.

Centipedes have a preference for
moist places, such as those under logs,
bark, and stones. They are very agile and
carnivorous in their eating habits, living
upon earthworms, cockroaches, and other
insects. They kill their prey with their

poison claws and then chew it with their mandibles. The common house centipede, *Cermatia forceps* (Figure 220), with fifteen pairs of legs, is often seen scurrying around bathrooms and damp cellars, where they catch insects. Most species are harmless to man. Some of the tropical centipedes may reach a length of 1 foot.

CLASS DIPLOPODA

These forms are called millipedes, which literally means "thousand legged" (Figure 221). Even though they do not have that many legs, they do have many appendages in proportion to their length and number of somites. Their cylindrical bodies are made up of 25 to 100 somites. The short thorax consists of four somites, each bearing one pair of legs; each abdominal somite has two pairs of appendages, a condition which may have arisen from the fusion of two somites. The head bears two clumps of simple eyes, a pair of antennae, a pair of mandibles, and a pair of maxillae. The general body structures are similar to those of centipedes with a few variations here and there. There are two pairs of spiracles on each abdominal somite. Each spiracle is located in front of a leg and opens into an

Figure 221. Millipede, *Spirobolus*. They have two pairs of jointed appendages on each of their segments except the short thorax of four somites, each of which has one pair of appendages. In some, the last one or two segments also have only one pair. Long abdomen is really composed of double segments which accounts for two pairs of appendages on each apparent somite. In contrast to centipedes, millipedes are usually vegetarian animals. (Courtesy Carolina Biological Supply Co., Elon College, N. C.)

air chamber which gives off the trachea air tubes, branched or unbranched. There are two genital apertures which are found toward the anterior end.

In most millipedes the appendages on the seventh somite are specialized for copulatory organs. After copulation the eggs are laid in a nest and carefully guarded by the mother. The larval forms have only one pair of legs to each somite. The adults have all the somites, except those of the thorax, fused in pairs, which explains the presence of two pairs of appendages on each somite.

Millipedes are not so active as centipedes and are herbivorous instead of carnivorous. They prefer dark, moist places under logs or stones. They eat decayed matter, whether plant or animal, although sometimes they eat living plants. When disturbed, they often roll up into a ball. Common examples of this class are *Spirobolus* and *Julus*, both of which have wide distribution.

ANNOTATED REFERENCES

Crustacea

Borradaile, L. A., and F. A. Potts. 1958. The Invertebrata, ed. 3 (revised by G. A. Kerkut). New York, Cambridge University Press. *A long chapter (pp. 340-419) with many figures is devoted to the crustaceans.*

Buchsbaum, R., and L. J. Milne. 1960. The Lower Animals, Garden City, Doubleday & Co., Inc. *Many fine descriptions of crustacean and other invertebrates.*

Calman, W. T. 1909. Crustacea. In Lankester, E. R.: A Treatise on Zoology, Part VII, 3rd fascicle. London, A. & C. Black, Ltd. *This account meets the high standards of this outstanding series of zoological treatises. Its taxonomy is outdated, but all serious students of the arthropods will find a wealth of information in it.*

Edmonson, W. T. (editor). 1959. Ward and Whipple's Fresh-Water Biology, ed. 2. New York, John Wiley & Sons, Inc. *Eight sections are devoted to the various fresh-water crustaceans in this imposing and comprehensive handbook of many specialists.*

Huxley, T. H. 1880. The Crayfish: An Introduction to the Study of Zoology. *A classical study which is often used as a model of clear and simple biological presentation.*

Pennak, R. W. 1953. Fresh-Water Invertebrate

of the United States. New York, The Ronald Press Co. *The many chapters on crustaceans in this fine work will arouse the interest of the student. Taxonomic keys with illustrative drawings are unusually clear. Extensive and up-to-date bibliographies add much to the usefulness of the work.*

Pratt, H. S. 1935. Manual of the Common Invertebrate Animals, ed. 2. Philadelphia, The Blakiston Co.

Smith, G., and W. F. R. Weldon. 1909. Crustacea. Cambridge Natural History, vol. 4. London, Macmillan & Co., Ltd. *A good account of the general structure and organization of crustaceans.*

Waterman, T. H. (editor). 1960. The Physiology of Crustacea, vol. I (Metabolism and Growth). New York, Academic Press. *This is the first volume of a planned two-volume work on crustaceans. It was made necessary by the accumulated mass of information on comparative physiology which has made great strides in the last few decades. A work of great importance to the specialist.*

chapter 18

Phylum Arthropoda

Subphylum Mandibulata—insects

PHYLUM ARTHROPODA
CLASS INSECTA

The insects are the most successful biologically of all the groups of arthropods. Although they comprise only one class out of more than fifty classes of animals, there are more species of insects than of all the others combined. It is estimated that the recorded number of insect species is between 600,000 and 700,000, with thousands of other species yet to be discovered and classified. There is also striking evidence that evolution is continuing among insects at the present time even though the group as a whole is considered to be very stable, according to the fossil record. Studies on *Drosophila* by Patterson, Dobzhansky, and others and on termites by Emerson afford some clear-cut cases of present-day evolutionary change.

It is very difficult to visualize the significance of this extensive group and its role in the biological pattern of animal life. Their bearing upon man's welfare, the competition they offer at nearly every stage of man's existence, and the many useful aspects of this highly specialized group pose problems that are a real challenge to all of man's ingenuity. The science of insects, **entomology**, occupies the time and resources of skilled men all over the world. Every civilized country spends enormous sums of money in the attempt to control insects. The struggle between man and his insect competitors seems to be an endless one, for no sooner are the suppressed at one point than they brea out at another. Yet such is the paradox c the whole matter that insects have so in terwoven themselves into the economy c things in so many useful roles that ma would have a difficult time without them

Distribution

Insects are among the most abundan and widespread of all land animals. The **have spread** into practically all habitat that will support life except that of th sea. They have shied away from sal water, and only an insignificant few ar found there. The marine water strider *(Halobates)* are about the only insects tha live on the open sea, but a considerabl insect fauna is found in brackish wate in salt marshes, and on sandy beache They are found in fresh water, in soils, i forests, in plants, in deserts and wast lands, on mountain tops, and as parasite in and on the bodies of plants and animal

Their wide distribution is made poss ble by their powers of flight and thei highly adaptable nature. In most case they can easily surmount barriers that ar well nigh impassable to many other ani mals. Their small size allows them to b carried by currents of both wind an water to far regions. Their well-protecte eggs can withstand rigorous condition and can be carried long distances by bird and animals. The qualities of agility an aggressiveness enable them to fight fo every possible niche in a location. When-ever they get a foothold they do not give up until the last one is completely eradicated. No single pattern of biological adaptation can be applied to them.

Size range

Insects range all the way from forms smaller than 1 mm. in length to those that are 7 or 8 inches long. Some of the tropical moths have a wing spread of 8 to 12 inches. The smallest forms are probably certain parasitic insects. As a general thing, the largest insects are found in tropical countries. Most insects, however, are rarely more than 1 inch long, and a considerable number fall below this dimension. Some beetles are only 1/100 inch long.

Relationships and origin

It is difficult to work out the ancestry of insects. Fossils give little help in solving the problem. All of the few thousand species of fossil insects that have been found in amber and volcanic ash were winged, but wingless forms (order Collembola) have been found in older rocks. Both chilopods and insects have sharply marked off heads, provided with antennae and jaws, but insects have a thorax, which is wanting in chilopods, and they lack the large digestive glands of the crustaceans. Some zoologists think they have come from a crustacean larval form such as the zoea; others believe they are derived from polychaete worms. One theory holds that insects arose from millepede ancestors by neoteny (sexual maturity in the larval stage).

Characteristics

1. Body of three clearly defined regions—**head, thorax, abdomen**
2. Head of six segments with two antennae and two mandibles and two pairs of maxillae; **mouth parts adapted for sucking, chewing, and lapping**
3. Thorax of three segments, each with a pair of jointed walking legs; thorax may have two pairs, one pair, or no pair of **wings**

4. Abdomen of not more than eleven segments and **modified posteriorly as genitalia**
5. Respiration by a many-branched **tracheal system** which communicates with the outside by **spiracles** on the abdomen
6. Digestive system of fore-, mid-, and hindgut and provided with salivary glands
7. Circulatory system of heart, aorta, and hemocoeles; no capillaries or veins
8. Excretion by **Malpighian tubules** which empty into the hindgut
9. Coelom very much reduced
10. Nervous system of a dorsal brain, subesophageal ganglia, and a double ventral nerve cord provided typically with a pair of ganglia to each somite
11. Sense organs consisting of simple and compound eyes, receptors for taste about the mouth, receptors for touch on various parts of body, and receptors for sound
12. Reproduction by separate sexes; paired gonads with single duct in each sex; fertilization internal; few reproducing by parthenogenesis; most exhibiting **metamorphosis**

Adaptability

Insects have marvelous powers of distribution, and the capacity to adjust themselves to new habitats. A survey of any particular community will reveal that insects have occupied more available biological niches than any other group of animals. Most of their structural modifications center around the wings, legs, antennae, mouth parts, and alimentary canal. One has only to examine the honeybee's legs to discover how remarkably they are adapted for such a variety of uses. This wide diversity of habits enables this vigorous group to take advantage of all available resources of food and shelter. Some are parasitic, some suck the sap of plants, some are predacious, some chew up the foliage of plants, and some live upon the blood of various animals. Within these different groups specialization occurs, so that a particular kind of insect will eat, for instance, the leaves of one kind of plant and others will dine only upon another kind. This specificity of eating habits lessens competition among them and to a great extent accounts for their biological success.

Insects have fitted themselves for a wide range of habitats, especially in dry and desert regions. The hard and protective chitinous exoskeleton prevents evaporation, but the insects also extract the utmost in fluid from food and fecal material as well as moisture from the water by-product of bodily metabolism.

Food habits

The food habits of insects are determined to some extent by their kind of mouth parts, which are usually biting or sucking in nature. The majority of insects feed on plant juices and plant tissues. Such a food habit is called **phytophagous**. Some insects will restrict their feeding to certain varieties of plants; others, such as the grasshoppers, will eat almost any plant that comes their way. It is well known that the caterpillars of many moths and butterflies will eat the foliage of only certain plants. Ants are known to have fungus gardens on which they subsist. Many beetles and the larvae of other insects (**saprophagous**) will live upon dead animals. Other insects are highly predaceous, catching and eating not only members of their own group but those of other groups as well. For these types of feeding, the mouth parts are adapted in a specialized way. The sucking, or suctorial, mouth parts are usually arranged in the form of a tube and can pierce the tissues of plants or animals. In butterflies and moths the well-known proboscis, which is usually coiled up when not in use, is fitted as a sucking tube for drawing nectar from flowers. Biting mouth parts are adapted for seizing and crushing food; those of most carnivorous insects are sharp and pointed in addition for piercing their prey.

The kind of mouth parts an insect has determines the type of spray used in destroying it. Those that bite and chew their food can be destroyed by applying poison directly to the food; those that suck

must be smothered with gaseous mixture which interfere with their respiration.

Many insects, adults as well as larvae are **parasitic**. Fleas, for instance, live on the blood of mammals, and the larvae of many varieties of wasps live upon spider and caterpillars. In turn, many are parasitized by other insects. Some of these are highly beneficial by controlling the numbers of injurious insects. When parasitic insects are themselves parasitized by other insects, the condition is known as **hyper**

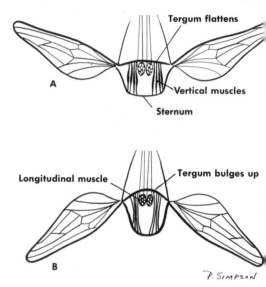

Figure 222. How an insect uses its wings. Chief muscles that move wings of insects and have no direct connection with wings but produce flight by changing shape of body wall to which wings are attached. Two sets of muscles attached to inner body wall necessary for flight movements. Vertical muscles, **A,** between tergum and sternum contract to flatten tergum and cause wings to rise. Longitudinal muscles, **B,** contract, causing tergum to bulge upward and wings to be lowered. Alternate contraction of these two sets produces flight. Other muscles attached directly to wings rotate wings as they are lowered and also draw wings to resting position when not in use. Lever-fulcrum attachment of wing is such that slight change in body wall movements produces wide range in wing tips. Wings of some insects, such as dragonflies, controlled entirely by direct muscles, which produce slight but rapid up-and-down vibrations of wings, which are always held in horizontal position. (Modified from Snodgrass.)

316

parasitism, which often becomes quite involved.

Power of flight

Insects share with birds and the flying mammals (bats) the power of flight. Most insects have two pairs of wings, one on the mesothorax, the other on the metathorax. However, the wings of insects are not homologous to those of birds and bats, for the latter are derived in an entirely different manner. Wings of insects are really extensions of the integument and thus are different from the limb buds of birds and mammals. They vary a great deal and are used for making distinctions in classification. When only one pair of wings is present (Diptera), the missing pair (the metathoracic) is represented by a pair of club-like threads called **balancers, or halteres.** In many cases the wings are thin and membranous and are called membranous wings. Beetles and some others have the front pair of wings thickened and hardened into **horny** wings (**elytra**) which protect the more delicate flying wings behind. Grasshoppers and closely related forms have the front wings modified into flexible **leatherlike** wings (**tegmina**). Butterflies and moths have their wings covered with fine scales which are easily shed when handled.

The wing beat, as well as the speed, of insects varies greatly with different insects. Many butterflies have very slow wing beats of only 5 or 6 per second; those of honeybees may be as many as 200 per second. Likewise, insects also vary

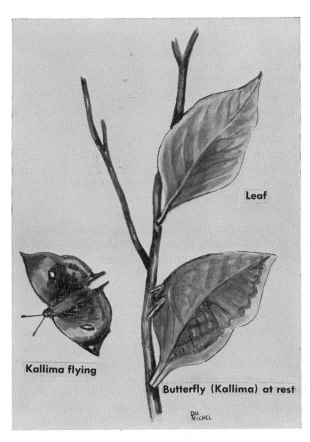

Figure 223. Striking case of protective resemblance in a butterfly, *Kallima,* which resembles a leaf when perched on a twig. This butterfly is native of the East Indies and was first described by the famous English naturalist Alfred Russell Wallace.

Phylum Arthropoda—subphylum Mandibulata—insects 317

greatly in their speed of flying. Some of the flies are reported by some observers to have great speeds, but when these flying records are carefully checked, they are usually found to be exaggerated. In a few orders of insects there are no wings at all, and others have generations without wings followed by generations with wings. For the mechanics of wing movement see Figure 222.

Protection and coloration

Insects as a group display many colors. This is especially true of butterflies, moths, and beetles. Even in the same species the color pattern may vary in a seasonal way, and there also may be color differences between males and females. Some of the color patterns in insects are probably highly adaptive, such as those for **protective coloration, warning coloration, mimicry,** and others.

Besides color, insects have other methods of protecting themselves. The chitinous exoskeleton affords a good protection for many of them; others, such as stink bugs, have repulsive odors and taste; and others protect themselves by a good offense, for many are very aggressive and can put up a good fight (for example, bees and ants); and still others are swift in running for cover when danger threatens.

Neuromuscular coordination

Insects are active creatures and this implies good neuromuscular coordination. Their muscles are strong and numerous (more than 4,000 have been found in a caterpillar) and are mainly of the striated variety. Their strength is all out of proportion to their size, for a flea can hop a distance a hundred times its own length, and a honeybee is known to pull many times its own weight. The nervous system of insects is similar to that of the earthworm, with a ventral double nerve cord and paired ganglia in each somite. In some insects there is a tendency toward centralization and cephalization, for the ganglia are concentrated toward the anterior end of the body. The skill and dexterity with which many insects can avoid danger are

well known, for everyone realizes how quickly flies can avoid swats and dragonflies can evade a butterfly net. Along with their neuromuscular coordinations, the sensory perceptions of insects are unusually keen, especially those involving sight and smell. The compound eyes of insects are adapted for detecting slight movements.

Sound production and reception

A sense of hearing is not present in all insects but appears to be well developed in those that produce sound. Everyone is familiar with many of the sounds of insects, such as the buzzing of bees, the chirping of crickets, and the humming of mosquitoes and flies. Sounds are produced in a variety of ways. Some are the result of the rubbing together of rough surfaces, such as those of the integument. Grasshoppers produce a sound effect by rubbing the femur of the last pair of legs over rough ridges on the forewings. Male crickets scrape their wing covers to produce their characteristic chirping. The hum of mosquitoes and bees is due mainly to the rapid vibration of their wings. Some Hymenoptera produce their sound by a combination of means, such as the vibration of the wings and the special leaflike appendages in the tracheal system. The sound of the cicada is a long drawn-out one produced in a special chamber between the thorax and abdomen. Within this chamber is a membrane connected to a muscle whose rapid contractions cause the membrane to vibrate at different pitches. The cavity amplifies the sound by acting as a resonance chamber.

The humming of bees varies with the temperament of the hive. When excited the more rapid vibration of the wings produces a difference in sound which is readily detected by those familiar with their ways. Sound may be a means of communication by which insects are able to warn of danger, to call their mates, etc.

Behavior

The keen sensory perceptions of insects enable them to respond to many stimuli

has been proved experimentally that their chemical senses are far more sensitive than they are in man. Most, if not quite all, of their responses are **reflexes.** Their **taxes** are in many cases clear cut and definite, such as the attraction of the moth for light, the detection of rotting flesh by carrion flies, and the avoidance of light by cockroaches. To attract their mates, many insects emit a delicate odor which is detected by the opposite sex. The taxis of contact (**thigmotaxis**) is illustrated by crickets and beetles, which are often found in narrow crevices; **rheotaxis,** or reaction to water currents, is shown by the caddis fly larvae which live in rapids.

Although insect behavior is mainly instinctive, their behavior patterns can be modified somewhat. Bees, for instance, can be taught to make simple associations between food and color, and ants will learn to make associations between certain odors and food supplies. Thus to some extent they have memory sufficient for the establishment of a conditioned reflex.

Reproduction

The sexes are always separate in insects, and fertilization is internal. Most are **oviparous,** but a few are **viviparous** and bring forth their young alive. **Parthenogenesis** occurs in aphids, gall wasps, and others. In a few (e.g., *Miastor*) a process called **pedogenesis** is found. This involves parthenogenesis by larval stages rather than by the adults. Many larvae are produced, some of which pupate to become male and female adults.

Methods of attracting the opposite sex are often quite involved among insects. Some, like the female moth, give off a scent which can be detected a long distance by the males. Fireflies use flashes of light for this purpose, whereas many can find each other by the sounds they make. Insects usually lay a great many eggs. Perhaps the greatest number of eggs is produced by the queen honeybee, which may lay more than a million eggs during her lifetime. At the other extreme some viviparous flies bring forth a single young

at a time. There seems to be a relation between the number of eggs produced and the care of the offspring. Forms that make no provision for their young bring forth many hundreds of eggs; those that have to provide provisions for the larvae, such as the solitary wasps and bees, lay much fewer eggs. Fewness of eggs in one generation may be offset by short life cycles. Houseflies and fruit flies require only about ten days to complete their cycles of development and growth. On the other hand, the number of offspring produced bears no relation to the number of eggs laid, for in some chalcid flies each egg gives rise to more than a hundred embryos (**polyembryony**).

Insects reveal marvelous instincts in laying their eggs. Butterflies will lay their eggs only on the particular kind of plant on which the caterpillar feeds, and the ichneumon fly with unerring accuracy seeks out a certain kind of larva on which her young are parasitic. Many, however, drop their eggs, which are often well protected, wherever they happen to be and make no further provision for them.

Metamorphosis and growth

Whenever the young of animals show a pronounced change in appearance during their development from the adults, the process is called **metamorphosis.** Although this condition is not restricted to insects, they illustrate this biological principle better than any other group. The transformation, for instance, of the hickory horned devil caterpillar (Figure 224) into

Figure 224. Great hickory horned devil. Largest caterpillar in North America; may exceed 5 inches in length. It develops into royal walnut moth.

the beautiful royal walnut moth represents an astonishing change in development. In insects metamorphosis is an outcome of the evolution of wings which are restricted to the reproductive stage where they can be of the most benefit. Not all insects show metamorphosis, but most of them do in some form or other.

Complete metamorphosis (which nine-tenths of all insects have) is of great adaptive value, for it separates the great physiological processes of growth (larva), differentiation (pupa), and reproduction (adult) from each other, so that each stage of development can function most efficiently without hindrance from the others. Metamorphosis speeds up the energy-transforming mechanisms of the insect life and gives a broader ecological niche relationship, for the larvae often live in an entirely different environment from the adults and have different food habits. This specialization of development stages promotes also the evolution rate because of greater possibilities of mutations.

Since the exoskeleton acts as a restrictive armor which prevents expansion of the body, an insect can change its form or size by the process of **molting,** or **ecdysis.** Thus when its cuticula becomes too small for it, a second epidermis is formed by the hypodermis and the old epidermis splits open along the back of the head and thorax and the insect works its way out of the old exoskeleton.

With regard to their growth and development, insects may be divided into four groups—no metamorphosis, and incomplete, gradual, and complete metamorphosis.

No metamorphosis. A few insects called collectively the **ametabola** have no metamorphosis at all. In these the young hatch from the egg in the same form as the adult insect and development consists in merely growing larger. Good examples among the various orders of insects are the Thysanura and the Collembola. The stages of development in the life cycle of these are (1) egg, (2) young, or juvenile, and (3) adult.

Figure 225. Dragonfly naiad. These naiads found in bottom of pools and streams.

Incomplete metamorphosis. In some insects (Ephemeroptera, Odonata, and Plecoptera) the eggs are laid in water and develop into aquatic naiads or nymphs which are quite different from the adult (Figure 225). The immature stages of these insects are thus spent in water while the adults are aerial. The naiads have tracheal gills and other modifications for an aquatic life. They grow by successive molts, crawl out of water, and after the last molt become winged adults. Since it includes a partial metamorphosis it is called **hemimetabola,** and the stages of its life cycle are (1) egg, (2) naiad, and (3) adult. The three orders which have this type of metamorphosis are not closely related phylogenetically but have evolved this type of larval adaptation independently.

Gradual metamorphosis. In this type the newly hatched individual resembles the adult in general bodily features but has no wings or genital appendages (Figure 226 and 227). The bodily proportions of the immature form (nymph) are also different from the adult. At each **instar** (growing stage) after each molt the nymph looks more and more like the adult. Wing buds appear in the later instars, and finally wings are developed. Both nymphs and adults have the same type of mouth parts and food habits. This type of metamorphosis is called **paurometabola** and is found among Orthoptera, Hemiptera, Homoptera, and many others,

320

Figure 226. Young praying mantes (nymphs) emerging from their egg capsule. Egg capsules (öothecae) are glued to shrubbery and other objects in late summer and fall. When eggs hatch in spring, enormous swarm of nymphs emerge from a single capsule.

Figure 227. Praying mantis, about life size. It gets this name from the way it holds its fore-limbs but is far more interested in preying on other insects than in pious devotions. Order Orthoptera. (Courtesy Joseph W. Bamberger.)

The stages of development in the life cycle of these are (1) egg, (2) nymph, and (3) adult.

Complete metamorphosis. A large num-ber of insect orders undergo changes in their larval development to adults which are referred to as complete metamorphosis (Figure 228) and the group as the **holo-metabola.** In this type the young emerge as wormlike segmented larvae with little difference between the head, thorax, and abdomen. These wormlike forms are called by various names, such as cater-pillars, maggots, bagworms, fuzzy worms,

Figure 228. **A,** Caterpillar of angulifera moth, *Callosamia angulifera*. **B,** Pupa of angulifera moth. **C,** Angulifera moth.

grubs, and others. The **instars,** which are the larvae between molts, increase in size by molting a number of times, then pass into a sort of resting period, the **pupa (chrysalis).** It forms around its body a **case** from its outer body covering or a **cocoon** by spinning silk threads around itself. Within the cocoon or case the final metamorphosis occurs, and finally the adult, or **imago,** appears. When it emerges, the adult is as large as it ever will be, for it undergoes no further molting. In complete metamorphosis, the stages of development are (1) egg, (2) larva, (3) pupa, and (4) adult.

Physiology of metamorphosis. The physiology of molting and metamorphosis has been much studied in the past few years and a great deal is known about the mechanism. It has been demonstrated that certain hormones control the processes of molting and metamorphosis in insects. I molting, for instance, secreting cells of the intercerebral gland in the brain first liberate a **molting hormone** which activates the prothoracic gland. Then the latter gland produces a **growth hormone** which sets in motion certain processes that lead to the casting off of the old skin (ecdysis) by proliferation of the epidermal cells. If the larval form is retained at the end of this process it is called simple molting; if the insect undergoes changes into pupa and adult it is called metamorphosis. Simple molting persists as long as a certain **juvenile hormone** is found in the blood, and each molting simply produces a larger larva. This hormone is produced by a pair of tiny glands (corpora allata) located near the brain. But when the corpora allata ceases to produce the juvenile hormone, the molting hormone alone is secreted into the blood and the pupa or adult emerges (metamorphosis). Experimental evidence shows that when the corpora allata (and thus the juvenile hormone) is removed surgically, the following molt will result in metamorphosis into the adult. Conversely, if the corpora allata from a young larva is transplanted into an old larva, the latter can be converted into a giant larva because no metamorphosis can occur.

What factors initiate the sequence role of these three different hormones? How are they correlated with cyclic events in the life histories of insects? Experimentally, it has been shown that low temperature activates the neurosecretory cells of the intercerebral gland of the brain which then sets in motion the sequence of events already related. The chilling of the brain seems to be all important in the initiation of metamorphosis. Adults cannot molt and grow because they have no prothoracic glands. Many aspects of the control mechanism of these interesting processes have not yet been worked out.

Diapause

Diapause refers to a condition or state of physiological dormancy or arrested development. Although the concept may apply to variant similar conditions in other animals, its original meaning has direct reference to insects. It is well known that there are periods in the life cycle of many insects when eggs, pupae, or even adults remain for a long time in a state of dormancy because external conditions of climate, moisture, etc. are too harsh or unfavorable for survival under states of normal activity. Because of diapause, the insect egg has a mechanism for preventing evaporation from dry surroundings, the pupa can withstand extreme cold, and the adult can synchronize its life cycle with an abundance of food. Altogether, it is an important adaptation in the embryonic larvae and pupal stages of most insects of the Northern Hemisphere. Diapause is that stage of the life cycle when the insect's morphogenesis is interrupted because of unfavorable environmental conditions and is resumed when climate, season, and food are favorable for development and survival. The evidence indicates that hormones are responsible for the control of diapause, for the latter occurs whenever the neurosecretory cells of the brain fail to secrete the molting hormone. Diapause always occurs at the end of an active growth stage of the molting cycle, so that when the diapause period is over, the insect is ready for another molt, or ecdysis.

Social instincts

Some insects, such as bees and ants, exhibit very complicated patterns of social instincts. It is true that most insects are more or less solitary and come together only for mating, and some are sometimes found together in large gregarious swarms, but others have worked out complex societies involving **division of labor.** In these societies the adults of one or both sexes live together with the young in a cooperative manner. The size and complexity of these insect organizations vary with the kind of insects. Among the bumblebees the groups are small and the groupings last only a season. The honeybee, however, has worked out one of the most striking examples in the insect world. Instead of lasting one season, their organ-

Figure 229. Paper nest of bald-faced hornet, *Vespa*, cut open to show one of horizontal combs. These nests are attached to bushes or trees and are composed of fibers of weather-worn wood. Larvae are reared in comb cells.

ization continues on for a more or less indefinite period. As many as 60,000 to 70,000 bees may be found in a single hive, of which there is a single **queen,** a few hundred **drones** (males), and the rest **workers** (infertile females). The workers carry on all the activities of the hive except lay eggs. They gather the nectar from flowers, manufacture honey, collect pollen, secrete wax, take care of young, and ventilate and guard the hive. Each worker appears to do a specific task in all this multiplicity of duties. Their life span is only a few weeks. One drone fertilizes the queen and stores sperm enough in her spermathecae to last her a lifetime. The life span of drones is usually for the duration of the summer, for they are driven out or killed by the workers. A queen may live as long as five seasons, during which time she may lay a million eggs. She is responsible for keeping the hive going during the winter, and only one queen will be tolerated in a hive at one time.

Ants and termites also have complicated social lives. An ant colony has a single fertile queen and, at times, fertile males (drones). Of the infertile females, some are soldiers, some are workers to gathe food, and some are nursemaids for th young, and so forth. Among termites, so cial life is still more complex. The colonies contain two castes. One of thes consists of fertile males and females; th other, of infertile males and females. Th reproductive individuals may or may n have wings. If they have wings, they leav the colony, mate, lose their wings, an start a new colony. Those reproductive in dividuals without wings may, under ce tain conditions, substitute for the kin and queen. The sterile members have r wings and make up the workers and so diers. Within the castes there are als different types. Ants and termites hav reached the peak of insect social evolu tion, for they have evolved striking pa terns of economic behavior, such as mal ing slaves, farming fungi, herding "a cows" (aphids), sewing their nests t gether with silk, and using tools.

Relation to man's welfare

It would require a large amount space to enumerate all the ways insec benefit and harm man's interests. Mos are probably injurious than helpful. Th **beneficial insects** (Figure 230) may b listed as follows:

1. Those insects that produce usefu products for man's use. Among these ma be mentioned first the products of th honeybee, such as honey, which amoun to several thousand tons each year, an beeswax, which amounts to many hu dred tons annually. Another valuab product is silk produced by the silkworn Some 25,000 cocoons are necessary make one pound of silk, and fifty millic pounds of silk are produced each yea Shellac is made from a wax secreted the lac insects which belong to fami Coccidae, and the dye cochineal former much used in histology, is made from th dried bodies of another coccid which liv on the cactus plant.

2. Insects that are necessary to cros fertilize the blossoms of fruits and crop useful to man. These include the bees th are indispensable in raising fruits an

lover and other crops. To raise the myrna fig in California it was necessary to make use of the small fig wasp (*Blastophaga*) which carries pollen from the non-edible caprifig.

3. Predaceous insects that destroy other insects harmful to man. Among these are tiger beetles, aphid lions, ant lions, praying mantids, lady beetles, wasps, and many others. Many insects control injurious insects by parasitizing them. Such insects usually lay their eggs on the larvae

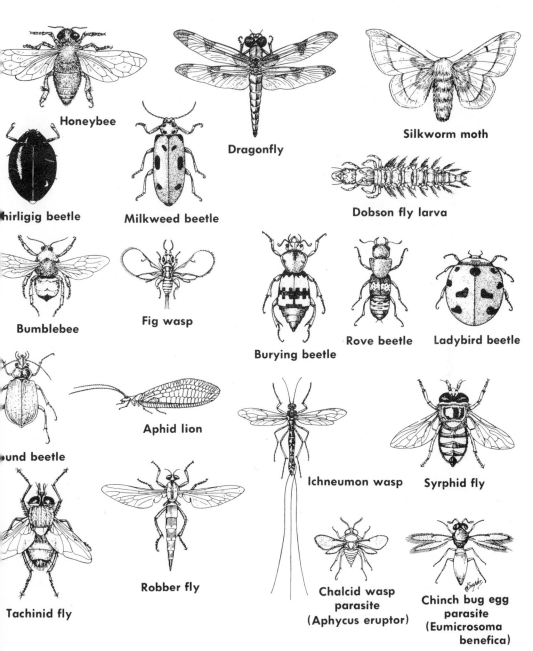

Honeybee

Dragonfly

Silkworm moth

hirligig beetle

Milkweed beetle

Dobson fly larva

Bumblebee

Fig wasp

Burying beetle

Rove beetle

Ladybird beetle

und beetle

Aphid lion

Ichneumon wasp

Syrphid fly

Tachinid fly

Robber fly

Chalcid wasp parasite (Aphycus eruptor)

Chinch bug egg parasite (Eumicrosoma benefica)

Figure 230. Beneficial insects. (Courtesy General Biological Supply House, Inc., Chicago.)

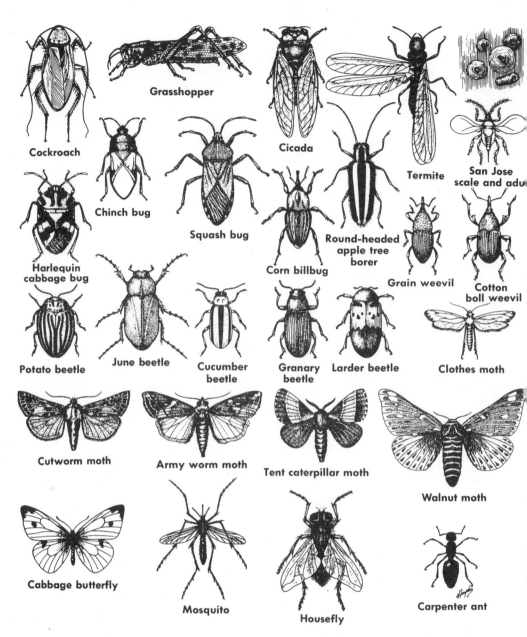

Labels within figure:

Cockroach

Grasshopper

Chinch bug

Cicada

Termite

San Jose scale and adu

Harlequin cabbage bug

Squash bug

Round-headed apple tree borer

Corn billbug

Grain weevil

Cotton boll weevil

Potato beetle

June beetle

Cucumber beetle

Granary beetle

Larder beetle

Clothes moth

Cutworm moth

Army worm moth

Tent caterpillar moth

Walnut moth

Cabbage butterfly

Mosquito

Housefly

Carpenter ant

Figure 231. Harmful insects. (Courtesy General Biological Supply House, Inc., Chicago.)

of the harmful ones, and the larvae hatched from these eggs slowly devour their host.

4. Insects that do good through their scavenger habits. Many beetles and flies live on both animal and plant refuse and litter. Dead animals are quickly taken care of by the maggots of flies which lay the eggs in the carcasses. Tumble bugs ro up balls of dung in which to lay the eggs; the developing larvae eat up th dung.

5. Insects as food. Many birds and an mals depend upon insects for their foo

upplies. Some fish also get a considerable art of their food supply from aquatic isects.

The **harmful insects** (Figure 231) may e grouped as follows:

1. Those insects that eat and destroy lants and fruits. These include grass-oppers, chinch bugs, Hessian flies, corn orers, cotton boll weevils, San Jose scales, Iediterranean fruit flies, grain weevils, ire worms, and scores of others; the mount of damage done by these insects more than a billion dollars each year. very cultivated crop is bothered to some xtent by insect pests.

2. Those insects that annoy and harm omestic animals. This is a large group nd includes lice, blood-sucking flies, war-le flies whose larvae burrow into the skin f cattle, larvae of botflies in the stomach f horses, etc.

3. Insects responsible for transmitting iseases. These have an enormous influ-nce on man, for some of our most devas-ting diseases are carried by insects. mong the chief vectors of disease are the iosquitoes, which carry malaria, yellow ver, and filariasis; houseflies, which arry typhoid fever and dysentery and ther diseases; tsetse flies, which carry frican sleeping sickness; fleas, which arry bubonic plague; and body lice, hich carry typhus fever.

4. Those insects that are destructive in the household. These include insects that injure or damage food, such as weevils, cockroaches, and ants, and those that damage clothing and furnishings, such as clothes moths (Figure 232), carpet beetles, and others. Among these are the termites which are highly destructive to buildings and wooden structures.

Romalea microptera— lubber grasshopper

The insects show a considerable variety of morphological characters. Some have a more or less generalized plan of body structure, and others, because of some spe-cial habit of food getting or living condi-tions, are specialized in certain particu-lars. The grasshopper, or locust, is a good representative of the generalized type and is commonly studied in our laboratories for that reason. The big lubber grass-hopper is a favorite one for study, but the description which follows may apply to grasshoppers in general, for their struc-tural patterns are similar.

Habitat. Grasshoppers have a world-wide distribution and are found where there are open grasslands and abundant leafy vegetation. The prairies of the west have immense hordes of them, for there they have abundant food and ideal places to breed. Most American grasshoppers do not migrate to any extent, but those in Europe and Asia do so frequently, often depleting the food in one region and then moving on to another. Such practices have been used at times in our western states whenever the food became scarce in an arid region and they moved en masse toward lush vegetation in the east, where they mostly settled down and remained. Moreover, some species have very short wings or no wings at all and thus are re-stricted in their range.

Grasshopper plagues. The early settlers of the great plains of our West often had to contend with great migratory swarms of grasshoppers which were driven out of an arid region where food was scarce to the cultivated fields of wheat and corn. Many farms there had to be abandoned because of the ravages of these pests.

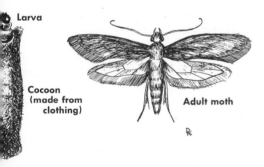

Larva

Cocoon (made from clothing)

Adult moth

igure 232. Clothes moth, *Tinea,* and its larval ase. Injury is restricted to larvae which build teir cocoons from the fabrics, usually woolen, pon which they feed. Adults lay eggs upon lothing or fabric not in daily use and kept more r less in the dark.

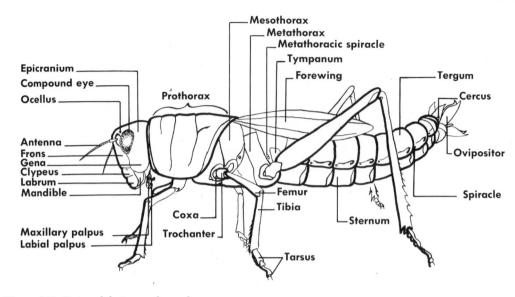

Figure 233. External features of grasshopper.

Stories are handed down of these great plagues. In Salt Lake City there is a monument to the gulls that saved the early Mormons from a grasshopper plague. So great were some of their swarms that railroad trains were unable to make their way through the teeming masses. The insects still flair up in those regions, but better control measures have usually kept them in check. The worst grasshopper plagues have probably been in the Old World, such as in Russia, Southern Europe, and Northern Africa. One of the worst locust plagues ever reported occurred in Tunis and Algiers in 1908, when swarms of locusts darkened the sun for days as they flew in from the deserts and arid regions. They literally ate up every form of vegetation wherever they were, devastated hundreds of square miles, and caused all railroad transportation to come to a standstill.

Various devices are used to control grasshoppers, such as sprinkling poisoned mash over the fields, collecting them in traps and ditches covered with oil (which suffocates them), and by early fall plowing, which destroys the eggs laid in the soil by the females during the summer.

External features. The body is composed of the typical insect plan of head, thorax, and abdomen (Figure 233). The head is made up of six fused somites; the thorax, three somites, on which are the legs and wings; and the abdomen, eleven somites. Covering the body is the **exoskeleton,** or **cuticle,** of chitin secreted by the epidermis underneath. The exoskeleton is divided into hard plates, **sclerites** which are separated from each other by soft cuticula (sutures), which permits the coat of armor to be moved freely. The head is made up of a dorsal portion, the **epicranium;** a region in front, the **frons** and the sides, or **genae.** Below the frons is the plate, **clypeus.** On each side of the head is a **compound eye,** and three simple eyes (ocelli) are located in the region between the compound eyes. A pair of slender **antennae** are also found on the head. On the ventral side of the head (Figure 234) are the chewing mouth parts consisting of (1) the upper lip, or **labrum** attached to the clypeus; (2) a membranous tonguelike **hypopharynx** just back of the mouth; (3) two heavy jaws, or **mandibles,** toothed for chewing food; (4) two **maxillae,** each with several parts; and (5) the lower lip, or **labium,** which is made up of a number of parts, including a pair of **labial palps.**

The **thorax** contains the anterior **prothorax,** which bears the saddlelike pronotum, a middle **mesothorax,** and the posterior **metathorax.** Each of these segments bears a pair of legs, and the mesothorax and metathorax also each bear a pair of wings. There are eleven sclerites in each somite, divided among a dorsal **tergum** of four, a **pleuron** of three on each side, and a ventral **sternum** of one. Each leg has the following segments: the **coxa** attached to the body; the **trochanter,** short and fused to the large **femur;** the slender **tibia;** and the **tarsus,** which contains three visible segments, of which the proximal one bears four pairs of ventral pads and the terminal one a pair of **claws,** between which is the fleshy **pulvillus.** The claws and pulvilli are used by the insect in clinging. The metathoracic legs are adapted for leaping. The **hindwings** are membranous. Many are veined and fold up under the narrow leathery **forewings** like a fan. These wings are outgrowths of the epidermis and consist of a double membrane which contains the tracheae. The **veins**

represent the thickened cuticle around the tracheae and serve to strengthen the wing. Although these veins vary in their patterns among the different species, they are constant in individuals of certain species, where they serve for classification.

The **abdomen** is elongated and tapers toward the end, where the terminal somite is specialized for copulation or egg laying. Ten pairs of **spiracles,** small openings into the respiratory system, are found along the lower sides of the abdomen. The first segment of the abdomen has its sternum united to the thorax, and its tergum bears on either side the oval **tympanic membrane** which covers the auditory sac of hearing. The terminal segments of the abdomen are modified in the two sexes for copulation and egg laying. For one thing the end of the abdomen in the male is rounded; that of the female, pointed. The first seven abdominal segments are alike. In both sexes, the terga of 9 and 10 are partly fused. In the male the tergum of 11 forms the **supra-anal** plate over the anus. A small process called the **cercus** projects on each side behind 10, and the sternum of 9 is long and bears the subgenital plate which terminates dorsally in two short projections. The subgenital plate covers the male genital apparatus. In the female the sternum of 9 is elongated and the abdomen terminates in two pairs of lobes, or valves, with a smaller pair hidden between the larger valves. The **ovipositor,** or egg-depositing mechanism, is made up of these three pairs of valves.

Internal features (Figure 235). The internal cavity of the grasshopper is a **hemocoele,** that is, contains blood, and is not a true coelomic cavity. **Muscles** of the striated type are grouped here and there for the movement of the mouth parts, wings, and legs. In the abdomen there are segmental muscles for respiratory and reproductive movements.

The most conspicuous organ system in the body is the **digestive** system. It consists of (1) a **mouth,** surrounded by the mouth parts, into which the **salivary glands** open; (2) a short tubular **esophagus;** (3) a thin-walled **crop;** (4) a **pro-**

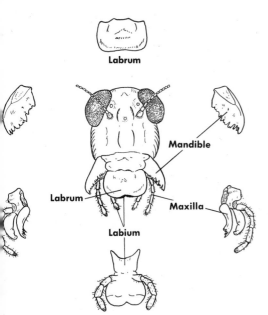

Figure 234. Mouth parts of grasshopper.

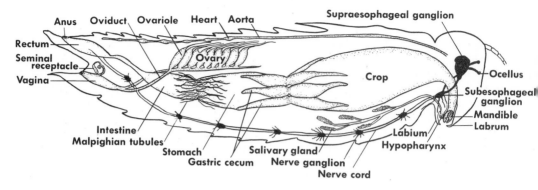

Figure 235. Internal structures of female grasshopper with right body wall removed (diagrammatic).

ventriculus, or gizzard, for grinding food; (5) a **stomach**, or **ventriculus**; (6) a series of six double thin-walled **gastric ceca**, which open into the stomach; (7) an **intestine**; (8) an enlarged **rectum**; and (9) an **anus**. The first four divisions mentioned form the **foregut**, the next two make up the **midgut**, and the last three the **hindgut**. Both the foregut and the hindgut are lined with chitin, and thus absorption of food is confined mainly to the stomach portion.

The **circulatory** system is much reduced compared with many other arthropods. There are (1) a tubular **heart** lying in the pericardial cavity close to the dorsal wall of the abdomen with small openings, the **ostia**; (2) a **dorsal aorta**, which extends from the heart into the head region;

and (3) a **hemocoele** made up of spaces between the internal organs. The system is an open one (lacunar), for there are no capillaries or veins. Its sole function appears to be the transportation of food, for the grasshopper, in common with other insects, has a separate tracheal system for respiration.

Respiration is taken care of by an extensive network of tubes, **tracheae** (Figure 236), that go to every part of the body. The tracheal tubes consist of a single layer of cells and are lined with cuticle which is shed at molting. The larger tubes are prevented from collapsing by spiral threads of chitin. The **spiracles** on each side of the body lead by branches into a longitudinal trunk. The finer air tubes, called **tracheoles**, are connected directly to the body tissues to deliver oxygen and carry away carbon dioxide. There are also several **air sacs** in the abdomen which pump air in and out of the tracheal system by the alternate contraction and expansion of the abdomen. The action of the spiracles is so synchronized that the first four pairs of spiracles are open at inspiration and closed at expiration, while the other six pairs are closed at inspiration and open at expiration.

The **excretory** system consists of the **Malpighian tubules** which are joined to the anterior end of the hindgut. Their free ends are closed, and they remove waste from the blood in the hemocoele and pass it into the hindgut.

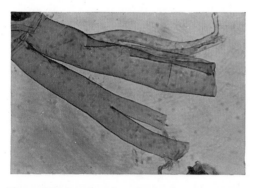

Figure 236. Portion of tracheae of an insect. Fine transversely striated appearance is due to spiral thickenings in walls to prevent them from collapsing. (Photomicrograph.)

330

The **nervous** system consists of (1) a brain of three fused ganglia (**supraesophageal ganglia**), which supply the head organs; (2) two **connectives**, which run around the esophagus from the brain to the **subesophageal ganglia**; and (3) the ventral **nerve cord**, made up of paired ganglia and longitudinal connectives. A pair of ganglia is found in each thoracic somite, and five pairs are scattered through the abdomen. The smaller number in the abdomen is explained by the fusion of certain ganglia. Nerves run from the ganglia to the visceral organs, legs, and wings. There is also an **autonomic nervous system** in two divisions. Nerves from this system supply the muscles of the digestive system, the spiracles, and the reproductive system.

Grasshoppers have all the major senses—touch, taste, smell, hearing, and sight. The chief sensory receptors are the **olfactory** organs on the antennae, **tactile hairs** on the antennae, palps, cerci, and legs, **taste organs** on the mouth parts, **compound eyes** concerned with vision, **ocelli** for light perception, and **auditory organs**, which are located on the sides of the first abdominal somite and consist of a tympanic membrane within a circular chitinous ring. Grasshoppers produce sound by rubbing the hind tibia with its rough surface against the wings.

Sexes are separate in grasshoppers, and distinction between male and female can be determined by the posterior ends of the abdomen. In the male it is round; in the female it is pointed because of the ovipositor. In the male the **reproductive system** (Figure 237) consists of the **two testes**, above the intestine; the two **vasa deferentia** that lead from the testes to the **seminal vesicles**, which unite to form the common **ejaculatory** duct; and the **copulatory** organ (penis). **Accessory glands** secreting a fluid open into the ejaculatory tube. In the female (Figures 235 and 237) are two **ovaries** made up of egg tubules (**ovarioles**), two **oviducts** from the ovaries, a median **vagina** formed by the union of the two oviducts, and a small **seminal receptacle**, which stores sperm

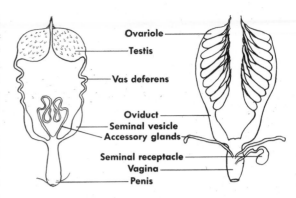

Figure 237. Reproductive organs of grasshopper. Male on left; female on right.

from copulation. The genital opening is between the plates of the ovipositor.

Fertilization and development. In copulation the male inserts his copulatory organ into the vagina of the female and transfers his sperm. The sperm are stored in the seminal receptacles until the eggs are laid. The mature eggs, 3 to 5 mm. long, pass down the oviduct and pick up the yolk and shell before fertilization. A small opening in the egg, **micropyle**, enables the sperm to enter and fertilize the egg. The female makes a tunnel in the ground with her ovipositor and then deposits her eggs. The eggs are usually laid in lots of twenty, and a single female may lay several lots. A few days later the adults die. Development lasts about three weeks and ceases when cold weather comes. Growth begins again in the spring when the temperature is warmer. The young **nymph** which hatches from the egg resembles the parent, but its head is disproportionally large and it lacks wings. As the young grasshopper grows and becomes too large for its chitinous exoskeleton, which is shed periodically, wings finally develop and it reaches the adult form.

Some structural variations

Since the grasshopper is about the only insect studied in our general zoology courses, it is well to point out a few of the modifications of its structural pattern shown by other insects. The grasshopper

Figure 238. Various types of insect antennae. From left to right: Water scavenger beetle (clavate); mosquito (plumose); May beetle (laminate); click beetle (serrate); and tenebrionid beetle (moniliform).

represents a generalized plan into which many other insects fit, but some are highly specialized in their habits and reactions, and this is often accompanied by a corresponding change in bodily structures. These differences are more pronounced in external characteristics than they are in internal features. Some of these variations are here described in order to get a view of their adaptive modifications. Others have already been mentioned in the first part of our discussion on insects.

Body form. There are many patterns of body shape. Some insects are of the thick plump variety, such as beetles (Figures 250 to 253); others have long slender bodies, such as the damsel fly, crane fly, and walking stick (Figure 242). Many have bodies of a distinct streamline form which is represented by aquatic bugs and beetles (Figure 250). Some insects are very much flattened (for instance, cockroaches, Figure 231) which is an adaptation for living in crevices. The termination of the abdomen often has a lot to do with

the impression one gets of the general shape of the body. The abdomen in insects has appendages only at the posterior end, and in the female of various species the ovipositor may be extremely long (ichneumon wasp, Figure 257). Some also bear modifications of the cerci, such as the horny forceps of earwigs (Figure 243) and those of stoneflies and silverfish. Some insects, such as moths, have hairy coverings. Bees have many bristles for collecting pollen (Figure 239).

Mouth parts. The mouth parts of insects are for chewing or sucking. The sucking type may be modified also for piercing, such as in the mosquito. Insects that live on vegetation usually have mandibles for crushing, whereas those of carnivorous insects are specialized for piercing and sucking. Those of the honeybee are fitted for both chewing and sucking. The chewing mouth type may be considered the generalized type; the piercing one usually has the labrum and epipharynx modified into a tubelike structure.

332

Antennae. Antennae may be long, as in cockroaches, some grasshoppers, and katydids, or short, as in dragonflies and most beetles. Some have plumed antennae, such as moths, and others have naked and club-shaped ones (Figure 238). Butterflies have little knobs on the ends of their antennae.

Legs. Legs of insects show modifications for special purposes. Terrestrial forms such as beetles have walking legs with terminal pads and claws. These pads may be sticky for walking upside down, as in houseflies. The mole cricket has the first pair of legs modified for burrowing in the ground. Water bugs and many beetles have paddle-shaped appendages for swimming. For grasping its prey, the forelegs of the praying mantis are large and strong.

The **honeybee** is a good example of how an insect's legs are developed for special purposes (Figure 239). The first pair of legs in this insect is suited to collect pollen by having a feathery **pollen brush** on the tarsus and a fringe of hairs along the medial edge of the tibia for cleaning the compound eye. A semicircular indentation lined with teeth is found in the metatarsus, and this is covered over with a spine, the **vellum** from the tibia. As the antenna is pulled through this notch, it is cleaned of pollen; hence this structure is called the **antennae cleaner.** The middle leg has a **pollen brush** on the first tarsal joint and a spur at the distal end of the tibia. This spur is for the removal of the wax from the wax glands located on the ventral side of the abdomen. The hindlimb is the most specialized of all, for it bears the **pollen basket,** the **pollen packer,** and the **pollen combs.** The pollen basket is made up of a concavity on the outer surface of the tibia with hairs along both edges. These hairs are kept moist with secretions from the mouth. The pollen packer consists of a row of stout bristles on the lower end of the tibia and the auricle, a smooth plate on the proximal end of the metatarsus. The pecten removes the pollen from the pollen comb of the opposite leg onto the auricle. When

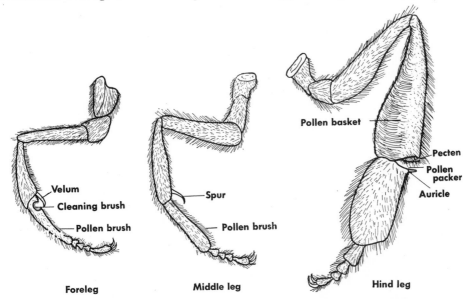

Figure 239. Adaptive legs of honeybee. In foreleg, toothed indentation covered with velum is used to comb out antennae. Spur on middle leg removes wax from wax glands on abdomen. Inside of hind leg bears pollen comb (not shown); long hairs of pecten remove pollen from comb of opposite leg, then auricle presses it into pollen basket when leg joint is flexed back. Bee carries load in both baskets to hive, pushes pollen into cell, to be cared for by other workers.

the leg is flexed, the auricle presses against the end of the tibia, compressing the pollen. Pollen combs are found on the inner surfaces of the metatarsus and consist of rows of stout spines.

Light production

Some four or five orders of insects are represented among forms that are self-luminous. Others may appear luminous, but this is probably due to luminous bacteria. The best-known insects that produce their own light are the glowworm and the firefly. The former may be the larvae of a fly (the New Zealand glowworm) or that of a beetle (Lampyridae, the common one of Europe and elsewhere). Some glowworms are wingless females. The firefly (which belongs to a family of the beetles) is famed for its dis-

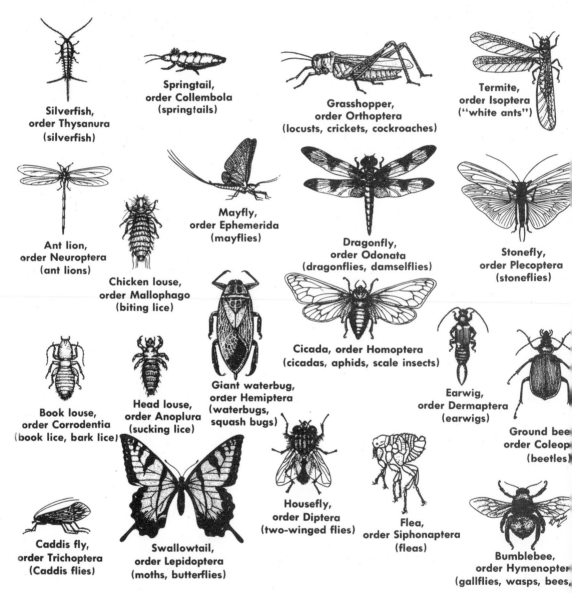

Silverfish,
order Thysanura
(silverfish)

Springtail,
order Collembola
(springtails)

Grasshopper,
order Orthoptera
(locusts, crickets, cockroaches)

Termite,
order Isoptera
("white ants")

Ant lion,
order Neuroptera
(ant lions)

Chicken louse,
order Mallophago
(biting lice)

Mayfly,
order Ephemerida
(mayflies)

Dragonfly,
order Odonata
(dragonflies, damselflies)

Stonefly,
order Plecoptera
(stoneflies)

Book louse,
order Corrodentia
(book lice, bark lice)

Head louse,
order Anoplura
(sucking lice)

Giant waterbug,
order Hemiptera
(waterbugs,
squash bugs)

Cicada, order Homoptera
(cicadas, aphids, scale insects)

Earwig,
order Dermaptera
(earwigs)

Ground bee
order Coleop
(beetles)

Caddis fly,
order Trichoptera
(Caddis flies)

Swallowtail,
order Lepidoptera
(moths, butterflies)

Housefly,
order Diptera
(two-winged flies)

Flea,
order Siphonaptera
(fleas)

Bumblebee,
order Hymenopter
(gallflies, wasps, bees,

Figure 240. Orders of insects. (Courtesy General Biological Supply House, Inc., Chicago.)

play of light all over the world. In these the photogenic organs are located on the ventral surface of the last abdominal segment and consist of two kinds of cells—those that serve as a reflector (dorsal mass) and large cells with granules which are the photogenic cells (ventral mass). Running into the mass of photogenic cells is an extensive network of tracheae which are connected to tracheal end cells. The organ is thus ensured of a good supply of oxygen. The actual source of the light is probably the granules in the cells. The organ appears to be under nervous control, for nerves run to it.

Brief review of insect orders

The following is a classification of insects with a brief description of each order (Figure 240).

Subclass Apterygota (ap-ter'y-go"ta) (Gr. *a-*, not, + *pterygotos*, winged). Primitive wingless insects, that is, have not come from winged ancestors; with little or no metamorphosis; usually stylelike appendages on pregenital abdominal segments in addition to cerci.

  Order 1. Protura (pro-tu'ra) (Gr. *proto*, first, + *oura*, tail). These are considered the most primitive of insects, for they have no wings, no antennae, no compound eyes, and no metamorphosis. Appendages are present on abdomen as well as thorax. They are small, around 1 mm. in length, and are found in damp places, such as under leaves, bark, and moss. Example: *Acerentulus.*

  Order 2. Collembola (col-lem'bo-la) (Gr. *kolla*, glue, + *bole*, dart)—springtails (Figure 240). These have no wings, compound eyes, or tracheae (usually). They have a peculiar springing organ (furcula) on the ventral side of the fourth abdominal segment. They derive their name from the sticky secretion from a gland near the labium by which they can adhere to objects. Most are under 5 mm. long. They are often found in damp places under leaves and bark. They are especially abundant sometimes in early spring on snowbanks. Example: *Achorutes.*

  Order 3. Thysanura (thy'sa-nu"ra) (Gr. *thysanos*, tassel)—bristletails (Figure 240). These are also wingless with long antennae. The abdomen is provided with two or three long, jointed cerci. Some are quite small and others may be more than 1 inch long. A common and familiar form is the silverfish *(Lepisma),* which is often found in homes, where they do damage by eating the starch of book covers and clothing. Another one is the firebrat *(Thermobia),* often found about fireplaces.

Subclass Pterygota (pter'y-go"ta) (Gr. *pterygotos*, winged). Usually winged, but if wingless the condition is acquired; no abdominal appendages except cerci.

  Division 1. Exopterygota (ek'sop-ter'i-go"ta) *exo,* outside, + *pterygotos,* winged). With gradual metamorphosis.

  Order 4. Orthoptera (or-thop'ter-a) (Gr. *orthos,* straight, + *pteron,* wing)—grasshoppers (locusts), crickets, cockroaches, etc. (Figure 240). Two pairs of wings are found in this order. The forewings (tegmina) are thickened and the hindwing is folded like a fan under the forewing. These

Figure 241. Mole cricket, *Gryllotalpa.* Note how forelegs are adapted for digging. Order Orthoptera.

Figure 242. Walking stick. Note resemblance to twigs. (Shown slightly less than life size.)

insects have chewing mouth parts and gradual metamorphosis. The group is a very extensive one and includes the grasshoppers, cockroaches, crickets, walking sticks, and praying mantes (Figures 241 and 242). Most of them are harmful, but the praying mantis (Figure 227) is very useful in destroying other insects.

Order 5. Dermaptera (der-map'ter-a) (Gr. *derma,* skin, + *pteron,* wing)—**earwigs** (Figures 240 and 243). The forewings of earwigs are very short, with large membranous hindwings. They have biting mouth parts and gradual metamorphosis. The tip of the abdomen bears a pair of curious forceplike cerci. *Forficula* is a common example.

Order 6. Plecoptera (ple-cop'ter-a) (Gr. *pleko,* fold, + *pteron,* wing)—**stone flies** (Figure 240). The four wings are membranous and held pleated on the back when not in use. Mouth parts (not always present) are for chewing, and the metamorphosis is incomplete. The larval form (naiad) is aquatic and bears tufts of tracheal gills.

Order 7. Isoptera (i-sop'ter-a) (Gr. *isos,* equal, + *pteron,* wing)—**termites** (Figure 240). These are often wrongly called white ants. They have chewing mouth parts and gradual metamorphosis. They can be distinguished from true ants by the broad union of the thorax to the abdomen. Sexual forms have four similar wings which they shed after mating; workers and soldiers are wingless and blind. Termites are one of the best examples of a social insect, for they live in large colonies. Their diet is exclusively wood, and in tropical countries they are among the most destructive of insects. They are also fairly common in the temperate zones. To aid in their digestion of wood, termites have in their intestines flagellate protozoans that secrete enzymes for the breakdown of cellulose. The mounds of the colonies in the tropics are often imposing affairs.

Order 8. Ephemerida (eph'e-mer"i-da) (Gr. *ephemeros,* lasting but a day)—**may flies**

Figure 243. Earwig. Forcepslike cerci at posterior end are usually better developed in the male and are used as organs for defense and offense. Order Dermaptera. (Stained preparation, greatly enlarged.)

336

(Figure 240). The wings are membranous, with the forewings larger than the hindwings. Adult mouth parts are vestigial, and the metamorphosis is incomplete. The naiads are aquatic, with lateral tracheal gills. *Ephemera* is a common form.

Order 9. **Odonata** (o-do-na′ta) (Gr. *odontos*, tooth)—**dragonflies, damsel flies** (Figure 240). This order gets its name from its toothlike biting mouth parts. These insects have two pairs of membranous wings, incomplete metamorphosis, and large compound eyes. They represent a beautiful group of insects that are often seen flying gracefully over ponds hawking for their food. The larval forms are aquatic (Figure 225), those of the dragonfly being provided with a long, hinged labium with which they capture their prey. The naiad has gills in its rectum and breathes by alternately drawing in and expelling water. *Gomphus* is a very common example.

Order 10. **Corrodentia** (cor′ro-den″ti-a) (L. *corrodens*, gnawing)—**book lice** (Figure 240). These are small insects with chewing mouth parts and four membranous wings (sometimes absent). Metamorphosis is gradual. They are sometimes found in books, since they have a fondness for the starch of the bindings, and also in bird's nests and under bark. *Troctes* is an example.

Order 11. **Mallophaga** (mal-loph′a-ga) (Gr. *mallos*, wool, + *phago*, to eat)—**biting lice** (Figure 240). These insects are less than ¼ inch long and are wingless. Their legs are adapted for clinging to the host, and their mouth parts are for chewing. Their metamorphosis is gradual. They live exclusively on birds and mammals, eating feathers, hairs, and skin debris. The common chicken louse is *Menopon*.

Order 12. **Embioptera** (em′bi-op″ter-a) (Gr. *embios*, lively, + *pteron*, wing)—**embiids.** These are small insects with elongated bodies, with wingless females and usually winged males. Their mouth parts are for chewing, and their metamorphosis is gradual. They make silk-lined channels in the soil and are colonial. They are mostly tropical forms. *Embia* is an example.

Order 13. **Thysanoptera** (thy′sa-nop″ter-a) (Gr. *thysanos*, tassel, + *pteron*, wing)—**thrips.** These are only a few millimeters long or smaller. Some are wingless, but others have four similar wings. They have sucking mouth parts and gradual metamorphosis. Parthenogenesis is common among them. They live by sucking the juices of plants. *Thrips* is an example.

Order 14. **Anoplura** (an′o-plu″ra) (Gr. *anoplos*, unarmed, + *oura*, tail)—**sucking lice** (Figure 240). The bodies of these insects are small and depressed, and they are wingless. Their mouth is adapted for piercing and sucking, and they have no metamorphosis. These are the true lice, and three kinds have become more or less a pest to man: (1) the head louse (*Pediculus capitis*), which lives on the head hair and lays its eggs (nits) there; (2) the body louse (*Pediculus corporis*), sometimes called the "cootie," which lives on the body and head, lays its eggs in the clothing and hair, and is responsible for carrying typhus fever, trench fever, and other diseases; and (3) the crab louse (*Phthirius pubis*), which often gets in the pubic hair. Many other kinds are found on various mammals.

Order 15. **Hemiptera** (he-mip′ter-a) (Gr. *hemi*, half, + *pteron*, wing)—**true bugs** (Figure 240). This is an extensive group of great economic importance. The front wings of these insects are thickened and leatherlike at the anterior half but membranous at the posterior half, while the hindwings are membranous and fold under the front ones. They have piercing and sucking mouth parts, and the metamorphosis is gradual. This order includes such groups as the water bugs, bedbugs, stinkbugs, chinch bugs, assassin bugs, and water striders (Figures 244 and 245).

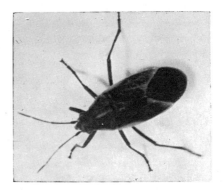

Figure 244. Box elder bug. These often become a nuisance in the fall when they enter houses in swarms, seeking place to hibernate. However, they do no damage to house contents. Order Hemiptera.

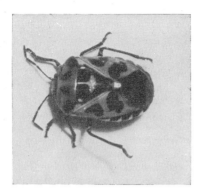

Figure 245. Harlequin cabbage bug, *Murgantia*. Order Hemiptera.

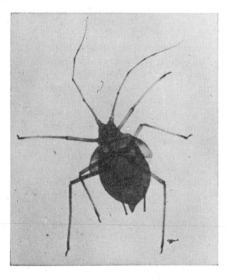

Figure 246. Aphid. Aphids not only have an interesting reproductive cycle but certain kinds also excrete honeydew for ants, which in turn take care of the aphid's eggs and preserve adults from harm. Order Homoptera. (Photomicrograph.)

Order 16. Homoptera (ho-mop'ter-a) (Gr. *homos*, same, + *pteron*, wing)—**cicadas, aphids, scale insects, leaf hoppers** (Figure 240). These insects have two pairs of wings (absent in some) of uniform thickness and texture. The mouth parts are for piercing and sucking, and there is gradual metamorphosis. One of the most noted members of this order is the cicada, or seventeen-year locust (*Magicicada septemdecem*). Eggs are laid in trees, where they hatch into nymphs, which then drop to the ground. Then for seventeen years they make their home in the soil, living on plant juices from the roots of trees. At the end of this time they crawl up a tree trunk undergo their final molt, and emerge as adults. Some southern species require only thirteen years for their cycle.

Another interesting member of the order is the aphid, or plant louse (Figure 246). Aphids have both sexual and parthenogenetic generations, and they are very destructive to plants. Scale insects are likewise very destructive by sucking plant sap. Some are protected by a soft cottony covering.

Order 17. Zoraptera (zo-rap'ter-a) (Gr. *zoros*, pure, + *apterygos*, wingless). These are small insects not exceeding 3 mm. in length. They have some resemblance to termites, for they occur in colonies and both winged and wingless forms are found in spite of their name. The winged forms have two pairs of wings which they shed like termites. The wingless forms are blind. Of sixteen species, only two occur in the United States. Unlike termites, they feed as predators or scavengers on small arthropods. They are commonly found under bark and in rotten logs.

Division 2. Endopterygota (en'dop-ter'y-go"ta) (Gr. *endon*, inside, + *pterygotos*, winged). With complete metamorphosis.

Order 18. Neuroptera (neu-rop'ter-a) (Gr. *neuron*, nerve, + *pteron*, wing)—**dobson flies, ant lions, lacewings.** This order takes its name from the many cross veins in the wings. The four wings are alike and are membranous. They have complete metamorphosis, with biting mouth parts.

Figure 247. Hellgrammite. Larval form of dobson fly, *Corydalis*, much prized by fishermen for bait. Order Neuroptera.

338

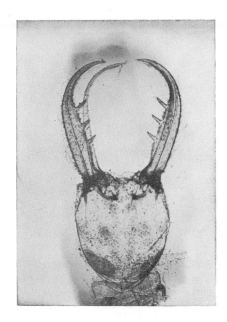

Figure 248. Head of ant lion larva, *Myrmeleon,* showing large mandibles for seizing its prey as it lies concealed in its pit. Order Neuroptera. (Photomicrograph.)

Figure 249. Conical crater pit of ant lion. When an ant starts to slide into sandy pit, ant lion helps out by undermining the sand beneath the ant and awaits it with open jaws.

Corydalis, the huge dobson fly, looks formidable with its large mandibles but is quite harmless (Figure 247). It is excellent bait for fish. The larva (doodlebug) (Figure 248) of the ant lion has the interesting habit of making a conical crater in the sand and lying concealed in it until its prey accidentally falls into it (Figure 249). With its very large jaws the larva quickly seizes and makes a meal of it.

Order 19. Coleoptera (co'le-op"ter-a) (Gr. *koleos,* sheath, + *pteron,* wing)—**beetles, weevils** (Figure 240). The beetles are the most extensive group of animals in the world. About one animal out of every three is a beetle. The forewings (elytra) are thick and leathery, while the hindwings are membranous and are folded under the forewings. Some beetles are wingless. They have chewing mouth parts and complete metamorphosis. This large group is divided into many families, each with thousands of species. Among the most familiar of these family groups are the ground beetles, tiger beetles, carrion beetles, whirligig beetles, click beetles, darkling beetles, stag beetles, fireflies, and diving beetles (Figures 250 to 253).

The other division of this important group is the weevil. Weevils have their jaws modified into snouts, and the most familiar one is the cotton boll weevil (*Anthonomus grandis*).

Order 20. Strepsiptera (strep-sip'ter-a) (Gr. *strepsis,* a turning, + *pteron,* wing)—**stylops.** There is a marked sexual dimorphism in these small forms, for the males have tiny or vestigial forewings and fan-shaped hindwings and the females no wings, eyes, or antennae. The mouth parts are for chewing, and the life cycle is complex (**hypermetamorphosis**). The females and larvae are wholly parasitic in bees, wasps, and other insects. There are relatively few species in the group. *Xenos* is a parasite in the wasp (*Polistes*).

Order 21. Mecoptera (me-cop'ter-a) (Gr. *mekos,* length, + *pteron,* wing)—**scorpion flies.** These have four narrow, membranous wings (some are wingless) and chewing mouth parts. Metamorphosis is complete. The male has a curious clasping organ at the tip of the abdomen, which resembles the sting of a scorpion; hence the name of the order. *Boreus,* which is often found on snow in the winter, is one of the more familiar forms.

Figure 250. Giant diving beetle, *Dytiscus*. This beetle is more than 1 inch long, is very active in water, and will eat any prey it can overcome. Order Coleoptera.

Figure 251. Common stag beetle, *Lucanus*, another coleopteran.

Figure 252. Colorado potato beetle, *Leptinotarsa*. Order Coleoptera.

Figure 253. Rhinoceros beetle, *Dynastes*, another coleopteran.

Order 22. **Lepidoptera** (lep'i-dop"ter-a) (Gr. *lepis*, scale, + *pteron*, wing)—**butterflies, moths** (Figure 240). These insects are famed for their great beauty and are known the world over. Two pairs of wings are membranous and are covered with overlapping scales. The mouth parts are for sucking and are kept coiled under the head when not in use. The metamorphosis is complete, and the larval form is called a caterpillar. Butterflies have a knob at the tip of the antennae; moths have plummed or feathered antennae as a usual thing. The larval forms are provided with glands for spinning their cocoons. The pupa is sometimes called a chrysalis. The major families are the tiger moths, the regal moths, the bagworm moths, the swallow-tailed butterflies, the sulphur butterflies, and the gossamer butterflies (Figure 254).

Order 23. **Diptera** (dip'ter-a) (Gr. *dis*, two, + *pteron*, wing)—**flies** (Figures 240 and 255). These are the true flies. They are unique among insects in having only two wings, although some are wingless. In place of hindwings, they have **halteres.** Their metamorphosis is complete, and they have piercing and sucking mouth parts. Their larval forms are often known as maggots and those developing in water as wigglers. They are commonly separated into two great divisions: the long-horned flies with antennae of more than five segments and the short-horned flies with antennae of five or less joints. Among the long-horned flies are the crane flies, mosquitoes, moth flies, midges, gnats, and black flies. Representatives of the short-horned flies are the

Figure 254. Swallow-tailed butterfly, *Papilio*. Order Lepidoptera.

fruit flies, flesh flies, botflies, houseflies, and bee flies.

Order 24. Trichoptera (tri-chop'ter-a) (Gr. *thrix*, hair, + *pteron*, wing)—**caddis flies** (Figure 240). These insects have two pairs of membranous wings with silky hairs. Metamorphosis is complete, and the mouth parts are vestigial. The larval forms have the interesting habit of living in fairly rapid waters in a case composed of sand and sticks bound together by their secretions.

Order 25. Siphonaptera (si'pho-nap"ter-a) (Gr. *siphon*, siphon, + *a*, without, + *pteron*, wing)—**fleas** (Figure 240). Fleas are wingless, with sucking mouth parts. Their bodies are laterally compressed with legs adapted for leaping. Compound eyes are lacking, and simple eyes may be suppressed. They are ectoparasites on mammals and birds. There are different species of fleas, but they readily change host whenever the opportunity offers. Some of them are vectors for the bubonic plague and typhus fever. The one that is most annoying to man is *Pulex irritans*.

Order 26. Hymenoptera (hy'me-nop"ter-a) (Gr. *hymen*, membrane, + *pteron*, wing)—**ants, bees, wasps.** This order gets its name from the four membranous wings which may be absent in some. They have complete metamorphosis and chewing or sucking mouth parts. Their wings have the pecularity of being held together with hooks (hamuli). The ovipositor in the female is modified into a stinger (Figure 256), piercer, or saw. Both social and solitary species are found. This group is a very large one and includes some of the most specialized members of the insect world

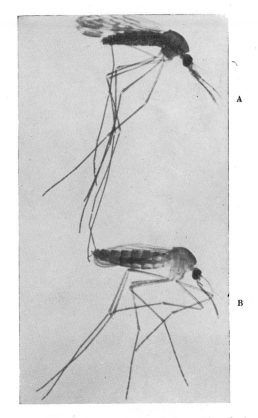

Figure 255. Two common mosquitoes (females). A, *Anopheles*, the malaria carrier, bears dark blotches on its wings. B, *Culex*. In feeding, *Anopheles* holds its body at an angle to surface, whereas *Culex* holds its body horizontally. Order Diptera.

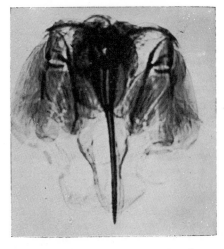

Figure 256. Stinger of honeybee after dissection. (Photomicrograph.)

Phylum Arthropoda—subphylum Mandibulata—insects 341

Figure 257. Ichneumon wasp. By means of long ovipositor, female can bore deep into tree and lay an egg near wood-boring beetle larva. There egg hatches into tiny larva which parasitizes beetle larva. Ichneumon wasps are large insects, this specimen having an over-all length of over 6 inches. Inset shows typical compound insect eyes, antennae, and mouth parts of ichneumon head. Order Hymenoptera.

Figure 258. Solitary wasp that has just been rudely awakened from his winter sleep. Brought in from his hibernation in February. Order Hymenoptera.

(Figure 257). Some are quite useful and others are destructive to man's interests. Among the bees the most familiar are the bumblebees, carpenter bees, honeybees, and mason bees. Mud-dauber wasps and bee wasps are among the most common of the wasps (Figure 258). The great family of ants has carried the social organization as far as any group of insects, and their marvelous instincts and reactions are among the most interesting in the animal kingdom.

Derivation and meaning of basic terminology

Asellus (L. asellus, a little ass).

autotomy (Gr. *autos,* self, + *tome,* cutting) The animal voluntarily breaks off a part of itself.

Branchiopoda (Gr. *branchia,* gills, + *podos,* foot).

Cambarus (Gr. *kammaros,* a sea crab).

chelicera (Gr. *chele,* claw, + *keraos,* horny).

Chelicerata (Gr. *chele,* claw, + *keraos,* horny) Instead of jaws these arthropods have a pair of jointed appendages which bear horny claws.

Chilopoda (Gr. *cheilos,* margin, + *podos,* foot).

chitin (Gr. *chiton,* tunic).

chrysalis (Gr. *chrysallis,* gold) Refers to gold-colored pupa.

Cirripedia (L. *cirrus,* curl, + *pes,* foot).

Diplopoda (Gr. *diploos,* double, + *podos,* foot) Each somite bears two pairs of legs.

ecdysis (Gr. *ekdysis,* put off) Shedding of outer cuticular layer; molting.

Entomostraca (Gr. *entomon,* insect, + *ostrakon,* shell) A resemblance to insects enclosed in a shell.

Eurypterida (Gr. *eurys,* broad, + *pteryon,* wing or fin) Refers to the shape of some of the appendages.

342

Homarus (OF. *homar*, a lobster).

Insecta (L. *insectum*, cut into) Refers to the marked constriction between the thorax and abdomen.

Latrodectus (L. *latro*, robber, + Gr. *dektes*, a biter).

Malacostraca (Gr. *malakos*, soft, + *ostrakon*, shell).

Mandibulata (L. *mandibula*, mandible) Division of arthropods with jaws for crushing and chewing.

metamorphosis (Gr. *meta*, after, + *morphe*, form) Marked change in form during post-embryonic development.

Miranda (L. *miranda*, wonderful).

Myriapoda (Gr. *myrios*, many, + *podos*, foot).

Onychophora (Gr. *onycho*, claw, + *phero*, to bear).

Pauropoda (Gr. *pauros*, small, + *podos*, foot).

pedipalps (L. *pes*, foot, + *palpo*, to feel) Second pair of appendages of arachnids.

pentastomida (Gr. *pente*, five, + *stoma*, mouth) Refers to the shallow pits near the mouth which give the latter the appearance of being five-parted.

Peripatus (Gr. *peripatos*, walking about).

Pycnogonida (Gr. *pyknos*, compact, + *gonas*, gonad) The gonads are packed away in the appendages.

Symphyla (Gr. *sym*, together, + *phylon*, tribe).

Tardigrada (L. *tardus*, slow, + *gradior*, to walk).

Trilobita (Gr. *tri*, three, + *lobos*, lobe) Dorsal shield is marked in three lobes.

Xiphosura (Gr. *xiphos*, sword, + *oura*, tail) Refers to the pointed tail.

ANNOTATED REFERENCES

Boardman, E. T. 1939. Field Guide to Lower Aquarium Animals. Bloomfield Hills, Mich., Cranbrook Institute of Science. *Many aquatic insects are described and illustrated in this work.*

Borradaile, L. A., and F. A. Potts, 1958. The Invertebrata, ed. 3 (revised by G. A. Kerkut). New York, Cambridge University Press. *This standard manual is one of the most comprehensive in the field, but no one volume can cover this extensive group adequately. Naturally, some invertebrates are given scanty treatment in this work. Drawings are mainly schematic and are below the standard one should expect in a book of this type.*

Borror, D. J., and D. M. Delong, 1954. An Introduction to the Study of Insects. New York, Rinehart & Co. *This up-to-date text emphasizes both the study and the identification of insects. Its taxonomic keys are very complete*

and both line drawings and photographs are included in the illustrations. *An excellent glossary, but lacking derivations, is included.*

Butler, C. G. 1955. The World of the Honeybee. New York, The Macmillan Co. *Honeybees have been much in the limelight since von Frisch's work of a few years ago. The time, therefore, is ripe for a monograph such as the present one on the organization and behavior of the honeybee community, in the light of recent knowledge (such is the force of new discoveries on old concepts!). The many photographs are clear and revealing.*

Comstock, J. H. 1940. An Introduction to Entomology, ed. 9. Ithaca, Comstock Publishing Co. *One of the best general texts in the field of entomology. Somewhat technical but can be understood by the beginner.*

Folsom, J. W., and R. A. Wardle. 1934. Entomology With Special Reference to Its Ecological Aspects, ed. 4. Philadelphia, The Blakiston Co. *Deals with the relation of insects to their environment. A good account of the habits and behavior of insects.*

Frisch, K. von. 1950. Bees: Their Vision, Chemical Senses, and Language. Ithaca, Cornell University Press. *An outstanding work on the way bees communicate with each other and reveal the sources of food supplies. A marvelous revelation of animal behavior.*

Goetsch, W. 1957. The Ants. Ann Arbor, University of Michigan Press. *A concise and authoritative account of ants and their ways. The author describes many of his own experiments on the reactions and behavior of these interesting forms.*

Graham, S. A. 1952. Forest Entomology. New York, McGraw-Hill Book Co., Inc. *A clear description of the insects that are injurious to forests.*

Herms, W. B. 1950. Medical Entomology, ed. 4. New York, The Macmillan Co. *A study of the insects that have a bearing upon the diseases of man. Good descriptions of the common vectors in the communication of diseases.*

Herrick, G. W. 1926. Insects Injurious to the Household and Annoying to Man. New York, The Macmillan Co. *The common insect pests of man around his home are described and methods for their control suggested. A very practical book for the beginning student.*

Jaques, H. E. 1951. How to Know the Beetles. Dubuque, Iowa, Wm. C. Brown Co. *A useful and compact manual for the coleopterist.*

Johannsen, O. A., and F. H. Butt. 1941. Embryology of the Insects and Myriapods. New York, McGraw-Hill Book Co., Inc. *A technical* work on the development of insects and some of their allies.

Lees, A. D. 1955. The Physiology of Diapause in Arthropods, Cambridge, Cambridge University Press. *The temporary lagging of growth or reproduction typical of many animals is called diapause and has received much attention and investigation in recent years. The author has spent many years on this phenomenon in red spider mites and has advanced evidence to show that it is controlled by hormones, although this is only one aspect of the problem. In insects, and perhaps other animals, the dormant and active periods are synchronized with available food supplies. Light reactions are thought to play a part here. This excellent monograph presents our present state of knowledge about this interesting physiological adaptation.*

Little, V. A. 1957. General and Applied Entomology. New York, Harper & Brothers. *An excellent work for beginning students in entomology. It treats the subject from the viewpoints of anatomy, physiology, metamorphosis, and control. Little attention is given to classification other than general surveys of the various orders. The illustrations include a number of excellent photographs. A selected bibliography is also included.*

Lutz, F. E. 1935. Field Book of Insects, ed. 3. New York, G. P. Putnam's Sons. *A good manual for field identification of insects.*

Miall, L. C. 1922. The Natural History of Aquatic insects. London, Macmillan & Co., Ltd. *Excellent descriptions of both adult and larval forms of aquatic insects. Interesting to beginner.*

Morgan, A. H. 1930. Field Book of Ponds and Streams. New York, G. P. Putnam's Sons. *Aquatic insects are given considerable treatment among other forms.*

Neider, C. (editor). 1954. The Fabulous Insects. New York, Harper & Brothers. *An anthology of selections dealing with interesting insects and written by eminent authorities. The beginner will greatly profit from the reading of this book.*

Pesson, P. 1959. The World of Insects. Translated by R. B. Freeman. New York, McGraw-Hill Book Co. Inc. *All zoology students will have their interest in insects quickened by this fascinating volume of illustrations (many of them in perfect kodachrome colors) and the excellent pithy descriptions of the natural history of this "most abundant and the most diverse of all animals."*

Pierce, G. W. 1949. The Songs of Insects, Cambridge, Harvard University Press. *The author, a physicist, has applied the apparatus and methods of physics to an investigation of the sounds made by insects and has made many revealing discoveries about the patterns of sound found in this group of animals. Many of his methods have been applied with great success to the problems of echo location in bats.*

Pringle, J. W. S. 1957. Insect Flight. New York, Cambridge Univeristy Press. *This little monograph summarizes the present state of knowledge of the complicated methods of flight of insects. The physiology, anatomy, and aerodynamics are discussed. There is an interesting chapter on the histology and physiology of the flight muscles.*

Scheer, B. T. (editor). 1957. Recent Advances in Invertebrate Physiology. Eugene, University of Oregon Publications. *This work is based on a symposium held at the University of Oregon on the various aspects of invertebrate physiology by eminent specialists. Among the interesting topics discussed are neuromuscular action, hormonal control, and patterns of rhythms.*

Swain, R. B. 1948. The Insect Guide. New York, Doubleday & Co., Inc. *A description of the orders and major families of North American insects. Contains some good color plates which help in identification.*

Wigglesworth, V. B. 1939. The Principles of Insect Physiology. London, Methuen & Co. Ltd. *A technical work suitable for the advanced student on the functional patterns of insects.*

Wigglesworth, V. B. 1954. The Physiology of Insect Metamorphosis. Cambridge, Cambridge University Press. *The author believes that metamorphosis is merely another case of polymorphism, which is almost universal among animals. He adduces evidence that all levels of complexity are determined by the supply or deficiency of raw materials that may be produced within an endocrine gland and circulate as a hormone.*

chapter 19

Phylum Mollusca*

BIOLOGICAL PRINCIPLES

Organ-system level of organization

1. All organ systems are present and well developed.

2. Adult body plan is different from any other invertebrate group but is sharply defined and easily recognized.

3. This is a highly successful phylum which is typically marine but has also invaded the land and fresh water. These represent the second largest invertebrate group.

4. Bilateral symmetry is the rule, although this has been modified in the snails (Gastropoda) into an asymmetrical plan.

5. They have evolved a body plan without any suggestion of metamerism except in the recently discovered Monoplacophora.

6. Great diversity of form is due to plasticity of mantle and related structures.

7. Within the phylum the members display a great range of organization from the lowest to the highest, as shown by a comparison of the relatively simple Amphineura with the highly modified and specialized Gastropoda and Cephalophoda.

8. Mollusks belong to the protostome branch, or schizocoelous coelomates, of the animal kingdom and have spiral and determinate cleavage.

Biological contributions

1. They introduce for the first time a fleshy **mantle** which in most cases secretes a shell.

2. Another unique organ in the invertebrate kingdom is the **radula**.

3. Shells in most types are well developed, but these are not peculiar to mollusks, although their use of the mantle in the shell formation may be considered a unique plan.

4. Another contribution to the animal blueprint is the ventral **muscular foot**, a distinct molluscan character.

5. The highly developed **eye** in the higher mollusks has arisen as a skin derivative in contrast to the brain eye of vertebrates. This independent evolution must be considered as an example of convergent evolution.

6. Morphologically, the invertebrate reaches its greatest size in mollusks.

Position in animal kingdom

1. Many mollusks have a trochophore larval form (veliger) which has a resemblance to the trochophore larva of marine annelids.

2. Since most mollusks are not segmented, they must have branched from the main evolutionary line before segmentation arose.

3. There is some evidence that mollusks and annelids have come from a common platyhelminth origin, probably a turbellarian form. The newly found monoplacophorans would indicate an annelid relationship.

GENERAL RELATIONS

Next to the arthropods the mollusks have the most named species in the animal kingdom. The name Mollusca (L. *molluscus,* soft) indicates one of their distinctive characteristics, a soft body. The group ranges in form from fairly simple organisms to some of the most complex invertebrates and in size from the almost microscopic to a length of 50 feet—the largest of all invertebrates.

Two structural features of the mollusks that set them aside from all other animals are the ventral muscular **foot** and the fleshy **mantle**. The mantle is a sheath of

---

*Mol-lus′ca (L. *molluscus,* soft).

skin which surrounds the soft parts and hangs down as a free fold around the body like a skirt, enclosing the mantle cavity space. It serves a variety of purposes. It secretes the shell and forms the siphons. The gills and other respiratory devices, such as the lungs of pulmonate snails, develop from the mantle. The exposed edge of the mantle in certain Gastropoda and Scaphopoda is used for respiration. Almost all the blood of Mollusca is oxygenated in some part of the mantle or its modification. In cephalopods the muscular mantle is used for locomotion and, mechanically, also for respiration.

The phylum is very old, with a continuous record since Cambrian time, as shown by certain bivalve and gastropod fossils. Perhaps no group has left more or better fossils than mollusks because their shells facilitated fossil formation. Mollusca is a well-organized phylum, the adults being quite distinct from those of other phyla, making it somewhat difficult to establish their relationships to other groups. The trochophore-like larva common in many marine mollusks, as well as their type of egg cleavage, indicate an affinity with the annelids. This view is supported by the recent discovery of the group Monoplacophora, which is segmented. Some mollusks also have a ladderlike nervous system similar to that of the turbellarian flatworms. Thus it is possible that both the annelids and the mollusks have diverged from a common platyhelminth form.

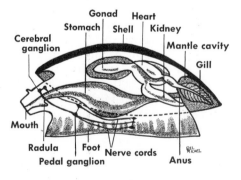

Figure 259. Hypothetical ancestral mollusk. This primitive mollusk type is supposed to fit structural ancestral pattern of all molluscan classes.

Relationship between the various mollusk classes is equally difficult, for each represents distinct evolutionary tendencies. Zoologists have tried to reconstruct a hypothetical primitive mollusk with features to fit the ancestor of all molluscan classes. Such a generalized ancestor (Figure 259) might have a body dorsally arched and bilaterally symmetrical, with calcareous shell; a strong, creeping muscular foot on the ventral side; a mantle cavity formed from the soft integument of the dorsal side; a simple digestive tube from front to rear; a pair of feather-shaped gills near the anus; and a pair of ganglia in the head with two nerve trunks at different levels. Amphineura *(Chiton)* is considered the most primitive molluscan class, although its fossil record dates from a more recent period than the other classes. Scaphopoda and Gastropoda both have a univalve shell and radula. Pelecypoda (bivalves) with their pointed foot and lack of head, eyes, or tentacles resemble the Scaphopoda. The highly advanced Cephalopoda (squids and octopods) seem isolated from the other classes but share some characteristics with the gastropods.

Mollusks are found in nearly all places that will support life, in all latitudes, and at altitudes up to 20,000 feet. Most are marine, living in shallow water, along the seashore, in the open sea, or at great depths. Some are found in fresh water, and some have been successful on land. The fossil evidence indicates that mollusks originated in the sea. Much of their evolution probably took place in littoral zones (along the shore) because such a region has an abundance of food, a variety of habitats, and a diversity of physical conditions. It is especially suitable for a group that stresses creeping and burrowing. The more mobile cephalopods are naturally pelagic (live in open water), but some live close to the bottom or near shore. Only gastropods have mastered land conditions.

Only the Gastropoda and the Pelecypoda left the sea and invaded the land and fresh water. These groups gradually became adapted to the conditions produced by tides and the reduced concentration of salt in estuaries. The mode of nutrition (filter feeding) of pelecypods restricted them to water. Many species are found in the estuaries of large rivers and are intermediate between the marine and fresh-water forms. Such mollusks tolerate a salinity between that of the sea and fresh water. Burrowing animals, such as mollusks, had a better chance to invade and tolerate the conditions of estuaries. In time estuarian forms became tolerant of fresh water and invaded the latter. The transformation of a marine pelecypod to a fresh-water type was not difficult, for both types breathe and feed in the same way. Among the gastropods, a vascular lining of the mantle cavity made possible the development of a lung. Only gastropods have actually invaded land because of their lung and other morphological changes. Whereas there are only a few genera of Pelecypoda in fresh water, gastropods have undergone an amazing adaptive radiation, especially on land. Terrestrial snails are mostly restricted in their range by humidity, by shelter from heat and light, and by the presence of lime in the soil. Many pulmonates have evolved an operculum for closing the apertures of their shells during hibernation or aestivation and can remain inactive for a long time. According to fossil records, pulmonate snails first invaded terrestrial habitats in the Carboniferous period. Gastropods usually have slow methods of dispersal, and the evolutionary factor of isolation (physical barriers) has operated to a greater extent with this group than with most other animals. Mutational forms had a better chance to become stabilized, because of fewer opportunities for hybridization.

Mollusks are most abundant and diverse of form in the tropics and subtropics. Here the most species are found, as well as the most strikingly beautiful color adaptations. Pelagic forms are usually colorless, whereas the nudibranchs may adopt the color of forms on which they feed (green algae, anemones, hydroids, etc.).

Life cycles are generally short, although some mollusks live for several years. Nudibranchs probably live only a year, oysters may live up to 10 years, *Unio* 12 years, fresh-water snails 4 to 5 years, squid *(Loligo)* up to 2 years, and giant squid 10 years (Spector).

In temperate and cold climates mollusks often hibernate in burrows, crevices, or mats of leaves. They withdraw into the shell and secrete a membrane (epiphragm) over the aperture, while body metabolism sinks to a low ebb.

CHARACTERISTICS

1. Body unsegmented (except in Monoplacophora) and typically bilaterally symmetrical (bilateral asymmetry in some)

2. External body with three typical divisions: an anterior head (absent in some) with mouth, appendages, and sense organs; a **ventral muscular foot** variously modified but chiefly for locomotion; and a dorsal **mantle** which usually secretes a shell (absent in some)

3. Body surface usually covered with ciliated epithelium bearing many mucosa glands and sensory nerve endings

4. Coelom reduced and represented mainly by the pericardium, gonadal cavity, and kidney

5. Digestive system complete with digestive glands and liver; with a rasping organ (**radula**) usually present

6. Circulatory system of heart, pericardial space and blood vessels; blood mostly colorless, with erythrocruorin restricted and hemocyanin more common

7. Respiration by gills, lungs, or direct

8. Excretion by one or two pairs of nephridia or a single nephridium opening internally into pericardium and externally onto body surface

9. Nervous system of paired **cerebral, pleural, pedal,** and **visceral ganglia,** with nerves; ganglia centralized in ring (Cephalopoda and Gastropoda)

10. Sense organs of touch, smell, taste, vision (in some), and statocysts for equilibrium

11. Reproduction dioecious or mono-ecious; one or two gonads with gona-ducts which may open into renal ducts or to exterior.

12. Fertilization external or internal

13. Spiral and determinate cleavage; trochophore-like larval form (**veliger**) in some

ECONOMIC IMPORTANCE

A group as large as the mollusks would naturally affect man in some way. As a food, oysters and clams are popular every-where, and snails are widely used in some areas. Pearl buttons are obtained from shells of bivalves. More than forty species of mollusks are suitable for this purpose. The Missouri and Mississippi river basins furnish material for most of this industry in the United States. In some regions supplies are becoming so depleted that attempts are being made to propagate them artificially. Pearls, both natural and cultured, are produced in the shells of clams and oysters, most of them in a marine oyster, *Meleagrina*, found around eastern Asia.

Brightly colored shells have been used as ornaments and also for utensils by primitive people in all ages. Purple snails (*Murex*) were used by the ancients for their chief source of dye. Cowries (brightly colored snails of the genus *Cypraea*) have been employed as money in the Far East and in the South Pacific.

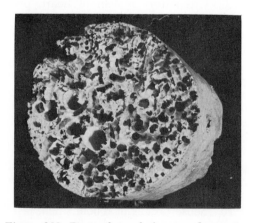

Figure 260. Piece of wood showing destructive burrows of shipworm, *Teredo*.

Some mollusks are destructive. The bur-rowing shipworm, *Teredo*, does great damage to wooden ships and wharves (Figure 260). *Teredo* has an elongated body with a pair of slender siphons on its posterior end. The anterior end of the animal has two movable valves by which the mollusk burrows into wood, sometimes as far as 3 or 4 feet. The siphons extend from its body to the water to provide oxy-gen and small particles of food as well as to discharge waste. Some of its food is in the wood which it excavates. To prevent the ravages of the shipworm, wharves are either creosoted or built of cement.

Snails and slugs are known to damage garden and other vegetation. In addition, snails often serve as intermediate hosts for serious parasites, such as the blood flukes (*Schistosoma*), liver flukes of sheep, and many others. *Urosalpinx* is second only to the sea star in destroying oysters.

CLASSES

The classes of mollusks are based on such features as type of shell, type of foot, and shape of shell. Five classes have been recognized for many years, but the dis-covery in 1952 of a few specimens of liv-ing mollusks two miles deep near the west coast of Mexico has caused a reap-praisal of the classes. These new mol-lusks (*Neopilina galatheae*) (Figure 261) are small, with a limpet-shaped (low and rounded) shell. They are bilaterally sym-metrical and have a complete digestive system, anterior mouth (with radula), stomach with crystalline style, two-branched liver, and posterior anus. Five pairs of gills are situated in rows on each side of the ventral foot. Internally there are five pairs of dorsoventral muscles, five pairs of nephridia, and five pairs of gill hearts. Sexes are separate, and sex cells from the gonad pass to the outside through nephridia. There is a well-de-veloped coelom and clearly marked in-**ternal segmentation.** The body is com-posed of five segments with three in the head. A 1957 appraisal of this "living fossil" suggested two possible taxonomic

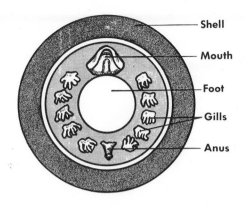

- Shell
- Mouth
- Foot
- Gills
- Anus

Figure 261. Schematic drawing of ventral view of monoplacophoran, *Neopilina*. These recently discovered mollusks, "living fossils," date back to more than 300 million years ago.

ranks. Some zoologists call it class Monoplacophora; others consider it an order (Monoplacophora) under class Amphineura. Anyway, we can no longer say that mollusks are unsegmented.

Class Amphineura (am'phi-neu"ra) (Gr. *amphi*, both, + *neuron*, nerve)—chitons. Elongated body with reduced head; bilaterally symmetrical; one order segmented; radula present; row of eight dorsal plates usually; large, flat ventral foot, which is absent in some; nervous system consisting of a ring around the mouth with two pairs of ventral longitudinal nerve cords; sexes usually separate, with a trochopore larva. Examples: *Chiton, Neopilina*.

Class Scaphopoda (ska-fop'o-da) (Gr. *skapha*, boat—elephant tusk shells. Body enclosed in a one-piece tubular shell open at both ends; conical foot; mouth with tentacles; head absent; mantle for respiration; sexes separate; trochophore larva. Example: *Dentalium*.

Class Gastropoda (gas-trop'o-da) (Gr. *gaster*, belly, + *pous*, foot)—snails and others. Body usually asymmetrical in a coiled shell (shell absent in some); head well developed, with radula; foot large and flat; mantle modified into a lung or gill; nervous system with cerebral, pleural, pedal, and visceral ganglia; dioecious or monoecious with or without pelagic larva. Examples: *Littorina, Physa, Helix*.

Class Pelecypoda (pel-e-cyp'o-da) (Gr. *pelekus*, hatchet, + *pous*, foot)—bivalves. Body enclosed in a two-lobed mantle; shell of two lateral valves of variable size and form, with dorsal hinge; no head, but mouth with labial palps; no eyes (except a few) or radula; foot usually wedge shaped; gills platelike; sexes usually separate with trochophore or glochidial larva. Examples: *Anodonta, Teredo, Venus*.

Class Cephalopoda (ceph'a-lop"o-da) (Gr. *kephale*, head, + *pous*, foot)—squids and octopuses. Body with a shell, often reduced or absent; head well developed with eyes and a radula; foot modified into arms or tentacles; siphon present; nervous system of well-developed ganglia, centralized to form a brain; sexes separate with direct development. Examples: *Loligo, Octopus, Sepia*.

REPRESENTATIVE TYPES
CLASS AMPHINEURA

The class Amphineura is the most primitive of all mollusks, having a fossil record extending back to the Ordovician period of the Paleozoic era. The members of this strictly marine group have an elongated, bilaterally symmetrical body, covered by a mantle bearing calcareous spicules embedded in a cuticle and often with transverse plates. A flattened foot may cover most of the ventral surface but is reduced in some. A mouth and anus at the ends and a reduced head without tentacles or eyes are characteristic of the

Figure 262. Dorsal view of *Chiton*.

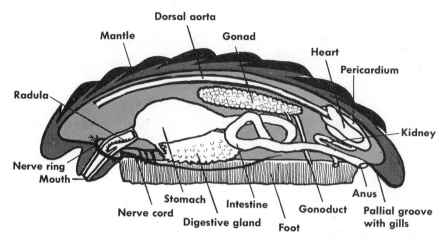

Figure 263. Longitudinal section of *Chiton,* showing internal anatomy.

class. Their name is derived from the two pairs of longitudinal nerve cords (pedal and pallial) which are connected anteriorly to a ring around the mouth region. There are two groups or orders—Polyplacophora (chitons) and Aplacophora (Solenogastres). If the newly found monoplacophorans are considered an order, then there are three groups in the class Amphineura.

The chitons (Figure 262) are the most numerous of the Amphineura. They are elongated, somewhat flattened animals with a convex dorsal surface which bears eight articulating limy plates or valves that overlap posteriorly. In early fossil forms the plates did not overlap. Most of them are only 1 or 2 inches long, and the largest (*Cryptochiton*) rarely exceeds 8 to 10 inches. A marginal **girdle** formed from the mantle surrounds or covers the central mass of plates. It may contain calcareous spines and scales which give it a shaggy appearance. The mantle, which secretes the plates, covers the dorsal and lateral surfaces, and a broad muscular foot covers most of the ventral surface very much like that of a snail. The **pallial groove** between the foot and mantle surrounds the animal. The head on the underside is separated from the foot by a narrow groove and bears the mouth, but it has no eyes or tentacles. Posteriorly the **anus** is found in the pallial groove.

The internal structure of *Chiton* (Figure 263) is made up of an **alimentary canal,** with a radula in the floor of the mouth cavity, two pairs of salivary glands, a short pharynx, a thin-walled stomach, and coiled intestine; a **circulatory system** of a heart (one ventricle and two auricles), surrounded by a pericardium in the posterodorsal region of the body, an anterior aorta, and two large sinuses; an **excretory system** of two long, folded kidneys (nephridia), which carry waste away from the pericardial cavity to the exterior; a **respiratory system** of gills (4 to 80) or ctenidia, which lie in the bottom of the pallial groove; a **nervous system** of two pairs of longitudinal nerve cords (with few or no ganglia) and connected in the buccal region by a cerebral commissure; a **sensory system** of shell eyes (in some) on the surface of the shell, a pair of osphradia (sense organs for sampling water) near the anus, and scattered small sense organs; and a **reproductive system** of a single gonad (of either sex) between the aorta and intestine, with paired gonoducts that open to the outside.

In general, chitons resemble the hypothetical ancestral mollusk described earlier. There are some differences, such as the gill arrangement, for the chiton usually has many, the ancestral prototype only a single pair.

Chitons are sluggish and creep slowly

350

on their flat foot. They live upon seaweed or other plant life along the sea floor or shore. Their broad feet can adhere to rocky surfaces along protected shores. A favorite depression in a rock that is exposed at low tide may be used for countless generations by chitons. Some attach to the underside of rocks. Chitons are mostly intertidal invertebrates, although some have been taken at great depths. Molested, they may roll up like a pill bug, because the plate joints are flexible. Females lay their eggs in masses or strings of jelly; fertilization is external. In the West Indies, the natives cook them ("sea beef"). *Nuttallina* and *Cryptochiton* are familiar along the west coast; the tiny *Chaetopleura* is one of the commonest east coast forms.

The Solenogastres (order Aplacophora) are wormlike forms with no foot or shell (except minute spicules in mantle). The body is completely enclosed in the mantle, the edges of which meet in a groove under the body. The digestive tract is straight and some have a radula. The vascular system is open (sinuses) and hemoglobin corpuscles may be present. Gills are restricted to a posterior cavity. The animals are hermaphroditic; sex cells are discharged into the pericardium and carried

out by the nephridia. The nervous system resembles that of the chiton. The status of the Solenogastres has been doubtful, some authorities maintaining that they are closer to the worms than to mollusks. Others think they represent Amphineura whose development has been arrested, or a sort of neoteny. They are usually found in fairly deep water and live on hydroids and corals. *Neomenia* and *Chaetoderma* are common species along the Atlantic coast.

CLASS SCAPHOPODA

These mollusks are commonly called the tooth shells or elephant tusk shells because of their resemblance to those structures. They have a slender, elongated body covered with the mantle which secretes a tubelike shell open at both ends. A burrowing foot protrudes through the larger end of the shell. The mouth, which is near the foot, is provided with a radula and contractile tentacles which are sensory and prehensile. Respiration takes place through the mantle, and the circulatory system consists merely of sinuses which are distributed among the different organs. They have two saclike kidneys which open to the outside near the anus. Their nervous system has the same basic

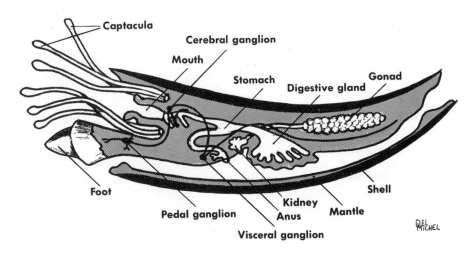

Figure 264. Internal anatomy of *Dentalium*. In nature it buries its head end in the sand, leaving posterior end projecting up into the water. Captacula (L. *captare*, to catch) are ciliated, contractile tentacles which are prehensile and used in capturing microscopic organisms.

plan as other mollusks. Members of this class are marine and live embedded in sand in shallow water or sometimes at great depths, and they feed upon animals and plants of microscopic size. The sexes are separate, and the larva is a trochophore. After developing a mantle, the larva sinks to the bottom. *Dentalium* (Figure 264) is a familiar example along our eastern seashore. Few living Scaphopoda are more than 3 inches long, but some fossil forms reached a length of 2 feet.

CLASS GASTROPODA

Among the mollusks, the class Gastropoda is by far the largest and most successful. It is made up of members of such diversity that there is no single general term in our language that can apply to them as a group. Their scientific name is derived from the Greek *gaster,* belly, and *podos,* foot. They include snails, limpets, slugs, whelks, conchs, periwinkles, and others. The group includes animals that basically are bilaterally symmetrical, but by torsion the visceral mass has become asymmetrical. A shell, when present, is always of one piece (univalve) and often coiled (some are cap shaped and uncoiled). The class has become adjusted to habitats on land and in fresh water, as well as in salt water. Their original habitat, as revealed by fossils, was the ocean. Land gastropods are among the largest group of land invertebrates. Their range of habitat is large. In the sea they are common in the littoral zones, at great depths, and some are even pelagic (free swimming). Some are adapted to brackish water and some to fresh water. On land they are restricted by such factors as the mineral content of the soil and extremes of temperature, dryness, and acidity. Some have been found at great altitudes and even in polar regions. Snails have all sorts of habitats—woodlands, pastures, small pools or large bodies of water, under rocks, in mosses, on cliffs, under-

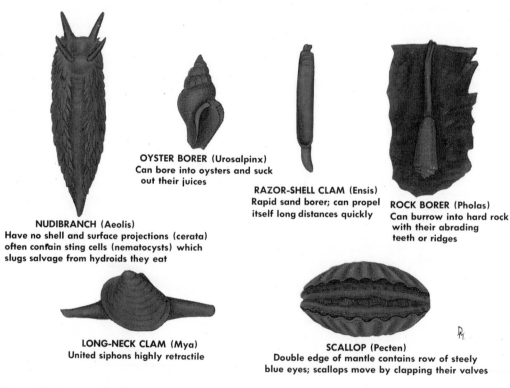

OYSTER BORER (Urosalpinx)
Can bore into oysters and suck out their juices

RAZOR-SHELL CLAM (Ensis)
Rapid sand borer; can propel itself long distances quickly

ROCK BORER (Pholas)
Can burrow into hard rock with their abrading teeth or ridges

NUDIBRANCH (Aeolis)
Have no shell and surface projections (cerata) often contain sting cells (nematocysts) which slugs salvage from hydroids they eat

LONG-NECK CLAM (Mya)
United siphons highly retractile

SCALLOP (Pecten)
Double edge of mantle contains row of steely blue eyes; scallops move by clapping their valves

Figure 265. Some mollusks with unusual habits or structures.

ground, in trees, and in fairly warm springs.

Gastropods range from microscopic forms to giant whelklike, marine snails that exceed 2 feet. Most of them are ½ inch to 3 inches. Some fossil gastropods were 5 or 6 feet long. Their life span is not well known but some live from 5 to 15 years.

Gastropods are usually sluggish, sedentary animals because most of them have heavy shells and slow locomotor organs. Some are specialized for climbing, swimming, or burrowing. Shells are their chief defense, although they are also protected by coloration and by secretive habits. Some are distasteful to other animals, and a few, such as *Strombus*, can deal an active blow with the foot which bears a sharp operculum. However, they are eaten by birds, beetles, small mammals, fish, and other predators. Serving as intermediate hosts for many kinds of parasites, snails are often harmed by the larval stages of the parasites.

Most gastropods live on plants or plant debris. Many marine forms live on seaweed and algae which they scrape from the rocks. A few live on detritus strained from the water. Many are scavengers, living on dead and decayed flesh; others are carnivorous, preying upon clams, oysters, and worms. Some carnivores are provided with an extensible proboscis for drilling holes in other mollusks to eat the soft parts. To obtain and rasp food, snails have a **radula**, which is a long ribbon beset with two rows of chitinous teeth and attached at each end by muscles. It works back and forth like a hand saw over a cartilage out of a pharyngeal cecum. The arrangement, shape, and number of teeth are useful in taxonomic determinations.

The phenomenon of **torsion** (Figure 266) which occurs in the early embryo sets gastropods off from all other mollusks. The early gastropod embryo is symmetrical, with anterior mouth and posterior anus—which is probably the primitive ancestral condition. Rather abruptly in the veliger stage there is a 180 degree counterclockwise rotation of the visceral mass

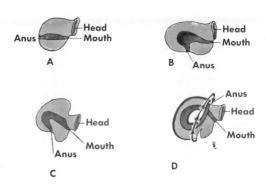

Figure 266. Body torsion in snail. Early larva is symmetrical, with mouth and anus at opposite ends of body, **A**. Most snails, however, undergo asymmetrical growth in which anus shifts downward, **B**, then forward and comes to lie near the mouth, **C**. Later, anus and other parts rotate upward and lie above head, **D**. This rotation of visceral mass counterclockwise through angle of 180 degrees is due to more rapid growth of left side of visceral mass. Spiral winding of shell and visceral mass of snail is different process from body torsion described. Spiral coiling of visceral mass is due partly to atrophy of original left-handed organs, causing mass to coil around an axis at right angles to torsion axis, giving a more compact form and reduced diameter to shell and contents. In left-handed (sinistral) snails, organs of left side are preserved whereas those on right atrophy.

upon the head and foot which results in the typical gastropod asymmetry; i.e., the anus, mantle, and gill (all of which formerly lay posteriorly) are now placed back of the head. There are two phases to the movement, which results in torsion. First, the posterior anus shifts forward with the ventral flexure of the intestine to lie below the mouth. Second, the anus, its mantle cavity, and other visceral parts rotate upward and come to lie above and to the right of the head, and the organs, which are shifted from the left side to the right, tend to disappear. There are varying degrees of torsion among the different groups of gastropods.

Torsion must be distinguished from the coiling or spiral winding of the shell, as they are separate processes. The coiling of the shell and visceral mass may occur simultaneously with the torsion process or earlier in some cases. The coiling may be caused by differential growth and muscular contraction so that a corkscrew-shaped cone is produced at right angles to the axis of the torsion. Coiling is not found in some snails or else is suppressed in some way (limpets). In nudibranchs a coiled shell is found in the embryo but is absent in the adult. The reasons for torsion are obscure, but it has been suggested that having the gills forward made better respiration possible. The direction of coiling (right- or left-handed) of the shell is determined by the orientation of the early cleavage spindle, and its heredity is unique in that the character of the coiling is determined in the egg before fertilization, by the action of the mother's genes.

Major groups of gastropods

There are three major groups of gastropods which some authorities call subclasses and others call orders. Each subclass or order is subdivided on the basis of distinctive characteristics.

Prosobranchia (subclass or order). In these gastropods the gills (ctenidia) are located anteriorly in front of the heart. Another name for this group is Streptoneura, which refers to the twisted nature of the nervous system (often in a figure eight). They have two tentacles, and the sexes are separate. An operculum is nearly always present. The Prosobranchia are divided into two groups or orders: Aspidobranchia, with a rather diffused nervous system and usually two auricles in the heart, and Pectinibranchia, with concentrated nervous system and one auricle. These two groups contain most of the marine snails and a few of the freshwater ones. They range in size from the periwinkles and small limpets (*Patella, Fissurella*) to the giant conch (*Strombus*), the largest univalve in America. Familiar examples of prosobranchs are the abalone (*Haliotis*), which has an ear-shaped shell; the giant whelk (*Busycon*) (Figure 267), which lays its eggs in double-edge, disk-shaped capsules attached to a cord a yard long; the common periwinkle (*Littorina*), introduced from Europe where it is widely used as food; the slipper or boot shell (*Crepidula*), which has an internal limy diaphragm;

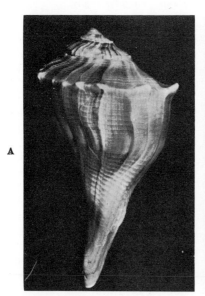

A   B

Figure 267. A, Shell of large marine snail or whelk, *Busycon*. **B,** Dry egg case of *Busycon*. This is secreted by a special gland. Disk-shaped egg cases are strung close together along a cord and each case contains many eggs.

the oyster drill (*Urosalpinx*), which bores into oysters and sucks out their juices; the rock shell (*Murex*), of which a European species was used for making the royal purple of the ancient Romans; and the fresh-water forms (*Goniobasis, Paludina*).

Opisthobranchia (subclass or order). In these the gill is displaced to the right side or rear of the body. Two pairs of tentacles are usually found, and the shell is reduced or absent. All are monoecious. They are all marine, most of them shallow-water forms, hiding under stones and seaweed; a few are pelagic. There are two groups or orders: Tectibranchia, with gill and shell usually present, and Nudibranchia, in which there is no shell or true gill but adaptive gills are present around the anus. The opisthobranchs are an odd assemblage of mollusks which includes sea slugs, sea hares, sea butterflies, canoe shells, and others. Among the Tectibranchia are the sea hare (*Tethys* or *Aplysia*), which grows to be more than 1 foot long and has large earlike anterior tentacles and vestigial shell; and the pteropods, or sea butterflies (*Carderia, Clione*), with the foot modified into fins for swimming; thus they are pelagic and form a part of plankton fauna.

The Nudibranchia are represented by the sea slugs, which are often brightly colored and carnivorous in their eating habits. The plumed sea slug (*Aeolis*), which lives on sea anemones and hydroids, often draws the color of its prey into the elongated papillae (cerata) which covers its back. It also salvages the nematocysts of the hydroids for its own use.

Pulmonata (subclass or order). This extensive group includes the land and fresh-water snails and slugs (and a few brackish or salt-water forms). They have a lung instead of a gill, one or two pairs of tentacles, and a single, monoecious gonad. The aquatic species have one pair of nonretractile tentacles, at the base of which are the eyes; land forms have two pairs of tentacles, the posterior pair bearing the eyes. Among the thousands of land species the most familiar American forms are *Helix, Polygyra, Succinea, Ang-*

uispira, Zonitoides, Limax, and *Agriolimax.* Aquatic forms are represented by *Helisoma, Viviparus, Campeloma, Lymnaea,* and *Physa.* The latter is a left-handed (sinistral) snail; that is, the snail coils to the left when viewed from the apex. Dextral shells (coiling to the right) are far more common among snails than sinistral. Genetical investigation has shown that the direction of coiling is always determined before the egg is fertilized.

Common snail

Structure. Any of the larger land forms may be taken as a type for study. Some of our most common terrestrial snails belong to genus *Polygyra,* but an imported European snail, *Helix aspersa,* is often studied in this country because of its size and the ease with which it can be collected. In some of our southern states it is known as the garden snail.

The snail has a well-developed **head** which bears two pairs of retractile **tentacles,** a pair of **eyes** on the longer tentacles, and **mouth** (Figures 268 to 270). The tentacles are hollow and can be inverted, while the eyes are adapted for light perception. A muscular **foot** is attached to the head, and the visceral mass forms a dorsal hump, on top of which is the **shell.** The visceral mass is surrounded by the **mantle,** which also secretes the shell. The mantle cavity is just beneath the mantle. When the soft parts are exposed they are protected by a mucous membrane. Other than the mouth, openings to the exterior include the **genital pore** on the right side near the mouth and the **anus** and **respiratory pore,** both located in the margin of the mantle at the edge of the shell. By means of the columella muscle, all soft parts can be withdrawn into the shell.

The **digestive** system is made up of the **mouth,** a **pharynx** bearing a **radula** (Figure 269), an **esophagus,** a thin-walled **crop,** a **stomach,** a coiled **intestine,** and the **anus.** A pair of salivary glands opens into the pharynx, and a large digestive diverticulum (sometimes called liver) high in

Figure 268. A, Common land snail, *Anguispira*, extended and travelling. B, Common garden snail, or slug, *Limax*.

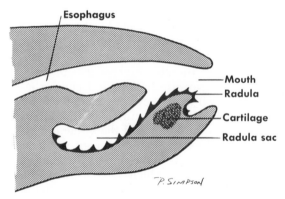

Figure 269. Median section through head and mouth of pond snail, showing radula (diagrammatic). With use of muscles, radula is worked backward and forward for rasping food. Radula is usually distinctive for each species and is useful for taxonomic studies.

the spiral shell leads to the stomach.

The **circulatory** system has a **heart** (one auricle and one ventricle) and arteries which deliver blood to the organs. In some snails (*Planorbis*) the blood contains erythrocruorin. For aeration of blood, land snails have a **lung** which is the modified mantle cavity provided with a network of blood vessels. Air is drawn in through the respiratory pore.

The **excretory** system is composed of a **nephridium** (kidney), which removes waste from the pericardial space and carries it to the mantle cavity.

The **nervous system** in snails is more condensed than it is in mussels, for the various ganglia (cerebral, buccal, pedal, and visceral) are concentrated around the pharyngeal region. Nerves from these ganglia run to the body organs. The sensory organs include the eyes and olfactory organs on the tentacles, a pair of **statocysts** for equilibration near the pedal ganglia, and tactile and chemical sensory organs in the head and foot.

These land snails are monoecious, and the reproductive gland, **ovotestis**, is located high in the shell surrounded by a coil of the liver. The ovotestis produces both eggs and sperm. From the ovotestis the **hermaphroditic duct** connects to the **albumin gland**, which furnishes albumin to the eggs. The hermaphroditic duct carries both eggs and sperm. Where the albumin gland joins the duct, two tubes, often imperfectly separated, are given off— the **vas deferens**, which conducts sperm to the **penis** at the **genital opening** and the **oviduct**, which leads to the **vagina** and also empties at the common genital opening.

356

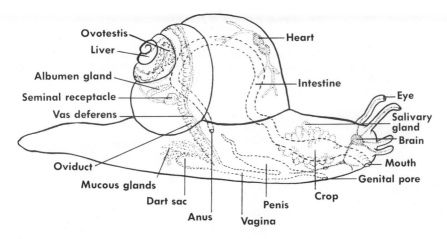

Figure 270. Internal structure of land snail.

To the vagina is connected the duct of the **seminal receptacle** as well as the **oviducal glands** and the **dart sac.** A slender flagellum by which sperm are formed into spermatophores is connected to the penis. Although this snail is hermaphroditic, cross-fertilization is the rule. In copulation each member inserts its penis into the vagina of the other and transfers a spermatophore. After separating, each deposits its eggs in shallow burrows in the ground, usually in damp places. Development is direct, and the young emerge as small snails.

Natural history and behavior. Snails are usually most active at night, when they glide by wavelike contractions of the foot muscle. A slime gland is located at the anterior end of the foot and deposits a mucous film over which the snail moves. Locomotion is very slow, a "snail's pace," and may not exceed ten to twelve feet per hour, although some snails are known to travel faster.

Their food consists of green vegetation which they rasp off by means of their radulas. They are partial to damp situations and by day are often found under patches of leaves or in burrows. When threatened with very dry weather, they form a temporary covering, or epiphragm, of mucus and limy secretions which covers the shell aperture. Some snails have a permanent **operculum** which covers the aperture when the body is in the shell.

CLASS PELECYPODA (LAMELLIBRANCHIATA)

This class includes the mussels, oysters, scallops, shipworms, and clams, found in both fresh water and salt water. Many of them burrow in the sand and mud; others crawl on or attach themselves to solid objects. The group includes more than 7,000 species, widely distributed over the world. The size range is from 1 mm. to 1 meter (giant clam); most are 1 to 2 inches. Most of them are specialized for a sedentary life and are provided with a filtering mechanism for obtaining their food.

The fresh-water mussel is often studied because of its typical structural pattern and the ease with which it can be procured. *Unio* and *Lampsilis* are similar to *Anodonta* and are often used in its place, for there are only minor differences among them.

Anodonta—fresh-water mussel

External structure. The shell is somewhat oval when examined from the side, being rounded at the anterior end and more pointed posteriorly (Figure 273). It is composed of symmetrical **right** and **left valves** which are thicker on the dorsal side. They are held together along the inner dorsal surface by an elastic hinge

HOW A PEARL IS FORMED

Parasite or foreign object becomes embedded between shell
valve and mantle edge; this causes mantle epithelium to secrete
pearly layers around object; pearl may later break through
mantle epithelium into mantle cavity or may become
attached to a valve

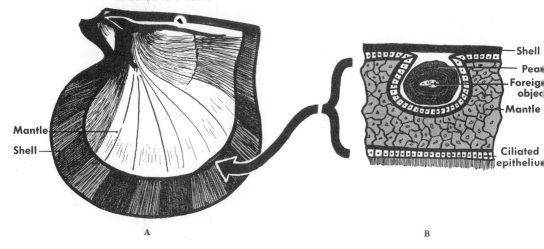

Figure 271. Pearl oyster, *Margaritifera*. **A**, Interior of valve with arrow pointing to site of
pearl formation. **B**, Enlarged section of mantle with pearl in position.

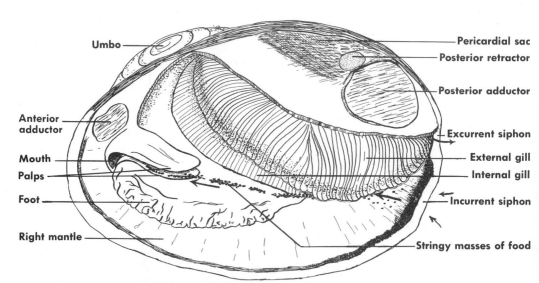

Food particles with sand and other debris carried in with
water stream through incurrent siphon by cilia on gills;
small particles of food entangled on stringy masses by mucous
secretions of gills and carried by cilia on gills and palps to
mouth; sand and other indigestible particles drop into mantle
cavity and are removed by ciliary action

Figure 272. Feeding mechanism of clam. Left shell and mantle removed.

358

ligament which draws the valves together dorsally, causing them to gape ventrally. A rounded projection, the **umbo,** is the oldest part of the valve. Surrounding the umbo are concentric lines of growth indicating the intervals between successive growth stages. Several lines may be formed in one season, some more prominent than others. In some forms, but not in *Anodonta,* there may be dorsal hinge **teeth** to help hold the valves together.

The shell consists of three layers: (1) the external horny **periostracum** (of an organic substance, conchyolin) which is often absent on the umbo; (2) the middle **prismatic** layer of crystalline calcium carbonate; and (3) the inner (lamellar) layer of iridescent **nacre,** or mother-of-pearl, which is formed of many thin layers of calcium carbonate. The nacre is thickest at the umbo, thinnest at the margin. In

the formation of the shell the nacre is produced by the whole surface of the mantle and the other two layers by its edge. The shell grows in surface size by additions at the margin and in thickness by additions within.

When a foreign substance, such as a grain of sand or larva of a worm, becomes enclosed between the mantle and the shell, the mantle secretes successive layers of nacre around it (Figure 271). The pearl thus produced is made up of concentric layers of calcium carbonate surrounding the irritating substance. Pearls are cultured by opening the oyster, inserting small particles into the mantle, and replacing the oyster, in a wire cage, back in the ocean. A few years later the cage is lifted and the oyster and pearl removed.

Internal structure. Inside the shell (Fig-

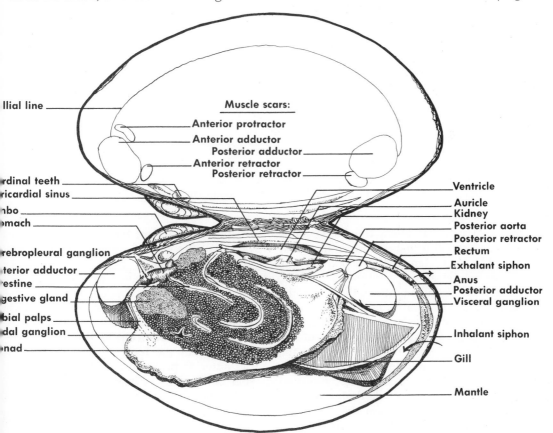

Figure 273. Structure of clam. Visceral mass shown in sagittal section.

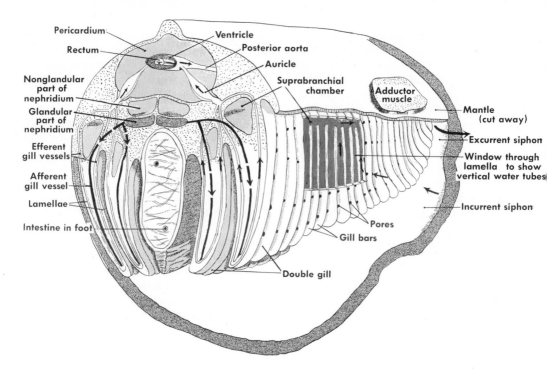

Figure 274. Anterolateral view of cross-section through heart region of clam to show relations of circulatory and respiratory systems (diagrammatic). Arrows indicate direction of blood flow and water currents. Scheme of blood circulation: ventricle pumps blood forward through anterior aorta to sinuses of foot and most of viscera and backward through posterior aorta to sinuses of rectum and mantle; blood from mantle returns to auricles, and from other organs to kidneys (nephridia); blood from kidneys to gills; then to auricles; from auricles to ventricle. Scheme of water circulation to aerate gills and transport food: water drawn in through incurrent siphon by cilia; food particles trapped in stringy masses of mucus from gills and carried by cilia to labial palps; water passes through gill pores into water tubes which run into suprabranchial chambers; water in its passage gives up oxygen to blood of gills, picks up carbon dioxide, feces, and sex cells, and finally discharges through excurrent siphon to outside.

ure 272) is a soft mass, the body, made up of a **visceral mass** and a muscular **foot.** The visceral mass is attached dorsally to the **mantle** and is continuous with it. Each lobe of the mantle adheres to the inner surface of a valve, and together they form the **mantle cavity** which encloses the entire body mass. The outer edge of the mantle attachment to the shell is the **pallial line.** The mantle secretes carbonate of lime which is added to the edge and inner surface of the shell. Posteriorly the mantle is modified to form the dorsal **excurrent siphon** and the slightly fringed ventral **incurrent siphon** which regulate the intake and outgo of water. Cilia on

the inner surfaces of the siphons and mantle direct the flow of water over two pairs of **gills (ctenidia).**

On the inner surface of a clean valve are conspicuous scars made by the attachments of various muscles. The **anterior** and **posterior adductors** draw the valves together; the **anterior** and **posterior retractors** pull the foot into the shell; and the **anterior protractor** aids in the extension of the foot (Figure 273).

The **digestive system** is made up of (1) the **mouth,** between the two pairs of fleshy **labial palps** which are provided with cilia to carry food into the mouth; (2) a short **esophagus** leading to (3) a dilated **stomach,** which receives digestive enzymes from the large **digestive gland** (liver); (4) the coiled **intestine;** (5) the dorsal **rectum** surrounded by the heart and pericardium; and (6) the **anus,** which opens near the dorsal excurrent siphon. Within the rectum is a longitudinal fold, the **typhlosole,** which increases the surface area of that portion of the alimentary canal. The food of the mussel is made up of microscopic plants and animals which are carried into the animal in the water by the incurrent siphon. As the water passes over and through the gills, the food particles are filtered out and entangled in the mucous secretions of the gills and mantle. Stringy masses of mucus and food are propelled by the cilia through the grooves between the palps and directed into the mouth. (See Figure 272.) In addition to extracellular digestion, amebocytes digest (intracellularly) and transport food products to the tissue cells. A cecum opening into the stomach may secrete a gelatinous rod (crystalline style) which is the source of a starch-digesting enzyme.

The **circulatory** system (Figure 274) is an open one and consists of a heart, arteries, sinuses, and veins. Water, however, cannot enter the system. The heart, which lies in the pericardial cavity, is made up of two auricles and a ventricle and beats at the rate of 6 times per minute. Blood is pumped through an **anterior aorta** to the foot and most of the viscera and through a **posterior aorta** to the rectum and mantle. Part of the blood is oxygenated in the mantle and returned to the ventricle through the auricles; the other part circulates through sinuses, passes in a vein to the kidneys, thence to the gills for oxygenation, and back to the auricles. Carbon dioxide and other wastes are carried to the gills and kidneys for elimination. The blood is colorless and contains nucleated ameboid corpuscles.

Respiration is carried on by both the mantle and the gills. A pair of gills (**ctenidia**) hangs down on each side of the foot. Each ctenidium is formed of two walls (**lamellae**) (Figure 275) joined together at their ventral margins. Each lamella contains many vertical **gill filaments** strengthened by chitinous rods. Water enters the gills through innumerable small **ostia** in the walls and is propelled by ciliary action. Partitions between the lamellae divide the gill internally into many vertical **water tubes,**

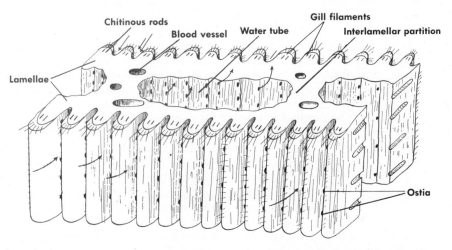

Figure 275. Section through portion of clam gill, showing relation of lamellae and water tubes. Cilia on gill surface draw water through small pores into tubes which carry it up to suprabranchial chambers and out excurrent siphon. Blood vessels in partitions bring blood close to oxygen supply in water. Females use water tubes of external gills as brood pouches for developing glochidia larvae during certain seasons.

which carry water upward (dorsally) into a common **suprabranchial chamber** and through it posteriorly to the excurrent siphon. Blood vessels or spaces in the interlamellar partitions are used for exchange of gases. The water tubes in the female double as brood pouches for the eggs and larvae during the breeding season. The different orders of Pelecypoda are based upon the types of gills they have.

Excretion is performed by two U-shaped **kidneys** just below the pericardium. Each kidney consists of an opening from the pericardial space into a ciliated tube which in turn leads to a bladder. The bladder empties into the suprabranchial chamber. The kidneys remove waste from both the blood (which circulates through the kidney network) and the pericardial space.

Coordination is effected by a **nervous system** of several ganglia scattered throughout the body in pairs (Figure 273). These include the **cerebropleural ganglia** near the mouth, the **pedal ganglia** in the foot, and the **visceral ganglia** just below the posterior adductor muscle. The members of each pair are linked by a commissure. Also, the three kinds of ganglia are joined to each other by connectives. Nerves lead from the ganglia to the organs. **Sensory** organs are not well developed, although light-detecting organs occur in the siphon margins, tactile organs along the mantle margins, a pair of **statocysts** for equilibrium in the foot, and an **osphradium** of yellow epithelial cells over each visceral ganglion. The osphradia may be used to test the chemical nature of incoming water.

The sexes are separate. **Reproductive organs** are much-branched, lobate masses, located around the intestinal coils of the visceral mass just above the foot. The vasa deferentia in the male or the oviduct in the female open into the suprabranchial chamber near the openings to the kidneys. There are no copulatory organs or accessory glands.

Development. The sperm cells are discharged into the suprabranchial chamber

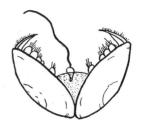

Figure 276. Glochidium or larval form of freshwater clam. When larva is released from brood pouch of mother, it may become attached to a fish by clamping its valves closed. It remains as a parasite on the fish for several weeks. (Size, about 0.3 mm.)

by the vas deferens and escape through the dorsal siphon to be carried in the water to a female. Eggs are retained in the body. When they are discharged by the oviduct into the suprabranchial chamber, they pass into the water tubes of the gills, which enlarge to form brood chambers (**marsupia**). Here the eggs are fertilized by sperm carried in through the ventral siphon. The fertilized egg, or zygote, undergoes cleavage, passes through blastula and gastrula stages, and forms a larva called the **glochidium** (Figure 276). In the brood chambers, the larvae may live on the epithelial cells of the gills during incubation. The time of fertilization varies with different species; in *Anodonta* it usually occurs in August. The glochidium has two valves (only one in the embryo at first) which are closed by an adductor muscle. The glochidia of *Anodonta* bear ventral hooks on their valves and a **larval thread** between the valves (absent in some species). The glochidia are discharged into the water through the excurrent siphon and are swept along by the water currents, or they may sink to the bottom, for they cannot swim. When they come into contact with the gills of a passing fish they attach themselves by snapping their valves closed. The larvae encyst and live as parasites on the fish for eight to twelve weeks. During this time they develop into miniature clams and the cysts break to release them. They then sink to the bottom where they begin their existence as independent clams. This larval behavior of hitchhiking helps distribute a form whose locomotion is very limited.

Behavior and natural history. Mussels move by extending the muscular foot anteriorly between the valves into the mud or sand. Blood flow swells the end of the foot and anchors it. Then longitudinal muscles in the foot contract and the clam is pulled forward. In lagoons and cutoffs from the main streams, the trails clams make through the mud can easily be seen. When the mussels are not moving, their behavior is restricted to the opening and closing of the two siphons which are sensitive to light, touch, and other stimuli. When disturbed in the vertical position, mussels often fall upon their sides.

Because of the composition of their shells, mussels are found in very "hard" water or water rich in limy salts. This factor of salt content often determines their abundance or scarcity.

For many years studies have been made of oysters—their habits, enemies, best habitats, food, and means of cultivation. Extensive oyster beds have been cultivated along our Atlantic coast and to some extent along the Pacific coast. Some of these beds are world famous for fine oysters. The larval forms (spats) swim about for two weeks before settling down to attach themselves to some hard surface. Before the larvae settle they are often netted and transported to desirable beds where they are provided with stones or cement for attachment. It takes about four years for an oyster to grow to commercial size. More than 400,000 tons are taken in the waters of the United States each year.

The evolution of the Pelecypoda has centered mainly around their feeding mechanism and the development of the ctenidia or gills. They have evolved a form of filter feeding which more and more involves the assistance of the ctenidia. Primitive forms, such as *Nucula*, had very small ctenidia but very elongated and ciliated palps which conveyed the food to the mouth, but more advanced pelecypods had larger ctenidia which directed ciliary currents with food of small organisms to the small palps which in turn passed it to the mouth. Thus the ctenidia have come to serve the double function of respiration and food collecting. However, such a specialized feeding mechanism imposed certain limitations on pelecypods, such as a

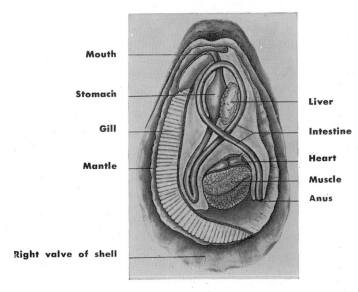

Mouth

Stomach

Gill

Mantle

Liver

Intestine

Heart

Muscle

Anus

Right valve of shell

Figure 277. Internal structure of oyster, *Crassostrea (Ostrea) virginica*, with left mantle and body wall removed (diagrammatic).

loss of a radula, poor cephalization, and a restriction to a water habitat.

The class Pelecypoda shows interesting adaptive radiation, especially with reference to one of their most important morphological units, the foot. Perhaps the most common method of locomotion is burrowing through sand and mud (*Venus, Anodonta*), but the creeping mode of locomotion is perhaps the primitive type and is represented by a few forms (*Solemya, Leptor*). Other pelecypods can swim (*Pecten, Lima*), leap over surfaces (*Yoldia*), climb up a surface (*Kellia*) bore or burrow into hard substances (*Pholas, Teredo*), and become attached by a byssus thread (*Mytilus*), or to rocks by a secretion (*Ostrea*).

Other members of class Pelecypoda

There are many species of clams other than *Anodonta* found in our fresh-water streams and ponds. Some of the more common ones are *Unio, Quadrula*, and *Lampsilis*. Some of them prefer a quiet pond or pool, but others are partial to moderately swift water. Those found in still water tend to have thinner shells. Clams found in our bigger lakes often have diurnal migratory habits, coming from the deeper water during the night and wandering about the shallow water near the shore. Early in daytime they migrate back to the deeper waters.

Belonging to this same class are the shipworms (*Teredo*) already mentioned. Some of the marine clams, such as *Pecten*, have the interesting habit of swimming by clapping their shells together and ejecting a stream of water. One pelecypod of great interest is the rock-drilling *Pholas* which manages to drill into fairly soft rock by means of its roughened shell.

Other marine forms of this class are *Mytilus*, which attaches itself to solid objects by secreting numerous byssal threads and is found hanging in masses on wharfs and rocks; *Venus*, or quahog, which is large with an oval shell and is widely used for food; *Sima*, also a swimming clam with a fringe of long tentacles along the mantle edge; *Nucula*, one of the most primitive living members of the class, with small ctenidia and large labial palps; and *Mya*, or long-necked clam, which is esteemed for chowders on our eastern coast, and is provided with long siphons.

Many members of this class have a trochophore-like larva, the **veliger**. In this form the larva swims about for a time, and, after acquiring a shell gland, sinks to the bottom of the water to become a bivalve. Because of the many hazards in their life cycles, most of the mollusks produce an enormous number of eggs. It is said that the oyster, for example, may produce more than 50,000,000 eggs in a single season.

CLASS CEPHALOPODA

This class is far more advanced than any other class of Mollusca and in some respects more advanced than any other invertebrates. All are marine and they include the squids, octopuses, nautiluses, devilfish, and cuttlefish. They derive their name from the Greek *kephale*, head, and *podos*, foot. This derivation describes one of their most unusual features, namely, the concentration of the foot in the head region. The edges of the foot are drawn out into arms and tentacles which bear sucking discs for seizing prey. Part of the foot (epipodium) is modified to form the funnel for carrying water from the mantle cavity. The group goes back to the Cambrian period, with remarkable fossil records. The largest invertebrate known is the giant squid (*Architeuthis*) which may be up to 50 feet long. *Rossia*, a squid on the west coast, is only 1½ inches long.

Mollusks appear to have differentiated along three lines of life habits. Bottom-dwelling filter feeders with a slow locomotion gave rise to pelecypods; herbivorous or carnivorous feeders with slow creeping movements evolved into gastropods; whereas a third group of active swimming predators became the cephalopods. As predators, the cephalopods are not only swift but they also have prehensile arms and tentacles for seizing and suckers for holding their prey. They can put out protective "smoke screens" and possess marvelous patterns of color changes. Although the earliest cephalopods bore heavy external shells, they overcame this handicap by making the shells buoyant with gas chambers separated by septa and connected to the body by a tube, the **siphuncle.** Later cephalopods reduced the shell until it was internal or absent and relied on their speed and an ink screen for protection.

Cephalopods probably originated from a form similar to the hypothetical mollusk ancestor. It is thought that the simple limpetlike shell became elongated as the visceral mass shifted away from the apex of the shell. Behind the visceral mass a septum was secreted at each growth period so that the shell became a series of successive compartments. As the fossil record shows, the shell was first straight (*Orthoceras* or *Michelinoceras*) but later became coiled, producing the *Nautilus* type of shell (Figure 278). The evolution of the nonshelled or reduced-shell forms is obscure because of lack of fossils, but the evolutionary tendency for a degenerate shell or none at all is evident.

The natural history of the cephalopods is known only in part. They are salt-water animals and appear sensitive to the degree of salinity. Few are found in the Baltic Sea where the water has a low salt content. The *Octopus* is often found in the intertidal zone, lurking among rocks and crevices; the active squids are rarely found in this zone. Cephalopods are found at various depths. *Nautilus* is usually taken from the ocean floor near islands (southwestern Pacific) where the water is several hundred meters deep. Some squids have been taken at 5,000 meters. Octopoda are usually in shallow water near shore but occasionally are found at great depths.

Color changes of cephalopods are produced in the skin by the contraction and expansion of special pigment cells called **chromatophores,** manipulated by tiny muscles attached to the edge of the cells. The pigment colors are black, brown, red, and yellow, so that a squid or octopus can assume a variety of colors when emotionally disturbed or for protection. All cephalopods except *Nautilus* have ink sacs from which they expel ink when attacked. The ink contains melanin (black) pig-

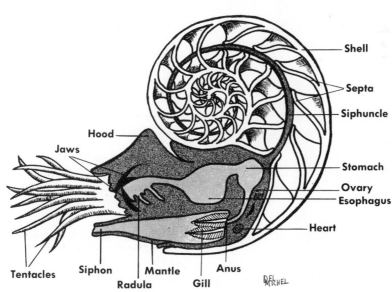

Figure 278. Median section through shell and viscera of *Nautilus*, showing internal anatomy (semidiagrammatic). This is only surviving genus of Tetrabranchia which flourished millions of years ago in tropical seas. It inspired O. W. Holmes' famous poem, "The Chambered Nautilus."

ment, which is formed by the oxidation of the amino acid tyrosin through the action of an enzyme. Some think the discharged ink assumes the shape of a "dummy" to distract an enemy predator. Or the ink may paralyze the enemy's sense of smell. All cephalopods are predaceous and carnivorous. Their chief food is small fish, mollusks, crustaceans, and worms. They are strong enough to pull clams apart; their horny beaks can quickly tear the flesh from a crustacean skeleton. They will even eat each other. Cephalopods are preyed upon by whales, seals, sea birds, and moray eels. The slender moray eel can go where the octopus hides and overcome it.

The sexes are separate in cephalopods. Females sometimes outnumber the males as much as 100 to 15. There is a certain amount of sexual dimorphism, too, so that it is possible to distinguish the sexes in some cases. One of the male arms is modified for transferring sperm to the female. The sperm are arranged in long tubes called **spermatophores**, which are formed in a special sac of the vas deferens. During mating, the male clasps the female and with his **hectocotylus** arm withdraws a bundle of spermatophores from his siphon and places them near her mouth or within her mantle cavity. In *Argonauta* (Figure 279) and a few others part of this arm is disengaged and left within the mantle chamber of the female; in others only the tip of the arm is detached. The hectocotylus arm is usually one of the fourth pair of arms in the squid, one of the third in the octopus, The squid lays her eggs in pencil-shaped masses of jelly and attaches them to some object. They are called "deadman's-fingers." The octopus lays eggs in long strings or bunches attached to a rock, where she remains to care for them.

Major groups of cephalopods

There are two orders of cephalopods: Tetrabranchia (four-gilled) and Dibranchia (two-gilled). Tetrabranchia is the more primitive. Its members populated the Paleozoic and Mesozoic seas but left only one genus, *Nautilus* (Figure 278), of which there are three species. This order is characterized by having external calcareous shells, which may or may not be coiled and (based on the only living form, *Nautilus*), two pairs of gills and nephridia, many tentacles, no suckers, no ink sac, eyes without lenses (Figure 280), and a passive mantle for holding the viscera and secreting the shell. Paleontologists divide the Tetrabranchia into two suborders: Nautiloidea, with simple septa between the chambers, and Ammonoidea, divided by fluted septa. The Nautiloidea are geologically older.

The order Dibranchia includes all liv-

Figure 279. Hectocotylized arm of cephalopod. In most male cephalopods one of the arms is modified (hectocotylized) for transferring sperm capsules (spermatophores) to mantle cavity of female. In some members of Octopoda (e.g., *Argonauta*) hectocotylus arm is autonomous, i.e., becomes detached and lodged in female.

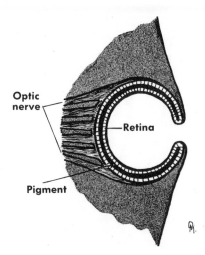

Figure 280. Eye of *Nautilus*. Example of pinhole camera eye. Such an eye corresponds to a stage of development in more complicated eyes of *Octopus* and *Loligo*. Such an eye focuses rays directly upon retina without a focusing device such as a crystalline lens.

Figure 281. School of young squids. As they course back and forth through aquarium, each individual carefully maintains his position and distance with reference to others. If this pattern is disturbed, squids quickly revert to their original position formation.

ing cephalopods except *Nautilus*. It has an internal shell or none at all, a cylindrical-shaped body which may have a fin, a pair of gills, a pair of kidneys, eight to ten arms or tentacles with suckers, eyes with lenses, and a muscular mantle for locomotion. There are two suborders: Decapoda with ten arms and large coelom and Octopoda with eight arms and reduced coelom. Squids belong to the Decapoda and the octopuses to the Octopoda.

Two of the decapod's arms are modified into tentacular arms for seizing prey. They can either be retracted into special pouches or doubled back upon themselves. They bear suckers only at the ends and are situated between the third and fourth arms on each side of the head. The suckers in squids are stalked (pedunculated), with horny rims bearing teeth; in octopuses the suckers are sessile and have no horny rims.

Loligo—squid

External structures. The squid (Figures 279 and 280) has an elongated torpedo-shaped body with a large head which

Figure 282. Squid, *Loligo*.

bears two large eyes and a mouth surrounded by ten arms provided with suckers. One pair of arms, the retractile tentacles, are longer than the others.

Along each side of the body is a fleshy triangular fin. The mantle encloses the mantle cavity in which are the internal organs. This mantle ends just behind the head in a free margin, the **collar.** Under the collar there projects a conical structure, the **siphon,** from which water can be forced by the contraction of the mantle. The shell, or **pen,** of *Loligo* is much reduced, consisting of a feather-shaped plate just beneath the skin of the back or anterior wall. It offers little protection but does stiffen the body. There is also cartilage support for the neck region, the siphon, and the fins.

Internal structures (Figure 283). The **digestive system** is made up of the usual divisions: mouth, pharynx, esophagus, stomach, cecum, intestine, and anus, which opens into the mantle cavity. The pharynx has a pair of horny **jaws** and two pairs of salivary glands, and the stomach has the ducts of the **liver** and **pancreas**

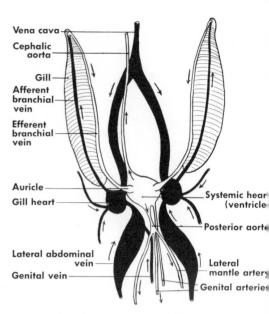

Figure 284. Cephalopod gills with "booster hearts" and related circulatory system. Well-developed circulatory system of most cephalopods is mainly a closed system with endothelial-lined arteries, veins, and capillaries. Blood is pumped to gills by gill hearts which are expanded portions of afferent branchial veins at base of gills. These hearts give a booster effect by ensuring efficient blood circulation through gills. As in most mollusks, kidneys are close to pericardium. Two thin-walled renal capsules enclose each division of afferent branchial vessel and terminal parts of lateral abdominal veins. Venous blood returning from body gives off waste to renal capsules before entering gills.

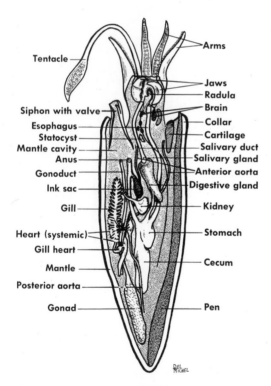

Figure 283. Internal anatomy of squid, *Loligo.* Body wall cut away on left side. Only one gill shown. (Semidiagrammatic.)

connected to it. A glandular **ink sac** opens into the mantle cavity near the anus. A **radula** is also present in the pharynx.

The circulatory system (Figure 284) is closed, with **branchial hearts** for pumping blood through the gills and a **systemic heart** which forces blood to the various other organs. A pair of **kidneys** connect the pericardial space with the mantle cavity. **Respiration** is carried on by a pair of **gills** in the lower part of the mantle chamber.

The **nervous system** contains many pairs of ganglia concentrated mainly in the head region. This region is protected by a cartilaginous case. The **sensory** organs are

fairly well developed. There are two complex **eyes** (Figure 285) which contain
cornea, lens, chambers, and retina with
rods. They can form real images, as do
the eyes of vertebrates; but as they are derived in a different manner, they are not
homologous. Other sense organs are a pair
of **statocysts** below the brain for equilibration and a pair of **olfactory organs.**

The sexes are separate, and from the
gonad in each sex a duct leads forward to
empty into the mantle cavity near the
anus. The male is provided with a hectocotylus arm (Figure 279) for transferring
sperm to the female.

Behavior. Squids have an interesting
method of locomotion which involves a
sort of "jet propulsion." When going backward, which they can do with great speed,
they take water into the mantle cavity, the
collar closes tightly around the neck, and
the water is forcibly ejected in a jet from
the siphon which is directed toward the
arms. In going forward, the siphon is directed backward. The two fins are used in
steering and for swimming.

Squids also have two important devices
for protecting themselves against their
enemies. One of these is their remarkable
power of changing color. Their skins contain many chromatophores with red, blue,
purple, and yellow pigments. By contracting or expanding these, it is possible for
the animals to assume rapidly many different shades of color, from the darker
hues to those that are paler. The other
method of protection involves the ink sac.
When the squid is escaping from its
enemies, this gland is made to secrete a
black fluid through the siphon to form a
"smoke screen."

Squids live upon fish, mollusks, and
crustaceans, which they capture with their
arms and specialized tentacles. The prey
is drawn by the arms to the mouth where
the horny jaws bite out pieces which are
then swallowed. The jaws and radula are
operated by the highly muscular pharynx.

Other members of class Cephalopoda

The squid *Loligo* is little more than 1
foot long, but the giant squid *Architeuthis*

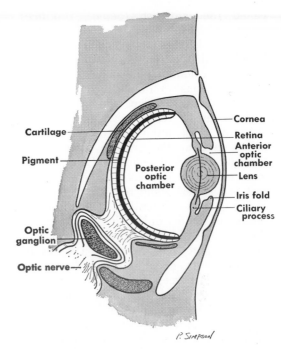

P. SIMPSON

Figure 285. Section through eye of cephalopod,
such as *Loligo.* Compare with simpler eye of
Nautilus, Figure 280.

Figure 286. Living octopus, *Octopus.* It is provided with eight arms which bear powerful
suckers for crawling over rocks and seizing prey
(mostly crabs). Conspicuous eye similar to vertebrate eye, but sensitive rods of retina face
toward light source instead of away from it, as in
vertebrates. (From film *Marine Life,* Encyclopaedia Britannica Films, Inc.)

may be more than 50 feet long, the largest of all invertebrates. It is found off the
coast of Newfoundland. Another squid,

called the cuttlefish *(Sepia)*, produces sepia-colored ink which is used by artists. The cuttlefish has a large pen or cuttle-bone which is often given canaries as a source of calcium.

The octopus, or devilfish, has no shell but possesses a large body and eight sucker-bearing tentacles (Figure 286). Some of these animals are only a few inches in diameter and are quite harmless, but the giant octopus of the Pacific may reach an over-all diameter of 30 feet and is very dangerous to divers.

The chambered nautilus is found on the bottom of the South Pacific seas. Its spiral shell in one plane is up to 10 inches in diameter and is made up of a series of compartments, each of which has been occupied in succession as the animal has grown larger. Thus each new chamber is larger than the preceding one. The animal occupies the outermost compartment. The unoccupied compartments are filled with gas, probably secreted by the **siphuncle**, a body mass of blood vessels and tissues enclosed in a tube which runs through the center of the partitions. The heads of these forms bear sixty to ninety arms. The simple "pinhole camera" eye of the nautilus is shown in Figure 280.

The paper nautilus *(Argonauta)* has a delicately coiled shell formed from glands in its tentacles. This shell is adapted for housing its eggs and for a nursery for the young after they hatch.

Derivation and meaning of basic terminology

Amphineura (Gr. *amphi*, both, + *neuron*, nerve).
Anodonta (Gr. *an*, without, + *odous*, tooth).
Busycon (Gr. *bu*, huge, + *sykon*, fig) Giant whelk.
Cephalopoda (Gr. *kephale*, head, + *pous*, foot).
Chiton (Gr. *chiton*, coat of mail) Refers to plates that cover this primitive mollusk.
Dentalium (L. *dens*, tooth).
Gastropoda (Gr. *gaster*, belly, + *pous*, foot).
glochidium (Gr. *glochin*, point, + *idion;* diminutive) Larva of a clam.
hectocotylus (Gr. *hekaton*, hundred, + *kotyle*, cup-shaped) Transformed arm which serves as a male copulatory organ in cephalopods.
Helix (Gr. *helix*, twisted).

Lamellibranchiata (L. *lamina*, plate, + Gr *branchia*, gills) Another name for class Pelecypoda.
marsupium (L. *marsupium*, pouch) A brood pouch.
Monoplacophora (Gr. *mono*, single, + *plakos* flat, + *phorein*, to bear) New group of mollusks discovered in 1952.
nacre (F. *nacre*, mother-of-pearl) Innermost layer of mollusk shell.
Nautilus (Gr. *nautilos*, sailor) This sole survivor of the most ancient mollusks is an active swimmer.
Nudibranchia (L. *nudus*, naked, + Gr. *branchia* gills) These gastropods have no shells.
Opisthobranchia (Gr. *opisthen*, behind, + *branchia*, gills) Gills are located posteriorly in these gastropods.
osphradium (Gr. *osphradion*, strong scent) A sense organ that tests incoming water.
Pelecypoda (Gr. *pelekys*, hatchet, + *pous*, foot)
periostracum (Gr. *peri*, around, + *ostrakon* shell) Outer horny layer of mollusk shell.
Physa (Gr. *physa*, bubble) Refers to bubble of air carried by snail when it submerges.
Polyplacophora (Gr. *poly*, many, + *plakos*, flat + *phorein*, to bear) An order of Amphineura with a shell of eight plates.
Polygyra (Gr. *poly*, many, + *gyros*, circle)
Prosobranchia (Gr. *proso*, front, + *branchia* gills) Order of gastropods with gills located anteriorly.
radula (L. *radula*, scraper) Rasping tongue of certain mollusks.
Scaphopoda (Gr. *skaphe*, boat, + *pous*, foot).
Solenogastre (Gr. *solen*, pipe, + *gaster*, belly).
Strombus (L. *strombus*, spiral snail) Giant conch.
umbo (L. boss of a shield) The part of a shell resembling a boss.
veliger (L. *veliger*, sail bearing) Larval form of certain mollusks.

ANNOTATED REFERENCES

Baker, F. C. 1898-1902. The Mollusca of the Chicago Area. Part I: The Pelecypoda. Part II: The Gastropoda. Chicago, The Chicago Academy of Science. *An authoritative work by a great specialist in this field. Excellent plates. Taxonomy somewhat outdated.*

Cambridge Natural History. 1895. Mollusca (Cooke, A. H.). London, Macmillan & Co., Ltd. *A standard work on mollusks. Good general descriptions.*

Edmonson, W. T. (editor). 1959. Ward and Whipple's Fresh-Water Biology, ed. 2. New York, John Wiley & Sons, Inc. *This is a re-*

vision of the well-known work of Ward and Whipple published many years ago. A taxonomic key to all the fresh-water families of mollusks is found together with illustrations of the principal members. The mollusks represent only one of the many fine features of this outstanding work of many specialists.

Encyclopaedia Britannica. 1956. Art: Mollusca and the Various Classes. Chicago, Encyclopaedia Britannica, Inc. *Clear descriptions and some illustrations in color.*

Grave, B. H. 1928. Natural History of the Shipworm, Teredo navalis, at Woods Hole, Mass. Biol. Bull., vol. 55, pp. 260-282. *An excellent account of the habits of this destructive mollusk.*

Lankester, E. R. (editor). 1906. A Treatise on Zoology. Part V: Mollusca (P. Pelseneer). London, A. and C. Black. *This is the best monograph on the mollusks so far published. All students of the group make use of this fine work as a source of information.*

Lemche, H. 1957. A New Living Deep-Sea Mollusc of the Cambro-Devonian Class Monoplacophora. Nature, London, vol. 179, p. 413. *An interesting account of the recently discovered Neopilina. This small limpet-shaped mollusk is segmented and poses, therefore, the problem of annelid relationship. This seg-*

mentation, however, may be independently acquired, for there is no evidence that these new forms belong to the primitive ancestors of Mollusca.

MacGinitie, G. E., and N. MacGinitie. 1949. Natural History of Marine Animals. New York, McGraw-Hill Book Co., Inc. *A section is devoted to a fine account of Mollusca with several excellent photographs of representative forms.*

Parker, T. J., and W. A. Haswell. 1940. A Textbook of Zoology, ed. 6, 2 vols. (revised by O. Lowenstein). London, Macmillan & Co., Ltd. *This standard text is very useful for a general survey of Mollusca.*

Pennak, R. W. 1953. Fresh-Water Invertebrates of the United States. New York, The Ronald Press Co. *A chapter each is devoted to the Gastropoda and the Pelecypoda. General descriptions of their structure, physiology, distribution, and ecology as well as taxonomic keys are given.*

Schechter, V. 1959. Invertebrate Zoology. Englewood Cliffs, N. J., Prentice-Hall, Inc. *A good elementary discussion.*

Spector, W. S. (editor). 1956. Handbook of Biological Data, pp. 183-184. Philadelphia, W. B. Saunders Co.

chapter 20

Phylum Echinodermata*

BIOLOGICAL PRINCIPLES

Organ-system level of organization

1. The echinoderms share with the annelids, mollusks, and arthropods the distinction of reaching the highest organization of the invertebrates.

2. Unlike the other three phyla, this group has radial symmetry, but this type of symmetry has been secondarily acquired, for their larval forms are bilaterally symmetrical.

3. As a phylum, echinoderms show a great degree of specialization which is manifested by bizarre characters not found elsewhere.

4. They have no segmentation or well-defined head region.

5. They belong to the deuterostome branch, or enterocoelous coelomates, of the animal kingdom, which include the phyla Chaetognatha, Echinodermata, Hemichordata, Chordata, and a few minor phyla.

6. Echinoderms have radial and indeterminate cleavage.

Biological contributions

1. Most of the echinoderm characters are so out of line that few of them are copied by other phyla.

2. Some of their unique features are the water-vascular system, tube feet, pedicellariae, dermal branchiae, and calcareous endoskeleton.

3. They have a **mesodermal endoskeleton** of plates which may be considered the first indication of the endoskeleton so well developed among vertebrates.

4. They have a remarkable power of autotomy (self-mutilation) together with that of regeneration of lost parts.

5. They have contributed a pattern of em-

---

*E-chi'no-der"ma-ta (Gr. *echinos*, spiny, + *derma*, skin).

bryonic development very similar to that of the highest group, the chordates. This pattern includes (a) an anus derived from the embryonic blastopore, (b) a mouth formed from a stomodaeum which connects to the endodermal esophagus, (c) a mesoderm from evaginations of the archenteron (enterocoelous), and (d) a chief nervous system in close contact with the ectoderm.

Position in animal kingdom

1. The echinoderms are a very ancient group of animals which, according to fossil records, were differentiated back in Cambrian time. The fossil record gives no clues as to their origin.

2. The most primitive echinoderms were probably the stalked members, and from these, the free forms arose. These early echinoderms were noncrinoid Pelmatozoa now wholly extinct.

3. From their larvae, the evidence indicates that their ancestors were bilaterally symmetrical and that their radial symmetry was secondarily acquired. Even in the adult condition certain aspects of bilateral symmetry can be discerned under the disguise of the radial.

4. Of all invertebrates, echinoderms are placed nearest to the chordates because of the features referred to under biological contributions.

5. Another strong evidence of their chordate affinities is the similarity between the larval type of echinoderms and that of the prechordate acorn worm (*Balanoglossus*).

6. From the evidence at hand, it appears that echinoderms and chordates may have originated from a common ancestor or at least from the same side of the phylogenetic tree.

7. Within the group, the holothuroids are supposed to have come from a common stem with the crinoids, whereas the asteroids, echinoids, and ophiuroids have risen from a common pelmatozoan but noncrinoid ancestry.

GENERAL RELATIONS

The echinoderms are marine forms and include the sea stars, brittle stars, sea urchins, sea cucumbers, and sea lilies. They represent a bizarre group sharply distinguished from all other members of the animal kingdom. Their name is derived from a characteristic of their integument (Gr. *echinos*, spiny, + *derma*, skin). A calcareous endoskeleton is found in all members of the phylum, either in the form of plates or represented by scattered tiny ossicles. Echinoderms are abundant along the seashore and extend to depths of many thousand feet. None can move rapidly and some are sessile. None of them are parasitic. There is a great variety of colors among the 6,000 species, including orange, reds, purples, blues, and browns.

The most marked characteristics of the echinoderms are (1) the spiny endoskeleton of plates, (2) the water-vascular system, (3) the pedicellariae, (4) the dermal branchiae, (5) the amebocytes, and (6) radial symmetry. Radial symmetry is not limited to echinoderms, but no other group with such complex organ systems has radial symmetry.

They are an ancient group of animals extending back to the Cambrian period. They have left an excellent fossil record which gives no indication, however, of echinoderm ancestors. For a long time Echinodermata were placed with Coelenterata and the two groups were called Radiata. There is every reason to believe that the echinoderms have descended from bilateral ancestors in spite of their present type of symmetry. This fact is the more evident when one considers the secondary character of the radial symmetry, for it appears late in development; the larvae are bilaterally symmetrical. Even in the adult, radial symmetry merely disguises an underlying bilateral symmetry. Of all invertebrates, the echinoderms are considered to be nearest in relation to the chordates. The type of larvae of echinoderms and of *Balanoglossus* (prechordate) are much alike. While these two forms of larvae could have arisen independently by convergent evolution, evidence indicates that their similarity has real evolutionary meaning and that both echinoderms and chordates have come from a common ancestor. Chordate segmentation could have arisen after the two groups diverged.

The phylogeny of the echinoderms is obscure. The extinct class of Heterostelea, one of the stem-bearing forms, has some of the qualifications of an ancestral type. It was bilaterally symmetrical. The free-moving forms (subphylum Eleutherozoa) have probably arisen from the more ancient and primitive stem-bearing varities (subphylum Pelmatozoa), which include the living crinoids and several extinct classes. Among the free-moving classes the sea stars (Asteroidea) and brittle stars (Ophiuroidea) seem to be closely related, whereas the sea cucumbers (Holothuroidea) no doubt arose from some crinoidlike ancestor.

CHARACTERISTICS

1. Body unsegmented with **radial symmetry**; often in **divisions of five**; body rounded, cylindrical, or star shaped

2. Three germ layers; mesoderm of endomesodermal origin

3. **No head;** body surface of five (or more) radiating areas (ambulacra) with alternating spaces, or interambulacra (interradii)

4. **Endoskeleton of dermal calcareous ossicles with spines;** covered by an epidermis (ciliated in most)

5. A unique **water-vascular system** of coelomic origin which pushes out the body surface as a series of tentacle-like projections, podia or tube feet, which are protruded or retracted by alterations of fluid (sea water or coelomic) pressure within them; an external opening (madreporite or hydropore) usually present.

6. Locomotion usually by **tube feet** (podia) which project from the ambulacral spaces

7. **Coelom extensive,** forming the perivisceral cavity and the cavity of the water-vascular system; coelom of entero-

coelous type; coelomic fluid with amebocytes

8. Digestive system usually complete; axial or coiled; anus absent in ophiuroids

9. Vascular system reduced; hemal or lacunar system enclosed in coelomic channels

10. Respiration by **dermal branchiae,** by **tube feet,** by **respiratory tree** (in some), and by **bursae** (ophiuroids)

11. Nervous system with circumoral ring and radial nerves; usually two or three systems of networks located at different levels

12. Sensory system (poorly developed) of tactile organs, chemoreceptors, podia, terminal tentacles, photoreceptors, statocysts

13. Excretory organs absent

14. Sexes separate (a few hermaphroditic) with large gonads, single (holothuroids) but multiple in most, with simple ducts

15. Fertilization usually external

16. **Development through specialized free-swimming larval stages** of many kinds with metamorphosis

17. Regeneration of lost parts conspicuous

ECONOMIC IMPORTANCE

Because of the spiny nature of their structure, echinoderms have a limited use as food for other animals. The eggs of these forms may serve as food, and the sea cucumber (trepang) is used by the Chinese for soup. Where echinoderms are common along a seashore, they have been used for fertilizer.

Sea stars feed mainly on mollusks, crustaceans, and other invertebrates, but their chief damage is to clams and oysters, for which they have a great fondness. A single star may eat as many as a dozen oysters or clams in a day. To rid shellfish beds of these pests, rope nets in which the sea stars become entangled are sometimes dragged over oyster beds, and the collected sea stars destroyed. A more effective method is to distribute lime over areas where they abound. Lime causes the delicate epidermal membrane to dis-

integrate; lesions are then formed which destroy the dermal branchiae and ultimately the animal itself.

The eggs of echinoderms are widely used in biological investigations, for the eggs are usually abundant and easy to collect and can be handled conveniently. The investigator can follow their developmental stages with great accuracy. Artificial parthenogenesis was first discovered in sea urchin eggs, when it was found that by changing the chemical nature of sea water development would take place without the presence of sperm.

Although most invertebrate groups have parasitic members, echinoderms have none so far as is known.

CLASSIFICATION

Echinoderms are divided into two subphyla: Pelmatozoa (chiefly stem-bearing forms) and Eleutherozoa (free-moving animals). There are about 4,000 to 6,000 living and 20,000 extinct or fossil species. Five classes of existing echinoderms are recognized and about that many extinct classes are known to invertebrate paleontologists. Most of the extinct classes belong to the subphylum Pelmatozoa, which now has only one living class (Crinoidea). Fossil classes differed mainly from existing classes (1) in having a heavy body wall of closely fitting plates (theca), (2) in having both mouth and anus on the oral side, and (3) in being sessile, attached by the aboral side. Some of these features are retained by living species.

Diagnostic features

Echinoderms belong to the Deuterostomia branch of the animal kingdom and are enterocoelous coelomates. The other phyla of this group are Chaetognatha, Hemichordata, and Chordata. It will be recalled that the deuterostomes have the following features in common: an anus from the blastopore, a coelom budded off from the archenteron (enterocoelous), radial and indeterminate cleavage, a nervous system in close contact with the ectoderm, and a larva (when present) of the **dipleurula** type. The primitive patern of the echinoderms seems to have included radial symmetry, radiating grooves ambulacra), and a tendency for the body penings (oral side) to face upward, as een in sessile forms. Radial symmetry with arm extensions would be an advantage to a sessile animal; it could get ts food from all directions. Living crin-ids follow this primitive pattern. Modi-ications of the plan are found in free-noving forms which have been favored by evolution, for attached forms, once plentiful are now reduced to the one class, Crinoidea.

Zoologists have constructed a hypo-thetical ancestral larval form (**dipleu-rula**), of which existing larval forms may be modifications. Dipleurula is pictured as an elongated, bilaterally symmetrical, two-sided animal without a skeleton and with a complete digestive system and a coelom of three paired sacs. Through attachment on one side and some degeneration or shifting of structures, this bilateral larva was transformed into the radial adult form. Although an attractive theory and widely accepted, many zoologists are doubtful about its usefulness. Perhaps a

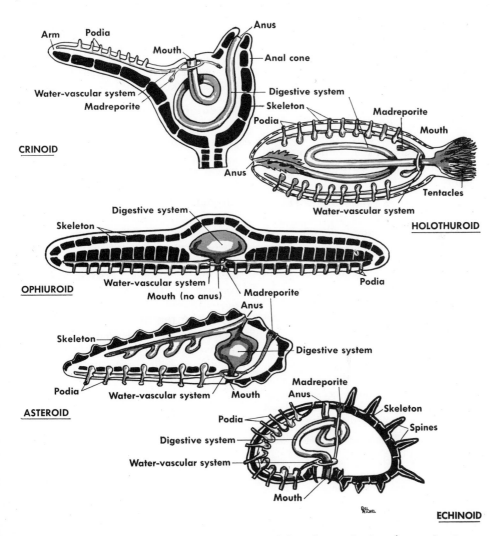

Figure 287. Schematic cross-sections of representatives of five classes of echinoderms, showing comparatively the skeletal, water-vascular, and digestive systems.

more satisfactory theory is the pentactula concept of five radial tentacles around the mouth, but this larval concept could be regarded as a later evolutionary development of the dipleurula. Embryological evidence indicates that the unique water-vascular system arose as hollow protrusions (tentacles) of the body wall carrying coelomic branches. Side branches of these protrusions became podia or tube feet which served originally as sensory or food-collecting structures. In sea stars, urchins, and cucumbers the podia have acquired suckers and are used in locomotion; food is no longer conveyed by ciliated grooves but is taken by mouth. The calcareous endoskeleton of most echinoderms is an important aspect of their evolution. Primitive echinoderms were heavily armored with complicated plates, but in existing forms the skeleton tends to be reduced for flexibility. In most groups it consists of closely fitting plates provided with spines and tubercles and held together by muscles and mesenchyme. Holothurians have almost no endoskeleton.

Subphylum Eleutherozoa (e-lu′ther-o-zo″a) (Gr. *eleutheros*, free, + *zoon*, animal)

   Class Asteroidea (as′ter-oi″de-a) (Gr. *aster*, star, + *eidos*, form)—**sea stars.** Star-shaped echinoderms with the arms not sharply marked off from the central disc; ambulacral grooves with tube feet on oral side; tube feet with suckers; anus and madreporite aboral; pedicellariae present (Figure 289). Example: *Asterias.*

   Class Ophiuroidea (o′phi-u-roi″de-a) (Gr. *opis*, snake, + *oura*, tail, + *eidos*, form)— **brittle stars.** Star shaped with the arms sharply marked off from the central disc; ambulacral grooves absent or covered by ossicles; tube feet without suckers and not used for locomotion; pedicellariae absent; anus absent (Figure 295). Example: *Ophiura.*

   Class Echinoidea (ech′i-noi″de-a) (Gr. *echinus*, spiny, + *eidos*, form) (Figure 287)— **sea urchins.** More or less globular echinoderms with no arms; compact skeleton or test; movable spines; ambulacral grooves covered by ossicles; tube feet with suckers; pedicellariae present (Figures 297 to 299). Example: *Arbacia.*

   Class Holothuroidea (hol′o-thur-oi″de-a) (Gr. *holothurion,* a sea cucumber, + *eidos* form)—**sea cucumbers.** Cucumber-shaped echinoderms with no arms; spines absent ossicles confined to thick muscular wall anus present; ambulacral grooves concealed tube feet with suckers; circumoral tentacle (modified tube feet); pedicellariae absent madreporite plate internal (Figures 301 and 302). Example: *Thyone.*

Subphylum Pelmatozoa (pel′ma-to-zo″a) (Gr. *pelmatos*, stalk, + *zoon*, animal)

   Class Crinoidea (cri-noi′de-a) (Gr. *crinon* lily, + *eidos*, form)—**sea lilies.** Body attached during part or all of life by an aboral stalk of dermal ossicles; mouth and anus on oral surface; five arms branching at base and bearing pinnules; ciliated ambulacral groove on oral surface with tentacle-like tube feet for food collecting; spines madreporite, and pedicellariae absent (Figures 303 and 304). Example: *Antedon.*

Larval forms of echinoderm classes

The early development of the larval form is similar in all echinoderms. The egg is usually fertilized in sea water or in brood pouches. It divides by total cleavage which is indeterminate. It passes through successive stages: a hollow single-layered blastula; a double-layered gastrula with an archenteron and a wide blastocoele; paired out-pocketings of the archenteron which form the coelom and water-vascular system; mesenchyme formed in the blastocoele from ecto-dermal and endodermal cells; and a mouth by the breaking through of a sto-modaeum; and eventually a free, pelagic larva (in most) which shows similarities as well as differences among the various classes.

In most cases this early larva is bilateral and free swimming, and it lacks a calcareous skeleton but has calcareous spines, probably for support. The coelom consists of three pairs of pouches and the future ventral side becomes concave. Some call this stage the dipleurula. Cilia which first covered most of the body are now restricted to a band around the concavity. This band, used in locomotion, is folded into loops which vary in the different larval forms.

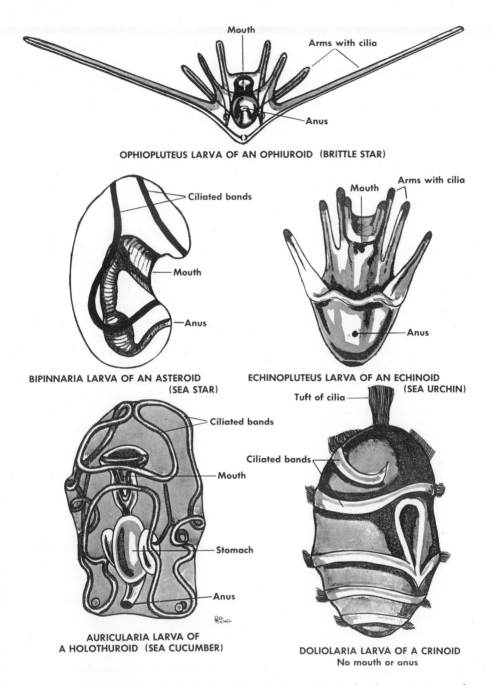

OPHIOPLUTEUS LARVA OF AN OPHIUROID (BRITTLE STAR)

Mouth

Arms with cilia

Anus

BIPINNARIA LARVA OF AN ASTEROID (SEA STAR)

Ciliated bands

Mouth

Anus

ECHINOPLUTEUS LARVA OF AN ECHINOID (SEA URCHIN)

Mouth

Arms with cilia

Anus

AURICULARIA LARVA OF A HOLOTHUROID (SEA CUCUMBER)

Ciliated bands

Mouth

Stomach

Anus

DOLIOLARIA LARVA OF A CRINOID
No mouth or anus

Tuft of cilia

Ciliated bands

Figure 288. Representative larva of each class of echinoderms. Early development stages of various classes are similar, and hypothetical common ancestor, "dipleurula" larva, has been proposed for all echinoderms. (After Lang and others.)

One of the most primitive of the echinoderm larvae is the **auricularia** (Holothuroidea). Its body is elongated, with a ciliated band partly around the preoral lobe and partly on body folds. The **bipinnaria** (Asteroidea) larva, which is similar to the auricularia, separates the preoral ring of cilia from the rest. In the other types of larvae the body lobes become elongated, with supporting rods, and the ciliated bands more elaborate. The transformation of the larvae into adults by metamorphosis is a complicated process and differs in several groups. This change involves shifting of the mouth position, development of the endoskeleton, torsion whereby the left side becomes the oral and the right side the aboral surface, development of a coelomic pouch into the water-vascular system, and assumption of radial symmetry.

REPRESENTATIVE TYPES
CLASS ASTEROIDEA

Sea stars are found in all oceans, usually on rocky seashores but also at great depths in the ocean far from the shore line. More than a thousand species are known. Although five rays is the usual number, there are species that have as many as forty or fifty; the number, however, is not constant if in excess of five or six. At low tide the rocks along the shore may have large numbers of sea stars upon them. They often cling so tenaciously that it is difficult to dislodge them without tearing loose many of the tube feet.

Asterias—sea star

External structure. Asterias is one of those genera which has five arms. The body consists of a central **disc** and five tapering arms, or **rays.** On the upper, or **aboral,** surface there are many spines, around the bases of which are grouped in rosettes the minute pincerlike **pedicellariae** (modified spines) (Figure 290). Between the spines are the soft, delicate **dermal branchiae** (papulae), or skin gills, which function in respiration. The pedicellariae, which have jaws manipulated by muscles, help keep the body free from debris, aid in capturing food, and protect the skin gills. On the aboral surface are the small **anus** and the conspicuous circular **madreporite,** which acts as a sieve leading to the water-vascular system. The axes, or imaginary lines that run from the center of the disc to the tips of the arms are known as **radii** and the spaces on the disc between them, as **interradii.** On the **oral,** or lower, surface, the **mouth** in the center of the disc is surrounded by the soft **peristomial membrane.** Along the oral surface of each ray a median **ambulacral groove** is bordered by large spines. From the groove project two or four rows of **tube feet** (podia). At the tip of each ray is a small **tentacle** and a red **eye spot** which marks the position of many pigment-cup **ocelli,** each lined with retinal cells.

Ciliated **epidermis** covers the entire body. Beneath it, and secreted by the dermis, is the mesodermal **endoskeleton** of small calcareous **ossicles** with projecting **spines** and tubercles. They are bound together in a definite pattern by muscle and connective tissue. On the spines the epidermis and its cuticle may be worn off. In the ambulacral groove the ossicles form a trough for the tube feet. Skin color is due to pigment granules in the epidermis.

Sea stars move their rays by muscles in the body wall. Transverse and longitudinal muscle fibers in the ambulacral grooves bend the rays aborally and part

Figure 289. Aboral surface of common sea star Asterias. Class Asteroidea.

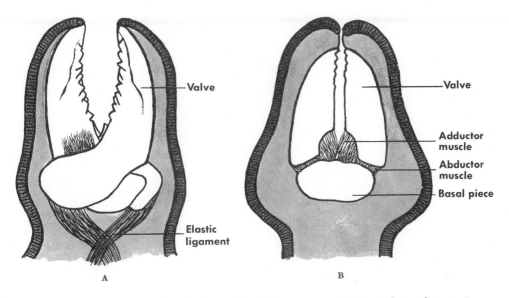

Figure 290. Two of the types of pedicellariae found in sea stars. **A**, Crossed-jawed type. **B**, straight-jawed type, opened by abductor muscles, closed by adductor muscles.

ially close the grooves by drawing in their margins.

Internal structure (Figures 292 and 93). The large, branched **coelom** is lined with ciliated epithelium (**peritoneum**). In it, circulating in a lymphlike **coelomic fluid**, are **amebocytes** (coelomocytes) which function in respiration, circulation, and excretion. The coelom extends into the dermal branchiae so that the fluid is brought close to the sea water for gas exchange. In excretion, waste is gathered by amebocytes which then escape through the walls of the dermal branchiae to the outside. The **digestive system** has a **mouth** on the oral side, with sphincter and radial muscles and a short **esophagus** leading to large saclike **stomach** composed of two parts. The lower **cardiac** part has thin folded walls and is attached to the body wall by **gastric ligaments** which prevent the stomach from being everted too far; the smaller **pyloric** stomach connects with ducts from five pairs of pyloric **ceca**. A short **intestine** with a pair of **rectal ceca** ends at the **anus** on the top (aboral) side. The pyloric ceca (digestive glands) fill a large part of each ray. The layers of the digestive tube, like those of the body wall and peristomial membrane, consist of epithelium, connective tissue, and muscle.

The **circulatory,** or **hemal,** system is made up of vessels enclosed in coelomic sinuses, or hyponeural canals. In each arm, under the radial canal of the water-vascular system, there is a radial hemal vessel which is divided into halves by a longitudinal septum. These vessels communicate with an oral-ring vessel which encircles the mouth. The hemal system is

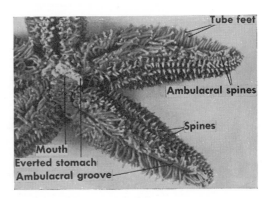

Figure 291. Portion of oral surface of sea star, showing arrangement of tube feet along ambulacral grooves.

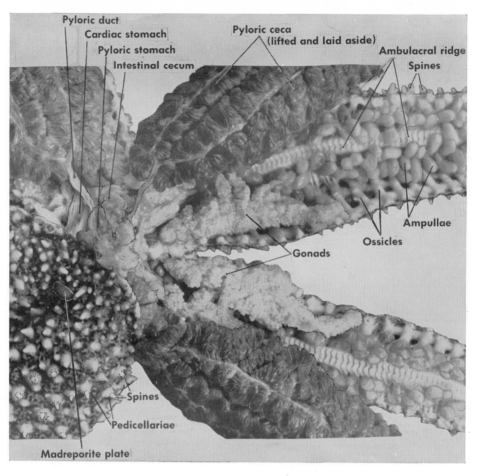

Figure 292. Sea star dissection, aboral view, showing portions of two arms with digestive glands lifted aside to expose gonads in interradial spaces and ampullae on either side of ambulacral ridge. At lower left two arms are left undissected to show madreporite and spines.

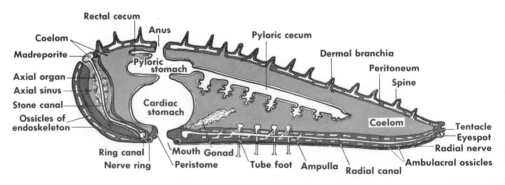

Figure 293. Diagram of longitudinal section through disc and arm of sea star, showing principal structures.

ot well developed in sea stars and is difficult to see. The **nervous system** is made up of three nervous units placed at different levels in the disc and arm. These are (1) the **oral (ectoneural)** nervous system, composed of a circumoral ring around the mouth and five radial nerve cords, one in each arm, just beneath the radial canals; (2) the **deep (hyponeural)** nervous system, consisting of a double circumoral ring above the ectoneural ring and giving off paired branches which run on each side of the radial nerve; and (3) the **coelomic (aboral)** nervous system, containing an anal nerve ring and nerves along the roof of the ray. Subepidermal plexuses or nerve nets freely connect these systems with the body wall and related structures. The ectoneural elements appear to coordinate the tube feet, while the deep regulate the muscular action of the rays. In sea stars the ectoneural and aboral systems are poorly developed. The **sense organs** are not well developed; tactile organs are found over the surface and an eyespot at the tip of each arm.

The sea star has separate sexes. The **gonads**, either **testes** or **ovaries**, look alike but can be distinguished by microscopic examination. They are made up of saclike masses which resemble tiny bunches of grapes, and there is a pair of them in each interradial space. The gonads are greatly enlarged at the breeding season. The ducts by which the eggs or sperm are discharged to the outside are minute pores on the aboral surface near the base of the arms. **Fertilization** is external and occurs in early summer when the eggs and sperm are shed into the water.

The **water-vascular** system, which is unique among the echinoderms, is made up of a system of canals and specialized tube feet and in sea stars serves as a method of locomotion (Figure 294). It is made up of (1) the **madreporite** on the aboral surface, a finely grooved sieve through which water enters; (2) the **stone canal**, which runs from the madreporite to (3) the **ring canal** around the mouth; (4) five **radial canals**, one in each ray above the ambulacral groove and concealed under the ambulacral bridge; (5) the **lateral canals**, which connect the tube feet with the radial canals and which are each provided with a valve; and (6) the **tube feet**. Each tube foot is a thin-walled cylinder with a rounded muscular sac, the **ampulla**, at its inner end and a **sucker** at its outer end. The ampullae lie within the ray; the tube feet proper are outside in the ambulacral groove. The tubes which connect the ampullae with the suckers pass through small pores between

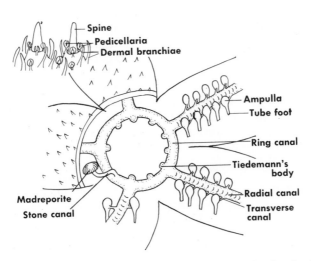

Figure 294. Diagram of water-vascular system of sea star. Upper left, detail of spines and skin gills (dermal branchiae).

the ambulacral ossicles. The ampullae contain circular muscles in their walls, whereas the tube feet have longitudinal muscles. On the inner wall of the ring canal are nine tiny spherical swellings, the **Tiedemann's bodies.** There is no evidence that they produce amebocytes as formerly supposed. The stone canal and the brownish, spongy axial gland close by are surrounded by a tubular coelomic cavity called the axial sinus. The axial gland is a part of the hemal system and some think it is the remnant of a heart.

Behavior. The sea star uses the water-vascular system for locomotion. When an ampulla contracts, the fluid within it is prevented by a valve from flowing back into the radial canal and thus is forced into the tube foot. The elastic tube foot extends and can twist about by its muscular wall. When the tube foot touches a substratum, it becomes attached by its sucker. Then the longitudinal muscles contract, shorten it, and force the water back into the ampulla. Thus the animal is drawn forward. The coordinated effort of all or many tube feet is sufficient to draw the animal slowly up a vertical surface. The muscles of the arms and tube feet are controlled by the motor nerves of the subepidermal plexus.

If the sea star happens to be on a soft surface, such as muck or sand, the suckers are little used, for then the tube feet are employed as legs. Locomotion now becomes mainly a stepping process involving a backward swinging of the middle portion of the podia, followed by a contraction, shoving the animal forward. Sea stars can move about six inches a minute. They can also move by twisting and bending their rays; when inverted, the sea star twists its rays until some of its tube feet attach to the substratum as an anchor and then it slowly rolls over.

The food of the sea star is mainly mussels, clams, oysters, snails, tube worms, and other slow-moving forms which the animal can overtake and overpower. Oysters and clams are the main diet. The sea star arches its body in a humped-up position over the shell and grips the op-

posite valves with the tube feet. Then begins a steady pull at right angles t the surface of the shell, using its feet i relays. A force of some 1,300 grams ca be exerted in this way. In half an hour o so the adductor muscles of the bivalv fatigue and relax. When the valves gap the star everts the lower part of its stom ach, inserts it between the two valves, an wraps it around the soft parts of the shel fish. Secretions from the stomach and d gestive glands digest the food in the shel Enzymes are known to be involved in th process. The partly digested food is pulle into the stomach and pyloric ceca, wher digestion is finished. Digestion is entirel extracellular. At the completion of th process, the sea star draws its stomac back into its mouth. This is not done b retractor muscles, as usually stated, bu by contraction of muscles in the stomac and gastric filaments and by relaxation o muscles in the body wall along with th return of coelomic fluid into the arms Very little indigestible material is taken in, so that only a tiny amount of feca matter is ejected through the anal pore

Sea stars are rarely active during the day, remaining quietly attached to som object. At night they are active, in searcl of food. Their reactions are mainly t touch, light, temperature, and chemicals Apparently they can be taught a simpl habit, such as righting themselves witl certain arms, as Professor Jennings dem onstrated many years ago.

Regeneration and autotomy. The se star can regenerate lost parts. The arm regenerate readily; if all are removed from the disc, all will grow back. A single ray with a small portion of the disc will re generate an entire animal. Sea stars als have the power of **autotomy**, or volun tarily discarding a part. An injured arn is cast off by the animal near the base although months may be required for it replacement.

CLASS OPHIUROIDEA

In this group, as in Asteroidea, the members have a central disc with five (sometimes more) distinct arms (Figure

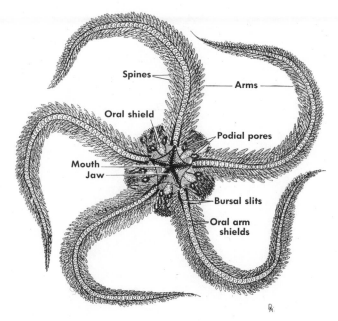

Figure 295. Spiny brittle star, oral view.

295). The arms, however, are long and slender and are sharply marked off from the disc. They represent the largest class of echinoderms in number of species. They are abundant wherever found. Basket stars have their rays branched in a complex fashion. Members of this class are found in shallow and deep water, and they have a wide distribution.

Some common ophiuroids along our Atlantic coast are *Amphipholis* (viviparous and hermaphroditic), *Ophioderma,* and *Ophiothrix.* Along the Pacific coast are *Orthasterias* (very long arms); in British Columbia, *Amphiodia;* and in California, *Ophioplocus* (viviparous). The basket star *(Gorgonocephalus)* is usually found at considerable depths. Some ophiuroids have varigated color patterns.

Brittle stars

Brittle stars, unlike sea stars, have no pedicellariae, ambulacral grooves, or dermal branchiae. They have tube feet, called tentacles, largely sensory in function and without suckers. They can pass food along the rays to the mouth and have a limited function in locomotion. Each of the jointed arms consists of a column of calcareous vertebrae connected by muscles and covered by plates. On the oral surface of the central disc are the **madreporite** and the **mouth** with five movable plates which serve as jaws. There is no anus. The skin is leathery, with dermal plates (ossicles) and spines arranged in characteristic patterns. Cilia are mostly lacking.

The visceral organs are confined to the central disc; the rays are too slender to contain them. The **stomach** is saclike and there is no intestine. Indigestible material is cast out of the mouth. Five pairs of **bursae** (peculiar to ophiuroids) open toward the oral surface by **genital slits** at the bases of the arms. Water circulates in and out of these sacs for respiration. On the coelomic wall of each bursa are small **gonads** that discharge into the bursa their ripe sex cells, which pass through the genital slits into the water for fertilization. Sexes are usually separate; a few are hermaphroditic. Some brood their young in the bursae; the young escape through the genital slits or by rupturing the aboral disc. The larva, called the **ophiopluteus** (Figure 288),

Figure 296. Ophiuroid with aboral disc wall cut away to show principal internal structures. Only bases of arms shown.

metamorphoses into the adult. Water-vascular, nervous, and hemal systems are similar to those of the sea stars; in each arm there is a small **coelom,** a **nerve cord,** and a **radial canal** of the water-vascular system.

Behavior. Brittle stars are often found under stones and seaweed at low tide, because they are negatively phototactic and positively thigmotactic. At high tide they are active, wandering about in search of small animals which they capture with their rays. They move with a writhing, serpentlike motion of the arms. They can swim with their rays, but they often hold to objects with one or more rays while pushing with the others. Regeneration and autotomy are even more pronounced in brittle stars than in sea stars. Many individuals are regenerating parts most of the time, for they are very fragile.

Sea urchins and sand dollars

These forms lack rays and hav rounded bodies made up of continuou endoskeletons of closely fitting plate (Figures 297, 298, and 299). Sea urchin are hemispherical, sand dollars are dis shaped, and heart urchins are ovoid. Se urchins with their long sharp spines re semble chestnut burrs. One of the mos common sea urchins of the eastern coas is *Arbacia punctulata,* found in both sha low and deep waters and often in tid pools concealed under seaweeds. Alon, the Pacific coast, *Strongylocentrotus* is th common form.

Structure. The **test,** or shell, is a com pact skeleton of ten double rows of plate which bear movable, stiff spines. Th plates are firmly sutured. Five pairs o these ambulacral rows are homologou

384

o the five arms of the sea star and have pores for the long tube feet. Alternating with the ambulacral rows are the interambulacral spaces. The plates bear small tubercles, or sockets, in which the round ends of the spines articulate. The spines move by small muscles around the bases. The four or five kinds of **pedicellariae** are three jawed and are mounted on long stalks; they help keep the body clean and capture small organisms. The **mouth** is surrounded by five converging **teeth** with an enclosing collar-shaped lip. Ten branched gills (modified podia) encircle the peristome. The rounded aboral end bears the centered **anus**, a number of **genital** openings, and the **madreporite**. This area contains a number of endoskeletal plates and is called the **periproct**.

Inside the test (Figure 298) is the coiled **digestive system**—the complicated **Aristotle's lantern** (Figure 300) to which the teeth are attached, a slender esophagus, a dilated stomach with ceca, an intestine, and a rectum which terminates at the anus. A peculiar tubelike ciliated siphon connects the esophagus to the intestine and enables the water to by-pass the

Pacific purple stars (Pisaster)

5-rayed star (Dermasterias)

21-rayed star (Pycnopodia)

21-rayed sun star

Sea urchin (Strongylocentrotus)

Common sea cucumber (Stichopus)

Figure 297. Group of common west coast echinoderms. (Courtesy Vancouver Public Aquarium, British Columbia.)

stomach to concentrate the food for digestion in the intestine. The hemal system consists of an esophageal ring and radial vessels to the inner surface of the test. Around the esophagus is the ring canal with five radial canals which extend along the interior of the test and connect to the tube feet. The ring canal is connected to the madreporite by the stone canal which is accompanied by a spongy axial gland. The chief **nervous system** consists of a nerve ring around the mouth, five radial nerves which run along the radial canals, and a subepidermal plexus which innervates the podia, spines, and pedicellariae. There are few special sense organs, but the podia, spines, and pedicellariae are also sensory. A number of **gonads** are attached to the inner aboral surface, and from each a duct leads to one of the genital openings. The sexes are separate and the larval form is a **pluteus**.

The sand dollar (Figure 299) *(Echinarachnius)* differs from *Arbacia* in having a flattened disc-shaped body and also in certain minor details, such as small cal-

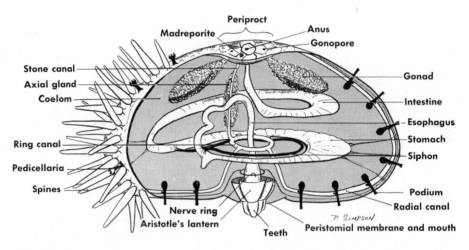

Figure 298. Semidiagrammatic view of some internal and external structures of sea urchin, *Arbacia.*

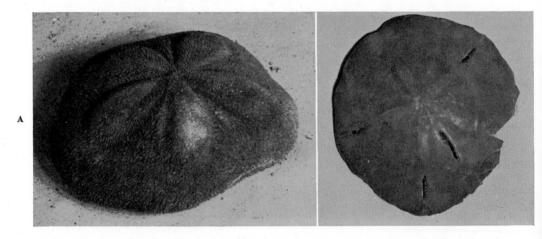

Figure 299. Tests of two types of sand dollars. **A,** Sea biscuit. **B,** Keyhole sand dollar. In latter, slitlike openings are called lunules, but their function is unknown. Class Echinoidea.

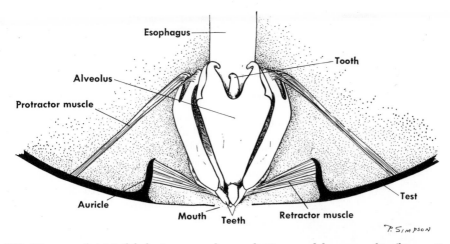

Esophagus

Tooth

Alveolus

Protractor muscle

Auricle

Mouth Teeth Retractor muscle

Test

T. SIMPSON

Figure 300. Diagram of Aristotle's lantern, complex mechanism used by sea urchin for masti-cating its food. Five pairs of retractor muscles draw lantern and teeth up into test; five pairs of protractors push lantern down and expose teeth. Other muscles produce variety of move-ments. Only major skeletal parts and muscles are shown in diagram.

careous spines and a marginal anus. The tests of some sand dollars are perforated with holes, called **lunules,** of unknown function.

Behavior. The echinoids live on sea-weed and dead animal matter. They move about by means of their spines and tube feet. Their spines and hard test afford them considerable protection. When prodded they will turn the spines toward the source of irritation. One sea urchin found along the coast of Florida and the Gulf of Mexico has poison-ous spines. However, echinoids are preyed upon by some fish and marine carni-vores.

CLASS HOLOTHUROIDEA

In a phylum characterized by odd an-imals, class Holothuroidea contains mem-bers that both structurally and physio-logically are among the strangest of all. These soft-bodied animals have a remark-able resemblance to the vegetable after which they are named (Figure 297). In their evolution they appear to be more closely related to Echinoidea than to any other echinoderms. They are bottom-dwelling forms, living mostly in sand and mud. Low-tide pools with mucky bot-toms are favorite places. Here they lie

buried with their tentacles sticking up into the clearer water.

Two common species along the eastern seacoast are *Cucumaria frondosa* and *Thyone briareus.* Along the Pacific coast there are several species of *Cucumaria* and the striking reddish brown *Sticho-pus,* with very large papillae. The follow-ing description applies to either *Thyone* or *Cucumaria.*

Sea cucumbers

Structure. The bodies of sea cucumbers are elongated. The **mouth** and retractile tentacles are found at the oral end and the **anus** at the aboral end. They have leathery skins in which are embedded microscopic calcareous plates. The ten to thirty retractile **tentacles** around the mouth correspond to the oral tube feet of other echinoderms. The **body wall** con-tains both circular and longitudinal mus-cles and is covered by a cuticle and non-ciliated epidermis. The dorsal side bears two longitudinal zones of tube feet; the ventral side has three. Podia are absent in some species. The ventral side often becomes flattened and is called the **sole.**

The **coelomic cavity** is large and is not divided into compartments. It is filled with a fluid similar to sea water and

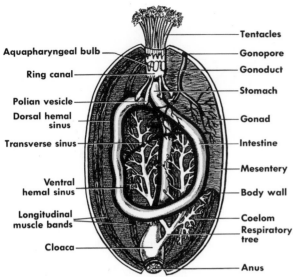

Figure 301. Longitudinal section of sea cucumber (similar to *Stichopus*), showing internal anatomy (semidiagrammatic).

Figure 302. Holothurian and its commensal fish, *Carapus* or *Fierasfer*. The fish (4 to 5 inches long) uses cloaca and respiratory tree for shelter. Only a small percentage of holothurians harbor the fish.

contains many coelomocytes. The **digestive system** contains a mouth, an esophagus, an oval stomach, a long, looped intestine (supported by mesenteries) which is enlarged at the posterior end into the cloaca, and the anus. A respiratory tree, two long, branched tubes though which the muscular cloaca pumps water, is formed by evaginations of the digestive tract and serves for both respiration and excretion. Water also passes through the walls of the respiratory tree into the coelom. The hemal system is well developed. It consists of a ring around the esophagus with radial vessels along the water canals

and two main sinuses along the digestive system. The hemal system is especially large in *Stichopus*.

The water-vascular system consists of an internal madreporite, a ring canal around the esophagus, and five radial canals that connect to the tube feet. Opening into the ring canal are a number of **polian vesicles**, elongated sacs hanging in the coelom and serving as expansion chambers for the water-vascular system.

The **nervous system** is made up of an oral nerve ring with five radial nerves. There appear to be sense organs for touch and light, and some species have stato-

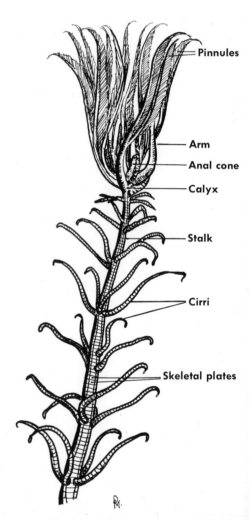

Figure 303. Crinoid with part of stalk. Some crinoids have stalks 2 feet long.

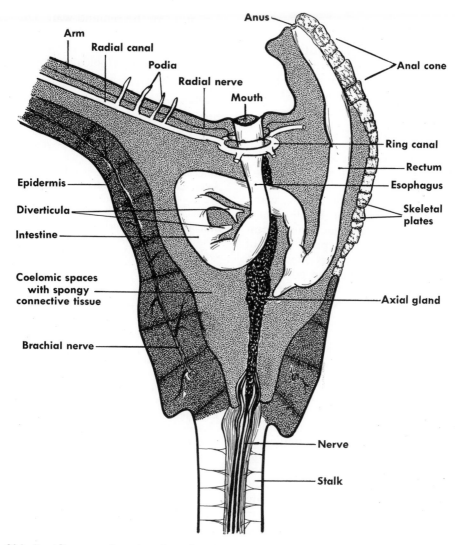

Labels in figure:
Anus
Arm
Radial canal
Podia
Radial nerve
Mouth
Anal cone
Ring canal
Rectum
Esophagus
Skeletal plates
Epidermis
Diverticula
Intestine
Coelomic spaces with spongy connective tissue
Axial gland
Brachial nerve
Nerve
Stalk

Figure 304. Semidiagram of section through calyx of typical crinoid, showing principal internal structures. (After Lang.)

cysts. The sexes are separate, but some holothuroids are hermaphroditic. There is one gonad in *Thyone* and *Cucumaria*, two in *Stichopus*. Each gonad is composed of numerous tubules united at their base to form a tuft, which may be quite large at sexual maturity. A common gonoduct empties the sex cells through a **gonopore** to the outside where fertilization occurs. The larval stage is called an **auricularia** (Figure 288). Some species brood the young either inside the body or somewhere on the body surface.

Behavior. Sea cucumbers are sluggish, moving partly by means of their ventral tube feet and partly by waves of contraction in the muscular wall which contains five powerful longitudinal muscle bands as well as circular muscle fibers. The dorsal tube feet are respiratory and tactile. The food consists of small organisms which they entangle in the sticky mucus of their tentacles and suck into the mouth. Sea cucumbers have a peculiar power of self-mutilation. Some, when irritated, may cast out a part of their viscera by a strong muscular contraction which may either rupture the body wall or evert its contents through the anus. The lost parts are soon regenerated. An interesting commensal relationship between a sea cucumber and certain fish is shown in Figure 302.

CLASS CRINOIDEA

The crinoids are the most primitive of the echinoderms. As fossil records reveal, they were once far more numerous than now. They are essentially a deep-water form although a few species live near shore. They differ from other echinoderms by being attached during part or all of their lives. The feather stars have long, many-branched arms and the adults are free swimming. At one stage of their life cycle they are attached to stalks, which they later absorb.

Sea lilies or feather stars

Structure. The body disc, or **calyx**, is covered with a leathery skin (tegmen) containing calcareous plates. Cuticle and epidermis are poorly developed. Five flexible arms branch to form many more arms, each with many lateral **pinnules** arranged like barbs on a feather. Calyx and arms together are called the **crown**. Sessile forms have a long, jointed **stalk** attached to the aboral side of the body. This stalk is made up of plates, appears jointed, and may bear **cirri**. The upper (oral) surface bears the **mouth** and the **anus**, which may be on a raised cone. Madreporite, spines, and pedicellariae are absent. Ciliated **ambulacral grooves** on the arms carry food to the mouth. Tube feet in the form of tentacles are also found in the grooves. The **water-vascular system** has the echinoderm plan. The **nervous system** is made up of an **oral ring** and a **radial nerve** which runs to each arm. The aboral, or entoneural, system is the main one in crinoids, in contrast to most other echinoderms. Sense organs are scanty and primitive. The sexes are separate. The gonads are simply masses of cells in the genital cavity of the arms and pinnules. The gametes escape without ducts through

a rupture in the pinnule wall. The larvae (doliolaria) are free swimming for a time before they become attached and metamorphose. Most crinoids are from 6 to 12 inches long.

Derivation and meaning of basic terminology

ambulacra (L. *ambulare,* to walk) Radiating grooves where podia of water-vascular system project to outside.

Arbacia (Gr. *Arbakes,* ancient king).

Asteroidea (Gr. *aster,* star, + *eidos,* form).

Bipinnaria (L. *bi,* double, + *pinna,* wing) Refers to shape of this asteroid larva.

Brachiolaria (L. *brachiolatus,* with arms) This asteroid larva has three preoral processes.

coelomocyte (Gr. *koiloma,* hollow, + *kytos,* cell) Another name for amebocyte, primitive or undifferentiated cell of the coelom, and the water-vascular system.

Crinoidea (Gr. *crinon,* lily, + *eidos,* form).

Dipleurula (Gr. *dis,* double, + *pleura,* side) This hypothetical echinoderm larva has bilateral symmetry.

Echinarachnius (Gr. *echinos,* hedgehog, + *rhachis,* spine).

Echinoidea (Gr. *echinos,* hedgehog, + *eidos,* form).

Eleutherozoa (Gr. *eleutheros,* free, + *zoa,* animals) This subphylum is made up of freely movable and unattached echinoderms.

Holothuroidea (Gr. *holothurion,* a sea cucumber).

lunules (L. *luna,* moon) These slitlike openings in the sand dollar test may be crescent shaped.

madreporite (L. *mater,* mother, + Gr. *poros,* pore, + *ite,* nature of) Sievelike structure which is the intake for the water-vascular system.

Ophiuroidea (Gr. *ophis,* serpent, + *oura,* tail, + *eidos,* form).

ossicle (L. *ossiculum,* small bone) Small separate pieces of endoskeleton.

pedicellaria (L. *pediculus,* a small foot).

Pelmatozoa (Gr. *pelmatos,* stalk, + *zoa,* animals) Members of this subphylum of echinoderms are attached.

periproct (Gr. *peri,* around, + *proktos,* anus) Region of aboral plates around the anus of echinoids.

pluteus (L. *pluteus,* a painter's easel) These echinoid larvae have elongated processes like the supports of an easel.

rosette (L. *rosa,* a rose) Arrangement or cluster resembling a rose.

ANNOTATED REFERENCES

Borradaile, L. A., and F. A. Potts. 1958. The Invertebrata, ed. 3 (revised by G. A. Kerkut). New York, Cambridge University Press. *A standard textbook on the invertebrates. A fair account of the echinoderms with schematic drawings.*

Buchsbaum, R. 1948. Animals Without Backbones, rev. ed. Chicago, University of Chicago Press. *Excellent illustrations of echinoderms.*

Cambridge Natural History. 1906. Echinodermata (E. W. MacBride). London, Macmillan & Co., Ltd. *Authoritative and detailed treatment of general structures.*

Carter, G. S. 1951. A General Zoology of the Invertebrates. London, Sidgwick & Jackson, Ltd. *An excellent work with emphasis on physiological aspects of the group.*

Encyclopaedia Britannica. 1956. Echinoderma. Chicago, Encyclopaedia Britannica, Inc. *A fine, concise account of echinoderms with clear illustrations.*

Harvey, E. B. 1956. The American Arbacia and Other Sea Urchins. Princeton, Princeton University Press. *A comprehensive monograph on this interesting group which have furnished so many basic concepts in the field of cytology and development.*

Hyman, L. H. 1955. The Invertebrates: Echinodermata. New York, McGraw-Hill Book Co., Inc. *The latest and most comprehensive work yet published on the echinoderms.*

Jennings, H. S. 1907. Behavior of the Starfish Asterias forreri De Loriol. Berkeley, University of California Publications in Zoology, vol. 4, pp. 339-441. *An account of the reactions of the starfish, including the righting movement.*

MacGinitie, G. E., and N. MacGinitie. 1949. Natural History of Marine Animals. New York, McGraw-Hill Book Co., Inc. *The section on echinoderms includes some good descriptions and photographs of representative forms, especially those of the Pacific coast.*

Lankester, E. R. (editor). 1900. A Treatise on Zoology. Part III. The Echinoderma (F. A. Bather). London, A. and C. Black. *The technical descriptions of echinoderms in this work will always be of great value.*

Parker, T. J., and W. A. Haswell. 1940. A Textbook of Zoology, ed. 6, 2 vols. (revised by O. Lowenstein). London, Macmillan & Co., Ltd. *Good general descriptions with considerable detail.*

Ricketts, E. F., and J. Calvin. 1952. Between Pacific Tides, ed. 3 (revised by J. W. Hedgpeth). Stanford, Stanford University Press. *In many ways this is an unique book of seashore life. It stresses the habits and habitats of the Pacific coast invertebrates (including echinoderms), and the illustrations are revealing. It includes an excellent systematic index and annotated bibliography.*

Schechter, V. 1959. Invertebrate Zoology. Englewood Cliffs, N. J. Prentice-Hall, Inc. *A short chapter is devoted to echinoderms. The bibliography stresses recent research articles of great value. Simple line drawings are presented.*

Smith, R. I., and others (editors). 1957. Intertidal Invertebrates of the Central California Coast. Berkeley, University of California Press. *This is a revision of S. F. Light's Laboratory and Field Text in Invertebrate Zoology. Consists mainly of taxonomic keys to the forms found in the intertidal zone.*

chapter 21

Phyla Hemichordata and Pogonophora

Phylum Hemichordata*

BIOLOGICAL PRINCIPLES

Organ-system level of organization

1. Hemichordates are a group that has a combination of both invertebrate (echinoderm) and chordate characteristics.

2. A chordate plan of structure is vaguely suggested by gill slits and a restricted tubular dorsal nerve cord.

3. Both classes (Enteropneusta and Pterobranchia) have a tripartite body composed of a proboscis, collar, and trunk, but one class is adapted for a sluggish burrowing habit and filter feeding; the other for a sessile, colonial existence and a ciliated lophophore method of feeding.

4. Each of the three body regions (segments) has its own body cavity, or coelom, which is unpaired in the proboscis but paired in the other two. The coelomic pouches of the proboscis and collar have pores (coelomostomes) to the exterior which are comparable to the water pores of echinoderms.

5. They belong to the deuterostome branch of the animal kingdom and are enterocoelous with radial cleavage.

6. Because of their close relationship to the chordates, this phylum and Pogonophora are called prechordates.

Biological contributions

1. The class Enteropneusta has developed the **filter-feeding** mode of life and the class

*Hem'i-kor-da"ta (Gr. *hemi*, half, + *chorde*, cord).

Pterobranchia, the sessile condition typical of the ancestral prevertebrates.

2. **A tubular dorsal nerve cord** (in collar zone) foreshadows the future condition in chordates, and a diffused net of nerve cells is similar to the uncentralized, subepithelial plexus of echinoderms.

3. The **gill slits** so characteristic of chordates are used primarily for filter feeding and only secondarily for breathing and are thus comparable to some of the protochordates.

4. The **stomochord** (**notochord** by tradition), an outpocketing forward from the roof of the mouth cavity, with its chitinous plate is of debatable phylogenetic status. It is sometimes called a buccal diverticulum.

Position in animal kingdom

1. The best evidence of relationship to the chordates are the gill slits and U-shaped tongue bars (which are absent in the Pterobranchia).

2. The affinity of the hemichordates with the echinoderms is more clear-cut, such as the embryological (larval) resemblance between two groups, general similarity of their nervous systems, and the functional similarity of the hydraulic mechanism of the proboscis-collar coelom with the water-vascular system of echinoderms.

3. The presence of both phosphocreatine (a vertebrate energy compound) and phosphoarginine (an invertebrate energy compound) in *Balanoglossus* may indicate that the latter is a connecting link between vertebrates and invertebrates.

GENERAL RELATIONS

The taxonomic status and phylogenetic relationship of the hemichordates has been somewhat of a puzzle among zoologists for many years. Many authorities still consider them a subphylum under the chordates and lump them among the subphyla Tunicata (Urochordata) and Cephalochordata to form the Protochordata. This classification was based mainly upon certain characteristics of the hemichordates, such as gill slits and a supposed rudimentary notochord which members of the phylum Chordata possess. Some hemichordates have the beginning of a dorsal hollow nerve cord which distinguishes the chordate nerve cord from that of the invertebrates. The group also is somewhat unique in having many invertebrate characteristics as well as chordate ones. Their affinity with the echinoderms is marked, for the **tornaria larva** of *Balanoglossus* is remarkably like certain echinoderm larvae. There are also other resemblances to echinoderms, such as the coelomic pouches which act like a water-vascular system and the general plan of the subepithelial plexus nervous system, characteristic of both groups. Both the hemichordates and the echinoderms also share many habits in common, such as feeding methods and ecological niches. Many zoologists are highly skeptical about the presence of a true notochord in Hemichordata but instead consider such an organ as a **stomochord,** which may not be homologous to the notochord of chordates.

Because of these and other reasons, the hemichordates are placed in a phylum of their own, phylum Hemichordata, which is made up of two classes, Enteropneusta and Pterobranchia. These two classes have many like as well as unlike features. Enteropneusta are highly specialized for burrowing and filter feeding; Pterobranchia are sessile and colonial, with lophophore feeding. All three groups—echinoderms, hemichordates, and chordates—are deuterostomous and have enterocoelous coeloms (as do the Chaetognatha and a few others). The class Pterobranchia shows affinities with the Ectoprocta, Brachiopoda, and others because of the lophophore and sessile habits. There is strong evidence to suggest that the early vertebrate ancestor may have been sessile but filter feeding with gill slits developed due to loss of the lophophore system.

CHARACTERISTICS

1. Soft-bodied animals of elongated (wormlike) or short, compact body with **stalk** for attachment; bilateral symmetry; body typically divided into **proboscis, collar,** and **trunk; stomochord** in posterior part of proboscis

2. Body wall of unicellular epidermis with mucus-secreting cells, basement membrane, musculature of smooth muscle, and mostly longitudinal

3. One group (Enteropneusta) free living and of burrowing habits; another (Pterobranchia) sessile with free-living and colonial members in chitinous tubes

4. Digestive tract straight and complete, or U shaped with a **lophophore** of two or many arms bearing ciliated bands (pterobranchs)

5. Coelomic cavities correspond to each of the three body regions; proboscis coelomic pouches single, other two paired; proboscis and collar coelomic pouches open to exterior by dorsal pores

6. Circulatory system of a median dorsal and a median ventral longitudinal vessel interconnected by small lateral vessels and jointed to a heart dorsal to the stomochord

7. Respiratory system of gill slits (few or none in Pterobranchia) forming a dorsolateral row in the pharynx behind the collar

8. Excretory system of a single glomerulus (proboscis gland) connected to blood vessels

9. Nervous system of a subepidermal plexus of cells and fibers which is thickened to form two longitudinal nerve cords, one mediodorsal and the other medioventral, with a ring connective between the two cords in the collar; dorsal nerve cord of collar hollow in some

10. Sexes separate in Enteropneusta with saclike gonads projecting into body cavity and arranged in a row on each side in the genital region of the trunk; in Pterobranchia reproduction may be sexual, with paired ovaries and pigmented oviducts or paired testes near the anus (a few monoecious), or asexual (in some) by budding; external fertilization; tornaria larva in some Enteropneusta but without larval stages in others; in *Rhabdopleura* (Pterobranchia) individuals bud from a stolon to form a colony of zooids

CLASSES

Class Enteropneusta (en'ter-op-neus"ta) (Gr. *enteron*, gut, + *pneustos*, breathed)—**acorn or tongue worms.** Body vermiform with no stalk; proboscis cylindrical and tapering to a blunt point; active, free living and burrowing; many gill slits in a row on each side of anterior region (pharynx) of trunk; alimentary canal straight with anus at terminal end; separate sexes with many saclike gonads arranged serially; tornaria larva in some. Examples: *Balanoglossus, Saccoglossus.*

Class Pterobranchia (pter'o-bran"chi-a) (Gr. *pteron*, feather, + *branchion*, gill)—**pterobranchs.** Compact body with stalk; proboscis shield shaped; sessile in chitinous tubes with lophophore bearing ciliated arms; a single pair of gill slits in pharynx or none; alimentary canal U shaped with anus near mouth; separate sexes or monoecious, budding in some. Examples: *Cephalodiscus, Rhabdopleura.*

(**Class Planctosphaeroidea**, represented by a few pelagic larvae, is recognized by some.)

REPRESENTATIVE TYPES

CLASS ENTEROPNEUSTA

These are vermiform hemichords which are common in sand or mud flats in rather shallow water, although specimens have been collected at great depths. They vary in length from an inch or two to several feet. The name *Balanoglossus* has been applied to many genera but should be restricted to one genus. This genus has a world-wide distribution. Several species of *Saccoglossus* (Figure 305) are found along both the east and west coasts. *Saccoglossus kowalevskii* is common along the east coast, *Saccoglossus pusillus* along

the California coast. Some of them have bright orange and red colors.

The body is made up of a **proboscis** **collar**, and an elongated **trunk.** In the hind part of the proboscis lies the **stomochord** (called the **notochord** until recently) which is an outpocketing of the dorsal wall of the buccal cavity. Its exact phylogenetic status is unknown, but it may be a primitive notochord. On the ventral surface of the stomochord is a chitinous skeletal plate which helps support the proboscis. The many **gill slits** form a dorsolateral row on each side just behind the collar. These slits serve as passages from the pharynx to the exterior. The external opening of each slit is a simple pore, but the inner opening into the pharynx is U shaped, produced by the downgrowth of branchial tongue bars.

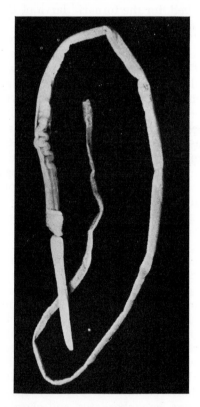

Figure 305. Tongue or acorn worm, *Saccoglossus.* Proboscis appears dense and rigid, with collar folded just behind it. Note coils of intestinal tract. Class Enteropneusta.

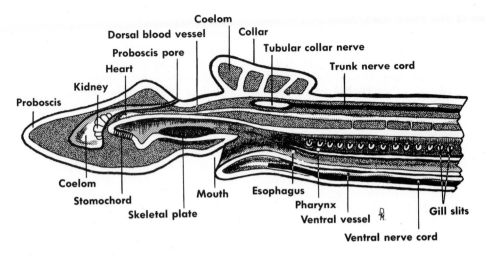

Figure 306. Diagram of longitudinal section through anterior end of *Saccoglossus*. Class Enteropneusta.

These tongue bars are provided with capillaries and function in respiration. The gill slits and pouches serve to pass outward the water that enters the pharynx and thus serve as food strainers. There is a single coelomic space in the proboscis, paired ones in the collar and trunk. The spaces in the proboscis and collar can fill with water through dorsal pores (usually paired), and thus the anterior end of the animal can become turgid as an aid in burrowing. The **digestive system** is made up of a wide mouth at the anteroventral margin of the collar, a buccal cavity within the collar, the pharynx with its gill slits, a straight intestine bearing dorsal hepatic ceca, and the anus at the terminal end. The alimentary canal is supported by the double walls of the longitudinal partition which divides the trunk coelom into two cavities. The anterior end of the digestive system is also divided into the dorsal pharynx and the ventral esophagus. The **vascular system** consists of a median dorsal and a median ventral longitudinal blood vessel which are interconnected by small branches especially in the pharyngeal region. A **heart vesicle** lies dorsal to the stomochord, but propulsion is probably done by peristaltic contractions of the large blood vessels. The blood is colorless (and may have

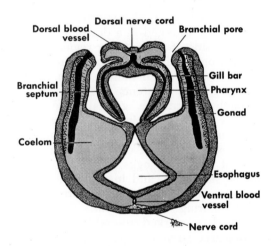

Figure 307. Cross-section through pharyngeal region of tongue worm. Class Enteropneusta. (After Lang.)

cells) and flows anteriorly in the dorsal blood vessel. In the proboscis, the vascular system gives rise to a network of blood sinuses (the proboscidal glomerulus), which may have excretory functions.

The body is covered by a thick, ciliated, unicellular epithelium which contains many mucous cells. This epithelium rests upon a basement membrane underneath which is the musculature that makes up most of the **body wall.** Most of the muscles are longitudinal, but a few may be circular or pseudocircular. Most of them give off an unpleasant smell like that of iodoform. The **nervous system** consists mostly of a subepithelial network or plexus of fibers and cells, to which processes of epithelial cells are attached. Thickenings or concentrations of this net form nerve cords along the mid-dorsal and mid-ventral lines of the trunk. These cords are united posterior to the collar by a ring connective, and the dorsal cord, which is here thickened and invaginated into a tubular form in some, continues on into the collar and furnishes many fibers to the plexus of the proboscis.

The sexes are separate in class Enteropneusta. The gonads, which are simple or branched sacs projecting into the body cavity, are arranged in a dorsolateral row on each side of the anterior region of the trunk from behind the collar to near the hepatic ceca. When mature, each gonad discharges its contents to the exterior through a separate genital pore. The gonads do not open into the coelom and new ones are constantly being formed at the posterior end of each row. Fertilization of the small eggs occurs externally in the sea water, and in some species, a pelagic, ciliated larva, the **tornaria,** is found during development. This larva has such a marked resemblance to the auricularia larva of certain echinoderms that it was at one time described as belonging to the echinoderm group. The tornaria larva differs, however, in having a perianal band of cilia and a pair of eyespots near the apical tuft of cilia. The familiar *Saccoglossus* of American waters does not have a tornaria stage.

Hemichordates are delicate, sluggish animals which use their proboscis and collar for burrowing through sandy or muddy sea bottoms. By taking in water through the pores into the coelomic sacs, the proboscis and collar are stiffened for burrowing. Then, by contracting the body wall musculature, the excess water is driven through the gill slits while the silt and mud, containing usable organic food, is passed along the ventral esophagus into the intestine where digestion occurs. Like earthworms, hemichordates pass a great deal of indigestible material through the alimentary canal.

CLASS PTEROBRANCHIA

The basic plan of this class is quite similar to that of the Enteropneusta, but certain structural differences are correlated with the sedentary mode of life of pterobranchs. The first pterobranch ever reported was obtained by the famed "Challenger" expedition of 1872-1876. Although first placed among the Polyzoa (Entoprocta and Ectoprocta), its affinities to the hemichordates were later recognized. Only two genera *(Cephalodiscus*

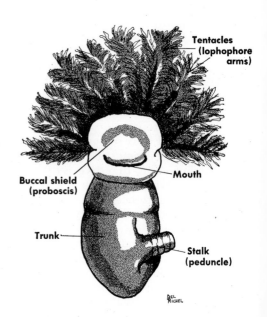

Figure 308. *Cephalodiscus,* a pterobranch. These tiny sessile forms do not exceed 2 mm. in length and live in chitinous tubes in which they can move about. Ciliated bands on arms carry currents of food toward mouth. Patches of stiff epithelial cells in pharyngeal region are called a notochord (?) by some. Pair of so-called gill slits serve merely as outlet for water. It is thought that these deep-sea organisms are close to ancestral stock of both echinoderms and chordates. (After Lang and others.)

and *Rhabdopleura*) are known in any detail. They are small animals, usually within the range of 1 to 7 mm. in length, although the stalk may be longer. The members of *Cephalodiscus* are free living, but many individuals live together in gelatinous tubes which often form an anastomosing system. Through apertures in these tubes they extend their crown of tentacles. They are attached to the walls of the tubes by body stalks which are very extensible and can jerk the owners back when necessary. The body of *Cephalodiscus* is divided into the three regions—proboscis, collar, and trunk—characteristic of the hemichordates. There is only one pair of gills, and the alimentary canal is U shaped with the anus near the mouth. The proboscis is shield shaped. At the base of the proboscis many pairs of branching arms (lophophores) with ciliated bands arise. By means of these cilia they collect their food. The two gonads open in front of the anus. Some species are dioecious and others monoecious. Asexual reproduction by budding may also occur.

In the other genus, *Rhabdopleura*, which is smaller than *Cephalodiscus*, the members remain together to form a colony of zooids, each with its contractile stalk enclosed in a chitinous tube. The collar in these forms bears two branching arms or lophophores. No gill clefts or glomeruli are present. New individuals are reproduced by budding from a creeping basal tube or stolon which branches on a substratum. There are two types of individuals in a colony—**budding** individuals and **feeding** individuals. In none of the pterobranchs is there a tubular nerve cord in the collar, but otherwise their nervous system is similar to that of the Enteropneusta.

The fossil graptolites of the middle Paleozoic era are often placed as an extinct class under Hemichordata. Their tubular chitinous skeleton and colonial habits indicate an affinity with *Rhabdopleura*. They are considered important index fossils of the Ordovician and Silurian geological strata.

Phylum Pogonophora*

BIOLOGICAL PRINCIPLES

Organ-system level of organization

1. This is a new phylum in the process of analysis. It is sometimes called Brachiata.
2. It is the only free-living metazoan phylum without a digestive system.
3. Other organ systems are present.
4. They belong to the Deuterostomia branch with enterocoelous formation of the coelom and unequal determinative cleavage.

Biological contributions

1. Body is typically divided into three regions—**protosome, mesosome,** and **trunk** (metasome); similar to hemichordate pattern.
2. There is some indication of segmentation in trunk.
3. A tentacular mass originates on the protosome.
4. The type of cleavage does not fit into either the spiral or radial type but is of a unique pattern.
5. Negative characteristics are the complete **lack of a digestive system** and the **absence of a blastopore** in gastrula formation.
6. The tentacles with pinnules form a device for collecting food and probably also for absorbing the extracellularly digested food.

Position in animal kingdom

Belonging to the deuterostomes, pogonophores (beard worms) are in the same group with the hemichordates, the echinoderms, and the chordates. Their tripartite body regions and coelom indicate a relationship to the hemichordates.

GENERAL RELATIONS

Specimens of this phylum, the most recently discovered in the animal kingdom, were collected from deep-sea dredgings (1900) in the waters off the coast of Indonesia. They have since been discovered in several seas and sufficient material for the phylum's appraisal has only recently been available. So far about twenty-two species have been described. These elongated tubicolous forms have left no known fossil record and show closest affinities to the hemichordates. Many

*Po'go-nof"er-a (Gr. *pogon*, beard, + *phora*, bear).

details of structure are vague and uncertain.

CHARACTERISTICS

1. **Body elongated** and **tripartite** (protosome, mesosome, and metasome; body enclosed in a **secreted tube;** faint evidences of segmentation in trunk; constrictions between the protosome and mesosome may or may not be present; mesosome and metasome separated by muscular diaphragm; dorsal and ventral sides not evident

2. Protosome small with one to more than 200 **tentacles,** each provided with **pinnules** or lateral projections; basal part of tentacles may be fused into a spiral; protosome terminating in rounded **cephalic lobe**

3. Body covered with **columnar epidermis** with cuticle; epidermis may be provided with glands and cilia; trunk with pair of raised girdles (**belts**) bearing chitinous adhesive organs

4. Coelom subdivided into a single protocoele (protosome) and a pair of coelomic sacs in each of the mesosome and metasome divisions

5. No digestive system

6. **Closed circulatory system** of two median longitudinal vessels, one of which may be enlarged to form a heart

7. No gills or special respiratory system.

8. Excretory system of a **pair of nephridial coelomoducts** which connect the unpaired protosomal coelom to the surface

9. Nervous system of a ring-shaped or elongated brain in the cephalic lobe with one or more median longitudinal cords; epidermal in position

10. Musculature of both circular and longitudinal fibers; special muscles in protosome and the septum or diaphragm

11. Sexes separate; gonads paired elongated bodies in the metacoele with gonopores to the exterior; spermatophores present

12. Fertilization occurring in tube; cleavage holoblastic and unequal; bilateral embryos develop in tube; gastrulation without blastopore.

CLASSIFICATION

Order Athecanephria (a-thec'a-nef"ri-a) (Gr. *a,* without, + *theca,* case, + *nephros,* kidney). Protosome-mesosome divided by constriction; coelomoducts with lateral nephridiopores; tentacles usually few and separate; postannular trunk with scattered adhesive papillae; fusiform spermatophores. Examples: *Oligobrachia, Siboglinum.*

Order Thecanephria (thec'a-nef"ri-a) (Gr. *theca,* case, + *nephron,* kidney). Protosome-mesosome usually without external constriction; coelomoducts with median nephridiopores; tentacles numerous and may be basically fused; postannular trunk with transverse rows of adhesive papillae; flat spermatophores. Examples: *Heptabrachia, Galathealinum.*

GENERAL FEATURES

External structure. Beard worms are cylindrical worms with elongated, slender bodies, which are enclosed in secreted tubes. The different species vary from 80 mm. to 350 mm. in length, and from 0.5 to about 2 mm. in diameter. The body is divided into a short anterior part, which in some is subdivided by a constriction into a protosome and a mesosome, and a very long, slender trunk (metasome). The latter is separated from the mesosome by a septum or diaphragm. The protosome bears the cephalic lobe, at the base of which originate the fringed tentacles (1 to 200 in number). In some, the tentacles may be fused together at their bases. All tentacles are hollow extensions of the coelom. A pair of ridges on the mesosome is known as the **bridle** and a pair of elevated girdles with platelets on the trunk are called the **belts.** That region of the trunk anterior to the belts is the **preannular region** with a median ciliated band; posterior to the belts is the postannular region. Adhesive papillae to anchor the worm in its tube are found on the trunk. Although classed among the coelomate Bilateria, dorsal and ventral surfaces are not evident.

Internal structure. The columnar epidermis may bear many glands. Beneath the epidermis are circular and longitud-

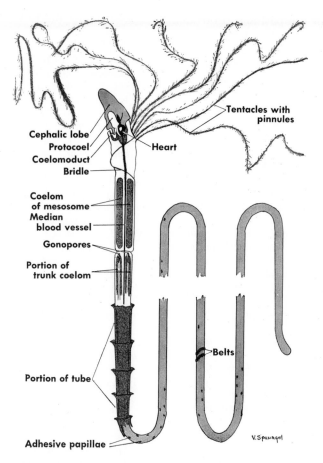

Figure 309. Diagrammatic view of pogonophore, showing principal external and internal structures. Portions of trunk have been omitted. (After Ivanov and others.)

In the diagram, the following labels appear:

- Cephalic lobe
- Protocoel
- Coelomoduct
- Bridle
- Coelom of mesosome
- Median blood vessel
- Gonopores
- Portion of trunk coelom
- Portion of tube
- Adhesive papillae
- Tentacles with pinnules
- Heart
- Belts
- V. Spanagel

inal muscles, and the protosome is provided with additional muscles. The coelom is divided into a single sac (protocoele) in the protosome and paired sacs in each of the mesosome and metasome divisions. Peritoneum is scanty. There is no digestive system or special respiratory system. The closed circulatory system usually consists of two median vessels, one of which may serve as a muscular heart. Tentacles and their pinnules are well supplied with blood. In the protosome the unpaired coelom opens to the surface by a pair of ciliated nephridial coelomoducts. The nervous system is epidermal in position and is made up of a ring-shaped or elongated brain in the cephalic lobe which gives rise to one or two longitudinal cords to the trunk region. The sexes are separate with paired gonads in the metacoele of the metasome, the ovaries and oviducts in the anterior part of the trunk, and the testes and sperm ducts in the posterior half. The sperm is found in spermatophores. Fertilization and development occur in the tube. The unequal but holoblastic cleavage produces a bilateral larva.

Natural history and behavior. Most pogonophores live in the ooze on the bottom of the ocean floor, but some have been found in littoral waters. They are obtained only by dredging. The tubes they secrete around themselves are usually longer than the animals and consist of cellulose (tunicin). They are not fastened

Phyla Hemichordata and Pogonophora 399

in these tubes but are partially protruded for food getting. Since they lack a digestive system, it has been suggested that they use their tentacles and pinnules as food-catching nets, where digestion also occurs. The digested products are then absorbed through the thin walls of the pinnules which are abundantly supplied with blood.

Derivation and meaning of basic terminology

Athecanephria (Gr. *a*, without, + *theca*, case, + *nephros*, kidney) Coelomoducts are far apart.

Balanoglossus (Gr. *balanos*, acorn, + *glossa*, tongue) Refers to the shape of the proboscis in this genus.

mesosome (Gr. *mesos*, middle, + *soma*, body) Collar or middle part of pogonophores and hemichordates.

metasome (Gr. *meta*, next, + *soma*, body) Posterior part of the body.

Pogonophora (Gr. *pogon*, beard, + *phora*, bearing).

protosome (Gr. *protos*, first, + *soma*, body) First body division or proboscis of pogonophores and hemichordates.

Saccoglossus (Gr. *sakkos*, sac, + *glossa*, tongue).

stomochord (Gr. *stoma*, mouth, + L. *chorda*, cord) The thick-walled forward evagination of the dorsal wall of the buccal cavity into the proboscis; the buccal diverticulum; may be a homologue of the notochord or a primitive notochord.

Thecanephria (Gr. *theca*, case, + *nephros*, kidney) Coelomoducts are close together.

Tornaria (L. *tornare*, to turn) This larva rotates in circles.

ANNOTATED REFERENCES

Hemichordata

Hyman, L. H. 1959. The Invertebrates: Smaller Coelomate Groups (Phylum Hemichordata), vol. 5. New York, McGraw-Hill Book Co., Inc. *The best up-to-date account.*

Kowalevsky, A. 1866. Anatomie des Balanoglossus. Mem. Acad. Imper. Sci. St. Petersbourg, ser. 7, vol. 10, no. 3. *A classical paper and the first accurate description of this group.*

Newell, G. E. 1951. The Stomochord of Enteropneusta, Proc. Zool. Soc., vol. 121, p. 741. *An appraisal of the status of the stomochord in comparison with a true notochord.*

Van der Horst, C. J. 1932. Enteropneusta. In W. Kunkenthal and T. Krumbach: Handbuch der Zoologie, vol. 3, pt. 2. *A detailed study of the phylum.*

Van der Horst, C. J. 1935. Hemichordata. In H. G. Bronn: Klassen und Ordnungen der Tierreichs, vol. 4, pt. 4, book 2.

Pogonophora

De Beer, G. 1955. The Pogonophora, Nature, vol. 176. *A brief survey and appraisal.*

Hyman, L. H. 1959. The Invertebrates: Smaller Coelomate Groups, vol. V. New York, McGraw-Hill Book Co., Inc. *The best appraisal in English of this strange group.*

Ivanov, A. V. 1955. The Main Features of the Organization of the Pogonophora. In C. S. (Doklady), Academy of Science, U.S.S.R., 100 (translated by A. Petrunkevitch in System. Zool. 4). *In this and other papers, Ivanov has given the most comprehensive account yet published on the beard worms.*

chapter 22

Phylum Chordata*

Ancestry and evolution; general

characteristics; protochordates

BIOLOGICAL PRINCIPLES

Organ-system level of organization

1. Chordates have most of the features of the higher invertebrate phyla, such as bilateral symmetry, three germ layers, coelomic cavity, and, in common with arthropods and annelids, metamerism. Metamerism, however, has arisen independently of the other groups.

2. Organ-systems are well represented and have reached a stage of development (vertebrates) greater than those in the highest invertebrates.

3. In general there is a marked regional differentiation of the body into a head, trunk, and tail.

4. A neck is found also in the lung-breathing forms (many vertebrates).

Biological contributions

1. A **living endoskeleton** is characteristic of the entire phylum. Two endoskeletons are present in the group as a whole. One of these is the rodlike **notochord** which is present in all members of the phylum at some time; the other is the **vertebral column**, which largely replaces the notochord in higher chordates.

2. The endoskeleton does not interfere with **continuous growth**, for it can increase in size with the rest of the body. There is, therefore, no necessity for shedding it as is the case with the nonliving exoskeleton of the invertebrate phyla. Moreover, the endoskeleton allows for almost indefinite growth, so that many chordates are the largest of all animals.

*Chor-da'ta (L. *chorda*, a cord).

3. The nature of the endoskeleton is such that it affords much surface for muscular attachment, and since the muscular and skeletal systems make up most of the bulk of animals, other bodily systems must also become specialized in both size and function to meet the metabolic requirements of these two great systems.

4. The endoskeleton in higher chordates consists of the **axial** and **appendicular** divisions. The axial is made up of the cranium, vertebral column, ribs, and sternum; the appendicular is composed of the pectoral and pelvic girdles and the skeleton of the appendages.

5. A **postanal** tail is a new addition to the animal kingdom and is present at some stage in most chordates.

6. A **ventral heart** is a new characteristic, and a closed blood system is better developed than it is in other phyla. Chordates have also developed a **hepatic portal system** which is specialized for conveying food-laden blood from the digestive system to the liver.

7. **Pharyngeal gills** are introduced for the first time. Gill slits or traces are present in the embryos of all chordates. Terrestrial chordates have developed lungs by modification of this same pharyngeal region.

8. A dorsal, hollow nerve cord is universally present at some stage.

Position in animal kingdom

1. All available evidence indicates that chordates have evolved from the invertebrates, but it is impossible to establish the exact relationship.

2. Two possible lines of ancestry have been proposed in the phylogenetic background of the

chordates. One of these is the annelid-arthropod-mollusk group; the other is the echinoderm-protochordate group.

3. The echinoderms as a group have certain characteristics which are shared with the chordates, such as **indeterminate cleavage, same type of mesoderm and coelom formation, anus derivation from blastopore with mouth of secondary origin,** and the same biochemical substance (phosphocreatine). Thus the echinoderms appear to have a close kinship to the chordate phylum.

4. Taking the phylum as a whole, there is more fundamental unity of plan throughout all the organs and systems of this group than there is in any of the invertebrate phyla.

BACKGROUND

This great phylum derives its name from one of the few common characteristics of this group—the **notochord** (Gr. *noton,* back, + L. *chorda,* a cord). This structure is possessed by all members of the phylum, either in the larval or embryonic stages or throughout life. The notochord is a rodlike, semirigid body of vacuolated cells which extends, in most cases, the length of the body between the enteric canal and the central nervous system. Its primary purpose is to support and to stiffen the body, that is, to act as a skeletal axis.

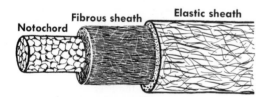

Fibrous sheath **Elastic sheath**
Notochord

Figure 310. Diagram of structure of notochord and its surrounding sheaths. Cells of notochord proper are thick walled, pressed together closely, and filled with semifluid. Stiffness due mainly to turgidity of fluid-filled cells and surrounding connective tissue sheaths. This primitive type of endoskeleton is characteristic of all chordates at some stage of life cycle. Notochord provides longitudinal stiffening of main body axis, base for myomeric muscles, and axis around which vertebral column develops. In most vertebrates it is crowded out of existence. In man, slight remnants are found in nuclei pulposi of intervertebral discs. (Modified from Eaton.)

The structural plan of chordates retains many of the features of invertebrate animals, such as bilateral symmetry, anterior-posterior axis, coelom, tube-within-a-tube arrangement, metamerism, cephalization, and others.

One distinguishing characteristic of the chordates is the **endoskeleton** which, as we have seen, is first found in the echinoderms. An endoskeleton is an internal structure which provides support and serves as a framework for the body. Most chordates possess two types of endoskeletons in their life cycle. The first is the **notochord** (Figure 310), possessed at some stage by all chordates. The second is the **vertebral column** and accessory structures such as the appendages. This second type of endoskeleton, which is more specialized and more adaptable for evolutionary growth, is possessed by only part, although the greater part, of the chordate phylum.

Even though the chordates have emphasized an endoskeleton, they have by no means cast aside the exoskeleton of the invertebrates. Many of the higher chordates (that is, the vertebrates) have keratinoid exoskeletons, although here the exoskeleton is mainly for protection and not for attachment of muscles. Another marked distinction is that the endoskeleton is a living tissue, whereas the exoskeleton is composed of dead noncellular material. The endoskeleton has the advantage of allowing continuous growth without the necessity of shedding. For this reason vertebrate animals can attain great size; some of them are the most massive in the animal kingdom. Endoskeletons provide much surface for muscle attachment, and size differences between animals result mainly from the amount of muscle tissue they possess. More muscle tissue necessitates greater development of body systems, such as circulatory, digestive, respiratory, and excretory. Thus it is seen that the endoskeleton is the chief basic factor in the development and specialization of the higher animals.

From an evolutionary viewpoint the

function of the skeleton, as represented by the exoskeleton and the endoskeleton, has shifted more from a protective one to that of support. The limy shells of clams and other mollusks and the chitinous armor of arthropods are excellent defensive armors even though they also serve for attachment of muscles and support of bodily structures. However, endoskeletons have their protective functions as well as supporting ones, as revealed by such excellent protective boxes as the cranium for the brain and the thorax for important visceral organs.

The animals most familiar to the student belong to the chordates. Man himself is a member and shares the common characteristics of this group. Ecologically the phylum is among the most successful in the animal kingdom. They are among the most adaptable of organic forms and are able to occupy most kinds of habitat. From a purely biological viewpoint chordates are of primary interest because they illustrate so well the broad biological principles of evolution, development and relationship. They represent as a group the background of man himself.

ANCESTRY AND EVOLUTION

That vertebrates have come from invertebrates is not doubted by most biologists. The best evidence available is that which involves the protochordates and the echinoderms. The great chasm, however, between the invertebrates and the chordates has never been bridged in spite of many attempts of biologists to do so. Whatever this ancestor may have been there are no fossil records to show. There is reason to believe that it was soft bodied, which would account for its failure to be preserved as a fossil. The primitive chordates which we refer to as the **protochordates** are so different from the invertebrates as a group that they throw little light on the problem. Apparently only the vertebrates were sufficiently hard and durable to be laid down as fossil forms. It has been possible to trace with considerable success the evolutionary patterns of most vertebrates, for the sequence of their fossil records is very convincing in many cases.

The ancestor of the chordates can be reconstructed to some extent from our present knowledge of existing protochordates. This ancestor probably was sessile and quite simple, having a filter device for collecting food, an alimentary canal, and a reproductive system, all enclosed in a soft body.

Echinoderm theory. Of the many theories to account for the probable invertebrate ancestor of chordates, only the echinoderm theory deserves serious consideration. Several lines of evidence of an embryological and biochemical nature strongly suggest a close relationship between the two groups. In the first place there is a marked resemblance between the bipennaria larva of certain echinoderms and the tornaria larva of the hemichordates (a phylum with some chordate characteristics), for both of them have similar ciliated bands in loops, sensory cilia at the anterior end, and a complete digestive system of ventral mouth and posterior anus. Both echinoderms and chordates have indeterminate cleavage; that is, each of the early blastomeres has equivalent potentialities with each of the other blastomeres. Echinoderms and chordates belong to the deuterostome branch of the animal kingdom; that is, the mouth is formed as a secondary opening and the blastopore of the gastrula becomes the anus. The coelom in these two phyla is enterocoelous and thus is budded off from the archenteron of the embryo.

Biochemically, with few exceptions, deuterostomes use phosphocreatine in the energy cycle of their muscular contraction; most of the protosomes (other phyla) use phosphoarginine for the same purpose. In this connection it is interesting to note that certain hemichordates use both phosphocreatine and phosphoarginine in their muscle cycle which may indicate that these forms are connecting links between vertebrates and invertebrates. Serological tests also show a closer relationship of vertebrates to echinoderms than to other phyla.

Earliest chordates (prevertebrates). If the phylum Chordata has an evolutionary relationship with the echinoderms, and probably sprang from the same ancestors, what was the nature of this primitive chordate and what chordate today is most like it? The fossil record cannot tell us, for it is unlikely that such a primitive form could be fossilized. The gap between the invertebrates and the vertebrates may always remain unbridged. What we can find out about these matters must be acquired from a comparative study of living forms, especially from their larval and embryological stages. The simplest chordates which exist today are a few lowly forms that possess a notochord but no vertebral column (backbone). These backboneless animals and those with a backbone, or the vertebrates, make up the phylum Chordata as we know it. The vertebrates comprise by far the greatest number of the chordates, so that the terms vertebrate and chordate are sometimes used as synonyms. The backboneless members are often referred to as the protochordates or prevertebrates and include two types or subphyla: (1) Cephalochordata, represented by the lancelet (*Amphioxus* or *Branchiostoma*); and (2) Urochordata (Tunicata), represented by *Ciona*. Closely linked to the protochordates and often included with them is the phylum Hemichordata which is made up of the acorn worms and the pterobranchs.

The American geologist Chamberlain, who gave us the theory of the fresh-water origin of vertebrates in 1900, also constructed a hypothetical protovertebrate which might be considered the ancestor of vertebrates. According to his scheme the chief features of such an ancestor would include a spindle-shaped or fusiform body, bilateral symmetry, a stiff axial rod and segmentally arranged muscles, a jawless mouth fitted for filter feeding, internal gills, a nervous system and brain, and a solid tail of muscle. Such an active swimming form is supposed to have been evolved under the influence of flow-ing continental streams or rivers where its ancestors were driven by enemies or by the necessity of finding algae or the rich detritus (organic material) of river mouths, or by seeking unoccupied ecological niches, etc. It is generally agreed among evolutionists that whatever the nature of this protovertebrate, it arose in fresh water and was adapted for filter feeding.

What existing or fossil animal best fits the form and organization of this hypothetical prevertebrate? There is no agreement about the answer to this question. Authorities, such as Colbert, insist that the classical *Amphioxus* (Figure 329) is still the logical structural ancestor of the vertebrates in spite of objections advanced by others regarding the specialization and aberrant nature of this well-known form. He regards the lancelet as a very primitive chordate which meets most of the requirements of the hypothetical ancestor.

Homer Smith's reconstruction of the hypothetical protovertebrate, as sketched in his well-known book, *From Fish to Philosopher,* has a remarkable resemblance to *Amphioxus.* Yet that authority denies that *Amphioxus* could be the prototype of chordates because it is impossible to derive the vertebrate nephron from the nephridial complex of the lancelet. Romer regards *Amphioxus* as degenerate and as a divergent side branch between the lower chordates and the vertebrates.

Another theory of chordate origin is the ascidian theory advocated by Garstang in 1928. This theory stresses the idea that the early chordate ancestors were filter feeding, marine, and sessile. For collecting food, gill slits were evolved, and these later became respiratory in function. The ascidians themselves may have come from the sessile pterobranchs, one of the divisions of the phylum Hemichordata. The ascidian tadpole larva, with its basic vertebrate organization, was evolved, according to this theory, from the sessile form and became pelagic in order to exploit the plankton of oceanic surface waters. After swimming around for a time, this larva usually attaches to a substratum, and, after a degenerative metamorphosis, assumes the sessile adult form. Certain of these tadpole larvae, it is believed, became neotenous (i.e., sexually mature in the larval stage), did not metamorphose into the adult sessile form, and entered the estuaries and river mouths where they could live upon the rich detritus brought down from the continents. Zoologists have long considered the class Larvacea of the tunicates as an example of neoteny in which later stages are omitted in its evolution. To invade the inland regions of the continents by way of streams, a correlated evolutionary change had to take place in these neotenous larvae. Invasion meant facing and overcoming the water currents flowing toward the sea, and morphological and physiological changes, such as strong locomotor equipment, increase in size of body, more alert senses, and a kidney adapted for a fresh-water existence, had to be evolved. Segmentation of the body, especially of the muscles, promoted the efficiency of the animal in swimming against currents. (This segmentation is thus independently acquired and does not indicate kinship with the annelids and arthropods.) Only a few groups of early Paleozoic animals managed to exploit the ecological niches of fresh water, and among these were the protovertebrates and the arthropods. According to this theory, *Amphioxus* may have been one of these early protovertebrates which evolved under the impact of fresh water but, returning to the sea to breed, became readapted to a filter-feeding marine existence. This theory of the ascidian origin of vertebrates has been revived and vigorously supported in recent years by Berrill of McGill University and Romer of Harvard University.

Romer also emphasizes the dual nature of the basic pattern of chordate organization. One of the two components of such an animal is the **visceral**, which is made up of the structures of the ancestral sessile adult, such as the food-collecting apparatus, the alimentary canal, the reproductive organs, and the regulative factors

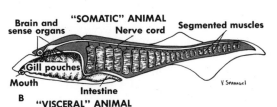

Figure 311. Double origin of chordate organization. **A**, Visceral component (lighter compact area) is supposed to represent adult tunicate, fitted for sessile existence and stressing digestive and reproductive systems. Somatic component (in darker shading) is larval tunicate, stressing locomotion by means of muscular, nervous, and sensory systems. **B**, Visceral and somatic components are integrated, as seen in ostracoderm, making new patterns of vertebrate morphology possible. Theory of anatomical duality has significant psychological implications (e.g., Freudism?). (Redrawn from Roe and Simpson: Behavior and Evolution, Yale University Press.)

(hormone and nervous) associated with the viscera. The second component is called the **somatic** and is represented by the new additions of the larval tunicate or active free-swimming form, such as the well-defined sensory and nervous systems and a locomotor apparatus of striated muscles built around a supporting notochord. Romer also points out that this anatomical duality is correlated with a duality of behavior, for the visceral or internal responses are regulated chiefly by sympathetic nerves and hormones; the somatic or external responses are regulated by means of somatic sensory, nervous, and muscular structures. Higher vertebrates have tended more to fuse the visceral and somatic components into an integrated and more functional whole, but the behavior patterns of all vertebrates can be interpreted on the basis of this dual nature.

Sequence of vertebrate origins. The foregoing account of the possible prevertebrate origin must always remain speculative, to some extent, in the absence of a fossil record. Among existing vertebrates the most primitive members belong to the class Cyclostomata which includes the lampreys and the hagfish. This group is often referred to as Agnatha (without jaws) and also includes some notable fossil members (ostracoderms). The adult cyclostomes cannot altogether be considered as primitive, for they have certain specialized structural features, such as the lack of a bony skeleton and the presence of a rasping tongue for a parasitic habit. However, the ammocoete larva of the lamprey has many resemblances to the chordate prototype as we have pictured it, and its archetypal characteristics are much stressed by evolutionists at the present time. Although this larva gives one an understanding of the basic structural plan of chordates, it cannot altogether be pinpointed as the exact ancestor of vertebrates. The fossil record must, therefore, be our main reliance for primitive vertebrates.

The first indication of fossil vertebrates were some scales or bony plates found in Ordovician fresh-water deposits in Colorado. These first evidences of vertebrates from the geological record are so fragmentary and incomplete that it is impossible to identify them with any particular animal, although some paleontologists consider them as belonging to the ostra-

coderms. During the Ordovician geological period the invertebrates were the dominant animals. In the next geological periods of upper Silurian and Devonian, the first true vertebrate fossils were found in considerable numbers. These were the well-preserved ostracoderms (shell or bony skin) which have aroused an enormous amount of interest since their discovery in Colorado, Canada, Europe, and especially Spitsbergen. The epoch-making investigation of Stensio (1927) has focused much attention on these ancient fish which are supposed to have flourished 400 million years ago. From the Devonian period onward the fossil record of the vertebrates begins to unfold with great clearness in the successive layers of the earth's crust. This sequence of vertebrate origin can best be considered in the following brief summary of the various vertebrate groups—when they flourished, how some became extinct, and how they are related to existing groups.

JAMOYTIUS. In 1946, White, an English paleontologist, described a primitive, unarmored jawless chordate (*Jamoytius*, Figure 312), from the Silurian rocks of England, which may supplant the ostracoderms as the earliest fossil vertebrates to be discovered. Whether or not this form is as old as the oldest ostracoderm may be questioned, but its morphology is, without doubt, more primitive. The fossil, which was mainly an impression in the deposits, is difficult to analyze satisfactorily. It may be a primitive ostracoderm. It was

Figure 312. *Jamoytius*, small jawless, fishlike fossil found in Silurian deposits in England. It has many requirements of chordate archetype, such as lateral fin folds, notochord, primitive myotomes, and lack of general internal skeleton and gills. As such it could well serve as ancestor of prevertebrates and ostracoderms. It is at present an enigma to paleontologists who await further discoveries and appraisals.

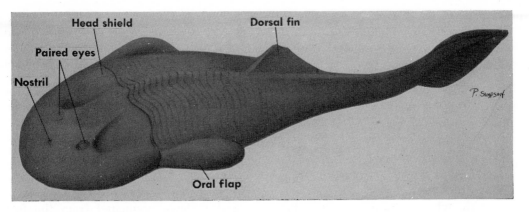

Figure 313. Diagram of dorsolateral view of ostracoderm. This group represents oldest fossil vertebrate group yet discovered. They rarely exceeded 1 foot in length and were related to living cyclostomes (lampreys, hagfish). Like larval forms of cyclostomes, ostracoderms were filter feeders. Many fine specimens have been found in Spitzbergen and elsewhere. Outstanding work of Stensio has revealed amazing amount of detail about these primitive jawless verte- brates, most typical being genus *Cephalaspis*. They were all covered by bony armor and some may have been provided with internal bony skeleton. They flourished from Ordovician to Devonian times, becoming extinct about 300 million years ago. Oral flaps are not considered to be homologous to pectoral fins of higher fish. (After Stensio and Romer.)

about 7 inches long, with a more or less fusiform body, on either side of which were lateral fin folds. A median dorsal fin fold was also present, and there were in- dications of muscle myotomes similar to the arrangement in *Amphioxus*. The only internal skeleton was a notochord, which gave support to the body. Its head was somewhat blunt and a little flattened. There were no gill slits. Its primitive na- ture could well qualify it as an ancestor of the amphioxus and ostracoderms. Pale- ontologists are not agreed on the exact status of this interesting form, and a few of them accept White's contention that it is near the archetypal chordate. Perhaps more fossils will have to be discovered be- fore it can be correctly appraised.

OSTRACODERMS. Paleontologists are agreed that the ancestors or forerunners of higher fish were the ostracoderms (Fig- ure 313) which belong to the jawless group known as Agnatha. They were abundant during the upper Silurian and Devonian periods and are the oldest known vertebrates. They were fresh-water forms, and many of them were preserved as fossils in the bottom sediments of

streams in many parts of the world, as mentioned before. They were represented by a great variety of types and some were no doubt highly specialized. Much of our knowledge about them has been due to the studies of Stensio on *Cephalaspis*, which belongs to the group of Cephala- spida. They were small animals, rarely ex- ceeding 1 foot in length, and were cov- ered by a well-developed armor, the head by a solid shield (rounded anteriorly) and the body by bony plates. They had no axial skeleton or vertebrae. The mouth was ventral and anterior, and they were jawless and toothless. Their paired eyes were located close to the mid-dorsal line. A pineal eye was also present, in front of which was a single nasal opening. At the lateroposterior corners of the head shield were a pair of flaplike appendages which may represent pectoral fins. The trunk and tail appeared to be adapted for ac- tive swimming. Between the margin of the head shield and the ventral plates there were ten gill openings on each side. They also had a lateral line system. They were adapted for filter feeding, which may explain the large expanded size of the head made up as it is of a large pharyngeal gill-slit filtering apparatus. Much of their structure is similar to that of lampreys, and the two groups are closely related and placed together in the Agnatha. Since ostracoderms had a bony external skeleton, bone rather than cartilage is considered a primitive characteristic.

It must be remembered, however, that fossil ostracoderms, as we find them, were specialized and the products of a long evolutionary past. They probably came from unarmored ancestors, such as *Jamoytius*. Although successful for a time during which they became adapted to many ecological niches, they could not in the end compete with the jawed fish that evolved in such diversity during the Devonian period.

PLACODERMS. The ostracoderms were probably the ancestors of the placoderms, the first fish to have **jaws**. The fossil record indicates that placoderms lived in fresh water also, such as streams and estuaries of rivers. Yet the fossil record fails to show any connecting link between the jawless and the jawed fish. The appearance of jaws represented a great revolution in vertebrate feeding, for now fish could evolve and spread into a great variety of habitats and make use of a greater variety of food. Many of them became predaceous, which led to the evolution of an efficient muscular system for locomotion. Predation also put a premium on the sensory and nervous system. Jaws were derived from gill arches. Some ostracoderms had as many as ten gill openings. Gill arches are skeletal structures or rods that afford support for the muscles opening and closing the slits. Jaws are supposed to have originated from the first pair of gill bars in front of the first gill slit.

Another great contribution of placoderms was **paired appendages**. Appendages may have had their beginning in lateral folds, such as those in *Jamoytius*. This fold may have broken up into a series of fins such as is found in certain primitive placoderms (acanthodians). In these, however, the anterior and posterior pairs were larger than the others and eventually became the pectoral and pelvic fins; the intermediate ones disappeared. Some paleontologists think, however, that these

Figure 314. Placoderm—first fish with jaws. Some of these early fish belonged to group called acanthodians, which was represented by common fossil genus *Climatius*. One of their interesting characteristics was smaller paired fins between larger pectoral and pelvic fins. These smaller fins may have evolved from lateral fin folds or they may have arisen independently. Placoderms arose in early Devonian period and must have played important part in early evolution of vertebrates before they became extinct. They are only vertebrate class of which there are no existing members. (Modified from Romer.)

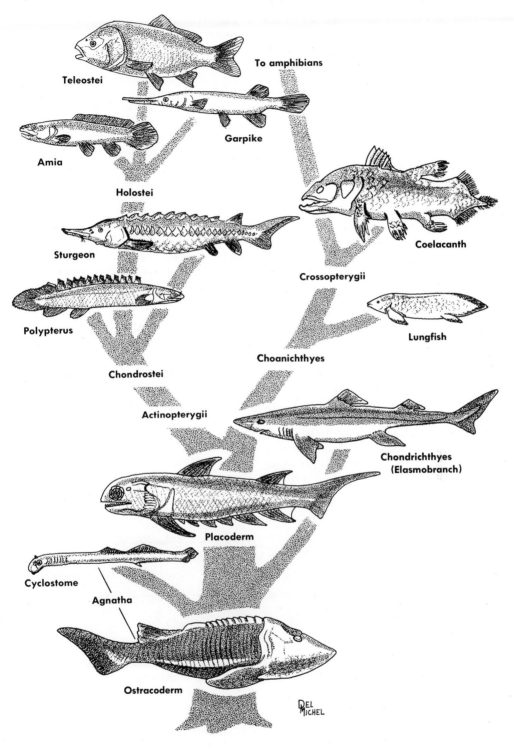

Figure 315. Evolutionary tree of major groups of fish (class Pisces). (After Colbert and others.)

numerous paired fins may have arisen independently as separate structures. Their internal skeleton so far as known was composed of bone.

Placoderms (Figure 314) evolved into a great variety of types. Many of them were aberrant and grotesque in appearance and some were quite large. They were armored fish and were covered either with diamond-shaped scales or with large plates of bone. All of them became extinct by the end of the Paleozoic era. The placoderms represent the only class of vertebrates to become wholly extinct; the other classes are all represented by certain living members.

HIGHER FISH (SHARKS AND BONY FISH). It is not known definitely that placoderms gave rise to the higher fish, but some placoderms were so primitive that they could well serve as the ancestors of the sharks and possibly the bony fish (Figure 315). The sharks (cartilaginous Chondrichthyes) did not appear in the fossil record until the mid-Devonian period; the bony fish (Osteichthyes) date from the early Devonian period. Sharks are thus not as old as bony fish, contrary to popular opinion. Moreover, bone is a primitive characteristic, and its absence in the cartilaginous Chondrichthyes is an indication of degeneration. Chondrichthyes are also degenerate rather than

primitive in other features as well. The higher fish were definitely superior to the ostracoderms and the placoderms because they were better swimmers and because they evolved along many lines for efficient feeding and for protection. Their success is attested by the fact that there are more species of fish than of all other vertebrates combined, and in population numbers they far exceed those of other vertebrate classes. The chief morphological changes these higher fish have introduced are (1) a better streamlined body, (2) an efficient array of fins (both median and paired), (3) a specialization of jaws (such as the hyomandibular support), (4) a more highly developed ossified internal and external skeleton (Osteichthyes), (5) a functional lung or swim bladder in many, and (6) better sensory and nervous regulation.

Both sharks and bony fish evolved in fresh water, the same as ostracoderms and placoderms, but many of them took up a marine existence later.

Bony fish differentiated into two great groups or subclasses—Actinopterygii and Choanichthyes. The first of these are the ray-finned fish which make up most of the existing fish (teleosts) today. The Choanichthyes include those fish with internal nostrils, or nostrils that open into the mouth. They comprise two small, but im-

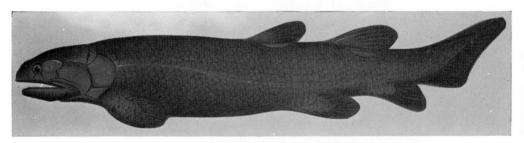

Figure 316. *Osteolepis*, primitive crossopterygian fish of middle Devonian times. This fish must be considered in direct line of descent between fish and amphibians because its type of skull was similar to that of primitive land vertebrates and its lobe fin was of a pattern that could serve as beginning of tetrapod limb. This type of fin (archipterygium) consisted of median axial bones, with small bones radiating out from median ones. Some of its bones can be homologized with limb bones of tetrapods, such as humerus or femur, and the ulna-radius or tibia-fibula elements. *Osteolepis* was covered by primitive cosmoid scales, not found in existing fish. These scales were of rhombic shape and consisted of basal bony layers, with a spongy layer of blood vessels covered with cosmine (dentine) and enamel. (After Romer.)

410

Figure 317. *Latimeria*, living representative of crossopterygian or lobe-finned fish. Lobe-finned fish were assumed to have become extinct at end of Cretaceous period nearly 70 million years ago. In 1938 a specimen was found near Madagascar; since then many related specimens have been collected. Although the crossopterygian fish are direct ancestors of land forms (tetrapods) through amphibians, *Latimeria* belongs to specialized side branch of crossopterygians known as coelacanths. Another branch, the rhipidistians, represented by such forms as *Osteolepis*, were actual ancestors of four-legged vertebrates. Rhipidistians were fresh-water fish and are now extinct; the coelacanths are marine, but their ancestors probably came from fresh water. Striking similarity between living *Latimeria* and fossil coelacanths of 300 million years ago indicate that these fish have been able to adapt to changing environment without structural changes. In this sense *Latimeria* may be called "living fossil," but it is not a "missing link," for it does not connect two known types of animals.

Figure 318. Labyrinthodont amphibian *Eryops*. Most primitive tetrapods were icthyostegids which have been found in Devonian deposits of Greenland and definitely classified as amphibians. These and other members of superorder Labyrinthodonta, such as *Eryops*, represent important group in early evolution of amphibians. Their head armor of bony plates and other features indicate that they have come from crossopterygian ancestors. For land adaptation, pectoral and pelvic fins of crossopterygians were transformed into arms and legs in labyrinthodonts.

portant groups—the Dipnoi, or lungfish, and the Crossopterygii, or lobe-finned fish. The Crossopterygii are ancestral to land forms (tetrapods). Although supposed to have been extinct since Cretaceous times, several lobe-finned fish (*Latimeria*) (Figure 317) have been collected in recent years off the coast of Africa and Madagascar. Their paired fins show a basic plan of a jointed series of bones that could evolve into the limbs of tetrapods. They also were lung breathers. Limbs and lungs were necessary qualifications for tetrapod evolution.

Phylum Chordata—ancestry, characteristics, protochordates 411

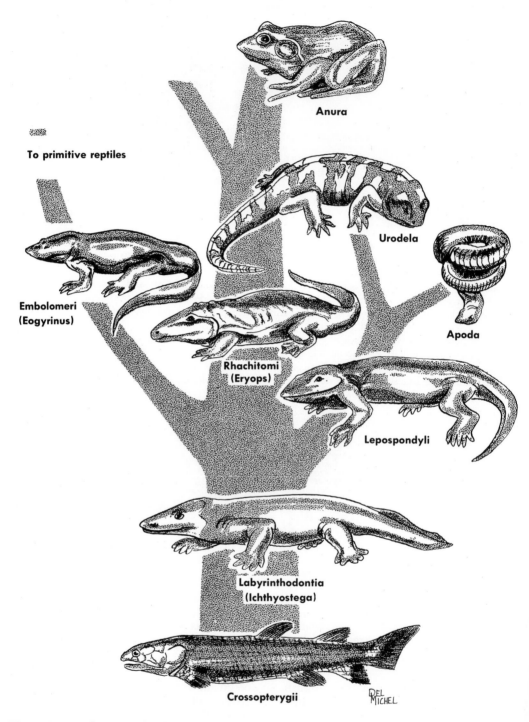

Figure 319. Evolutionary development of amphibians. Some fossil type genera are shown in parentheses. Reptiles probably arose from stock close to Embolomeri. (After Colbert and others.)

412

AMPHIBIANS. Paleontologists agree that the first amphibians arose from certain crossopterygians. The fossil *Ichthyostega*, from the late Devonian period, was found in Greenland in 1932 and possessed both crossopterygian and amphibian characteristics. The earliest amphibians known were the labyrinthodonts, so called because of the infolding of their teeth. Why did the crossopterygians leave the water and go on land? It is known that they lived in fresh water, and if they happened to be in places where there was a seasonal drying up of pools, there would be a great incentive to move to more favorable ones. The search for food may also have been a factor. Since they had the prerequisites for a tetrapod limb, it is not difficult to see how such limbs could be evolved. Labyrinthodonts did not look much like modern amphibians, for their flat heads were covered with bony armor, their body was rounded in section with bony scales at least on the belly, and their legs were short and placed at right angles to the body. Some were more than 2 feet long. The Permian labyrinthodont, *Eryops* (Figure 318), was more than 6 feet long and was able to compete with the reptiles of its time.

Changes are also found in the auditory organ, for the first embryonic gill slit became the Eustachean tube, an ear ossicle (stapes) was formed from the hyomandibular arch to conduct sound waves, and a tympanic membrane for detecting sound was also found. The labyrinthodont amphibians became extinct at the end of the Triassic period, after giving rise to two great groups, the anuran amphibians (frogs and toads) and the reptiles. The other amphibians, salamanders and caecilians, which are in existence today came from another group of primitive amphibians, the lepospondyls, which were contemporary with the labyrinthodonts (Figure 319). The lepospondyls were small snakelike forms which were adapted to ecological niches in undergrowth and swamps where labyrinthodonts were not commonly found.

REPTILES. Reptiles first appeared during

Figure 320. *Seymouria*, fossil tetrapod which serves as connecting link between amphibians and reptiles. Although too specialized to be direct ancestor of reptiles, its transition characteristics indicate that it must have come from ancestors close to basal stock of stem reptiles. Many of its characteristics are similar to those found in labyrinthodont amphibians.

the Carboniferous period and became the dominant terrestrial vertebrates of the Mesozoic era. The transition between the primitive amphibians and the reptiles is well shown in the famous form *Seymouria* (Figure 320) which has a combination of both amphibian and reptile characteristics. This interesting fossil was found near the town of Seymour, Texas, in 1917, and few fossils have attracted more attention among paleontologists. The first reptiles were cotylosaurs, to which *Seymouria* belonged. They were not greatly different from labyrinthodont amphibians which are supposed to be the ancestors of the cotylosaurs. The establishment of a land existence was made possible by the development of the **amniotic egg.** Most amphibians have to return to water to lay their eggs, but the reptiles even before they took to land developed an egg that had a tough outer shell and shell membrane and amniotic membrane enclosing the amniotic fluid. In this fluid the embryo floats, protected from injury and drying out, and is provided with an adequate supply of yolk. Such an egg required internal fertilization and the development of mating habits. Reptiles were thus freed from an aquatic life and could become true terrestrial tetrapods. Most reptiles had become terrestrial tetrapods by the end of the Paleozoic era.

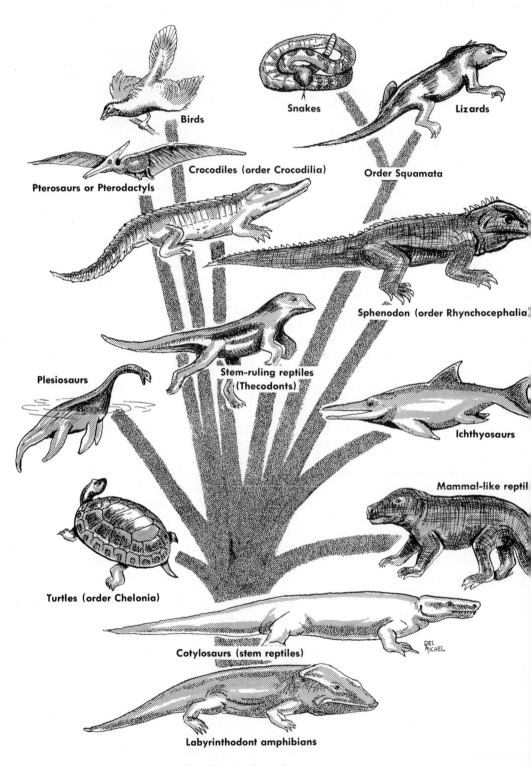

Birds

Snakes

Lizards

Pterosaurs or Pterodactyls

Crocodiles (order Crocodilia)

Order Squamata

Sphenodon (order Rhynchocephalia)

Plesiosaurs

Stem-ruling reptiles
(Thecodonts)

Ichthyosaurs

Mammal-like reptil

Turtles (order Chelonia)

Cotylosaurs (stem reptiles)

Labyrinthodont amphibians

Fig. 321. For legend see opposite page.

Figure 322. *Icthyosaurus*, extinct marine reptile which flourished during the Jurassic and Cretaceous periods. This fishlike reptile was more than 10 feet long, and its legs were modified into paddles which were used for balance and steering. It breathed by means of lungs, and many of this group brought forth their young alive. This return to water of a reptile is illustrated by many others, as shown by the fossil record. (After Romer.)

Perhaps no group of vertebrate animals has ever displayed more evolutionary diversity and adaptive radiation than has the reptiles. They gave rise to adaptations which enabled them to invade the land, the water, and the air. From the basic cotylosaur stem there developed reptiles of small and insignificant size to those like the dinosaurs, which were the largest terrestrial animals that have ever existed. Some reptiles were grotesque and bizarre, with spines and other structures. Others were adapted for aquatic life (ichthyosaurs, Figure 322). The glory of the reptiles passed with the Mesozoic era; the present-day reptiles are mere vestiges of their former conditions.

Morphologically, the greatest advance shown by reptiles as a group over the amphibians was the development of a locomotor pattern in which limbs furnished the propulsive power instead of the body undulation and belly dragging of the amphibians.

Among the many diverse groups of reptiles, two of them resulted in the great classes of birds and mammals (Figure 321).

BIRDS (AVES). Structurally, birds are so close to reptiles that they have often been referred to as "glorified reptiles" (Huxley). Birds arose from a group of reptiles called the archosaurans, which also gave rise to the order Pterosaura (flying reptiles), or pterodactyls, in the Jurassic period. These reptiles flew by means of membrane wings which were supported mainly by elongated last fingers. Some pterosaurs had a wing spread of 25 feet, but most were smaller. Their bodies

Figure 321. Adaptive radiation of reptiles. First vertebrates to possess land were reptiles, amazing in their variety. Transition from certain labyrinthodont amphibians to reptiles occurred in Carboniferous period of Mesozoic times. This transition was effected by development of amniote egg which made land existence possible, although egg may well have developed before oldest reptiles had ventured far on land. Explosive adaptation by reptiles may have been due partly to variety of ecological niches into which they could move. Fossil record shows that five lines which arose from stem reptiles led to turtles, mammal-like reptiles, ichthyosaurs, plesiosaurs, and stem-ruling reptiles. Some of these returned to the sea. Later radiations led to flying reptiles, birds, dinosaurs, and others. Of this great assemblage, the only reptiles now in existence belong to four orders shown above (Chelonia, Crocodilia, Squamata, and Rhynchocephalia). How are the mighty fallen! (From several sources.)

Figure 323. Cast of *Archaeopteryx,* lizard bird. (Courtesy Ward's Natural Science Establishment, Inc., Rochester, N. Y.)

Figure 324. *Cynognathus,* mammal-like reptile of Triassic age. Mammal-like reptiles evolved early in evolutionary history of reptiles, and some attained size of large dog. These reptiles, called therapsids, flourished until ruling reptiles (dinosaurs) emerged. First true mammals, which arose from mammal-like reptiles about Jurassic times, were small and unimportant during reign of dinosaurs. When latter became extinct at end of Mesozoic era, great adaptive radiation of mammals occurred, so that Cenozoic era is called Age of Mammals.

were relatively small and their bones light and hollow. Whatever resemblance they had to birds was due to convergent evolution, for birds had a separate evolution. They became extinct before the end of the Cretaceous period.

The first known birds appeared during Jurassic times. Our knowledge about these earliest birds is obtained from two fossil specimens found in limestone in Bavaria, Germany. They are called *Archaeopteryx* (Figure 323). These fossils show plainly the presence of feathers which the pterosaurs did not have, but they had many reptilian characteristics, such as teeth and elongated tails. It has been suggested that

416

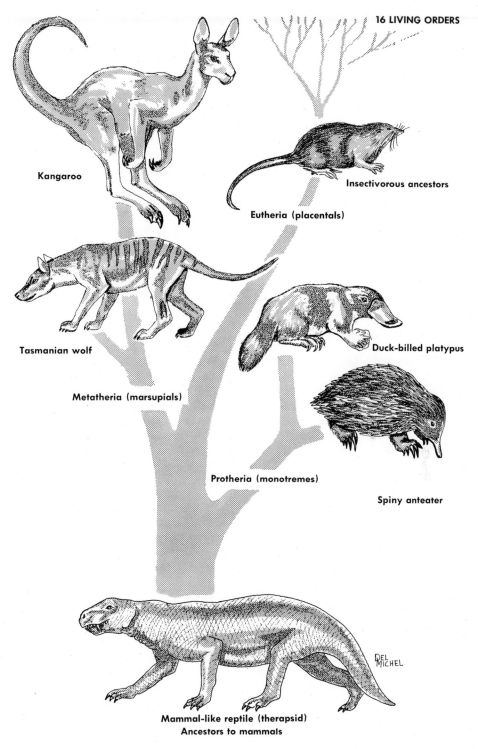

16 LIVING ORDERS

Kangaroo

Insectivorous ancestors

Eutheria (placentals)

Tasmanian wolf

Duck-billed platypus

Metatheria (marsupials)

Protheria (monotremes)

Spiny anteater

Mammal-like reptile (therapsid)
Ancestors to mammals

Figure 325. Diagram of evolution of major groups of mammals. (Modified from several sources.)

bird flight may have originated from rapid running on the ground (some reptiles were specialized that way) and the flapping of their fore limbs, or it could have originated from the habit of gliding to the ground from trees. Many physiological changes also occurred before birds could become efficient flyers, such as a constant temperature, highly specialized sensory reactions, and efficient neuromuscular coordination for balancing. It was not until Cretaceous times that birds became modernized in such respects as the fusion of the skull bones, development of pneumatic bones, coalescence of the pelvis and sacrum, suppression of the tail, and many others.

MAMMALS. Mammals arose from mammal-like reptiles—the Synapsida in the Jurassic period—although some may have appeared earlier. One of these mammal-like reptiles was *Cynognathus* (Figure 324) which was an early Triassic carnivore about the size of a large dog. Related forms were much smaller. This type showed many mammalian as well as reptilian characteristics. These mammals at first were small and insignificant and were no match for the ruling reptiles of that time. When the large dominant reptiles (dinosaurs, ichthyosaurs, etc.) disappeared, many ecological niches were now opened to the mammals, and by great adaptive radiation they were able to fill many of these niches during the Cenozoic era. The early fossil record of mammals is very scanty and incomplete, but the Mesozoic mammals were establishing the types which later developed into the successful group as we now know it. By the close of the Cretaceous period mammals had developed into two main groups, the marsupials and the placentals, which had probably arisen independently from the Pantotheria. Mammals underwent many changes morphologically and physiologically from their reptilian ancestors. The most striking of these changes involved a greater brain with a higher degree of intelligence, reproduction and care of young with the development of characteristic behavior patterns, develop-ment of a constant body temperature, transformation of the articulating elements between jaw and skull into the ear ossicles, a differentiated dentition of canine, incisors, and molar teeth, and many skeletal changes involving the fusion of the pelvic bones to form a single element, the appearance of two occipital condyles instead of one (reptiles), and alterations in the ribs and digits.

The early placental mammals of the Cretaceous period are known only from a few fossils. They were small and were the direct ancestors of the most primitive group of living mammals, the Insectivora (moles and shrews), which may be the ancestors of all other placental mammals. By adaptive radiation from this stem all the great variety of mammals arose (Figure 325).

CHARACTERISTICS OF CHORDATES

1. Bilateral symmetry; segmented body; three germ layers; coelom well developed

2. **Notochord** (a skeletal rod) present at some stage in life cycle

3. **Nerve cord dorsal and tubular;** anterior end of cord usually enlarged to form brain

4. **Pharyngeal gill slits present at some stage in life cycle** and may or may not be functional

5. A **postanal tail** usually projecting beyond the anus at some stage and may or may not persist

6. **Heart ventral** with dorsal and ventral blood vessels; closed blood system

7. Complete digestive system

8. Exoskeleton often present; well developed in some vertebrates

9. A cartilage or bony **endoskeleton** present in the majority of members (vertebrates)

The three distinctive characteristics which set chordates apart from all other phyla are the **notochord, dorsal tubular nerve cord,** and **pharyngeal gill slits.** These characteristics are always found in the early embryo, although they may be altered or disappear altogether in later stages of the life cycle.

These three features are so important that each merits a short description of its own.

Notochord. This rodlike body develops in the embryo as a longitudinal outfolding of the dorsal side of the alimentary canal. It is endodermal in origin, although in some forms there is a possibility that the other germ layers have contributed to its formation. In most it is a rigid, yet flexible, rod extending the length of the body. It is the first part of the endoskeleton to appear in the embryo. As a rigid axis on which the muscles can act it permits undulatory movements of the body. In most of the protochordates and in primitive vertebrates the notochord persists throughout life. In all vertebrates a series of cartilaginous or bony vertebrae are formed from the connective tissue sheath around the notochord and replace it as the chief mechanical axis of the body.

Dorsal tubular nerve cord. In the invertebrate phyla the nerve cord (often paired) is ventral to the alimentary canal and is solid, but in the chordates the cord is dorsal to the alimentary canal and is formed as a tube. The anterior end of this tube in vertebrates becomes enlarged to form the brain. The hollow cord is produced by the infolding of ectodermal cells on the dorsal side of the body above the notochord. Among the vertebrates the nerve cord lies in the neural arches of the vertebrae, and the anterior brain is surrounded by a bony or cartilaginous cranium.

Pharyngeal gill slits. Pharyngeal gill slits are perforated slitlike openings which lead from the pharyngeal cavity to the outside. They are formed by the invagination of the outside ectoderm and the evagination of the endodermal lining of the pharynx. The two pockets break through when they meet to form the slit. In higher vertebrates these pockets may not break through and only grooves are formed instead of slits; all traces of them usually disappear. In forms that use the slits for breathing, gills with blood vessels are attached to the margins of the slits and make the gaseous exchange with the water which enters the mouth and passes through the pharyngeal gill slits. The slits have in their walls supporting frameworks of gill bars. Primitive forms such as *Amphioxus* have a large number of slits, but only six or seven are the rule in the fish. The transitory appearance of the slits in land vertebrates is often used as evidence for evolution.

WHAT ADVANCEMENTS DO CHORDATA SHOW OVER OTHER PHYLA?

Certain structures in chordates give them some advantage over other animals. One of these is the **endoskeleton.** With the exception of the echinoderms and a few others which have vague beginnings of an endoskeleton, the chordates are the only phylum that has gone all out with this important mechanical device. The endoskeleton is a living tissue, composed of living cells, and grows and undergoes changes the same as other tissues. Thus the endoskeleton grows along with the other parts of the body and does not have to be shed periodically to allow for growth as is the case with the invertebrates that have chitinous exoskeletons. The endoskeleton may lack a little of the mechanical advantage of the exoskeleton, but it more than compensates for this by allowing greater freedom of movement.

Another advantage chordates have is their method of **breathing.** An efficient respiratory system has gone hand in hand with a well-developed circulatory system. It is true that certain arthropods with their direct tracheal system have evolved a very efficient respiration, but such a plan is fitted to animals of small size only. In either the gills of aquatic forms or the lungs of terrestrial forms, the blood circulates freely through the respiratory organs, ensuring rapid and efficient exchange of gases. Moreover, the blood system of chordates is admirably fitted to carry on so many functions that it has become a general factotum for bodily functions.

No single system in the body is more correlated with functional and structural advancement than is the **nervous system.**

Throughout the invertebrate kingdom we have seen that there has been a more or less centralization of nervous systems. This tendency has reached its climax in the higher chordates where we find the highly efficient tubular nervous system. Such a system allows the greatest possible utilization of space for the nervous units so necessary for well-integrated nervous patterns. Along with the advanced nervous system goes a better sensory system, which partly explains the power of this group to adapt itself to a varied environment.

COMPARISON OF CHORDATA WITH INVERTEBRATA

Some of the most striking differences between chordates and higher invertebrates may be seen by the following summary of comparisons.

Nervous system. The nerve cord is dorsal in chordates, ventral in higher invertebrates. Both have dorsal brains.

Circulatory system. The heart is ventral in chordates, dorsal in invertebrates. In the dorsal blood vessel the blood flows posteriorly in chordates, anteriorly in invertebrates.

Endoskeleton. Chordates have an endoskeleton in the form of a notochord or a more highly developed vertebral system; invertebrates lack this.

Digestive system. In all larval and in some adult chordates the anus terminates anterior to the posterior part of the body, producing a postanal tail; higher invertebrates have the anus terminating at the posterior part of the body. Pharyngeal gill slits are found in the pharynx of chordates (at some stage) but are lacking among the invertebrates.

SUBPHYLA

There are three subphyla under phylum Chordata. Two of these subphyla are small, lack a vertebral column, and are of interest primarily as borderline or first chordates (protochordates). Since these subphyla lack a cranium, they are also referred to as Acrania. The third subphylum is provided with a vertebral column and is called Vertebrata. Since this phylum has a cranium, it is also called Craniata.

Protochordata (Acrania)

Subphylum Urochordata (u'ro-chor-da"ta) (Gr. *oura,* a tail, + L. *chorda,* cord) (**Tunicata**). Notochord and nerve cord only in free-swimming larva; adults sessile and encased in tunic. Example: *Molgula.*

Subphylum Cephalochordata (ceph'a-lo-chor-da"ta) (Gr. *kephale,* head, + L. *chorda,* cord). Notochord and nerve cord found along entire length of body and persist throughout life; fish-like in form. Example: *Amphioxus (Branchiostoma).*

Craniata

Subphylum Vertebrata (ver'te-bra"ta) (L. *vertebratus,* backbone). Bony or cartilaginous vertebrae surround spinal cord; notochord in all embryonic stages and persists in some of the fish. This subphylum may also be divided into two groups (superclasses) according to whether or not they have jaws.

> **Class Agnatha** (ag'na-tha) (Gr. *a,* not, + *gnathos,* jaw). Without true jaws or appendages. Example: *Petromyzon.*
>
> **Class Gnathostoma** (na-thos'to-ma) (Gr. *gnathes,* jaw, + *stoma,* mouth). With jaws and (usually) paired appendages. Example: *Homo.*

PROTOCHORDATA: FORERUNNERS OF VERTEBRATA

Two of the three subphyla of the chordates are often referred to collectively as the **protochordates,** that is, the first or early chordates. These primitive borderline forms have little economic importance but are of great interest to biologists because they exhibit the characteristics of chordates in simple form.

SUBPHYLUM UROCHORDATA (TUNICATA)

The tunicates (Figure 326) have a wide distribution, being found in all seas from near the shore line to great depths. Most of them are sessile, at least as adults, although some are free living. The name tunicate is suggested by the nonliving tunic which surrounds them and contains cellulose. A common name for them is sea squirt because some of them discharge water through the excurrent siphon when

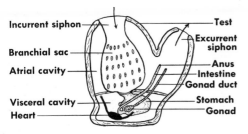

Incurrent siphon
Test
Excurrent siphon
Branchial sac
Atrial cavity
Anus
Intestine
Gonad duct
Visceral cavity
Stomach
Gonad
Heart

Figure 326. Scheme of internal structures of tunicate (sea squirt).

irritated. They vary in size from microscopic forms to several inches in length.

As a group they may be considered as degenerative or specialized members of the chordates, for they lack many of the common characteristics of chordates. For a long time they were classified among the mollusks. In 1866 Kowalevsky, the Russian embryologist, worked out their true position.

Urochordata is divided into three classes—**Ascidiacea, Larvacea,** and **Thalacea.** Of these, the members of **Ascidiacea,** commonly known as the ascidians, are by far the most common and are the best known. One of this group is described below as the type of tunicates. The ascidians are often considered as a group that has regressed in its evolution, for most of them as adults are attached, but have evolved from free-moving ancestors. Ascidians may be solitary, colonial, or compound. Each of the solitary and colonial forms has its own test, but among the compound forms many individuals may share the same test. In some of these compound ascidians, each member has its own **incurrent siphon,** but the **excurrent opening** is common to the group. Most ascidians are monoecious, but some are dioecious, and they can also reproduce asexually by budding or gemmation. The larvae may develop outside or in the atrium of the parent. Ascidians vary in color, such as black, pink, and scarlet.

The **Larvacea** and **Thaliacea** are pelagic forms of the open sea and are not often found in the intertidal zones where ascidians are common. The members of **Larvacea** are small, tadpolelike forms under 5 mm. in length and appear to be ascidian tadpoles. They may represent persistent larval forms which have become neotenous. They secrete around themselves cellulose tunics and are filter feeders. *Oikopleura* is a larvacean form often collected in tow-net samplings of ocean plankton. The class Thaliacea is made up of members that may reach a length of 3 or 4 inches. Their transparent body is spindle shaped or cylindrical and is surrounded by bands of circular muscles, with their incurrent and excurrent apertures at opposite ends. They are mostly carried along by currents, although by contracting their circular muscle bands they can force water out of their excurrent siphons and move by jet propulsion. Many are provided with luminous organs and give a brilliant light at night. Most of their body is hollow, with the viscera forming a compact mass on the ventral side. They appear to have come from attached ancesters like the ascidians. Some of them have complex life histories. In forms like *Doliolum,* there is alternation of generations between sexual and asexual forms. After hatching from the egg the larval tadpole changes into a barrel-shaped nurse or asexual stage which produces small buds on a ventral stolon. These buds break free, become attached to another part of the parent, and develop into three kinds of individuals, one kind of which breaks free to become the sexual stage. *Salpa* also has alternation of generations and is a common form along the Atlantic coast.

Adult ascidian—Molgula

Molgula is globose in form and is attached by its base to piles and stones. Lining the test or tunic is a membrane or **mantle.** On the outside are two projections, the **incurrent** and **excurrent siphons** (Figure 326). Water enters the incurrent siphon and passes into the pharynx through the mouth. On the midventral side of the pharynx is a groove, **endostyle,** which is ciliated and secretes mucus. Food material in the water is entangled by the mucus in this endostyle and car-

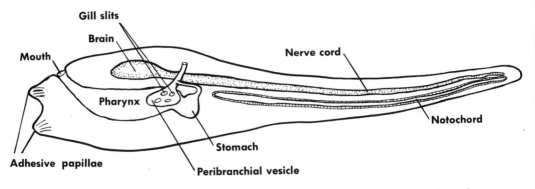

Figure 327. Structure of tunicate larva (ascidian tadpole), showing all three chordate characteristics: notochord, dorsal nerve cord, and gill slits.

ried into the esophagus and stomach. The intestine leads to the anus near the excurrent siphon. The water passes through the pharyngeal slits in the walls of the pharynx into the atrial cavity. As the water passes through the slits, respiration occurs.

The circulatory system contains a ventral **heart** near the stomach and two large vessels, one connected to each end of the heart. The action of the heart is peculiar in that it drives the blood first in one direction and then in the other. This reversal of blood flow is found in no other animal. The excretory system is a sort of nephridium near the intestine. The nervous system is restricted to a nerve ganglion and a few nerves which lie on the dorsal side of the pharynx. A notochord is lacking. The animals are hermaphroditic, for both ovaries and testes are found in the same animal. Ducts lead from the gonads close to the intestine and empty near the anus. The germ cells are carried out the excurrent siphon into the surrounding water, where cross-fertilization occurs.

It will be seen that of the three chief characteristics of chordates, adult tunicates have only one, the pharyngeal gill slits. However, the larval form gives away the secret of their true relationship.

Ascidian tadpole. The tadpole larvae (Figure 327) among the different ascidians vary in certain details, but the basic plan is much the same in all. The de-

velopment of the egg through the blastula and gastrula stages is somewhat similar to that of *Amphioxus.* However, cleavage is determinate, and the mesoderm arises not from pouches but from clumps of cells of the archenteron. After a development of about two days the embryo hatches out into an elongated transparent larva about 1 to 5 mm. long. Its tail is four or five times as long as its trunk. The tail is provided with a slender cuticular fin and contains the following structures: a **notochord** of vacuolated cells arranged in a single row; a hollow dorsal **nerve cord** extending from the tip of the tail to the sensory vesicle and made up of small cells; and a striated muscle band on each side of the notochord. Some mesenchymal cells are also found in the tail. In the larger head and trunk regions are found the three adhesive papillae; a digestive system of dorsal mouth, a short esophagus, a large pharynx with endostyle and **gill slits** which open into the atrium, a stomach, intestine, and anus opening into the atrium; the brain which is a continuation of the nerve cord of the tail; a sensory vesicle containing an otolith for balance; and a dorsal median eye with lens and pigmented cup. A coelom and a circulatory system are present, but the heart is not formed until after metamorphosis. The larva does not feed but swims around for some hours, during which time it is at first positively phototactic and negatively geotactic but later becomes

422

negatively phototactic and positively geotactic. By its adhesive papillae it now fastens itself vertically to some solid object and then undergoes retrograde metamorphosis to become an adult. In this process the tail is absorbed by phagocytes; the notochord, muscles, and nervous system (save a trunk ganglion) degenerate; the branchial sac enlarges with many gill slits; and the alimentary canal and circulatory system (with a heart) enlarge and develop. The body also undergoes a rotation so that the mouth and atrial openings (siphons) are shifted to the upper unattached end. Gonads and ducts arise in the mesoderm, and the whole animal becomes enclosed in a test or tunic.

The evolutionary significance of the ascidian tadpole has already been discussed.

SUBPHYLUM CEPHALOCHORDATA

This subphylum is the most interesting of all the protochordates, for one of its members is Amphioxus (Branchiostoma), one of the classical animals in zoology. This group is found mainly on the sandy beaches of southern waters where they burrow in the sand with the anterior end projecting out. One American species, Branchiostoma virginiae, is found from Florida to Chesapeake Bay. They can swim in open water by swift lateral movements of the body.

Amphioxus is especially interesting, for it has the three distinctive characteristics of chordates in simple form, and in other ways it may be considered a blueprint of the phylum. It has a long, slender, laterally compressed body 2 to 3 inches long (Figures 328 and 329), with both ends pointed. There is a long **dorsal fin** which passes around the tail end to form the **caudal** fin. A short **ventral** fin is also found. These fins are reinforced by **fin rays** of connective tissue. The ventral side of the body is flattened and bears along each side a **metapleural fold**. There are three openings to the outside; the ven-

Figure 328. Amphioxus (Branchiostoma), best known of protochordates. This is mature specimen (about ×2). Note myotomes and block-shaped gonads.

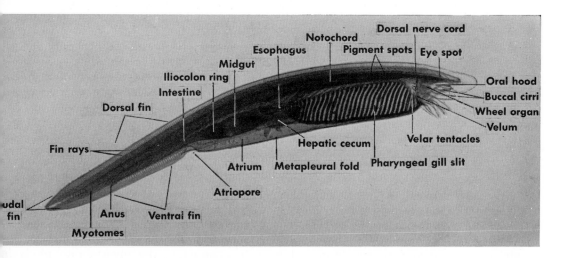

Figure 329. Structure of Amphioxus. Photomicrograph of juvenile; gonads not present.

Phylum Chordata—ancestry, characteristics, protochordates   423

tral anterior **mouth,** the **anus** near the base of the caudal fin, and the **atriopore** just anterior to the ventral fin.

The body is covered with a soft **epithelium** one layer thick resting upon some connective tissue. The **notochord,** which extends almost the entire length of the body, is made up of cells and gelatinous substance enclosed in a sheath of connective tissue. Above the notochord is the tubular dorsal **nerve cord** with a slight dilation at the anterior end known as the **cerebral vesicle.** Along each side of the body and tail are the numerous V-shaped **myotomes,** or muscles, which have a metameric arrangement. The myotomes are separated from each other by **myosepta** of connective tissue. The myotomes of the two sides alternate with each other. The anterior end of the body is called the **rostrum.** Just back of this and slightly below is a median opening surrounded by a membrane, the **oral hood,** which bears some twenty **oral tentacles** (**buccal cirri**). The oral hood encloses the chamber known as the **vestibule,** at the bottom of which lies the true **mouth** with a membrane, the **velum,** around it. Around the mouth are twelve **velar tentacles.** The cirri and tentacles serve to strain out large particles and have sensory functions. Ciliated patches on walls of buccal cavity in front of velum produce a rotating effect and are called the **wheel organ,** which propels water currents. Just behind the mouth is the large compressed pharynx with more than a hundred pairs of **gill slits,** which act as strainers in filter feeding as well as in respiration. From the pharynx the narrow tubular **intestine** extends backward to the anus. On the ventral side of the intestine is a large diverticulum, the **hepatic cecum.** The **coelom** is reduced and is confined to the region above the pharynx and around the intestine. Connecting the coelom to the atrium are about a hundred pairs of ciliated **nephridia** of the solenocyte type, a modified kind of flame cell (Figure 115, *B*). The big cavity around the pharynx is the **atrium;** it is lined with ectoderm and is therefore not a coelom. The pharynx has

a mid-dorsal groove called the **hyperbranchial groove** and a mid-ventral one known as the **endostyle.** Both of these grooves are lined with cilia and gland cells. Food is entangled by the mucus of the endostyle and carried to the intestine; the water passes through the gill slits into the atrium and gives up oxygen to the blood vessels in the **gill bars.**

Although there is no heart, the **blood system** is similar to that of higher chordates. The blood moves posteriorly in the **dorsal aorta** and anteriorly in the **ventral aorta;** a **hepatic portal** vein leads from the intestines to the liver. Blood is propelled by contractions of the ventral aorta and is carried to the dorsal aorta by vessels in the gill bars. The blood is almost colorless with a few red corpuscles. The **nervous system** is above the notochord and consists of a single dorsal **nerve cord** which is hollow. This nerve cord gives off a pair of nerves alternately to each body segment, or myotome, the dorsal root having both sensory and motor functions and the ventral root having motor functions only. Ciliated cells with **sensory** functions are found in various parts of the body. Sexes are separate, and each sex has about twenty-five pairs of gonads located on the wall of the atrium. The sex cells are set free in the atrial cavity and pass out the atriopore to the outside, where fertilization occurs. Cleavage is total (holoblastic) and a gastrula is formed by invagination. The larva hatches soon after deposition and gradually assumes the shape of the adult.

No other chordate shows so well the basic diagnostic chordate characteristics as does the amphioxus. Not only are the three chief characters of chordates—**dorsal nerve cord, notochord,** and **pharyngeal gill slits**—well represented but also secondary characteristics, such as postanal tail, liver diverticulum, hepatic portal system, and the beginning of a ventral heart. Indicative also of the condition in vertebrates is the much thicker dorsal portion of the muscular layer. This is in contrast to the invertebrate phyla in which the muscular layer is about the

424

same thickness around the body cavity. The metameric arrangement of the muscles suggests a similar plan in the embryos of vertebrates. The separation of the dorsal and ventral spinal nerves may indicate the early condition in the vertebrate ancestors. From these and other considerations, this interesting animal is often placed close in affinity to the higher chordates, the vertebrates. Just where it is placed in the evolutionary blueprint of the chordates and the vertebrates is a controversial point. It is placed by many authorities near the primitive fish, ostracoderms, but whether it comes before or after these fish in the evolutionary line is not settled. Many regard the amphioxus as a highly specialized or degenerate member of the early chordates and believe that the overdeveloped notochord was developed in them as a correlation to their burrowing habits. The forward extension of the notochord into the tip of the snout may be one of the reasons for the small development of the brain of the amphioxus.

Among other serious objections that have been advanced against *Amphioxus* as a generalized ancestral type of chordates are its solenocyte type of protonephridia, such as is found in certain polychaetes, and which has no resemblance to the glomerular-tubular nephron of vertebrates, its unique atrium which has no counterpart in vertebrates and its vast number of gill slits. Many authorities, therefore, assign *Amphioxus* to a divergent side branch of some stage intermediate between the early filter-feeding prevertebrates and the vertebrates.

CRANIATA
SUBPHYLUM VERTEBRATA

The third subphylum of the chordates, Vertebrata, has the same characteristics that distinguish the other two subphyla, but in addition it has a number of features that the others do not share. The characteristics that give the members of this group the name Vertebrata or Craniata are the presence of a brain case, or **cranium**, and a spinal column of verte-

brae which forms the chief skeletal axis of the body.

Characteristics

1. The chief diagnostic features of chordates—**notochord, dorsal nerve cord,** and **pharyngeal gill slits**—are all present at some stage of the life cycle.

2. They are covered with an **integument** basically of two divisions, an outer **epidermis** of stratified epithelium from the ectoderm and an inner **dermis** or corium of connective tissue derived from the mesoderm. This skin has many modifications among the various classes, such as glands, scales, feathers, claws, horns, and hair.

3. The notochord is more or less replaced by the spinal column of vertebrae composed of cartilage or bone or both. The vertebral column with the cranium, visceral arches, limb girdles, and two pairs of jointed appendages form the distinctive **endoskeleton.**

4. Many **muscles** are attached to the skeleton to provide for movement.

5. The complete **digestive system** is ventral to the spinal column and is provided with large digestive glands, liver, and pancreas.

6. The circulatory system is made up of the **ventral heart** of two to four chambers, a closed blood vessel system of arteries, veins, and capillaries, and a blood fluid containing red blood corpuscles and white corpuscles. Paired aortic arches connect the ventral and dorsal aortae and give off branches to the gills among the aquatic vertebrates; in the terrestrial types the aortic arch plan is modified into pulmonary and systemic systems.

7. A **coelom** is well developed and is largely filled with the visceral systems.

8. The **excretory system** is made up of paired kidneys (opisthonephric or metanephric types) provided with ducts to drain the waste to the cloaca or anal region.

9. The brain is typically divided into five vesicles.

10. Ten or twelve pairs of cranial nerves with both motor and sensory func-

tions is the rule; a pair of spinal nerves supplies each primitive myotome; and an autonomic nervous system controls involuntary functions of internal organs.

11. An **endocrine system** of ductless glands scattered through the body is present.

12. The sexes are nearly always separate, and each sex contains paired gonads with ducts which discharge their products either into the cloaca or into special openings near the anus.

13. The **body plan** consists typically of **head, trunk,** and postanal **tail.** A **neck** may be present in some, especially terrestrial forms. Two pairs of appendages are the rule, although they are entirely absent in some. The coelom is divided into a pericardial space and a general body cavity; in addition, mammals have a thoracic cavity.

AMMOCOETE LARVA AS CHORDATE ARCHETYPE

As pointed out in a previous section, the oldest known group of vertebrates was the Agnatha, which included the extinct ostracoderms and the existing cyclostomes (lampreys and hagfish). It is logical, therefore, to look for a vertebrate ancestor among these primitive forms. Is there a living form which can serve as a generalized vertebrate ancestor? What features must such a prototype possess? Adult cyclostomes are too specialized and too degenerative in many respects for meeting the requirements of such a generalized type. The ammocoete larva of lampreys, however, possesses many of the basic structures one should expect to find in a chordate archetype. Many of its structures are simple in form and similar to those in higher vertebrates. It has a heart, ear, eye, thyroid gland, and pituitary gland which are characteristic of vertebrates but are lacking in *Amphioxus*. This larva is so different from the adult lamprey that it was for a long time considered to be a separate species, and it was not until it was shown to metamorphose into the adult lamprey that the exact relationship was explained. This eel-like larva spends

several years buried in the sand and mud of shallow streams, until it finally emerges as an adult which may continue to live in fresh water (fresh-water lampreys) or else migrate to the sea (marine lampreys).

Since Stensio's important work on ostracoderms in 1927, the similarity of this ammocoete larva to the cephalaspids of that ancient group of fish has become more and more apparent, and many zoologists are substituting it for *Amphioxus* as a basic ancestral type. It is true that the ammocoetes has some degenerative specializations of its own, for it lacks the bony exoskeleton, an important feature in ostracoderms. Stensio, Romer, and other paleontologists have emphasized that a hard or bony exoskeleton is characteristic of ancestral vertebrates and that cartilaginous structures in the adult represent a specialized embryonic condition which has been retained. Homer Smith has suggested that the heavy armor of the ostracoderms was a protection not against predators but against the osmotic effect of passing from salt to fresh water, where a rapid and fatal absorption of water into the organism would occur unless checked by the bony exoskeleton. Romer has shown that cartilage serves a real purpose in the embryo. Cartilage is not present in dermal bones, such as certain skull bones which are laid down directly in membrane and have simple growth, but only in internal bones where it is necessary to maintain complicated relationships with blood vessels, muscles, and other bones throughout the entire growth period. Bone grows only by accretion and does not have the power to expand, which cartilage can do, and thus the latter represents an ideal embryonic material before the adult elements are fully formed.

Some of the generalized characteristics of the ammocoete larva will be pointed out in the following summary of its basic structures.

General chordate features. The ammocoetes has a long, slender body with the front end broader and blunter (Figure 330). A median membranous fin fold ex-

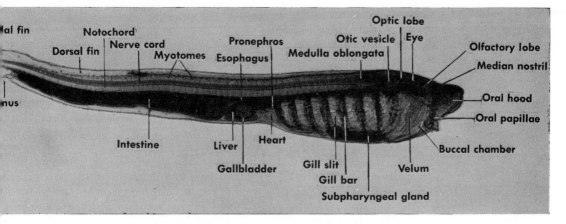

Figure 330. Structure of ammocoete larva. Photograph of stained slide.

tends along most of the posterior dorsal border, passes around the caudal end, where the fin is broader, and then continues forward on the ventral side. The **notochord** is large and extends from the very tip of the tail to a region near the anterior end of the brain. The **dorsal nerve cord,** unlike the amphioxus, is enlarged anteriorly to form a complete brain. Instead of the many gill slits of the amphioxus, there are only seven pairs of gill pouches and slits in the ammocoetes (there are six pairs in shark embryos). Muscular segmentation is also found in the form of myotomes along the dorsal part of the body. The skeleton is meager and in a degenerate condition. Such parts as are found are entirely cartilaginous, such as the gill bars of the branchial basket, the scattered plates of the brain case, and the small vertebrae near the notochord. The well-developed notochord is the chief supporting skeleton. There are no paired fins or jaws.

Digestive and respiratory systems. At the ventral anterior end of the larva there is a cup-shaped **oral hood** which encloses the buccal cavity. Numerous **oral papillae,** or branched projections, are attached to the sides and roof of the oral hood and surround the mouth cavity. They have a sensory function. Between the buccal cavity and the **pharynx** is the **velum,** made up of a pair of flaps which help create currents of water entering the mouth. The expanded pharynx makes up a large part of the alimentary canal and bears in its lateral walls the seven pairs of **gill pouches.** Each of these pouches opens to the exterior by a **gill slit.** Each gill slit has a fold or **gill** on both its anterior surface and posterior surface, and the wall of the pharynx between adjacent gill slits contains supporting rods of cartilage (**gill bars**). The gills are richly supplied with blood capillaries and are bathed by currents of water which enter the mouth and pass to the exterior through the gill slits. Oxygen from the water enters the blood in the gills and carbon dioxide is given off by the blood in exchange. The **endostyle (subpharyngeal gland),** a closed furrow or tube extending for the length of four gill pouches, is found in the floor of the pharynx. It secretes mucus which is discharged into the pharynx by a small duct. This sticky mucus entangles the food particles brought in by water currents produced by muscular contractions of the pharynx. Cords of food thus formed are carried into the intestine by the ciliated groove in the floor of the pharynx. During metamorphosis a portion of the endostyle is converted into the **thyroid gland** which secretes the thyroid hormone containing iodine.

The pharynx narrows at its posterior end to form a short **esophagus** which opens into the straight **intestine.** Opening into the intestine by the **bile duct** is the

Phylum Chordata—ancestry, characteristics, protochordates 427

liver with which is associated a very large and conspicuous **gallbladder. Pancreatic cells** are found in the wall of the anterior part of the intestine but do not form a distinct gland. The intestine opens posteriorly into the cloaca which also receives the kidney ducts. The **anus** is found a short distance in front of the post-anal tail.

The generalized vertebrate features of the ammocoetes are thus seen to be its jawless filter feeding, its relatively undifferentiated alimentary canal, its gill arrangement, and its endostyle characteristic of primitive feeding organisms. The development of the thyroid gland from part of the endostyle, as well as the muscular branchial movement, also represents a plan which higher vertebrates have followed.

Circulatory system. The hypothetical, primitive chordate plan of four major longitudinal blood vessels—**dorsal aorta, subintestinal, right cardinal vein,** and **left cardinal vein**—and two major connections between these blood vessels—**right** and **left ducts of Cuvier** and the **aortic arches** —is generally followed in the ammocoetes with certain modifications. The posterior end of the subintestinal has become modified to form the **hepatic portal vein,** the anterior portion to form the **heart** of one **auricle** (atrium), and one **ventricle** arranged in tandem. From the ventricle the short **ventral aorta** runs forward and gives off eight pairs of **aortic arches** to the gill pouches. Each arch is composed of an **afferent branchial artery** carrying blood to the capillaries of the gills and an **efferent branchial artery** carrying aerated blood from the gill capillaries to the **dorsal aorta.** The dorsal aorta gives off many branches to the body tissues, and a large posterior branch, the **intestinal,** to the intestine. The **cardinal veins** return blood from the tissues to the right and left **ducts of Cuvier,** which empty into the **sinus venosus,** a thin-walled chamber which empties into the atrium, and thence to the ventricle of the heart. Each cardinal vein is made up of an **anterior cardinal** and a **posterior cardinal branch.** The he-

patic portal vein picks up blood laden with nutrients from the intestine and carries it to the liver. The **hepatic vein** carries blood from the liver to the **sinus venosus,** and so back to the heart.

Excretory system. The ancestral vertebrate kidney is supposed to have extended the length of the coelomic cavity and was made up of segmentally arranged uriniferous tubules. Each tubule opened at one end into the coelom by a nephrostome and at the other end into the common archinephric duct. Such a kidney has been called an **archinephros** or **holonephros** and is found in the embryos of hagfish. The kidneys of higher vertebrates presumably developed from this primitive plan. Embryological evidence indicates that vertebrates pass through successive developments of three different regions (pronephros, mesonephros, and metanephros) of this primitive archinephros. Evolutionary differences in the internal environment of the different vertebrate groups have produced a differential complexity of tubules in specifiic regions of the ancient kidney.

In the amniotes (reptiles, birds, and mammals) each individual, therefore, in its development passes through stages that correspond to a region of anterior tubules (pronephros), a region of middle tubules (mesonephros), and a region of posterior tubules (metanephros). The pronephros and mesonephros disappear in amniotes, leaving only the metanephros as the functional kidney, although the mesonephros may function during embryonic life. However, in forms lower than the amniotes, the pronephros and mesonephros grades of tubules are functional in varying combinations of the two regions. Thus cyclostomes have stressed the pronephric type of tubules, whereas fish and amphibians have emphasized the mesonephric type. Among fish and amphibians, however, the adult mesonephros has developed posteriorly into the region of the metanephros of higher forms and is given the name of **opisthonephros.**

In summary, we may state that the evolutionary sequence of adult vertebrate

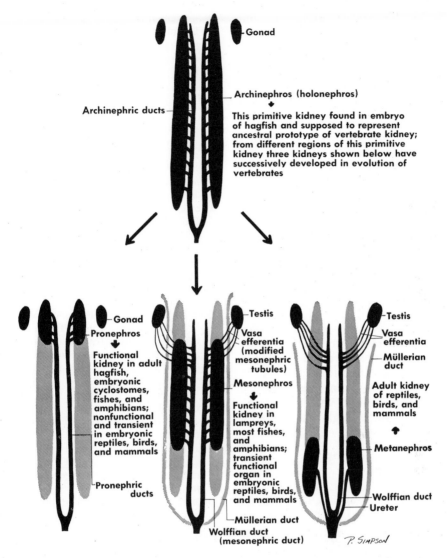

Figure 331. Diagram showing evolution of vertebrate kidney. Actual functional structures shown in black; degenerate or undeveloped parts shaded. Some authorities substitute for mesonephros the term opisthonephros (most fish and amphibians) which includes also part of metanephric region.

kidneys has been archinephros, opisthonephros, and metanephros.

It is seen that the excretory system of the ammocoetes conforms to the basic chordate plan, whereas the solenocyte type of flame cell found in *Amphioxus* is altogether different.

Reproductive system. The **gonads** are paired ridgelike structures on the dorsal side of the coelom. Each gonad appears

to have been formed by the fusion of a number of units. Since they lack genital ducts, the adult lampreys shed their gametes into the coelom where an opening into the **mesonephric duct** allows the gametes to escape to the outside through the **urogenital papillae.**

Nervous and sensory system. Both brain and spinal cord conform to the basic chordate plan. The **brain** has the typical three divisions of **forebrain, midbrain,** and **hindbrain.** Each of these divisions is associated with an important sense organ—olfactory, vision or eyes, and auditory, respectively. From the dorsal side of the forebrain there are two outgrowths or stalks, each of which bears a vestigial **median eye,** the only instance among vertebrates of two median eyes. Other vertebrates may have two outgrowths, but the anterior one is the parietal body, which appears to have been a median eye, and the posterior one (epiphysis) is the pineal gland. In no living vertebrate does a median eye function as such. In some vertebrates only the pineal gland or body is present. A **pituitary gland,** formed from an evagination (infundibulum) of the forebrain and the **hypophysis** from the **nasohypophyseal canal** of the pharynx, is found on the ventral side of the brain. The functional **eyes** of the ammocoetes are small and develop from the forebrain. The spinal cord gives off a pair of **dorsal roots** (mainly sensory) and a pair of **ventral roots** (motor) in every muscle segment. The dorsal and ventral roots do not join as they do in higher vertebrates, nor do the nerves have myelin sheaths.

Derivation and meaning of basic terminology

Amphioxus (am'phi-ox"us) (Gr. *amphi,* double, + *oxys,* sharp) Often used as a synonym for *Branchiostoma,* the correct generic name; the lancelet.

Archaeopteryx (ar'ke-op"ter-iks) (Gr. *archaio,* ancient, + *pteron,* wing) A fossil reptilelike bird.

Ichthyostega (ich'thy-os"te-ga) (Gr. *ichthyo,* fish, + L. *os,* bone, + Gr. *tegos,* covering) A fossil with both fish and amphibian characters of the late Devonian period.

Ostracodermi (os'tra-co-der"mi) (Gr. *ostrakon,* shell, + *derma,* skin) A fossil class of fishlike animals of Silurian and Devonian rocks; the oldest recorded vertebrates.

Placodermi (plac'o-der"mi) (Gr. *plakos,* plate,

+ *derma,* skin) The extinct class of armored fish of the late Silurian and Devonian rocks.

Seymouria (sey'mou-ri"a) (after Seymour, Texas) A fossil cotylosaur with both amphibian and reptilian characters.

ANNOTATED REFERENCES

Beer, de, G. R. 1951. Vertebrate Zoology, rev. ed. London, Sidgwick and Jackson, Ltd. *The student will glean a knowledge of representative types of vertebrates and how they fit into the evolutionary scheme from this excellent work which should be read by all serious students of the zoological sciences.*

Berrill, N. J. 1955. The Origin of Vertebrates. Oxford, Oxford University Press. *The author stresses the tunicates as the basic stock from which other protochordates and vertebrates arose. He believes that such a sessile filter feeder was really the most primitive animal and was not a mere degenerate side branch of chordate evolution.*

Colbert, E. H. 1955. Evolution of the Vertebrates. New York, John Wiley & Sons, Inc. *A clear and well-written presentation of the history of the backboned animals through time. One of the best treatises in the field.*

Roe, A., and G. G. Simpson (editors). 1958. Behavior and Evolution. New Haven, Yale University Press. *A masterpiece which integrates two great disciplines—evolution and behavior.*

Romer, A. S. 1945. Vertebrate Paleontology. Chicago, University of Chicago Press. *An authoritative work of the first rank by a master paleontologist.*

Romer, A. S. 1959. The Vertebrate Story. Chicago, University of Chicago Press. *A comprehensive background of the evolutionary trends and relationships of the various vertebrate groups leading up to that of man himself.*

Smith, H. M. 1960. Evolution of Chordate Structure. New York, Holt, Rhinehart & Winston, Inc. *This excellent introduction to comparative anatomy gives a fine appraisal of the basic structures of primitive chordates.*

Stirton, R. A. 1959. Time, Life, and Man. New York, John Wiley & Sons, Inc. *An up-to-date account of the fossil record of both invertebrates and vertebrates.*

chapter 23

Phylum Chordata

Classes Cyclostomata and Chondrichthyes

PRIMITIVE AND CARTILAGINOUS FISH

It is customary to group vertebrates into two major groups: (1) Pisces (fish), which includes the classes Cyclostomata, Chondrichthyes, and Osteichthyes; and (2) Tetrapoda (four-footed), which includes the classes Amphibia, Reptilia, Aves, and Mammalia. The former is made up of strictly aquatic forms and the latter, of the land-dwelling animals. A second method of grouping is (1) Anamnia, or those without fetal membranes (Cyclostomata, Chondrichthyes, Osteichthyes, Amphibia); and (2) Amniota, or those with fetal membranes (Reptilia, Aves, and Mammalia).

The present arrangement of grouping the cyclostomes and the chondrichthyes together is mostly one of convenience, although both groups have many primitive chordate characteristics and afford the student an explanation of the generalized plan of vertebrate morphology found in the embryonic history of higher vertebrates. There is no question of the advancement of the sharks over the cyclostomes, for the former have jaws, paired appendages, true teeth, scales, and reproductive ducts which are entirely lacking in the latter. Both are cartilaginous, but this probably has little significance. In evolutionary origin there is no logical basis for placing the two classes together. As emphasized previously, it is quite logical to assume that living cyclostomes and the fossil ostracoderms came from the same common stock of primitive ancestral

vertebrates, so that the two groups are placed in the same taxonomic group—Agnatha, or jawless vertebrates. With Chondrichthyes and Osteichthyes, however, it is impossible to pick out any ancestral type from such a varied assemblage as the placoderms. It was formerly thought that the chondrichthyes, because of their complete absence of bone and other characteristics, were very primitive and that they appeared on the evolutionary scene before the bony fish. This view is no longer held; cartilage is considered degenerative rather than primitive. The fossil record indicates that the chondrichthyes appeared after the bony fish. It appears that this class had its origin in fresh water, the same as did other vertebrates, but quite early took to the sea and mostly disappeared from fresh water. A few species are known to inhabit fresh water permanently or temporarily. In the sea they have undergone many evolutionary specializations and have been a very successful and highly compact group of fish. Altogether, there are about 3,000 species of Chondrichthyes as compared with the 20,000 species of bony fish.

PHYLUM CHORDATA

CLASS CYCLOSTOMATA*—lampreys and hagfish

These forms derive their name from their circular mouth. They are the lowest vertebrates and the only existing ones

---

*Si′klo-sto″ma-ta (Gr. *cyklos*, circular, + *stoma*, mouth).

without jaws (superclass Agnatha) and are thus distinguished from the remaining vertebrates which have jaws (superclass Gnathostomata). Cyclostomata is represented by about 50 species, almost equally divided between two orders. Because of their close relationship to the extinct ostracoderms, some authorities consider Agnatha as a class made up of two subclasses (Ostracodermi and Cyclostomata). There are also other taxonomic arrangements of these two groups.

Characteristics

1. Body slender, **eel-like**, rounded, with **soft skin** containing **mucous glands** but **no scales**
2. Median fins with cartilaginous fin rays, but **no paired appendages**
3. **Fibrous** and **cartilaginous** skeleton; notochord persistent
4. **Ventral suctorial mouth; single nasal sac**
5. Heart with one auricle and one ventricle; aortic arches in gill region; blood with erythrocytes and leukocytes
6. Six to fourteen pairs of gills
7. Two **pronephric** kidneys (mesonephros or opisthonephros in adult) with ducts to urogenital papillae
8. Dorsal nerve cord with differentiated brain; eight to ten pairs of cranial nerves
9. Digestive system lacking a stomach, and the intestine provided with a fold, **typhlosole**
10. Sensory organs of taste, smell, hearing, and sight present; each auditory organ with one to two semicircular canals
11. Sexes separate in lampreys; hermaphroditic in hagfish; gonad single and no duct; fertilization external; long larval period in lampreys

Classification

Body is cylindrical with well-developed dorsal fin; skin smooth without scales; jaws absent; mouth suctorial with horny teeth; nasal aperture single; appendages absent; gill pouches, six to fourteen pairs.

432

Order 1. Petromyzontia (pet'ro-my-zon"ti-a) (Gr. *petros*, stone, + *myzon*, suck)—**lampreys.** Mouth suctorial with horny teeth; nasal sac not connected to mouth; gill pouches, seven pairs. Examples: *Entosphenus, Petromyzon.*

Order 2. Myxinoidea (mik'si-noi"de-a) (Gr. *myxa*, slime, + *oidea*, type of)—**hagfish and slime eels.** Mouth terminal with four pairs of tentacles; buccal funnel absent; nasal sac with duct to pharynx; gill pouches, ten to fourteen pairs; partially hermaphroditic. Examples: *Myxine, Bdellostoma.*

ORDER PETROMYZONTIA (HYPEROARTII)— lampreys

All the lampreys of the northern hemisphere belong to the family Petromyzonidae. The destructive marine lamprey, *Petromyzon marinus,* is found on both sides of the Atlantic Ocean (America and Europe) and may attain a length of 3 feet. Other genera, such as *Entosphenus* and *Lampetra,* also have a wide distribution in North America and Eurasia and are usually from 6 to 24 inches long. There are 19 species of lampreys in North America. About half of these belong to the nonparasitic brook type; the others are parasitic. According to Hubbs, a noted authority on lampreys, the nonparasitic species have arisen from the parasitic forms by degeneration of the teeth, alimentary canal, etc. The genus *Ichthyomyzon,* which contains three parasitic and three nonparasitic species, is restricted to eastern North America. On the west coast of North America the chief marine form is represented by *Entosphenus tridentatus.* The southern hemisphere is represented by two families—Geotriidae and Mordaciidae.

All lampreys, the marine as well as the fresh-water forms, spawn in the spring on shallow gravel beds in streams of fresh water. With their buccal funnels, the males clear away the pebbles from a sandy bottom and form a sort of pit (Figure 333). When a female anchors herself to a pebble over one of these pits, a male seizes her, winds his tail around her, and discharges his sperm over the eggs as they are extruded from her body into the

Figure 332. Ammocoetes, larval form of lamprey. This one is about 2 inches long and has undergone its metamorphosis in bottom sand of stream. Compare with earlier stage in Figure 330.

333

334

Figure 333. Lamprey nest with four individuals hard at work removing pebbles. (About ⅓ natural size.) (Courtesy John W. Jordan, Jr.)

Figure 334. Eggs of brook lamprey, *Lampetra lamottei*. (About 2 times natural size.) (Courtesy John W. Jordan, Jr.)

depression. More than one pair may spawn in the same nest. The adults soon die after their spawning act. The eggs hatch in about two weeks into small larvae (ammocoetes) which stay in the nest until they are about ½ inch long; they then burrow into the mud and sand in quiet water and emerge at night to feed on the organic ooze that is caught in mucus strings on the floor of the pharynx. The ammocoete period lasts from 3 to 7 years, according to species. During this time the

Figure 335. Whitefish with sea lamprey, *Petromyzon marinus,* attached. When lamprey attaches itself with its sucking mouth it proceeds to rasp off small bits of flesh with its chitinous teeth. Lamprey then injects an anticoagulant and sucks blood of host fish. Such wounds often prove fatal to fish, especially if point of attachment is in abdominal region of body. In many Great Lakes regions commercial fishing has been reduced annually from many millions of pounds to just a few thousand pounds. Many devices have been used to control lampreys, such as poison and electrical barriers, but none have been wholly effective. (U. S. Fish and Wildlife Service.)

ammocoetes grows, and then in the fall, rapidly metamorphoses into an adult. This change involves the development of larger eyes, the replacement of the hood by the oral disc with teeth, a shifting of the nostril to the top of the head, and the development of a rounder but shorter body. Parasitic lampreys either migrate to the sea, if marine, or else remain in fresh water where they attach themselves by their suckerlike mouth to fish and with their sharp horny teeth rasp away the flesh and suck out the blood. To promote the flow of blood, the lamprey injects an anticoagulant into the wound. When gorged, the lamprey releases its hold but leaves the fish with a large gaping wound which may prove fatal. The parasitic fresh-water adults live a year or more before spawning and then die; the marine forms may live longer. The nonparasitic lampreys do not feed after emerging as adults, for their alimentary canal degenerates to a nonfunctional strand of tissue. Within a few months they also spawn and die.

The invasion in recent years of the upper Great Lakes by the sea lamprey has posed a great economic problem to the fisheries of that region. It has been estimated that upward of nine-tenths of the lake trout and white fish have been destroyed by the depredations of this parasite. Control methods of trapping and preventing the lampreys from spawning have been only partially successful.

Distinctive characteristics of adult lamprey

The anatomy of different species of lampreys varies somewhat, especially between parasitic and nonparasitic members, but in general they all have the same basic plan. Their skin is smooth and slimy, with many unicellular glands. There are no scales. They have no jaws or paired fins but do have median fins with fin rays on the posterior dorsal region and tail. The mouth or buccal disc is suckerlike and, together with the muscular protrusible tongue, is provided with horny, epidermal teeth (degenerate in nonparasitic forms). The tongue creates suction by acting like a plunger. The primitive skeleton is cartilaginous with persistent notochord. No vertebral centra are formed. The seven pairs of gills are not connected directly with the pharynx but are found in spherical pouches which open into a respiratory chamber and to the outside through tubes. The opening into the respiratory chamber is controlled

434

by a flap, or velum. When the animal is attached, water for respiration passes into as well as out of the gill slits. The single nasal opening is on top of the head and opens internally into the olfactory sac which connects with the cavity of the pituitary. The simple digestive system (degenerate in nonparasitic lampreys) consists of an esophagus and an intestine which has a spiral longitudinal fold (typhlosole) or spiral valve. A liver and a gallbladder (in some) are present. No spleen or pancreas (as a definite gland) is found. The compact paired kidneys (mesonephroic divisions of the archinephroi) open by ureters into a urogenital papilla. The circulatory system is similar to that of the ammocoete larva. No renal portal system is present. Among its sense organs there is a lateral line system. The sexes are separate, and the single gonad with no duct discharges its gametes through the urogenital sinus.

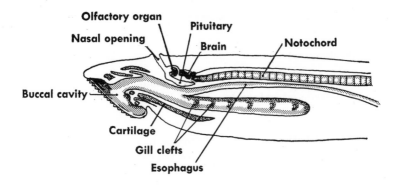

LONGITUDINAL SECTION THROUGH HEAD END OF LAMPREY

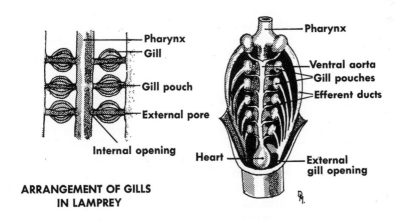

ARRANGEMENT OF GILLS
IN LAMPREY

ARRANGEMENT OF GILLS
IN HAGFISH (Myxine)

Note that efferent ducts on side all unite and open to outside by a common opening

Figure 336. Some structural features of cyclostomes. (Partly redrawn from Atwood: A Concise Comparative Anatomy, The C. V. Mosby Co.)

Phylum Chordata—classes Cyclostomata and Chondrichthyes 435

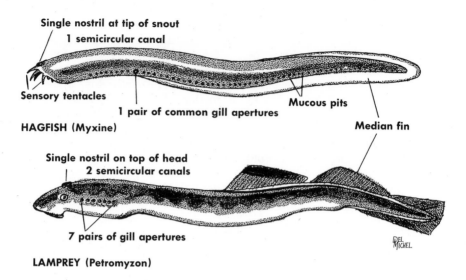

Single nostril at tip of snout
1 semicircular canal

Sensory tentacles

1 pair of common gill apertures

Mucous pits

HAGFISH (Myxine)

Median fin

Single nostril on top of head
2 semicircular canals

7 pairs of gill apertures

LAMPREY (Petromyzon)

Figure 337. Comparison of hagfish and lamprey (class Cyclostomata). Mucous pits indicate enormous amount of mucin produced by hagfish.

ORDER MYXINOIDEA (HYPEROTRETI)—
hagfish and slime eels

The members of this order are often called "borers" because of their habit of burrowing into fish for flesh consumption. They are really internal parasites. They are all marine and spawn on the ocean floor. Some may reach a length of 36 inches. The slime eel *(Myxine)* on the Atlantic coast and the hagfish *(Polistotrema)* on the Pacific coast are the most common species in North America. Other species are found off the coasts of Japan, Africa, and South America.

They differ from lampreys in several ways. The dorsal fin is not divided and may be absent. Their nostril near the front of the head opens into a canal which runs into the roof of the pharynx. Their eyes are vestigial. They have no buccal funnel but have a suctorial mouth with one large epidermal tooth. Around the mouth and nostril there are six tentacles. Their gills (six to fourteen pairs) are located far behind the head region and their efferent ducts join into a common external opening on each side. Their brain is poorly developed, and the dorsal and ventral roots of spinal nerves are united. A single semicircular canal is

found in the ear. The yolk-filled egg may be nearly 1 inch in diameter and is enclosed in a horny shell. There is no larval stage and growth is direct. They are hermaphroditic but can produce only one kind of gamete at a time; a single individual may produce sperm at one season and eggs the next, or vice versa.

The evolutionary studies of the cyclostomes have been discussed under ammocoete larva as a chordate archetype, page 426.

CLASS CHONDRICHTHYES*
(ELASMOBRANCHII)—sharks

This group includes the sharks, rays, and chimaeras. They have many resemblances to the true fish, but they also have many differences. The group is a very ancient one and has left many fossil forms. One of their distinctive features is their cartilaginous skeleton which must be considered degenerate instead of primitive. Although there is some calcification here and there, bone is entirely absent throughout the class. Sharks are extensively studied in nearly all vertebrate an-

---

*Chon-drich'thy-es (Gr. *chondros,* cartilage, + *ichthys,* fish).

436

atomy classes, for their basic structural plan is also the pattern found in the embryos of higher forms. This early blueprint of vertebrate structure is modified in forms above sharks into plans characteristic of each particular group.

Characteristics

1. **Body fusiform or spindle shaped,** with a **heterocercal** caudal fin (see Figure 350); paired pectoral and pelvic fins; two dorsal median fins; pelvic fins in male modified for "claspers"; fin rays present

2. **Mouth ventral; two olfactory sacs which do not break into the mouth cavity;** jaws present

3. Skin with **placoid** scales (Figure 359) and **mucous glands;** teeth modified placoid scales which have both an ectodermal and mesodermal origin

4. **Endoskeleton entirely cartilaginous;** notochord persistent; vertebrae complete and separate; appendicular, girdle, and visceral skeletons present

5. Digestive system with a J-shaped stomach and intestine with a spiral valve; liver, gallbladder, and pancreas present

6. Circulatory system of several pairs of aortic arches; dorsal and ventral aorta, capillary and venous systems, hepatic portal and renal portal systems; two-chambered heart

7. Respiration by means of five to seven pairs of gills with separate and exposed gill slits; **no operculum**

8. No **swim bladder**

9. Brain of two olfactory lobes, two cerebral hemispheres, two optic lobes, a cerebellum, and a medulla oblongata; ten pairs of cranial nerves

10. Sexes separate; gonads paired; reproductive ducts into cloaca; oviparous or ovoviviparous; direct development; fertilization internal

11. Kidneys of opisthonephros type

Classification

Streamlined form with heterocercal tail; cartilaginous skeleton; leathery skin with placoid scales (dermal denticles); restricted notocord; mouth and two nostrils ventral; jaws and paired appendages; males with claspers; eggs with large yolks.

Subclass Elasmobranchii (e-las′mo-bran″chi-i) (Gr. *elasmos*, plate, + *branchia*, gills). Gills in separate clefts along pharynx; a spiracle behind and above each jaw; cloaca present.

> **Order Selachii** (se-la′chi-i) (Gr. *selachos*, a fish having cartilage instead of bones)—**modern sharks.** Body spindle shaped; five to seven pairs of lateral gills not covered by operculum; pectoral fins not enlarged. Example: *Squalus (Acanthias).*

> **Order Batoidei** (ba-toi′de-i) (Gr. *batos*, a kind of ray, + -oid)—**skates and rays.** Body spread out; pectoral fins enlarged and attached to head and body; five pairs of gill slits on ventral side; spiracles large. Examples: *Raja* (common skate), *Dasyatis* (sting ray).

Subclass Holocephali (hol′o-ceph″a-li) (Gr. *holos*, entire, + *kephale*, head)—**chimaeras or ghost fish.** Gill slits covered with operculum; aberrant shape; jaws with tooth plates; single nasal opening; without scales; accessory clasping organs in male; lateral line an open groove. Example: *Chimaera.*

With the exception of the whale, sharks are the largest living vertebrates. The larger sharks may reach 40 to 50 feet in length. The dogfish sharks so widely used in zoological laboratories rarely exceed 3 feet. Sharks are noted for being voracious, and some of them have attained great notoriety in this respect. The man eater, *Carcharodon*, which often reaches a length of 30 feet, will not hesitate to attack a human being when the opportunity offers. Another shark, *Sphyrna*, known as the hammerhead, has a head in the form of a transverse projection with an eye at each end.

Distinctive characteristics

The body of a shark, such as a dogfish shark (Figure 338), is fusiform or spindle shaped. In front of the ventral mouth is a pointed **rostrum;** at the posterior end the vertebral column turns up to form the **heterocercal** tail. The fins consist of the paired **pectoral** and **pelvic** fins supported by appendicular skeletons, two median **dorsal** fins (each with a spine in *Squalus),* and a median **caudal** fin. A median **anal**

Figure 338. Dogfish shark.

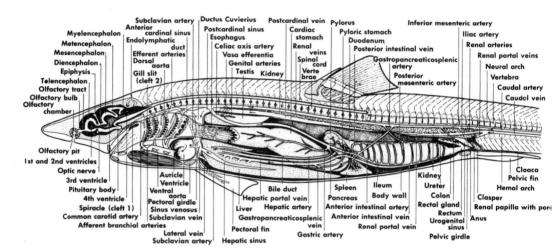

Figure 339. Dogfish shark, *Squalus acanthias*. Longitudinal section. (From Wodsedalek: General Zoology Laboratory Guide, Wm. C. Brown Co.)

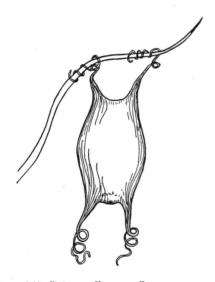

Figure 340. "Mermaid's purse."

fin is present in the smooth dogfish (*Mustelus*). In the male, the medial part of the pelvic fin is modified to form a **clasper** which is used in copulation. The paired **nostrils** (blind pouches) are ventral and anterior to the mouth. The lateral eyes are lidless, and behind each eye is a spiracle (remnant of the first gill slit). Five gill slits are found anterior to each pectoral fin. The leathery skin is covered with placoid scales (dermal denticles), each of which consist of a wide basal plate of dermal dentine and a spine covered with vitrodentine, or a shiny enamel-like dentine. These scales are modified to form teeth in the mouth and are the remnants of the dermal plates of placoderms. A lateral line sensory system is made up of canals which extend along the side of the

438

trunk and tail and over the head region.

Internally, the cartilaginous skeleton is made up of a **chondrocranium,** which houses the brain and auditory organs and partially surrounds the eyes and olfactory organs; a vertebral column, a visceral skeleton, and an appendicular skeleton. The jaws are suspended from the chondrocranium by ligaments and cartilages. Both the upper and the lower jaws are provided with many sharp, triangular teeth which, when lost, are replaced by other rows of teeth. Teeth serve to grasp the prey, which is usually swallowed whole. The muscles are segmentally arranged and are especially useful in the undulations of swimming. The mouth cavity opens into the large **pharynx** which contains openings to the separate gill slits and spiracles. A short, wide esophagus runs to the J-shaped stomach. A **liver** and **pancreas** open into the short, straight **intestine** which contains the unique **spiral valve** that delays the passage of food and increases the absorptive surface. The chambers of the **heart** are arranged in tandem formation and the circulatory system is basically the same as that of the embryonic vertebrate and of the ammocoetes. The opisthonephroi, or kidneys, are two long, slender organs above the coelom and are drained by the **Wolffian ducts** which open into a single urogenital sinus at the **cloaca.** The Wolffian ducts also carry the sperm from the testes of the male, which uses a clasper to deposit the sperm in the female oviduct. The Müllerian tube or oviduct (paired) carries the eggs from the **ovary** and coelom and is modified into a **uterus** where a primitive placenta may attach the embryo shark until it is born. Such a relationship is really **viviparous reproduction;** others simply retain the developing egg in the uterus without attachment to the mother's wall (**ovoviviparous reproduction**). Some sharks and rays deposit their fertilized eggs in a horny capsule called the "mermaid's purse" (Figure 340) which is attached by tendrils to seaweeds. Later the young shark emerges from this "cradle."

The nervous system is more advanced

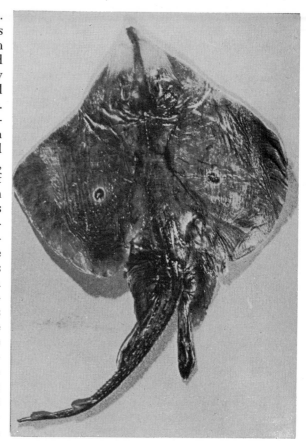

Figure 341. Common skate, *Raja.* Order Batoidei. Note in this male the large leglike claspers of pelvic fins for internal fertilization of eggs in female.

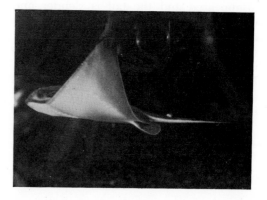

Figure 342. Stingray swimming by flapping pectoral fins. Tail is slender, whiplike, and provided with one or more dangerous spines which may inflict a blood-poisoning wound. (Courtesy Vancouver Public Aquarium, British Columbia.)

than the ammocoete larva and is developed directly from the dorsal nerve cord of the embryo. The brain is typically made up of the three basic parts of the vertebrate brain—forebrain, midbrain, and hindbrain. These parts form five subdivisions or regions—telencephalon, diencephalon, mesencephalon, metencephalon, and myelencephalon—each with certain functions. There are ten pairs of cranial nerves which are distributed largely to the head regions. Surrounding the spinal cord are the neural arches of the vertebrae. Along the spinal cord a pair of spinal nerves with united dorsal and ventral roots is distributed to each body segment.

Members of the order Batoidei (skates and rays) (Figures 341 and 342) are specialized for bottom dwelling. In these the pectoral fins are greatly enlarged and are used in swimming like wings. The gill openings are on the underside of the head, and the spiracles are unusually large. Water for breathing is taken in through these spiracles to prevent clogging the gills, for their mouth is often buried in sand. Their teeth are adapted for crushing their prey, which consists mainly of mollusks, crustaceans, and an occasional small fish. Two members of this group are of especial interest—the sting rays (Figure 342) and the electric rays. In the sting rays the caudal and dorsal fins have disappeared and the tail is slender and whiplike. The tail is armed with one or more saw-edged spines which can inflict very dangerous wounds. Such wounds may heal slowly and leave complications. Electric rays have smooth, naked skins and have certain dorsal muscles modified into powerful electric organs which can

give severe shocks and stun their prey. Sting rays also have electric organs in the tail.

Sharks have considerable economic importance. Most are highly destructive to fish, lobsters, and crabs. In some localities sharks are used as food by man. Commercially, shark-liver oil is extracted and used in medicine as a source of vitamins A and D, and sharkskin leather is made into many useful articles.

ANNOTATED REFERENCES

Applegate, V. C., and J. W. Moffett. 1955. The Sea Lamprey, Scientific American, April, 1955, p. 36. *An account of the life history of this lamprey and the destruction it has wrought on the game fish of the Great Lakes.*

Daniel, J. F. 1934. The Elasmobranch Fishes, ed. 3, Berkeley, University of California Press. *A very useful study of this group for the advanced student.*

Gage, S. H. 1893. The Lake and Brook Lampreys of New York. Wilder Quarter-Century Book. Ithaca, Comstock Publishing Co.

Goodrich, E. S. 1909. Cyclostomes and Fishes. In Lankester: Treatise on Zoology. London, A. and C. Black, Ltd. *A good appraisal of these groups for the specialist.*

Hubbs, C. L. 1937. A Revision of the Lamprey Genus Ichthyomyzon. Miscellaneous Pub. No. 35, Museum of Zoology, University of Michigan. Ann Arbor, University of Michigan Press. *An up-to-date revision of the group. Of great interest to the specialist.*

Hubbs, C. L. 1956. Cyclostomata (Encyclopaedia Britannica). Chicago, Encyclopaedia Britannica, Inc. *Gives the distinctive characteristics, life history, and evolution of this oldest existing group of vertebrates.*

Young, J. Z. 1950. The Life of Vertebrates, New York, Oxford University Press. *Well-written chapters are devoted to the cyclostomes and the elasmobranchs in this imposing work. Well illustrated.*

chapter 24

Phylum Chordata

Class Osteichthyes

BONY FISH

The bony fish include many species and are most familiar of all the fishlike animals. Their skeletons are, at least in part, bony, and most are covered by dermal scales. The skull and pectoral girdles are covered by investing bony plates in the dermal skin. The bony fish are also characterized by having the gills covered by opercular folds which are provided with bony supports. This extensive group is found in a great variety of aquatic habitats. Some are strictly fresh-water dwellers, whereas others divide their time between the two kinds of aquatic habitats, but most species are marine.

Bony fish have been the most successful of all aquatic forms. Their 20,000 species indicate that they are the most numerous of all vertebrates, at least in number of species and probably also in number of individuals. Although some groups of fish have flourished and declined in the past, the class as a whole (especially the Teleostei) has reached at the present time a degree of success never attained in the past.

From whence came the bony fish? There are two great subclasses of existing fish—the Actinopterygii and the Choanichthyes. When first detected in the fossil record of the middle Devonian fresh-water deposits, they were both well-defined groups. Their common ancestor is unknown. Two of their most characteristic features were their bony skeletons and their air or lung sacs. In most of the bony fish the lung is modified into the hydrostatic organ, the air or swim bladder. Some aspects of their organization pattern show a resemblance to that found in certain placoderms (acanthoderms), and some authorities think that the early bony fish ancestor had a close affinity to the ancestor of the placoderms.

PHYLUM CHORDATA
CLASS OSTEICHTHYES (PISCES)*
Characteristics

1. **Skeleton more or less bony** which has replaced the primitive cartilaginous skeleton; vertebrae numerous; notochord may persist in part; **tail usually homocercal**
2. Skin with mucous glands and with embedded dermal scales of three types: **ganoid, cycloid,** or **ctenoid**; some without scales; no placoid scales
3. Fins both median and paired with **fin rays of cartilage or bone**
4. **Mouth terminal** with many teeth (some toothless); jaws present; olfactory sacs paired and may or may not open into mouth
5. Respiration by gills supported by bony gill arches and covered by a **common operculum**

---

*Os'te-ich"thy-es (Gr. *osteon*, bone, + *icthys*, a fish). Pis'ez (L. *pises*, fishes).

6. **Swim bladder** often present with or without duct connected to pharynx

7. Circulation consisting of a two-chambered heart, arterial and venous systems, and four pairs of aortic arches; blood of nucleated red cells

8. Nervous system of a brain with small olfactory lobes and cerebrum and large optic lobes and cerebellum; ten pairs of cranial nerves

9. Sexes separate; gonads paired; fertilization usually external; larval forms may differ greatly from adults

Fish vary greatly in size. Some of the minnows are less than 1 inch long; some forms may exceed 10 feet in length. The swordfish is one of the largest and may attain a length of 12 to 14 feet. Most fish, however, are around 1 to 3 feet.

Classification

Body primitively fusiform, but variously modified in many; body divided into three regions—head, trunk, and tail; skeleton mostly bony; mouth usually terminal; skin usually with embedded dermal scales; paired and lateral fins supported by dermal fin rays usually present; gills on bony gill arches in a common chamber on each side of pharynx and covered by an operculum.

Subclass Actinopterygii (ak'ti-nop'ter-yg'i-i) (Gr *actis*, ray, + *pteryx*, fin)—ray-finned fish. Paired fins supported by dermal rays and without basal lobed portions; one dorsal fin (may be divided); nasal sacs open only to outside.

Superorder Chondrostei (chon-dros'te-i) (Gr *chondros*, cartilage, + *osteon*, bone)—primitive ray-finned fish.

Order Acipenseroidei (as'i-pen'ser-oi"de-i (L. *acipenser*, sturgeon, + *oideus*, like) Ossified dermal skull and unossified chondral skull; endoskeleton mostly of cartilage; body mostly scaleless except for rows of bony (ganoid) scutes; snout and barbels; mouth on underside of head; no teeth in adult; dorsal swim bladder may be present; tail heterocercal; notochord slightly constricted by vertebrae; spiral valve. Examples: *Acipenser* (common sturgeon), *Polyodon* (paddlefish).

Order Polypterini (pol'ip-ter"i-ni) (L. *polypterus*, a certain fish, + *inus*, like). Ossified skeleton; dorsal fin divided into eight or more finlets; body slender with thick ganoid scales; lobed pectoral fins; caudal fin diphycercal; ventral air bladder of two lobes and

Figure 343. White sturgeon, *Acipenser*. These grow to a large size and ascend rivers to spawn. Superorder Chondrostei.

Figure 344. Long-nosed gar, *Lepidosteus*. Extremely voracious, feeds on fish, and is commercially unimportant. Superorder Holostei.

442

Figure 345. C-O sole, *Pleuronichthys*. Common name derived from markings on tail. It is a bottom-dwelling flatfish; protruding eyes can see while rest of body is buried in sand. Superorder Teleostei. (Courtesy Vancouver Public Aquarium, British Columbia.)

Figure 346. Climbing perch, *Anabas*, can move along ground and climb low trees by means of paired fins and spines on gill covers and anal fin. It has a special air-breathing chamber or labyrinthic organ above the gills. Superorder Teleostei. (Courtesy Vancouver Public Aquarium, British Columbia.)

opens into pharynx by a common duct. Example: *Polypterus* (bichir).

Superorder Holostei (ho-los'te-i) (Gr. *holos*, entire, + *osteon*, bone)—intermediate ray-finned fish.

Order Protospondyli (pro'to-spon"dy-li) (Gr. *protos*, first, + *spondylos*, vertebra). Body covered with overlapping cycloid scales; dorsal fin long and low; modified heterocercal tail; chondrocranium partly ossified and not closely integrated with the bony dermal skull; bilobed swim bladder may serve for respiration. Example: *Amia* (bowfin).

Order Ginglymodi (jing'li-mo"di) (Gr. *ginglymos*, hinge joint). Body slender and cylindrical and covered with thick, ganoid scales; long jaws armed with teeth; swim bladder may serve for respiration; small dorsal and anal fins. Example: *Lepidosteus* (gar pike).

Superorder Teleostei (tel'e-os"te-i) (Gr. *teleos*, complete, + *osteon*, bone)—climax bony fish. Body covered with thin scales without bony layer (cycloid or ctenoid) or scaleless; dermal and chondral parts of skull closely united; caudal fin mostly homocercal; mouth terminal; notochord a mere vestige; swim bladder mainly a hydrostatic organ and usually not opened to the esophagus; endoskeleton mostly bony; more than 30 different orders and some 350 families recognized. These orders may be placed in two basic groups: Isospondyli, or soft-rayed fish, and Acanthopterygii, spiny-rayed fish, Five clear-cut and distinctive major groups (orders) are recognized in this scheme.

Order Isospondyli (i'so-spon"dy-li) (Gr. *isos*, equal, + *spondylos*, a vertebra). Fins with soft dermal rays; pelvic fins in posterior abdominal position; open duct to

Figure 347. Piranha or piraya fish, *Serrasalmo*, is noted for attacking living animals; but accounts of its ferocity are probably exaggerated. It operates in packs and is a native of South American rivers. Superorder Teleostei. (Courtesy Vancouver Public Aquarium, British Columbia.)

Figure 348. Starry flounder, *Platichys*. In common with other flatfish, this one has both eyes on same side of head. Note twisted, distorted mouth. Flounders have remarkable powers to change colors in imitation of their background. Superorder Teleostei. (Courtesy Vancouver Public Aquarium, British Columbia.)

Phylum Chordata—class Osteichthyes 443

Figure 349. Sea horse, *Hippocampus*. Male is provided with brood pouch for sheltering eggs. Superorder Teleostei.

air bladder; most primitive teleosts. Examples: *Clupea* (herring), *Oncorhynchus* (Pacific salmon), *Salmo* (Atlantic salmon), *Sardinops* (Pacific sardine).

Order Apodes (ap′o-des) (Gr. *apodos*, footless). Body long and slender; fins with soft rays; scales vestigial or absent; pelvic fins usually absent; air bladder with duct. Example: *Anguilla* (fresh-water eel).

Order Mesichthyes (me-sick′thy-es) (Gr. *mesos*, middle, + *ichthys*, fish). Intermediate teleosts; fins with soft rays; pelvic fins abdominal; jaws with many teeth; air bladder with open duct. Example: *Esox* (common pike).

Order Ostariophysi (os-ta′ri-o-phy″si) (Gr. *ostarion*, dim. of *osteon*, a bone, + *physa*, bladder). Fins with some rays spiny; chain of little bones (ossicles) connecting air bladder with internal ear (Weberian organ); body covered with cycloid scales or bony plates or naked; barbels (in some). Examples: *Catostomus* (sucker), *Cyprinus* (common carp), *Ictalurus* (channel catfish), *Electrophorus* (electric eel).

Order Acanthopterygii (ac′an-thop′ter-yg″i-i) (NL., fr. *acantho*, spine, + Gr. *pteryx*, fin). Teleosts with spiny rays on dorsal, anal, and paired fins; maxilla short; air bladder without duct; pelvic fins forward beneath thoracic region or head; scales

mostly ctenoid. Examples: *Perca* (perch), *Gadus* (codfish), *Hippocampus* (sea horse), *Pomoxis* (crappie), *Symphurus* (sole), majority of teleosts.

Subclass Choanichthyes (cho′a-nich″thy-es) (Gr. *choana*, funnel, + *ichthys*, fish)—**lobe-finned or air-breathing fish.** Body primitively fusiform, but slender to thick in existing forms; diphycercal tail; nostrils connected to mouth cavity; paired fins lobed or axial; two dorsal fins; primitive cosmoid scale modified to thin cycloid type.

Order Crossopterygii (cros-sop′te-ryg″i-i) (Gr. *crossoi*, a fringe, + *pteryx*, fin)—**lobe-finned fish.** Heavy bodied; paired fins lobed with internal skeleton of basic tetrapod type; premaxillae, maxillae present; scales large with tubercles and heavily overlapped; three-lobed diphycercal tail; skeleton with much cartilage; bony spines hollow; air bladder vestigial; gills hard with teeth; intestine with spiral valve; spiracle present.

Suborder Coelacanthini (se′la-kan″thi-ni) (NL., fr. Gr. *koilos*, hollow, + *akantha*, thorn, spine) (**Actinista**). Examples: *Latimeria, Malania.*

Order Dipnoi (dip′noi) (Gr. *di*, twice, + *pnoe*, breath)—**lungfish.** All median fins fused to form diphycercal tail; fins lobed or of filaments; scales of cycloid bony type; teeth of grinding plates; no premaxillae or maxillae; air bladder of single or paired lobes and specialized for breathing; intestine with spiral valve; spiracle absent. Examples: *Epiceratodus, Protopterus, Lepidosiren.*

Evolutionary patterns of bony fish

No group of vertebrate animals has surpassed the bony fish in evolutionary diversity. Nowhere else do we see better examples of adaptive radiation where, from certain generalized types, species have evolved whose adaptations fit them for nearly every kind of aquatic ecological niche. Although the oldest of vertebrate groups existing very early in the earth's organic evolution, bony fish have persisted, become diversified, and passed from one type to another, always meeting the challenge of their environment. Their many varieties of body form and size are correlated with particular aquatic habitats. Some have fusiform or streamlined bodies for reducing friction and other adaptations for rapid swimming. Predaceous fish not only have trim, elongated bodies but also powerful tail fins and other mechanical advantages for swift pursuit. Sluggish bottom-feeding forms have flattened bodies for movement and concealment on the ocean floor. Many have striking protective coloration. Some are fitted for deep-sea existence. Scores of other types, even more striking, could be mentioned. Any particular type of teleost fish will reveal an amazing array of specialized structures for food getting, for offense and defense, for reproduction, and for other purposes.

The fossil record reveals that the actinopterygian bony fish, which were found in the fresh-water deposits of the Middle Devonian period, were small with large eyes and extended mouths. Their tails were **heterocercal** (Figure 350). They had a single dorsal fin and a single anal fin; paired fins were represented by the anterior pectoral fins and the posterior pelvic fins. Their skeletons were largely bone. Their trunks and tails were incased in an armor of heavy, rhombic scales (**ganoid**). Most of these early fish had functional lungs, but these were used chiefly as swim bladders (hydrostatic organs). All had gills (five pairs or less) and spiracles. These early actinopterygians belong to the order Palaeoniscoidea (now extinct). One common genus of this order was *Cheirolopis*, a generalized type which had some resemblance to certain acanthodians (placoderms). From such an ancestor the actinopterygians have evolved. In their evolution, they passed successively through the stages represented by the superorders Chondrostei, Holostei, and Teleostei. Certain evolutionary trends are evident in this succession. The first two superorders represented today by only a few forms, flourished in the early development of the bony fish (Permian, Triassic, and Cretaceous periods). Although the teleosts are thought to have originated in fresh water, and many of the existing lower forms are fresh-water forms, the major evolution of

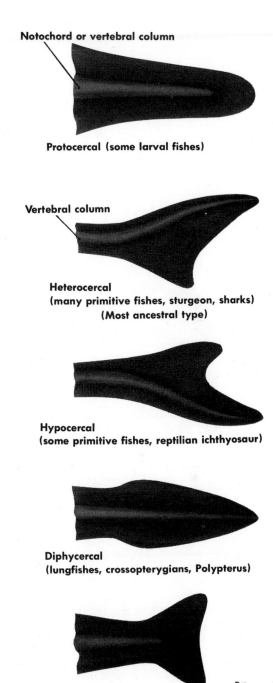

Figure 350. Types of caudal fins among fish. Some functional correlations may be seen among these different types. Heterocercal tail, for example, is found in fish without swim bladder, for it tends to counteract gravity while swimming.

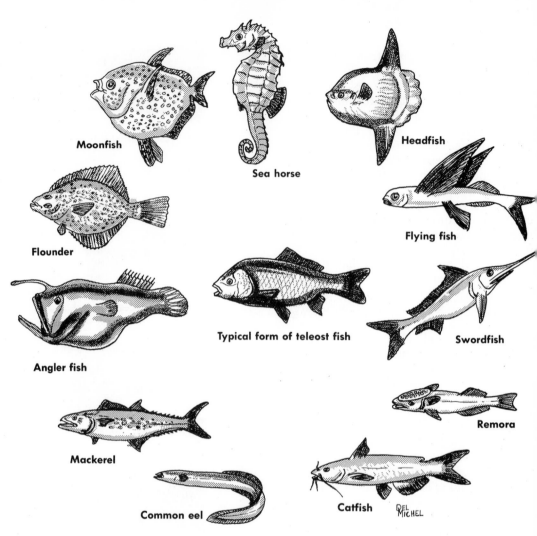

Figure 351. Adaptive radiation of bony fish (teleosts). Variety of body forms have fitted them for many diverse habitats and conditions of existence. It is not always possible, however, to explain all their adaptive shapes and structures.

the group occurred in the sea, where the majority of species now live. The first true teleost recognized by paleontologists is *Leptolepis,* a small Triassic fish that had definite primitive and generalized characteristics, such as soft dermal fin rays, pelvic fins in the abdominal position, and air bladders with ducts. There is no satisfactory explanation for this constant replacement of one type by another. Aquatic media are fairly stable in comparison with land habitats. Bony fish do vary, but there is no reason to suspect a higher mutation rate among this group than that of others. It is known that convergent or independent evolution occurs among fish. No definite statements can be made with certainty about any criteria of success as they apply to modern teleosts. But the diversity within the group is attested by the many thousands of different species.

In what ways are modern fish different from their ancient ancestors? What major changes have been made in structural adaptations in this deployment of fish types? In the first place there has been an almost inconceivable variety of different body forms in present teleosts as compared with the normal fusiform or spindle-shaped body of primitive fish. This is shown in such fish as flounders, eels, flying fish, swordfish, batfish, sea horses, sargassum fish, catfish, lizard fish, headfish, moonfish, toadfish, remora, and many other specialized types. The skeleton of primitive fish was largely ossified, but this condition regressed to a partly cartilaginous state among many of the Chondrostei and Holostei. Teleosts, however, have an internal skeleton almost completely ossified like the primitive members. The dermal investing bones of the skull (dermatocranium) and the chondrocranium (endocranium) around the brain and sense organs form a closer union among the teleosts than they did in the primitive bony fish. Other evolutionary changes among the teleosts were the movement of the pelvic fins forward to the head and thoracic region, the transformation of the lungs of primitive forms into air bladders with hydrostatic functions and without ducts, the changing of the heterocercal tail of primitive fish and of the intermediate superorders into a homocercal form, and the development of the thin cycloid and ctenoid scales from the thick ganoid type of early fish. Among other changes were the loss of the spiracles and the development of stout spines in the fins, especially in the pectoral, dorsal, and anal ones.

The other great subclass (Choanichthyes) of bony fish has had a less spectacular evolutionary development than the actinopterygians, but it is of far greater interest and importance in an evolutionary sense, for its members are close to the ancestral stock of the higher vertebrates. This subclass has nostrils that open into the mouth, swim bladders that can act as lungs, and paired **lobed fins.** The ray-finned fish are an important part of vertebrate evolution and adaptive radiation but are a side issue in the evolutionary line of higher vertebrates. The lobe-finned fish apparently originated and evolved in fresh water and flourished during late Paleozoic times. The subclass is divided into the Crossopterygii (fringe finned) and the Dipnoi (lungfish). They first appeared in Devonian times, and one of the common generalized forms was *Osteolepis,* a crossopterygian which has been found in Old Red Sandstone of Great Britain. Among the primitive characteristics of this ancient form were the fusiform shape, the position of the paired fins, the presence of two dorsal fins, and a heterocercal tail. The paired fins in this or similar types also bore some resemblance to a tetrapod limb, for they consisted of a basal arrangement of median or axial bones with other bones radiating out from these median ones. Some of the proximal bones seem to correspond with the three chief bones of the tetrapod limb. The scales of these primitive fish were of the **cosmoid** type, a thick complex scale of dentinelike cosmine, enamel, and vascular pulp cavities. This type of scale is not found in modern fish but has been replaced by the bony **cycloid** type. From these and related forms the early amphibians arose.

Osteolepis belonged to a crossopterygian group which were mainly freshwater fish. The coelacanths were marine forms which appeared in late Devonian times and flourished during the Mesozoic era. They were derived apparently from the osteolepids but had certain characteristics of their own. Although the tail was of the **diphycercal** type, they also possessed a small lobe between the upper and lower caudal lobes, producing a threepronged structure. Coelacanths also show some degenerate features, such as more cartilaginous parts and a swim bladder that was either calcified or else persisting as a mere vestige. Although this form was supposed to have become extinct in the Cretaceous periods, several specimens of *Latimeria,* a living coelacanth, have been collected near Madagascar since 1938. The other order (Dipnoi) (Figure 352) of the subclass Choanichthyes is considered to be a specialized and aberrant offshoot of the primitive crossopterygians. They are commonly known as **lungfish** and were

Figure 352. Lungfish, *Protopterus,* just removed from its mud "cocoon" in which it has lived during dry season. This fish is a native of Africa. Subclass Choanichthyes, order Dipnoi. (Courtesy General Biological Supply House, Inc., Chicago.)

PROTOPTERUS (Africa)

**Side branch of dipnoan evolution
Can burrow in mud when water dries up**

LEPIDOSIREN (South America)

**Side branch of dipnoan evolution
Can burrow in mud when water dries up**

EPICERATODUS (Australia)

**Direct descendant of ancient lungfish
Cannot withstand complete drying up of water**

Figure 353. Lungfish, *Dipnoi.* In all three the air bladder is a lunglike structure by which they can breathe air when necessity arises.

once supposed to be the ancestors of the amphibians—a view no longer held. They have many structures in common with the crossopterygians, such as internal nares, the cycloid scale modified from the cosmoid type, and paired fins which are somewhat lobe shaped. Fossil primitive lungfish show a closer relationship to the crossopterygians than do existing forms, for they had a heterocercal tail, two dorsal fins, and a well-ossified skull—structures which have undergone considerable modification in modern lungfish. The major evolutionary trends of this ancient group, which probably originated in Middle Devonian times, were specializations, such as bone reduction, change in dentition toward tooth-bearing plates for crushing hard food, the fusion of the median fins into a symmetrical diphycercal tail, and the development of functional lungs not unlike those of tetrapods. The fossil record shows the genus *Dipterus* to be the earliest lungfish. From this genus, dipnoan evolution led directly to the genus *Ceratodus*, a Triassic form that had a wide distribution over the earth. From *Ceratodus*, lungfish evolution led directly to the living Australian lungfish, *Epiceratodus*, which may attain a length of 5 feet. This lungfish is able to survive in stagnant pools by coming to the surface and gulping air into its single lung, but it cannot live out of water. The South American lungfish, *Lepidosiren*, and the African lungfish, *Protopterus*, are evolutionary side branches of the Dipnoi and can live out of water for long periods of time by breathing through openings connecting their mud burrows with the surface. All three types of lungfish live in habitats which alternate between wet and dry seasons.

Some interesting structural adaptations of fish

Swim bladder. The swim bladder, which is found in all bony fish except a few bottom forms (*Lophius*, etc.), is a development from the paired lungs of primitive Osteichthyes or their ancestors the placoderms, that lived in alternate wet and dry regions where lungs were necessary for survival. The generalized condition of the lungs in these primitive forms may have been similar to the lungs found in the existing *Polypterus*, a chondrostean fish of the fresh waters of tropical Africa. The crossopterygians which gave rise to the amphibians no doubt had similar structures, although there are only vestigial lungs in *Latimeria*. Functional lungs are also present in existing lungfish. In all other bony fish the lungs have mostly lost their original function and have become swim bladders.

In *Amia* and *Lepidosteus* (Holostei), the bilobed swim bladder functions in breathing, but in other actinopterygians the swim bladder may serve as a hydrostatic organ, as a sense organ, or as an organ of sound production. The swim bladder, which in teleosts functions chiefly as a hydrostatic organ, can alter the specific gravity of the fish by filling itself with gas (lessening the hydrostatic pressure) or by emptying itself (increasing the hydrostatic pressure). The fish can thus float higher or sink lower in the water accordingly. In those fish in which the swim bladder is not connected to the pharynx by a duct (Physoclisti), gases (oxygen, carbon dioxide, and nitrogen) are mostly secreted into the bladder by a special anterior gland, **red gland,** with its remarkable network of blood vessels, **rete mirabilia.** A posterior **oval gland** of the swim bladder has the power to absorb these gases to lessen its size. In those fish with a swim bladder connected to the pharynx (Physostomi) the bladder may be filled by gulping air. Gas secretion and resorption are under the control of the autonomic nervous system.

The lung or swim bladder originates as a diverticulum from the ventral side of the pharynx, the position occupied by the lungs of *Polypterus*, *Lepidosiren*, *Protopterus*, and tetrapods. This position tended to make aquatic forms top heavy, and so the swim bladder shifted to the dorsal side of the pharynx in most bony fish. *Epiceratodus*, the Australian lung-

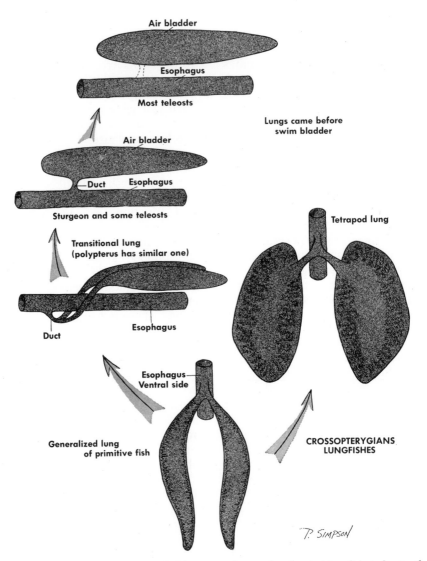

Air bladder

Esophagus

Most teleosts

Lungs came before
swim bladder

Air bladder

Duct Esophagus

Sturgeon and some teleosts

Tetrapod lung

Transitional lung
(polypterus has similar one)

Esophagus

Duct

Esophagus
Ventral side

Generalized lung
of primitive fish

**CROSSOPTERYGIANS
LUNGFISHES**

P. Simpson

Figure 354. Evolution of lungs and air bladders. Fossil records of primitive fish indicate that most of them were provided with lungs which were adapted to climatic conditions existing during the early evolution of fish. Lung originated on ventral side as a double sac connected to throat by single duct. Embryologically, it may have started as gill pouches. From this generalized lung condition two lines of evolution occurred. (1) One line led to swim or air bladder of modern teleost fish. Various transitional stages show that the air bladder and its duct (which is eventually lost) have shifted to a dorsal position above esophagus to become structurally a hydrostatic organ for flotation instead of for breathing. (2) Second line of evolution has led by extensive internal foldings, but no radical change in position, to the tetrapod lung found in land forms.

fish, still retains, however, the ventral duct connection to the pharynx.

Sound production in fish which mainly involves the swim bladder is discussed in Chapter 41, Animal Behavior Patterns.

Fins. Fins in fish are always of two kinds: (1) **paired**, which include the **pectoral** and **pelvic** fins; and (2) **unpaired** which consist of the **dorsal**, **caudal**, and **anal** fins. Among the various species the

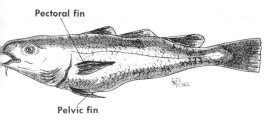

Pectoral fin

Pelvic fin

Figure 355. Tomcod, *Microgadus*. Has pelvic fins anterior to pectoral fins. Many other fish have the pelvic fins well forward, an adaptation which fish morphologists think prevents the fish from rising in water when it stops.

fins vary as to location and number. Fish swim mainly by lateral movements of the tail and tail fin, while the paired fins are held closely against the side and the other unpaired fins are spread out to keep the animal in a vertical position. In their undulations they make use of alternate contractions of their segmentally arranged muscles. When swimming quietly they may use their paired lateral fins. The shape or form of a fish has an important bearing on its rate of locomotion. Some bodies have a more efficient "streamline" resistance than others. The mackerel family is especially well adapted for fast swimming. The only vertebrate parasite of man, the candiru of the South American catfish, has a slender body adapted for entering the sex organ orifices of man.

The flying fish use their large and extended pectoral fins for gliding, and the climbing perch of India use their gill cover and anal spines for ascending the branches of shrubs and trees found in their habitats (Figure 356).

Kidneys and osmoregulation. The kidney in fish is called an **opisthonephros** because it is the spatial equivalent of both the mesonephros and metanephros, although it is at the **mesonephros** (which is its classical term) level. The primitive kidney was adapted for a fresh-water existence because it originated in primitive fresh-water fish. These early kidneys were designed mainly to get rid of excess water just like the contractile vacuole of fresh-water amebae. In fresh-water fish the blood and tissues have salt (NaCl) concentration of about 0.6%, and there is a tendency for water from the outside to enter the body through the gills and mouth membrane because of this difference in osmotic pressure (the outside fresh water having only a negligible amount of salt).

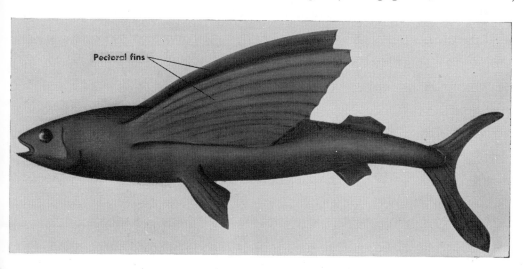

Pectoral fins

Figure 356. Flying fish, *Cypselurus,* example of highly structural and functional adaptation among fish. Flying fish do not fly but glide with their modified pectoral fins held in rigid position. By vigorous side-to-side swimming movements of their tails they taxi for several feet on surface and gain sufficient momentum for their take-off. Their flight usually lasts only a few seconds and the distance of their glide varies from a few feet to several hundred feet.

Phylum Chordata—class Osteichthyes 451

Figure 357. Yellow perch, *Perca flavescens*. This fish is of commercial importance and may attain a length of more than 14 inches. It has been introduced into many states where it is not native. (Courtesy Vancouver Public Aquarium, British Columbia.)

The protovertebrates that entered fresh water from the sea had kidneys segmentally arranged, with each coelomic segment provided with a pair of tubules, each of which had one end (nephrostome) opened into the coelom and the other to the outside. This method served to drain the coelomic fluid with its waste to the exterior. But such a method was inadequate to cope with a fresh-water existence and so a tuft of blood capillaries (glomerulus) enclosed in a capsule was developed in the tubules for filtering under high blood pressure the excess water from the blood. In time the nephrostome

disappeared from the kidney tubules of higher vertebrates and the glomerulus alone did all the work of the kidneys. A few primitive fish, such as *Amia,* still retain the nephrostome which serves to return coelomic fluid to the circulation by emptying into a venous sinus. In freshwater fish the **nephron** then consists of the renal corpuscle (glomerulus plus Bowman's capsule) and the uriniferous tubule. The latter tube is typically divided into two segments, a proximal and a distal part, and receives blood from the efferent glomerular artery and the renal portal vein. As the blood filtrate passes down this uriniferous tubule, food and salt molecules are resorbed by its walls. Much of the nitrogeneous waste in fresh-water fish is excreted through the gills in the form of ammonia and urea; a little, such as uric acid, is excreted through the nephron.

In marine fish the problem is to keep the body from losing water, because of the high osmotic pressure of sea water (3.5% NaCl) against the lower osmotic pressure (1.5% NaCl) of the fish's blood. Marine fish therefore tend to get rid of the glomerulus and depend more upon tubular excretion which does not require the filtration of water. Some marine fish, such as the toadfish (*Opsarus*), have no glomeruli (aglomerular). Such fish swallow a great deal of water and get rid of

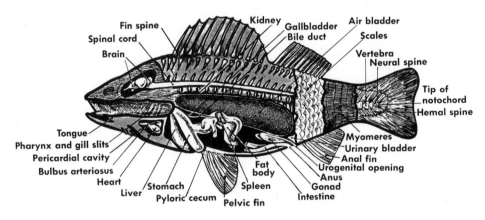

Figure 358. Diagram of visceral organs of teleost fish, such as yellow perch, *Perca flavescens.* Part of intestine cut away.

452

excess salt by means of special chloride-secreting cells in the gills. That marine fish have not entirely rid themselves of glomeruli indicates perhaps that they have left fresh water too recently to have acquired completely this adaptation.

Osmoregulation, which varies greatly among fish, determines the ability of some to live in either fresh water or salt water. Many have little or no powers of regulating their osmotic pressure or adjusting themselves to a water concentration different from their normal habitat. Those that can tolerate only very narrow ranges of salt concentration in water are called **stenohaline;** those with wide toleration are **euryhaline.** Some fish, such as *Anguilla,* may be both stenohaline and euryhaline during the life cycle. Those fish that migrate from the sea to spawn in fresh water are **anadromous,** such as salmon, shad, and marine lampreys; on the other hand, fresh-water forms that resort to the sea to breed are **catadromous,** such as the fresh-water eel *(Anguilla).* In such cases, adjustments to either fresh-water or sea water involve osmotic regulation of salt and water balance, which may be under the control of hormonal activity, especially that of the thyroid gland.

"Bloodless fish." Although fish have the characteristic vascular pattern of vertebrates, such as red blood, nucleated corpuscles, and specialized hemoglobin for transporting oxygen, in recent years certain fish collected from the Antarctic regions are exceptions to this rule. The icefish *(Chaenocephalus)* has transparent blood with little iron and no red blood corpuscles; white corpuscles, however, are present. Oxygen transportation appears to take place only by physical solution in the plasma with low oxygen capacity. Such fish apparently are able to survive only in very cold water, but they do show that vertebrates may exist without hemoglobin.

Color. Many fish have striking colors, although the common game fish are rather modestly attired. The males of some species, such as the horned dace and darters, have beautiful colors during the breeding season, but the most striking colors are found in tropical fish, especially those that live in and around coral reefs. Color is chiefly due to the presence of pigment cells (**chromatophores**) found in the dermal layer of the skin. The pigments are red, orange, black, and yellow. Various combinations of these can produce other shades of color. **Guanine** present in certain cells gives the silvery appearance often noticed in fish. An absence of pigment produces a whitish appearance.

Many fish can change their color patterns to harmonize with their surroundings by contracting or expanding the pigment in the chromatophores. The flounder is one of these. Placed on artificial mosaic backgrounds, these fish assume the same kind of pattern by the manipulation of their chromatophores. Other fish can alter their color to a lesser extent.

The mechanisms for explaining color changes are not clear in all cases, but the neurohumoral theory, which states that the neurons to the chromatophores produce acetylcholine and adrenaline (sympathin) for dispersing or aggregating the pigment, respectively, has received wide acceptance.

Scales. Both fish and reptiles bear scales in their skin, but the scales are not homologous in the two groups. In reptiles, scales are epidermal (ectodermal) in origin; in fish they are dermal (mesodermal) structures. Some fish, such as catfish, have no scales at all, but most do possess at least one of the three types found in the group—**ganoid, cycloid,** and **ctenoid** (Figure 359). Scales usually overlap like the shingles on a roof, but they may be separated, as they are in eels.

Ganoid scales are platelike bony forms covered externally with enamel. They vary greatly in variety and form among the various species. In some they are rhombic plates fitted side by side. **Cycloid** scales are rounded and thicker in the center, like the boss on a shield. They are marked by concentric lines and are arranged to overlap. **Ctenoid** scales are also rounded, but the exposed parts which are not overlapped bear teeth. Intermediate

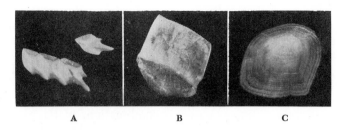

Figure 359. Types of fish scales. **A**, Ganoid. **B**, Cycloid. **C**, Ctenoid.

types are also found between the cycloid and ctenoid varieties. Also the same fish may bear both cycloid and ctenoid scales. Flounders, for instance, have ctenoid scales dorsally and cycloid ventrally.

Scales grow throughout the life of the fish. The age of certain fish, such as salmon and trout, can be determined on the scales by the interruptions (winter marks, or annuli) between regular groups of circuli. During winter there is slower growth which results in fewer lines of growth spaced close together; in summer there is more growth with the growth lines farther apart.

Reproduction. Most fish have separate sexes, and sexual dimorphism is found in some. The teleosts shows many types of sexual reproduction patterns. Although the hermaphroditic condition may occasionally occur abnormally in many species, only one or two families (e.g., Serranidae) are truly hermaphroditic. In hermaphroditic forms the gonads are each divided into testicular and ovarian zones.

The **testes** are usually elongated, whitish organs divided into lobules which contain cysts of maturing germ cells. Within each cyst the maturing cells are always of the same stage of development. The lobules open into the spermatic duct (with secretory lining) which runs into the urogenital sinus. Males often become sexually mature before the females, and their testes may be active throughout the year; in others the testes have seasonal rhythms in reproductive activity. The **ovaries** may run the length of the abdominal cavity and are made up of many ovarian follicles supported by connective tissue. The ovary

with its membraneous covering may be continuous with the oviduct, or the ovaries may be naked and discharge their eggs into the peritoneal cavity, whence they are picked up by the oviducts (Müllerian ducts). The paired oviducts may open through a common urogenital pore behind the anus or they may open through genital pores. Some fish, such as trout and salmon, have no oviducts; others, such as the fresh-water eel, have neither sperm ducts nor oviducts. Usually eggs are produced during a seasonal rhythm and the ovaries are quiescent at other times. A few (e.g., hake) are known to have active ovaries at all times. Some fish, such as the cod, produce enormous numbers of eggs (9,000,000) in a single specimen.

Most teleost fish are oviparous, laying eggs that are fertilized in the water by the sperm discharged by the male, usually in close contact with the female. Gametes in water have limited viability unless they are united. Certain fish, however, are ovoviviparous (young born alive but nourished by egg yolk in mother) or viviparous (young with sort of placental attachment to wall of uterus). Ovoviviparity or viviparity is found in the mosquito fish *(Gambusia)* and certain sea perch (Embiotocidae), as well as a few others.

Male fish have evolved many devices for transferring sperm into the female. Copulatory organs include the urogenital papillae, anal fins, and other specialized structures. Fertilization usually takes place while the egg is still in the ovarian follicle. In *Rhodeus*, the female lays her eggs in the gill spaces of a fresh-water mussel by means of a very long uro-

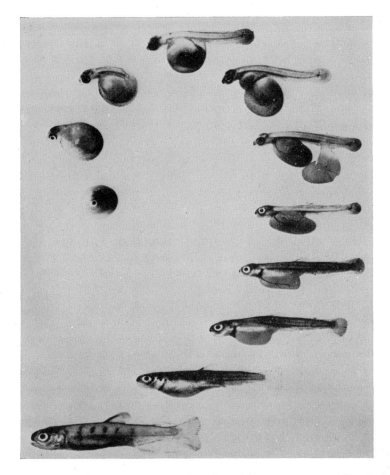

Figure 360. Development of salmon from egg to fingerling. (Courtesy Homer Kelly, U. S. Fish and Wildlife Service.)

genital papilla. In fish that are ovoviviparous, the young develop within a cavity of the ovary.

Soon after eggs are laid in water, they take up water and harden. Cleavage (meroblastic) occurs in the blastodisc of the zygote, and a blastoderm is formed. As cleavage continues, the blastoderm spreads over and encloses the yolk mass. The space between the blastoderm and yolk is the segmentation cavity, or blastocoele. Development proceeds, and eventually a larval form of fishlike appearance with a large yolk sac is hatched. Temperature has a great effect on regulating the speed of hatching and subsequent development.

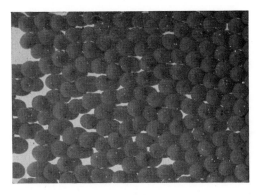

Figure 361. Chinook salmon eggs—"eyed" stage. Eyes of young fish visible as two black spots. (Courtesy W. F. Kubichek, U. S. Fish and Wildlife Service).

Derivation and meaning of basic terminology

Actinopterygii (Gr. *actino,* ray, + *pteron,* wing or fin).

anadromous (Gr. *ana,* up, + *dromos,* running) Refers to those fish that migrate up streams to spawn.

catadromous (Gr. *kata,* down, + *dromos,* running) Refers to those fish that migrate from fresh water to the ocean to spawn.

Choanichthyes (Gr. *choane,* funnel or nostril, + *ichthys,* fish) Nostrils of these fish are connected to the mouth cavity.

Chondrostei (Gr. *chondros,* cartilage, + *osteon,* bone) Their skeleton is a mixture of cartilage and bone.

Crossopterygii (Gr. *crosso,* tassel, + *pteryx,* fin) These fish have lobed fins.

Dipnoi (Gr. *di,* two, + *pnoe,* breath) So called because they can breathe both by gills and by swim bladders.

euryhaline (Gr. *eurys,* broad, + *hals,* salt) Such fish can tolerate wide ranges of salt-water concentrations.

Holostei (Gr. *holos,* entire, + *osteon,* bone).

Osteichthyes (Gr. *osteon,* bone, + *ichthys,* fish).

Physoclisti (Gr. *physa,* bladder, + *kleistos,* closed) Swim bladder not connected to pharynx by duct.

Physostomi (Gr. *physa,* bladder, + *stoma,* opening) Swim bladder connected to pharynx by duct.

rete mirabilia (L. *rete,* network, + *mirabilia,* wonder) A network of small blood vessels so arranged that the incoming blood runs parallel to the outgoing blood and thus makes possible a counter exchange between the two blood streams. Such a mechanism ensures a constancy of gases in the swim bladder.

stenohaline (Fr. *stenos,* narrow, + *hals,* sea) Such fish have restricted ranges of salt-water concentrations.

ANNOTATED REFERENCES

Berg, L. S. 1940. Classification of Fishes Both Recent and Fossil. Ann Arbor, Edwards Brothers, Inc. *A comprehensive treatise of great value.*

Brown, M. E. (editor). 1957. The Physiology of Fishes. Volume I, Metabolism; Volume II, Behavior. New York, Academic Press, Inc. *An up-to-date treatise by many eminent specialists.*

Curtis, B. 1949. The Life Story of the Fish. New York, Harcourt, Brace & Co., Inc. *Interesting life histories of fish. Can be understood by the beginner.*

Dean, B. 1895. Fishes, Living and Fossil. New York, The Macmillan Co. *A classical work but somewhat outdated.*

Hubbs, C. L., and K. F. Lagler. 1947. Fishes of the Great Lakes Region. Bloomfield, Mich., Cranbrook Institute of Science.

Lagler, K. F. 1956. Freshwater Fishery Biology, ed. 2. Dubuque, Iowa, Wm. C. Brown Co. *This is an excellent treatise on the principles and methods of fresh-water fishery and research. Nearly every aspect of the subject is treated and the work is well documented throughout.*

Norman, J. R. 1931. A History of Fishes. London, Ernest Benn, Ltd. *An authoritative work of great value.*

Schultz, L. P., and E. M. Stern. 1948. The Ways of Fishes. New York, D. Van Nostrand Co., Inc. *A somewhat popular discussion of the behavior of fish. Especially good for the beginning student in zoology.*

Young, J. Z. 1950. The Life of Vertebrates. New York, Oxford University Press. *Many chapters in this excellent treatise are devoted to the structure, evolution, and adaptive radiation of fish.*

chapter 25

Phylum Chordata

Classes Amphibia and Reptilia

HOW ANIMALS HAVE CHANGED TO A LAND EXISTENCE

The vertebrates already considered are adapted to a strict aquatic life. The dipnoans, it is true, showed a modification of the aquatic breathing system to meet the conditions of a terrestrial life, but this case is a mere incident in the transition to land. The other classes of vertebrates we are to consider are modified more or less for the great change of terrestrial existence. Amphibians are on the borderline between the aquatic and the land modes of life. Aquatic and terrestrial modes of living entail differences in nearly every system of the body.

PHYSICAL CONTRAST BETWEEN AQUATIC AND LAND HABITATS

There are many drastic differences between water and land habitats. In general, animals that live in water have more restrictions than terrestrial forms.

Oxygen content of water and air. Air contains much more oxygen per unit volume than does water. Air has about 210 ml. of oxygen per liter; in water the amount is usually about 3 to 9 ml. per liter. This variation is sometimes striking, for example, in lakes at high altitude. Equilibrium is reached between the oxygen of the air and the small amount of oxygen in the water, which, as in the lakes of the high Andes, may be too small to support life at all.

Dissolved substances in water. Most water contains dissolved salts and other substances leached out of the soil. In sea water the salt content may vary from 3 or 4% in our large seas to 27% in some of our salt lakes. Pollution by refuse is also an important factor.

Temperature contrasts on land and in water. Temperature changes are more radical in terrestrial habitats than in water. Water tends to have more constant temperature. Climatic conditions vary more on land so that one region may undergo freezing, thawing, drying, flooding, and other changes.

Cover and shelter. Land habitats as a rule afford a greater variety of cover and shelter than do aquatic habitats. Aquatic animals in open water depend on speed to avoid enemies. Forms near shore find crevices and cover spots for shelter. Land forms, on the other hand, have numerous types of refuge, such as grasslands, forests, rocks, soil, and holes in trees and ground.

Medium for locomotion. Water affords support for the body which is largely lacking in air. Land also provides a variety of habitats which demand different forms of locomotion.

Breeding places. Land affords a greater variety of breeding places than does water. Shelters, as well as nests and burrows, are used for this purpose. Many aquatic forms use the shore and shallow water for breeding, but many discharge their eggs directly into the water before or after fertilization.

HOW ANIMALS HAVE MET TERRESTRIAL MODE OF LIFE

The transition from water to land was gradual and certain of the modifications were more striking than others. Some of the structural modifications may be summarized.

Skin. Terrestrial forms are protected from drying out by having hard dry skins. Instead of the soft epidermis of aquatic forms, the outer layers of land forms are cornified and composed of dead cells.

Amniotic egg. Existence on land required an egg that could be laid on land. Such an egg must be protected against drying out and mechanical injury and thus is provided with a tough but porous shell, large yolk, and special sacs and membranes (amnion, chorion, and allantois). Since it requires internal fertilization, many modifications of mating habits occurred. This type of egg is first found in reptiles and may well have first developed in animals not yet adapted for land existence. The lack of it has kept the amphibians close to water.

Breathing. Terrestrial forms have developed lungs instead of gills. This adaptation was not difficult, for lungs are primitive and the ancestral crossopterygians had them. The breathing organs of land forms must be situated deeper in the body to protect their delicate structure from the drying action of air. Along with this change in position has come the development of special air passageways, such as pharynx, trachea, and bronchi, which have no counterparts in aquatic animals.

Circulation. In connection with the development of the lungs, there are corresponding changes in the circulatory system. In fish the gill circulation (aortic arches) is placed directly in the path of the blood from the ventral aorta. Terrestrial forms have modified this aortic arch plan into a double circulation—a **systemic** circulation over the body and a **pulmonary** circulation to the lungs. No longer will the tandem arrangement of the heart chambers of fish suffice; the heart must take on additional chambers so that part of the double heart receives blood from the body and the other part from the lungs.

Locomotion. The paddlelike fins of aquatic animals are replaced on land by jointed appendages which became specialized for walking, running, climbing, flying, etc.

Sensory organs. Changes also occurred in sensory organs in the transition from water to land. Perhaps olfactory organs undergo some degeneration in land forms, for in water these organs carry a greater burden of sensory impression because of the poor development of other sense organs. Accordingly, the olfactory lobes in many fish are exceptionally large. In most terrestrial animals the eye is protected with a lid to prevent drying out. The lens is accommodated for distant vision whereas fish are mostly nearsighted. It is doubtful whether fish can hear in the ordinary sense of the word, although they are sensitive to vibrations through their lateral line organs. Sound waves are carried through the water more easily than through the air which probably accounts for the better ear in land animals.

SUBPHYLUM VERTEBRATA
CLASS AMPHIBIA*—frogs, toads, and salamanders

Amphibians were the first animals to attempt the transition from water to land. Strictly speaking, their crossopterygian ancestors were the animals that made the first attempt with any success—a feat that would have a poor chance now because present well-established competitors would make it impossible for a poorly adapted transitional form to gain a foothold. Amphibians are not completely land adapted and hover between aquatic and land environments. This double life is

---

*Am-fib'e-ah (Gr. *amphi,* both or double, + *bios,* life).

expressed in their name. The group is unique in many ways. Structurally they are between the fish on the one hand and the reptiles on the other. Although more or less adapted for a terrestrial existence, few of them can stray far from moist conditions, but many have developed devices for keeping their eggs out of water where the larvae would be exposed to enemies.

In their transition from water to land, amphibians have developed limbs in place of fins, lungs in place of gills, and some skin changes. Their circulatory system provides for lung circulation. All of them as larval forms retain a link with the aquatic life by having gills, and some retain gills throughout life. There are also other structural differences from fish which are mainly correlated with their mode of life, such as skeletal and muscular differences.

Characteristics

1. Skeleton mostly bony with varying number of vertebrae; ribs present in some, absent in others; notochord does not persist; **exoskeleton absent**

2. Body forms vary greatly from an elongated trunk with distinct head, neck, and tail to a compact, depressed body with fused head and trunk and no intervening neck

3. **Limbs usually four (tetrapod),** although some are legless; forelimbs of some much smaller than hind limbs, in others all limbs small and inadequate; **webbed feet often present**

4. **Skin smooth and moist with many glands,** some of which may be poisonous; **pigment cells (chromatophores)** common, of considerable variety, and in a few capable of undergoing various patterns in accordance with different backgrounds; **no scales,** except concealed dermal ones in some

5. Mouth usually large with small teeth in upper or both jaws; **two nostrils open into anterior part of mouth cavity**

6. Respiration by gills, lungs, skin, and pharyngeal region either separately or in combination; external gills in the larval

form and may persist throughout life in some

7. **Circulation with three-chambered heart,** two auricles and one ventricle, and a double circulation through the heart; skin abundantly supplied with blood vessels

8. Excretory system of paired opisthonephroi

9. Ten cranial nerves

10. Separate sexes; fertilization external or internal; metamorphosis usually present; **eggs with jellylike membrane coverings**

Major groups

Amphibians are divided into three chief orders as follows:

Order **Gymnophiona** (gym'no-phi"o-na) (Gr. *gymnos*, naked, + *ophioneos*, serpentlike) (**Apoda**). Wormlike; legless; dermal scales embedded in skin. Example: caecilians.

Order **Urodela** (u'ro-de"la) (Gr. *ura*, tail, + *delos*, visible) (**Caudata**). Tail present; no scales; two pairs of limbs usually present. Examples: salamanders, newts.

Order **Salientia** (sa'le-en"she-a) (L. *saliens*, leaping) (**Anura**). Tail absent; no scales; gill openings absent in adult; two pairs of limbs. Examples: frogs, toads.

Relationships

Amphibians arose from some fishlike ancestor similar to the primitive Osteichthyes. This ancestor must have possessed both pectoral and pelvic fins which were similar in their general structure. No existing fish has exactly this kind of fin pattern. The osteolepids, members of Crossopterygii, had some of the characteristics of the early amphibians, such as internal and external nares and a form of lung; and the pentadactyl limb of amphibians is supposed to have arisen from such fins as the osteolepids possessed. It may be surmised that the early ancestor developed girdles and fins that were useful not merely for swimming but also for supporting the body while crawling from one desiccated basin of water to another. The primitive fossil form, *Ichthyostega*, found in Greenland has both crossopterygian and amphibian characteristics. Early amphibians, such as the Gymnophiona, still possess small scales in the skin, and the lateral line system so well developed in fish is retained in the larvae of present-day Amphibia. In the geological time scale, however, the osteolepids flourished during the Devonian period; the earliest amphibians are from the Lower Carboniferous period. The latter period is often referred to as the "age of amphibians."

An extinct superorder of amphibians, the Labyrinthodontia, may throw some light on the origin of the Amphibia (Figure 319). These were forms that resembled salamanders and had the head enclosed with dermal bones or plates. Many of them also had large teeth, and some may have been 15 feet long. One group of these, the Embolomeri, may have given rise to the reptiles. However, there are no convincing links between these early labyrinthodonts and modern amphibians, for intermediate fossils have not been discovered. Although some modern amphibians have resemblances to living dipnoans, it is thought that there is no direct genetic affinity between the two and that the likenesses are due to convergence or parallel evolution.

Structural and natural history of amphibian orders

Gymnophiona (Apoda). There are about 50 species of this little-known order (Figure 362). They are mostly found in Africa, Asia, and South America and are commonly called caecilians. In North America no species is found north of Mexico. Aside from the long, slender, worm-like body, they are characterized by having small scales in the skin, many vertebrae, long ribs, small concealed eyes, no limbs, and terminal anus. They are strictly burrowing forms and rarely seen above the surface. Their food is mostly worms and small invertebrates which they find underground. Fertilization is internal, and the male is provided with a protrusible cloaca by which he copulates with the female. The eggs are usually deposited in moist ground near the water; the larvae

may be aquatic or the complete larval development may occur in the egg. In some species the eggs are carefully guarded in folds of the body during their development. None of this group has ever been found in a fossil form. *Ichthyophis* is a common form in southeast Asia; *Typhlonectes* is a South American aquatic caecilian which is ovoviviparous.

Urodela (Caudata)—salamanders and newts. Order Urodela has about 150 spesies. Although found to a limited extent in other parts of the world, the temperate part of North America is the chief home of the tailed amphibians. The largest caudate known is the Japanese salamander, more than 5 feet long. Most of those in North America are from 3 to 6 inches long, although a few are longer *(Necturus)*. These forms have primitive limbs set at right angles to the body with the fore and hind limbs about the same size. In some the limbs are rudimentary *(Amphiuma)* (Figure 363), and in others *(Siren)* there are no hind limbs. Many of these amphibians never leave the water

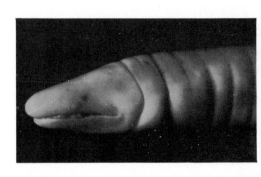

Figure 362. Head and anterior region of caecilian. Order Gymnophiona (Apoda). These legless and wormlike amphibians may reach length of 18 inches and diameter of ¾ inch. Among their odd characteristics are their body folds (which give them appearance of segmented worm), presence in some of embedded mesodermal scales, a mouth with many sharply pointed teeth, pair of tiny eyes mostly hidden beneath skin, small tentacle between eye and nostril, viviparous (in some species), and presence in males of protrusible copulatory organ. (Courtesy General Biological Supply House, Inc., Chicago.)

460

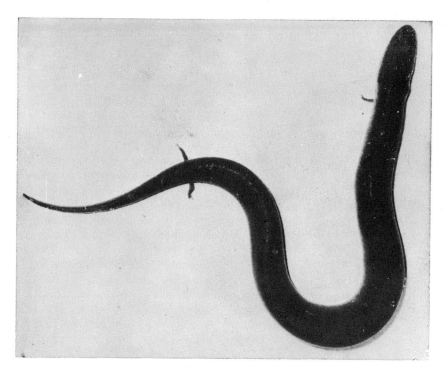

Figure 363. Congo eel, *Amphiuma*.

in their entire life cycle, although others assume a terrestrial life, living in moist places under stones and rotten logs, usually not far from the water. All have gills at some stage of their lives; some lose their gills when they become adults. Those that retain their gills are called **perennibranchs;** those that lose them are called **caducibranchs.**

Although some species have lungs in place of gills, others have neither and depend upon their skin and pharyngeal region (buccopharyngeal respiration). This is true with the family Plethodontidae, a common group in North America. This interesting family is supposed to have originated in swift mountain streams of the Appalachian mountains. Mountain brook water, which is cool and well oxygenated, is excellent for cutaneous breathing. The cold temperature of the water slows down metabolism and thus less oxygen is required. This family also has an interesting structural adaptation, the nasolabial groove (Figure 364), which helps clear the nostrils

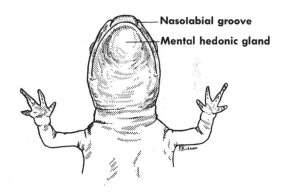

Figure 364. Ventral side of head of male plethodontid salamander, showing mental hedonic gland and nasolabial grooves. Hedonic gland, most prominent during breeding season, is flat, slightly raised area of chin and is restricted to males. It is really a cluster of glands supposed to stimulate female during courtship. Nasolabial grooves are also confined to family Plethodontidae and may function in clearing nostrils of water.

of water. The groove is flushed out by the secretions of a gland which empties into it and by cilia which carry the excess

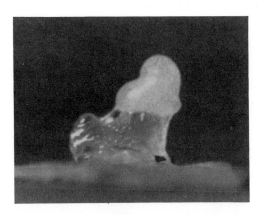

Figure 365. Spermatophore of *Plethodon gluti-nosus*. Males of most salamanders produce these mushroom-shaped bodies which consist of jelly stalk and sperm cap. During courtship display, in which male apparently stimulates female by pressing his mental hedonic gland against her skin, female is induced to detach sperm cap with lips of her cloaca and fertilize her eggs internally. Spermatophores are deposited by males on leaves or other solid objects. (Courtesy James A. Organ, Museum of Zoology, University of Michigan.)

Figure 366. Cluster of developing salamander eggs, showing little embryos. (Courtesy Charles Alender.)

water away. Some plethodontids, such as *Aneides,* have large blood sinuses in the tips of the toes for digital respiration. It is thought that lungs are absent in some because they may act as hydrostatic organs and would prevent their possessors from hiding quickly under aquatic covers.

In color, salamanders and newts are usually modest and unassuming but are occasionally strikingly brilliant. Color changes are not nearly so pronounced among them as with their relatives, the frogs.

Neither do the caudates show as much diversity of breeding habits as Salientia. Both external and internal fertilization are found in the group, but in a number the males have the interesting habit of depositing their sperm in capsules called **spermatophores** (Figure 365). These are placed on leaves, sticks, and other objects, and the female picks them up with her cloacal lips and thus fertilizes her eggs. Aquatic species lay their eggs in clusters (Figure 366) or stringy masses in the water; terrestrial forms may also lay their eggs in the water or in moist places. In *Salamandra,* a European form (Figure 367), the eggs are retained within the body of the female, until the larvae have completed part of their development. Many species of salamanders show distinctive courtship behavior patterns. Plethodontid males often have a secondary sex character in the form of a hedonic or mental gland under the chin (Figure 364). This gland can be detected as a slight elevation or swelling and is probably a modified mucous gland. In some species, hedonic glands may be found on other parts of the body, such as the tail or groin. Such glands are supposed to produce a secretion which excites the female during courtship.

Blind salamanders are found in many limestone caves in certain parts of the United States and Austria. One of the best known of these species is *Typhlotriton spelaeus,* which has functional eyes in the larval form and lives near the mouth of caves. As an adult, it withdraws deeper into the caves and the eyes degenerate. An interesting experiment has been performed with these salamanders. If the larval forms are kept in the light, they retain functional eyes when they mature; if they metamorphose in the dark, they lose the sight of their eyes. There is no evidence that this blind effect 'is hereditary, for the larvae always have eyes.

Some urodeles exhibit **neoteny**, that is,

462

sexual reproduction during larval periods. This is strikingly shown by the tiger salamander, *Ambystoma tigrinum*. This species is widely distributed over the United States into Central Mexico. The larvae, known as **axolotls** (Figure 368), breed in Mexico and in the southwestern part of the United States. When transferred to the eastern states, they lose their gills, assume lungs, and become native tiger salamanders. At one time axolotls were considered a separate species, for the eastern *Ambystoma tigrinum* after a short larval period becomes mature. In their native regions axolotls apparently never transform.

Salamanders and newts live on worms, small arthropods, and small mollusks. Most of them will eat only things that are moving. Their food naturally is rich in proteins, and as a usual thing they do not store in their bodies great quantities of fat or glycogen. Since they are cold-blooded animals and are not particularly active they have a low metabolism and do not need much energy.

SOME COMMON AMERICAN SALAMANDERS. Most North American salamanders belong to the family Plethodontidae which contains more species than all the other families combined. All the species illustrated in Figures 369 to 374 belong to family Plethodontidae. The most common genus of this family in the eastern United States is *Desmognathus* (the dusky salamander), of which there are several species. On the west coast the more familiar genera of plethodontids are *Aneides* and *Batrachoseps*. The primitive family. Salamandridae is represented in America by the American newt (*Diemictylus viridescens*) which is found all over the eastern United States. This salamander is widely used in zoological research and is of especial interest because it usually passes through a land phase (eft) in its development before becoming an aquatic adult. The California newt (*Taricha torosa*) is common in the coast ranges of California. Another common family is Ambystomidae, which includes such familiar salamanders as the tiger salamander, spotted salamander (*Ambystoma maculatum*), and Jefferson salamander (*Ambystoma jeffersonianum*). Certain species of this family are also found on the Pacific coast. Family Cryptobranchidae is represented by the giant salamander *Cryptobranchus* which may reach a length of more than 2 feet. There are two species that are restricted to certain river systems in Pennsylvania and the midwest. This salamander and those of Sirenidae are the only American salamanders that have external fertilization.

Salientia (Anura)—frogs and toads. The behavior and adaptations of frogs and toads are among the most interesting of any group of animals. In certain lines of

Figure 367. Spotted salamander of Europe, *Salamandra salamandra*. This common salamander with black and yellow markings gives birth to larvae which complete their development in the water. (Courtesy Vancouver Public Aquarium, British Columbia.)

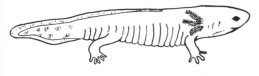

Figure 368. An axolotl, larval form of tiger salamander, *Ambystoma tigrinum*. In Mexico and southwestern states larva does not metamorphose but breeds in this form.

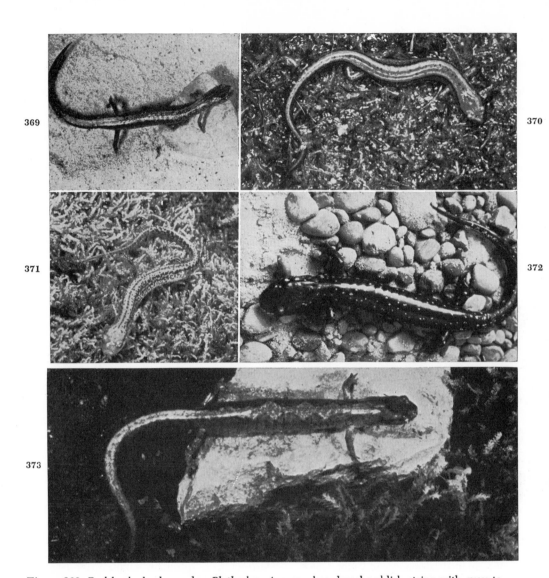

Figure 369. Red-backed salamander, *Plethodon cinereus,* has dorsal reddish stripe with gray to black sides.

Figure 370. Two-lined salamander, *Eurycea bislineata,* is yellow to brown with two dorsolateral black stripes.

Figure 371. Long-tailed salamander, *Eurycea longicauda,* is yellow to orange with black spots that form vertical stripes on sides of tail.

Figure 372. Slimy salamander, *Plethodon glutinosus,* is black with white spots.

Figure 373. Zigzag salamander, *Plethodon dorsalis,* has zigzag pattern on back.

behavior, anurans are not surpassed anywhere in their diversified adaptations. This is especially true of their breeding habits, which are discussed more fully in Chapter 40, Some Interesting and Striking Adaptations. The present section will be devoted to other aspects of their behavior and adaptations.

The skin of both frogs and toads has many variations among the different species. Toads usually have warty skins, and frogs tend to have smooth, slimy skins.

Figure 374. Cave salamander, *Eurycea lucifuga*, one of the most beautiful and also one of the rarest of Middle West. They are reddish orange with black spots.

The kind of habitat determines to a great extent the nature of the skin. Whenever they live in or near the water, their skins are more or less smooth and slimy; in deserts or dry regions, however, their skins are rough and warty. Unlike the salamanders, the skin does not adhere closely to the underlying muscles, so that it is easy to "skin a frog." The skin of Salientia is usually well supplied with glands. One type secretes mucus used mainly as a lubricant; the other type includes the larger poison glands. Mucus itself may have poisonous properties in some, but the granular poison obtained from the poison glands is highly irritating. In some this poison is so caustic that it burns the hands of anyone who handles the specimen. The poison of *Dendrobates*, a South American frog, is used by Indian tribes to poison the points of their arrows. An interesting skin modification is found in the so-called "hairy frog," *Astylosternus*, found in the Cameroons of Africa (Figure 376, *B*). The males have developed fine cutaneous filaments on the thighs, groins, and sides which have a remarkable resemblance to hair. Some authorities think these curious structures have a respiratory function and others think they are sensory.

Anurans are usually considered defenseless, and in the temperate zones many of them are. But in the tropics and subtropics many frogs and toads are aggressive, jumping and biting at their potential enemies. Some defend themselves by feigning death ("playing possum"). Nearly all anurans can blow up their lungs so that they are difficult to swallow. When disturbed along the margin of a pond or brook, a frog will often remain quite still; when it thinks it is detected it will jump, not always into the water where enemies

Figure 375. Giant South American toad, *Bufo marinus*. Some of these are more than 6 inches long. Their large parotid glands produce most poisonous secretions to be found among amphibians, which may account for their wide distribution and abundance. (Courtesy C. P. Hickman, Jr.)

Phylum Chordata—classes Amphibia and Reptilia 465

Figure 376. Three frogs with unusual features. **A,** "Flying" frog of Borneo, *Polypedates nigropalmatus*. Large webs between digits of feet aid it in gliding from higher elevation to lower one. **B,** Hairy frog of Africa, *Astylosternus*. Hairlike filaments on groins and sides of male are really cutaneous papillae, probably used for respiration. These filaments are unusually well developed during breeding season. **C,** Bell toad of northwestern Pacific coast, *Ascaphus truei*. Male's cloacal appendage serves as copulatory organ for fertilizing female's eggs. This frog and certain ovoviviparous frogs of Africa are only known salientians which have internal fertilization. (From various sources.)

may be awaiting it but into grassy cover on the bank. When held in the hand a frog may cease its struggles for an instant and then leap violently, at the same time voiding its urine. Their best protection is their ability to leap and their use of poison glands. Bullfrogs in captivity will not hesitate to snap at tormentors and are capable of inflicting painful bites.

As a group, anurans are vociferous, for most of the males at certain seasons can give rise to distinctive sounds. Everyone is familiar with the chorus of frog voices on a warm, rainy spring night in some pond or marsh. Their utterances range all the way from the deep bass gutturals of the bullfrog to the soft birdlike trill of certain tree frogs. The first vertebrates to

466

have a voice, they have developed this characteristic well. The chief function of their voice appears to be the attraction of their mates; many can call under water. When giving their call notes during the breeding season the males keep their mouths and nostrils tightly closed. The air is driven back and forth between the lungs and mouth. Many have resonating organs or sacs, which are diverticula of the mouth and mouth cavity. In some these sacs balloon out either under the chin or on either side of the throat when they are calling (Figure 377). Frogs can give loud shrill screams when seized. In such cases the mouth is held widely agape. This pain cry may serve to warn other frogs.

Migration of frogs and toads is correlated with their breeding habits. Males usually return to a pond or stream in advance of the females, whom they then attract by their calls. The initial stimulus for migration in many cases is due to a seasonal cycle in the gonads plus hormonal control which increases their sensitivity to temperature and humidity changes. It has been known for some time that frogs may be induced to discharge their sex cells when injected with hormones from the anterior pituitary. How frogs and toads find water for their breeding is a problem of speculation. According to some, amphibians are sensitive to moisture gradients or to the odors of aquatic vegetation. It is also suggested that migration may be an instinctive return to the ancestral breeding grounds.

Unlike the salamanders, which mostly have internal fertilization, nearly all frogs and toads fertilize their eggs externally. When the female lays her eggs, the male embraces her and discharges his sperm over the eggs as they extrude from her body (Figures 378 and 379). A notable exception is the famed bell toad (*Ascaphus*) of the Pacific coast region (Figure 376, *C*). This small toad (family Ascaphidae), which is only about 2 inches long, is found in swift mountain streams of low temperature from British Colum-

Figure 377. Spring peeper, *Hyla crucifer*, with its resonating vocal sac enlarged just before it gives its high note which can be heard a long distance. It will be noted that the whole body as well as the vocal sac is inflated. (Courtesy Robert Fuson.)

Figure 378. Toad eggs. Toads lay eggs in strings; frogs lay theirs in clusters. (Courtesy Charles Alender.)

bia to northern California and has a conspicuous extension of cloaca which serves as an intromittent or copulatory organ for fertilizing internally the eggs of the fe-

Figure 379. Pair of toads in amplexus. As eggs are extruded from cloaca of female, male fertilizes them with his sperm. (Courtesy Charles Alender.)

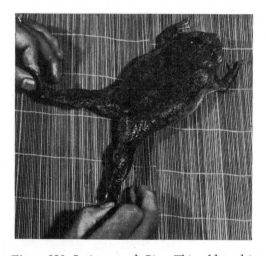

Figure 380. Surinam toad, *Pipa*. This odd toad is quite flat and has a triangular head but no tongue. This one is male; female carries eggs in little pockets on her back. Fully metamorphosed young emerge in about three months. (Courtesy Vancouver Public Aquarium, British Columbia.)

male. *Ascaphus* is the only American frog that has ribs in the adult condition. A related genus, *Liopelma*, is found in New Zealand. The only frog to bring forth its young alive is the ovoviviparous *Necto-*

phrynoides of Africa. This frog also has internal fertilization but has no external copulatory organ.

The largest anuran is known as *Rana goliath*, which is more than 1 foot long from tip of nose to anus; it is found in west Africa. This giant will eat animals as big as rats and ducks. On the other hand, the smallest frog recorded is *Phyllobates limbatus*, which is only about ½ inch long. This tiny frog, which is more than covered by a dime, is found in Cuba. Our largest American frog is the bullfrog (*Rana catesbeiana*), which reaches a length of 8 or 9 inches. Most of our common species are only a few inches long, and the tree frogs are considerably smaller than this.

Brief classification

Class Amphibia. Body with moist skin which contains many glands; no scales; usually two pairs of limbs; two nostrils, connected to mouth; skull with two occipital condyles; more than 2,000 species of all orders.

Order 1. Gymnophiona (Apoda). Body worm-like; limbs and limb girdle absent; mesodermal scales may be present in skin; tail short or absent.

Family Caeciliidae. Example: *Ichthyophis.*

Order 2. Urodela (Caudata). Body with head, trunk, and tail; no scales; usually two pairs of equal limbs.

Family Proteidae. Body depressed; tail with fin; gills and lungs; no eyelids; aquatic. Example: *Necturus.*

Family Cryptobranchidae. Body depressed with fleshy folds and large; gills absent; no eyelids; teeth larval. Example: *Cryptobranchus.*

Family Ambystomidae. Body small to large; lungs; neotenic forms with gills; eyelids present; vomerine teeth; nasolabial groove absent. Example: *Ambystoma.*

Family Salamandridae. Body small to large; lungs; nasolabial groove absent; adults usually without gills; eyelids present; vomeropalatine teeth diverge posteriorly. Example: *Diemictylus.*

Family Amphiumidae. Body large and eel-like; lungs; no eyelids; limbs diminutive; no nasolabial groove; larval teeth. Example: *Amphiuma.*

Family Plethodontidae. Body small to medium; nasolabial groove present; no lungs or gills; some neotenic species; vomerine and palatine teeth usually present; eyelids present. Example: *Plethodon.*

Family Sirenidae. Body elongated and eel-like; anterior limbs present, hind limbs absent; three pairs of gills; eyelids absent; larval teeth. Example: *Siren.*

Order 3. Salientia (Anura). Head and trunk fused; no tail; no scales; two pairs of limbs; mouth large; lungs; vertebrae 10, including urostyle.

Family Pelobatidae (Scaphiopodidae). Hind foot with horny spade on inner margin; pupil of eye elliptical and vertical; snout blunt. Example: *Scaphiopus.*

Family Bufonidae. Skin with many warts; large parotid gland behind each eye; pupil not vertical; maxillary teeth absent. Example: *Bufo.*

Family Hylidae. Body small; teeth in both jaws usually; hind leg long; toes with adhesive discs; terminal bone of each digit usually claw shaped. Example: *Hyla.*

Family Ranidae. Body with large tympanum; teeth in upper jaw; toe discs absent; warts absent; no parotid glands. Example: *Rana.*

Family Ascaphidae. Male with tail-like copulatory organ; female with short anal tube; pupil vertical; tympanum not visible; ribs present. Example: *Ascaphus.*

CLASS REPTILIA*—lizards, snakes, turtles, and crocodiles

Reptiles represent the first class of vertebrates that have gone all out for a terrestrial life. They include snakes, lizards, turtles, tortoises, alligators, and crocodiles. So closely affiliated in structures are they with birds that the two classes are sometimes referred to as the Sauropsida. There are more than 5,000 species of reptiles in the world and of these more than 300 species are found in the United States. Common as they are now they were far more common and dominant in the dim geological past; the Mesozoic period is called the Age of Reptiles. This group was the first vertebrate class to break away from breeding in the water. Although many of them, such as alligators, snakes, and turtles, live in or near the water, they always return to the land to lay the eggs. The name of the class (L. *repere* to crawl) refers to the method of locomotion common among many of them.

Origin and adaptive radiation of reptiles

It is generally agreed that reptiles arose from labyrinthodont amphibians sometime before the Permian period. The stem reptiles belonged to the order Cotylosaura (stem reptiles) which is represented by two basic members—*Seymouria* and *Limnoscelis*. *Seymouria*, a small, partly aquatic tetrapod fossil found in Texas, has long enjoyed the distinction of being a connecting link between the amphibians and reptiles, for it has characteristics of both groups. Paleontologists are not certain about its exact status. The other basic member, *Limnoscelis*, was found in New Mexico and dates from the early Permian period. This form was larger than *Seymouria* and had many characteristics which fit it as a prototype of the reptilian class. It had more reptilian characteristics than the other, but its skull and other skeletal features were definitely amphibian. However, both *Seymouria* and *Limnoscelis* appeared too late in the geo-

---

*Rep-til'i-a (L. *repere*, to creep).

logical record to be considered true ancestral reptiles, for the latter were already established by Permian times.

From the stem reptiles (cotylosaurs) there sprang a great evolutionary development of reptiles, both as to form and adaptation. This adaptive radiation, especially pronounced in the Triassic period, was correlated with the new ecological niches provided by the climatic and geological changes which were taking place at that time, such as a variable climate from hot to cold, mountain building and terrain transformations, and a varied assortment of plant life. According to most paleontologists, there were five major lines of reptilian evolution: (1) the mammal-like reptiles, which connected the primitive reptiles with the mammals; (2) the ichthyosaurs, which were adapted for a marine existence; (3) the plesiosaurs, long-necked marine forms; (4) the turtles; and (5) the archosaurs or ruling reptiles, which included a most varied assortment of reptilian lines, such as the thecodonts, crocodiles, dinosaurs, pterosaurs, and birds.

The Mesozoic was the age of reptiles. At this time the class reached the climax of its development, and its importance cannot be overestimated. This group was the turning point in the invasion of land. With the exception, perhaps, of the bony fish, no animals have displayed more amazing patterns of evolutionary morphology. From rather small stem reptiles they evolved into some of the most bizarre and powerful creatures ever known (dinosaurs); some became adapted for flying and gliding (pterodactyls); others returned to water (ichthyosaurs); some had bipedal locomotion (thecodonts); many were carnivorous (theropods) and others herbivorous (sauropods). Their striking fossil record shows no fewer than fourteen different orders at their heyday of evolution; only four of these orders are found among present-day reptiles which are still an active group but are mere shadows of their former greatness. Two of their great evolutionary lines led directly to the birds and mammals. Why did reptiles decline

from their former greatness? Most of the great reptilian orders died out completely by late Cretaceous times. No one factor can be blamed, for groups in wholly different environments became extinct. A combination of climatic and ecological factors, excessive specialization, low reproduction rate, etc. may have been responsible, but all are speculative. Why did some survive against the fierce competition of the mammals? Turtles had their protective shells, snakes and lizards evolved in habitats of dense forests and rocks where they could meet the competition of any tetrapod, and crocodiles because of their size and natural defense and offense had few enemies in their aquatic habitats.

Characteristics

1. Body variable in shape; compact in some, elongated in others; **body covered with an exoskeleton of horny epidermal scales** with the addition sometimes of bony dermal plates; **integument with few glands**

2. **Limbs paired, usually with five toes,** and adapted for climbing, running, and paddling; absent in snakes

3. Skeleton well ossified; ribs with sternum forming a complete thoracic basket; **skull with one occipital condyle**

4. Respiration by lungs; **no gills;** cloaca used for respiration by some; branchial arches in embryonic life

5. **Three-chambered heart; crocodiles with four-chambered heart;** usually one pair of aortic arches

6. Kidney an opisthonephros (paired)

7. Nervous system with the optic lobes on the dorsal side of brain; **twelve pairs of cranial nerves** in addition to nervus terminalis.

8. Sexes separate; fertilization internal; meroblastic (amniote) **eggs which are covered with leathery shells**

9. Embryonic membranes including the **amnion, chorion, yolk sac** and **allantois** present during embryonic life

Orders

Order 1. Squamata (squa-ma′ta) (L. *squamatus,* scaly). Skin of horny epidermal scales or

470

plates which is shed; teeth attached to jaws; quadrate freely movable; vertebrae usually concave in front; anus a transverse slit. Examples: snakes, lizards, chameleons. 3,800 species of lizards; 3,000 species of snakes.

Order 2. Testudinata (tes-tu'di-na"ta) (L. *testudinatus,* a tortoise) (**Chelonia**). Body in a bony case of dermal plates with dorsal carapace and ventral plastron; jaws without teeth but with horny sheaths; quadrate immovable; vertebrae and ribs fused to shell; anus a longitudinal slit. Examples: turtles and tortoises. 400 species.

Order 3. Crocodilia (croc'o-dil"i-a) (L. *crocodilus,* a crocodile). Four-chambered heart; vertebrae usually concave in front; forelimbs usually with five digits, hind limbs with four digits; quadrate immovable; anus a longitudinal slit. Examples: crocodiles and alligators. 25 species.

Order 4. Rhynchocephalia (rhyn'cho-ce-pha"li-a) (L. *rhyncho,* snout, + Gr. *kephale,* head). Vertebrae biconcave; quadrate immovable; parietal eye fairly well developed and easily seen; anus a transverse slit. Eample: *Sphenodon*—only species existing.

How Reptilia show advancement over Amphibia

The fact that reptiles are adapted for a complete existence on land in contrast to amphibians that are still tied more or less to water or moist habitats indicates that reptiles have certain adaptations not found in amphibians. Some of these advancements shown by reptiles are as follows:

1. Reptiles have developed some form of copulatory organ so necessary for internal fertilization.

2. The amniote eggs of reptiles are leathery and limy which resist desiccation and air exposure. Amphibians have gelatinous covering for their eggs.

3. Reptiles have dry, scaly skin which is adapted to land life.

4. Reptiles have protective embryonic membranes which are lacking in amphibians.

5. Reptiles also have a partial or complete separation of the ventricle, thus ensuring a higher type of oxygenation, but there is some mixing of venous and arterial blood through right and left arches.

6. Most reptiles have developed limbs well adapted for efficient locomotion on land.

Distinctive structures of reptilian body

In contrast to the soft, naked body of amphibians, reptiles have developed an **exoskeleton** which is largely waterproof. This exoskeleton consists of dead horny scales which are formed of keratin, a protein substance found in the epidermal layers of the skin. Reptilian scales are not homologous to fish scales, which are derived from the dermis and represent a kind of bone. Reptilian scales may be flat and fitted together like a mosaic, or they may be widely separated; in some cases they overlap like roof shingles. Underneath each scale is a special vascular papilla from the underlying dermis or corium. This papilla supplies nutriment to the basal layer of the epidermis, which becomes thickened in that region to form the actual scale. In some, the outer layer of the scales are continually being shed, either in small bits or sloughed off periodically in one piece. In some snakes and lizards, these cast skins show perfectly the continuity of the horny skin. Turtles, however, add new layers of keratin under the old layers in the scales. Modified forms of scales are found in the reptile group. The scutes of a turtle shell are large, platelike scales. Also, in some reptiles, the epidermal scales are reinforced by dermal plates (osteoderms). Scales are of great diagnostic value in the identification of some reptiles such as snakes.

The **skeleton** of the early reptiles (cotylosaurs) was quite similar to the labyrinthodont amphibians. Most changes in later reptiles involved a loss of skull elements (by fusion or otherwise) and adaptable transformations for better locomotion and other functions. The nostrils of an alligator or crocodile are on the dorsal side of the head and the internal nares are at the back of the throat, which can be closed off by a fold. Thus the reptile can breathe while holding its prey submerged. The reptilian skull has developed a more flexible joint with the vertebral column, and more efficient girdles were evolved for supporting the body. The toes are provided with claws. Their peglike teeth vary somewhat but do not show the differentiation of the mammal; they may be set in sockets (thecodont) or fused to the surface of the bone (acrodont). In many, the teeth are found in two rows along the edges of the premaxillae and maxillae, in the upper jaw, and along the dentaries of the lower jaw. Teeth may also be present on some of the palate bones. They are absent in turtles, where only a horny beak is present.

Muscular development has kept pace with the greater limb movements of reptiles as compared with amphibians. Trunk muscles show less importance, although their segmented nature is conspicuous in some. Much of the muscular arrangement of reptiles is quite similar to that found in mammals.

The **body cavity** of reptiles is mostly divided into sacs by mesenteries, ligaments, and peritoneal folds. The heart is always enclosed in a pericardial sac. Among the turtles the lungs lie outside the peritoneal cavity. In lizards there is a posthepatic septum which divides the peritoneal cavity into two divisions, and there is a similar one in crocodiles which contain muscle and may function in respiration. This partition, however, is not homologous to the mammalian diaphragm.

Most reptiles are carnivorous and their **digestive system** is adapted for such a diet. All are provided with a tongue. This is large, fleshy, and broad in crocodiles and turtles. In crocodiles a tongue fold with a similar fold of the palate can separate the air passage from the food passage. In some reptiles (chameleon) the tongue is highly protrusible and is used in catching their prey. When not in use the anterior part of such a tongue is telescoped into the posterior portion. Buccal glands vary a great deal. In snakes the upper labial glands may be modified into poison glands. The stomach is usually spindle-shaped and contains gastric glands. Pebbles or gastroliths are found in some reptiles (crocodiles) for grinding the food. A short duodenum receives the ducts from the liver and pancreas. The walls of the midgut are thrown into folds, but there

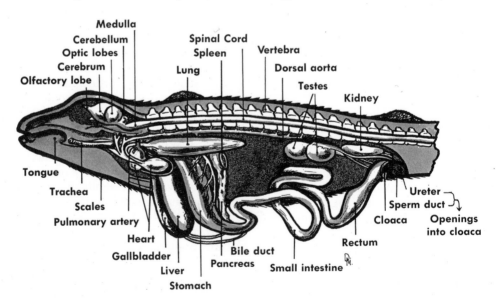

Figure 381. Internal structures of male lizard. Reptilian body shows advancement over amphibians in having (1) scaly skin for dry land, (2) better ossified skeleton and more efficient limbs, (3) heart partly or completely separated into four chambers, (4) amniotic egg for land existence, and (5) beginning regulation of body temperature by behavior patterns.

472

are few glands. The **cloaca** which receives the rectum, ureters, and reproductive ducts may be complicated. A urinary bladder is found in *Sphenodon*, turtles, and most lizards and opens into the ventral wall of the cloaca.

The **excretory** system is made up of the paired elongated or compact kidneys (opisthonephroi) which contain no nephrostomes. Ureters carry the urine (fluid in turtles and crocodiles; semisolid with insoluble urates in the others) to the cloaca.

All reptiles have **lungs** for breathing. The glottis behind the tongue is closed by special muscles. The larynx box contains arytenoid and cricoid cartilages but no thyroid cartilages. The trachea is provided with semicircular cartilage rings to keep it open. Lungs are mainly simple sacs in *Sphenodon* and snakes (where one is reduced), but in turtles and crocodiles they are divided into irregular chambers, with the alveoli connected to branched series of bronchial tubes. In chameleons long, hollow processes of the lungs pass posteriorly among the viscera and represent forerunners of the air sacs of birds. Air is drawn into the lungs by the movements of the ribs and, in crocodiles, by the muscular diaphragm.

Since there is no branchial circulation in reptiles, on each side the fifth aortic arch is lost, the third becomes the carotid arch, the fourth the systemic arch, and the sixth the pulmonary arteries. The systemic arches are paired in contrast to the single one of birds and mammals. In crocodiles there are two completely separated ventricles; in the other groups the ventricle is incompletely separated. *Crocodiles are thus the first animals with a four-chambered heart.* The conus and truncus arteriosus are absent. Venous blood is returned to the sinus venosus of the heart through the paired precaval and the single postcaval veins. Renal and hepatic portal systems are present. The blood contains oval, nucleated corpuscles which are smaller than those of amphibians.

The male reproductive system consists

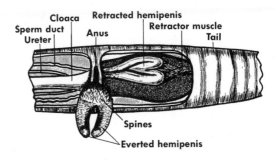

Figure 382. Paired hemipenes of male snake. These copulatory devices of snakes and lizards are fingerlike sacs in lateral wall of cloaca. In copulation one hemipenis is everted (like fingers of glove) with spines outward, inserted into female cloaca, and held there by the spines until completion. Sperm are conducted in grooves to female oviducts. When not in use, hemipenes are drawn back into tail pockets by retractor muscles.

of paired elongated testes which are connected to the vasa deferentia (the Wolffian or mesonephric ducts). The latter carry sperm to the copulatory organ which is an evagination of the cloacal wall and is used for internal fertilization. These copulatory organs are single in crocodiles and turtles but paired in lizards and snakes, where they are called **hemipenes** (Figure 382). The female system is made up of large paired ovaries, and the eggs are carried to the cloaca by oviducts which are provided with funnel-shaped ostia. The glandular walls of the oviducts secrete albumin and shells for the large amniote eggs. The two embryonic membranes, amnion and allantois, first appear in reptiles and are used for the protection and respiration of the embryo.

The reptilian nervous system shows many advancements over that of the amphibians. The parts of the brain are enlarged and fiber connections are increased; relatively, however, the brain is small, never exceeding 1% of the body weight. There are twelve pairs of cranial nerves in addition to nervus terminalis. A better developed peripheral nervous system is associated with the better limbs of reptiles. Sense organs vary among the different reptilian groups, but in general they are well developed. The lateral line system, however, is entirely lost. All reptiles have a middle and inner ear, and crocodiles have an outer one as well. The middle ear contains the ear ossicle (stapes) and communicates with the pharynx by the Eustachian tube. A unique sense organ, Jacobson's organ is a separate part of the nasal sac and communicates with the mouth; it is especially well developed in snakes and lizards. It is innervated by a branch of the olfactory nerve and is used in smelling the food in the mouth cavity. This organ in some form is found in other groups, including the amphibians.

Structure and natural history of the different orders

Squamata. This order is made up of snakes, lizards, and chameleons. All of them shed the outer dead layers of the skin periodically, for their scales are bound together in a continuous armor. The group is usually divided into suborders Lacertilia, which includes the lizards, and Ophidia, which includes the snakes. Lizards have movable eyelids, external ear opening, and legs (usually); snakes lack these.

Lizards are extremely diversified (Figures 383 and 384), ranging in length from 1 or 2 inches to several feet. They are found in habitats equally diversified, from the hottest desert to forested regions and the water. *Draco,* a lizard found in India, is able to volplane from tree to tree because of skin extensions on the side. Its limbs are well developed for running and climbing. A few lizards, such as the glass lizard, are limbless. The skin of lizards is flexible, with the scales arranged in rows. On the ventral surface they have small

383

384

Figure 383. Five-lined skink, *Eumeces,* widely distributed lizard of North America.

Figure 384. Carolina anole, *Anolis.* Family Iguanidae. These are popularly called chameleons, because they can change their color like true chameleons of the Old World.

474

Figure 385. Pilot blacksnake, *Elaphe obsoleta*—a harmless snake and one of four largest snakes in United States. This living specimen more than 6 feet long, but some known to grow longer. Kills its prey by constriction.

overlapping scales instead of transverse scutes which snakes have.

Some lizards have evolved methods for regulating their body temperature within narrow limits. Bogert and others have shown that lizards are able to do this even when the surrounding temperatures may vary widely. Although they lack the internal temperature controls of warm-blooded animals, lizards can obtain a differential effect of the sun's rays by orienting their bodies, either at right angles to the sun for maximum effect or parallel to the rays for minimum effect. Thus basking becomes a fine art with these animals. They can also regulate the absorption of heat by expanding their skin chromatophores when they are cold or contracting them when the body becomes too warm. Their optimum temperature zone for activity seems to center around 93° F.

The tongues of some lizards, chameleons in particular, have the power of being extended quickly to catch insect prey. Lizards often lose their tails, which they

easily regenerate. Lizards also have a bladder connected to the cloaca, and the male is provided with two **hemipenes** in the side of the cloaca. In copulation these hemipenes are everted and projected into the female cloaca.

The only poisonous lizard in the United States is the Gila monster. Its habitat is mainly in the southwestern states, Arizona in particular. Although somewhat sluggish, it can move its head quickly in biting. With poison fangs in the lower jaw it works its poison into its prey by chewing movements. It adapts readily to captivity and requires little care. In the same region with the Gila monster is *Phrynosoma*, the so-called "horned toad," which is really a lizard. Although its grostesque spines give it a formidable appearance, it is quite harmless and makes an interesting pet.

Snakes (Ophidia) with their limbless, elongated form represent one of the most specialized groups of animals in the world. This loss of limbs is not restricted to

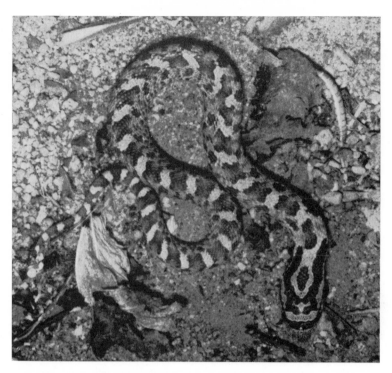

Figure 386. Young hog-nosed snake, *Heterodon contortrix*. This small snake is quite harmless but puts up a great bluff by flattening its head and hissing. It also feigns death by turning over upon its back.

the appendages but also applies to the pectoral and pelvic girdles (the latter being found as vestiges in pythons). Snakes also differ from lizards in having no sternum, eyelids, external ear openings, or bladder. The jaws of snakes are loosely connected to the skull, so that the mouth may be greatly expanded. Because their ribs are not attached ventrally and because of the great expansion of their mouths, snakes can swallow food much greater in diameter than their own bodies. While swallowing their prey they hold it firmly with their teeth, which are pointed backward, and by moving the jaws first on one side and then the other the snake gradually swallows the prey. In order to breathe while swallowing a large object, snakes have their glottis located far anterior in the floor of the mouth just behind the teeth.

Like lizards, snakes bear rows of scales which overlap like shingles on a roof. In some snakes the scales are keeled and in others smooth. Nearly all snakes have on their ventral surface from chin to anus a single row of transverse scales or scutes and one or two rows on the ventral surface of the tail. In moving, the snakes make use of these scutes by projecting their margins and using them for clinging against a surface while the body is driven forward by lateral undulations. On very smooth surfaces snakes cannot move forward easily. Snakes also move by alternately throwing the body into coils and then straightening it out. Most species are good swimmers; they swim by lateral convolutions of the body.

The forked tongue of the serpent is neither poisonous nor harmful; it is merely a sensory organ for detecting chemical stimuli. The tongue can be withdrawn into a sheath in the floor of the mouth. When the mouth is closed the tongue can also be thrust out of a groove between the two jaws. The teeth are sharp and curved backward and are used for hold-

476

ing the prey in the swallowing process. In poisonous snakes a pair of teeth on the maxillary bones are modified as fangs. These are grooved or tubular for conducting the poison from the poison sac (a modified salivary gland) into the prey that is bitten. This mechanism is, therefore, on the order of a hypodermic needle.

The internal organs of snakes are correlated with the elongated body, for most of the organs are also elongated. Usually only the left lung is present, and the alimentary canal is mostly a straight tube.

Organs such as the kidneys are at different levels in the body cavity to conserve space.

Most snakes lay eggs (oviparous), but some bring forth the young alive. There is no evidence to show that snakes swallow their young to protect them. How this idea arose is hard to guess. Someone may have cut into an ovoviviparous snake and released the young ones from the parent's body and erroneously concluded that she had swallowed them.

There are more than 100 species of

Figure 387. Ring-necked snake, *Diadophis*. This harmless species rarely exceeds 1 foot in length and is seldom seen because of its secretive habits.

Figure 388. Coral snake, *Micrurus*, very poisonous snake which inhabits southern United States and tropical countries. Only representative of cobra family in North America. Body bands black, red, and yellow. (Courtesy F. M. Uhler, U. S. Fish and Wildlife Service.)

snakes in the United States, of which fewer than 20 species are venomous. The latter include the rattlesnakes, copperheads, water moccasins, and coral snakes (Figure 388). All of these are pit vipers (except the coral snakes) and derive their name from a small cavity just anterior to the eye. This pit is a specialized sense organ which reacts to temperature and enables the snake to detect a warm-blooded animal. Nearly all pit vipers have long, curved fangs that lie against the upper wall of the mouth when not in use. When striking, however, these fangs (Figure 389) are erected to a position at right angles to the mouth surface and are driven straight into their prey and the venom injected at the same time. Just how many people are bitten each year by venomous snakes in the United States is not accurately known but probably not more than a few hundred. Of those bitten,

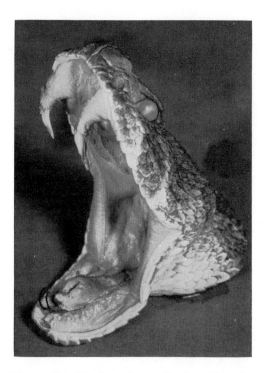

Figure 389. Head of diamondback rattlesnake, showing long fangs in roof of mouth, glottis, and forked tongue in sheath in floor of mouth. Anterior position of glottis enables snake to breathe while slowly swallowing prey.

only a small percentage die. More people are bitten by the copperhead, *Agkistrodon mokasen,* than by any other species, although more deaths are caused by the Texas diamondback rattlesnake, *Crotalus atrox* (Figure 390). Rattlesnakes are characterized by the **rattle,** which consists of horny, ringlike segments held loosely together, on the end of their tails. When aroused, the snake vibrates these rapidly, producing a buzzing sound. Whenever the skin is shed, the posterior part remains behind to form another ring of the rattle. The number of rattles is not an accurate indication of age, for the snake often sheds more than once a year, and rings of the rattle are frequently lost. The practice of vibrating the tail when excited is common in many species of snakes, venomous or nonvenomous. The famed bushmaster *(Lachesis muta)* of Central America is often referred to by the natives as the "silent rattler" because it has this habit of vigorous vibration of its tail. Our largest poisonous snake in the United States is the eastern diamondback rattlesnake *(Crotalus adamanteus)* which may reach a length of 8 feet.

The tropical and subtropical countries are the homes of most species of snakes, both of the venomous and nonvenomus varieties. However, even here most of the members are nonpoisonous. Among warm countries only a few regions, such as New Zealand, are free from native snakes. Madagascar has no poisonous snakes. In India the death toll from snake bites averages about 25,000 annually. Many used to die from poisonous snakes in South America until antivenom serums were developed effectively. The tropics also furnish the enormous constrictor snakes (Figure 391), some of which, like the regal python of the Malay Peninsula, attain a length of 30 feet; the anaconda of South America is another large snake. The many fantastic stories about the power of these constrictors to seize and swallow animals as big as oxen and man are without foundation. Most of these big snakes are fairly sluggish and their prey rarely exceeds the size of a good-sized pig. The largest of the

Figure 390. Texas diamondback rattlesnake, *Crotalus atrox*. More deaths caused by this snake than by any other species of poisonous snakes in United States. (Courtesy E. P. Haddon, U. S. Fish and Wildlife Service.)

Figure 391. Boa constrictor. This specimen was kept at DePauw University for 23 years, until its death (1961) at nearly 30 years of age. During its vigorous years it ate from 15 to 30 rats or pigeons each summer (by first constricting them to death) but refused to eat in winter. During its last years it ate only 4 or 5 rats a year. It grew 2 to 3 feet in captivity; was nearly 9 feet long.

venomous snakes are the king cobra (hamadryad), which may reach 15 to 18 feet in length, and the bushmaster *(Lachesis)* of Central and South America which, although never exceeding 10 feet in length, is thick and muscular. Our own Florida diamondback rattlesnake also ranks among the large poisonous snakes of the world.

From the standpoint of type of fangs, poisonous snakes are usually divided into two groups: the vipers with long movable fangs and the Elapidae with anterior short immovable fangs which chew their venom into the blood of their prey. Examples of Elapidae are the Australian blacksnakes, the cobras, the mambas, and the coral snakes. Most of the back-fanged snakes (Opisthoglypha) are mildly poisonous.

Phylum Chordata—classes Amphibia and Reptilia   479

Closely related to the cobras are the very venomous sea snakes (Hydrophiidae). Pit vipers, mostly found in the new world, are represented by the bushmaster, fer-de-lance, rattlesnakes, water moccasins, and copperheads. Among the pitless vipers are the great Gaboon viper and the river jack of Africa and Russell's viper of India.

Snake venom is produced by modified parotid salivary glands.

Why this gland is modified in some snakes into such a deadly weapon is a problem for the evolutionist. The mouth secretions (saliva) of all harmless snakes possess some toxic properties and it is logical that this toxic tendency could be stressed by certain species. Venom is frequently collected from snakes by "milking" the glands. This is done by holding the snake by the neck, placing a small beaker in the jaws, and manipulating the gland with the fingers. Certain venoms have a medicinal value, such as alleviating the pain of cancer; they are also used in making antivenom serums. Snake poison varies with the type of snake. It is usually a thick, yellowish, slightly cloudy liquid which, on exposure to the air, will crystallize into yellow crystals. In a container these crystals may remain toxic for a long time. They are soluble in weak salt solutions. The toxic power of the venom may be destroyed by agencies such as heat and radium.

According to the type of poison, venomous snakes are divided into two groups. One type acts mainly on the nervous systems (neurotoxic), affecting the optic nerves (causing blindness) or the phrenic nerve of the diaphragm (paralysis of respiration). The other type is hemolytic; that is, it breaks down the red blood corpuscles and blood vessels and produces extensive extravasation of blood into the tissue spaces. Many venoms have both neurotoxic and hemolytic properties. Some venoms may be swallowed without danger, for the gastric juice destroys them, but this is not true of the poison produced by the cobra and the vipers of Africa.

The student may be curious about the relative toxicity of the venoms of differ-ent snakes. Is the cobra of India more deadly than a diamondback rattlesnake? Several factors determine the degree of harm the bite of a venomous snake may do. Usually the larger the specimen, the more venom it may inject. Or if the snake has recently bitten another animal its poison glands may not have produced their full amount of poison. But aside from these factors, venoms do differ in degree of toxicity. This is determined by the minimal lethal dose on laboratory animals. By this standard, the venom of *Bothrops insularis,* a member of the fer-de-lance family in South America, appears to be the most deadly of poisons drop for drop.

Even the most deadly snakes have enemies. In the United States the king snakes *(Lampropeltis)* will eat other snakes, especially poisonous ones. The slender king snake will encircle even the big diamond-back rattlesnake in its coils and squeeze it to death. The king snake is immune to the poison of the rattler. Where venomous snakes abound, natural enemies in some form are sure to act as a curb on their numbers. In India the mongoose *(Herpestes),* a little mammal, attacks and eats the hooded cobra and other poisonous snakes. Many snakes feed upon other snakes, which is the case with the king cobra of southeastern Asia, but the snakes it kills are mostly harmless. In South America, the fer-de-lance has two deadly enemies, the skunk *(Conepatus)* and musurana *(Clelia),* a mild-appearing snake of the Brazilian forests. Snakes have many bird enemies, especially some of our large hawks.

Testudinata (Chelonia). Tortoises and turtles are enclosed in shells consisting of a dorsal carapace and a ventral plastron. The shell is so much a part of the animal that it is built in with the thoracic vertebrae and ribs. Into this shell the head and appendages can be retracted for protection. No sternum is found in these forms and their jaws lack teeth but are covered by a horny sheath. The nasal opening is single. They have lungs, although aquatic forms have vascular sacs in the cloaca which serve for breathing when the ani-

480

Figure 392. Life history of turtle. **A**, Egg. **B**, Early embryo. **C**, Embryo and large yolk sac enclosed in amniotic membrane, just before hatching. **D**, Baby turtle.

Figure 393. Green sea turtle, *Chelonia*. Note that limbs are modified into flippers. Such turtles are strictly aquatic except when they lay their eggs on sandy shore. Some of these turtles may weigh as much as 400 to 500 pounds and are greatly prized for turtle soup. (Courtesy Vancouver Public Aquarium, British Columbia.)

Figure 394. Common box turtle, *Terrapene*.

Figure 395. Western painted turtle, *Chrysemys*, common turtle of ponds and lakes.

mals are submerged. On their toes are horny claws for digging in the sand, where they lay their eggs. Some of the marine forms have paddle-shaped limbs for swimming. Fertilization is internal by means of a cloacal penis on the ventral wall of the male cloaca. All turtles are oviparous and the eggs have firm, calcareous shells (Figure 392).

Turtles range from a few inches in diameter to the great marine ones which may weigh a thousand pounds. Sea turtles usually grow larger than land forms, although some of the latter in the Galápagos Islands may weigh several hundred pounds. Most turtles are rather sluggish in their movements which may account for their longevity; some are supposed to live more than a hundred years.

Turtles eat both vegetable and animal products. Many marine forms capture fish and other vertebrates. Land tortoises live on insects, plants, and berries. The common box turtle (*Terrapene*) (Figure 394) grows very fat during the wild strawberry season.

The term tortoise is usually given to the land forms, whereas the term turtle is reserved for the aquatic ones (Figure 395). Among the former, the box turtle (*Terrapene*) is one of the most familiar. It is about 6 inches long. It has a high arched carapace with the front and rear margins curled up. The lower shell is hinged, with two movable parts, so that it can be pulled up against the upper shell. The color markings vary, but usually the shell is a dark brown color with irregular yellow spots. Box turtles are found in woods and fields and sometimes in marshes. In spite of their slow movement they do get around; marked individuals have often been found a considerable distance away from the point of release. They lay their eggs in cavities dug out of loose soil and cover them over.

The diamondback terrapin (*Malaclemys*) is widely used as food. This turtle dwells in salt marshes and derives its common name from the markings on its shell. In some eastern regions terrapin farms are maintained on a commercial basis

482

Diamondbacks grow to be about 10 inches long.

Snapping turtles (*Chelydra*) are found in nearly every pond or lake in the eastern half of this country. They grow to be 12 to 14 inches in diameter and 20 to 40 pounds in weight. They are ferocious and often referred to as the "tigers of the pond." They are entirely carnivorous, living on fish, frogs, waterfowl, or almost anything that comes within reach of their powerful jaws. They are wholly aquatic and come ashore only to lay their eggs. They are dangerous to handle, for they strike with lightning speed and hold on with fierce tenacity.

Crocodilia. Crocodiles are the largest members of Reptilia; some have been captured which were more than 25 feet long. This order is divided into crocodiles and alligators. Crocodiles have relatively long slender snouts; alligators have short and broader snouts. With their powerful jaws and sharp teeth they are formidable antagonists. Although all are carnivorous, many will not attack man. The "man-eating" members of the group are found mainly in Africa and Asia. The estuarine crocodile (*Crocodylus porosus*) found in southern Asia grows to a great size and is very much feared. Alligators are usually less aggressive than crocodiles. Alligators are almost unique among reptiles in being able to make definite sounds. The male alligator can give loud bellows in the mating season. Vocal sacs are found on each side of the throat and are inflated when he calls. In the United States there is a single species of alligator (*Alligator mississipiensis*, Figure 396) and one of crocodiles (*Crocodylus americanus*). The latter is confined to Florida and is almost extinct. The American alligator is found from North Carolina to Florida and west to Texas. Few specimens are now caught more than 12 feet long. Although alligators can put up a severe fight when cornered, they are timid toward man and will avoid him. There is no authentic case of an American alligator attacking man, and bathers in southern waters need have no fear of them. The crocodile found in Florida is likewise a harmless animal to man.

Alligators and crocodiles are oviparous. Usually from twenty to fifty eggs are laid in a mass of dead vegetation. The eggs are about 3 inches long. The penis of the male is an outgrowth of the ventral cloaca.

Rhynchocephalia. This order, which has many fossil forms, is represented by only one living species, the tuatara (*Sphenodon punctatum*) of New Zealand (Figure 397). This "living fossil" is found on one or two islands in Cook Straits and is protected by the New Zealand government. It is a lizardlike form about 2 feet or less in length and has a number of primitive characteristics, such as unique skull peculiarities, abdominal ribs, amphicoelous vertebrae, and a well-marked

Figure 396. Small alligator, *Alligator mississipiensis.*

Phylum Chordata—classes Amphibia and Reptilia 483

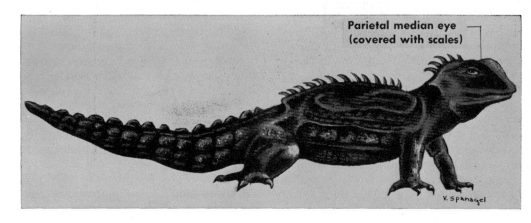

Parietal median eye
(covered with scales)

V. Spanagel

Figure 397. *Sphenodon,* only living representative of order Rhynchocephalia. This "living fossil" reptile has well-developed parietal eye with retina and lens on top of head. Eye is covered with scales and is considered nonfunctional but may have been important sense organ in early reptiles.

parietal eye which is less degenerate than in other animals and is one of its most distinguishing structures. This eye even has evidences of a retina. The upper surface of the animal is covered with small scales, and the ventral region is covered with transverse rows of squarelike plates. Sphenodon lives in burrows among the rocks, is nocturnal in habits, and eats small animals. This form may not be an ancestor from which modern lizards have descended but may represent an independent specialized type. The members of this order appeared in the Triassic period and all became extinct during the Mesozoic, save only *Sphenodon.* The latter, in spite of a long evolution of 170 million years, has retained many primitive characteristics and represents one of the slowest rates of evolution known among vertebrates.

Brief classification

Class Reptilia. Body covered with horny (ectodermal scales or plates; usually four limbs, each with five claws; skeleton ossified; one occipital condyle; lungs throughout life.

Order 1. Testudinata (Chelonia). Body enclosed in a shell of dorsal carapace and ventral plastron; jaws with horny sheaths; no teeth; quadrate bone immovable; vertebrae and ribs fused to shell usually.

Family Chelydridae—snapping turtles. Head, neck, and limbs cannot be withdrawn into shell; plastron small with ten plates; upper jaw hooked; carapace and tail tuberculated. Example: *Chelydra.*

Family Kinosternidae—musk and mud turtles. Plastron hinged at both ends; edge of carapace not flaring; plastron with nine to eleven plates; odor musky. Example: *Sternotherus.*

Family Testudinidae—tortoises and terrapins. Carapace with flaring edges; plastron with twelve plates. Example: *Chrysemys.*

Family Chelonidae—sea turtles. Body large; limbs like flippers; marine; shell with smooth horny shields. Example: *Chelonia.*

Family Trionychidae—soft-shelled turtles. Carapace leathery without horny plates or scales; snout long and flexible. Example: *Amyda.*

Family Dermochelidae—leatherback turtles. Marine; limbs flipperlike; carapace leathery; large. Example: *Dermochelys.*

Order 2. Rhynchocephalia. Parietal organ (third eye) present; scales granular; mid-dorsal row of spines; quadrate bone immovable; vertebrae biconcave. Example: *Sphenodon.*

Order 3. Squamata. Skin with horny epidermal scales; quadrate bone movable; vertebrae procoelus usually; copulatory organ (hemipenes) present; anus a transverse slit.

Suborder 1. Sauria (Lacertilia)—lizards. Body slender, usually with four limbs; rami of lower jaw fused; eyelids movable; copulatory organs paired.

Family Gekkonidae—geckos. Body small; toes with adhesive pads usually; eyes without movable lids usually; vertebrae biconcave; tongue protrusible. Example: *Phyllodactylus*.

Family Iguanidae—New World lizards. Head and body scales small; teeth homodont; tongue not protrusible; eyelids present. Example: *Anolis*.

Family Agamidae—Old World lizards. Teeth heterodont; tongue short and thick; throat sacs present in some. Example: *Draco*.

Family Chamaeleontidae—chameleons. Body somewhat bilaterally compressed; tail prehensile; toes suited for grasping; tongue prehensile; large eyes independently movable; lungs with air sacs; color changes. Example: *Chamaeleo*.

Family Lacertidae—Old World lizards. Body covered with small granular or wedge-shaped scales; pleurodont teeth; head covered with large shields; scales of trunk in transverse rows. Example: *Lacerta*.

Family Scincidae—skinks. Body with large and smooth scales; skin folds lacking on side; tongue with indented tip and papillae; legs small. Example: *Eumeces*.

Family Amphisbaenidae—worm lizards. Body elongated, wormlike; limbs absent or rudimentary; scales not overlapping; ears not visible. Example: *Rhineura*.

Family Helodermatidae—poisonous lizards. Body with beadlike scales; tail short and thick; tongue protrusible; lower jaw with grooved poison fangs. Example: *Heloderma*.

Family Anguidae—plated lizards. Body elongated; scales large and squarish; fold of skin along each side; limbs small or absent; tongue long and forked; tail long and fragile. Example: *Ophisaurus*.

Suborder 2. Serpentes (Ophidia)—snakes. Body elongated; limbs and ear openings absent; mandibles joined anteriorly by ligaments; eyes lidless and immovable; tongue bifid and protrusible; teeth conical and on jaws and roof of mouth.

Family Leptotyphlopidae—blind snakes. Body small, wormlike; blind; teeth on lower jaw only; vestiges of femur and pelvic bones. Example: *Leptotyphlops*.

Family Boidae—boas and pythons. Body with smooth scales; pupils vertical; vestiges of pelvic girdle and hind limbs; tails short and obtuse. Example: *Python*.

Family Colubridae—common snakes. Body with smooth or keeled scales; facial bones movable; squamosals loosely attached to skull; teeth in both jaws. Example: *Drymarchon*.

Family Elapidae—immovable-fang snakes. Body with rounded tail; pupil round; front pair of upper teeth forming short poisonous fangs; very venomous. Example: *Naja*.

Family Crotalidae—pit vipers. Pupil vertical; deep pit between eye and nostril; pair of poison fangs in front part of roof of mouth, folded back when not in use. Example: *Crotalus*.

Order 4. Crocodilia (Loricata). Body long; head large with long jaws; teeth many and conical; short limbs with clawed toes; tail long and heavy and bilaterally compressed; thick leathery skin with horny scutes; tongue nonprotrusible; anal opening longitudinal.

Family Gavialidae—gavials. Snout very long; first and fourth lower teeth bite into a groove in upper jaw; nasal bones not part of nasal aperture; teeth about equal; scutes on neck and back the same. Example: *Gavialis*.

Family Alligatoridae—alligators and caimans. Head short and broad; first and fourth lower teeth bite into pits in upper jaw; nasal bones form part of nasal aperture; teeth unequal; scutes on neck may be distinct from those on back. Example: *Alligator*.

Family Crocodylidae—crocodiles. The head is long and narrow; the first tooth bites into a pit; the fourth into a groove in upper jaw; nasal bones form part of nasal aperture; teeth unequal; scutes on neck may be distinct from those on back. Example: *Crocodylus*.

Derivation and meaning of basic terminology

Ambystoma (Gr. *amby*, blunt, + *stoma*, mouth) Often erroneously called Amblystoma, although Ambystoma is the original term.

Amphibia (Gr. *amphi*, both or double, + *bios*, life).

Anura (Gr. *an*, without, + *oura*, tail).

Archosauria (Gr. *archos*, chief ruler, + *sauros*, lizard) Great subclass of fossil reptiles which dominated the Age of Reptiles, and from which some of our existing reptiles have come.

axolotl (Sp. *axolotl*, servant of the water).

Cotylosauria (Gr. *kotyle*, cup, + *sauros*, lizard) Fossil stem reptiles that gave rise to the various groups of later reptiles.

Crocodilia (L. *crocodilus*, crocodile).

Gymnophiona (Gr. *gymn*, naked, + *ophioneos*, like a serpent).

Ichthyostega (Gr. *ichthys*, fish, + *stegos*, a covering) This genus of fossil forms is considered to be the oldest amphibians. They had some crossopterygian characteristics and are considered close to the amphibian ancestral stock.

Labyrinthodontia (Gr. *labyrinthos,* tortuous passage, + *odontos,* tooth) An important group (superorder) of fossil primitive amphibians from which most amphibians evolved. Their teeth had complex patterns of enamel infolding.

Lacertilia (L. *lacertus,* lizard).

Ophidia (Gr. *ophis,* snake) Suborder of Squamata which includes the snakes.

Rhynchocephalia (Gr. *rhynchos,* snout, + *kephale,* head).

Salientia (L. *saliens,* leaping).

Sphenodon (Gr. *sphen,* wedge, + *odontos,* tooth).

Squamata (L. *squamatous,* scaly).

Testudinata (L. *testudinatus,* tortoise).

Urodela (Gr. *oura,* tail, + *delos,* visible).

ANNOTATED REFERENCES

Amphibia

Barbour, T. 1926. Reptiles and Amphibians. New York, Houghton Mifflin Co. *An interesting account of the habits of amphibian and reptiles.*

Bishop, S. C. 1943. Handbook of Salamanders. Ithaca, Comstock Publishing Co. *The best handbook on the habits and taxonomy of the salamanders of the United States and Canada.*

Blanchard, F. N. 1938. Natural History of Vertebrates. Ann Arbor, Edwards Brothers, Inc. *A considerable part of this work is devoted to field studies of amphibians. An excellent bibliography is included.*

Conant, R. 1958. A Field Guide to Reptiles and Amphibians of Eastern North America. Boston, Houghton Mifflin Co. *A handy pocketsized guide which is indispensable to the field worker on these two groups.*

Dunn, E. R. 1926. The Salamanders of the Family Plethodontidae. Northampton, Smith College. *An excellent and comprehensive monograph of this interesting family of salamanders. A model for all such treatises.*

Noble, G. K. 1931. Biology of the Amphibia. New York, McGraw-Hill Book Co., Inc. *A good general account of the structure, life histories, and classification of the group.*

Oliver, J. A. 1955. The Natural History of North American Amphibians and Reptiles. Princeton and New York, D. Van Nostrand Co. Inc. *This is an excellent work for beginners, for it appraises many aspects of natural history.*

Stebbins, R. C. 1951. Amphibians of Western North America. Berkeley, University of California Press. *An up-to-date account of our western amphibian fauna, including both life histories and classification.*

Wright, A. H., and A. A. Wright. 1949. Handbook of Frogs and Toads of the United States and Canada. Ithaca, Comstock Publishing Co. *The best work of its kind in existence.*

Young, J. Z. 1950. The Life of Vertebrates. Oxford, Oxford University Press. *A pretentious work which attempts the integration of all aspects — embryology, anatomy, physiology etc.—of vertebrate life. It is a book for the serious student, for it gives a unified view of vertebrate life and its evolution.*

Reptilia

Barbour, T. 1934. Reptiles and Amphibians, ed. 2. Boston, Houghton Mifflin Co. *Many interesting reptiles are described in this work.*

Buckley, E. E., and N. Porges. 1956. Venoms. Washington, American Association for the Advancement of Science. *This is an excellent appraisal of the many problems connected with animal poisons. This volume is made up of the papers contributed to the First International Conference on Venoms. The reader will be amazed to learn how widespread this method of defense and offense is among animals. Nearly very phylum from Protozoa to Chordata is represented, and little is known about the nature of the various toxins which animals employ.*

Carr, A. F., Jr. 1952. Handbook of Turtles. Ithaca, Cornell University Press. *One of the best handbooks on the subject.*

Conant, R. 1951. The Reptiles of Ohio, ed. 2. Notre Dame, University of Notre Dame. *This work is one of the better state surveys of reptiles and is useful for studying the reptiles also in adjacent states.*

Ditmars, R. L. 1944. Snakes of the World. New York, The Macmillan Co. *A general and popular account of the group by one of the world's greatest authorities.*

Gadow, H. 1901. Amphibia and Reptiles (Cambridge Natural History). London, Macmillan & Co., Ltd. *A classical but somewhat outdated survey. Good morphological descriptions.*

Klauber, L. M. 1956. Rattlesnakes, 2 vols. Berkeley, University of California Press. *If you want to learn about rattlesnakes read these two ponderous volumes! Everything about their habits and life histories, together with a full description of all species, is included in this amazing handbook.*

Morris, P. A. 1944. They Hop and Crawl. Lancaster, The Jaques Cattell Press. *A popular description of the more common reptiles and amphibians. An excellent work for beginners.*

Pope, C. H. 1937. Snakes Alive and How They Live. New York, The Viking Press. *An accurate, well-written, semipopular account.*

Pope, C. H. 1955. The Reptile World. New York, Alfred A. Knopf, Inc. *All the four major groups of reptiles are represented in this interesting and revealing work. Each of these groups is introduced by such general topics as food, size, enemies, intelligence, reproduction, hibernation, locomotion. The numerous photographs cannot be surpassed.*

Schmidt, K. P., and D. D. Davis. 1941. Field Book of Snakes of the United States and Canada. New York, G. P. Putnam's Sons. *One of the most useful field manuals on snakes. Interesting to the beginner.*

Smith, H. M. 1946. Handbook of Lizards of the United States and Canada. *An excellent and authoritative manual. The illustrations are mostly photographs which add to the value of the work.*

Wright, A. H., and A. A. Wright. 1957. Handbook of Snakes of the United States and Canada, 2 vols. Ithaca, Comstock Publishing Associates. *This fine, definitive work on snakes is in the best traditions of animal group handbooks. It is constructed along the same lines as that of the author's great work on frogs and toads. The authors are really field naturalists and their emphasis in this work is on snakes as they are found in the wild. The introduction gives an excellent account of the general characteristics of snakes, and the remainder of the work is devoted to a description of the various taxonomic units. Photographs are clear and numerous. Distribution maps spot the location of the different species.*

chapter 26

Phylum Chordata

The frog as a vertebrate type

SUBPHYLUM VERTEBRATA

CLASS AMPHIBIA

Why frogs are used in laboratory study

The frog is widely used for vertebrate study in introductory zoology. Since it is a transition form between the strictly aquatic and the strictly land animals, it is convenient for making comparisons between the more primitive and the higher vertebrate types. The frog is easy to dissect, easy to procure, and inexpensive. On the other hand, the frog is a highly specialized animal, and in some ways it cannot be considered a truly representative vertebrate. However, a knowledge of its structures and bodily functions provides a background for the study of the higher forms, including man.

Frogs as a group

Frogs share with toads the subclass (or order, according to some authorities) Salientia (Anura—a-nu'ra, Gr. *an*, without, + *oura*, tail), which includes more than 1,600 species widely distributed over the world, except in the polar regions and certain oceanic islands. The distinction between frogs and toads is not sharp, for they have so many features in common. Toads are more terrestrial than frogs and are provided with warty skins and with parotid glands behind the head. The true toads also lack teeth on either jaw. The most

common family of frogs is Ranidae (true frogs) which is made up of twenty-eight species and subspecies in the United States and Canada. The three species most commonly studied in the laboratory are the bullfrog (*Rana catesbeiana*, Figure 398), the green frog (*Rana clamitans*, Figure 399), and the leopard frog (*Rana pipiens*, Figure 400). Of these the bullfrog is by far the largest, often reaching a length of more than 8 inches, and is exceeded only by the giant frog (*Rana goliath*) of Africa. Other interesting frogs commonly met with are the wood frog (*Rana sylvatica*), the pickerel frog (*Rana palustris*), and the tree frog or toad (Hylidae).

Habitats and distribution of frogs

The frogs as a group are usually found close to water, although some, such as the wood frog (*Rana sylvatica*), spend most of their time on damp forest floors, often some distance from the nearest water. The wood frog probably returns to pools only for breeding in early spring. The larger frogs, *Rana catesbeiana* and *Rana clamitans*, are nearly always found in or near permanent water or swampy regions. The leopard frog (*Rana pipiens*) often has a wider variety of habitats. Sluggish streams running through grassy regions or meadows are favorite places for them. *Rana pipiens*, with all its subspecies and phases, is perhaps the most wide-

Figure 398. Bullfrog, *Rana catesbeiana*, is largest of all American frogs.

Figure 399. Green frog, *Rana clamitans*, next to bullfrog in size. Body usually green, especially around jaws; has dark bars on sides of legs.

Figure 400. Leopard frog, *Rana pipiens*. Has light-colored dorsolateral ridges, and irregular spots.

Figure 401. Spring peepers, *Hyla crucifer*, the darlings of warm spring nights, when their characteristic peeping is so often heard. Is small (1 to 1½ inches) and light brown, with an "X" marked on back.

Figure 402. Swamp cricket frog, *Pseudacris nigrita triseriata*, common tree frog of early spring. About size of spring peeper. A small frog (1 to 1½ inches) with smooth skin and three dark longitudinal bands on back.

Figure 403. Gray tree frog, *Hyla versicolor*. Note large adhesive discs on ends of digits. Its sound is one of most familiar on summer night.

(Figures 398 to 403 courtesy Charles Alexander.)

spread in its distribution of all the North American frogs. It has been found in some form in nearly every state but is sparingly represented along the extreme western part of the Pacific coast. It also extends far into northern Canada and as far south as Panama. In some places it has been introduced artificially. The bullfrog (*Rana catesbeiana)* is native east of the Rocky Mountains but has been introduced into most of the western states. *Rana clamitans* is confined mainly to the eastern half of the United States, although it has been introduced elsewhere. Within the range of any species of frogs, they are often restricted to certain habitats (for instance, to certain streams or pools) and may be absent or scarce in similar habitats of the range. The pickerel frog *(Rana palustris)* is especially noteworthy this way, for it is known to be abundant only in certain localized regions.

General behavior and activities of frogs

Frogs of different species show considerable differences in behavior. Most of our larger frogs are solitary in their habits, although during the breeding season a considerable number may be found in a single pool. During the breeding period most of them, especially the males, are very noisy and their characteristic calls are familiar to all. At such times each male usually takes possession of a particular perch where he may remain for a long time, trying to attract a female to that spot. At times other than the breeding season frogs are mainly silent and their presence is not detected until they are disturbed. Many of them, such as the leopard frog, are very agile and excellent jumpers. The members of this species may often be found some distance away from water and, when pursued, will leap swiftly toward the pool, often in a zigzag manner. Extremely agile individuals may leap a distance of five to six feet in a single jump. When they reach the water, they dart about swiftly and reach the bottom of the pool, where they kick up a cloud of muddy water. In swimming, they hold the forelimbs near the body and kick backward with the webbed hind limbs, which propel them forward. When they come to the surface to breathe, only the head and foreparts are exposed, and as they usually take advantage of any protective vegetation, they are difficult to see.

Frogs can croak under water as well as on land, and they make their character istic noises by forcing the air back and forth over the vocal cords into the lungs. Most species utter characteristic croak which identify them. One of the loudes is the familiar "jug-o-rum" of the bull frog. The bass notes of the green frog are banjolike, and those of the leopard frog are long and guttural. Many frog sounds are now available on phonograph records.

Frogs are mainly carnivorous and feed on worms, insects, tadpoles, etc. The large species will eat the smaller ones if the chance affords. Stationary objects hold n attraction for them, but they will snap with their protrusible tongue, which i attached at the front end and free behind, at any moving object within their range. The free end of the tongue i highly glandular and produces a sticky secretion with which it adheres to the prey.

During the winter months most frog **hibernate** in the soft mud of the bottom of pools and streams. The wood frog hibernates under stones, logs, and stump in the forest area. Naturally their life processes are at a very low ebb during their hibernation period, and such energy a they need is derived from the glycoge and fat stored in their bodies during the spring and summer months.

Adult frogs have many enemies such a snakes, aquatic birds, turtles, raccoons man, and many others; only a few tad poles survive to maturity.

Parasites in frogs

In common with most animals, frog serve as hosts for many different kind of parasites. The number and kind o parasites they have depend upon man factors. Rarely are frogs found withou some form of parasite, although some ar more heavily parasitized than others. I certain surveys made, protozoan para sites seem to be more common in tadpole and young frogs than they are in adults although in *Rana pipiens* and the toad some protozoans, such as *Opalina*, ar found in all stages. The tadpoles of *Rana clamitans* and *Rana catesbeiana* are especially parasitized with protozoan forms. There is a regional distribution of frog parasites in accordance with the difference in frog species. Frogs in California, for instance, usually have many parasites not shared with species in other geographical ranges. The widely introduced bullfrog in California is not parasitized by the parasites of frogs native to that state, while in turn the bullfrog's parasites do not live in native frogs. Frogs in captivity tend to shed their parasites rapidly and in a week or so may show few specimens, especially if the frogs are not fed. According to some authorities, the degree of parasitism depends upon the abundance of food. Another factor is abundance of rainfall, which may account for the wide prevalence of parasites among a frog population or the reverse when conditions are

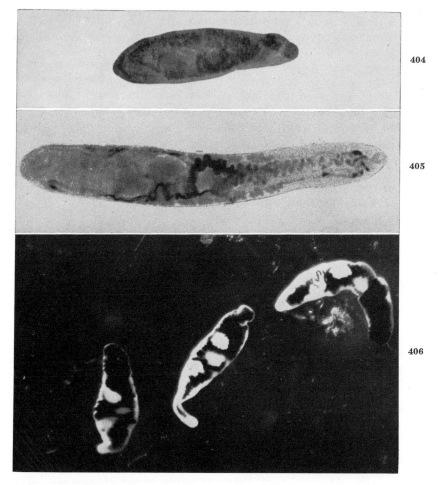

404

405

406

Figure 404. Common lung fluke, *Pneumobites*, parasite of frog. These flukes have complicated life history. Eggs are shed from frog and ingested by snails. In snails, cercariae are produced which later find their way into rectum of dragonfly larva, or naiad, where they encyst as metacercariae and remain throughout metamorphosis of nymph into dragonfly. Cycle is completed when frog snaps up dragonfly.

Figure 405. Stained preparation of *Haematoloechus*.

Figure 406. Lung fluke, *Haematoloechus*. These living specimens photographed just after removal from lung of freshly killed frog.

dry. Land forms have fewer parasites than aquatic ones.

Among the protozoans, the large ciliates, *Opalina* and *Nyctotherus*, are most frequently found in the intestine and rectum. Flagellates, such as *Hexamita* and *Trichomonas*, are also often found in the same region. *Entamoeba raravurn* occurs in the intestine. In the blood, *Trypanosoma* and *Haemogregarina* are frequently present. In addition to these, many ectozoic protozoans may be found on the skin and gills of tadpoles, such as *Epistylis*, *Vorticella*, *Opercularia*, and *Trichodina*. The latter is often found as an endoparasite in the urinary bladder of frogs.

Tapeworms (Cestoda) are not common in frogs. Some members of the family Proteocephalidae have been recorded in *Rana clamitans*, and in the same species a new form of tapeworm, *Ophiotaenea saphena*, has been described in recent years.

The most striking parasites of the frog belong to the trematodes (Figures 404 to 406), usually found in the lungs and the urinary bladder. Most of the lung flukes belong to the genus *Haematoloechus* (old name, *Pneumonoeces*), of which about sixteen species have been described. In the bladder are found flukes of the genus *Gorgodera*, represented by at least two species, and the genus *Gorgoderina*, of which at least six species have been described. Another common trematode is *Clinostomum attenuatum* which is often found encysted in the mesenteries and under the peritoneum of *Rana pipiens* and *Rana catesbeiana*. In many species of frogs genus *Megalodiscus* is sometimes present in the rectum, whereas two species of *Loxogenes* are known to occur in cysts on the liver or in the bile duct of three of four different species of frogs. The intestine may harbor many parasites, such as *Cephalogonimus* and *Glypthelmins*, each genus being represented by two or three species. In the mouth or pharynx two or three species of *Halipegus* occur in certain frogs, including *Rana pipiens*.

Nematode parasites have not been studied as extensively as the trematodes. Nematodes are found chiefly in the lungs, intestine, and heart, although they may be found elsewhere. Some of the more common ones found are representatives of the following genera: *Rhabdias*, *Isociella*, *Oswaldocruzia*, *Falcustra*, and *Aplectana*. The common hair worms (Gordiacea) are also known to be parasitic in the frog during part of their larval history.

The frog as morphological type

The frog, although specialized, is a fairly typical vertebrate with an arrangement of organ systems in line with those of land vertebrates, where increased skeletal and muscular tissue demand more nutrition, more oxygen, and a more efficient elimination of waste. A form that is adapted for land locomotion requires an entirely different pattern of skeletal and muscular elements. The simple sheetlike (myotome) muscles of fish, for instance, must be highly modified to meet the requirements of a skeleton fitted for locomotion on land.

The following description applies mainly to *Rana pipiens*, which is commonly used for laboratory study.

External features of frog

Body plan. The body of the frog is divided into **head** and **trunk** without an intervening neck region. There are two pairs of **legs** but no tail. The head bears a pair of nostrils, or **external nares**, a large transverse **mouth**, two protruding **eyes** (which can be depressed into their orbits when the frog closes its eyes), and, behind each eye, a flat **tympanic membrane**, or eardrum. A posterior terminal **cloacal opening** represents the external orifice of the **cloaca**. On top of the head just in front of the eyes is the light-colored **brow spot** (frontal organ), which represents the vestigial pineal eye.

The front legs are short and turned in, and each has four digits. On male frogs the inner digit is thickened into the **nuptial pad** for clasping the female during mating. The long hind limbs are adapted

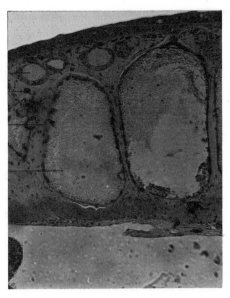

Epidermis
Mucous gland
Chromatophores
Spongy layer of dermis
Poison gland
Compact layer of dermis

Figure 407. Histological section of frog skin. Stratified epidermis is seen as dark layer at surface with thicker dermis below. Note small mucous glands and large poison glands in dermal layer.

for jumping and swimming and are folded together when the frog is not active. The five slender toes of the hind limbs are connected by broad webs which are swimming adaptations.

Integument. The skin of the frog is thin and moist and is attached loosely to the body only at certain points. Behind each eye a dorsolateral fold, or **dermal plica,** is formed by a thickening of the skin. Histologically, the skin is made up of two layers—an outer stratified **epidermis** and an inner spongy **dermis** (Figure 407). The outer layer (**stratum corneum**) of the epidermis consists of flat, horny cells which are shed periodically. Beneath the stratum corneum are other cells which rest upon the columnar basal cells of the Malpighian layer, or **stratum germinativum.** As the stratum corneum is shed, new cells formed from the stratum germinativum push up to take its place. The frog molts a number of times during its active months. In the process the stratum corneum is split down the back and is worked off as one piece. The dermis is made up mostly of glands, pigment cells, and connective tissue. On its outer por-

tion are the glands— small **mucous glands,** which secrete mucus, for keeping the skin moist, and the larger **poison** glands, which secrete a whitish fluid that is highly irritating to enemies. Both of these glands are epidermal in origin, although located in the dermis, and both pour their secretions onto the skin surface by means of ducts.

Skin color in the frog is produced by pigment granules scattered through the epidermis and by special pigment cells, **chromatophores,** located in the dermis. The latter are represented by a number of types, such as **guanophores,** which contain **guanine** (white crystals), **melanophores** with black and brown pigment, and **lipophores** (xanthopores) with red and yellow pigment. Frogs have some power to change color to suit their background by the manipulation of their various chromatophores or pigment. All the chromatophores have branched cytoplasmic processes. Darkened effects result whenever the pigment granules become scattered through the branched processes; light effects occur whenever the pigment becomes concentrated toward the center of the pigment cell. There is evidence to show that pigment changes are due, in part at least, to influences through the eye, although the specific regulation is hormonal and nervous in nature.

Dermal scales are lacking in modern amphibians (except caecilians) although their ancestors were well provided with them. The lack of them has made possible the well-developed glandular system of the skin, as an accessory breathing mechanism as well as for protection.

Symmetry and nomenclature of body regions. The typical **bilateral symmetry** of all higher forms is found in the frog. A median longitudinal plane will separate its body into mirrored halves. Convenient terms for locating the regions of a frog's body are the **anterior,** or head, end; **posterior,** or the end opposite the head; **dorsal,** or back, which is uppermost in the normal position; **ventral,** or lower (belly) position; **medial,** or toward the middle of the body; and **lateral,** or toward the sides. **Cephalic** also refers to the head end; **caudal,** to the tail region. **Distal** parts of the animal are away from the center of the animal, whereas **proximal** parts are nearer the center. More specific terms are the **chin** and **throat** regions under the head, the **pectoral** region near the forelegs, and the **pelvic** region between the hind legs.

Internal structures

Mouth cavity (buccal cavity). The mouth of the frog is proportionally large for the size of the animal (Figure 408). On the margin of the **upper jaw** are the conical **maxillary teeth,** and on the roof of the mouth are two patches of **vomerine** teeth. The teeth serve only to hold their prey and are replaced when lost. Lateral to the vomerine teeth are the two openings, **internal nares,** which connect with the external nares. Air passes into and out of the mouth cavity through these nares. Behind the internal nares are the large swellings of the eye sockets. When the eyes are depressed into these sockets and the floor of the mouth is raised, swallowing is thereby aided. Near the posterior

494

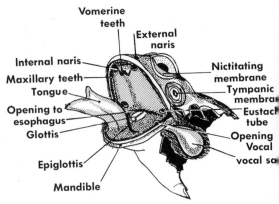

Figure 408. Head and mouth region of frog, with vocal sac exposed.

angle of each jaw is the opening into the **Eustachian tube** which connects with the middle ear and equalizes the air pressure on each side of the tympanic membrane. The **lower jaw** has no teeth. The large muscular tongue is attached in front to the floor but is notched and free at its posterior end which bears a sticky secretion for capturing prey. Taste buds are located on the **papillae** of the tongue. The **glottis** is a longitudinal slit in the larynx which allows air passage to the lungs. Across the larynx are the two elastic bands, the **vocal cords,** which the frog uses in croaking. The posterior part of the mouth cavity is the **pharynx** which leads into the opening of the esophagus. In each inner angle of the lower jaw of the male is the opening into a vocal sac. These paired vocal sacs are inflated to intensify the sounds made by the frog, especially during the mating season. The roof of the mouth, as well as the pharyngeal region, is lined with ciliated epithelium which carries food and liquids toward the esophagus and into the digestive tract.

Coelomic cavity and its structures. The body cavity, or **coelom,** is lined with thin transparent membrane (**parietal peritoneum**) and the viscera are covered with a thin transparent membrane **visceral (peritoneum).** The double-layered peritoneum that holds the various organs to the dorsal body wall is called the **mesenteries.** The organ systems which are revealed when the body cavity is opened are the digestive, circulatory, respiratory, excretory, and reproductive systems. Beginning at the anterior end of the coelomic cavity are the pear-shaped **heart** enclosed in the **pericardial sac,** with the roots of the large blood vessels connected to it, the reddish brown **liver** with the greenish **gallbladder** between its lobes, the short **esophagus** back of the liver, the J-shaped **stomach,** and the coiled **small intestine** terminated by the short straight **large intestine** or rectum. In the space between the stomach and duodenum is the whitish **pancreas,** and in the mesentery near the beginning of the large intestine is the small, round reddish **spleen.** Above the peritoneum and close to the midventral line are the flat, elongated **kidneys,** and the bilobed **urinary bladder** is attached to the ventral side of the **cloaca** into which the rectum opens. In the male the small bean-shaped **testes** with connected **fat bodies** are found at the anterior ends of the kidneys; in the female the large ovaries with small dark eggs are found on the ventral side of the kidneys, and the two much-convoluted **oviducts** are close to the dorsal wall of the body cavity.

Four systems of the frog's body lie more or less outside of the coelomic cavity. They are the skeletal, muscular, nervous, and sensory systems. These systems have the important roles of support, protection, movement, regulation and coordination, and reception of stimuli.

Skeletal system

The exoskeleton is practically nonexistent in modern amphibians, for their glandular skin has no hard, ectodermal structures. The well-developed **endoskeleton** (Figure 409) of bone and cartilage provides support and a framework for the muscles in movement, as well as protection for the viscera and nervous system. In the early development of the frog the endoskeleton is entirely of cartilage, but in the adult most of its parts are of bone, with cartilage on the ends of bones and other scattered places. The frog's skeleton is correlated with its specialized body.

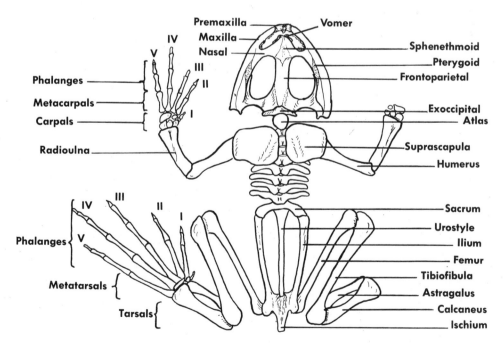

Figure 409. Dorsal view of frog skeleton.

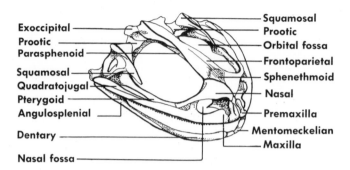

Figure 410. Dorsolateral view of frog skull.

This is marked in the hind limbs fitted for jumping, in the absence of the tail and ribs, and in the reduction of the vertebrae.

Like other vertebrates, the frog skeleton may be divided into main divisions: **axial** and **appendicular** skeletons. The axial skeleton is made up of the skull, vertebral column, and sternum; the appendicular consists of the girdles (pectoral and pelvic) and limbs.

The **skull** of the frog (Figure 410) is made up mainly of dermal bones with a few replacement bones, that is, those which have replaced cartilage. It is flat and broad and is made up of **cranial** and **visceral** parts. The cranial division consists of the brain case, or cranium, the olfactory and auditory capsules, and the optic orbits. The visceral portion contains the two jaws, the hyoid cartilage, and the laryngeal cartilages.

The bones of the **cranium** are distributed as follows: two frontoparietals on the dorsal side, two nasals over the nasal capsules, the single sphenethmoid which runs forward from the parietals, two prootics which are around the inner ears, and two exoccipitals on the posterior end of the skull. Each exoccipital bears a process, the **occipital condyle**, which articulates with the first vertebra (atlas) of the vertebral column. Between the condyles is the **foramen magnum**, through which the spinal cord enters to join the brain; on the ventral side of the cranium are the two vomers which bear the vomerine teeth, the single daggerlike parasphenoid, the palatine bones which attach the **upper jaw**, the two premaxillae in front of the external nares, the two maxillae forming the greater part of the sides of the jaw and which, with the premaxillae, bear teeth, the two quadratojugal bones along the maxillae, and the two squamosals and two pterygoids which attach the upper jaw to the posterior end of the cranium.

The **lower jaw**, or mandibular arch, is made up of two small mentomeckelian bones at the tip of the lower jaw, two dentaries, and two angulosplenials. The **hyoid apparatus** found in the floor of the mouth beneath the tongue is made up chiefly of a flat cartilaginous plate (body), the anterior cornua which become attached to the prootic bones of the cranium, and the posterior cornua which support the larynx. The lower jaw articulates with the quadrate cartilage on each side of the cranium.

The **vertebral column** which supports the body and houses the spinal cord consists of nine vertebrae and the **urostyle**, in which the end of the spinal cord terminates. Each vertebra is typically made up of the **centrum** of compact bone, surmounted by a bony ring, the **neural arch**, through which the nerve cord passes. On top of the neural arch is the **neural spine**, on each side is a **transverse process**, and at either end is a pair of **articular processes** (anterior and posterior zygapophyses). Between these articular processes and the cartilage pads of the centra of the vertebrae are the **intervertebral foramina** though which the spinal nerves

496

leave the spinal cord. No ribs are found in the frog.

The **pectoral girdle** serves as a support for the forelimbs and as a protection for structures within that region of the body. On each side the girdle is made up of a dorsal flat cartilaginous **suprascapula**, a lateral **scapula**, and, on the ventral side, a slender **clavicle** and a broad **coracoid**. Both clavicles and coracoids join the breastbone, or **sternum** (a part of the axial skeleton), which consists anteriorly of the cartilaginous plate, **episternum**, followed by the rodlike **omosternum**, the larger **mesosternum**, and the broad **xiphisternum**. The clavicles and coracoids from both sides are connected by a pair of cartilage bars, the **epicoracoids**, on the midventral region. The **glenoid fossa**, a concavity in which the head of the humerus of the forelimb fits, is located at the junction of the scapula and coracoid on each side.

Each **forelimb** is made up of a **humerus**, which articulates with the girdle at the glenoid fossa, the **radioulna**, consisting of two fused bones in the forearm, the **carpus** of six small bones in two rows in the wrist, five **metacarpals** in the palm of the hand, and ten **phalanges** in the four functional **digits**. The rudimentary thumb, or first digit, is represented by the first metacarpal, whereas the second and third digits have two phalanges each, and the fourth and fifth digits have three phalanges each.

The **pelvic** girdle consists of two **innominate** bones, each of which is made up by fusion of the long anterior **ilium**, the posterior **ischium**, and the ventral **pubis**. The three bones meet at the **acetabulum** (cotyloid cavity), the concavity into which the **femur** bone of the hind limb fits. The pelvic girdle is attached to the vertebral column by means of the ilia which articulate with the transverse processes of the ninth or **sacral vertebra**.

The bones of the **hind limb** correspond in general with those of the forelimb. The thigh contains the **femur**; the shank, or crus, is made up of the fusion of two bones into the **tibiofibula**; the ankle, or

tarsus, consists of two elongated bones (astragulus, or talus, and calcaneus, or fibulare) and two smaller bones; the upper portion of the foot is comprised of the five **metatarsals;** and the five toes, or digits, have fourteen **phalanges** among them. Of these phalanges, the first and second toes contain two each; the third and fifth toes, three each; and the fourth toe, four. A rudimentary sixth digit (prehallux, or calcar) is found near the upper part of the metatarsal bone of the first digit and corresponds to the great toe of the human being or the vestigial first digit (thumb) of the frog's forelimb.

A **joint** is the meeting place of two bones. Some joints are immovable (**synarthroses**), such as those between skull bones; others are freely movable (**diarthroses**), including **hinge** joints, such as those of the knee and elbow, and **ball-and-socket** joints found at the hips and shoulders. There are a number of specialized structures at a joint. Where the bones meet each other, there are cartilage pads between them to reduce friction. Little

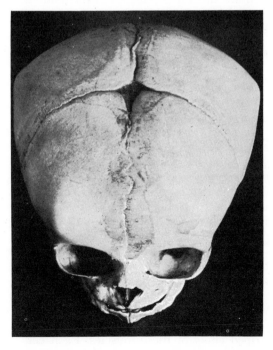

Figure 411. Skull of infant, showing sutures between skull bones. Example of synarthrosis joint.

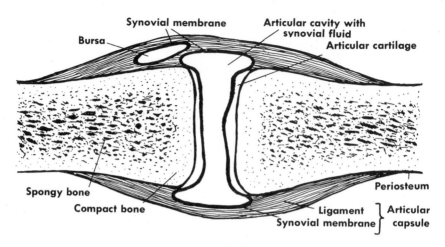

Figure 412. Structures of diarthrosis joint (longitudinal section).

closed sacs (**bursae**) are formed by these cartilage surfaces for supplying the **synovial fluid** used in lubrication. The joint cavity is surrounded by a fibrous, liquid-tight capsule which aids in holding the bones together by atmospheric pressure. Running over and around the joint capsule are the various muscles and tendons needed to manipulate the movements of the joint.

Muscular system

Types of muscles. Three types of muscle fibers are found in vertebrates: **skeletal** (striated), **smooth**, and **cardiac**.

SKELETAL OR STRIATED MUSCLES. Striated muscle fibers, or cells, are elongated and are bound together to make up the gross muscles which form most of the musculature of the body. They are under the control of the will and are thus vitally concerned with voluntary movement. The long, blunt muscle fibers (cells) in the human being are from 2 or 3 mm. to 41 mm. long and from 10 to 100 microns in thickness (Figure 413). Each fiber consists of many longitudinal **myofibrils** which bear alternate light and dark segments, or striations; these account for the striped effect of these muscles. Each cell possesses a number of nuclei. Skeletal muscles act faster, tire more easily, and

are less capable of stretching than other types of muscle fibers.

SMOOTH MUSCLES. Smooth muscles (Figure 415) are found in the walls of the digestive system, blood vessels, urinary bladder, gallbladder, and glands and their ducts. The spindle-shaped cells in man never exceed 0.5 mm. in length, and each has a single nucleus located in the center of the cell. Their myofibrils have no cross-striations. Smooth muscles are often found in sheetlike arrangements encircling a hollow organ. They are supplied with nerves from the autonomic nervous system and are thus involuntary and slow in action. This kind of muscle is more characteristic of invertebrates than is the striated type.

Figure 413. Photomicrograph of skeletal muscle, showing several striated fibers lying side by side. (Courtesy Joseph W. Bamberger.)

498

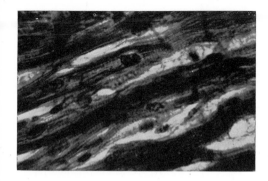

Figure 414. Photomicrograph of heart, or cardiac, muscle. Syncytial arrangement of fibers can be seen. (Courtesy Joseph W. Bamberger.)

Figure 415. Group of smooth muscle cells.

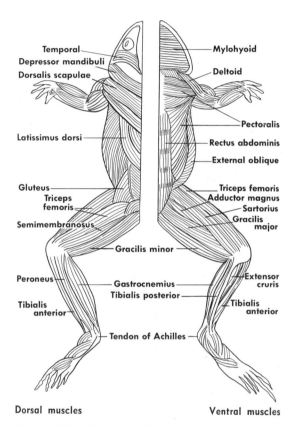

Dorsal muscles   Ventral muscles

Figure 416. Chief superficial muscles of frog (diagrammatic).

CARDIAC MUSCLE. Cardiac muscle (Figure 414) is found only in the hearts of vertebrates. It has some resemblance to both the other types of muscles. It consists of fibers, but these fibers branch and anastomose with each other to form a network. Heart muscle is actually a **syncytium,** for there are many nuclei but no cell boundaries. The nuclei are located near the center of the fiber much like those of smooth muscles. Myofibrils with cross-striations are also found in the strands and give cardic muscle its striated effect. In action, cardiac muscle is neither as fast as skeletal nor as sluggish as smooth muscle.

Structure of a gross muscle. A gross muscle is made up of a number of striated fibers bound together with connective tissue. The opposite ends of the muscles are usually connected to bones by means of modified connective tissue extensions called **tendons.** Gross muscles vary in shape and form according to their functions. Some are long and tapering, some are broad and sheetlike, others are short and thick, and still .others form sphincters with circular arrangement of the fibers. The less movable end of a muscle is called the **origin;** the more movable end, the **insertion.** The middle mass of muscle is the **belly,** and the shining connective tissue that encloses the muscle is the **fascia.** A *muscle's only action is to contract,* which

causes it to become shorter and thicker in the belly. Muscles are usually arranged in antagonistic groups, so that movement is effected by the contraction of one group and the relaxation of the opposite group. Muscles may be classified according to their action.

abductor Moves the part away from median axis of body (**deltoid**)

adductor Moves the part toward the median axis of the body (**adductor magnus**)

flexor Bends one part on another part (**biceps brachii**)

Phylum Chordata—the frog as a vertebrate type   499

Table 5. Principal superficial muscles of frog—origin, insertion, and action

Name	Origin	Insertion	Action
Muscles of jaws and tongue			
Temporal	Side of skull	Posterior end of lower jaw	Elevates lower jaw and closes mouth
Masseter	Zygomatic process of tympanic bone and quadratojugal	Lower jaw	Elevates lower jaw and stretches tympanic
Depressor mandibuli	Behind tympanic ring and dorsal fascia	Tip of mouth and jaw	Depresses lower jaw and opens mouth
Mylohyoid (sub-maxillary)	Medial surface of mandible	Median line of lower jaw	Raises floor of mouth in breathing and swallowing
Geniohyoid	Tip and border of lower jaw	Processes and body of hyoid	Lowers mandible and elevates hyoid
Sternohyoid	Sternum and coracoid	Ventral surface of hyoid	Lowers floor of mouth in breathing
Hyoglossus	Thyroid process of hyoid	Tongue	Retracts tongue
Genioglossus	Lower jaw	Tongue	Protracts tongue
Muscles of trunk			
Dorsalis scapulae	Dorsal surface of supra scapula	Lateral side of humerus	Extends arm
Latissimus dorsi	Dorsal fascia	Lateral border of humerus	Raises forelimb upward and backward
Longissimus dorsi	Anterior third of urostyle	Skull	Extends back and elevates head
Coccygeosacralis	Lateral anterior half of urostyle	Arch and transverse process of 9th vertebra	Draws back nearer urostyle or turns back to one side
Coccygeoiliacus	Lateral side of urostyle	Ilium	Fixes urostyle with respect to pelvic girdle
External oblique	Dorsal fascia and ilium	Linea alba	Supports and reduces abdominal cavity
Transversus	Ilium, dorsal fascia, and transverse processes of vertebrae	Linea alba, sternum, and coracoid	Constriction of abdomen
Rectus abdominis	Pubic symphysis	Sternum	Supports abdomen and fixes sternum in place
Pectoralis	Sternum and fascia of rectus abdominis muscle	Deltoid ridge of humerus	Adducts, flexes, and rotates arm

Table 5—Cont'd

Name	Origin	Insertion	Action
Muscles of thigh			
Sartorius	Pubic symphysis	Just below head of tibia	Bends shank and adducts thigh; draws limb forward
Adductor magnus	Ischial and pubic symphysis	Distal end of femur	Adducts thigh and leg; draws thigh ventrally
Adductor longus	Ventral part of ilium	Femur; joins adductor magnus	Adducts thigh
Triceps femoris	One head from acetabulum and two heads from ilium	Below head of tibia; upper end of tibiofibula	Adducts thigh; extends shank
Gracilis major	Posterior margin of ischium	Proximal end of tibiofibula	Adducts and extends thigh; flexes or extends shank, depending upon its position
Semitendinosus	Ischium	Proximal end of tibiofibula	Adducts thigh and flexes shank
Biceps femoris (ileofibularis)	Dorsal side of ilium	Tibiofibula	Flexes shank and extends thigh
Semimembranosus	Dorsal half of ischium	Back of head of tibiofibula	Adducts or extends thigh and flexes or extends shank, according to its position
Gluteus	Outer dorsal side of ilium	Head of femur	Rotates femur forward
Iliacus	Ilium and pubis	Middle third of femur	Flexes and rotates thigh
Muscles of shank			
Gastrocnemius	Distal end of femur and triceps femoris	Tendon of Achilles	Extends ankle and foot; flexes shank
Tibialis posticus	Posterior surface of tibiofibula	Proximal end of tibiale (astragalus)	Extends foot when flexed; flexes foot when fully extended
Tibialis anticus	Distal end of femur	Fibulare (calcaneum) and tibiale	Flexes foot and extends shank
Extensor cruris	Distal end of femur	Tibiofibula	Extends shank
Peroneus	Distal end of femur	Lower end of tibiofibula; head of calcaneum	Extends shank; when foot extended, extends it further; if flexed, flexes it further

Phylum Chordata—the frog as a vertebrate type 501

extensor Straightens out a part (**triceps brachii**)
depressor Lowers a part (**sternohyoid**)
levator Elevates a part (**masseter**)
rotator Produces a rotary movement (**gluteus**)

Some of the principal superficial muscles of the frog, together with their **origin, insertion,** and **action,** are listed in Table 5. Most of the muscles are paired, and most of them have the same names and action as those of man.

Nervous system

The nervous system coordinates and integrates the various physiological processes of the organs of the body as it adjusts to its environment. The system is specialized to interpret the stimuli and sensations it receives and originate the proper responses. The basic structure of all nervous systems is the **neuron,** a highly specialized cell. Neurons are arranged in complex patterns, but the whole structure works as a unit. The system is commonly divided into (1) the **central nervous system,** made up of the brain and spinal cord; (2) the **peripheral nervous system,** consisting of the cranial and spinal nerves; and (3) the **autonomic nervous system.** This division is mainly one of convenience, for the entire system is unified to work as a unit.

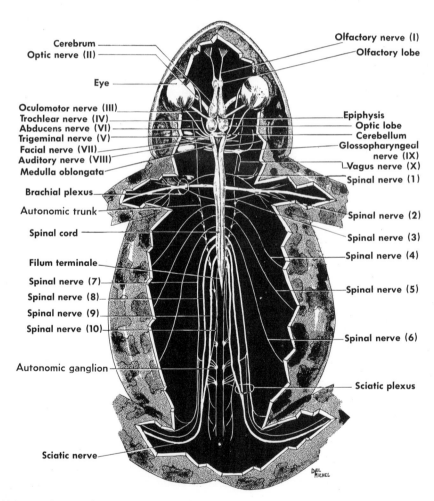

Figure 417. Dorsal view of nervous system of frog.

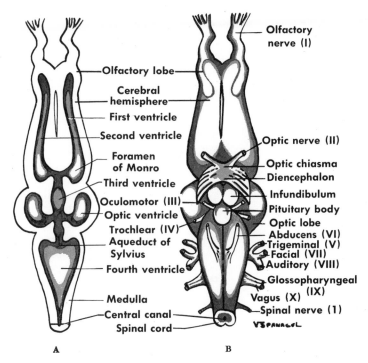

Figure 418. Brain of frog. **A,** Longitudinal section, showing dorsal view of ventricles. **B,** Ventral view of brain and cranial nerves.

The brain and spinal cord are well protected by bone, for the brain is confined to the cranium of the skull and the spinal cord to the neural canal of the vertebral column. Both the brain and the spinal cord are surrounded by two connective tissue membranes, called **meninges.** Next to the bone is the **dura mater,** a relatively tough structure; close against the nervous tissue is the **pia mater,** more delicate, pigmented, and vascular. When exposed, the brain reveals dorsally the following structures.

1. Two **cerebral hemispheres,** long oval bodies that are constricted into the **olfactory lobes** at their anterior ends. The hemispheres are the seat of memory and perhaps other faculties not very advanced in the frog. The olfactory lobes are concerned with the sense of smell.

2. **Diencephalon,** or 'tween-brain, a depressed region behind the cerebral hemispheres that gives rise to the **pineal body,** a delicate stalk that runs to the **brow**

spot. The diencephalon is concerned with balance and vision.

3. Two **optic lobes,** prominent rounded bodies posterior to the diencephalon and resting on the **midbrain.** They inhibit spinal cord reflexes.

4. **Cerebellum,** a transverse ridgelike body that is much smaller in frogs than in most other vertebrates. It controls equilibrium.

5. **Medulla oblongata,** that part of the brain connected to the spinal cord. The frog is less dependent upon its brain for body activities than are higher vertebrates. If its medulla is intact it can still do most of the things a frog can do.

A ventral view of the brain reveals these additional structures:

1. **Optic chiasma,** the crossing of the optic nerves after their origin from the diencephalon.

2. **Infundibulum,** a bilobed extension of the diencephalon, just posterior to the optic chiasma which bears the hypophysis.

3. **Pituitary,** or **hypophysis,** a rounded

Phylum Chordata—the frog as a vertebrate type 503

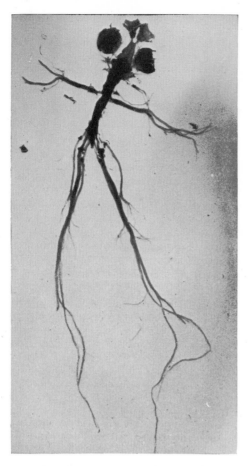

Figure 419. Nervous system of frog prepared by a maceration method of nitric acid. Note eyes and olfactory capsules.

glandular body posterior to the infundibulum. This is an important endocrine gland which helps regulate many of the body functions.

The cavities, or **ventricles,** of the brain are four in number. The first two are inside the cerebral hemispheres. These connect to the third ventricle in the diencephalon by a narrow passage, the interventricular foramen. From the third ventricle a small aqueduct of Sylvius leads to the large fourth ventricle in the medulla oblongata. The optic ventricles of the optic lobes open into the aqueduct of Sylvius. **Cerebrospinal fluid** circulates through these ventricles, through the hollow spinal cord, and in the spaces between the meninges. Two important plexuses of blood vessels are found in connection with the surface of the brain: the **anterior choroid plexus** over the diencephalon and the **posterior choroid plexus** over the medulla. These structures are concerned with the nourishment and metabolism of the brain.

The spinal cord is a continuation of the medulla oblongata and occupies the neural canal of the vertebral column. Posteriorly it ends as a fine, nonnervous filament, **filum terminale,** in the urostyle. It is enlarged in two places, the **brachial enlargement** opposite the forelimb and the **sciatic** or **lumbar enlargement** anterior to the filum terminale. These are associated with the greater nerve supply to the limbs and are absent in fish and snakes. The spinal cord has **dorsal** and **ventral fissures,** as well as a **central canal,** which is a continuation of the ventricles of the brain. The outer portion of the spinal cord is **white matter** composed of nerve fibers; the inner portion is **gray matter** consisting chiefly of nerve cells. The cord gives rise laterally to ten pairs of **spinal nerves** which leave the neural canal between the vertebrae to be distributed on the dorsal wall of the abdomen just under the peritoneum. Each spinal nerve is attached to the cord by two roots, a **dorsal sensory root** and a **ventral motor root.** The sensory root carries impulses into the spinal cord and the motor root carries impulses out from the cord to the body. On each side the second spinal nerve and branches of the first and third nerves combine near the cord to form the **brachial plexus** which sends nerves to the forelimbs and shoulder region. The seventh to ninth nerves on either side form the **sciatic plexus** which innervates the hind limb.

The **peripheral nervous system** is made up of the spinal nerves already described and the **cranial** nerves of the brain. The autonomic nervous system is sometimes included in this division. In the frog there are ten pairs of cranial nerves. These arise from the lateral and ventral surfaces of the brain and make their way through the foramina of the skull to the head, throat, and trunk. Fish share with frogs the possession of ten pairs of cranial nerves, whereas the higher vertebrates—reptiles, birds, and mammals—have twelve pairs. An additional pair of cranial nerves, the **nervus terminalis,** has been found in some vertebrates. Found at the anterior end of the brain, it carries sensory impulses from the skin and blood vessels of the nasal region to the brain. The nervus terminalis is not often included among cranial nerves at present.

The nerves, origin, distribution, and functions of the frog cranial nerves are given in Table 6.

The **sympathetic nervous system** in the frog consists of a pair of slender nerve trunks which start at the cranium and run along the dorsal wall of the coelomic cavity. Each trunk has **ten ganglia** which are connected by nerves (**rami communicantes**) with the adjacent spinal nerves. From these ganglia branches are given off, many of them uniting to form plexuses (solar, urogenital, etc.) which distribute nerves to the stomach, liver, kidneys, intestines, and many other visceral organs. The chief role of the sympathetic system is to regulate many internal involuntary functions, such as the heartbeat, movements of the alimentary canal, secretions of the digestive juices, tone of blood vessels, action of the urogenital, respiratory, and reproductive systems, etc.

Sensory system

The sensory system of the frog is made up of sense organs, or receptors, which receive information of changes in the external or internal environment. These

Table 6. Cranial nerves of frog—origin, distribution, and function

No.	Name	Origin	Distribution	Function
0	Terminal	Forebrain	Lining of nose	Sensory (probably)
I	Olfactory	Olfactory lobe	Lining of nose	Sensory for smelling
II	Optic	Diencephalon	Retina of eye	Sensory for vision
III	Oculomotor	Ventral side of midbrain	Four muscles of eyes	Motor
IV	Trochlear	Dorsal side of midbrain	Superior oblique muscle of eye	Motor
V	Trigeminal	Side of medulla	Muscles of jaw; skin of face and mouth; tongue	Sensory and motor
VI	Abducens	Ventral region of medulla	External rectus muscle of eye	Motor
VII	Facial	Side of medulla	Chiefly muscles of face	Motor and sensory, mostly motor
VIII	Auditory (acoustic)	Side of medulla	Inner ear	Sensory for hearing and equilibrium
IX	Glossopharyngeal	Side of medulla	Tongue, hyoid, pharynx	Sensory and motor
X	Vagus, or pneumogastric	Side of medulla	Larynx, lungs, heart, esophagus, stomach, intestine	Sensory and motor

changes are manifested as stimuli acting upon the specialized receptors (sense organs). Sensory nerves carry the nervous impulses aroused by the stimuli to the central nervous system where they are interpreted by the frog as characteristic sensations. The receptors of the frog include (1) the sense organs of the skin, (2) the sense organs of the mouth, and (3) the more specialized sense receptors of smell (olfactory), hearing (ear), and vision (eye).

Sense organs of skin. Both the epidermis and dermis of the frog's skin are richly supplied with nerve endings. Some of these endings are merely a network of nerves scattered among the cells; others are in the form of compact **corpuscles** mostly embedded in the dermis and projecting into papillae of the epidermis. The skin is sensitive to many kinds of stimuli, such as touch, chemicals, temperature, humidity, and light. The tadpole has a **lateral line** system which is similar to that of fish and is concerned with vibrations in the water, but this system is absent in the adult.

Sense organs of mouth. The mouth epithelium contains many general nerve endings whose functions are not very well known, but there are many **taste buds** on the tongue and on the floor and roof of the mouth. The taste buds are located on the surface of the fungiform papillae and are concerned with tasting or sampling the food which is taken into the mouth.

Specialized sense receptors. **Smell** in the frog is located in the **olfactory epithelium** lining the nasal cavity. **Olfactory cells** have tufts of fine cilia on their outer ends and nerve connections on their inner ends.

Frogs have only two portions of the vertebrate ear, the middle and the internal. The external ear is absent in frogs. The middle ear is closed externally by the **tympanic membrane,** or eardrum, which is a conspicuous structure on frogs. Just underneath the eardrum is the cavity of the middle ear which communicates with the mouth through the Eustachian tube. Connecting the eardrum to the internal ear is a rod-shaped **columella** which extends across the cavity of the middle ear and transmits vibrations of the tympanic membrane to the oval window of the internal ear. The latter is a membranous labyrinth surrounded by cartilage and bone. It is filled with a fluid, **endolymph,** and bears the sensory nerve endings of the auditory (eighth) cranial nerve. Sound waves transmitted to the inner ear cause the endolymph to vibrate and sound impressions are registered by the sensory end organs of the auditory nerve. The sense of equilibrium is taken care of in the inner ear by the **semicircular canals** which are filled with fluid. The pressure of this fluid stimulates certain nerve endings which carry the impulses over a branch of the auditory nerve to the brain where they are interpreted as sensations of equilibrium.

The **eye** is specialized for responding to light. The frog's eyes are built on the same plan as those of man. The eyeballs are globular in form and are placed in the orbits, where each eye is manipulated by six muscles attached to its posterior wall. Two of these muscles are called the **external oblique** and the **internal oblique** muscles, and the other four are called the **rectus** muscles. The outer covering of the eyeball is the tough white **sclerotic coat** of connective tissue which is modified anteriorly to form the transparent **cornea.** Underneath this coat is the **choroid coat,** pigmented and vascular, which has an opening in its pigmented **iris,** the **pupil.** The innermost coat is the **retina,** containing the sensory **rods** and **cones.** Light impulses are carried from the rods and cones by means of the optic nerve (second cranial) to the brain. Behind the pupil, which contracts or dilates to regulate the amount of light entering, is the spherical crystalline **lens.** Unlike the lens of the human eye, the frog's lens does not change its shape or position, so the frog's eye can form images of objects only beyond a certain distance. The lens is held in place by the **ciliary processes** which extend from the lens to the choroid wall. The region over the cornea and beneath the lids is lined with the transparent **conjunctiva.** A third eyelid, a thin membranous **nictitating membrane,** can be drawn up over the eye for protection. A more detailed description of the eye structure will be found in Chapter 33.

Digestive system

The plan of the digestive system of the frog is similar in most respects to that of other vertebrate animals. Its primary function is to break up by physical and chemical means the complex foods into products that can be absorbed and used by the body—a process known as **digestion.** The general pattern of the system consists of a tube with specialized compartments extending from mouth to anus, together with digestive glands which secrete the important digestive ferments, the **enzymes.**

The first part of the digestive system is the **mouth,** or **buccal,** cavity which secretes mucus for lubricating the food, for there are no salivary glands in the frog.

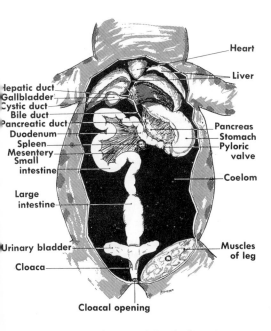

Figure 420. Ventral view of frog's digestive system. Liver lobes pushed aside to show gallbladder.

Back of the mouth is the dilated region known as the **pharynx** which leads into the short but highly distensible **esophagus.** The latter is provided with some glands and with muscular walls which force the food along toward the **cardiac end** of the **stomach.** The stomach, crescent shaped and tapering toward the **pyloric end,** is an organ for storage and digestion of food. It is fastened to the dorsal wall of the peritoneal cavity by a mesentery, the **mesogaster.** The stomach has relatively thick walls compared with the rest of the alimentary canal. Its walls show in cross-section the following four layers from without in: (1) the **serosa,** a thin outer layer of peritoneum; (2) the **muscularis,** a thin layer of longitudinal muscles (mostly connective tissue) and an inner layer of circular muscle; (3) the **submucosa,** connective tissue containing blood vessels and nerves; and (4) the **mucosa,** the stomach lining of columnar epithelium and glands.

Stomach glands are unicellular and multicellular. The multicellular, or gastric, glands of the cardiac end are long and branched, whereas those of the pyloric end are shorter. The product of these glands is acid in reaction because of the presence of free hydrochloric acid, and it contains the enzyme **pepsin** which breaks down proteins to soluble **peptones.** Fats and carbohydrates are not acted upon in the stomach. The **pyloric sphincter** is the constriction between the stomach and the small intestine.

The small intestine is made up of the short **duodenum** and the longer, **coiled ileum.** Its walls have about the same layers as the stomach. The small intestine is attached to the mid-dorsal wall by mesenteries. Into the duodenum the **common bile duct** from the gallbladder and the **pancreatic duct** from the pancreas empty by a common opening. Bile, which emulsifies fat, is a secretion of the liver and is stored in the gallbladder before being poured into the intestine. Pancreatic juice is an alkaline fluid which contains a number of enzymes, such as **trypsin,** which acts upon protein; **lipase,** which acts on fats;

and **amylopsin,** which acts upon carbohydrates. **Intestinal** juice may be produced by glands of the small intestine, and it probably contains such enzymes as **erepsin** (proteins) and **maltase** (carbohydrates). Most digestion and absorption take place in the small intestine. The undigested residue passes from the small intestine into the large intestine. Emptying of the rectum is called **egestion** (*not* excretion).

The wider large intestine is the storage place for **feces,** the rejected and undigested part of the food. The posterior part of the large intestine opens into the **cloaca,** which also receives the ducts of the urogenital system. The cloaca opens to the outside by the **cloacal opening.** The large intestine is supported by a part of the digestive tract mesentery, the **mesorectum.**

Circulatory system

The circulatory system of the frog is a closed system carrying red blood in its circuit. Its principal functions are to carry digested food products to the tissues, to carry oxygen from the lungs and skin to the various organs, to carry carbon dioxide and other waste products away from the tissues, and to carry hormones and blood sugar to wherever they are needed. The system is made up of a heart, arteries, capillaries, veins, lymphatic vessels, and the fluid medium, blood and lymph.

Blood contains a colorless liquid, the **plasma,** in which are suspended various types of cells, the formed elements of the blood. Blood plasma is formed of water, blood proteins, salts, sugars, various waste products, and other soluble substances. Plasma has the power to coagulate whenever a blood vessel is injured and the blood comes in contact with a foreign substance. In this process the spindle cells, or **thrombocytes,** in the plasma release an enzyme, **thrombin,** which changes fibrinogen (one of the blood proteins) into the insoluble **fibrin.** Fibrin, with the blood corpuscles, forms the **clot.** The formed elements of the blood include (1) the **erythrocytes,** or red corpuscles, which are elliptical in shape, nucleated, bear the respiratory pigment **hemoglobin,** and are about 22 microns long; (2) the **leukocytes,** or white corpuscles, which are colorless and nucleated and are of different types; and (3) the spindle cells, or **thrombocytes,** which are elongated and nucleated. The red corpuscles, which number from 250,000 to 450,000 per cubic millimeter of blood, are mainly responsible for carrying oxygen; the white corpuscles (about 5,000 to 7,000 per cubic

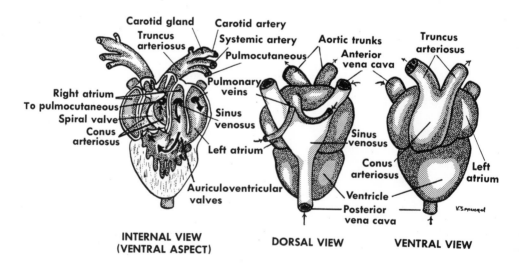

Figure 421. Structure of frog's heart.

508

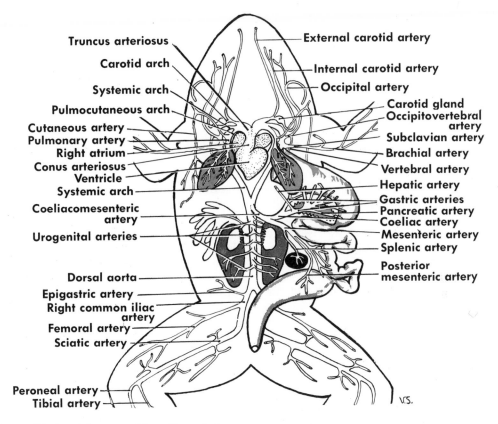

Figure 422. Arterial system of frog. Ventral view.

millimeter) are phagocytic against bacteria; and the spindle cells may be involved in blood clotting or the formation of red corpuscles. The various blood cells are formed in **bone marrow** and in the **spleen;** the latter also destroys the worn-out cells.

The **heart** is the pump responsible for driving the blood through the blood circuit. It is a muscular organ provided with three chambers and lies in the anterior part of the body cavity, just ventral to the liver. It is enclosed in a two-layered sac, the **pericardium.** The heart consists, posteriorly, of a single conical **ventricle** with thick walls, two anterior **atria** (auricles) with thin walls, a triangular **sinus venosus** on the dorsal surface of the heart, and the large, tubular **conus arteriosus** on the ventral surface. The chambers are separated by valves to keep the blood

flowing in one direction. Between the atria and the ventricle on the outside there is a marked constriction, the **auriculoventricular groove,** and between the left and right atria on the inside is the **interatrial septum.** The action of the heart can best be understood by following the course of the blood through the heart. Blood is brought by the venous system to the sinus venosus, which forces it into the right atrium. The left atrium receives blood from the lungs. Contraction of the two atria then drives the blood into the ventricle. For a long time it was thought that the **spiral valve** in the conus arteriosus directed the blood from the right atrium (the first blood to enter the ventricle) into the pulmocutaneous arches and the blood from the left atrium into the systemic and carotid arches. In this way the unoxygenated blood would be shunted to the lungs and skin for oxygen, while the oxygenated blood would be sent to the body tissue. Experimental evidence shows that the two kinds of blood actually mix and that some of the unoxygenated blood is pumped to the tissues along with the oxygenated blood. Contraction of the heart is called **systole**; its relaxation is termed **diastole**.

The **arterial** system (Figure 422) of the frog may be said to begin with the **truncus arteriosus** which divides into left and right branches, each of which subdivides into three arches: the **pulmocutaneous**, the **systemic**, and the **common carotid**. Each pulmocutaneous branch gives rise to a **pulmonary artery** to the lungs and a **cutaneous artery** to the skin for oxygenation of the blood. Each common carotid arch gives off the small **external carotid**, or lingual, to the tongue and adjacent regions and the larger **internal carotid** with

its enlarged **carotid glands.** The internal carotid gives rise to the **palatine** to the roof of the mouth, the **cerebral carotid** to the brain, and **ophthalmic** to the eye.

The two systemic arches pass dorsally around the alimentary canal and unite to form the **dorsal aorta,** which runs toward the posterior part of the body. In its course each systemic arch gives off the **laryngeal** to the throat region, the **occipitovertebral** to the back of the skull, the upper jaw, and the vertebral column, the **subclavian,** which goes to the shoulder region and continues as the **brachial** to the arm. The **dorsal aorta** runs just underneath the vertebral column and gives off the **coeliacomesenteric,** which quickly branches into the **coeliac** to the stomach, pancreas, and liver; and the **anterior mesenteric** to the intestine, spleen, and cloaca. Posterior to the coeliacomesenteric a number of **urogenital arteries** arise from

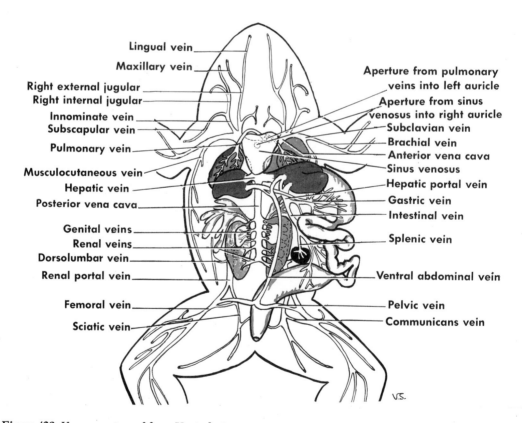

Figure 423. Venous system of frog. Ventral view.

the dorsal aorta and pass to the kidneys and reproductive organs. Near these arteries, but originating from the dorsal wall of the aorta, are the **lumbar arteries** running to the dorsal body wall. Toward the end of the dorsal aorta the single **posterior mesenteric** passes to the large intestine, and just behind this artery the dorsal aorta bifurcates into the two large arteries, the **common iliacs.** Each common iliac gives rise to (1) the **epigastric** to the ventral body wall, (2) the **rectovesical** to the rectum and bladder, (3) the **femoral** to the hip and upper thigh, and (4) the **sciatic** to the leg regions.

The **venous** system (Figure 423) includes those blood vessels in which the blood flows toward the heart. Veins are usually thinner but are larger in diameter than corresponding arteries. The left atrium of the heart receives blood from the lungs through the **pulmonary veins;** the **sinus venosus** receives blood from three large trunks: the paired **anterior venae cavae** and the single **posterior vena cava.** Each anterior vena cava collects blood from (1) the **external juglar,** which drains the region of the tongue and floor of the mouth; (2) the **innominate,** which receives blood from the head by way of the **internal juglar** and from the shoulder by way of the **subscapular;** and (3) the **subclavian,** which receives blood from the forelimb by means of the **brachial** and from the side of the head and body by the **musculocutaneous.** The **posterior vena cava** receives two large **hepatic** veins from the liver, **renal veins** from the kidney, and **spermatic** or **ovarian** veins from the reproductive organs. Two **portal** systems are found in the frog. Such a system does not return the venous blood directly to the heart but to a capillary system in some organ from whence another vein returns the blood to the heart. One of these is the **hepatic portal system** which picks up the blood from the stomach and intestine and carries it to a sinusoid system in the liver. The blood is then passed on to the hepatic veins which enter the posterior vena cava. The purpose of the hepatic portal system is to carry the digested food products to the liver which either stores them or acts upon them in some way before releasing them to the circulation. Connected to the hepatic portal vein in the region of the liver is the **ventral abdominal vein,** which is formed by the union of the two **pelvic veins** from the hind limbs and by veins from the bladder and ventral body wall. The other portal system is the **renal portal system,** which carries blood to a capillary system in the kidneys. It is made up of two **renal portal veins,** which pass to the outer margins of the kidneys. Each renal portal vein receives the **femoral** and **sciatic** veins from the thigh and the **dorsolumbar veins** from the back. By this plan the blood from the hind limbs may return to the heart either by way of the ventral abdominal vein to the liver (hepatic portal system) or by way of the kidneys (renal portal system). There is no renal portal system in man.

Capillaries are the small blood vessels that connect the arteries with the veins. Whenever an artery approaches a capillary bed it branches into **arterioles** which, by contraction and dilation of their muscular walls, largely regulate the supply of blood to an organ. Arterioles subdivide into capillaries which are provided with thin walls for the exchange of materials between the blood and tissues. For the defense of the body white blood corpuscles can migrate through the walls (**diapedesis**) into the tissues, from whence they are carried back into the blood by the lymphatic system. To complete the circuit through the capillaries small **venules** join to form the veins that carry the blood toward the heart. To see capillary action at its best advantage the networks in the web of the frog's foot is a classical demonstration.

The **lymphatic system** of the frog is more primitive than that of higher vertebrates. There are an abundance of subcutaneous lymph sinuses all over the body, especially under the skin, which partly accounts for the looseness of the skin. The lymph spaces are separated by connective tissue septa, and the larger ones are lined with thin endothelial cells.

One of the most important is the **sub-vertebral lymph sinus** (**cisterna magna**) which extends above the kidneys along most of the dorsal body wall. The colorless **lymph** contains leukocytes and various constituents of blood plasma. It is formed by the filtering of blood plasma through the capillaries. Lymph flow is sluggish and inconstant but is aided by the pulsating of two pairs of **lymph hearts.** One pair, found near the transverse processes of the third vertebra, pumps lymph into the vertebral vein of the internal jugular; the other pair, on either side of the tip of the urostyle, pumps the lymph into a branch of the renal portal veins. The lymphatic system functions as an accessory transportation system between the blood and the tissues.

Respiratory system

Respiration is effected in the frog both through the moist surface of the outer skin and through the lungs, with some gaseous exchange taking place through the lining of the buccal cavity. The lungs, of course, are the most important, but when the frog is hibernating, the skin does most of the breathing. The skin can function both in and out of water. Whether through the skin or lungs, the basic plan is the same, for before oxygen can diffuse into the blood it must first dissolve in a moist surface. That is why frogs stay where their skin remains moist and does not dry out.

The respiratory system (Figure 424) of the frog consists of the external nares, nasal cavities, internal nares, mouth, glottis, larynx, two bronchi, and two lungs.

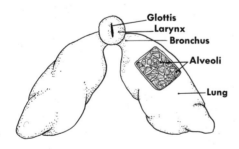

Figure 424. Respiratory organs of frog.

The **glottis,** a slitlike structure in the mouth cavity, opens into the **larynx,** or voice box. The larynx has cartilages to reinforce it and is provided with the elastic vocal cord by which the frog can make its sounds. From the larynx a short bronchus leads to each lung. The lungs are ovoid, saclike, and elastic. Their inner surfaces are divided by a network of folds into small chambers called **alveoli,** the walls of which are richly supplied with blood vessels for the gaseous exchange. The alveoli are lined with thin epithelium. The lungs are covered with peritoneum. Respiration involves two phases, **inspiration** and **expiration.** To draw air into the lungs (inspiration), the frog closes its glottis and depresses the floor of its mouth. This enlargement of the mouth cavity draws air through the nares into the mouth. By closing the external nares and compressing the mouth chamber the air is now forced through the opened glottis into the lungs. To force the air out (expiration), the flanks are drawn in, compressing the lungs and forcing out the air. In addition to the phases of inspiration and expiration, the frog performs certain oscillatory throat movements by which air passed in and out of the mouth through the nares. During this process the glottis remains closed, and no air enters or leaves the lungs, but gaseous exchange takes place through the mucous membrane lining of the buccal cavity. Also, the air thus drawn in and out of the mouth renovates the air discharged from the lungs after each expiration. When a frog is at rest, these throat movements may continue for some time before the flank movements indicate that the lungs are being emptied.

Excretory system

Excretion is the removal of the end products of metabolism. Frogs, in common with other vertebrates, have a number of organs for the disposal of waste, such as the skin, lungs, bile of the liver, and, more especially, the regular excretory system. The latter is made up of two kidneys, certain ducts (ureters), and a

512

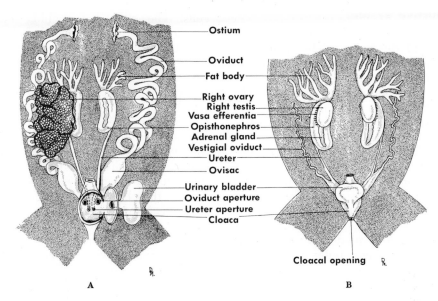

Figure 425. Urogenital system of frog, *Rana pipiens*. **A,** Female; **B,** male. Ventral view. Male leopard frog is only common frog that has vestigial oviduct, which indicates that in early embryo there are beginnings of organs of both sexes (bisexuality).

Labels: Ostium / Oviduct / Fat body / Right ovary / Right testis / Vasa efferentia / Opisthonephros / Adrenal gland / Vestigial oviduct / Ureter / Ovisac / Urinary bladder / Oviduct aperture / Ureter aperture / Cloaca / Cloacal opening

urinary bladder. Because of the intimate association of the excretory and reproductive systems in the frog they are often considered together as the **urogenital system** (Figure 425). The **kidneys** (opisthonephroi) are two flat, reddish organs lying dorsal to the coelom and peritoneum in the large lymph space, **cisterna magna.** On the ventral surface of each kidney is the **adrenal** gland (an endocrine gland to be referred to later). The histological structure of a kidney reveals about 2,000 units or **nephrons.** Each nephron consists of (1) a **renal corpuscle** containing a double-walled Bowman's capsule enclosing a knot of capillaries (glomerulus) and (2) a **uriniferous tubule** surrounded by capillaries. The role of these nephrons is the separation of waste and certain other products from the blood by the process of filtering, etc.

The various uriniferous tubules of a kidney join collecting tubules which enter the **ureter,** or Wolffian duct, which runs along the lower lateral margin of the kidney to the dorsal wall of the **cloaca.** The liquid waste, **urine,** passes down the ureters into the cloaca, where it passes to the outside through the anus or else is stored temporarily in the bilobed, thin-walled bladder which is attached to the ventral side of the cloaca. Interesting histological structures known as **nephrostomes** are found on the ventral surface of the kidney. They are ciliated funnels which open by one end into the coelom and by the other into the renal veins or, in tadpoles, into the uriniferous tubules. They pass waste from the coelom to the blood and represent an interesting stage in the evolution of the nephron.

Endocrine system

Endocrine glands produce hormones, which are diffused directly into the blood or lymph instead of being discharged upon a surface by ducts. **Hormones** have an important role in stimulating or inhibiting other parts of the body. The frog probably has most of the endocrine glands characteristic of higher vertebrates. The action of these glands, however, is better known in higher animals. Vertebrate endocrine glands and their hormones will be discussed in Chapter 32.

Reproductive system

Morphologically the sexes in frogs show few external differences. The male possesses vocal sacs, which are noticeable when in use, and the nuptial pads on the inner digits of the forelegs. These are lacking in the female. Internally, however, there are marked differences between the male and female reproductive systems.

The **male reproductive system** (Figure 425) consists of two testes and a series of tubules for carrying the sperm from the testes. Each **testis** is a whitish, oval body attached by a mesentery (mesorchium) near the anteroventral surface of the kidney. Each testis is made up of a coiled mass of **seminiferous tubules** in which the sperm are produced. From each testis a number of delicate tubules, the **vasa efferentia,** pass through the mesorchium, penetrate the inner margin of the kidney, and connect onto the anterior uriniferous tubules. The ureter, or Wolffian duct, serves to convey the sperm down to the cloaca. The posterior end of the ureter is enlarged as a **seminal vesicle** in which the sperm may be stored temporarily. The ureter in the male thus serves a double function, for it carries urine from the kidneys and sperm from the testes. Near the anterior end of the testes are the yellowish, much-branched **fat bodies** which provide food reserves for hibernation and for the functioning of the sex glands. A pair of vestigial structures, the Müllerian ducts, which are homologous to the oviducts in the female, are found as small wavy tubes near the kidneys. They enter the cloaca near the ureters.

The **female reproductive system** (Figure 425) of the frog is made up of two ovaries and two oviducts for carrying the eggs to the cloaca. Each ovary is fastened to the dorsal body wall of the coelom by a mesentery (**mesovarium**). In the inactive condition each ovary is a small grayish mass; during the mating season it is a large swollen gland filled with large numbers of dark round eggs. In structure an ovary is a lobed hollow sac made up of a double wall. Between the layers of this wall the eggs lie enclosed in follicles of cells. The ciliated funnel-like openings (**ostia**) of the two **oviducts** do not connect directly to the ovaries but are placed anteriorly in the body cavity near the lungs. The oviducts are whitish in color, much convoluted, and provided with glands which secrete gelatinous coats around the eggs. Just before entering the cloaca, the oviducts are dilated into enlargements, the **ovisacs**, where the eggs are collected before being discharged to the outside through the cloaca. When the ripe eggs ovulate they break through the thin ovarian walls into the body cavity. By the action of the cilia which cover the peritoneum and by muscular movements of the abdominal cavity, the eggs are moved anteriorly to the ostia. Within the oviducts the eggs are moved down by ciliary action and pick up their gelatinous coats in their passage.

Life cycle

Frogs are cold-blooded (poikilothermous) animals and thus their body temperature depends upon the environment. Their distribution and activities are therefore controlled by seasonal changes and climatic conditions. Their activities are restricted to the warmer seasons of the year, when they breed, feed, and grow. During the winter months in colder climates they spend their time in hibernation. During hibernation they are lethargic, do not feed, and live upon their food reserves (fat bodies, glycogen of liver, etc.). Naturally their metabolic states are at a very low ebb at this time. Their breathing is slow, their heartbeat is decreased, and their body temperature is only slightly above that of their surroundings.

The time of spring emergence varies with different species. One of their first interests after leaving their dormant period is breeding. At this time the males are very vociferous with their croaking, for which the males of many species have vocal sacs to increase the amplitude of their sounds. Although the females are mostly silent during this time, they have the power to croak, which they do when

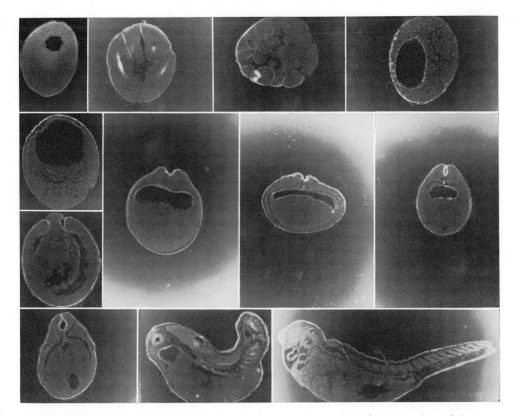

Figure 426. Embryology of frog. Upper row, left to right: unfertilized egg, early and late cleavage, and blastula. Second row, left to right: gastrula, with yolk plug stage below it, and three stages of developing neural grove. Third row: neural tube stage and two tadpole stages. (Courtesy Charles Alender.)

they are seized by predators or when in pain. The breeding season usually extends for several weeks. When their eggs are ripe, the females enter the water and are mounted and clasped by the males in the process called **amplexus.** The male holds the female by pressing the nuptial pads of his thumbs against her breast just back of her forelegs. As the female lays her eggs, the male discharges his seminal fluid containing the sperm over the eggs. The sperm, by movements of their tails, work their way through the jelly layers of the eggs and come in contact with the egg. Only one spermatozoan is necessary to fertilize an egg, and when one penetrates the egg, other sperm in the immediate vicinity are kept out by changes in the egg substance. After fertilization, the jelly layers absorb water and swell. Eggs

are laid in great masses, which may include several thousands in the leopard frog. The egg masses are usually anchored to vegetation or debris by the sticky jelly layers around the eggs. Not all the eggs have a chance to develop, for some may not be fertilized and others are eaten by turtles, insects, and other enemies.

Development of the fertilized egg (zygote) begins about two to three hours after fertilization. The process involves cleavage, or segmentation of the egg. Cleavage occurs more rapidly at the black, or animal, pole, for there is more protoplasm there. The yolk or white (vegetative) pole delays the process of cleavage. Because of this inequality of cell division there gradually result many small cells at the animal pole side of the egg and fewer larger cells at the vegeta-

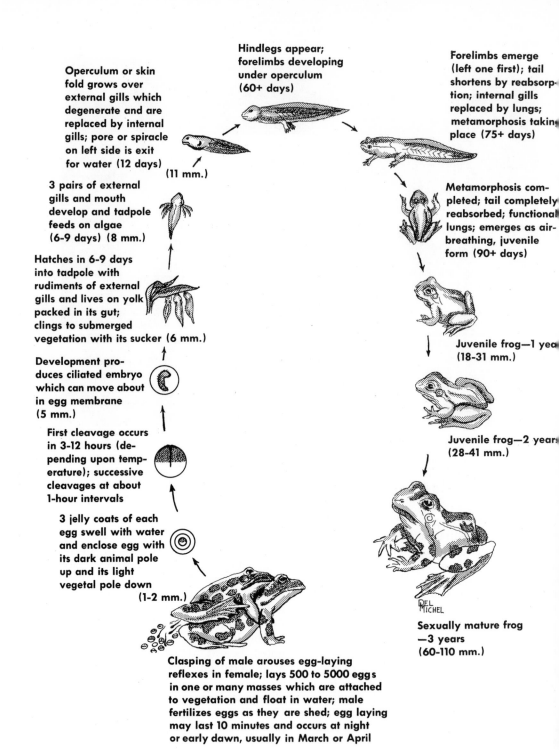

Hindlegs appear; forelimbs developing under operculum (60+ days)

Forelimbs emerge (left one first); tail shortens by reabsorption; internal gills replaced by lungs; metamorphosis taking place (75+ days)

Operculum or skin fold grows over external gills which degenerate and are replaced by internal gills; pore or spiracle on left side is exit for water (12 days)

(11 mm.)

3 pairs of external gills and mouth develop and tadpole feeds on algae (6-9 days) (8 mm.)

Metamorphosis completed; tail completely reabsorbed; functional lungs; emerges as air-breathing, juvenile form (90+ days)

Hatches in 6-9 days into tadpole with rudiments of external gills and lives on yolk packed in its gut; clings to submerged vegetation with its sucker (6 mm.)

Development produces ciliated embryo which can move about in egg membrane (5 mm.)

Juvenile frog—1 year (18-31 mm.)

First cleavage occurs in 3-12 hours (depending upon temperature); successive cleavages at about 1-hour intervals

Juvenile frog—2 years (28-41 mm.)

3 jelly coats of each egg swell with water and enclose egg with its dark animal pole up and its light vegetal pole down (1-2 mm.)

DEL MICHEL

Sexually mature frog —3 years (60-110 mm.)

Clasping of male arouses egg-laying reflexes in female; lays 500 to 5000 eggs in one or many masses which are attached to vegetation and float in water; male fertilizes eggs as they are shed; egg laying may last 10 minutes and occurs at night or early dawn, usually in March or April

Figure 427. Life cycle of frog.

tive pole. By collecting masses of frog eggs early in the morning it is possible to find eggs in various stages of development, such as two-, four-, and eight-cell stages. Generally one finds them still further along in development. Factors such as temperature influence the rate of development. Eggs usually hatch into tadpoles within a period of three to twenty days. At the time of hatching, the tadpole has a distinct head and body with compressed tail. The mouth is located on the ventral side of the head and is provided with horny jaws for scraping off vegetation from objects for food. Behind the mouth is a ventral adhesive disc for clinging to objects. In front of the mouth are two deep pits which later develop into the nostrils. Swellings are found on either side of the head and these later become external gills. There are finally three pairs of external gills which are later replaced by three pairs of internal gills within the gill slits. On the left side of the neck region is an opening, the **spiracle,** through which water passes after entering the mouth and over the internal gills. Of the limbs, the hind legs appear first, while the forelimbs are hidden by the folds of the operculum. In time the forelimbs break through the skin, the left leg usually coming out first through the spiracle. The process of metamorphosis varies in length for different species of frogs. During this process the tail is resorbed, the intestine becomes much shorter, the mouth undergoes a transformation into the adult condition, lungs are developed, and the gills resorbed. The leopard or meadow frog usually completes its metamorphosis within a year or less; the bullfrog takes two or three years to complete the process.

ANNOTATED REFERENCES

Holmes, S. J. 1928. The Biology of the Frog, ed. 4. New York, The Macmillan Co. *A standard reference book on frogs for the elementary student. Stresses their structure and behavior.*

Marshall, A. M. 1928. The Frog, ed. 12. New York, The Macmillan Co. *The well-known English work on the morphology of the frog. Practical and descriptive directions.*

Noble, G. K. 1931. The Biology of the Amphibia. New York, McGraw-Hill Book Co., Inc. *Morphology, behavior, and classification of frogs and other amphibians.*

Orton, G. L. 1952. Key to the Genera of Tadpoles in the United States and Canada. The American Midland Naturalist, vol. 47, pp. 382-395.

Parker, G. H. 1948. Animal Colour Changes and Their Neurohumours. Cambridge, Cambridge University Press. *Parts of this work on the color changes of animals are devoted to the amphibians.*

Schmidt, K. P. 1953. A Checklist of North American Amphibians and Reptiles. American Society of Ichthyologists and Herpetologists. Chicago, University of Chicago Press. *This work gives the latest scientific names and the distribution of the various species.*

Wright, A. A., and A. H. Wright. 1949. Handbook of Frogs and Toads of the United States and Canada. Ithaca, Comstock Publishing Co. *Authoritative account of the life histories and classification of frogs.*

chapter 27

Phylum Chordata

Class Aves

SUBPHYLUM VERTEBRATA

CLASS AVES*—birds

Birds are one of the most interesting and most widely known groups of animals. There are more than 9,000 species of birds distributed all over the world. Their taxonomy has been thoroughly worked out and most authorities do not expect to find many new species in the future. Birds have wide appeal for amateurs. Bird clubs are found in nearly every community, and enthusiasts never tire of learning about the ecological relations, songs, and identifying characteristics of birds.

Although birds are gifted more than most animals in ease of moving from one habitat to another, some of them are restricted to special regions. One island or mountain valley may have species found nowhere else. These cases, however, are usually exceptional; birds ordinarily range far and take in varied habitats. Many birds have adapted themselves to certain climatic zones and do not stray from them. Thus the arctic and tropic regions have extensive bird life which is unique for those areas.

Birds share with mammals the highest development in the animal kingdom. The nervous system of mammals shows greater advancement, but in most body parts,

---

*A'vez (L. *avis,* a bird).

birds have greater specialization, much of which is correlated with their powers of flight. They are very active forms; this accounts for their higher rate of metabolism and higher body temperature.

Origin and relationships

Since the bones of birds are light and disintegrate quickly, it is only under the most favorable conditions that their remains are preserved as fossils. This explains the difficulty of working out their early relationships. The earliest known bird is *Archaeopteryx,* two specimens of which were found embedded in Jurassic slate in Bavaria several years ago. One of these forms is slightly different from the other and is called *Archaeornis.* This land form was about the size of a crow, with a skull not unlike the skulls of modern birds. There were bony teeth in the jaw sockets, and the jaws were elongated into a beak. The tail was long and bore two rows of feathers set obliquely, and each wing had three fingers, each bearing a claw. The foot consisted of a tarsometatarsus with four digits. With the exception of feathers, these birds had a general resemblance to dinosaurs. Other toothed birds of later geological periods have also been found, especially in the United States. The evidence, therefore, is strikingly in favor of a reptilian ancestor of birds. The ancestors of birds no doubt came from a branch of the archosaurians (the ruling reptiles), which in turn were derived from the thecodonts. Their exact ancestors are not known. Over the years more and more fossil birds have come to light. By 1950 over 700 different fossil species had been recorded. The modernization of birds took place chiefly during the Cretaceous period, and they were thoroughly modern by early Cenozoic times. Two well-known fossil birds, *Ichthyornis* and *Hesperornis*, were obtained from Cretaceous chalk beds of Kansas. Teeth were present in both these forms, and *Hesperornis*, an aquatic form, had almost completely lost its wings. The famous Rancho La Brea asphalt pits of Los Angeles have yielded many fossil birds of great importance.

Adaptive radiation among birds has produced many types for different methods of life. Just when this adaptive radiation occurred is not clear from the fossil record. Paleontologists think that the basic plan of bird structure was determined early in their evolution, because of the restrictions of flight. They believe that few structural changes have occurred in them during the past fifty or sixty million years. But there are evidences that some birds have evolved during the Cenozoic period. Many types have become extinct and have been replaced by others.

Available evidence seems to indicate that birds have evolved from a single ancestor and thus have a **monophyletic** origin. Some authorities have contended that flying birds have had a different origin from flightless forms (**diphyletic** origin).

Existing birds are divided into two groups: (1) **ratite** (Ratitae—ra-ti'tae, L. *ratis*, raft), or those that have a flat sternum with poorly developed pectoral muscles and are flightless and (2) **carinate** (Carinatae—car'i-na"tae, L. *carina*, a keel), or those that have a keeled sternum with large pectoral muscles and can fly. Most paleontologists think that the carinate group are the more primitive and that the flightless forms were derived from those that could fly. Most flightless forms are found where there are few carnivorous enemies, or else where they can outrun predators so that wings are not necessary for ground-feeding birds.

On the basis of the differences between ancient and modern birds, they are commonly divided into the following groups:

Subclass Archaeornithes (ar'chae-or"ni-thes) (Gr. *archios*, ancient, + *ornithos*, bird). This included *Archaepteryx* and possibly one or two other genera.

Subclass Neornithes (ne-or'ni-thes) (Gr. *neos*, new, + *ornithos*, bird). Modern birds are placed in this group. Some extinct species with teeth (Figure 428) are also included here because of their likeness to modern forms.

So far as essential details are concerned, birds as a group present a marvelous uniformity of structure. Many authorities maintain that there is less diversity in the entire class than there is in an order of other animals. Perhaps the uniformity of

Figure 428. Restoration of *Hesperornis*, a toothed bird that lived during Cretaceous period. This bird was an aquatic flightless form, and fossils of it have been found in United States. (Courtesy Chicago Natural History Museum.)

the class is tied up with the closely knit specialized character of the group.

Characteristics

1. Body usually spindle shaped, with four divisions: head, neck, trunk, and tail; **neck disproportionately** long for balancing and food gathering

2. Limbs paired with the **forelimbs usually adapted for flying;** posterior pair variously adapted for perching, walking, and swimming; foot with four toes

3. Epidermal **exoskeleton of feathers** and **leg scales;** thin integument of epidermis and dermis; no sweat glands; oil or preen gland at root of tail; **pinna of ear rudimentary**

4. **Skeleton fully ossified with air cavities or sacs;** skull bones fused with **one occipital condyle;** jaws covered with **horny beak;** small ribs; vertebrae tend to fuse, especially the terminal ones; sternum well developed, with keel or reduced with no keel; **no teeth**

5. Circulatory system of **four-chambered heart** with the **right aortic arch persisting;** reduced renal portal system; nucleated red blood cells

6. Respiration by slightly expansible lungs with thin air sacs among the visceral organs and skeleton; **syrinx (voice box) near junction of trachea and bronchi**

7. Excretory system by metanephric kidney; ureters open into cloaca; **no bladder; urine of urates, semisolid**

8. Sexes separate; testes paired, with the vas deferens opening into the cloaca; **females with left ovary and oviduct;** copulatory organ in ducks, geese, ratites, and a few others.

9. Fertilization internal; **eggs with much yolk and hard calcareous shells;** embryonic membranes in egg during development; **incubation external;** young active at hatching (**precocial**) or helpless and naked (**altricial**)

What is a feather?

Birds are the only animals that have feathers. Feathers are modified from the epidermis just as hair is in mammals and serve for insulation, support of the body

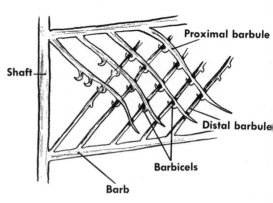

Figure 429. Diagram of interlocking mechanism between adjacent barbs in feather vane of a bird. Minute barbicels (hooklets) hold opposing rows of barbules loosely together to form a continuous surface (vanes).

in flight, protection of the skin, and regulation of body heat. A typical feather consists of a hollow **quill,** or calamus, thrust into the skin and a **shaft,** or rhachis, which is a continuation of the quill and bears the **barbs.** An aftershaft is also present in some birds (grouse, quail) at the junction of the principal shaft and quill. On the sides of each barb are the smaller **barbules,** whose opposing rows are held together by small **barbicels** with hooks (hamuli). Some flightless birds (ostrich) lack this interlocking mechanism and have a fluffy plumage. If the barbs and barbicels form a flat expansive surface, the structure is called a **vane;** when the barbs form only a fluffy mass, it is called **down.** By means of muscles in its skin, a bird can ruffle its feathers.

A feather originates in much the same way as an epidermal scale. Both are formed from a dermal papilla which pushes up against the overlying epidermis (Figure 430). However, instead of flattening like a scale, the feather is rolled into a cylinder or feather bud and is covered with epidermis. This feather bud sinks in slightly at its base and comes to lie in a feather follicle from which the feather will protrude. A layer of keratin is produced around the cylinder or bud and encloses the pulp cavity of blood vessels.

This surface layer of keratin splits away from the deeper layer to form a sheath. The deeper layer now becomes frayed distally to form parallel ridges, the median one of which grows large to form the shaft (contour feathers) and the others the barbs. Then the sheath bursts and the barbs spread flat to form the vane. The pulp cavity of the quill dries up when growth is finished, so that the quill is hollow with openings (umbilici) at its two ends. If the feather is to be a down feather, the sheath bursts and releases the barbs without the formation of a shaft or vane. Pigments (lipochromes and melanins) are added to the epidermal cells during growth in the follicle.

The feathers are divided into three types (Figure 431):

1. The **contour feather** is one of the most typical and consists of a central shaft and parallel barbs, arranged to form a vane. The shaft may be either straight or curved, depending upon the position of the feather in the body. These feathers give shape to the bird's body by the overlapping of the vanes and also afford a good heat-conserving surface. There are several types of contour feathers, such as the wing feathers (**remiges**) which include primaries on the hand, secondaries on the forearm, and tertiaries on the upper arm (humerus), and tail feathers (**retrices**). Each feather is usually covered above and below by rows of other feathers known as **coverts** (Figure 432).

2. **Down feathers** are entirely of down and are found interspersed among the contour feathers. They are useful for increasing insulation. They have short quills and short barbules. They are especially abundant on the breasts and abdomens of certain birds, such as water birds and birds of prey.

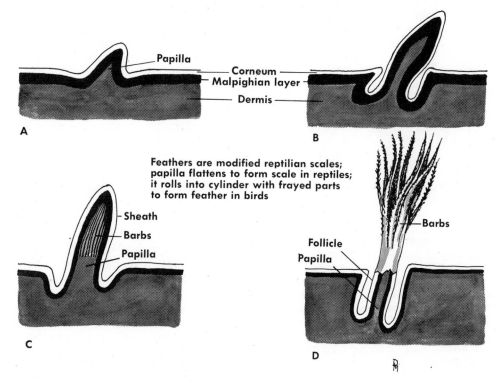

Figure 430. Development of a down feather. **A** to **D** are successive stages. In contour feather one ridge or rib (as in **C**) forms a shaft, and when sheath splits, barbs around medium shaft spread out to form the vane. Pulp cavity of quill or original dermal papilla with blood vessels dries out and forms hollow tube with opening at each end (umbilici).

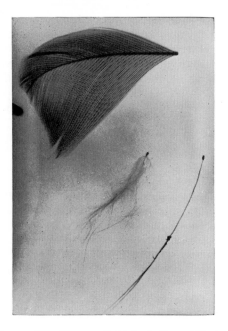

Figure 431. Types of bird feathers. Contour feather above, down feather in middle, and filoplume feather below.

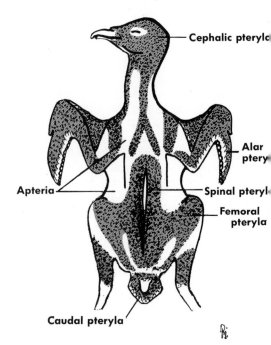

Figure 433. Distribution of feather tracts (pterylosis) of pigeon (dorsal view). Feathers are restricted to certain areas (pterylae); bare areas are called apteria. There are usually eight major feather tracts in birds. In kiwis and penguins feather tracts are lacking and the feathers are uniformly distributed.

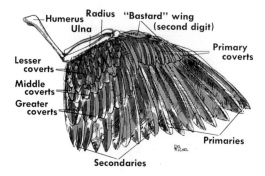

Figure 432. Spread right wing of typical bird. Forelimb of bird modified for flight by changes in carpus and hand. Humerus, ulna, and radius are little changed, but there are only two free carpals (ulnare and radiale); other carpal bones fuse with metacarpals to form carpometacarpus. Of the three digits (2, 3, and 4), second has short metacarpal and one phalanx and bears alula or bastard wing; third has long metacarpal and two phalanges; fourth has one long metacarpal and one phalanx. (Compare with Figure 434.) Note primary flight feathers are supported by the "hand" (digits 3 and 4 and metacarpus), secondary flight feathers by ulna and radius, and tertiary feathers (if present) by humerus.

3. **Filoplume feathers** are a kind of hair feathers in which the shaft is greatly reduced with few or no barbs. They are the pinfeathers which remain on a plucked bird. Modified filoplumes form rictal bristles about the mouth of flycatchers and whippoorwills.

Feathers are distributed over certain areas known as feather tracts, or pterylae (Figure 433). The bare spaces between are the apteria. These tracts are not all of the same pattern, for they vary with different species. In penguins feathers occur all over the skin. The term **plumage** refers to all the feathers collectively. **Molting** is the shedding and replacement of feathers, which is an orderly process that takes place gradually so that bare spots are avoided. At certain seasons, usually spring and fall, the molting continues until it is complete. There are many varia-ions of molting. Usually a bird has four moltings during its first year of life, such as postnatal, postjuvenal, first prenuptial, and first postnuptial. Birds in poor health may omit a molt entirely. A molt usually requires about six weeks.

Feather counts vary greatly with the different species. A hummingbird may have less than 1,000 feathers, whereas a whistling swan may have more than 25,000. The same species may show a seasonal variation in number, the greatest being in the winter. The remiges and retrices are remarkably constant in number.

Advancements made

Although birds are grouped quite often with the reptiles (Sauropsida) and share with the latter many common features, birds have made certain advances of their own. Some of these bird characteristics may not belong strictly to the category of advances and advantages but are developments of structures correlated with the specialized lives of birds. However, some definite advancements have been made by this great class of vertebrates.

1. A high body temperature carefully regulated and correlated with the animals' great energy.

2. A method of locomotion perhaps the most efficient in the animal kingdom.

3. The four-chambered heart initiated in some reptiles (crocodiles) is firmly established in birds, thus ensuring a complete separation of arterial and venous blood in the heart.

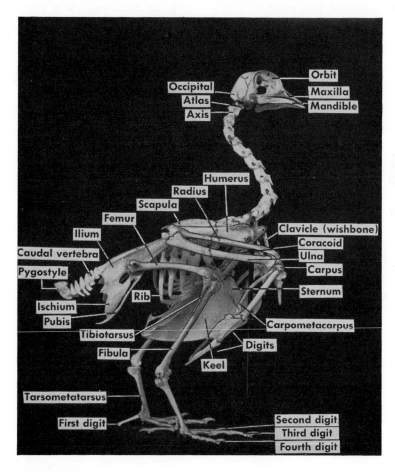

Figure 434. Skeleton of bird.

4. Birds have developed the voice with all the varied features of songs and calls—in striking contrast to the silent reptiles.

5. Finally, birds have developed patterns of behavior, such as parental care of young, nest building, courtship, attachment of mates, migration, etc., which are practically unknown in their near relatives, the reptiles.

Some peculiarities of structure

A highly specialized group of animals such as birds must have many unique features. Many of these peculiarities center around their power of flight. Just as in airplane design, certain things must be stressed to promote efficient flight, so in birds should we expect the same basic plan to be followed. Although birds have the same fundamental blueprint of body structures as other higher forms, they have modified these parts to meet their own unique adaptations.

Skeleton (Figure 434). The bones are light and delicate, although strong, and many contain air cavities. The bird's skeleton affords an interesting study in adaptation. Because of the specialized nature of the forelimb for flying, birds' skulls and jaws are modified for the performance of many of the duties commonly carried on by the forelimbs of mammals. The skull is mostly fused into one piece in the adult. The rounded brain case and orbits are large, and the anterior bones of the skull are elongated to form the beak. The beak is made up of a horny sheath (bill) and the jaws. The upper jaw consists of the enlarged premaxillae, the maxillae, and a few other bones; the lower jaw, or mandible, is a complex of many bones. The lower jaw has a loose articu-

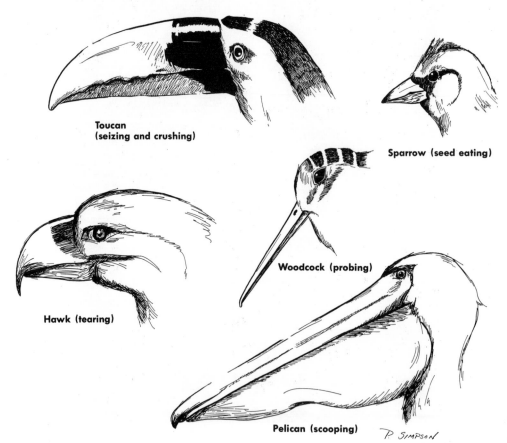

Toucan
(seizing and crushing)

Sparrow (seed eating)

Woodcock (probing)

Hawk (tearing)

Pelican (scooping)

P. SIMPSON

Figure 435. Some bills of birds, showing variety of adaptations.

524

lation with the movable quadrate which connects to the squamosal, making possible a larger mouth opening. Another unique feature of the jaws is the ability of some birds to move the upper jaw. In parrots, for instance, there is actually a movable hinge between the premaxillae and the anterior part of the skull. This is made possible by the arrangement of certain bones (pterygoid, palatine, etc.) between the quadrate and the upper jaw. When the quadrate moves forward the upper jaw is pushed upward. This device ensures greater adaptability of the beak in food manipulation and other performances. The beak of birds varies with the food habits—from generalized types such as the strong, pointed beaks of crows to grotesque, highly specialized ones of flamingos, hornbills, and toucans (Figure 435). The palatal structure of the jaws also affords a basis for classifying birds into two groups—**neognathous** (new jaw), with long palatines and movable pterygoids, and **palaeognathous** (old jaw), with short palatines and immovable pterygoids. Most flying birds are neognathous and most flightless ones are palaeognathous.

The bones of the pelvis (ilium, ischium, and pubis on each side) are fused with the lumbar and sacral vertebrae to form the **synsacrum,** which bears on each side a socket (acetabulum) for the head of the femur. Each leg is made up of the **femur,** the **tibiotarsus** (formed by the fusion of the tibia and proximal tarsals), the **tarsometatarsus** (formed by the fusion of the distal tarsals and metatarsals), and the four **toes** (three in front and one behind). A sesamoid bone (the patella) is found at the knee joint. There are two to five phalanges in each toe. Woodpeckers and others have two front and two hind toes.

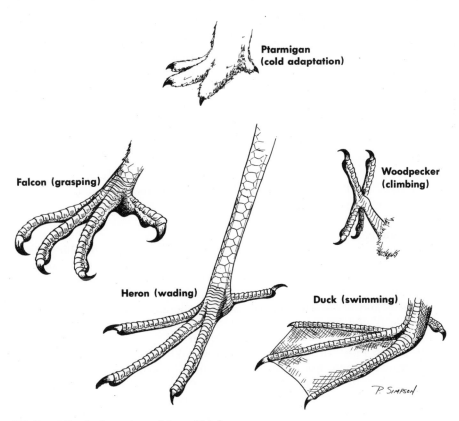

Figure 436. Specialized adaptations of feet of birds.

A few birds have only three toes, and the ostrich has two toes, unequal in size. Bird feet show a wide range of adaptations— walking, climbing, seizing, swimming, wading, etc. (Figure 436).

The trunk is rigid, owing mainly to the fusion of the vertebrae and fusion of the ribs with the vertebrae and sternum. Special processes called **uncinate processes** form an additional brace by passing posteriorly from one rib over the one behind. This rigidity affords a firm point of attachment for the wings. To assist in this support and rigidity, the pectoral girdle of scapulae, clavicles, and coracoids is more or less firmly united and joined to the sternum. Only the flexible neck of eight to twenty-four cervical vertebrae and the caudal vertebrae (four free and pygostyle) are free for movement in the axial skeleton. In all flying birds the sternum is provided with a marked keel for the insertion of the two major flight muscles. The forelimbs, or wing appendages, are the most highly modified of the paired appendages. Each consists of a **radius** and **ulna**, two **carpals**, and three **digits** (II, III, and IV). The other carpals are fused to the three metacarpals to form the **carpometacarpus**, which consists of two long bones. Of the digits, the middle one is longest, consisting of two phalanges; the second and fourth usually have only one. The second digit is called the **alula**, or bastard wing.

Muscular system. In birds the muscles are specialized for bipedal locomotion and for flight. Most of their muscles are concerned with the head, neck, and limbs. Segmental arrangements of muscles are scarce. The largest muscle is the **pectoralis major,** which depresses the wing in power flight. It originates on the sternal crest and clavicle and is inserted on the ventrolateral side of the humerus. In flying birds its fibers are red, but in flightless birds it forms most of the "white meat" of the barnyard fowl. For elevating the wing the **pectoralis minor,** or deep pectoral, lies under the pectoralis major. This muscle originates on the sternum and is inserted on the dorsomedial part of the

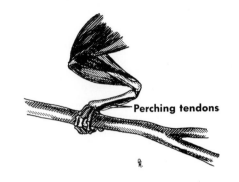

Figure 437. Perching mechanism of bird. When bird alights on perch, a grip reflex is initiated by a sensory receptor on plantar part of foot so that, by means of several tendons from flexor muscles, toes flex and lock as bird settles into resting or sleeping position.

humerus by a tendon that passes through the foramen triosseum, an opening formed by the clavicle, scapula, and coracoid bones. When the pectoralis minor contracts, its tendon works through this foramen like a rope in a pulley to raise the wing.

Other muscles besides the pectoralis group are involved in flight. Many of these help the pectoralis minor, some assist the pectoralis major, and others have various roles in movements around the shoulder region. The muscles of the back are greatly reduced, whereas those of the leg are enlarged and strong. There are few muscles on the shank and feet; this accounts for their slender and delicate appearance in most species. Long tendons attached to muscles in the upper part of the legs are used to move the toes. To prevent the bird from falling while asleep on a perch, there is a **perching mechanism** (Figure 437), consisting of several leg muscles (ambiens, gastrocnemius, peroneus longus, flexors of the digits, etc.) whose tendons pass behind the heel and shank to be inserted separately on the toes. When the foot touches a perch and squats, a grip reflex flexes the toes and locks the bird to its perch. Other muscles (extensors) open the toes.

Digestive system. The digestive system of birds is adapted for rapid and efficient digestion, for birds are selective in their diet and eat food that can be largely utilized. The **rectum** is short because the fecal matter is relatively small. There are no teeth in the mouth, and the poorly developed salivary glands rarely secrete diastatic enzymes but mainly mucus for lubricating the slender, horny covered **tongue.** There are few taste buds. Hummingbirds and some others have sticky tongues, and woodpeckers have tongues that are barbed at the end. From the short **pharynx** a relatively long elastic **esophagus** extends to the **stomach.** In many birds there is an enlargement (**crop**) at the lower end of the esophagus.

In pigeons and some parrots, milk is produced by the breakdown of the epithelial cells lining the crop, producing "bird milk" which is regurgitated by both male and female into the mouth of the young squabs. This milk has a much higher content of fat than cow's milk.

The stomach proper consists of a **proventriculus,** which secretes gastric juice, and the muscular **gizzard,** which grinds the food. To assist in the grinding process, birds swallow coarse, gritty objects or pebbles which lodge in the gizzard. Certain birds of prey, such as owls, form pellets of indigestible materials, e.g., bones and fur, in the proventriculus and eject them through the mouth. At the junction of the **intestine** with the rectum there are paired **ceca,** which may be well developed in some birds. Two **bile ducts** from the **gallbladder** and two or three **pancreatic ducts** empty into the duodenum, or first part of the intestine. The **liver** is relatively large and bilobed. The terminal part of the digestive system is the **cloaca,** which also receives the genital ducts and ureters; in young birds the dorsal wall of the cloaca bears the bursa Fabricii of unknown function.

Circulatory system. The general plan

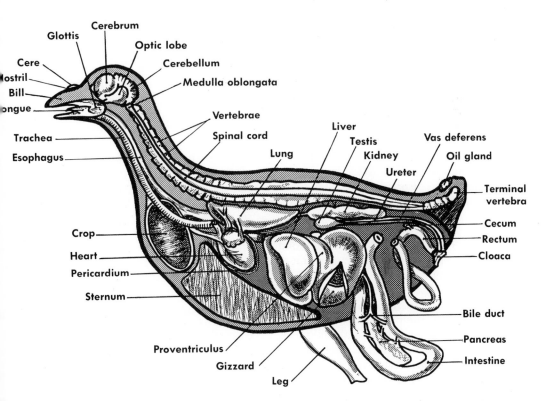

Figure 438. Internal structure of pigeon, *Columba* (semidiagrammatic). Only part of intestine shown.

of bird circulation is not greatly different from that of mammals. However, there are a few unique characteristics. The **four-chambered heart** is large, with strong ventricular walls, and thus they share with mammals a complete separation of the respiratory and systemic circulation. The **right aortic arch,** instead of the left as in the mammals, leads to the dorsal **aorta.** The two **jugular veins** in the neck are connected by a cross vein, an adaptation for shunting the blood from one jugular to the other as the head is turned around. The **brachial** and **pectoral** arteries to the wings and breast are unusually large. There is a well-developed **hepatic portal system,** but the renal portal system is much reduced compared with that in reptiles. The heartbeat is extremely fast, varying usually from 300 to 1,000 per minute. It is slower in large birds than it is in small ones. Bird's **blood** contains nucleated, biconcave red corpuscles which are somewhat larger than those of mammals. The phagocytes, or mobile ameboid cells, of the blood are unusually active and efficient in birds in the repair of wounds and in destroying microbes.

The high body temperature (104° to 112° F.) is correlated with the high basal metabolic rate but can be quite variable. Its fluctuation rhythm of 10° F. or more can be influenced by the time of day, activity, amount of food in the stomach, etc. Experimentally, Fuller and Hiestand found that the lethal maximum temperature for the domestic fowl (*Gallus domesticus*) was between 45° and 46° C. (113° F.). These investigators concluded that birds live closer to their maximum temperature ceiling than do mammals.

Respiratory system. The high metabolism of birds makes necessary many unique features in their respiratory system. The oval-shaped nostrils or **external nares** open near the base of the bill and connect to the **internal nares** which open into the pharynx. From the floor of the pharynx a **glottis** leads into a **trachea** (windpipe) which is stiffened by a series of bony and cartilaginous rings. This trachea may be extremely long in some aquatic birds, such as the whooping crane. At the upper end of the trachea is the **larynx** which consists of three cartilages and is rudimentary in birds. The trachea branches at its lower end into two **bronchi.** At this junction the **syrinx,** or voice box, of birds is located. The syrinx is made up of modified tracheal and bronchial rings which form a chamber containing a pair of semilunar membranes with muscles. The latter, which are complicated in singing birds, alter the pitch of the sound.

The **lungs** of birds have a different method of gaseous exchange from that of mammals and is not fully understood. The two compact lungs are small, with little elasticity. After branching from the trachea, each bronchus passes through the lungs, giving off a number of smaller **bronchioles.** From the bronchioles a complicated series of ramifying and anastomosing air passages (parabronchi, ventrobronchi, and dorsobronchi) are formed. There are no blind pouches or alveoli; instead there are **air capillaries** connected to the air passages that serve as respiratory membranes for exchange of the gases O_2 and CO_2. From the lungs, branches of the bronchi or bronchioles pass through them to the unique system of thin-walled and nonvascular **air sacs** which are distributed among the viscera and even into some of the larger bones. There are nine of these sacs in the pigeon, and they fill up much of the body cavity. Their function is not to lighten the body, as was once supposed, but to cool the body by internal evaporation or dissipation of heat and also to take care of the residual (dead) air, thus ensuring a complete renewal of air in the lungs in the breathing process. In **inspiration** the lungs (attached to the ribs) dilate by contraction of rib muscles and other muscles and air flows through the passageways of the lungs and into the air sacs. In **expiration,** which is the active part of respiration, thoracic and abdominal muscles compress the air sacs which force the air out by about the same route it entered. The act of flying also aids breathing by the muscular contraction of the thorax. Unlike other vertebrates, the air in birds passes completely through the lungs at each breath. In flying, even the residual air of the air sacs is completely renewed.

The great demand for oxygen requires a high breathing rate in birds, but they can adjust themselves quickly to external conditions. House wrens, for example, have been shown to have a breathing rate of 28 at 74° F. but 340 at their normal body temperature (104° + F.).

Excretory system. The paired metanephric kidneys are three-lobed and are attached to the dorsal wall of the synsacrum. From these, the ureters run to the **cloaca.** A urinary bladder is absent and the urine is semisolid, consisting mostly of urates. The whitish material in bird feces is due to these urates. Much of the water is absorbed in the cloaca, and as in reptiles, the excretion of nitrogen waste as uric acid instead of urea involves the use of little water, for uric acid is mainly insoluble in water and precipitates out easily. The fecal matter of sea birds may accumulate in large deposits, such as the famed guano beds off the coast of South America. Such guano forms a rich fertilizer in demand all over the world.

Nervous and sensory systems. The nervous system in birds is characterized by unusually large **optic lobes** and **cerebellum.** The well-developed optic lobes, together with very large eyes, indicate **keen sight,** a sense that is probably unsurpassed in the animal kingdom. Hearing is also well developed in birds; taste and smell, however, are poor. The large and much-convoluted cerebellum is correlated with delicate equilibrium and great muscular coordination. In the vitreous humor of the eye is the highly vascular and fan-shaped body, the **pecten,** which may aid in nutrition and accommodation. Birds also possess a **nictitating membrane,** vestigial in the mammalian eye, which can be drawn across the eyeball from the inner angle of the eye.

Tactile sense organs are not well developed except in a few places where they would be of adaptive value, such as the bill, in ducks or other aquatic birds, which is used for probing around in the mud and debris of stream bottoms. Rictal bristles of night hawks have sensory nerve endings at their base and can be used for sensory detection. But the bird depends mainly upon **vision** for its sensory impression. Vultures or turkey buzzards detect their carrion by sight, not smell. The side position of the eyes indicates monocular vision, that is, each eye having its own field of vision. The forward position of the owl's eyes may enable it to have binocular vision. Many birds, moreover, have two sensitive spots (foveas) on the retina—the central one for sharp monocular views and the posterior one for binocular vision. The ease with which birds can turn their heads makes possible a wide field of vision. Woodcocks can probably see binocularly both forward and backward. Bitterns in their freezing stance of bill pointing up can also see binocularly. The visual acuity of a hawk is thought to be eight times that of a man, and an owl's ability to see in dim light is ten times that of the human eye. Birds have some color vision, especially toward the red end of the spectrum.

Reproductive system. In the male, the paired **testes** and accessory ducts are similar to those in many other forms, but the female has only the left ovary and left oviduct, the right ones being vestigial. Some birds, including ducks and geese, have a large, well-developed **copulatory organ** (penis). It is a modified and thickened portion of the ventral wall of the cloaca; it is provided with a groove on its dorsal side for the transfer of sperm. The inactive penis has its distal end invaginated by an elastic ligament. The ostrich has a solid penis which can be drawn back into a sheath of the cloaca. With most birds, however, copulation is a mere matter of bringing the cloacal surfaces of the two sexes into contact—the so-called "cloacal kiss." From the **testes** of the male the **vasa deferentia** run to the cloaca. Before being discharged, the sperm are stored in the **seminal vesicle,** the enlarged distal end of the vas deferens.

This seminal vesicle may become so large with stored sperm during the breeding season that it causes a cloacal protuberance. The high body temperature which tends to inhibit spermatogenesis in the testes is probably counteracted by the cooling effect of the abdominal air sacs. The testes of birds undergo a great enlargement at the breeding season, shrinking to tiny bodies afterward.

In the female, the **ovary** is close to the left kidney. Eggs discharged from the ovary are picked up by the expanded end of the oviduct, the **infundibulum.** The oviduct runs posteriorly to the cloaca. While the eggs are passing down the oviduct, **albumin,** or egg white, from special glands is added to them; and farther down the oviduct, the shell membrane, shell, and shell pigments are also secreted about the egg. Fertilization takes place in the upper oviduct several hours before the laying of the eggs. Some hawks and owls have two ovaries, each capable of producing eggs. Birds may be determinate layers and lay only a fixed number (clutch) of eggs in a season. If any of the eggs of a set are removed, the deficit is not made up by additional laying (herring gull). Indeterminate layers, however, will continue to lay additional eggs for a long time if some of the first-laid eggs are continually removed (flickers, ducks, domestic poultry). Most birds are probably determinate layers. Many birds, such as songbirds, lay an egg a day until the clutch is completed; others stagger their egg laying and lay every other day or so. Domestic geese usually lay every other day, which is probably the pattern for the large birds of prey.

Endocrine system. Birds have well-developed regulatory systems of endocrine glands such as are characteristic of mammals and other animal forms. Much investigation has been conducted on this system in birds. Glands such as the **thyroid** in the neck, the **pituitary** at the base of the brain, the **islets of Langerhans** in the pancreas, the **adrenals** on the ventral surface of the kidneys, and the endocrinal tissue of the **gonads** are all well represented. The functions of these various glands are, on the whole, typical of such glands in other forms. Song and coloration, for instance, are controlled by hormones from the gonads.

Adaptive structures and natural history

Flight. Before birds acquired the power of flight they may have passed through a sequence pattern of swift running, flying leaps, tree climbing, parachute gliding from tree to tree, and a general arboreal existence. Many of their adaptations, such as the perching mechanism and active climbing habits, indicate such an apprenticeship. So far as birds are concerned, feathers were an absolute requirement for true flight, for there is no reason to suppose that they passed through a stage of wings composed of skin membranes such as the pterodactyls had. Other flight adaptations (streamline body, skeleton, internal organs, bodily functions, etc.) have already been mentioned. In ordinary flying, birds have to make use of the same principles and solve the same problems that confront human heavier-than-air aircraft. When such objects move through air there is a lift force acting upward which must be sufficient to sustain the weight of the object and a contrary force or drag force which tends to stop the motion. Both of these forces are proportional to the square of the speed, and no object can stay aloft in still air unless its speed produces a lift force equal to its weight.

Wings are required to function both as propellers and planes. In flying, birds elevate the wings, and then pull them forward, downward, and backward. This is accomplished by the large pectoralis major muscles. The wings are lifted back into position by a quick flip of the pectoralis minor muscles. When the wing is moved downward, the air is displaced and the bird is kept up or raised; the backward movement gives horizontal velocity to the body; and the air resistance which retards the forward movement also has a lifting force because the bird's wing is convex above and offers less resistance than the lower concave surface. Between strokes the loss of altitude may be slight in swift flying, but it is quite evident in the up-and-down flight of woodpeckers and goldfinches. Rapidity of flight within limits lessens the energy required in flight. It is estimated that the energy expended by a pigeon in taking off is five times as great as that needed to attain its regular speed.

There are three types of bird flight: gliding, flapping, and soaring.

GLIDING FLIGHT. In this type a bird attains a certain velocity and then planes without moving the wings, or having reached a certain altitude it descends without wing stroke. Birds use this method in landing. A gliding bird nearly always loses altitude when gliding, but wind direction and speed of take-off determine how far it can go without sinking. This is probably the most primitive method of flying.

FLAPPING FLIGHT. This type (already described) refers to the up-and-down movement of the wings and represents the most complicated mechanism of flight. It is ordinary bird flight and is often described as a screwlike wing motion with the primary feathers acting as propellers and the secondaries furnishing the plane lift.

There are different shapes of wings for different types of flying. The factors that determine the kind and shape of wing are as follows:

1. The relationship of wing area to the load it carries. Small wings are necessary for swift flapping flight, whereas a large wing area allows slow flight and good soaring. Large birds have relatively larger wings in comparison to their bodies than do small birds if they are to have the same wing area per gram of weight, for the weight increases as the cube and the wing area as the square. This wing surface per body weight ratio is not the same, however, for small and large birds. In the crow the ratio is 3 kilograms of body weight to 1 square meter of wing area; in warblers it may be 1 to 1. Smaller birds, therefore, have a greater margin of safety.

2. Aspect ratio, that is, the ratio between the wing length and breadth. A high aspect ratio allows a slow rate of descent while gliding and requires a small expenditure of energy. This is found mainly in birds that fly fast by flapping flight, for they tend to stall at slow soaring rates. In the albatross the ratio is 25 to 1; in the sparrow, 5 to 1.

3. The shape of the wing as related to the type of flying. A pointed wing is found only in fast flyers and is provided with large hand (primary) feathers; short broad wings are more suitable for slower but more maneuverable flyers and stresses the arm feathers.

4. The curvature, or camber, of the wing. The upper convex surface of the wing allows air to flow off the feathers when the wing is raised and produces a positive pressure on the underside of the wing. To minimize air turbulence and to promote a smooth flow of air over the surfaces, slots are formed at the tips of the wings, especially on the upbeat.

SOARING. In soaring flight, birds usually take advantage of updrafts and air currents so that flapping is dispensed with for considerable periods of time. The long, narrow wings of gulls and albatrosses and the short, broad wings of hawks are equally effective for this type of flight. Hawks often make use of the ascending warm air which arises from warmed areas of the earth to mount in circles to great heights. In soaring, albatrosses take advantage of currents of air of unequal velocity at different heights (faster at greater heights) which are found at low levels over the sea. The bird glides down the wind with great speed to a lower level, then turns, and rises with reduced velocity into a faster-moving layer of air. In this way the albatross without visible wing stroke can soar with or against the wind for some time.

How fast can birds fly? Many of our small songbirds are feeble flyers compared with swifts, swallows, and many birds of prey. How fast they fly depends to a great extent upon the conditions of the air. Against a strong headwind their speed is naturally cut down. Under favorable conditions most small songbirds fly from 20 to 40 miles per hour. Larger birds such as ducks usually fly from 40 to 80 miles per hour. Some swifts are known to fly more than 100 miles per hour, and some birds of prey probably exceed this in diving after their prey. Many estimates of speed, however, are purely guesswork and lack accurate measurement.

Coloration. Perhaps no group of animals has more beautiful and more striking colors than do the birds. This beauty reaches its peak in tropical birds, but many that dwell in the temperate zones are also renowned for their colors. Numerous birds are undoubtedly protectively colored by their plumage, and the brighter colors assumed by the male during the breeding season gave rise to Darwin's conception of sexual selection, a theory that has not found favor with most zoologists.

The color is partly due to pigments and partly to interference colors produced by light reflection and refraction. Some of the pigments (melanins) are granules of yellow, black, red, and a few others. Other pigments are the lipochromes, such as, zooxanthin (yellow) and zooerythrin (red). Colors produced this way always appear the same, but those due to reflection and refraction may appear different, depending upon the conditions under which they are seen. White is produced by reflection. The surface markings, as well as the internal structure, play a part in this interference coloration. Whenever there is an absence of pigment, an albino may result.

Nearly all birds undergo **molting,** a seasonal shedding and replacement of feathers. Molting may be accompanied by a change in the color of the plumage. The ptarmigan is white in winter and mottled brown at other seasons. The juvenile plumage in young birds may resemble that of the adult female. When the colors of males and females of the same species differ, the condition is called **sexual dimorphism.** In such cases the male is usually the brighter. Examples are the cardinal and scarlet tanager.

Songs. The vocal organ in the bird is the **syrinx** already mentioned. When air passes through this organ, the semilunar membrane vibrates to produce sounds. In some species the range and variety of songs is most striking; in others it is definitely restricted. In the song sparrow more than 800 different song variations have been recorded. Nearly all songbirds studied have different songs for different purposes, many of which convey precise information. The more bird songs are studied, the more amazing seems to be the scope and meaning of them. Much remains to be done before the language of birds can be unraveled, but better techniques and electronic devices for analyzing bird songs have yielded much significant information.

In addition to songs, which are far more common in the males during the breeding season, birds have distinctive call notes which are uttered when they are alarmed or are used for attracting mates or young, as well as for territory rights. The pelican and some others are voiceless. Many birds have great powers of mimicry; among these are the brown thrasher, catbird, mockingbird, myna, and, of course, the parrot.

Food. Because birds are very active their food requirement is large. Their body metabolism and body temperature are the highest known among animals. The food habits of the various species vary enormously. Many birds are strictly vegetarian, consuming great quantities of foliage, seeds, fruits, etc. because of the less concentrated nature of the food. Many game birds belong to this group. Others, such as birds of prey, are entirely carnivorous. Many small songbirds, such as flycatchers and woodpeckers, live exclusively upon insects. Still other birds are omnivorous, eating both vegetable and animal foods. The young of some birds may live on different foods than do the adults. During the nesting period many songbirds feed their nestlings insects, although the adults themselves are vegetarians. Some birds, such as the hummingbird that lives upon the nectar of flowers and the kingfisher that lives upon fish, have rather restricted food habits. The hummingbird requires so much food that it would starve to death at night except that it goes into a hibernation state with low breathing rate, low heart rate, and low body temperature. Perhaps no bird has a wider range of diet than has the common American crow, which may account for its wide distribution and large numbers. Carrion-eating birds, such as the condor and buzzard, may eat so much at times as to be unable to fly.

A striking example of a bird's changing its eating habits is found in the case of the New Zealand parrot *(Nestor notabilis)* which formerly lived on fruits, seeds, and nuts. When sheep were introduced into that country the parrot acquired the habit of digging out the kidneys and fat of sick or weakened animals.

How marine birds drink salt water. All marine birds drink salt water instead of fresh water. Since marine water is more than 3% salt and the blood of birds less than 1% salt, the excess salt must be eliminated. Since using kidneys for this purpose would involve loss of water, sea birds have evolved special salt glands on the head, either over each eye or between the eyes and the nasal cavity, for eliminating this salt. These glands consist of many parallel lobes, each with many branching tubules. Blood capillaries carry the blood containing the salt to the tubules, where the sodium and chloride ions against an osmotic gradient pass from the lower salt concentration of the blood to the higher salt concentration of the tubules. From the glands, ducts carry to the nasal cavities the salt secretions (sometimes more than 5% salt), which then drips from the nostrils and beak.

Sea reptiles, such as marine turtles, have glands behind the eyeball that function in a similar way and for a similar reason.

Care of young. To produce offspring, all birds lay eggs which must be incubated by one or both parents. Cowbird eggs require only nine or ten days for hatching; most songbirds, about fourteen days; the hen, twenty-one days; and ducks and geese, at least four weeks. Most of the duties of incubation fall upon the female, although in many instances both parents share in the task and occasionally only the male performs this work.

Most birds build some form of nest in which to rear their young. These nests vary from depressions on the ground to huge and elaborate affairs (Figures 439 to 443). Some birds simply lay their eggs on the bare ground or rocks and make no pretense of nest building. Some of the most striking nests are the pendant nests constructed by orioles, the neat lichen-covered nests of hummingbirds and fly-catchers, the chimney-shaped mud nests of cliff swallows, and the hugh brush pile nests of the Australian brush turkey. Most birds take considerable pains to conceal their nests from enemies. Woodpeckers, chickadees, bluebirds, and many others place their nests in tree hollows or other cavities; kingfishers excavate tunnels in the banks of streams for their nests; and birds of prey build high in lofty trees or on inaccessible cliffs. A few birds, such as the American cowbird and the European cuckoo, build no nests at all but simply lay their eggs in the nests of birds smaller than themselves. When the eggs hatch, the young are taken care of by their foster parents. Most of our songbirds lay from three to six eggs, but the number of eggs laid in a clutch varies from one or two (some hawks and pigeons) to eighteen or twenty (quail).

When birds hatch, they are of two types: **precocial** or **altricial.** The precocial young, such as quail, fowl, ducks, and most water birds, are covered with down when hatched and can run or swim as soon as their plumage is dry. The altricial ones, on the other hand, are naked and quite helpless at birth and remain in the nest for a week or more. The young of both types require care from the parents for some time after hatching. They must be fed, guarded, and protected against rain and the sun. The parents of altricial species must carry food to their children almost constantly, for most young birds will eat more than their weight each day. This enormous food consumption ex-

439 440 441

442 443

Figure 439. Pendant nest of Baltimore oriole.

Figure 440. Nest of red-eyed vireo.

Figure 441. Nest of phoebe—is always placed in sheltered position, such as under bridges, shelving rocks, and buildings.

Figure 442. Nest of cardinal—usually placed in thickets and brambles and not easily detected.

Figure 443. Mud-lined nest of robin.

plains the rapid growth of the young and their quick exit from the nest. The food of the young, depending upon the species, includes worms, insects, seeds, fruit, etc. Pigeons are peculiar in feeding their young with "pigeon milk," the sloughed-off epithelial lining of the crop.

Many birds, such as the eagle and some of the songbirds, are known to mate for life. Others mate only for the rearing of a single brood. There are also cases in which one female mates with several males (**polyandry**), as illustrated by the European cuckoo; in other cases one male mates with several females (**polygyny**); for example, the ostrich. Elaborate courtship rituals are found in many birds, such as the prairie chicken, sage grouse, bower birds, great crested grebes, and others.

Simpler ritual forms are found among most songbirds and consist mainly of male displays and songs.

Do birds hibernate? For many centuries, bird observers believed that birds hibernate in the mud of ponds, in stony crevices, and in other places. Aristotle had views of this kind, and Gilbert White, in his delightful book, *The Natural History of Selborne,* tries to account for the sudden appearance of swallows in the spring in this way. This belief has largely been discredited by trained observers, and yet in recent years some bird students have revived the idea. Among these is Professor E. C. Jaeger of California, who found poorwills in dormant conditions in rock crevices in his native state. His observations seem to verify what certain

English observers had previously discovered in Persia, where they found swallows apparently hibernating in burrows. Whether such practices are common is to be doubted, but such observations are of considerable interest.

Bird populations. Many censuses have been taken to ascertain bird populations within a particular area. The National Audubon Society and the Federal Fish and Wildlife Service have sponsored many such counts. Some are concerned with game birds and species on the verge of extinction. Emphasis is often placed upon breeding birds, making use of the territorial singing of the males. Some birds lend themselves to more accurate counts than others, such as those that nest in colonies or have particular nesting habitats. Students of birds use various techniques for identifying birds, such as sight, song, type of flying, call notes, etc. In 1914 a bird census made in the northeastern United States revealed about 125 pairs of birds per 100 acres (open farms) and 199 pairs per 100 acres of woodland. In 1949 a survey made in a spruce-fir forest in Maine gave a count of 370 pairs of breeding birds per 100 acres. Another count in the same region in 1950 showed 385 pairs of breeding birds per 100 acres.

Many censuses are incomplete and unreliable. With individual differences among observers not all reports are of the same accuracy. There are many other sources of error in samplings. Birds tend to congregate where food is abundant, for instance, in an orchard. At certain seasons quail may be found in large numbers in a wheat field but be scarcely noticed elsewhere. As for numbers of species, in the eastern half of the United States robins and house sparrows are most common near dwellings, whereas in the woodlands other species are more common. Many species tend to be localized in distribution.

Selection of territories. A pair of birds will usually select a territory on which to raise a brood. This territory is selected in the spring by the male who jealously guards it against all other males of the same species. The male sings a great deal to help him establish priority on his domain. Eventually he attracts a female, and the pair start mating and nest building. The female apparently wanders from one territory to another until she settles down with a male. How large a territory a pair takes over depends upon location, abundance of food, natural barriers, etc. In the case of some birds, such as robins, a house may serve as the dividing line between two adjacent domains, and each pair will usually stay close to the lawn on its particular side of the house. When members of another species trespass, the pair usually pay little attention. Competition is greatest among the members of the same species. Song sparrows, however, try to keep off members of other species as well as their own.

This concept of territory claims by birds was greatly developed by H. E. Howard, an English ornithologist, in 1920. Since that time other competent students have verified and extended the concept. One of these was Mrs. M. M. Nice, whose work on the song sparrow is now classical; another was Lack, an English ornithologist, who worked with the English robin.

Many modified aspects of territory are found. Some birds restrict their territories to nesting regions and share feeding grounds with others. Among hummingbirds, the female has a separate nesting site which she defends herself. Territories are usually deserted at the close of the nesting season and new ones are staked out the following spring. Song sparrows, however, keep their territories the year around. Territories are not absolutely fixed areas, but vary as the economic pressures vary.

Behavior and intelligence. Birds have some of the most marvelous instincts in the animal kingdom. This would indicate a complex and well-organized nervous system. Among their amazing behavior reactions are the elaborate and skillfully built nests characteristic of many species, the migratory instinct which enables birds to travel thousands of miles without deviating from their courses, the dexterity they show in food capture, the courtship and mating rituals of some, and, not least, their power of producing sweet and beautiful music.

Birds as a group are well blessed with sense perception. Their sense of sight is perhaps the keenest in the animal kingdom. A hawk gliding several hundred yards in the air can spot the movements of a mouse hidden in the grass below. Most birds, too, can hear well. Owls at night can hear slight rustling sounds not detectable to the ears of most animals. Smell and taste, however, are not highly developed in birds, for they depend mainly upon sight and hearing for their information.

In studying the behavior of birds, it is not always possible to distinguish between strictly inborn reflexes and acquired associations. Many of the former are found in newly hatched birds, for they are able to perform them without previous experience, but the parents are undoubtedly responsible for furnishing the stimuli in the development of the instinctive behavior of the young. The power birds have of radically changing their food and nesting habits, examples of which are well known, indicates that they can establish simple associations. Birds, thus, may be credited with a limited power of adjusting their behavior in accordance with simple trial-and-error experimentation. Many behavior patterns of birds have never been satisfactorily explained—for instance, "anting," the habit some birds (usually passerines) have of rubbing crushed ants (sometimes other objects) over and under their primary feathers. Some think that its primary purpose is to get rid of ectoparasites.

Bird banding. Bird banding is a method of marking live specimens with a special aluminum band which bears a serial number and other data. When these specimens are recovered, returns are made usually to some official organization, such as the United States Fish and Wildlife Service. Much useful information about birds has been acquired by this method, such as migration routes, distribution, and popula-

tion dynamics. Bird banding, to be effective, requires the cooperation of many banders and responsible organizations. Bird banders now number several thousand in the United States and Canada. Special federal and state permits are required of bird banders. Various forms of traps are employed for catching specimens. A funnel trap, in which birds can find their way in but not out, is a popular type.

Economic importance

Birds are both useful and harmful to man's interests. Many birds, such as fowls, geese, ducks, turkeys, pigeons, and others, have been domesticated, and their total value in flesh and eggs is great. Game birds, such as pheasants, quail, and grouse, are hunted both for food and for the zest of hunting.

The value of birds in consuming insect and weed seed pests should not be underrated. Hawks and owls help control vermin that might otherwise overrun agricultural crops. They undoubtedly do some damage to poultry and game birds, but even here they may do a service by getting rid of the sick and weakly.

Birds also serve another useful purpose, and that is the esthetic interest that is manifested in them in nearly all civilized countries. To study birds, thousands of people take to the fields and woods. This has proved fruitful in several ways, for such interests have also led to better bird protection and conservation.

Résumé of orders

Class Aves (birds) is made up of about twenty-seven orders of living birds and a few fossil orders. More than 30,000 species and subspecies have been described. Probably only a relatively few species remain to be discovered and named, but many subspecies are added yearly. With their powers of flight and wide distribution, most species of birds are more easily detected than many animals. Only those that are solitary, shy, and restricted to remote regions have a chance of remain-

Cassowary (Casuarius)
(Australia and adjacent islands)

Kiwi (Apteryx)
(New Zealand)

These flightless birds (ratites) have evolved from flying ancestors but live either in localities where there are few carnivorous enemies, such as in Australia and New Zealand, or on plains where they can see and outdistance their potential predators

Ostrich (Struthio)
(Africa)

Rhea (Rhea)
(South America)

DEL MICHEL

Figure 444. Group of ratite birds.

ing undiscovered for any length of time. Altogether, the species are grouped into 170 families. Of the twenty-seven recognized orders twenty are represented by North American species.

The first four orders in the following list make up the group of **ratite**, or flightless, birds (Figure 444); the remainder are the **carinate**, or flying, birds.

Order Struthioniformes (stru'thi-on'i-for"mes) (Gr. *struthio*, ostrich, + form)—**ostriches**

The ostrich (*Struthio camelus*) is the largest of living birds, some specimens being 8 feet tall and weighing 300 pounds. These birds cannot fly.

The feet are provided with only two toes of unequal size covered with pads, which enable the birds to travel rapidly through sandy country. The ostrich is found in the desert country of Africa and Arabia. Usually ostriches occur in small groups of hens with one cock that shares the task of incubation. Their great speed and strong legs afford them excellent protection from enemies. One egg of considerable size is laid by each hen, and all the hens of a troop lay their eggs in the same nest. Ostrich feathers are highly prized, and ostrich farming is extensive in South Africa, California, and elsewhere. There are four species, of which *Struthio camelus* is the largest.

Figure 445. Rookery of king penguins, showing enormous number that may be found in one locality. These birds, which during summer months hatch eggs in folds of flesh between their legs, do not build a nest at all. They breed in large "rookeries," usually on hard level beaches close to water. Order Sphenisciformes. (Courtesy Nature Magazine, Washington, D. C.)

Order Rheiformes (rhe'i-for"mes) (Gr. *Rhea*, mother of Zeus, + form)—**rheas**

These flightless birds are restricted to South America and are often called the American ostrich. There are three species of them; they are much smaller than the true ostrich, although they have a general resemblance to them. A feature found in no other bird is the entire separation of the terminal vertebrae from the rest of the vertebral column.

Order Casuariiformes (cas'u-ar'e-i-for"mes) (NL. *Casuarius,* genus of cassowary, + form)—**cassowaries and emus**

This is a flightless group of birds found in Australia, New Guinea, and a few other islands. Some specimens may reach a height of 5 feet. Each feather is provided with two shafts of equal length, one of which is the aftershaft.

Order Apterygiformes (ap'ter-yg'i-for"mes) (Gr. *a,* not, + *pteryx, wing,* + form)—**kiwis**

This is a flightless order of birds about the size of the domestic fowl, found only in New Zealand. They all belong to the genus *Apteryx,* of which there are three species. As an adaptation for scenting their prey (worms) at night, the nostrils are found at the very tip of their long beak. Only the merest vestige of a wing is present. The egg is extremely large for the size of the bird.

Order Tinamiformes (ti-nam'i-for"mes) (NL. *tinamus,* type genus of tinamou, + form)—**tinamous**

These are flying birds found in South America and Mexico. They resemble the ruffed grouse and are classed as game birds. There are more than sixty species in this order.

Order Sphenisciformes (sphe-nis'ci-for"mes) (Gr. *spheniscus,* wedge, + form)—**penguins**

Penguins (Figures 445 and 446) are found in the southern seas, especially in Antarctica. Although carinate birds, they use their wings as paddles rather than for flight. The largest penguin is the emperor penguin (*Aptenodytes forsteri*) of the Antarctic which breeds in enormous rookeries on the shores of that region. Penguins are of great interest because of their strange and elaborate behavior patterns. Since Admiral Richard Byrd made his explorations into Antarctica some years ago, many studies have

Figure 446. Group of emperor penguins. Order Sphenisciformes. (Courtesy Chicago Natural History Museum.)

Figure 447. Great northern diver, or common loon. Weird, lonesome cry of loon heard on our northern lakes is unforgettable sound. Usually only a pair of these birds found on a single lake. Order Gaviiformes. (Courtesy Chicago Natural History Museum.)

been made of this group of birds and their interesting ways.

Order Gaviiformes (ga′vi-i-for″mes) (L. *gavia,* sea mew, + form)—**loons**

Another name for the loon is the diver. Loons' legs are set far back on the body, so that walking is difficult for them. Remarkable swimmers and divers, they live exclusively on fish and small aquatic forms. The familiar great northern diver *(Gavia immer)* (Figure 447) is found mainly in northern waters. Its cry, one of the wildest sounds in nature, is easily recognized. During courtship, loons are remarkable for a peculiar ceremony in which the males glide over the surface of the water in an erect position.

Order Colymbiformes (co-lym′bi-for″mes) (Gr. *kolymbos,* diving bird, + form)—**grebes**

The pied-billed grebe, or dabchick *(Podilymbus podiceps),* is a familiar example of this order. These birds are found on ponds and lakes all over the eastern half of the United States. They are shy, secretive birds, and dive quickly when disturbed. Grebes are most common in old ponds where there are extensive growths of cattails, rushes, and water flags, of which they build their raftlike nests that float on the surface of the water. Although graceful in the water, grebes are very awkward on land. They live mainly upon fish and small aquatic animals.

Order Procellariiformes (pros′el-lar′i-i-for″mes) (L. *procella,* a tempest, + form)—**albatrosses, petrels, fulmars, shearwaters**

So far as wing span is concerned (nearly 12 feet in some) albatrosses are the largest of flying birds. Their fifteen species have a world-wide distribution. Albatrosses and shearwaters are known for their remarkable homing instincts. Petrels vomit oil when disturbed.

Order Pelecaniformes (pel′e-can′i-for″mes) (L. *pelicanus,* pelican, + form)—**pelicans, cormorants, gannets, boobies, and others**

All the members of this group have all their four toes included within the web.

Order Ciconiiformes (si-ko′ni-i-for″mes) (L. *ciconia,* a stork, + form)—**herons, bitterns, storks, ibises, spoonbills, flamingos** (Figure 448)

A familiar wading bird of eastern North America is the great blue heron *(Ardea herodias)* which frequents marshes and ponds. It usually nests in tall trees and the nests are added to year after year until they become quite large. It is a very shy bird. While searching for its prey, it has the habit of standing motionless in the water

Figure 448. European white stork. This bird is woven into folklore of many European countries, such as Holland and Denmark, where it often nests on tops of chimneys. Order Ciconiiformes. (Courtesy Chicago Natural History Museum.)

Phylum Chordata—class Aves   539

Figure 449. Pair of trumpeter swans. These rare birds are almost extinct and are rigidly protected in their few nesting sites. Order Anseriformes. (Courtesy Winston E. Banko, U. S. Fish and Wildlife Service.)

Figure 450. Bald eagle. This eagle is national emblem of our country but is found in only a few restricted areas. Order Falconiformes. (Courtesy Chicago Natural History Museum.)

for several minutes at a time and then striking suddenly at the prey.

The American bittern *(Botaurus lentiginosus)*

is one of the shyest birds of the swamps and marshes. Its favorite haunts are cedar swamps, cattail beds, and stagnant marshy regions where its concealment coloration makes it extremely difficult to see. Its peculiar notes, uttered in the mating season, resemble the sounds of pumping and stake driving.

Order Anseriformes (an′ser-i-for″mes) (L. *anser,* goose, + form)—**swans, geese, ducks** (Figure 449)

The members of this order have the web restricted to the front toes and have a long breast bone with a low keel. In some of the swans this keel serves as a chamber in which a long loop of the trachea is enclosed.

Order Falconiformes (fal′ko-ni-for″mes) (L. *falco,* falcon, + form)—**eagles, hawks, vultures, falcons, condors, buzzards** (Figures 450 to 453)

These are the great birds of prey and are represented by many species. There are two American species of eagles, the American golden eagle *(Aquila chrysaëtos)* and the bald eagle *(Haliaeetus leucocephalus).*

Order Galliformes (gal′li-for″mes) (L. *gallus,* a cock, + form)—**quail, grouse, pheasants, ptarmigan, turkeys, domestic fowl** (Figures 454 to 456)

Some of the most desirable game birds are in this order. The bobwhite quail *(Colinus virginianus)* is found all over the eastern half of the United States. The ruffed grouse *(Bonasa umbellus),* or partridge, is found in about the same region, but in the woods instead of the open

540

Figure 451. Osprey. Another name for this widely distributed bird is fish hawk, for it lives almost exclusively upon fish along our large water courses and coasts. Order Falconiformes. (Courtesy Nature Magazine, Washington, D. C.)

pastures and grain fields which bobwhite frequents. The drumming of the ruffed grouse is one of the most pleasing sounds of spring. The drumming sound is produced by the striking of the wings against the air and the feathers of the breast. It occurs during the mating season and acts both as a call to females and as a warning to male rivals.

The American wild turkey (*Meleagris gallopavo*) is now confined to the wilder parts of the south and a few of the northern states.

Order Gruiformes (gru'i-for"mes) (L. *grus*, crane, + form)—**cranes, rails, coots, gallinules**

Order Charadriiformes (cha-rad'ri-i-for"mes) (NL. *charadrius*, genus of plovers, + form)—**shore birds, such as gulls, oyster catchers, plovers, sandpipers, terns, etc.** (Figure 457)

Order Columbiformes (co-lum'bi-for"mes) (L. *columba*, dove, + form)—**pigeons, doves**

Order Psittaciformes (sit'ta-ci-for"mes) (L. *psittacus*, parrot, + form)—**parrots, parakeets**

Order Cuculiformes (cu-cu'li-for"mes) (L. *cuculus*, cuckoo, + form)—**cuckoos, roadrunners**

The common cuckoo (*Cuculus canorus*) of Europe lays its eggs in the nests of smaller birds,

Figure 452. South American or Andean condor, *Vultur*, largest flying bird in the world. It may have a wing spread of more than 12 feet, lives chiefly on carrion. Order Falconiformes. (Courtesy Smithsonian Institution, Washington, D. C.)

Figure 453. Harpy eagle, *Harpia*, fierce bird of prey which ranges forests of tropical America and lives mainly on monkeys and sloths. Order Falconiformes. (Courtesy Smithsonian Institution, Washington, D. C.)

Phylum Chordata—class Aves   541

454

455

Figure 454. Willow ptarmigan, showing marked difference between winter and summer plumage. Order Galliformes. (Courtesy Chicago Natural History Museum.)

Figure 455. Ruffed grouse, one of the most prized of American game birds. Order Galliformes. (Courtesy Chicago Natural History Museum.)

Figure 456. Pair of ring-necked pheasants. These birds have been successfully introduced as game birds in many sections of our country. Order Galliformes. (Courtesy Chicago Natural History Museum.)

542

Figure 457. Woodcock on nest. Vesper flight song of male is interesting courtship ritual. Order Charadriiformes. (Courtesy Rex Gary Schmidt, U. S. Fish and Wildlife Service.)

who rear the young cuckoos. In England the common hedge sparrow is most often victimized. In the spring a female cuckoo will take over a territory and slyly lay an egg here and there in the nests which she has had under observation. She waits until the rightful parents are away and quickly glides onto the nest, removes one of the eggs there, and deposits her own in its place. A single hen cuckoo may lay twenty or more eggs in a single season. The incubation period of the cuckoo's egg is about twelve days, often less than the eggs of the foster parents. When hatched, the young cuckoo works its way under its companions and backs them out of the nest one by one. The process of ejection has been photographed and filmed. The ejected young starve on the ground while their parents feed the usurper.

The American cuckoos, black billed and yellow billed, rear their own young.

Order Strigiformes (stri'gi-for"mes) (Gr. *strix,* owl, + form)—**owls** (Figures 458 and 459)

Owls are chiefly nocturnal birds and have probably the keenest eyes and ears in the animal kingdom. Their eyes are unusually large, and their pupils can enlarge enormously and quickly to receive light rays. In bright light the pupils are mere slits, but owls can see some in daylight. There are many species of this interesting group of birds, and most of them are quite useful in keeping down harmful rodents.

Order Caprimulgiformes (cap'ri-mul'ji-for"mes) (L. *caprimulgus,* goatsucker, + form)—**goatsuckers, nighthawks, poorwills**

The birds of this group are most active at night and in twilight. They have small, weak legs, wide mouths, and short, delicate bills. The

Figure 458. Barred owl. Order Strigiformes. (Courtesy Nature Magazine, Washington, D. C.)

mouth is fringed with bristles in most species. The whippoorwills (*Antrostomus vociferus*) are common in the woods of the eastern states, and the nighthawk (*Chordeiles minor*) is often seen and heard in the evening flying around city buildings. The call of the whippoorwills is well known, and a few may give the deceptive impression that there are many of them. Neither the whippoorwill nor the nighthawk makes a nest; the whippoorwill deposits its two eggs on the leaves in a secluded woods; the nighthawk

Phylum Chordata—class Aves 543

Figure 459. Barn owl, often called the monkey-faced owl, is one of the most useful of the owls, for it destroys rats and other vermin around barns. Order Strigiformes. (Courtesy Nature Magazine, Washington, D. C.)

deposits its eggs on the flat roof of a building. They feed on night-flying insects.

Order Apodiformes (a-pod′i-for″mes) (Gr. *apous,* footless, + form)—**swifts, hummingbirds**
The swifts get their name from their speed on the wing. The familiar chimney swift *(Chaetura pelagica)* fastens its nest in chimneys by means of saliva. They seek their insect food in the air from morning until night. They are never known to rest on the ground or trees; when not flying they cling to the vertical walls of chimneys or buildings. Their nests are made of small twigs glued together into a shallow but strong nest. In the fall, just before migration, it is not unusual to see hundreds of these birds descend upon a chimney and after many maneuvers drop one by one into the cavity of the chimney.
A swift found in China *(Collocalia)* builds a nest of saliva which is used by the Chinese for soup making.
Most species of hummingbirds (Figure 460) are found in the tropics, but there are fourteen species in the United States, of which only one, the ruby-throated hummingbird, is found in the eastern part of the country. Hummingbirds are

among the smallest of birds, and they get their name from the rapid vibration of their wings. They seem motionless as they hover over a flower, but this is only apparent, for their wings are vibrating faster than the human eye can see. In recent years with rapid-exposure cameras the wing movements have been caught on film. Most hummingbirds live upon nectar which they suck up with their highly adaptable tongue, although some catch insects also.
The nest of the ruby-throated hummingbird is exquisite. About the size of a thimble, it is usually saddled on a small limb or twig and made of downy fibers and spider's web. It blends into the surroundings as though it were a small knot on the limb. The outside of the nest is covered with tree lichens. The tiny white eggs are two in number. In the care of the young, few birds are more courageous than hummingbirds.

Order Coliiformes (ko′li-i-for″mes) (Gr. *kolios,* woodpecker, + form)—**mousebirds**
Africa.

Order Trogoniformes (tro-gon′i-for″mes) (Gr. *trogon,* gnawing, + form)—**trogons**
Tropical.

Order Coraciiformes (kor′a-si′i-for″mez) (Gr. *korax,* crow or raven, + form)—**kingfishers, hornbills, and others**
In the eastern half of the United States the belted kingfisher *(Megaceryle alcyon)* is common along most waterways of any size. It makes a nest in

Figure 460. Ruby-throated hummingbird. Of the fourteen species of hummingbirds in United States, the ruby-throated is only one found east of the Mississippi. Order Apodiformes.

544

a burrow in a high bank or cliff along a water course. It prefers steep, sandy banks for it excavates with its bill and scratches out the soil with its feet. The nest is found in a chamber at the end of the zigzag burrow. The call note of the kingfisher is a harsh rattle which it often utters as it darts along a water course. Its food is mostly fish, but it also catches frogs, crayfish, and other aquatic forms.

Order Piciformes (pis'i-for"mes) (L. *picus*, wood pecker, + form)—**woodpeckers, toucans, puffbirds, etc.**

Woodpeckers are adapted for climbing with stiff tail feathers and toes with sharp claws. Two of the toes extend forward and two backward. They have long, sharp bills which they drive into the wood with rapid blows and protrusible tongues for sucking up the insects they uncover. There are many species of woodpeckers in North America, the more common of which are the flicker, downy, hairy, red bellied, red headed, and yellow bellied. The largest is the pileated woodpecker which is rare and found only in deep and remote woods.

Order Passeriformes (pas'er-i-for"mes) (L. *passer*, sparrow, + form)—**perching birds**

This is the largest order of birds and is made up of sixty-nine families. To this order belong the songbirds found in all parts of the world. Among these are the skylark, nightingale, hermit thrush, mockingbird, meadow lark, robin, and hosts of others. Others of this order, such as the swallow, magpie, starling, crow, raven, jay, nuthatch, and creeper, have no songs worthy of the name. They have a wide range of ecological habits. Many are insectivorous, some are seed eaters, and others are omnivorous. Of all the orders of birds, these have been studied most extensively, and thousands of books and articles have been written about them.

Derivation and meaning of basic terminology

pecten (L. *pecten*, comb) A pigmented, vascular, and comblike process which projects into the vitreous humor from the retina at point of entrance of optic nerve (reptiles and birds). Its functions are obscure, but its peculiar shadow on the retina may make the bird more sensitive to movement in the visual field. It may also enable the bird to determine the position of the sun.

syrinx (Gr. *syrinx*, pipe) The voice box of birds. It is not homologous to the larynx (also found in birds) but is a modification of the trachea and bronchi and is situated where the two main bronchi begin. Voice is produced by the vibrations of a bony ridge (pessulus) and certain membranes.

ANNOTATED REFERENCES

Allen, A. A. 1936. Ornithology Laboratory Notebook. Ithaca, Comstock Publishing Co. *A workbook for exercises on the birds, with descriptions and photographs of nests together with distribution maps.*

Allen, R. P. 1947. The Flame Birds. New York, Dodd, Mead & Co., Inc. *A popular account of the roseate spoonbill and its sanctuaries in the southern states.*

Audubon, J. J. 1937. The Birds of America. New York, The Macmillan Co. *This is a reissue of the famous work first published in 1828-1838. This masterly treatise with superb pictures is without equal in the field of ornithology.*

Broun, M. 1949. Hawks Aloft. New York, Dodd, Mead & Co., Inc. *An account of the migration of hawks as observed from Hawk Mountain, Pennsylvania, with observations on the problem of protecting desirable birds of prey.*

Forbush, E. H. 1939. Natural History of the Birds of Eastern and Central North America. Boston, Houghton Mifflin Co. *A somewhat abbreviated edition of the author's great work, Birds of Massachusetts. The plates are excellent and the descriptions are full.*

Gilliard, E. T. 1958. Living Birds of the World. New York, Doubleday and Co., Inc. *A superb book of birds with illustrations (many in colors). Note, among others, the fine kodachrome of the European robin, famed in tradition and folklore, opposite page 272. Without a doubt the finest book of its kind.*

Griscom, L. 1945. Modern Bird Study. Cambridge, Harvard University Press.

Hausman, L. A. 1948. Bird Hiking. New Brunswick, Rutgers University Press. *A good, little book for the beginner.*

Headstrom, R. 1949. Birds' Nests. New York, Ives Washburn, Inc. *Good photographs of nests with descriptions. Nests are grouped according to a scheme of nest construction.*

Herrick, F. H. 1905. The Home Life of Wild Birds. New York, G. P. Putnam's Sons. *A good account of the methods in studying birds. Some pioneer work on bird photography.*

Hudson, W. H. 1920. The Birds of La Plata, 2 vols. New York, E. P. Dutton & Co., Inc. *An interesting account of the life habits of birds found in the Argentine. Many of those described are the familiar birds of the Northern Hemisphere which winter in Argentina and Patagonia.*

Kendeigh, S. C. 1952. Parental Care and Its Evolution in Birds. Urbana, The University of Illinois. *The author believes that parental care has evolved independently in the different phyla and that the complex patterns for the care of the young are definitely correlated with the development of the nervous and sensory systems.*

Lincoln, F. C. 1950. Migration of Birds. Washington, U. S. Government Printing Office. *An excellent and authoritative account of the origin and migratory routes of birds.*

Peters, J. L. 1931. Checklist of Birds of the World. Cambridge, Harvard University Press.

Peterson, R. T. 1947. Field Guide to the Birds, ed. 2. Boston, Houghton Mifflin Co. *One of the best field manuals for ready identification.*

Pettingill, O. S., Jr. 1946. A Laboratory and Field Manual of Ornithology. Minneapolis, Burgess Publishing Co.

Pettingill, O. S., Jr. 1947. Silent Wings, Madison, Wisconsin Society for Ornithology, Inc. *A pathetic account of the extinction of the passenger pigeon.*

Rand, A. L. 1956. American Water and Game Birds. New York, E. P. Dutton & Co. *A finely illustrated book with clear text descriptions of the various forms considered. Silhouettes add a great deal of interest and value to the work.*

Sturkie, P. D. 1954. Avian Physiology. Ithaca, Cornell University Press. *Dealing with the specialized physiology of birds and intended primarily for research workers, it includes data on nearly all aspects of birds' organ systems and their physiology. The book is well documented.*

Van Tyne, J., and A. J. Berger. 1959. Fundamentals of Ornithology. New York, John Wiley & Sons, Inc. *An up-to-date account of the structure, physiology, distribution, and taxonomy of one of the most interesting groups of animals. The chapter on migration is only one of many fine accounts about the behavior patterns of birds.*

Wallace, G. J. 1955. An Introduction to Ornithology. New York, The Macmillan Co. *An up-to-date book on nearly every aspect of bird life. For the beginner there is no better introductory work on birds. It is clearly written and well illustrated.*

Wolfson, A. (editor). 1955. Recent Studies in Avian Biology. Urbana, University of Illinois Press. *This summary by various specialists is important to all serious students of birds, for it includes an evaluation of the recent concepts and problems of evolution, systematics, anatomy, migration, breeding behavior, diseases, etc. Excellent bibliographies are included.*

Wood, N. A. 1951. The Birds of Michigan. Ann Arbor, University of Michigan Press. *Description of habits and life histories.*

chapter 28

Phylum Chordata

Class Mammalia

SUBPHYLUM VERTEBRATA
CLASS MAMMALIA*—mammals

The term Mammalia was given by Linnaeus (1758) to that group of animals which are nourished by milk from the breasts of the mother. The term is derived from the Latin *mamma,* breast. This group as a whole is considered the highest in the animal kingdom. Their advancement over other groups is quite pronounced from whatever viewpoint they are considered. Many other groups show a greater evolutionary diversity, for there are only between 4,000 and 5,000 named species of mammals, together with many thousand subspecies. In their structure most mammals are less spectacular than other vertebrates. Mammals have stressed the nervous system as their contribution to animal evolution. They have been a successful group, for they adapt themselves readily to new situations and to new food habits. As a climax to the evolutionary development of the nervous system, man himself has been the outcome.

Origin and relationships

It is universally accepted by zoologists that mammals have arisen from reptilian ancestors (cotylosaurs). Because there are many fossil remains of mammalian parts, it has been relatively easy to trace their evolution. The ancestor of all mammals

---

*Mam-ma′li-a (L. *mamma,* breast).

appears to have been a therapsid reptile that lived when the dinosaurs flourished during the Jurassic period. These small mammal-like reptiles probably survived because of their speed. Some of them may have been no larger than mice and dwelt in trees. One of these early reptiles was *Varanope,* whose fossils have been discovered in Texas. This and other similar forms left no direct descendants, but later mammal-like reptiles were larger and their descendants have been better traced.

By the Triassic period the mammal-like reptiles had become a relatively important part of the fauna of the world. One of the most advanced of these mammal ancestors was *Cynognathus,* discovered in South Africa. It was 4 or 5 feet long and oddly resembled a cross between a lizard and a dog. Its sharp teeth indicated carnivorous habits. The fossil record is not clear enough to draw the line between the therapsid reptiles and mammals. When the huge dinosaurs disappeared the small mammal-like animals came into their own. Probably at least five different groups of the mammal-like reptiles developed mammal-like characteristics and were mammalian in at least 50% of their osteological features. Modern taxonomists recognize these as three different subclasses: Prototheria, Metatheria, and Theria. The oldest known fossil mammals are the Pantotheria, an extinct group of the subclass Theria. From this primitive group the marsupials and the insectivora appear to

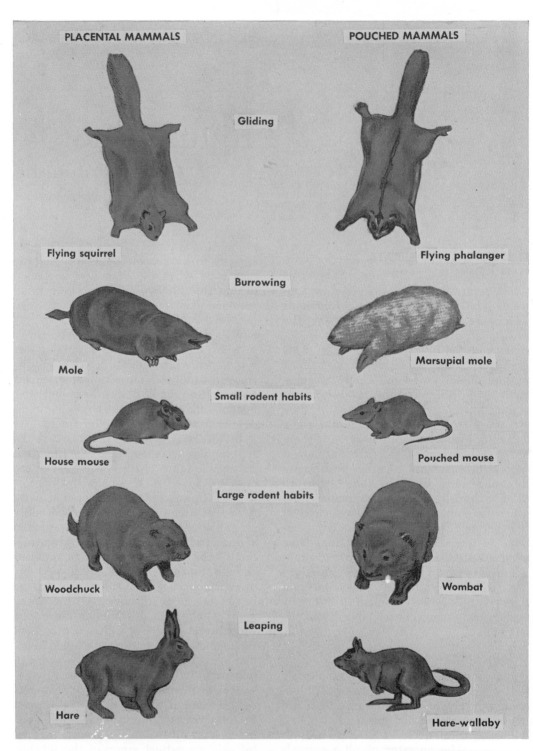

Figure 461. Convergent evolution among mammals. Two groups of mammals not closely related (placentals and marsupials) have independently evolved similar ways of life and occupy similar ecological niches. It will be noted that for every member of an ecological niche in one group there is a counterpart in the other group. This correspondence is not restricted to similarity of habit but also includes morphological features. (From many sources.)

have arisen independently, probably in the Late Jurassic period. From these primitive insectivora the other placental mammals (most of the living orders of mammals) arose. As a result of convergent evolution the marsupials and placentals have evolved similar ways of life (Figure 461). Throughout the Cenozoic era the mammals became dominant. That mammals have had a checkered career is shown by the fact that so many orders of mammals are extinct.

Although mammals have evolved from reptiles, the two groups show many important structural differences. Some important comparisons follow:

1. Most mammals have a body covering of hair instead of scales, although some scales persist, as on the tails of certain mammals.

2. Mammals have two occipital condyles instead of one as in reptiles and they have a larger brain case.

3. The muscular diaphragm of the mammal is found nowhere else. (Birds have a nonmuscular septum.)

4. The lower jaw in mammals is composed of one bone; the reptiles have more.

5. In mammals the lower jaw articulates directly with the skull and not through a quadrate bone which is found in reptiles.

6. Mammals have a chain of three bones in the middle ear: incus, malleus, and stapes; reptiles have only one columella (stapes) in the ear and retain the other two at the angle of the jaw.

7. The polyphyodont teeth of reptiles are replaced by the deciduous and permanent teeth of mammals.

8. Mammals have a four-chambered heart and only the left aortic arch.

9. Mammals have developed the voice apparatus (larynx and epiglottis) which is rudimentary in reptiles.

10. One of the most unique methods of nourishing the young is the milk-secreting glands of mammals.

Some characteristics which are highly developed in mammals are only primitive in reptiles; others have no counterpart at all. Some reptilian characteristics are retained by mammals, such as scales on the tails of rodents and on the body of certain anteaters.

Adaptive radiation

During the age of the dinosaurs, mammals were usually small and played a minor role in the late Mesozoic fauna. But when the dinosaurs vanished near the beginning of the Cenozoic era, mammals suddenly erupted into varied evolutionary patterns. This sudden expansion was due partly to the numerous ecological niches vacated by reptiles into which the mammals could move as their divergent adaptations fitted them. During the Eocene and Oligocene periods most of the orders of mammals as we know them originated so that, including those that later became extinct, the number of orders at that time far exceeded those of the present day. Only a few of our existing mammalian orders arose later. This pattern of adaptive radiation among mammals is a wide-spread phenomenon among all animal populations in which the members branch out to form types suited for particular niches.

The limb structure among mammals best shows this concept (Figure 462). According to this scheme, the early ancestral (stem) mammal had rather short limbs with no specialized adaptations except for a terrestrial existence, such as shrews have at the present time. From this stem type of mammal, by modification of limbs and other structures, there diverged the various types of locomotion such as running (horse, deer), burrowing (moles, gophers), flying (bats), and swimming (seals, whale). There are also modifications of these five basic patterns of locomotion, such as gliding (flying squirrels) and leaping (kangaroo). The student will recall the principle of homology in this adaptive radiation plan. He will note that the limb involved in each case of adaptation is a modification of the pentadactyl limb of the stem mammal, a fact that indicates common relationship.

Figure 462. Adaptive locomotion among mammals. Primitive mammal may have been terrestrial or arboreal, but ambulatory or walking method may well have been the one from which many of the others have arisen. (From several sources.)

Advancements made

What has enabled mammals to flourish and to adapt themselves to such a variety of environments? The one factor above all others is their nervous system; in other respects nonmammals are probably as well equipped as mammals. Another factor is that they are warm blooded, which enables them to be independent of environmental changes. They can survive frigid polar regions or adapt to temperate or torrid zones. Reptiles must hibernate during much of the year except in torrid zones.

Other helpful factors are their methods of nursing and caring for their young and their behavior patterns. Their active curiosity has led them to explore and to hold onto places they have occupied. This behavior pattern of ingenuity in man enables him not only to adjust to varied conditions but also to alter them for his own welfare.

Characteristics

Body covered with hair, but reduced in some; **integument with sweat, sebaceous, and mammary glands**; skeletal features of skull with two occipital condyles, **seven cervical vertebrae** (usually), and often an elongated tail; mouth with teeth on both jaws; **movable eyelids** and **fleshy external ears**; four limbs (reduced or absent in some) adapted for many forms of locomotion; circulatory system of a four-chambered heart, **persistent left aorta**, and **nonnucleated red blood corpuscles**; respiratory system of lungs and a voice box; **a muscular partition between thorax and abdomen**; excretory system of metanephros kidneys and ureters which usually open into the bladder; nervous system of a well-developed brain and twelve pairs of cranial nerves; **warm blooded**; cloaca present only in monotremes; separate sexes; reproductive organs of a penis, **testes (usually in a scrotum)**, ovaries, oviducts, vagina; internal fertilization; **eggs develop in a uterus with placenta attachment** (except monotremes); **fetal membranes (amnion, chorion, and allantois)**; young nourished by **milk from mammary glands**.

Size ranges

The smallest mammal known is the pigmy shrew (*Sorex*) which has a body length of less than 1½ inches and weighs only a fraction of an ounce. The largest, of course, is the whale, certain species of which may reach a length of 103 feet and weigh more than a hundred tons. The whale is the largest animal that has ever lived and is larger than the extinct dinosaurs. The African elephant, which may reach a height of 11 feet at the shoulders and weigh 7 to 8 tons, is the largest living terrestrial mammal. In no other group of animals do we find such a great size range, which indicates the wide adaptability of mammals.

General structures

External appearance. The bodies of mammals are divided into head, neck, trunk, tail, and appendages. The general body form varies enormously, depending upon the species and its adaptations. Aquatic mammals are streamlined for swimming. The **head** in most mammals is large in proportion to the rest of the body because of the well-developed brain. The face typically projects forward to form a snout. The location of the **eyes** depends upon the habits of the animal. Animals such as the rabbit, which is a vegetarian, have eyes on the side for watching their enemies; carnivorous forms have the eyes placed more in front of the head for seeing their prey. External **ears**, characteristic of mammals, are large and movable in many, such as the rabbit and horse, but are small in animals that burrow and may be absent in aquatic mammals. The neck in burrowing forms is short and may be absent altogether in the whale, whereas the giraffe has a neck length out of proportion to the rest of the body. The body **trunk** ranges all the way from heavy and ponderous in the rhinoceros and elephant to slender, as the weasel. **Tails** are used for a variety of purposes. Some are long and bushy (squirrels), flat and rubberlike (beaver), ropelike (elephants), and long and prehensile (monkeys).

Limbs are modified in mammals for

Figure 463. Mole, showing adaptations for life underground. Note enlarged forelimbs (for digging), reduced eyes and ears, and naked snout and tail, both of which have tactile hairs for orientation in its tunnel system. Order Insectivora.

walking or running, climbing, swimming, digging (Figure 463), jumping, and flying. The typical mammal plan has four limbs with **five toes** on each foot but this is found only in generalized forms, such as man and the primates. Many mammals have a reduced number of toes modified for various adaptations.

INTEGUMENTS AND ITS MODIFICATIONS. In general the skin is thicker in mammals than in other classes of vertebrates, although it is made up of the two typical divisions—epidermis and corium (dermis). Among the mammals the corium becomes much thicker than the epidermis. The epidermis varies in thickness. It is relatively thin where it is well protected by hair, but in places subject to much contact and use, such as the palms or soles, its outer layers become thick and cornified with keratin. Some mammals have unusually thick skins, such as the pachyderms (elephants).

Many structures are modifed from the integument. Most of these come from the epidermis, such as nails, claws, hoofs, horns of various animals, glands, and hair. The antlers of deer are exceptional in being bony outgrowths of the skull with a covering of the skin, or "velvet." When this velvet is worn off, the antlers are bare bones and may be said in this condition to have no relation to the integument. Also of epidermal origin is the keratin-fiber horn of the rhinoceros which arises from the cornified layer of the epidermis and is made up of a compact mass of keratin fibers cemented together. Wherever scales are found in mammals, such as the bony plates of armadillos, they are of mesodermal origin. However, in most mammals the scales are replaced with hair, although they persist to some extent in odd forms, such as the scaly anteater, and on the scaly tails of the beaver, rat, opossum, lemur, and shrew.

Some mammals have extensive masses of subcutaneous fat for insulation. Whale blubber is an example.

HAIR. Hair is characteristic of mammals, although in the whale and some other aquatic mammals it is reduced to only a few bristles on the upper lip. Hairs are epidermal and are formed by a column of cells (hair shaft) from this layer pushing down into the corium and enclosing there a tiny cup of blood vessels known as the dermal papilla (Figure 498). Epidermal cells grow in around the hair root to constitute the **root sheaths**. The **hair fol-**

licle is made up of these sheaths and the hair root. Opening into the follicles from the side is the sebaceous gland whose oily secretion keeps the hair moist. The hair usually has three layers: the medulla or pith in the center of the hair, the cortex with pigment granules next to the medulla, and the outer cuticle composed of imbricated scales.

Hair follicles are provided with smooth muscles (**arrector pili**) which cause the hair to assume an erect position. This is the cause of the tingling scalp sensation in a badly frightened man and the erect hairs on the neck of an angry dog.

Hairs are said to be homologous with the scales and feathers of reptiles and birds. However, hair probably originated from the tactile sensory pits (prototriches) of fish and amphibians, probably from apical bristles which at first were of sensory function. The distribution was the same as that of scales, since reptilian sensory pits were located on the apices of epidermal scales. This primitive pattern of distribution has been lost in advanced mammals.

The hair in cross-section may be elliptical or circular. The circular ones are usually straight, whereas the flattened ones are curly. Mammals usually have two kinds of hair: (1) the thick and soft underhair next to the skin for insulation and (2) the coarser and longer guard hair for protection against wear. Around the nose and eyes of many are the long tactile **vibrissae.** The hair covering, or **pelage,** varies greatly with different mammals. Animals in northern climates usually have much denser fur than those in warmer regions. Hair is usually shed once or twice a year. Many northern animals, such as hares, have a white coat in winter and a brown one in summer. Some hairs, such as those in the mane of a horse, may persist throughout life. The hair making up the furs of most animals ceases to grow after reaching a certain length, but those on the scalp of man may continue to grow unless they are shed.

Among interesting varieties of hair are the **spines** of the porcupine (Figure 464) and hedgehog, the stiff **bristles** of hogs, and the **wool** of sheep.

COLORATION. Mammals show many color patterns, although in this respect they do not rival the birds. Most mammals have somber colors mainly for protective purposes. Rarely do mammals have solid colors, such as the polar bear, but most of them have different shades of color on various parts of the body with stripes and bars common. The color is due principally to pigmentation in the hair, although in a

Figure 464. Porcupine. The hair has been modified to form spines. Order Rodentia. (Courtesy L. K. Couch, U. S. Fish and Wildlife Service.)

Phylum Chordata—class Mammalia   553

few, bare surfaces of skin may be found with bright hues, such as in the cheeks and sternal callosities of the mandrill (a species of baboon), which may be due to pigment or to blood capillaries in the skin. At least two types of chromatophores are found in mammals—melanophores (black and brown pigment) and xanthopores (red and yellow pigment). Pigment granules may also lie outside the regular pigment cells. Although the color of hair may fade to some extent, any marked change in the color of a mammal's fur coat must be brought about by molting.

The color patterns of most mammals fit into the color of the environment. This may be due to natural selection, for there is no reason to believe that the environment itself could affect the colors of the animals which live in it. Some think that climatic factors, such as humidity, may play a part in determining the color patterns of animals.

An interesting aspect of color is the pair of rump patches of the pronghorn antelope which are composed of long white hairs erected by special muscles. When alarmed, the animal can flash these patches in a manner visible for a long distance. They may be used as a warning signal to other members of the herd.

Dichromatism, or two-color phases in the same species, is found in foxes and some other mammals. The silver fox, prized for its pelt, may occur in a litter of red foxes. **Albinism,** or a lack of pigment, may happen in most kinds of mammals, as also may **melanism,** or an excess of black pigment.

GLANDS. Mammals have a great variety of integument glands. Whatever the type of gland, they all appear to fall into one of three classes: eccrine, apocrine, and holocrine (Figure 465).

The **eccrine glands,** to which the regular sweat glands belong, are found only in hairless regions (foot pads, etc.) in most mammals, although in some apes and in man they are scattered all over the body and are important devices for heat regulation. These glands have developed by the

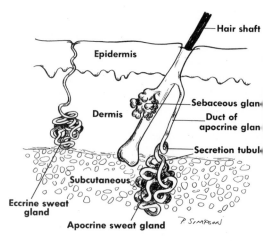

Figure 465. Sweat glands (eccrine and apocrine). Phylogenetically, apocrine glands are older. Eccrine glands are best developed in primates, few and scattered in other mammals. They develop from epidermis and play important role in temperature regulation. Most glands in dog, pig, cow, horse, etc. are apocrine, but these have declined in man, along with hair, for they develop from follicular epithelium. Apocrine glands are not involved in temperature regulation, but their odorous secretions, characteristic of different mammals and different races of man, play a part in sexual attraction.

time of birth and are true secretory or merocrine glands; that is, the cell remains intact or is not destroyed in the process of secretion. Their secretory coils are restricted to the dermal region.

Apocrine glands are larger than eccrine glands and have longer and more winding ducts. Their secretory coil is in the subdermis. They always open into the follicle of a hair or where a hair has been. Phylogenetically they are much older than the eccrine gland and are found in all mammals, some of which have only this kind of gland. The Negro has more apocrine glands than the whites, and women have twice as many as men. They develop about the time of sexual puberty and are restricted (in man) to the axilla, mons pubis, breasts, external auditory canal, prepuce, scrotum, and a few other places. Their secretion is not watery like ordinary sweat (eccrine gland) but is a milky, whitish or yellow secretion which dries on the skin to form a plastic film. Only the tip of the secretory cell is destroyed in the process of secretion. Their secretion is not involved in heat regulation, but their activity is known to be correlated with certain aspects of the sex cycle among other possible functions.

The third type of gland (**holocrine**) is one in which the entire cell is discharged in the secretory process and must be renewed for further secretion. Most of them open into hair follicles, but some are free and open directly onto the surface. The sebaceous gland is the most common example. In most mammals sebaceous glands are found all over the body; in man they are most numerous in the scalp, forehead, and face.

It is not always possible to state from which of the three major types of glands a particular mammalian gland has evolved. Mammary glands, anal glands, inguinal glands of rabbits, and the glands of the auditory canal are supposed to be modified apocrine glands.

Among the most common glands are the **scent** glands found in all terrestrial species. Their location and function vary greatly. Some are defensive in nature, others convey information to members of the same species, and still others are involved in the mating process. These glands are often located in the preorbital, metatarsal, and interdigital regions (deer); preputial region near the penis (muskrats, beaver, canine family, etc.); base of tail (wolves, foxes); and anal region (skunk, mink, weasel). These last, the most odoriferous of all glands, open by ducts into the anus and can discharge their secretions forcefully for several feet. During the mating season many male mammals give off strong scent for attracting the females.

Sweat glands are used mainly to regulate the body temperature. They are very common on such animals as the horse and man but are greatly reduced on the carnivores (cats) and are entirely lacking in shrews, whales, and others. Dogs are now known to have sweat glands all over the body. In the human, racial differences are pronounced. Negroes, who have more than whites, can withstand warmer weather. **Sebaceous** glands which open into the hair follicles keep the skin and hair soft and glossy. A modified sebaceous gland known as the Meibomian gland is found at the edge of each eyelid and provides an oily film between the eyelids and eyeball. **Lacrimal,** or tear, glands keep the surface of the eye moist and clean.

Mammary glands, which give the name to the group, occur on all female mammals and on most, if not all, male mammals; on the latter they are often covered by hair. They develop by the thickening of the epidermis to form a milk line along each side of the abdomen in the embryo. On certain parts of these lines the mammas appear while the intervening parts of

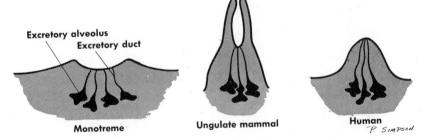

Figure 466. Types of mammalian nipples. Monotremes have no nipples and the young lick up the milk from ridged depression as milk exudes from mother's skin. Mammary glands are supposed to have originated from apocrine sweat glands. Primitive arrangement of nipples (which vary in number) consists of two series or milk lines along abdomen. Composition of milk varies among different species of mammals. Whale milk, for instance, contains four times more protein and ten times more fat than that of cow, but it lacks sugar.

the ridge disappear. They secrete milk for the nourishment of the young. When distended with milk, the glands produce marked integumentary swellings, the breasts, or mammas. The outlets of the gland are by elevated nipples (absent in monotremes) (Figure 466). The glands are located on the thorax of primates, bats, and a few others but on the abdomen or inguinal region in other mammals. Nipples vary in number from two in the human, horse, bat, etc. to twenty-five in the opossum. The number is not always constant in the same species. Mammary glands are periodic in their functioning, growing during pregnancy and secreting during the nursing period of the young.

TEETH. All mammals, with the exception of certain species of whales, monotremes, and anteaters, have teeth. The character of the dentition is correlated with the food habits of the mammal. Typically, mammals have two sets of teeth: deciduous and permanent. They are set in sockets in the jaw and the various types are molars, premolars, incisors, and canine. The rounded or pointed eminence on the masticating surface is called a **cusp.** Each type of tooth is specialized for some aspect of food getting or mastication. Incisors with simple crowns and slightly sharp edges are mainly for snipping or

biting; canines with long conical crowns are specialized for piercing; premolars with compressed crowns and one or two cusps are suited for shearing and slicing; and the molars with large bodies and variable cusp arrangement are for crushing and mastication. Molars always belong to the permanent set.

Each tooth is made up of **dentine** from the corium and the covering **enamel** from epithelium. **Cementum** from the corium lies around the **root** of the tooth within which is the **pulp cavity** of nerves and blood vessels. Certain insectivora cut only milk teeth. This condition is called **monophyodont;** in contrast is the **diphyodont** dentition of both deciduous and permanent teeth. Teeth that are alike are called **homodont,** which is characteristic of lower vertebrates; when they are differentiated to serve a variety of purposes, they are called **heterodont.** Teeth were already differentiated into these four types in the higher mammal-like reptiles. Carnivorous animals have teeth with sharp edges for tearing and piercing. They have well-developed canines, but some of the molars are poorly developed. In the herbivores, the canines are suppressed, whereas the molars are broad, with enamel ridges for grinding. Such teeth are also usually high crowned in contrast to the low

Figure 467. Wart hog, a native of Africa, is example of animal in which canine teeth have become modified into tusks. Order Artiodactyla. (Courtesy Smithsonian Institution, Washington, D. C.)

556

crowns of carnivores. The incisors of rodents have enamel only on the anterior surface, so that the softer dentine behind wears away faster, resulting in chisel-shaped teeth that are always sharp. Moreover, rodents' incisors grow throughout life and must be worn away to keep pace with the growth. If two opposing incisors fail to meet, the growth of the incisors continues and results in serious consequences to the animal.

The **tusks** of the elephant and the wild boar are modifications of teeth (Figure 467). The elephant tusk is a modified upper incisor and may be present in both males and females; in the wild boar the tusk is a modified canine present only in the male. Both are formidable weapons.

The number and arrangement of permanent teeth are expressed by a **dental formula.** The figures above the horizontal line represent the number of incisors, canines, premolars, and molars on one-half of the upper jaw; the figures below the line indicate the corresponding teeth in one-half of the lower jaw.

Man	Dog
2-1-2-3	3-1-4-2
2-1-2-3	3-1-4-3

Internal structures. Internally the structure of the mammals is basically the same as that of other vertebrates. The coelomic cavity, however, is divided into thoracic and abdominal cavities, separated by a unique muscular diaphragm. The thoracic region is divided into three coelomic cavities: two lateral pleural cavities and a median pericardial cavity.

DIGESTIVE SYSTEM. A **hard palate** of bone and tissue separates the nasal chambers from the mouth and is supplemented behind by the fleshy **soft palate.** The passageway from the mouth to the pharynx is known as the **fauces,** which has the tonsils on each side of it. The **glottis,** which is the opening into the trachea, has the flaplike **epiglottis** over it to prevent the entrance of food. Both mucous and salivary glands pour their secretions into the mouth. The **tongue** is unusually well equipped with numerous **papillae** and **taste buds.** It has

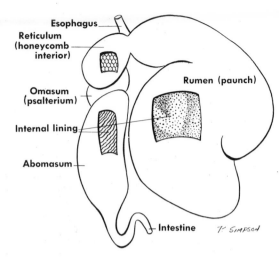

Figure 468. Stomach of a ruminant. By rapid eating, ruminants fill paunch with partially masticated food which is reduced to pulp by bacteria and ciliates. When animal "chews the cud," masses of food enter reticulum in which they are rolled into a cud, regurgitated, and thoroughly masticated in the mouth. When swallowed the second time, the cud goes first to omasum and then on to abomasum to be mixed with gastric juice for digestion before it enters intestine.

many uses, such as drawing grass into the mouth in herbivores, licking up ants in the anteater, and smoothing out the fur in fur-bearing forms.

Among the interesting features of the digestive tract is the four-chambered stomach of ruminants (cattle, camels, deer, etc.) which "chew the cud." The stomach compartments are (1) **rumen,** a large cavity; (2) **reticulum,** a space lined with shallow pits; (3) **omasum,** much folded; and (4) **abomasum,** which is the only compartment that contains glands (Figure 468). These animals collect food rapidly, mix it with saliva, and pass it to the rumen. After feeding, the animal lies down and regurgitates the food into the mouth, thoroughly chews it, and then swallows it. The food then passes through the other three compartments. In the walls of the rumen and reticulum of camels there are water cells in which these animals can store large amounts of water for desert journeys.

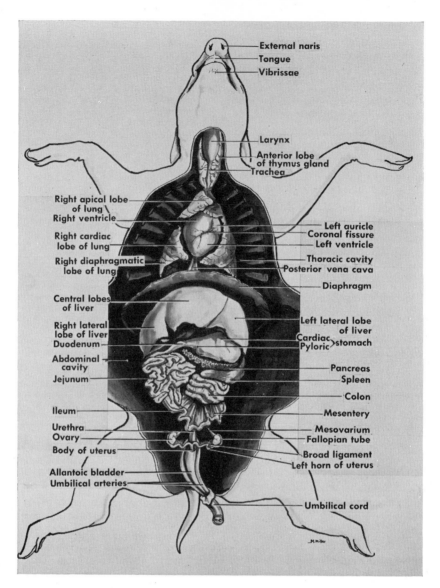

Labels in figure:
External naris
Tongue
Vibrissae
Larynx
Anterior lobe of thymus gland
Trachea
Right apical lobe of lung
Right ventricle
Right cardiac lobe of lung
Right diaphragmatic lobe of lung
Central lobes of liver
Right lateral lobe of liver
Duodenum
Abdominal cavity
Jejunum
Ileum
Urethra
Ovary
Body of uterus
Allantoic bladder
Umbilical arteries
Left auricle
Coronal fissure
Left ventricle
Thoracic cavity
Posterior vena cava
Diaphragm
Left lateral lobe of liver
Cardiac
Pyloric
stomach
Pancreas
Spleen
Colon
Mesentery
Mesovarium
Fallopian tube
Broad ligament
Left horn of uterus
Umbilical cord

Figure 469. Visceral organs of female fetal pig, ventral view.

The vampire bat has the fundus of its stomach drawn out into a long diverticulum, or pouch, in which it stores blood drawn from its victims.

The **cecum** between the small and large intestine has many modifications. Herbivorous mammals usually have large ones, but carnivores have small ones or none at all. In monotremes and female marsupials a **cloaca** is present, but in other mammals the anus is separated from the openings of the urinary and reproductive systems.

CIRCULATORY SYSTEM. Mammals share with birds in having the most efficient blood systems in the animal kingdom. The heart is four chambered and the systemic and pulmonary systems are separated. The left aorta persists instead of the right, as in birds. A hepatic portal system is found in mammals, but the renal portal system has disappeared.

RESPIRATORY SYSTEM. Mammals in their breathing make use of the complete separation of the thorax from the abdomen. The partition between these two cavities is the muscular **diaphragm** which is in the form of a dome with the convex side anteriorly. The **lungs** are located in the thorax in spaces called the pleural cavities. When the thoracic cavity is expanded by the elevation of the ribs and the depression of the diaphragm, air is drawn into the lungs. Relaxation of the muscles of the ribs and diaphragm forces the air out. The voice box (larynx) is well developed in most mammals.

EXCRETORY SYSTEM. All mammals have the third, or metanephros, kidney (or that part which develops from the caudal region of the archinephros), although during embryonic life they have a mesonephros. Connecting the kidney with the urinary bladder are the two ureters. The bladder opens to the outside by the **urethra,** except in monotremes, in which it empties into the cloaca.

NERVOUS SYSTEM. The cerebrum and cerebellum especially show marked advancements over other vertebrates. Only the monotremes have a reptilian type of brain. Higher mammals have the cerebral surface thrown into many convolutions, and all have the cerebellum convoluted as in birds. The two optic lobes of other classes are divided, becoming the four **corpora quadrigemina** in mammals. The general trend in the mammalian brain is for the upper part and sides of the end brain to expand and become the cerebral cortex. Here cortical centers differentiate for localization of functions which, in other vertebrates, are controlled at lower levels. The spinal cord in mammals does not reach the end of the bony vertebral canal which is filled with roots of spinal nerves below the end of the cord forming the so-called **cauda equina.** In common with birds and reptiles, mammals have twelve pairs of cranial nerves.

SENSORY SYSTEM. In correlation with the highly developed nervous system, mammals are well endowed with sense organs. Cutaneous sense organs, which reach their highest development in mammals, are represented by many forms of corpuscles and free nerve endings. The middle ear is now provided with three ossicles, malleus, incus, and stapes, and the sense of hearing is acute. The external ear (pinna) is found in most mammals. The nictitating membrane so well developed in the eye of birds tends to be reduced in mammals. The chemical senses of smell and taste reach a high stage of development in mammals, although some, such as whales, have little or no chemical sense.

ENDOCRINE SYSTEM. The endocrine glands of mammals are better known than those of any other group. They include the pituitary, thyroid, parathyroid, islets of Langerhans, adrenals, and gonads.

REPRODUCTIVE SYSTEM. The sexes are always separate in mammals, as they are in practically all vertebrates. The paired **testes** of the male are usually enclosed in a scrotal sac which hangs down from the body in a more or less pendulous condition (Figure 470). In some (rodents, bats, and camels) the testes descend into the scrotum only during the breeding season, and at other times they are withdrawn into the body cavity. In monotremes, elephants, whales, and others, they always remain in the body cavity. The penis of mammals is a closed tube, except in monotremes, where the urethra is a groove. The glans penis is double in opossums, and in some carnivores, seals, cetaceans, moles,

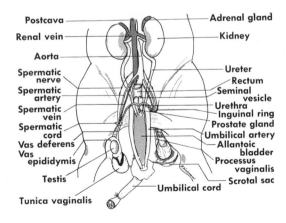

Figure **470.** Male urogenital organs of fetal pig.

Labels (top to bottom, left):
Postcava
Renal vein
Aorta
Spermatic nerve
Spermatic artery
Spermatic vein
Spermatic cord
Vas deferens
Vas epididymis
Testis
Tunica vaginalis

Labels (top to bottom, right):
Adrenal gland
Kidney
Ureter
Rectum
Seminal vesicle
Urethra
Inguinal ring
Prostate gland
Umbilical artery
Allantoic bladder
Processus vaginalis
Scrotal sac
Umbilical cord

bats, and some monkeys, the penis is stiffened by a penis bone, **os priapi.**

The female organs (Figure 469) are the paired **ovaries,** the **Fallopian tubes** (oviducts), the **uterus,** and the **vagina.** Basically, the uterus is double but is found in different degree of fusion among the various mammals. In rodents the horns of the uterus enter the vagina separately (**duplex**); in carnivores they fuse at the base (**bipartite**); in ungulates the fusion is more complete, forming a common chamber for the embryos (**bicornuate**); and in apes and man the fusion is complete and the uterus is a single chamber (**simplex**).

MUSCULAR SYSTEM. The better-developed appendages of mammals are correlated with an increase in their musculature to meet the varied uses of adaptive radiation. On the other hand, the trunk muscles have been reduced and changed. Some muscles have divided or migrated. Only the intercostal, intervertebral, and rectus abdominis muscles show segmentation. Some new developments in muscles also appear. Integumental, or cutaneous, muscles, such as the **panniculus carnosus,** appear in marsupials and reach a high degree of development in the horse and other forms but become greatly reduced in primates. Another addition is the diaphragm muscle, probably a derivative of the neck myotomes. Many of the muscles in mammals are similar to those in lower vertebrates except that mammals have greatly stressed those on the head, neck, and limbs. Division and migration have often made it difficult to homologize mammalian muscles with those of birds and reptiles.

SKELETAL SYSTEM. The general plan of the mammalian endoskeleton is similar to the skeleton of birds and reptiles. Some marked differences, however, are found in the axial skeleton. The bones of the cranium are firmly knit together and the lower jaw is more firmly articulated. Birds, reptiles, and fish have loose connections between the skull and lower jaw. Usually these vertebrates have a series of bones that serve for the connection between the skull and the lower jaw so that the latter is suspended from, rather than directly articulated with, the skull. There is also a considerable fusion of bones in mammals. The mammalian shoulder girdle shows several advances beyond the reptilian ancestors of mammals. The **coracoid,** except in monotremes, is no longer a separate bone but is a process on the scapula. The scapula has acquired shelves and projections for the attachment of muscles for the varied forms of locomotion. The vertebral column of mammals, with few exceptions, contains seven cervical vertebrae. With regard to the thoracic and lumbar vertebrae, mammals vary to some extent. **Amphiplatyan** vertebrae (that is, those flat on both ends) are the chief type in mammals, but some other types are found here and there. The vertebrae of mammals also represent a fusion of the centrum with bony discs, a process unlike that of other vertebrates.

Natural history and behavior

No group of animals has more interesting behavior patterns than the mammals. With their highly developed nervous system, alertness, and adaptations, mammals display a remarkable range of activity. Mammals demonstrate the highest range of intelligence patterns in the animal kingdom and have worked out ingenious devices for survival.

Body temperature. Part of the great activity of mammals may be attributed to the fact that they are warm blooded (homoiothermic or endothermal). Many of the larger members have temperatures from 100° to 103° F. Man's temperature is 98.6° F. Yet many mammals have an unstable temperature which fluctuates or is seasonal in character. Daily rhythms are found in practically all, including man. Rectal temperature is 1° to 2° F. higher than mouth temperature, and skin temperature is 7° to 9° F. lower than the internal temperature (man). Primitive mammals (monotremes) have a variation of about 10° F. in their temperatures. Such mammals are called **heterothermal** and their temperature is regulated chiefly by variations of heat production (increased by activity) and by the surrounding temperature. To this group belongs also newly born mammals, spiny anteater (*Echidna*), armadillos, bats, and all true hibernating mammals. Sloths placed in cold surroundings will have a drop in temperature of 15° to 20° F. Mammals in hibernation may have a temperature that fluctuates like a cold-blooded form. The upper limits of high temperatures (lethal) for mammals is between 104° and 112° F.; lower limits may extend down to a few degrees from freezing for some species.

Distribution. Mammals are found in most habitats which support life, but few of them are adaptable as to be able to live in the wide range of all the conditions found in most of our continents. Some, however, are able to range far wider than others. One of these is the shrew (*Sorex cinereus*), which is found from Alaska and northern Canada to our southern and southwestern states. Within such a wide area this tiny animal is able to adapt itself to a great variety of ecological habitats. On the other hand, some gophers and bats are restricted to small regions. This is particularly the case with forms that may be more or less isolated by the nature of the terrain. Factors that are mainly responsible for the distribution of mammals are natural barriers of water and land, temperature, climate, food, shelter, and enemies.

Aquatic mammals live in varied environments as shown by strictly aquatic forms, such as whales and porpoises; by seashore forms which spend a part of the time in the water, such as seals and walruses; and by fresh-water forms, such as beavers, muskrats, and mink.

Mammals, however, are mainly terrestrial and are found in nearly every kind of habitat on land. Woodlands attract them for the shelter, nesting sites, and protection they afford. Squirrels, monkeys, and various carnivores which are strictly arboreal are rarely found on the ground. Others, such as moles, shrews, rabbits, and hares, are found on the surface of soil or within burrows. Mammals are found at nearly all altitudes on our high mountain ranges, some of them far above timber line, such as mountain sheep and conies. Treeless and grassy regions often support large populations of gophers, prairie dogs, and other rodents, as well as many hoofed animals. Many mammals are active only at night and spend the daytime in their shelters and places of retreat.

Home range. One interesting aspect of mammal distribution is the territory rights of the members of a particular species. Many of the larger mammals literally "stake out" claims where they will not tolerate other members of the same species. This seems to be the case with the larger carnivores that are solitary in their habits, such as the grizzly bear and the mountain lion. The grizzly bear, for instance, has a range of many square miles which it guards zealously against all other grizzlies. Just how these animals establish priority or mark the boundaries of their ranges is not exactly known. It is known that some of them leave claw marks on trees which may serve as a warning to intruders, and some mark their rights with urine. Whenever a new territory is being colonized the first individuals to enter are usually the males, as Darling found in his famous study on the red deer. The practice of territory claims may be far more common than we yet know.

The home range refers to the area an animal covers in its normal activities of living. This is often determined by the nature of the territory, the supply of food, and the shelter. Small herbivorous animals, such as rabbits, ground squirrels, and squirrels, have relatively small ranges; carnivorous forms must range farther in seeking their prey. A woodchuck, for instance, may stay within its own half acre of a luxurious clover field, but a mink is known to travel several miles in a single night. Both the home range and territory of the same animal often vary during its life cycle.

Population surveys. Many surveys have been made to determine the number and kind of mammals found within a given area. These surveys, for which a certain amount of error must be allowed, are made by trapping, observation, tracks, signs, and other devices. Surveys are of great practical importance in conservation programs and ecological studies. There are several different techniques employed. Actual counts of all the individuals of a species population may be made on a given area, such as Darling did with various herds of red deer, provided conditions are favorable. Also used are indirect methods of marking captured specimens, releasing them, and, from the ratio of recaptures to the marked numbers, estimating the number in the whole population of the species in the area being studied. Another common method is the sampling method; individuals are counted on a specific part of a large area and then an estimate of the total on the large area is made from the number on the sample area. Results of these surveys show that the population of any species of mammal tends to vary from year to year. The population of most mammals is greatest just after the breeding season because of the additional young members.

Fluctuations of animal populations are often known as cycles. A cycle may take several years, during which time a species may build up to a peak and then decline. Meadow mice, for instance, usually have a cycle of about three to four years; the snow shoe hare, ten years; and squirrels, five years. Usually smaller mammals have a shorter cycle than larger species. The factors responsible for these cyclic variations may be such things as the abundance of food, the pressure of enemies, epidemic diseases, reproductive rate, weather conditions, etc. The abundance of one species may be correlated with that of another. The cycle of the Canadian lynx is closely correlated with the cycle of the rabbit or hare, for the lynx preys on these animals. Whenever a species declines rapidly, an epidemic disease is suspected. Many such outbreaks have been observed. The denser the population, the more rapidly such diseases spread.

Population densities of the various species of mammals depend upon shelters, food, enemies, and kind of species. Small mammals are usually far more common per unit area than are larger ones. Mice and shrews under favorable conditions may number 100 to 200 or even more per acre; jack rabbits about 10 to 20 per square mile; and deer about 12 to 15 per square mile.

Ecologic density, which refers to the habitable parts of any total area being studied, is also an important concept in population studies. Rarely do we find an area as big as a township which has a uniformity of ecological conditions all over it. Such an area may include grassland, forest, marsh, and streams, and any particular species population will be far more concentrated in those habitats for which it is best adapted.

Homes and shelters. Nearly all mammals have places where they rear their young or shelter themselves when they are not actively engaged in feeding or other pursuits. Many have permanent quarters from which they seldom stray far and to which they return to rest. Others, such as deer, which range far and wide to forage, are usually not restricted to a permanent home but take advantage of whatever is at hand. In winter even deer have tramped-out yards in remote forests near which they are always found. But the smaller mammals usually establish their residency in some protected home for long periods or even for life. Arboreal species, squirrels, raccoons, opossums, and mice make use of holes in trees. Rabbits, woodchucks, prairie dogs, coyotes, and skunks excavate burrows in the ground. Some squirrels and mice build elaborate nests (Figure 471) in the branches of trees. Many mammals make snug nests in their shelters, notably the muskrat, beaver, and chipmunk.

Food and storage. On the basis of food habits, animals may be divided into herbivorous, carnivorous, omnivorous, and insectivorous. Within each of these dietary classes the food of a species may show considerable variation, as mammals are highly adaptable. **Herbivorous** animals feed upon grasses and vegetation. This

Figure 471. Nest of fox squirrel, used for both a winter and a summer home. Nest 30 feet from ground.

group is large and includes most domestic animals, deer, elephants, rabbits, squirrels, and hosts of others. The **carnivorous** forms feed mainly upon the herbivorous animals and include foxes, weasels, cats, dogs, fishers, wolverines, lions, tigers, and others. **Omnivorous** mammals live on both plants and animals. Examples of these are man, raccoon, rats, and bears. Many carnivorous forms eat fruits, berries, and grasses when hard pressed. The fox, which usually feeds upon mice, small rodents, and birds, will eat frozen apples, beechnuts, and corn when the normal sources are scarce. Those that subsist chiefly on insects are called **insectivorous**, and mammals having these food habits are the bats, moles, shrews, etc. Many other mammals, such as bears, raccoons, mice, and ground squirrels, will catch and eat insects.

Mammals will often consume amounts of food out of all proportion to their size. Many will eat an amount of food in twenty-four hours equal to their own body weight. Shrews and moles will starve if deprived of food for a few hours. A large carnivorous mammal, such as the mountain lion, is known to kill an average of at least one deer each week and, when game is abundant, even more.

Mammals have many problems in obtaining food. Seasonal changes in food supplies are marked in temperature zones when inclement weather may cut off most normal supplies. Mammals have many ways to meet these emergencies. Some migrate to regions where food is more abundant. Others hibernate and sleep through the winter months. Many carnivores which do not migrate have to range far and wide to eke out an existence. Even so they undergo periods of fasting between feeding periods. But some provident mammals build up stores during periods of plenty. This habit is most pronounced in many of our rodents, such as squirrels, chipmunks, gophers, and certain mice. All the tree squirrels, red, fox, and gray, collect nuts, conifer seeds, and fungi and bury these caches for winter use. Later they locate these caches by their marvelous sense of smell. The chipmunk is one of the greatest providers, for it spends the autumn months in collecting nuts and seeds. Some of its caches may exceed a bushel in amount. Even carnivorous animals do a certain amount of storing, usually temporarily buried in the ground or under rubbish from which they do not stray far until it is all consumed.

Migration and emigration. Migration refers to the periodic passing from and the return to a region. Birds are renowned for their migratory habits, but many mammals also have the practice, though their ranges of migration are less striking. Ecologists recognize several types of migration. Some of the factors causing migration among mammals are the seasonal scarcity of food (alimental migration), severe climatic conditions (climatic migration), and the desire to have suitable places for rearing their young (gametic migration). One of the most remarkable migratory mammals is the fur seal (Figure 472). The breeding grounds of these animals are on the Pribilof Islands off the coast of Alaska. During the winter the females and young winter

Figure 472. Fur seal rookery. Fur seals have many interesting behavior patterns, not the least of which is their remarkable migration. (Courtesy V. B. Scheffer, U. S. Fish and Wildlife Service.)

far to the south of the islands. The old bulls do not go so far south. Toward spring all of them migrate back to the islands for breeding and for rearing their young. For the females this means a journey of 2,000 to 3,000 miles. On their return the young are born and cared for during the summer months. Late in the fall the various seals return to their winter quarters. This is an example of seasonal migration. The caribou of Alaska and Canada perform great mass migrations. Availability of food seems to be the primary reason. Some species of deer and mountain sheep undergo altitudinal migrations, spending the summer on the high mountains and returning to lower altitudes for the winter. Some of the bats spend the winter in caves in the northern regions; others migrate as far as the West Indies for the winter (seasonal and latitudinal migration).

Emigration means the movement away from a territory with no intention of returning. It may be induced by lack of food or overpopulation or by a combination of factors. **Immigration,** is the coming into a new region. The lemming (*Lemmus*) of Norway and Sweden is one of the best known cases of emigration. These small rodents are found on the high plateaus where they live on the moss and vegetation of that rough terrain. Usually they produce one or two litters of four or five young each season. But every four or five years their reproductive power is greatly increased, probably caused by a hormone or vitamin that they get from their food, and they will have three or four litters of eight to eleven young. This leads to overpopulation and mass emigration is the result. They overflow into the lower land masses, into the rivers and fiords, and even into the sea, where they perish. Mass movements of gray squirrels were frequent during pioneer days, and there are many authentic accounts of these within recent years. Emigration of the Norway rat accounts for the large number of these rodents in places where they were uncommon before.

Hibernation. Many mammals solve the problems of winter scarcity of food and low climatic temperatures by undergoing (1) a state of drowsy inactivity and intermittent sleep or (2) true hibernation. In the first of these processes the mammal becomes dormant for several weeks during which time it has intermittent periods of sleep and wakefulness. When asleep it responds quickly to stimulation and its metabolic processes are only a little lower than those of an active animal. There is little to no lowering of temperature. Such animals may remain in a dormant condition for considerable lengths of time, but the light sleepers frequently interrupt their winter sleep by stirring around. Good examples of this type of winter sleep are skunks, bears, opossums, badgers, and raccoons. True hiberation, on the other hand, involves a whole syndrome of physiological states different from normal activity. It involves an inactive state in which bodily processes are lowered, with a marked fall in temperature, which may be only slightly higher than that of the surroundings, and an inability to control the body temperature. For instance, in a ground squirrel, the respiratory rate may be nearly 200 during activity but only 4 or 5 while hibernating; comparable values for the heart rate are 150 and 5.

Although drowsy, torpid, and difficult to awaken while in their sleep, hibernating animals will awaken when their surroundings approach freezing, to keep from freezing to death. All true hibernating animals usually store up great amounts of fat before going into hibernation, although this is also true of some that are not true hibernators (bears). All hibernating animals are heterothermal animals and their temperature during active states is somewhat lower than nonhibernators. American mammals that hibernate include ground squirrels, woodchucks, bats, and jumping mice. The primary stimulus for starting hibernation may be a lack of food supplies, low temperature, and other factors not well understood.

Summer torpor, or **aestivation,** is practiced by some mammals, especially by ground squirrels in the western parts of our country. During the hot months of July and August, these animals seek out deep burrows and remain sleeping there during these hot and dry months. Aestivation in warm and tropical countries is quite common among a great variety of animals.

Enemies. Practically all mammals have enemies. Most herbivorous animals are preyed upon by flesh-eating animals, and some of the carnivorous forms are eaten by larger carnivores. Many birds of prey, hawks, owls, and eagles, live on the smaller mammals, such as squirrels, rabbits, and mice. Snakes eat many mammals. Man kills predator mammals which prey on his livestock and catches fur-bearing mammals for their fur. All mammals are parasitized, and many diseases are peculiar to them. Epidemic diseases are known to decimate mammal populations whenever they become too crowded.

Behavior patterns. Mammals are in a group by themselves in acquiring new behavior through learning and in their general intelligence. Their learning powers are so great that it is often difficult to distinguish between actions that are instinctive and those that are acquired. The range in this respect varies, of course, from the low to the higher levels of mammals. A mouse or shrew, for instance, will not demonstrate the same learning ca-

Figure 473. Black bear. (Courtesy E. P. Haddon, U. S. Fish and Wildlife Service.)

Phylum Chordata—class Mammalia 565

pacity as a chimpanzee. In nearly all varieties of learning, however, mammals will score much higher than other groups, whether it is conditioned responses, selective learning, insight solutions of problems, or elementary reasoning. The subject of mammalian intelligence is discussed more fully in Chapter 41, Animal Behavior Patterns, but two or three aspects of their behavior may be mentioned here. In the first place, the psychological superiority of man over other mammals is due chiefly to his capacity for language communication involving a systematic code of symbol expression whereby he is able to convey meaning to others. There is no evidence that nonhuman mammals have such language activities. But they do have limited powers of communication by which they can influence each other. They can do this by mimetic signs, by voice, and in other ways.

Most mammals can make use of their voices for warning each other, for scaring their enemies, for calling their young to them, for mating, and for calling each other together. Some apparently make sounds just to get rid of their emotions and pent-up energies. Some mammals, such as cattle, moose, and many monkeys, have powerful voices which can be heard for long distances. Many female mammals make characteristic sounds to their young. Just what meanings primates, such as apes, can convey with their utterances are not known. Bats use their ultrasonic notes to guide them in their flight, for these notes echo from nearby objects and so the bats can avoid such obstacles.

Recently a most striking behavior pattern has been observed among shrews (*Crocidura*) on the continent of Europe. Known as the caravan formation, it was photographed for the first time in 1957. It is a method employed by a mother shrew for removing all her litter of offspring at one time from a place of danger (Figure 474). In tandem formation the first youngster seizes the mother's fur near the root of her tail, is in turn seized the same way by the next youngster in the procession, and so on. The behavior may be partly innate but learning is involved, for considerable practice seems to be necessary before an efficient caravan is attained. The behavior has not been observed in other shrews, but variant forms of it have been found in field mice and other mammals.

Reproduction and secondary sex characteristics. Mammals have interesting mating habits, for much of their general behavior is centered around their breeding activity. Fertilization is always internal, and they are all viviparous, except the monotremes, which lay eggs. Most mammals have definite mating seasons, usually in the winter or spring. Many males are capable of fertile copulation at any time, but the female mating function is restricted to a periodic cycle known as the **estrus cycle,** or "heat." At times other than during this period they will not allow the male to approach them. The estrus cycle is marked by certain characteristic changes in the vagina and uterus. The cycle is divided into the **anestrum,** or resting period; **proestrum,** or preparation for mating; **estrum,** or period of accepting the male; and **metestrum,** or period of

Figure 474. Caravan formation of the European shrew, *Crocidura,* by which mother transports her litter to place of safety when danger threatens. Evidence indicates that the young must be taught and that the method is not instinctive. Modifications of this method have been observed among other small mammals, such as mice.

regressive changes in the uterine and vaginal walls. Animals vary as to the time of ova discharge from the ovary, but usually it occurs during the estrus period or shortly thereafter. How often females are in heat also varies greatly among the different mammals. Unless she has fruitfully mated, the female rat comes in estrus about every four days; the female dog, about every six months; the female house mouse, every four to six days; and the cow, every twenty-one days. Female rabbits are supposed to breed at any time. Those animals which have only a single estrus during the breeding season are called **monestrus;** those which have a recurrence of estrus during the breeding season are called **polyestrus.** Dogs, foxes, and bats belong to the first group; field mice and squirrels are all polyestrus. In the anthropoid primates, the female may be receptive and the male potent throughout the reproductive cycle, although the estrus period may have some influence on the time of mating.

Gestation, or period of pregnancy, varies greatly among the mammals. Mice and rats have about twenty-one days; rabbits and hares, thirty to thirty-six days; cat and dog, sixty days; cow, 280 days; and the elephant, twenty-two months. The marsupials (opossum) have a very short gestation period of thirteen days; at the end of that time the tiny young leave the vaginal orifice and make their way to the marsupial pouch where they attach themselves to nipples. Here they remain for more than two months (Figure 476).

The number of young produced by mammals in a season depends upon many factors. Usually the larger the animal, the smaller the number of young in a litter. Perhaps one of the greatest factors involved is the number of enemies a species has. Small rodents which serve as prey for so many carnivores produce, as a rule, more than one litter of several young each season. Field mice are known to produce seventeen litters of four to nine each in a year. Most carnivores have but one litter of three to five young a year. Large mammals, elephants and horses, have only one young, and the same is true for many others.

The condition of the young at birth also varies. Those young born with hair and open eyes and ability to move around are called **precocial** (ungulates and the jack rabbit); those that are naked, blind, and helpless like carnivores and rodents are known as **altricial.** Mammals exhibit a great deal of parental care and will fiercely fight in defense of their young. When disturbed they will often carry their young to more secure places.

Differences between the sexes of the same species of mammals are not so marked as in birds. The male is often larger and more powerful, especially in the larger mammals. The male fur seal may be four or five times as large as the female, although such disparity in sex sizes is uncommon. Scent glands may be more common in the male. Sexual variation in color is not common. The male of some monkeys may have a different shade from the female. Male deer are provided with antlers which are lacking in the female. Most of the smaller mammals have few or no secondary sex characteristics.

Economic importance

Man's welfare has been closely related to that of other mammals. He has domesticated the horse, cattle, sheep, pig, goat, dog, and many others. He uses these for beasts of burden, for food, and for clothing and many other products.

The fur-bearing animals have proved useful to man in all stages of his culture. For early man they were indispensable. Still basically a hunter, man hunts mammals for pleasure as well as for profit. This is why we have conservation programs. Of fur-bearing mammals, the muskrat at present seems to be the most valuable. Many mink and fox farms have proved very profitable. Although many wild fur-bearing animals have been almost exterminated, the annual value of furs in this country amounts to many millions of dollars.

Many mammals, including the small ones, destroy insects and seeds and are thus helpful. Skunks feed on grubs and cutworms. Moles and shrews consume enormous numbers of insect larvae.

Some mammals, however, are inimical to man's interests. Many rodents, rabbits, field mice, and woodchucks damage crops and fruit trees. Gophers and prairie dogs (Figure 483) do damage with their burrows and by destroying valuable crops. A dozen jack rabbits will eat as much as a sheep. Predatory mammals, wolves, coyotes (Figure 478), and panthers destroy much livestock.

Mammals also carry disease. Bubonic plague and typhus are carried by house rats. Tularemia, or rabbit fever, is transmitted to man by the wood tick carried by rabbits, woodchucks, muskrats, and other rodents. Rocky Mountain spotted fever is carried by ticks on ground squirrels. Trichina and tapeworms are acquired by man through hogs, cattle, and other mammals.

Probably the most destructive mammal is the house rat. The amount of damage done by this crafty rodent can scarcely be estimated. Recently, more effective controls have been used against rats, but so adaptable is this animal that it will probably be a menace for a long time.

Résumé of more important orders

Many authorities think that when all mammals are classified there will be some 20,000 species and subspecies. Fifteen thousand or more species and subspecies have been named, divided among sixteen or seventeen living **orders.** Mammals are classified according to blood relationships so far as possible. A physiological approach is receiving more consideration in modern taxonomy. Taxonomic study on mammals is forced to do a great deal of lumping, splitting, and shifting of genera from one group to another. This accounts

Figure 475. Mammal that lays eggs—duck-billed platypus, *Ornithorhynchus anatinus.* Order Monotremata. These monotremes are found only in restricted regions of Australia and Tasmania where they are found in rivers and ponds; they feed on insects and shellfish. They make complicated burrows in banks of their water habitats. Eggs are about ¾ inch in size and are incubated by the mother for about two weeks before hatching. The young suck from her fur the milk which seeps from her milk glands. (Courtesy New York Zoological Society.)

Figure 476. Mother opossum with four young. The young are first carried in her abdominal pouch and later on her back. Order Marsupialia. (Courtesy Frank M. Blake, U. S. Fish and Wildlife Service.)

for the variation in classified lists as new studies are published.

The classification of mammalian orders is based upon major differences, such as the character of the teeth, modifications of the limbs or digits, the presence or absence of claws and hoofs, and the complexity of the nervous system. The following summary of living orders will acquaint the student with some of the representative forms.

Classification of mammals varies somewhat with different authorities. According to Simpson's classification of mammals, there are eighteen living and fourteen extinct orders of mammals. Of the living orders, many of their families and genera are also extinct. Class Mammalia is divided into two subclasses as follows: Subclass **Prototheria** includes the monotremes, or egg-laying mammals. Subclass **Theria** includes two infraclasses, the **Metatheria** with one order, the marsupials, and the **Eutheria** with the rest of the orders, all of which are placental mammals.

Subclass Prototheria (*proto*, first, + *ther*, animal). The egg-laying mammals.

Order Monotremata (mon'o-tre″mah-tah) (Gr. *monos*, single, + *tremos*, hole)—egg-laying mammals, e.g., duck-billed platypus, spiny anteater (Figure 475)

This order is represented by the duckbills and spiny anteaters of Australia and New Guinea. The most noted member of the order is the duck-billed platypus (*Ornithorhynchus anatinus*). The adults are about 18 inches long and are adapted for an aquatic life, with webbed toes, a bill similar to that of a duck, and a thick coat of fur. Only the young have teeth. The males have on the hind feet horny spurs which are connected to poison glands. The females have mammary glands with no nipples and lay eggs (one to three, about 0.6 inch in diameter) similar to those of reptiles. They have a cloaca instead of separate openings for the digestive and urogenital systems. They make burrows in river banks where they rear their young. Their food consists mostly of small water forms.

The spiny anteater (*Tachyglossus*), about 17 inches long, is covered with coarse hair and spines. It has a long, narrow snout adapted for feeding on ants which are its chief food. The female carries the one egg in her marsupium on the abdomen. This species is found in Australia, but a larger one (*Zaglossus*) is in New Guinea. Monotremes represent the only order that is oviparous, and there is no known group of extinct mammals from which they can be derived. Their fossils date from the Pleistocene age.

Subclass Theria (*ther*, animal)

Infraclass Metatheria (*meta*, after, + *ther*, animal). The marsupial mammals.

Order Marsupialia (mar-su′pi-a″li-a) (Gr. *marsypion*, pouch)—**pouched mammals**, e.g., opossums, kangaroos, kaola, etc. (Figure 476)

Next to the monotremes, these are the most primitive mammals. They are characterized by an abdominal pouch, the **marsupium**, where they rear their young which are born in an immature condition. Although the young are nourished in the uterus for a short time, there is rarely a placenta present. The period of gestation is only thirteen days. When born, the immature young (seven to fourteen in number) find their way from the urogenital orifice to the pouch, where each is attached to a nipple. After several weeks the young leave the pouch but stay close to the mother and re-enter the pouch to feed or for shelter. This order is represented by the opossum, the kangaroo, the kaola, the Tasmanian wolf, the wombat, and many others. Only the opossum is found in the Americas, but the order is the dominant group of mammals in Australia.

The opposum is widely hunted in the United States for its fur and for food. It is omnivorous, feeding upon carrion, fruits, bird's eggs, etc. When disturbed, the adults frequently feign death ("playing possum").

It is thought that the American opossum (*Didelphis virginiana*) is but little modified from an ancestral stock of North American origin and of the Cretaceous period which, on the one hand, gave rise to the American opossums and, on the other, to the marsupials of Australia. There are at least two other subspecies of *Didelphis* in North America—the Florida and the Texas opossums. There are a number of genera and species of the opossum family in South America.

Infraclass Eutheria (*eu,* true, + *ther,* animal) The placental mammals.

Order Insectivora (in'sec-tiv"or-a) (L. *insectum,* an insect, + *vorare,* to eat)—insect-eating mammals, e.g., shrews, hedgehogs, moles (Figures 463 and 474)

The principal food of animals in this order is insects. The most primitive of placental mammals, they are widely distributed over the world, except Australia. Placental mammals and marsupials are thought to have arisen independently from common ancestors during the Cretaceous period, but in time the placentals became dominant in most parts of the world because of their superior intelligence. Insectivora are small, sharp-snouted animals that spend a great part of their lives underground. The shrews are the smallest of the group; some of them are the smallest mammals known. They have soft fur and sharply pointed muzzles, and their teeth show little differentiation. The North American forms are the long-tailed (*Sorex*) and the short-tailed shrews (*Blarina*), and also *Notiosorex, Microsorex, Cryptotis,* and others. *Sorex* with its many species and subspecies is distributed over most of North

America; *Blarina* with fewer species is restricted to the eastern half of North America. They live in burrows, spending some time on the surface at night. Cats frequently catch them but will not eat them because of their rancid odor. Shrews have enormous appetites and can fast only a short time.

Moles differ from shrews in being larger and in having an enormous development of the shoulder girdle. The forelimb is enlarged and flattened for digging. Like the shrews, moles have a soft, velvety fur. Most of their time is spent burrowing just under the surface of the ground. The ridges of their runways are always in evidence wherever these animals are found. They do damage to gardens and flower beds not by eating the plants or their roots but by uprooting and disturbing the plants. The common North American forms are the common mole (*Scalopus*) in the eastern states, the star-nosed mole (*Condylura*) and *Scapanus* on the west coast, and *Parascalops*. Their eyes are closed and the external ear is absent.

Order Chiroptera (chi-rop'ter-a) (Gr. *cheir,* hand, + *pteron,* wing)—flying mammals (Figure 477)

The bats are in some respects the oddest of all mammals, for they are provided with wings. The wings are modified forelimbs in which the second to fifth digits are elongated to support a thin integumental membrane for flying. The first digit (thumb) is short with a claw. The shoulder girdles are better developed than the

Figure 477. Large brown bat, often found in old barns and church steeples. They often hang head down as this one is doing. The single young is usually born in June. Order Chiroptera.

570

Figure 478. Coyote. His cunning in avoiding capture and his destruction of wild stock has made him a serious pest in certain localities. Order Carnivora, family Canidae. (Courtesy E. P. Haddon, U. S. Fish and Wildlife Service).

pelvic. The hind limbs have clawed digits by which the bats hang upside down when sleeping. They are most active in late evening and at night when they fly around in pursuit of insects. During the day they are mostly to be found in bell towers, caves, and abandoned attics. The Carlsbad Caverns in New Mexico are famed for the enormous number of bats that live in them, emerging in the evening in swarms of millions to seek food.

There are many families and species of bats the world over. The common North American forms are the little brown bat *(Myotis)*, the free-tailed bat *(Tadarida)*, which lives in the Carlsbad Caverns, and the large brown bat *(Eptesicus)*. In the Old World tropics, the "flying foxes" *(Pteropus)* are the largest of bats, with a wing spread of four to five feet, and live chiefly on fruits. Bats have left a very poor fossil record, and there are no known intermediate stages between them and the insectivore which they resemble. Their evolution may have been rapid and their fossils date from the Eocene age.

The tropics have many kinds of bats, including the famed vampire bat *(Desmodus)*. This bat is provided with highly specialized and sharp incisor teeth with which it can shave or rasp away the epidermis of the skin and expose the underlying capillaries. The bat then laps up the blood and pumps it into its specially modified stomach as the blood oozes from the wound. The vampire's saliva may contain an anticoagulant for promoting the blood flow. The vampire is very

Figure 479. Giant panda. This interesting animal belongs to raccoon family. Order Carnivora, family Procyonidae. (Courtesy Chicago Natural History Museum.)

sly in procuring its blood, taking advantage of sleeping victims who are usually unaware of what is going on.

Order Dermoptera (der-mop'ter-a) (Gr. *derma*, skin, + *pteron*, wing)—**flying lemurs**

These are related to the true bats and consist of

Phylum Chordata—class Mammalia 571

Figure 480. Spotted hyena. Hyena's food is chiefly carrion, and it often robs graves in regions where it is found. Note the low hind quarters. Order Carnivora, family Hyaenidae. (Courtesy Chicago Natural History Museum.)

Figure 481. Pair of cheetahs, *Acinonyx*. These are swiftest of all mammals (60 to 75 m.p.h.) and are native to Africa and some parts of Asia. Although placed in family Felidae, their claws are not retractile and their foot pads are doglike. Easily tamed, they make docile pets. They have been useful in running down coyotes in the southwest. Order Carnivora, family Felidae. (Courtesy Smithsonian Institution, Washington, D. C.)

a single genus, *Galeopithecus* or *Cynocephalus*. They are found in Malay and the East Indies. They cannot fly in the strict sense of the word but glide with their parachutes like flying squirrels.

Order Carnivora (car-niv′o-ra) (L. *caro*, flesh + *vorare*, to eat)—**flesh-eating mammals, e.g. dogs, wolves, cats, bears, weasels** (Figures 478 to 482)

This order is one of the most extensive group

Figure 482. Young raccoon. Often dips its food in water before eating it. Intelligent animal and an interesting pet. Order Carnivora, family Procyonidae.

of mammals, and its members are among the swiftest, keenest, and strongest of animals. They all have predatory habits, and their teeth are especially adapted for tearing flesh, since the incisors and canines are well developed and the molars specialized for cutting. In most of them the canines are used for killing their prey. They are divided among two suborders: (1) **Fissipedia**, whose feet contain toes, and (2) **Pinnipedia**, with limbs modified for aquatic life. Suborder Fissipedia consists of the well-known carnivores—wolves, tigers, dogs, cats, foxes, weasels, skunks, and many others. They vary in size from certain tiny weasles to the mammoth Alaskan bear and Bengal tiger. They are distributed all over the world, except in the Australian and Antarctica regions, where there are no native forms. Many of them are of great economic importance, such as keeping the balance of nature by preying upon other forms and for the great value of their fur. This suborder is divided into certain familiar families, among which are **Canidae** (the dog family), consisting of dogs, wolves, foxes, and coyotes; **Felidae** (the cat family), whose members include the domestic cats, tigers, lions, cougars, and lynxes; **Ursidae** (the bear family), made up of bears; and **Mustelidae** (the fur-bearing family), containing the martens, skunks, weasels, otters, badgers, minks, and wolverines.

Suborder Pinnipedia includes the aquatic carnivora, sea lions, seals, and walruses. Their limbs have been modified as flippers for swimming. They are all salt-water forms and their food is mostly fish. The well-known fur seal (*Callorhinus*) is found on the Pribilof Islands off the coast of Alaska, where it spends the summer, but for nine months it wanders far away in the sea.

In their evolution the Carnivora have left a better fossil record than many other groups and their history can be traced back to the Tertiary period. The ancestors of all carnivores appear to be the creodonts, slender, weasel-like forms with sharp claws. From these or similar carnivores (the miacids) there occurred in Oligocene and Pleistocene times a rapid adaptive radiation of various groups of carnivores to fill the ecological niches left vacant by the large predator reptiles which became extinct at the end of the Cretaceous period. One of these early groups was the fissipeds, the modern land forms of the Carnivora. Another group, the pinnipeds, appeared about the Miocene period and represent the aquatic carnivores. The evolution of the different groups of carnivores has varied greatly. Some have changed little from primitive ancestors (civets), others have undergone moderate rates of evolution (dogs), and some (bears) are quite recent.

Order Tubulidentata (tu′bu-li-den-ta″ta) (L. *tubulus,* a tube, + *dens,* tooth)—**aardvarks**

The aardvark is the Dutch name for earth-pig, a peculiar animal with piglike body found in

Figure 483. Prairie dog feeding. Where they are numerous, these rodents do a great deal of damage by burrowing and by destroying crops. Order Rodentia, family Sciuridae. (Courtesy D. A. Spencer, U. S. Fish and Wildlife Service.)

Figure 484. Muskrat, most common fur-bearing animal in America. Order Rodentia, family Muridae.

Figure 485. Beaver. Trapped almost to point of extinction, this desirable animal is now rapidly increasing in numbers under rigid protection. Order Rodentia, family Castoridae. (Courtesy Nature Magazine, Washington, D.C.)

Africa. The order is represented by only one genus *(Orycteropus)* with three or four species. These animals have donkeylike ears and a long snout with a tubular mouth and extensible tongue for collecting ants or termites, their principal food. With their strong claws they are expert diggers. The fossil record dates from the Pliocene epoch and indicates that they were once more widely distributed than they are now. They are

supposed to have affinities with the condylarths, one of the extinct orders of mammals.

Order Rodentia (ro-den'ti-a) (L. *rodare*, to gnaw)—**gnawing mammals, e.g., squirrels, rats, woodchucks, etc.** (Figures 483 to 485)

The rodents are the most numerous of all mammals. Most of them are small. They are found on all continents and many of the large islands. They have no canine teeth, but their chisel-like incisors (never more than four) grow continually. They live mostly on plants and plant products. They are of economic importance; some are household pests, such as rats and mice; some damage domestic crops, such as woodchucks and field mice; and some transmit diseases, for example tularemia carried by wood ticks on rodents. Some rodents are useful for their fur. The beaver *(Castor)*, the largest rodent in the United States, has a valuable pelt. Many rodents are utilized as food by carnivores and by man. The common families of this order are Sciuridae (squirrels, woodchucks), Muridae (rats, mice), Castoridae (beavers), Erethizontidae (porcupines), and Geomyidae (pocket gophers).

The rodents are the most successful order of mammals because of their diverse adaptive radiation which has enabled them to occupy so many ecological niches. The most primitive living rodents are the Sciuromorpha (suborder), which include squirrels, beavers, pocket gophers, marmots, and others. The other rodents are supposed to have evolved from basic sciuromorphs, but some, like the porcupine-like rodents, quite early branched off from the main original stock. The most primitive living rodent is the tailless sewellel *(Aplodontia)* or mountain beaver found in a restricted region of the Pacific coast.

Order Pholidota (phol'i-do"ta) (Gr. *pholis*, a horny scale)—**pangolins**

In this order there is one genus *(Manis)* with seven species. They are an odd group of animals whose body is covered with overlapping horny scales which have arisen from fused bundles of hair. Their home is in tropical Asia and Africa. They live upon ants and may have come from the same ancestors as the true edentates. Their fossil record throws no light upon their ancestors or relations.

Order Lagomorpha (lag'o-mor"pha) (Gr. *lagos*, a hare, + *morphe*, form)—**rabbits, hares, pika**

The chief difference between this order and Rodentia is the presence of four upper incisors, one pair of which is small, and the other large, with enamel on the posterior as well as on the terior surface of the tooth. Order Lagomorpha includes several species of rabbits and hares, all of which have long ears and long hind legs for jumping. Their food is almost entirely vegetarian, and they eat enormous quantities of clover, grasses, bark, shoots, and twigs. Rabbits are also known to feed on snails and insects. The little pika (*Ochotona*) lives at high altitudes in the Rocky Mountains and Eurasia and has the interesting habit of collecting grass, curing it in the sun, and storing it for winter food. Nothing is known definitely about the origin of the Lago-morpha, but fossils indicate they were common in the Oligocene epoch.

Order Edentata (e′den-ta″tah) (L. *edentatus*, toothless)—**toothless mammals, e.g., sloths, anteaters, armadillos** (Figures 486 and 487)

These forms are either toothless or else have degenerate teeth without enamel. The group includes the anteaters, sloths, and armadillos. Most of them live in South America, although the nine-banded armadillo (*Dasypus novemcinctus*) may extend up into Texas. The sloths are very

Figure 486. Group of giant anteaters, *Myrmecophaga*. These animals with their long heads and sticky, extensible tongues for collecting ants are among most specialized of mammals. Order Edentata. (Courtesy Chicago Natural History Museum.)

Figure 487. Armadillo. Although timid and inoffensive, armadillo has survived mainly because of its protective coat of armor. Order Edentata. (Courtesy Smithsonian Institution, Washington, D. C.)

sluggish animals which have the queer habit of hanging upside down on branches. The hairs of sloths have tiny pits in which green algae grow and render them invisible against a background of mosses and lichens. There are two types—the two-fingered and the three-fingered sloths. Ant-eaters have elongated snouts, slender and protrusible tongues, and no teeth. There are three living anteaters—giant, lesser, and pigmy. They live entirely on ants and termites. Armadillos are provided with a dorsal shell over skin and bony plates and can roll up into a pill shape when disturbed. Their food is mostly insects and small invertebrates. There are about twenty species of armadillos.

The first endentates date from early Tertiary fossils, and the present forms are considered to be primitive and also highly specialized. Quite early geologically they evolved by adaptive radiation into two branches. One branch included the tree sloths and the anteaters; the other became the armadillos. One of the extinct groups was the ground sloths which were represented by some members as large as small elephants, such as *Megatherium*.

Order Cetacea (se-ta'ce-a) (L. *cetus*, a whale)—fishlike mammals, e.g., whales, dolphins, porpoises

This order is well adapted for aquatic life. Their anterior limbs are modified into broad flippers; the posterior limbs are absent. Some have a fleshy dorsal fin and the tail is divided into transverse fleshy flukes. The nostrils are represented by a single or double blow hole on top of the head. Teeth may be absent, but when present they are all alike and lack enamel. They have no hair except a few on the muzzle, no skin glands except the mammary and those of the eye, and no external ear, and their eyes are small. Members of this order are the largest animals in the animal kingdom. There is even reason to believe that their ancestors were land forms which became modified for an aquatic life. The order is divided into two suborders, Odontoceti and Mysticeti. Suborder **Odontoceti** is made up of toothed members and is represented by the sperm whales, porpoises, and dolphins. With the exception of the sperm whale, which may attain a length of 75 feet, most Odontoceti are not as large as the members of the other suborder. Their food consists of fish, cuttlefish, seals, and other forms. The killer whale (*Orcinus*), the most savage member, is the tiger of the sea for, although rarely longer than 20 feet, it does not hesitate to attack the larger whales and to tear huge mouthfuls from their bodies. The killer is also destructive to seal rookeries. The sperm

whale (*Physeter*) is the source of sperm oil which is obtained from the head. A peculiar substance, ambergris, is formed in its stomach and is much used in perfumes. This substance may be derived from squids which form the principal food of sperm whales. Porpoises and dolphins, which also belong to this suborder, are only 6 or 7 feet long and feed mainly on gregarious fish. Another member of this group is the narwhal (*Monodon*) which has one of its two teeth modified into a twisted tusk eight to ten feet long which projects forward like a pike.

The other suborder, **Mysticeti**, or whalebone whales, include many species, some of which are gigantic. Instead of teeth they have a peculiar straining device of whale bone (baleen) attached to the palate. They live on the microscopic animals at the surface (plankton) which they strain out of the water with the whalebone. Thus the largest animals in the world live upon the smallest. The largest of the whales is the blue whale (*Balaenoptera*), which has a dorsal fin and may grow 100 feet long and weigh 150 tons. Whales can submerge for several minutes and then emerge to blow air through the blow hole. The warm air from the lungs is condensed by the cool sea air to form the familiar spout. Though found in all seas some of the more wanted species prefer northern waters. Whales have been hunted for their blubber, the fatty layer under the skin which is boiled down into oil, and for their whalebone, until they are near extermination.

The cetaceans, the most specialized of mammals, appeared in Tertiary times and seemed to have separated from the other mammals quite early. The most primitive cetaceans were the extinct archaeoceti, which probably did not give rise to present-day whales. Their fossil record throws little light upon their origin, and there are no connecting types between them and the other placentals. There are even some doubts about a common origin for the two suborders. Cetaceans apparently took over the ecological niche vacated by the aquatic reptiles, ichthyosaurs, and in doing so demonstrated marked evolutionary convergence, for there are many adaptations common to the two groups.

Order Proboscidea (pro'bos-cid"e-a) (Gr. *pro*, before, + *boscein*, to feed)—proboscis mammals, e.g., elephants

This order includes only the elephants, the largest of living land animals. They have large heads, massive ears, and thick skins (pachyderm). Hair is confined mainly to the tip of the tail. The two upper incisors are elongated as tusks, and the molar teeth are well developed.

There are two genera of elephants; the Indian (*Elephas maximus*), with relatively small ears, and the African (*Loxodonta africana*), with large ears. There is also a small African form, the pigmy elephant (*Elephas cyclotis*), which is found in West Africa. The larger elephants may attain a height of 10 to 11 feet and a weight of 6 to 7 tons. The Asiatic, or Indian, elephant has long been domesticated and is trained to do heavy work. The taming of the African elephant is more difficult but was extensively done by the ancient Carthaginians and Romans, who employed them in their armies. Barnum's famous "Jumbo" was an African elephant. Strictly herbivorous, elephants consume several hundred pounds of food each day.

Order Hyracoidea (hy'ra-coi"de-a) (Gr. *hyrex*, a shrew)—hyraxes, e.g., conies

Conies are restricted to Africa and Syria. They have some resemblance to short-eared rabbits but have teeth like rhinoceroses, with hoofs on their toes and pads on their feet. They have four toes on the front and three toes on the back feet. They are herbivorous in their food habits and live among rocks or in trees. Their fossils first appeared in the Oligocene period, and they appear to be distantly related to the Proboscidea.

Order Sirenia (si-re'ni-a) (Gr. *seiren*, sea nymph)—sea cows, e.g., manatees (Figure 488)

Sea cows, or manatees, are large, clumsy aquatic animals. They have a blunt muzzle covered with coarse bristles, the only hairs these queer animals possess. They have no hind limbs, and their forelimbs are modified into swimming flippers. The tail is broad with flukes but is not divided. They live in the bays and rivers along the coasts of tropical and subtropical seas. There are only two genera living at present: *Trichechus,* found in the rivers of Florida, West Indies, Brazil, and Africa, and *Halicore,* the dugong of India and Australia. They are entirely herbivorous, living upon the water grasses in the bays and rivers where they are found. The fossil record indicates that this order was formerly more widely distributed than now. They date back to the Eocene period and their fossil record gives no indication of their relationship, but they may be distantly related to the Proboscidea.

Order Perissodactyla (pe-ris'so-dac"ty-la) (Gr. *perissos,* odd, + *dactylos,* toe)—odd-toed hoofed mammals (Figure 489)

The odd-toed hoofed mammals have an odd number (one or three) of toes, each with a cornified hoof. They are often referred to as **ungulates,** or hoofed mammals, with teeth adapted for chewing. They include the horses, the zebras, the tapirs, and the rhinoceroses. The horse family (Equidae), which also includes

Figure 488. Manatees, or sea cows, are aquatic mammals that sometimes reach a length of 10 feet and live in estuaries of tropical and subtropical America. Order Sirenia. (Courtesy Chicago Natural History Museum.)

Figure 489. Malay tapir. Order Perissodactyla. (Courtesy Smithsonian Institution, Washington, D. C.)

Figure 490. Group of Alaskan caribou. Order Artiodactyla. (Courtesy Chicago Natural History Museum.)

asses and zebras, has only one functional toe. There are two species of tapirs: *Tapirella,* in Central and South America, and *Tapirus,* in Malay and Sumatra. They have four toes on the front feet and three on the hind feet. They have a short proboscis formed from the upper lip and nose. The rhinoceros (*Rhinoceros*) includes several species found in Africa and southeastern

Asia. Their most striking character is the horn (one or two) on top of the snout. This horn is modified from hair. Rhinoceroses have three toes on the hind limb and three or four on the front. All are herbivorous.

The evolution of the horse is treated elsewhere. The ancestral form of this order is not supposed to be very different from *Hyracotherium,* the Eocene horse from which by adaptive radiation the various groups of perissodactyls evolved. There are two main lines or groupings: the suborder Hippomorpha (horses and related forms) and the suborder Ceratomorpha (tapirs and rhinoceroses).

Order Artiodactyla (ar'ti-o-dac"ty-la) (Gr. *artios,* even, + *dactylos,* toe)—**even-toed hoofed mammals** (Figures 490 to 493)

The even-toed ungulates include swine, camels, deer, hippopotamuses, antelopes, cattle, sheep, and goats. Most of them have two toes, although the hippopotamus and some others have four. Each toe is sheathed in a cornified hoof. Many, such as the cow, deer, and sheep, have horns. Many of them are ruminants, that is, animals that chew the cud. Like Perissodactyla they are strictly herbivorous. They are found all over the world. The group is divided into nine living families and many extinct ones and includes some of the most valuable domestic animals. This extensive order is commonly divided into three suborders: (1) the Suina (pigs, peccaries, hippopotamuses), (2) the Tylopoda (camels), and (3) the Ruminantia (deer, giraffes, sheep, cattle, etc.). The ancestor of this order dates back at least as far as the Eocene period, and one of these early forms was *Diacodexis,* which has been found as a fossil in North America. During the Eocene period the perissodactyls were dominant, but since then the artiodactyls have flourished and have become by far the most numerous of ungulates.

In the odd-toed ungulates the middle, or third, digit is stressed (second and fourth also in some), and the main axis of weight passes through this. In the even-toed ungulates the third and fourth toes (sometimes also the second and fifth) are stressed, and the main axis of the leg passes between the third and fourth toes, so they bear equally the weight of the animal.

Order Primates (pri-ma'tez) (L. *prima,* first)— **highest mammals, e.g., lemurs, monkeys, apes, man**

This order stands first in the animal kingdom in brain development, although other structural features may be equaled or excelled by lower mammals. Most of the species are arboreal, apparently

derived from tree-dwelling insectivores. As a matter of fact, primates, bats, edentates, living insectivores, and some others are grouped as Unguiculata (L. *unguis,* nail) which are directly derived from the primitive insectivores. The primates then represent the end product of a line that branched off early from other mammals and have retained many primitive characteristics. It is thought that their tree-dwelling habits of agility in capturing food or avoiding enemies were largely responsible for their advances in brain structure. The brain of primates is so well developed that the cerebral hemi-

Figure 491. A, Bactrian camel, *Camelus.* B, Llama, *Lama,* with young. Common ancestors of camels and llamas developed and flourished in North America during late Eocene, but during Pleistocene one branch migrated to Asia to become the Old World camels and the other to South America to become the llamas. The North American forms later died out. Hump of Old World camels is later adaptation for storage of fat. Order Artiodactyla. (Courtesy Smithsonian Institution, Washington, D. C.)

Figure 492. Hippopotamus and young. Order Artiodactyla. (Courtesy Smithsonian Institution, Washington, D. C.)

Figure 493. Pair of mule deer. Name of these large deer derived from size of ears which are disproportionately large in fawns. Order Artiodactyla. (Courtesy E. P. Haddon, U. S. Fish and Wildlife Service.)

spheres cover the rest of the brain, especially in the higher primates. As a group, they are generalized with five digits (usually provided with flat nails) on both forelimbs and hind limbs. All have their bodies covered with hair, except man, in whom it is confined to certain regions. Forelimbs are often adapted for grasping, as are the hind limbs sometimes. The group is

580

singularly lacking in claws, scales, horns and hoofs.

There are three suborders:

1. **Suborder Lemuroidea** (lem'u-roi"de-a) (L. *lemures,* ghost) (Figure 494)

These are primitive arboreal primates, with their second toe provided with a claw and a long nonprehensile tail. They look like a cross between squirrels and monkeys. They are found in the forests of Madagascar, Africa, and Malay. Their food is mostly plants and small animals.

2. **Suborder Tarsioidea** (tar'si-oi"de-a) (Gr. *tarsus,* first foot)

There is only one genus *(Tarsius)* in this group. Tarsiers are small, solitary primates that live in the Philippines and adjacent islands. The snout is shortened and the eyes have been shifted into a position for binocular vision. The tarsal region of the foot is long, and two of the toes on each foot are provided with claws. The tips of all digits bear pads.

3. **Suborder Anthropoidea** (an'thro-poi"de-a) (Gr. *anthropos,* man)

This suborder consists of monkeys, apes, and man. They have well-developed, convoluted cerebral hemispheres, and their eyes have greater clarity of vision. This suborder represents the most advanced type of animal as far as the nerv-

Figure 495. Chimpanzee. Order Primates, superfamily Hominoidea. (Courtesy Smithsonian Institution, Washington, D. C.)

ous system is concerned. There are three superfamilies:

(1) **Superfamily Ceboidea** (se-boi'de-a) (Gr. *kebos,* a long-tailed monkey) (**Platyrhinii**)

These are New World monkeys, characterized by the broad flat nasal septum and by the absence of ischial callosities and cheek pouches. Their thumbs are nonopposable and their tails are prehensile. Familiar members of this superfamily are the capuchin monkey *(Cebus)* of the organ grinder, the spider monkey *(Ateles),* and the howler monkey *(Alouatta).*

(2) **Superfamily Cercopithecoidea** (sur'ko-pi'the-koi"de-a) (Gr. *kerkops,* long-tailed monkey, + *theca,* pouch) (**Catarrhinii**)

Figure 494. Ring-tailed lemur. Order Primates, suborder Lemuroidea. (Courtesy Chicago Natural History Museum.)

These Old World monkeys have the external nares close together and many have internal cheek pouches. They never have prehensile tails, there are calloused ischial tuberosities on their buttocks, and their thumbs are opposable. Examples are the savage mandrill *(Cynocephalus)*, the rhesus monkey *(Macacus)* widely used in biological investigation, and the proboscis monkey *(Nasalis)*.

(3) **Superfamily Hominoidea** (ho'min-oi"de-a) (Gr. *hominis*, man)

The higher (anthropoid) apes and man make up this superfamily. Their chief characteristics are lack of a tail and lack of cheek pouches. There are two families: Pongidae and Hominidae. The Pongidae family includes the higher apes, gibbon *(Hylobates)*, orangutan *(Simia)*, chimpanzee *(Anthropopithecus)* (Figure 495), and the gorilla *(Gorilla)*. Varying powers of intelligence are found among the members of the family. Chimpanzees seem to learn faster than others. The gorilla is the most powerful ape and may attain a weight of 500 pounds. The other family, Hominidae, is represented by a single genus and species *(Homo sapiens)*, modern man. Man differs from the members of family Pongidae in being more erect, in having shorter arms and larger thumbs, and in having lighter jaws with smaller front teeth. Most of the apes also have much more prominent supraorbital ridges over the eyes. Man's brain is larger, especially the cerebrum. Many of man's differences from the anthropoid apes are associated with his higher intelligence, his speech centers in the brain, and the fact that he is no longer an arboreal animal.

Derivation and meaning of basic terminology

Condylarthra (Gr. *condyl*, knuckle, + *arthron*, joint) Extinct order of mammals which gave rise to the ungulates.

Cotylosaur (Gr. *kotyle*, cup-shaped, + *sauros*, lizard) Primitive extinct order of reptiles from which all reptiles have stemmed.

Credontia (Gr. *kreas*, flesh, + *odontos*, tooth) The first order (extinct) of the carnivores.

Cynodont (Gr. *kyon*, dog, + *odontos*, tooth).

Fissipedia (L. *fissi*, split, + *pes*, foot) Carnivora with toes.

Lemuroidea (L. *lemures*, ghost) Name probably refers to their flitting nocturnal habits and large eyes.

Ornithorhynchus (Gr. *ornithos*, bird, + *rhynchos*, beak).

Pantotheria (Gr. *pantos*, all, + *therion*, animal) Extinct order of Jurassis mammals from which

placentals and marsupials may have arisen.

Pinnipedia (L. *pinna*, a fin, + *ped*, foot) Carnivora with fins.

placenta (Gr. *plakous*, flat cake) Vascular structure through which the embryo and fetus are nourished in the uterus.

Polyphyodont (Gr. *poly*, many, + *phy*, to grow, + *odontos*, tooth) A dentition which is made up of many teeth.

Protothrix (pl. prototriches) (Gr. *protos*, first, + *thrix*, hair) A tactile sensory pit of fish and primitive amphibians. In reptiles these pits counteracted the hard, sensory-impervious skin. The hair of mammals may have arisen from certain sensory bristles which are known to occur in these pits of small lizards. Later these tactile hairs acquired temperature control and other functions. Hairs are not homologous to scales.

Simian (L. *simia*, ape).

ungulate (L. *ungula*, hoof) Hoofed mammals.

ANNOTATED REFERENCES

Anthony, H. E. 1928. Field Book of North American Mammals. New York, G. P. Putnam's Sons. *An excellent manual on the classification, distribution, and characteristics of mammals.*

Blair, W. F., A. P. Blair, P. Brodkorr, F. R. Cagle, and G. A. Moore. 1957. Vertebrates of the United States, New York, McGraw-Hill Book Co., Inc. *This work is of great importance to all students of vertebrates, especially to those who are interested in taxonomy. The taxonomic keys are illustrated and identify all vertebrates down to species. The introduction includes a great deal of information about the characteristics of vertebrates, their physiology, and their distribution. A helpful glossary is provided, as well as a bibliography.*

Burns, E. 1953. The Sex Life of Wild Animals. New York, Rinehart & Co. *An interesting account of the mating reactions of many mammals.*

Cockrum, E. L. 1955. Manual of Mammalogy. Minneapolis, Burgess Publishing Co. *A practical and comprehensive manual which considers the morphology, classification, ecology, and life histories of mammals.*

Collins, H. H. 1959. Complete Field Guide to American Wildlife. New York, Harper & Brothers. *A section of this excellent field manual is devoted to mammals. Some color plates and distribution maps.*

Glass, B. P. 1951. A Key to the Skulls of North American Mammals. Minneapolis, Burgess Publishing Co. *A helpful aid to the student of mammalian structures.*

Hall, E. R., and K. R. Kelson. 1959. The Mammals of North America, 2 vols. New York, The Ronald Press Co. *This is a magnificent and definitive work on North American mammals, giving full descriptions of all species and subspecies with distribution maps. Taxonomic keys, records, and revealing line drawings of skull characteristics are included in a work that will be the final authority on mammals for a long time. An extensive index and bibliography add much to the usefulness of this fine work.*

Hamilton, W. J., Jr. 1939. American Mammals. New York, McGraw-Hill Book Co., Inc. *A well-written account of their habits and life histories.*

Hartman, C. G. 1952. Possums. Austin, University of Texas Press. *An excellent account of the life history and behavior by one who has extensively studied this odd animal.*

Lyon, M. W., Jr. 1936. Mammals of Indiana. Notre Dame, The University Press. *A thorough coverage of the mammals of the state, including their classification, type descriptions, and behavior.*

Sanderson, I. T. Living Mammals of the World. Garden City, Hanover House. *A beautiful and informative work of many photographs and concise text material. It is a delight to any zoologist regardless of his specialized interest.*

Scheffer, V. B. 1958. Seals, Sea Lions, and Walruses. A Review of the Pinnipedia. Stanford, Stanford University Press. *This is the first comprehensive review of these aquatic mammals since Allen's monograph of more than sixty years ago. It treats the group from the standpoint of their evolution, characteristics, and classification. Many fine photographs and a good bibliography are included.*

Seton, E. T. 1925-1928. Lives of Game Animals, 4 vols. New York, Doubleday, Doran & Co.

Simpson, G. G. 1945. The Principles of Classification and a Classification of Mammals. Bulletin of the American Museum of Natural History, vol. 85. New York, American Museum of Natural History.

Wolstenholme, G. E. W., and M. O'Connor (editors). 1959. The Lifespan of Animals. The Ciba Foundation Colloquia on Ageing, vol. 5. Boston, Little, Brown, & Co. *This interesting colloquium of many specialists deals with longevity and related problems in man and other animals.*

Young, J. Z. 1957. The Life of Mammals. New York, Oxford University Press. *This is an imposing work on nearly every aspect of mammalian life. It affords an excellent background for the student who wishes to know about mammals, especially their anatomy, histology, physiology, and embryology. Classification, however, is not treated.*

Part Three

Résumé of organ systems with particular reference to man

chapter 29

Support, protection, and movement

GENERAL STRUCTURE*

There are logical reasons for considering the integumentary, skeletal, and muscular systems together. They are all concerned in the problem of protection and support of the body structures, for together they guard the frontier of the body, serving as the bulwark between the delicate and vulnerable systems within and the environment without the body. Moreover, the skeletal and muscular systems work together in the great function of movement. Such an analysis is simply a matter of convenience. In the performance of almost any function of the body, many, if not at all, systems are involved to some extent.

INTEGUMENT AMONG VARIOUS GROUPS OF ANIMALS

The skin is not merely a protective wrapping; it has many and varied functions. Except for openings, it is continuous all over the external surface of the body. In most forms it is tough and pliable, is impervious to water (land forms), and is resistant to most germs. It protects underlying cells from the rays of the sun and prevents excessive loss of water from the animal. In the simpler forms its functions are less varied than in higher animals. In warm-blooded animals it is vi-

---

*Refer to Chapter 5, Principle 10.

tally concerned with the regulation of body heat. The skin can be considered a sensory organ, for it contains the receptors of many senses. It has excretory and, in some forms, respiratory functions as well. It can also form derivatives of many types and functions.

Invertebrate integument (Figure 496). Many protozoans have only the delicate cell membranes or plasma membranes for external coverings; others, such as paramecium, have developed a protective pellicle. In this sense, the term integument may be applied even to protozoans. Most invertebrates have a tissue covering—the **epidermis,** which consists of a single layer of cells, except in chaetognaths. Others have added a noncellular **cuticle** or secreted covering of another sort. Sessile coelenterates, such as *Obelia*, have a protective chitinoid covering over the epidermis. The hydra has only an epidermis. The nature of the epidermis and noncellular cuticle varies with different invertebrates. An epidermis is entirely lacking in trematodes and cestodes. The epidermis is ciliated in some flatworms, bryozoans, and mollusks. The integument of the annelids consists of a single layer (epidermis) of columnar cells resting on a basement membrane. Among the epidermal cells are goblet cells for mucus secretions and sensory cells. Over this epidermis is the thin, delicate striated cuticle. Setae are modified from the integument.

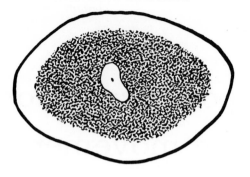

Differentiation of clear surface ectoplasm with its plasma membrane from inner granular endoplasm in certain protozoans is beginning of an integument

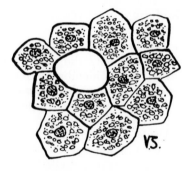

Surface of ectoplasm may differentiate to form pellicle which may be homogeneous or patterned in ridges, depressions, or spiral striations

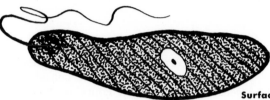

Flat, polygonal epithelial cells (pinacocytes) with bulging nuclei or a syncytium with scattered nuclei form surface layer (epidermis) of some sponges

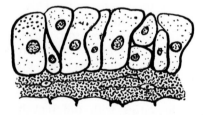

Coelenterate epidermis consists of epithelial cells of varying types, often interspersed with glands, sensory cells, and cnidoblasts; cuticle or perisarc may be secreted by epidermis

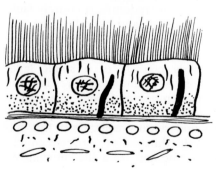

Free-living flatworms have one-layer epidermis of flat or columnar cells, generally ciliated, and sometimes syncytial.

Figure 496. Comparative structure
of invertebrate integument.

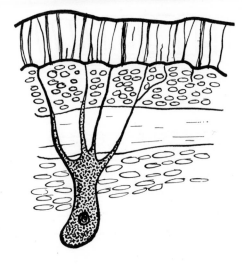

Epidermis lacking in parasitic flatworms (trematodes
and cestodes); a resistant cuticle rests upon subcuticular musculature and is secreted by special mesenchymal cells

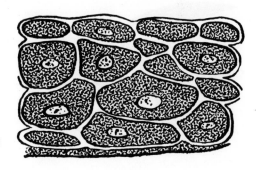

Acanthocephs unique in having syncytial epidermis
with lacunar system of fluid-filled spaces which distribute food

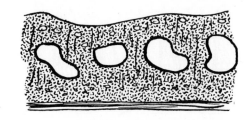

Chaetognaths are only invertebrates with stratified
epidermis

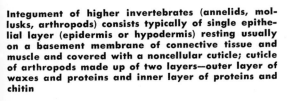

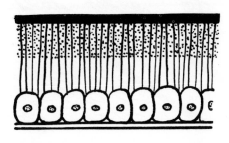

Integument of higher invertebrates (annelids, mollusks, arthropods) consists typically of single epithelial layer (epidermis or hypodermis) resting usually
on a basement membrane of connective tissue and
muscle and covered with a noncellular cuticle; cuticle
of arthropods made up of two layers—outer layer of
waxes and proteins and inner layer of proteins and
chitin

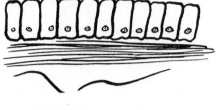

Simple chordates (*Amphioxus*, tunicates) and closely related phyla (hemichordates, echinoderms) have single-layered epidermis and connective tissue dermis; may have cilia, glands, and pigment; tunicates enclosed by overlying tunic of tunicin (cellulose) secreted by mesenchymal cells

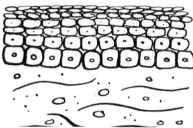

Vertebrate skin made up of stratified epidermis (ectodermal) and dermis of connective tissue, muscle, blood vessels, etc. (mesodermal) with many derivatives and modifications

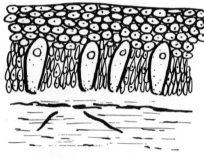

Cyclostome integument is smooth without scales but contains many unicellular mucous glands, some of which are club shaped and others thread cells; thin noncellular cuticle covers body

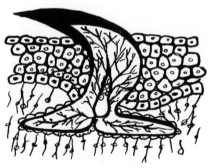

Tough epidermis of sharks contains much keratin and many mucous glands; scattered placoid scales are of dentine from mesodermal odontoblasts and enamel-like vitrodentine from mesoderm with enamel organs

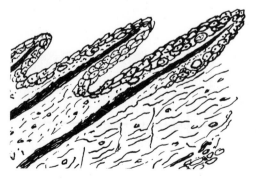

In most bony fish, entire epidermis alive but keratinized except for superficial cells which die and are replaced; many mucous glands; scales of many types formed by dermis and restricted to that region; chromatophores in epidermis and dermis; in scaleless forms, skin is thick, tough, and leathery

Figure 497. Comparative structure of vertebrate integument.

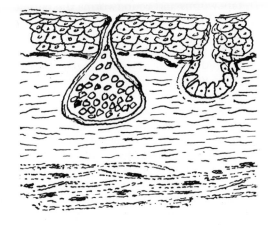

Superficial layer of amphibian integument cornified and shed at intervals; glands multicellular and specialized (mucous and poison); local thickenings of epidermis common, such as toad warts; scales absent (except Apoda); chromatophores in both epidermis and dermis

Integument of reptiles dry, lacking in glands, and provided with horny epidermal scales covered with cornified epidermis; entire horny layer, including scales, shed at intervals; bony plates may be found in dermis; pigment cells both epidermal and dermal

Birds have loose, dry skin with only cutaneous gland (uropygial); cornification mainly restricted to feathers; epidermal scales on legs.

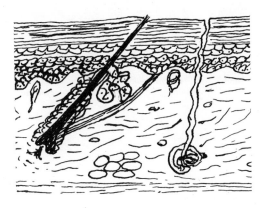

In mammals, epidermis varies from thin to thick (pachyderms), usually in 4 or 5 layers; epidermal scales restricted; many derivatives, mostly epidermal; hair and cutaneous glands of many types

Support, protection, and movement 591

In tapeworms and roundworms the cuticle is very thick and resistant. The molluscan epidermis is delicate and soft and contains mucous glands. The mantle is covered with epidermis containing many glands, some of which secrete the calcium carbonate of the shell. The cephalopod has developed a more complex integument, consisting of a cuticle, a simple epidermis, a layer of connective tissue, a layer of reflecting cells (iridocytes), and, finally, a thicker layer of connective tissue. Iridocytes are responsible for the pearly luster of the skin in many members of this group. Chromatophores, or color-bearing cells, in cephalopods are composed of sacs of pigment surrounded by radiating muscle fibers. In arthropods the epidermis (hypodermis) is a single layer of cells, from which is secreted the chitinous exoskeleton.

Vertebrate integument (Figure 497). The basic plan of the vertebrate integument is a thin outer stratified epithelial layer, the **epidermis**, derived from ectoderm and an inner, thicker layer, the **corium** (dermis), which is of mesodermal origin and is made up of nerves, blood vessels, connective tissue, pigment, etc. (Figure 498). Only in cyclostomes is a noncellular dead cuticle found. The epider-

mis consists usually of several layers of cells and varies in thickness in different animals and in different parts of the same animal. The basal part of the epidermis is made up of columnar cells which undergo frequent mitosis to renew the layers that lie above. Thus the outer layers, mostly cornified and dead, are sloughed off constantly. In many vertebrates (fish and amphibians) the epidermis is provided with mucous glands which lubricate the exterior surface of the body. Granular poison glands are also found in some amphibians. Land forms, such as reptiles, birds, and mammals, have a thicker epidermis, the outer layer of which is much cornified with keratin. This is for added protection to prevent drying out. Mammals are well provided with glands (Figure 499). Indeed, the entire epidermal cutaneous system of the amniotes may be considered a glandular system and, with the exception of the sweat glands, mostly holocrine in nature. The keratinized outer lays, secreted by the basal epidermal cells, are constantly being shed in small fragments (mammals) or in a single piece (some reptiles). Hair, feathers, keratin, and sebum (all dead cells when shed) may be considered as a secretion of the epidermis.

The **color** of the skin is often due to special pigment which may be in the form of granules scattered through the layers of the epidermis (mammals) and to special pigment cells, **chromatophores** (Figure 500), which are found chiefly in the dermis (fish and amphibians).

The skin is variously modified in different vertebrates to form the so-called skin derivatives. In addition to glands, hair and feathers, already mentioned elsewhere, are the bony and horny structures such as scales, claws, nails, horns, and antlers. True bony structures develop in the dermis, and bony plates were very common in such primitive forms as ostracoderms and placoderms. Certain bony plates of the head were modified to form the dermocranium of the skull. Fish scales (Figure 501), with the exception of the placoid scale which may have dermal

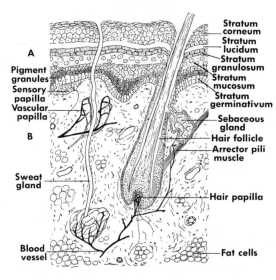

Figure 498. Histological section of mammalian skin. A, Epidermis B, Dermis.

Stratum corneum
Stratum lucidum
Stratum granulosum
Stratum mucosum
Stratum germinativum
Sebaceous gland
Hair follicle
Arrector pili muscle
Hair papilla
Fat cells

Pigment granules
Sensory papilla
Vascular papilla
Sweat gland
Blood vessel

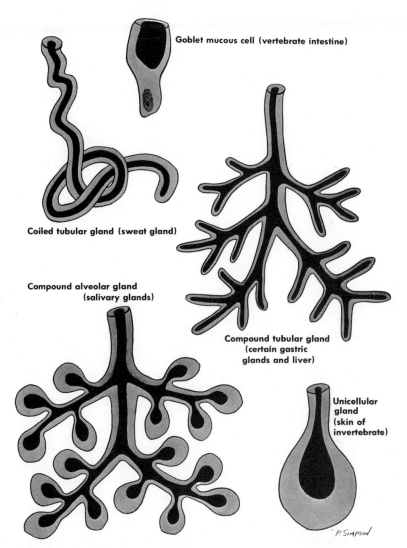

Figure 499. Types of exocrine glands. Exocrine glandular products are either secretions (formation of useful products from raw materials of blood) or excretions (waste products from blood). They are carried outside cells that form them, either to interior of certain organs or to surface. Secretory function is usually displayed by epithelial tissue but sometimes also by nervous and connective tissue. Invertebrates often have glands that resemble those of vertebrates, but invertebrates usually have greater variety of unicellular glands. Most glands form secretions in three ways: (1) merocrine, in which secretion is formed by cell; (2) apocrine, in which part of cell forms secretion; and (3) holocrine, in which entire cell is discharged in secretion.

and epidermal components, are bony dermal plates which are covered with live epidermis bearing a superficial layer of dead cells that are constantly being replaced. Amphibians have moist naked skins without scales (except the tiny dermal scales of the order Apoda). The superficial layer of their epidermis contains keratin which is replaced when lost. In strictly land tetrapods, keratinized epithelial structures have largely replaced the bony plates. Reptiles have horny scales (of epidermal origin) which prevent loss of water. These scales are also found on

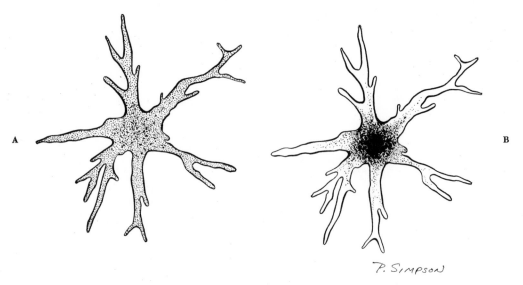

P. SIMPSON

Figure 500. Pigment cells (chromatophores). **A,** With pigment dispersed; **B,** with pigment concentrated. Pigment cell does not contract or expand; color effects produced by streaming of cytoplasm carrying pigment granules into cell branches for maximum color effect or to center of cell for minimum effect. Chromatophore of cephalopod, however, does change shape by muscular contraction. Control over dispersal or concentration of pigment is mostly through light stimuli of eye which may cause direct nervous stimulation of chromatophores or may cause nerve fiber endings to secrete neurohumors which diffuse to the pigment cells. Some hormones (intermedin) are known to influence activity of chromatophore. Types of chromatophores depend upon pigments they bear, e.g., melanophores (brownish black), xanthophores (yellow or red), and guanophores (white).

the legs and feet of birds and on the tails of certain mammals. In the pangolin the entire body is covered with large horny scales. In crocodiles and some turtles the scales form horny plates which overlie the bony dermal plates of the back and belly. Some lizards also have bony plates as well as horny scales. Horny scales are formed by the folding of the epidermis over mesodermal papillae, the upper surface of which becomes the cornified scale.

Three kinds of horns or hornlike structures are found in mammals. **True horns** found in ruminants consist of hollow sheaths of hardened epidermis which fit over a core of bone arising from the skull. Such horns are not shed, are not branched (although they may be greatly curved), and are found in both sexes. The American antelope is an exception, for its epidermal sheath may be branched and is shed periodically, and a new one is formed over the small core of dermal bone. The

antlers of the deer family (Figure 502) are entirely bone in the mature condition but during the growth period have a covering of a vascular hairy epidermis (velvet), which is gradually worn away. Antlers are shed annually and each replacement usually has more prongs or branches than the previous one. With the exception of the caribou and the reindeer, antlers are restricted to the males. Giraffes also have bony horns, but they are not shed. The **horns** of the rhinoceros are formed from hairlike horny fibers which arise from dermal papillae and are cemented together.

All claws, nails, and hoofs are keratinized epidermal structures. Mammals have inherited the reptilian claws and have modified them into nails and hoofs. A claw is shaped to cover the sides, top, and tip of a terminal joint; a nail is flattened and covers the dorsal surface of the distal phalange; and a hoof extends across the end of the digit and covers the plantar

594

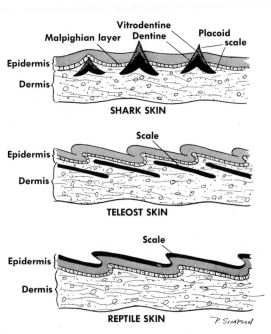

Figure 501. Diagrams of integument in classes Chondrichthyes, Osteichthyes, and Reptilia, showing different types of scales. Placoid scales of sharks are derived from dermis and have given rise to teeth in all higher vertebrates. Teleost fish have bony scales from dermis and reptiles have horny scales from epidermis. Only dermal scales are retained throughout life; epidermal scales are shed.

surface also. In the horse, the hoof, which is developed from the claw of one toe, is the only part of the foot touching the ground. Other hoofed animals may have spongy pads or other parts of the foot on which to walk.

The skin in birds and mammals plays an important part in regulating the heat of the body, for both these classes are warm blooded. Hair and feathers help in this process, but in many there are **sweat glands** which also aid in heat regulation. To prevent heat loss in cold water, such mammals as seals and whales have deep layers of fat (blubber) just beneath the skin, for hair is an efficient insulator only when air is entrapped within it.

SKELETAL SYSTEMS

Exoskeleton and endoskeleton. Two types of skeletons are recognized in the animal kingdom. Some animals have only an exoskeleton, others have mainly endoskeletons, and still others have both; neither is present in some. Protection seems to be the major function of the exoskeleton. Hard structures built up on the outside of the body may take the form of shells, spicules, calcareous plates, or other forms of defensive armor. An exoskeleton also provides inner surfaces for the attach-

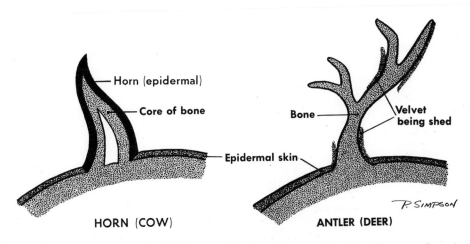

Figure 502. Diagram to show chief differences between horns and antlers. Bone, a dermal (mesoderm) derivative, forms basic part of each type, and when epidermal velvet with its hair is shed, bone forms all of the antlers. Antlers are shed annually (in winter) when zone of constriction below burr appears near skull. Horns do not branch and are not shed.

ment of muscles. It may be rigid, as in shells, but in higher invertebrates, such as arthropods, it is jointed and movable, both on the appendages and the trunk. An endoskeleton is formed inside the body, is surrounded by soft tissues, and is composed of bones and cartilages. Its manner of formation is different from that of the exoskeleton. It is formed from the mesoderm, whereas the exoskeleton comes chiefly from ectoderm. The cells which secrete most exoskeletons deposit the hard substance in layers outside the cells; in the endoskeleton the cells secrete the limy salts between the cells. This enables the endoskeleton to grow for a long period of time, for it is a living tissue.

How invertebrates meet problems of support and protection (Figure 503). Invertebrates have various ways to support and protect themselves. One of the earliest forms of exoskeleton is found in some of the protozoans which are enclosed in a shell made up of grains of sand held together by a secretion. Others of this phylum have exoskeletons formed of calcium carbonate or silica. Sponges rely upon spicules or networks of spongin for support. Some of the hydroid coelenterates *(Obelia)* have a chitinous perisarc. Mollusks, corals, and brachiopods have exoskeletons of calcium carbonate, noncellular and nonliving, which are not shed during their lives but merely increase at their margins and thicken with age. Exoskeletons have reached their greatest advancement in the arthropods, where they are formed chiefly of **chitin** secreted by the epidermis (hypodermis) and are flexible at the joints of the appendages and between the body somites. Some arthropods have a chitinous covering reinforced with limy salts (crayfish). These nonliving exoskeletons cannot increase in size; therefore the animal must shed (molt) them periodically. After a molt the body increases in size before the new exoskeleton is formed and hardened.

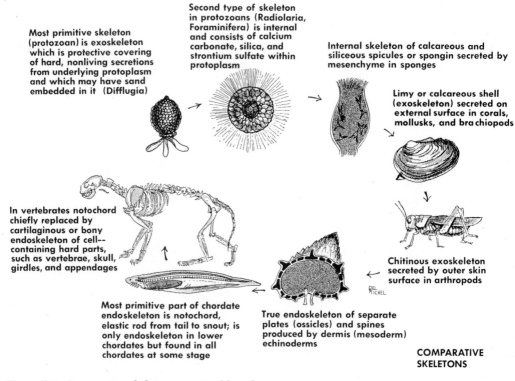

Most primitive skeleton (protozoan) is exoskeleton which is protective covering of hard, nonliving secretions from underlying protoplasm and which may have sand embedded in it (Difflugia)

Second type of skeleton in protozoans (Radiolaria, Foraminifera) is internal and consists of calcium carbonate, silica, and strontium sulfate within protoplasm

Internal skeleton of calcareous and siliceous spicules or spongin secreted by mesenchyme in sponges

Limy or calcareous shell (exoskeleton) secreted on external surface in corals, mollusks, and brachiopods

In vertebrates notochord chiefly replaced by cartilaginous or bony endoskeleton of cell--containing hard parts, such as vertebrae, skull, girdles, and appendages

Most primitive part of chordate endoskeleton is notochord, elastic rod from tail to snout; is only endoskeleton in lower chordates but found in all chordates at some stage

True endoskeleton of separate plates (ossicles) and spines produced by dermis (mesoderm) echinoderms

Chitinous exoskeleton secreted by outer skin surface in arthropods

COMPARATIVE SKELETONS

Figure 503. Comparative skeletons in animal kingdom.

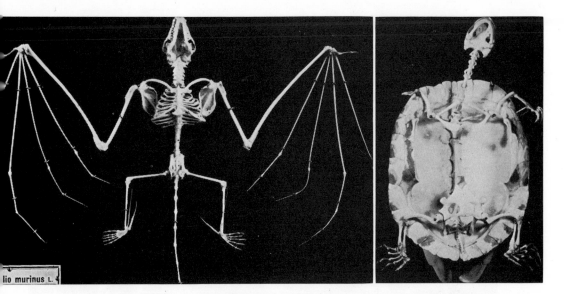

Figure 504. Two highly modified vertebrate skeletons. In the bat, forelimbs are adapted for flying. In the turtle, various divisions of endoskeleton are more or less consolidated into compact structure.

Many vertebrates also have exoskeletons, for traces of this external skeleton are found in the form of scales, fingernails, hair, feathers, and other cornified structures. The first appearance of the endoskeleton is the mesodermal plates of echinoderms; thus this form of skeleton, so well developed among the vertebrates, had its origin in the invertebrate group.

Vertebrate plan of skeleton. The characteristic skeleton of vertebrates is the endoskeleton. The endoskeleton is an internal framework of bone and cartilage which varies among the different classes of vertebrates. It is a living tissue made of cells and cell products, with the hard material deposited among the cells. The earliest form of endoskeleton to appear is the **notochord,** a semirigid rod in the protochordates. This axial rod gives partial support to the body and serves as an axis for the working of the muscles. The notochord persists in *Amphioxus* and cyclostomes, but in the other classes it is surrounded and replaced by the backbone of separate vertebrae. In these, however, vestiges of the notochord often remain. The basic constituents of the endoskeleton, bone and cartilage, vary with the different groups of vertebrates. Cyclostomes and elasmobranchs have cartilaginous skeletons; the other vertebrates have bony ones with some cartilage interspersed. Fossils and other lines of evidence indicate phylogenetically that bone is more primitive than cartilage, which may be considered an embryological material. An adult condition of cartilage instead of bone in later vertebrates (sharks, sturgeons) may indicate a degenerate or specialized skeleton, or else such forms have retained their embryonic cartilage.

The intercellular substance which forms the vertebrate skeleton may be a chondromucoid material and collagenous fibrils (cartilage), or calcium, collagenous fibrils, and phosphorus salts (bone). Most bone develops from cartilage (cartilage bone), but a few bones, such as certain ones in the face and cranium, are formed directly from sheets of mesenchyme tissue (membrane bones).

Divisions of endoskeleton. The axial division of the skeleton consists of the skull, vertebral column, ribs, and sternum; the appendicular division includes the

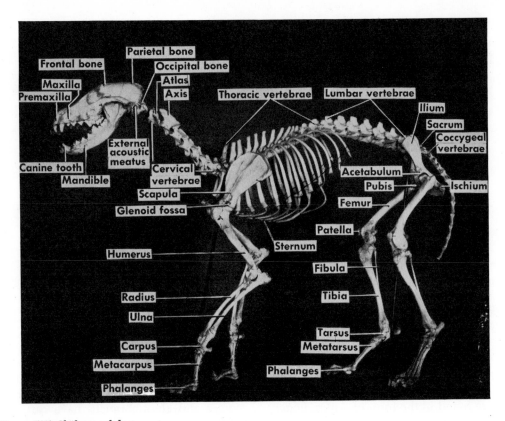

Figure 505. Skeleton of dog.

pectoral and pelvic girdles and the skeleton of the appendages. The skull is basically made up of the cranium, which houses the brain; the olfactory, optic, and otic capsules for the organs of smell, sight, and hearing; and the visceral skeleton, which makes up the jaws, hyoid apparatus, and supports for the gill pouches. In elasmobranchs the skull is cartilaginous, but in higher forms most of it is replaced by bones, with a closer union of the capsules and upper jaw. In land vertebrates the visceral skeleton has undergone a great transformation, because of the development of an entirely different method of breathing, and parts of it are converted to other structures, such as the bones of the middle ear and lower jaw and the cartilages of the larynx and epiglottis. The skull, moreover, has undergone great changes among the various vertebrates, especially in number of bones. Primitive forms tend to have a larger number of skull bones than recent forms. Some fish may have 180 skull bones; amphibia and reptiles, 50 to 95; and mammals, 35 or fewer. Man has 29.

The evolutionary history of the skull shows that it is derived from three sources: (1) the **endocranium**, or neurocranium, which is the original skull that surrounds the brain and is best seen in its primitive basic plan in the sharks; (2) the **dermocranium**, which represents the outer membranous bony cap which originated from fused dermal scales of the head and overlies the endocranium (best seen in the bowfin, *Amia*); and (3) the **splanchnocranium**, which is the endoskeletal part of the visceral skeleton that supports the gills and is also represented in a fairly primitive plan in sharks. The jaws are formed by certain visceral or gill arches which are a part of the splanchnocranium, as shown in Figure 506. In the lower vertebrates these three skull com-

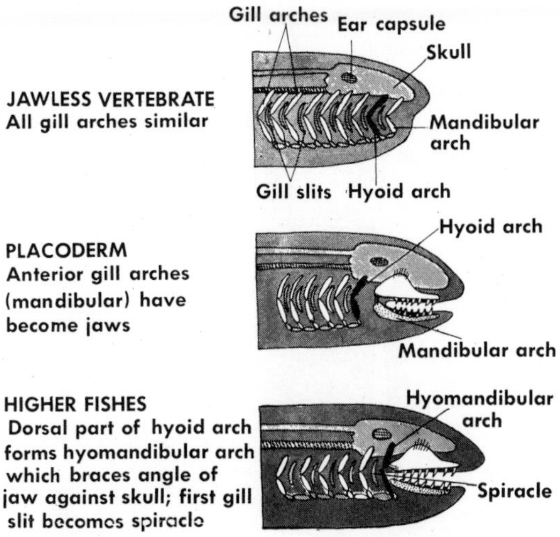

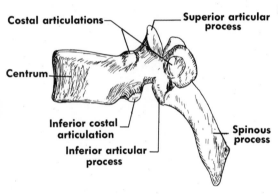

JAWLESS VERTEBRATE
All gill arches similar

Gill arches Ear capsule
Skull
Mandibular arch
Gill slits Hyoid arch

PLACODERM
Anterior gill arches (mandibular) have become jaws

Hyoid arch
Mandibular arch

HIGHER FISHES
Dorsal part of hyoid arch forms hyomandibular arch which braces angle of jaw against skull; first gill slit becomes spiracle

Hyomandibular arch
Spiracle

Figure 506. How vertebrate got its jaws. First two arches in order are mandibular and hyoid; the mandibular forms the jaws and the hyoid a supporting accessory structure. Jaws at first are separate from cranium, but later the two are consolidated. (From several sources.)

with different animals and with different regions of the vertebral column in the same animal. In the caudal region of many vertebrates each vertebra has a ventral **hemal arch** around the blood vessels of that region; this arch is modified into rib-like processes in the trunk region. The vertebral column in fish is differentiated only into **trunk** vertebrae and **caudal** vertebrae; the column in many of the other vertebrates, into **cervical** (neck), **thoracic** (chest), **lumbar** (back), **sacral** (pelvic), and **caudal** (tail) vertebrae. In birds and also in man, the caudal vertebrae are reduced in number and size, and the sacral vertebrae are fused. The number of vertebrae varies among the different animals. The python seems to have the largest number, 435. In man, there are 33 in the child, but in the adult 5 are fused to form the **sacrum** and 4 to form the **coccyx**. Besides the sacrum and coccyx, man has 7 cervical, 12 thoracic, and 5 lumbar vertebrae. The first cervical vertebra is modified for articulation with the skull and is

Costal articulations
Superior articular process
Centrum
Inferior costal articulation
Spinous process
Inferior articular process

Figure 507. Side view of thoracic vertebra.

ponents are more or less separated from each other; in higher forms they are all fused together or incorporated into a single unit, the vertebrate skull. There is a basic plan of homology in the skull elements of vertebrates from fish to man; evolution has meant reduction in numbers of bones through loss and fusion in accordance with size and functional changes.

The vertebral column supplants the notochord quite early in the phylogeny of the vertebrates. Vertebrae vary greatly

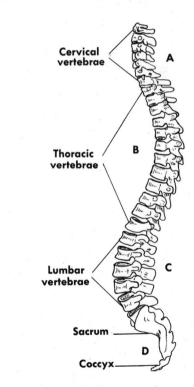

Cervical vertebrae — A

Thoracic vertebrae — B

Lumbar vertebrae — C

Sacrum
D
Coccyx

Figure 508. Vertebral column of man.

Support, protection, and movement 599

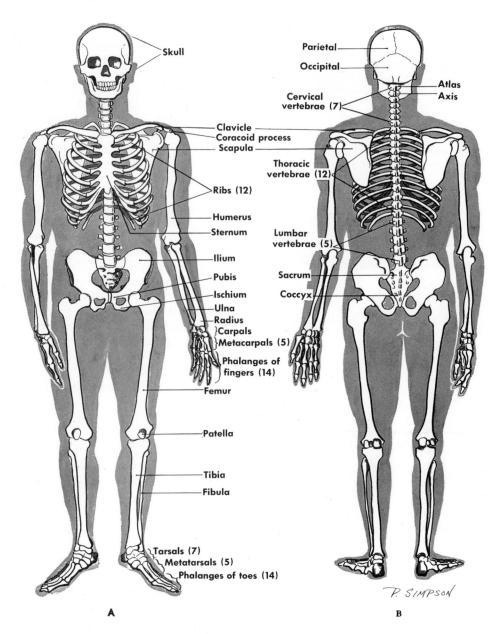

Labels on figure A (ventral view):
Skull
Clavicle
Coracoid process
Scapula
Ribs (12)
Humerus
Sternum
Ilium
Pubis
Ischium
Ulna
Radius
Carpals
Metacarpals (5)
Phalanges of fingers (14)
Femur
Patella
Tibia
Fibula
Tarsals (7)
Metatarsals (5)
Phalanges of toes (14)

A

Labels on figure B (dorsal view):
Parietal
Occipital
Atlas
Axis
Cervical vertebrae (7)
Thoracic vertebrae (12)
Lumbar vertebrae (5)
Sacrum
Coccyx

P. SIMPSON

B

Figure 509. Human skeleton. **A,** Ventral view. **B,** Dorsal view. Numbers in parentheses indicate number of bones in that unit. In comparison with other mammals, man's skeleton is a sort of patchwork of primitive and specialized parts. Erect posture brought about by specialized changes in legs and pelvis enabled primitive arrangement of arms and hands (arboreal adaptation of man's ancestors) to be used for manipulation of tools. Development of skull and brain followed as a consequence of the premium natural selection put upon dexterity, better senses, and ability to appraise environment.

called the **atlas.** The number of cervical vertebrae (7) is very constant in nearly all mammals. Manatees and the two-toed sloth, however, have 6, whereas the three-toed sloth has 9.

Ribs show many variations among the

vertebrates. The basic plan seems to have been a pair of ribs for each vertebrae from head to tail, but the tendency has been to reduce the number from lower to higher forms. Certain fish have two ventral ribs for each vertebra, and in some fish there are sometimes dorsal and ventral (pleural) ribs on the same vertebra (*Polypterus,* many teleosts). In tetrapods, the single type of rib is supposed to correspond to the dorsal one of fish. The ribs of many land vertebrates are joined to the sternum. The sternum is lacking in snakes. The ribs of vertebrate animals are not all homologous, for they do not all arise in the same way. Ribs, however, are not universal among vertebrates; many, including the leopard frog, do not have them at all. Others, such as the elasmobranchs and some amphibians, have very short ribs. Man has twelve pairs of ribs, although evidence indicates that his ancestors had more. The ribs together form the thoracic basket which supports the chest wall and keeps it from collapsing.

Most vertebrate animals have paired appendages. None are found in cyclostomes, but both the cartilaginous and bony fish have pectoral and pelvic fins which are supported by the pectoral and pelvic girdles, respectively. Forms above the fish (except snakes) have two pairs of appendages, also supported by girdles. The basic plan of the land vertebrate limb (tetrapod) is called the **pentadactyl,** for it terminates in five digits. Among the various vertebrates there are many modifications in the girdles, limbs, and digits which enable the animals to meet special modes of life. For instance, some amphibians have only three or four toes on each foot, and the horse has only one. Also, the bones of the limbs may be separate or they may be fused in various ways. Whatever the modification, the girdles and appendages in forms above fish are all built on the same plan and their component bones can be homologized. In man the pectoral girdle is made up of 2 scapulae and 2 clavicles; the arm is made up of humerus, ulna, radius, 8 carpals, 5 metacarpals, and 14 phalanges. The pelvic gir-

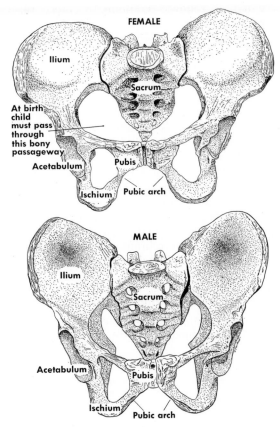

Figure 510. Chief difference between male and female skeletons is structure of pelvis. Female pelvis has less depth with a broader, less sloping ilia, a more circular bony ring (pelvic canal), a wider and more rounded pubic arch, and a shorter and wider sacrum. Most structures of female pelvis are correlated with child-bearing functions. In evolution of human skeleton, pelvis has changed more than any other part because it has to support weight of erect body.

dle (Figure 510) consists of 2 innominate bones, each of which is composed of 3 fused bones, ilium, ischium, and pubis; the leg is made up of femur, patella, tibia, fibula, 7 tarsals, 5 metatarsals, and 14 phalanges. It will be noted that each bone of the leg has its counterpart in the arm, with the exception of the patella. This kind of correspondence between anterior and posterior parts is called **serial homology.**

To summarize the bones in man, the 206 bones he normally possesses are divided as follows: cranium, 8; face, 14; hyoid, 1; ears, 6; vertebrae, 26; ribs, 24; sternum, 1; pectoral girdle, 4; arms, 60; pelvic girdle, 2; and legs, 60.

MUSCULAR SYSTEM

One of the basic properties of protoplasm is its power of contraction. However, certain cells have been specialized for this function, forming one of the major tissues of the body—**muscle.** Muscles are specialized for shortening when stimulated and thus can pull the parts to which they are attached. When the stimulation has ceased, the muscle simply relaxes and returns to its original form. Most movements in both vertebrate and invertebrate animals are produced by the contraction of muscles.

Devices for movement in invertebrates

Invertebrates have various ways of producing movement (Figure 511). Some of their movements are definitely not muscular. *Amoeba* makes use of protoplasmic streaming in contracting or extending its body. Protozoans, such as *Paramecium* and *Euglena,* use cilia and flagella for locomotion. Some protozoans, such as *Vorticella,* have special contractile **myonemes.** For their contractile elements coelenterates have the epitheliomuscular cells suggestive of the circular and longitudinal muscles in higher phyla. Muscle fibers are used by flatworms to produce movements in different planes. Roundworms have only longitudinal muscles; thus they move by dorsoventral bending of their bodies or by alternate contractions of the muscles on opposite sides of the body. Most annelids have well-developed circular and longitudinal muscles and can either shorten or elongate their bodies. All the higher invertebrates—mollusks, echinoderms, and arthropods—are well provided with muscles, not only in the

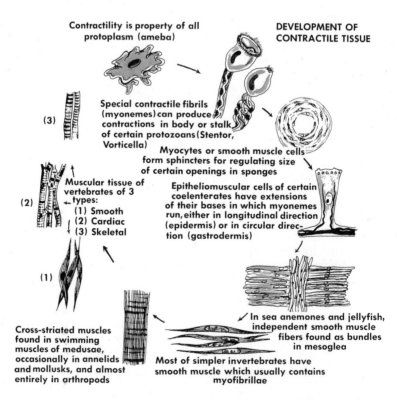

Figure 511. Development of contractile tissue (muscle) in animal kingdom.

body wall but also in many other parts of their bodies. Because of their rigid exoskeletons, arthropods have developed separate muscles which are attached at one end to the inner surface of the exoskeleton and at the other to the appendages or other parts. Certain types of striped muscle also appear in this phylum, forerunners of the skeletal muscles of vertebrates.

Muscular system of vertebrates

The great activity of most vertebrates is correlated with well-developed muscles. In the lower forms the muscles are predominantly segmented (Figure 512). In protochordates such as *Amphioxus* there are sixty or more pairs of muscle somites arranged alternately along the sides of the body. In most fish and amphibians, and, to some extent, reptiles, there is a segmental organization of muscles alternating with the vertebrae. This pattern is greatly altered in birds and mammals which no longer travel by the undulatory movements characteristic of the lower vertebrates. Segmental muscles in the higher vertebrates are found between the vertebrae and the ribs and in the abdomen. In the higher vertebrates muscles have become specialized for certain

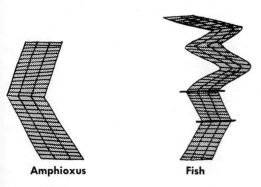

Amphioxus   **Fish**

Figure 512. Diagram of pattern of segmented muscle arrangement in lower chordates. Primitive plan (*Amphioxus*) is V-shaped chevron with point toward head; in many fish the zigzag form and sharp angles of myomeres are related to swift movements of trunk and tail. (Redrawn from Atwood: A Concise Comparative Anatomy, The C. V. Mosby Co.)

activities. From the sheet form of musculature in the low vertebrates there arose, by splitting, by fusion, and by shifting, the varied muscles of birds and mammals. Thus each specialized body part developed the type of muscles best suited for its manipulation. The shapes and sizes of muscles are correlated with their tasks. Limb muscles are often fusiform for conservation of space; muscles around the shoulders and hips, where origins are broad and insertions are narrow, are more or less triangular; abdominal muscles and diaphragm are definitely sheet-like.

Physiology of muscle

Striated muscle. Skeletal muscle fibers in a gross muscle are arranged in groups of about 100; each group is under the control of a single motor nerve fiber (Figure 513) and is called a **motor unit.** For this arrangement the single nerve fiber gives off many terminal branches, each of which innervates a muscle fiber. The attachment of a nerve to the muscle is called a **motor end plate** (Figure 513), consisting of many terminal, beaded axons which form a characteristic pattern in the underlying muscle sarcoplasm. Norepinephrine is released by these motor end plates in nervous mediation of the muscles.

The number of motor units in a muscle depends mainly upon the size of the muscle. Thus the gastrocnemius muscle of a cat has about 43,000 muscle fibers which would be divided among about 430 motor units. Motor units are supposed to obey the all-or-none law; that is, if they contract at all, they do so to their fullest extent. However, the gross muscle does not obey this law, for its extent of contraction depends upon the number of its motor units that are active at any particular time. A few motor units in operation will produce a feeble contraction; many units in action will result in a stronger contraction. In this way many gradations of contraction may be found in a gross muscle.

In living animals, muscles contract when stimulated by nerve impulses; in

Figure 513. Motor end plates of motor nerves on muscle fibers. (Courtesy J. W. Bamberger.)

the laboratory, artificial stimuli, such as induced electric currents, will cause them to contract. A single stimulus applied to a striated muscle results in a **simple twitch.** The gastrocnemius muscle of a frog may be removed with its motor nerve, the sciatic, and set up so that its contractions are recorded on a kymograph. In a simple twitch the graph will show a **latent period** between the application of the stimulus and the beginning of contraction; a **contraction period** during the actual shortening of the muscle; and a **relaxation period,** when the muscle returns to its resting condition. Repeated stimuli with sufficient time intervals for relaxation will result in **incomplete tetanus; if** the stimuli are too rapid to permit relaxation, the muscle will be thrown into a sustained contraction, producing a smooth curve on the kymograph until the cessation of stimuli or fatigue ensues, when the

lever will rapidly descend to the base line This is called **complete tetanus.**

The duration of the simple muscle twitch of the frog is commonly given as 0.01 second for the latent period, 0.04 second for contraction, and 0.05 second for relaxation. The whole time duration for the twitch is thus 0.1 second. In warm-blooded forms, muscles contract more rapidly. Remember that the simple muscle twitch is a laboratory phenomenon and is convenient for analysis, but the normal contractions of muscle in the living body are always those of the tetanic type, in which many stimuli are sent to muscles in varying degrees of rapidity.

The extent or force of muscle contractions in the illustrations mentioned depends upon the strength of the stimulus. If the stimuli are gradually increased, the muscle response will be greater, recording higher and higher contraction points until a maximum strength of stimulus is reached, after which no further increase in contraction will result. Another interesting phenomenon occurs when the muscle is excited to a maximal contraction several times in rapid succession, as in incomplete tetanus. Each twitch will be higher than its predecessor, a condition called **staircase,** or **treppe.** The explanation is that the chemical changes produced by one contraction promote a better one the next time.

Muscle tonus. Muscle **tone** refers to that state of partial contraction present in all living skeletal muscles even when they appear to be completely relaxed. It is thought that about 5% of the motor units are contracted at any one time to produce tone and that they act in relays, so that none are overworked. Whenever a nerve to a particular muscle is cut, tone in that muscle ceases. Curare, injected, abolishes tone by blocking the motor end plate between nerve and muscle.

Chemistry of muscle contraction. When a muscle fiber contracts, its myofibrils are the cell constituents which do the contracting. The changes which take place in the muscle following stimulation are not all known, although the problem has been

604

studied by many investigators. We know that many physical and chemical changes occur in the contraction process. Work is performed; therefore energy is required. Muscles apparently use 20 to 40% of the energy value of food molecules in contraction; the rest is converted into heat. About four-fifths of all the body heat comes from this source. In some way the energy released from certain biochemical reactions produces the physical changes necessary for the shortening of the muscle fiber. Much of this energy appears to be used during the relaxation phase rather than during contraction. In a contracting muscle, oxygen is used, carbon dioxide is produced, glycogen disappears, lactic acid forms, and heat production increases.

In addition, there are changes in two organic phosphates—**phosphocreatine** and **adenosine triphosphate**—which are found in muscle. According to the present state of knowledge, whenever a stimulus reaches a muscle cell adenosine triphosphate (ATP) is broken down and releases energy under the influence of an enzyme myosin, which with another muscle protein (actin) forms actomyosin. The latter is the chief contractile structure of the myofibrils. This chemical energy so released causes the protein molecules of the myofibrils to shorten either by coiling or folding or by the myosin and actin filaments sliding past each other. In the breakdown of ATP, adenosine diphosphate (ADP) is formed by the release of a molecule of phosphoric acid. To restore ATP for additional contraction, ADP combines with phosphagen (phosphocreatine) which contains a high-energy reservoir of phosphate. But phosphagen is being used up and must also be restored. To furnish energy for this process, glycogen is metabolized to lactic acid. Part of this lactic acid is oxidized to carbon dioxide and water; the other part is converted into glycogen. Only this latter step requires O_2 (aerobic); the preceding ones do not (anaerobic).

To summarize the process of muscle contraction, the sequence of chemical phases in abridged form may be expressed thus:

(1) ATP $\rightleftarrows$ ADP + H_3PO_4 + Energy for contraction
(2) Phosphagen $\rightleftarrows$ Creatine + H_3PO_4 + Energy for resynthesis of ATP
(3) Glycogen $\rightleftarrows$ Lactic acid + Energy for resynthesis of phosphagen
(4) 1/5 lactic acid + O_2 $\rightarrow$ CO_2 + H_2O + Energy for resynthesis of remaining 4/5 of lactic acid to glycogen

Since about 20% of glycogen is not restored but is lost in the oxidation of the lactic acid, this amount must be replenished by sugar from the glycogen of the liver or from the food that enters the blood. This is one of the basic reasons for nutrition.

Experimental evidence for this theory of muscular contraction was afforded by Szent-Györgyi, Hungarian biochemist of the United States, who showed that artificial fibers of actomyosin will contract when they are placed in a solution of ATP.

Rigor mortis, or the rigor after death, is also explained by the theory, for under such conditions the ATP molecules are used up in the contraction of the actomyosin fibers and enzyme systems are destroyed so that no recovery or relaxation can take place.

A muscle is able to contract in the complete absence of oxygen, but it fatigues faster. The reason is that lactic acid accumulates rapidly when the muscle is deprived of oxygen. Fatigue is thus caused primarily by an excess of lactic acid. In complete fatigue the exhausted muscle refuses to respond to nervous stimuli but it may still respond to certain direct mechanical stimuli. There is evidence that the site of this fatigue is the junction between nerve and muscle, or the motor end plate.

Oxygen debt. Ordinarily the oxygen supply to muscles is adequate for taking care of the lactic acid as it is formed in muscular contraction. However, in vigorous exercise an excess of lactic acid accumulates, for one cannot breathe fast enough to furnish the oxygen necessary to

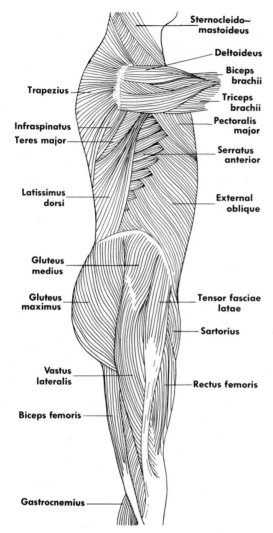

Figure 514. Lateral view of human muscles.

oxidize the lactic acid. The muscles incur what is called an **oxygen debt,** because the excess lactic acid must be oxidized by extra oxygen. The limit of oxygen debt is about 100 grams of lactic acid for the trained athlete, less for the untrained. When this limit is reached, the individual is exhausted until he recovers by rapid breathing.

Action of gross muscles

The human body contains approximately 696 skeletal muscles, most of which are paired. Apparently the muscular system is undergoing evolutionary changes in the body, for some muscles are tending to disappear and others are emerging. Most muscles are arranged in antagonistic pairs for the manipulation of the skeleton. This antagonistic action is seen also in most lower animals. Worms use their circular muscles to elongate and their longitudinal ones to contract. In the enterons of animals the circular and longitudinal muscles alternate in their action to propel the contents along (peristaltic movement).

Not all striated muscles are attached to bones. Some are of the sphincter type in which a set of circular muscles closes an opening and another set pulls radially away from the opening. Sphincters are found around the mouth and anal regions (striated muscles), at the pyloric and cardiac ends of the stomach, and in the iris of the eye (smooth muscle).

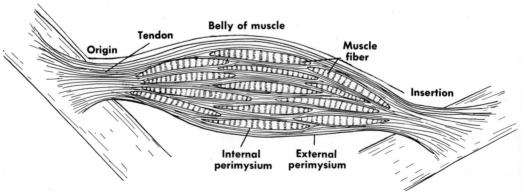

Figure 515. Diagram of a gross muscle.

Contraction of involuntary muscle

Smooth muscle contraction is much slower than that of skeletal muscle. Smooth muscles require a stronger stimulus to excite them, and all phases of contraction are prolonged. When they have developed tension, they can hold it for a longer period. Much of their action is slow and rhythmic.

In cardiac muscle the phases of contraction are slower than in striped muscle, and its contraction is mostly rhythmic. Each beat of the heart is a single twitch. This muscle has a long **refractory period,** which is that period following one stimulus when it will not respond to another one. One cannot tetanize heart muscle.

Muscles and animal electricity

Is there such a thing as animal electricity? To answer this question Luigi Galvani, an Italian physiologist, in 1786 performed his classical experiments which resulted in many fruitful concepts in this and related fields. Quite by accident Galvani found that dissected out frog legs suspended by their nerves to copper hooks twitched whenever the legs were swung against the iron bar to which the hooks were attached. Galvani concluded that the frog tissue had a peculiar kind of electricity which in some way caused the muscles to contract. In his time there was the popular belief that nerves caused muscles to contract by discharging a special fluid into them. A contemporary, Volta, showed that the contraction of the muscles was actually caused by an electric current induced by the contact of two dissimilar metals, iron and copper, which with the frog muscle acting as a conductor formed an electric arc. It was from this and similar experiments that the principle of the electric battery was developed by Volta who showed that whenever two dissimilar metals separated by material moistened with salt water were connected, an electric current would flow. However, in other experiments Galvani did demonstrate animal electricity, for he found that if the nerve of a muscle were made to touch another muscle at two points, one

uninjured and one injured, the muscle attached to the nerve would contract. The principle found by Galvani can easily be demonstrated by placing a small copper strip on one side of the tongue and a zinc or silver one on the other side and touching the metal strips together. The resulting current can be detected as an odd taste by the sensitive tongue.

OTHER FORMS OF MOVEMENT

Protoplasmic streaming. The streaming movements of protoplasm are found in Protozoa and also in such cells as eggs undergoing division. These movements may involve the entire cytoplasm or only part of it. It is most easily studied in the slime molds. Theories to account for these flowing movements are not satisfactory in all particulars. The passage of water into and out of the protoplasmic mass could produce disturbances in the form of streaming. The change from sol to gel and the reverse might be the mechanism. Differences in the electric potentials between different regions of the cell resulting in electric currents would set up flowing of the cell constituents. Whatever the cause of movements, the energy involved appears to come from respiration.

Ameboid movement. Amebae move by pushing out protoplasmic projections and then flowing into them. These pseudopodia are formed at the cell surface and could be produced by local changes in surface tension. Not all the protoplasm moves with the current; a stable gel layer surrounds the flowing sol protoplasm. This outer layer may exert a squeezing effect on the sol, thus pushing it forward. Viewed from the side, some of the pseudopodia seem to touch the substratum only with their tips, as though the animal were walking. An ameba cannot move by itself unless it is in contact with a surface. The whole process of ameboid movement with the chemical reactions necessary to supply the energy may be similar to that of muscular contraction.

Ciliary movement. Many protozoans use fine, protoplasmic hairs, called **cilia,** in swimming. The cilia are numerous and well coordinated, so that the animal can go forward or backward. The cilia extend through pores of the outer pellicle, connected to basal granules which are joined by a network of threads. Each cilium is made up of an elastic outer layer enclosing a number of contractile fibrils within it. It is thought that the contraction of the fibrils on one side of the cilium causes it to bend in that direction and that the elasticity of the outer layer causes it to return. Moving the cilia forcibly in one direction and returning them less forcibly would result in progressive movement. Cilia beat in rhythmic waves or in unison. Cutting through the basal network of threads will destroy the rhythmic wavelike action.

Cilia are also found in metazoans, both invertebrate and vertebrate. Examples are the body surface of Planaria, the pharynx of the frog, and the gonad ducts of most animals.

Action of flagella. Flagella are usually several times larger than cilia and much fewer in number wherever found. Most cells have only one or two. They move in a whiplike manner or with rotary motion, with the undulation passing from base to tip. In flagellate protozoans they are located at the anterior end, and by their movement the animal is pulled along. Like cilia, they consist of an elastic outer sheath surrounding contractile fibrils. Flagella are also found in higher forms. Most spermatozoa have posterior flagella which propel them forward. The collar cells of sponges are flagellated to create currents of water.

ANNOTATED REFERENCES

Adams, L. A., and E. Eddy. 1949. Comparative Anatomy. New York, John Wiley & Sons, Inc. *Good descriptions of the skeleton and muscles.*

Arey, L. B. 1957. Human Histology. Textbook in Outline Form, Philadelphia, W. B. Saunders Co. *This unique text should be on the desk of all zoology students.*

Carlson, A. J., and V. Johnson. 1948. The Machinery of the Body, ed. 3. Chicago, University of Chicago Press. *Good discussion of the physiology of the muscles.*

Eaton, T. H., Jr. 1960. Comparative Anatomy of the Vertebrates, ed. 2. New York, Harper & Brothers. *Good discussions of the skeleton and muscles.*

Hickman, C. P. 1940. Functional Human Anatomy. New York, Prentice-Hall, Inc. *This work attempts to explain the mechanical basis of skeletal and muscular components.*

Kahn, F. 1953. Man in Structure and Function, New York, Alfred A. Knopf, Inc. *Unique illustrations of the mechanics of muscle and bone. A well-written treatise.*

Katchalsky, A., and S. Lifson. 1954. Muscle as a Machine. Scientific American, vol. 190, pp. 72-76 (March).

Montagna, W. 1956. The Structure and Function of the Skin. New York, Academic Press, Inc. *An up-to-date account of this important organ. There is an interesting description of the relatively new concept of the apocrine sweat gland.*

Montagna, W. 1959. Comparative Anatomy, New York, John Wiley & Sons, Inc. *A clearly written presentation of the comparative anatomy of the skin, skeleton, and muscles.*

Morehouse, L. E., and A. T. Miller, Jr. 1948. Physiology of Exercise. St. Louis, The C. V. Mosby Co. *Clear descriptions of the properties and the metabolism of muscles.*

Morton, D. J. 1952. Human Locomotion and Body Form. Baltimore, Williams & Wilkins Co. *An excellent account of the mechanics of movement with relation to body form.*

Rothman, S. 1954. Physiology and Biochemistry of the Skin. Chicago, University of Chicago Press. *A highly technical account of the skin, its physical properties, its physiological functions, and its chemical constituents. Especially for the advanced student.*

Smith, H. M. 1960. Evolution of Chordate Structure. An Introduction to Comparative Anatomy. New York, Holt, Rinehart & Winston, Inc. *A text which gives a fine appraisal of the evolutionary background of vertebrate morphology. The serious student who wishes to know the why and wherefore of structural patterns will be amply repaid by studying this superb treatise.*

chapter 30

Digestive, circulatory, respiratory, and excretory systems

The animal requires energy for its living processes and materials for growth and repair. The source of materials for both energy and building is **food.** Most food cannot be utilized directly. It must be made over into a form that can enter the protoplasm of the body. First the larger molecules must be broken down into smaller molecules for absorption. Then they must be carried to wherever they are needed, to be built into body tissues or burned to provide energy. Finally the waste products generated by these processes must be eliminated. The sum total of all these chemical and physical processes is called **metabolism.** The metabolic process is one of the basic characteristics of living things. Metabolism has two phases, or aspects: **anabolism** and **catabolism.** The first is concerned with the building up of substances into new tissue or into storage materials; the second is concerned with the breaking down of complex materials to simpler ones for the release of energy.

DIGESTIVE SYSTEM
Historical background of the study of digestion

The most classical investigation in the field of digestion was made by the American, William Beaumont, during the years 1822 to 1833. His observations were made on a Canadian wood ranger named Alexis St. Martin who had accidentally shot himself with a shotgun. When the wound healed, a permanent opening, or fistula, was formed which enabled an observer to see directly into the stomach. For several years Dr. Beaumont kept St. Martin under observation and made careful note of what occurred during the process of digestion. He was able to observe how the lining of the stomach changed under different conditions, how foods varied in time of digestion, the effect of emotional states upon the motility of the stomach and its rate of digestion, and many other facts about the whole cycle of digestion.

To study the nature of gastric juice, Ivan Pavlov, a Russian physiologist, in 1887 devised his well-known stomach pouch in dogs. He constructed a pouch by sewing off a part of the stomach of a living animal in such a way that this artificial pouch opened to the outside through a hole in the abdominal wall. This pouch was lined with mucous membrane and retained its nerve supply. Whenever the main stomach functioned in response to food, emotion, and other factors, this artificial pouch also secreted gastric juice, which could be collected in a pure form. By this method, Pavlov was able to learn about the factors that stimulated or inhibited gastric digestion, the amount and consistency of gastric juice, and the phases in the cycle of digestion.

W. B. Cannon in 1898 found that by having animals (including man) swallow test meals mixed with bismuth salts, which are opaque to x-rays, the contours of the various divisions of the alimentary canal could be photographed with the rays. By taking photographs of the successive phases of digestion, it was possible to get an accurate picture of gastrointestinal movements as the food contents passed through the tract. Another American worker, A. J. Carlson (1915), added further knowledge to the movements of the stomach during normal and fasting periods by the balloon technique, by which balloons fastened to rubber tubes were swallowed and blown up in the stomach. The various movements of the stomach produced pressure changes in the balloons which could be transmitted through the rubber tubes to the tambour of a kymograph, where records were made.

Sequence of metabolic stages

The metabolism of any particular substance, in its broadest sense, includes all the chemical reactions that the substance undergoes from the time it enters the body until it is stored or oxidized for energy. Let us review the stages of metabolism briefly.

Ingestion of food takes place in most animals through the mouth; in some lower forms it is directly through the body surface. **Digestion** is the simplification of the food, by physical and chemical means, into smaller molecules in solution for absorption. These digested products are now **transported** by the circulatory system to all tissues of the body for utilization. **Assimilation** is the incorporation of the digested products into the protoplasm of the cells. There they may remain as a part of the protoplasm or they may undergo changes for the release of energy. Oxygen is also carried by the blood to the tissues where it is needed for **oxidation** of the food products. As a result of this burning process, energy and heat are produced for carrying on life processes, secretions are synthesized for many purposes, and waste substances (metabolites), such as carbon

dioxide and water, are formed as by-products. These by-products of metabolism are **excreted** through the lungs, the skin, and the excretory system. Food products unsuitable for digestion are rejected by the digestive system and are **egested** in the form of feces. Much food is not immediately oxidized but is **stored** for future use. Simple sugars can be stored in the liver and muscles as glycogen and easily reconverted as needed. Excess sugars are stored as adipose (fat) tissue. Proteins are not stored as such, but their amino acids are split up and some eliminated as waste, some converted into energy, and some stored as fat.

Digestion in invertebrates

The chemical breakdown of complex foods may occur within cells (**intracellular**) or outside cells (**extracellular**) (Figure 516). In the ameba and other Protozoa, digestion occurs intracellularly. Simple animals like these do not need special organs for taking in food or for simplifying it, although some of these have gullets (ciliates and flagellates). In these the food is retained in a droplet of water (**food vacuole**) and enzymes are secreted into it to perform the digestive process. This type of digestion is also found in metazoan forms, such as sponges, in which the collar cells take in food, digest it within the cell, and pass the food products to other cells. Most other metazoans have evolved a cavity of some kind which takes care of most of the digestion. Coelenterates and flatworms have a cavity which is known as a **gastrovascular cavity**; it takes on both digestive and circulatory functions. Into this cavity secretions with enzymes are poured, so that at least part of the food is digested **extracellularly**. Such a digestive system is not a complete digestive system, for the fecal material is egested through the mouth. A complete digestive system has a mouth, enteron, and anus. Differentiation of this tube into organs (pharynx, esophagus, stomach, and intestine) also occurs. Roundworms and nemerteans were the first animals to have a complete digestive system, and

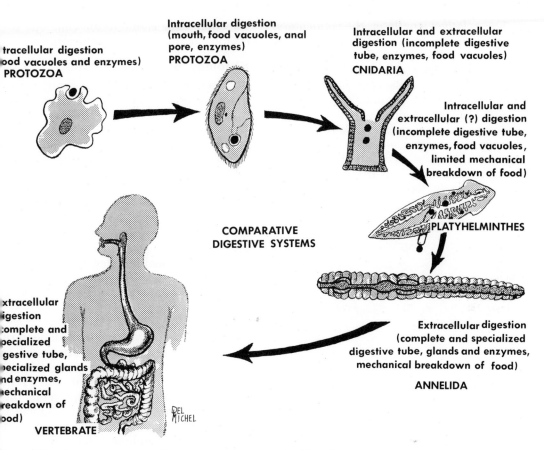

Intracellular digestion
(food vacuoles and enzymes)
PROTOZOA

Intracellular digestion
(mouth, food vacuoles, anal
pore, enzymes)
PROTOZOA

Intracellular and extracellular
digestion (incomplete digestive
tube, enzymes, food vacuoles)
CNIDARIA

Intracellular and
extracellular (?) digestion
(incomplete digestive tube,
enzymes, food vacuoles,
limited mechanical
breakdown of food)

**COMPARATIVE
DIGESTIVE SYSTEMS**

PLATYHELMINTHES

Extracellular
digestion
(complete and
specialized
digestive tube,
specialized glands
and enzymes,
mechanical
breakdown of
food)
VERTEBRATE

Extracellular digestion
(complete and specialized
digestive tube, glands and enzymes,
mechanical breakdown of food)

ANNELIDA

Figure 516. Comparative types of digestive systems in animal kingdom.

the higher invertebrates (annelids, mollusks, and arthropods) extended its differentiations.

Digestion in vertebrates

The vertebrate digestive plan is similar to that of the higher invertebrates, with a more highly differentiated alimentary canal and with a number of devices for increasing surface area. This increase may be effected by greater length, by inside folds, or by side diverticula. Elongation may be in the form of coils and loops which can be packed away among other visceral organs and in spaces in the body cavity. In this way digestive systems may be many times as long as the abdominal cavity. Some invertebrates have made use of folds, for example, the earthworm with its typhlosole. Lower vertebrates, such as cyclostomes and elasmobranchs, have longitudinal folds or spiral valves. Higher vertebrates have developed elaborate folds called **rugae** and small projections called **villi.** So effective is this method that in some animals the mucosa lining is ten times as great in area as the external surface of the tract. Diverticula are the side pouches or ceca which arise from the main canal.

Some fish have many **pyloric ceca** at the junction of the stomach and intestine. Higher vertebrates have **colic ceca** at the junction of the small and large intestines. In the rabbit, the colic cecum is larger than the large intestine. In man, this cecum is represented by the vestigial **vermiform appendix.** The large intestines of many mammals have pushed-out enlargements known as **haustra.**

The relative length of the alimentary canal depends upon food habits. Herbivorous animals, such as sheep, cattle, and rabbits, have long alimentary canals, for their food is so little concentrated that they must eat large quantities. Carnivorous animals which live upon highly concentrated food do not require so long a tube. In man, the length of the alimentary canal is given as twenty-five to thirty feet (post mortem); in the living condition it is only ten to twelve feet long.

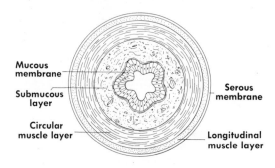

Figure 517. Diagram of cross-section of alimentary canal.

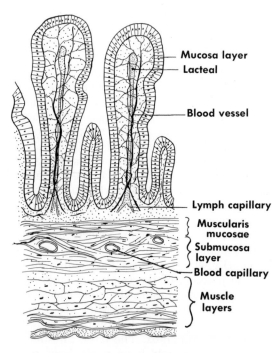

Figure 518. Diagram of villi from mammalian small intestine.

612

This difference is due to the complete relaxation of the muscles at death.

Histology of digestive tube

A section through the wall of any vertebrate alimentary canal reveals about the same histological plan with four typical layers (Figures 517 and 518). The inner **mucosa** is chiefly epithelial, simple in the stomach and intestine, stratified elsewhere. It is concerned with secretion and absorption and may be considered the chief functional component. The **submucosa**, mostly connective tissue, carries the capillaries and lymphatics. The **muscularis** layer is made up of inner circular and outer longitudinal muscles, by which peristalis is effected. The outer thin **serosa** layer is a continuation of the peritoneum.

Regions of digestive system

The structural plan of the alimentary canal among the various vertebrates is quite similar, whether we study the digestive system of a frog or of man (Figure 519). The following represents the essential parts of the system—mouth, pharynx, esophagus, stomach, small and large intestines, and mesenteries.

Mouth and mouth (buccal) cavity. The buccal cavity is surrounded by the cheeks, hard palate, soft palate, tongue, and pharynx. This region captures and takes in food. The mouth is provided with **teeth** for grasping and masticating food and with the **tongue** for manipulating, sampling, and swallowing the food. The **salivary glands,** which empty into the mouth cavity, lubricate the food and, in man at least, perform a limited amount of digestion. In man, two sets of teeth are formed during life—the temporary and the permanent sets. The former, known as "milk teeth," consists of 4 incisors, 2 canines, and 4 molars in each jaw (20 teeth). These are replaced by the permanent set of 4 incisors, 2 canine, 4 bicuspids (premolars), and 6 molars in each jaw (32 teeth). Teeth are attached to the jaw by different methods as indicated in Figure 520.

Pharynx. This is the throat cavity and is shaped like an inverted cone. It serves

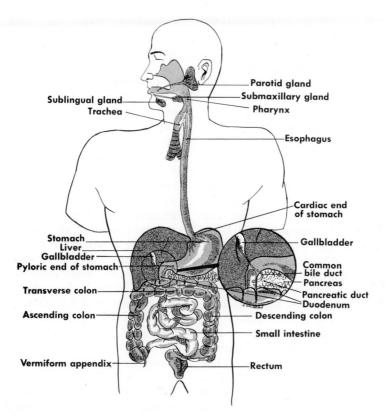

Figure 519. Digestive system of man. Window inset shows relation of gallbladder, common bile duct, and pancreatic duct to small intestine (duodenum).

for the passage of food and is the place where the air crosses the path of the food. It has undergone modifications among vertebrates. In fish and some others it is the region of the gills and serves as the point of origin for the swim bladder; in land animals the lungs and certain other structures originate in this area. In man and many other animals it has seven openings: (1) two internal nares from the nasal cavity, (2) the opening from the mouth, (3) two Eustachian tubes to the middle ear, (4) the opening into the esophagus, and (5) the glottis into the trachea.

Esophagus. The esophagus connects the pharynx with the stomach, and its length depends mainly upon the presence or absence of a neck. In the frog it is very short; in man, about thirteen inches long. The crop in birds is a differentiation of this tube and so is part of the complex

stomach of ruminants. The esophagus opens into the stomach by the **cardiac** opening, although low vertebrates have no demarcation at all between esophagus and stomach. The few glands in the esophagus are mostly of a lubricating nature, but there are well-developed muscles in

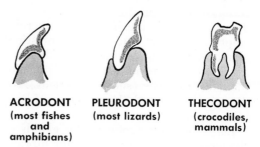

ACRODONT (most fishes and amphibians) **PLEURODONT** (most lizards) **THECODONT** (crocodiles, mammals)

Figure 520. Types of tooth attachment. Acrodont teeth are fastened to surface of jaw and pleurodont teeth to inner margin of jaw and thecodont teeth are set in sockets.

Digestive, circulatory, respiratory, excretory systems   613

its wall to aid in swallowing. The muscles at the beginning of the tube are striped; those lower down are smooth.

Stomach. The stomach in the lower vertebrates is an enlargement of the food tract between esophagus and intestine. In the higher vertebrates it assumes a great variety of shapes—saclike, spindle shaped, loop or J shaped, and the bag-shaped pouch. The stomach of man is similar to the last type and is divided into regions called the **fundus, cardiac region,** and **pyloric region.** The anterior entrance to the stomach is called the **cardiac** and the posterior exit the **pylorus.** The latter is provided with the pyloric sphincter valve which regulates the passage of the food into the small intestine. In most vertebrates there are gastric glands which secrete important enzymes for digestion, although these glands may be absent. In ruminants the stomach is divided into four compartments—the paunch, or **rumen, reticulum, omasum,** and **abomasum.** The first of these receives the food which is later recalled to the mouth to be chewed and then passed through the other compartments for digestion.

Small intestine. All vertebrates have an **intestine** which may be differentiated into **small** and **large intestines.** In the small intestine most of the digestion occurs and the food is absorbed into the blood stream for distribution to all parts of the body. In higher vertebrates, including man, the small intestine is divided into three regions: **duodenum, jejunum,** and **ileum.** These regions have certain histological differences. Two large digestive glands, the **liver** and **pancreas,** empty into the duodenum. **Intestinal glands** found along the entire length of the small intestine furnish a digestive fluid, the intestinal juice (succus entericus). All digestive juices, with the exception of liver bile, contribute enzymes for digestion.

Large intestine (colon). The glands of the large intestine are mainly for lubrication and not for digestion. Villi are absent. Usually the diameter of the colon is greater than that of the small intestine. In man, the large intestine is divided into ascending, transverse, and **descending** portions, with the posterior end terminating in the **rectum** and **anus.** At the junction of the large and small intestines is the **colic cecum** with its **vermiform appendix.** These latter structures are modified parts of the large intestine. Longitudinal muscles of the colon do not form a continuous layer but are collected into three bands, the **taeniae coli,** which cause the wall to form pouches, **haustra.** Unlike the frog and many other animals, there is no **cloaca** in mammals (with the exception of the monotremes), but the rectum has its own separate opening, the **anus,** which is regulated by a sphincter muscle.

Mesenteries. The stomach, small intestine, and large intestine are all suspended in the body cavity by **mesenteries** which are modified from two layers of the peritoneum, the lining of the coelom and the covering of the stomach and intestine. Organs, such as liver, spleen, and pancreas, are also held in place by mesenteries, which serve to carry blood and lymph vessels as well as nerves to the various visceral organs. Fat is often stored in mesenteries.

In the frog and lower vertebrates, the coelom is divided into two compartments —the **pericardial** cavity around the heart and the **pleuroperitoneal** cavity containing the other visceral organs. Mammals have the body trunk divided into two regions by the **diaphragm**—the **thoracic** region, containing two **pleural** cavities and the pericardial cavity between them, and the **abdominal** region, containing the **peritoneal** cavity. Each pleural cavity contains a lung, and the peritoneal cavity contains the other visceral organs except the excretory organs.

Physiology of digestion

Digestion involves both mechanical and chemical alterations of food. Digestion is the breakdown of complex products into simpler substances so the latter can be absorbed through the intestinal walls. Mechanical factors which aid in the process are teeth, for tearing and masticating, grinding organs (gizzards of earthworms and birds), and muscular action of the stomach and intestinal walls (segmentation movements). Chemical reactions in the breakdown of foods are regulated by the **enzymes,** organic catalysts which are highly specific, so that each enzyme will act upon only one kind of food. Only chemical alteration of food is found in animals that bolt their food down in large pieces.

Action of enzymes. Most digestive enzymes produce their action by the process of **hydrolysis,** in which a molecule of water is added to the food molecule which then separates into two other molecules. In hydrolysis, cleavage may involve several stages before the final molecules are obtained. In proteins, for example, the first stage in hydrolysis will yield molecules of several amino acids, and additional hydrolytic reactions will be necessary before amino acids will be split off. Before they can be absorbed, proteins must be split into amino acids; carbohydrates into simple sugars; and fats into glycerol and fatty acids. Specific enzymes for each of these processes are found in various regions of the alimentary canal. One enzyme may finish what another has started. Glands that secrete the various enzymes are controlled during digestion by nervous reflexes or by special hormones from the endocrine system.

Digestion in mouth. In the mouth, food is broken down mechanically by the teeth and chemically by certain enzymes. Chemical reactions are usually restricted because of the short time food is retained in the mouth. Food is masticated and mixed with **saliva** which is secreted by three pairs of salivary glands: **parotid, submaxillary,** and **sublingual.** Saliva contains two enzymes, **ptyalin** and **maltase,** which act upon carbohydrates. Ptyalin splits starch and other complex carbohydrates into the double sugar **maltose.** Maltase breaks down maltose to glucose. Salivary digestion continues in the stomach after the food enters there, but as soon as the gastric contents become acid, the process ceases.

Swallowing. When the food mass in the mouth is ready, the act of swallowing is begun voluntarily by the tongue and cheeks pushing the food backward into the pharynx. Then by involuntary reflex action the soft palate and uvula are elevated to close off the nasal cavity, and the larynx rises to meet the lowering of the epiglottis, thus closing off the windpipe. By these devices food is prevented from getting into the wrong channels. Food slides over the epiglottis, and contraction of esophageal muscles (peristalsis) forces the food into the stomach. This movement involves the constriction of muscles just behind a food bolus with a relaxation of muscles in front of it. It takes about 10 seconds for food to pass to the stomach, although fluids can pass in a much shorter time. The cardiac sphincter opens reflexly as the food bolus approaches, and the bolus glides into the stomach. Then the sphincter closes again to avoid regurgitation of food back into the esophagus. The nerve center of swallowing, involving both sensory and motor nerve components, is located in the medulla.

Digestion in stomach. Food is subjected to both muscular movements and chemical reactions in the stomach. The movements thoroughly mix the food with the gastric juice, secreted by the gastric glands. These contractions follow a definite pattern, for they start about the central portion of the stomach and move toward the pyloric end of the stomach. Succeeding waves of contractions originate more and more anteriorly and eventually arise near the cardiac end of the stomach. The enzymes (**pepsin** and **rennin**) of gastric juice act mainly upon protein foods. Pepsin in the inactive form, **pepsinogen,** is converted into active pepsin by hydrochloric acid and also by other pepsin already present. Pepsin is active only in an acid medium and splits large molecules of protein into smaller molecules of proteoses and peptones. The enzyme rennin coagulates milk by changing **casein** (a milk protein) from a soluble to an insoluble form. Rennet used in making junket pudding is made of rennin, and rennin extracted from the stomachs of calves is used in cheese making. The fat-splitting **gastric lipase** is thought by some to be present in the gastric juice.

The factors that cause the pyloric sphincter valve to open are complex but involve fluidity and acidity of the gastric contents, degree of filling of stomach, parasympathetic nerve activity, and effect of enterogastrone.

The mechanism responsible for avoiding self-digestion includes a thick lining of mucus secreted by special cells; this prevents direct contact of enzymes on the wall. There is also the possibility of anti-enzymes. Sometimes the mechanism does break down, as in gastric ulcers.

Digestion in small intestine. The major part of digestion occurs in the small intestine. Into this region of the digestive system three secretions, **pancreatic juice, intestinal juice,** and **bile,** are poured. The pancreatic juice has many enzymes and recent work has revealed new ones. The protease formerly considered as trypsin is now known to consist of several enzymes. One of these is **trypsin,** whose inactive zymogen is trypsinogen. The activation of the latter into trypsin by entero-kinase from the intestinal wall has been disputed, but trypsinogen freed from its inhibitor can be activated by small amounts of trypsin. This latter activity is called an **autocatalytic reaction** and may be a general phenomenon of enzymatic activities. Trypsin can act upon natural proteins and reduce them to proteases and peptones; if the proteins have been partly hydrolyzed by pepsin, trypsin can break them down to amino acids. Another protease is **chymotrypsin** which is found in an inactive form as chymotrypsinogen. The latter is activated into chymotrypsin by trypsin. Chymotrypsin also acts upon proteins and clots milk. One of the peptidase group of enzymes in pancreatic juice is called **carboxypeptidase.** It acts upon polypeptides and splits off amino acids. Of the other pancreatic juice enzymes, **amylopsin** (diastase) reduces whole or partly digested starches to maltose, and **pancreatic lipase** converts fats to fatty acids and glycerol. All these enzymes work best in an alkaline medium which is brought about by the carbonates of the pancreatic and intestinal juices.

Intestinal juice from the glands of the mucosal lining furnishes a number of enzymes. One of these, **erepsin,** completes the gastric digestion of peptones and proteoses and splits them into amino acids. Three other enzymes are concerned with carbohydrate splitting: **maltase,** which converts maltose to glucose; **sucrase,** which splits sucrose to glucose and fructose; and **lactase,** which breaks down lactose (milk sugar) into glucose and galactose. The acid contents from the stomach also cause the intestinal mucosa to release the hormone **secretin,** which, carried in the blood to the pancreas, stimulates the flow of pancreatic juice.

Bile contains no enzymes. It is made up of water, bile salts, and certain pigments. Bile is usually stored in the gallbladder and is stimulated to flow down the common bile duct when food enters the small intestine. A hormone, **cholecystokinin,** secreted by the intestinal lining, plays a part in regulating the flow of bile. Bile salts (sodium taurocholate and sodium glycocholate) emulsify fat into small particles, so that the fat-splitting enzymes may have a chance to reduce them. The bile pigments (**bilirubin** and **biliverdin**) are produced from the breakdown of hemoglobin in the destruction of red blood cells. They give bile its color which varies with different animals. Human bile is a golden yellow color. Bile pigments also color the feces. Excess cholesterol is excreted by the liver and may be the source of gallstones.

Bile is produced by the liver, the largest and most versatile gland in the body. Among the liver's many functions are the following: a storehouse for glycogen, production of fibrinogen in blood clotting, production of plasma proteins, site of protein synthesis, detoxification of nitrogenous waste by changing ammonia into urea, destruction of worn-out erythrocytes, formation and storage of the anti-anemia factor of the blood, deamination of the amino acids, storage of vitamins A and D, and a center for fat and carbohydrate metabolism.

Digestion in large intestine. The **colon** produces no digestive juices, but bacteria there secrete enzymes which work upon proteins and cellulose of plants. These enzymes are not very important in man, but in herbivorous animals they digest cellulose. Material that reaches the large intestine has most of its nutrients taken from it, although it is still in a liquid state. The colon stores the indigestible products and waste as feces and eliminates them from the digestive tract. Peristaltic movements force the contents slowly along until they reach the rectum. Peristaltic movements are greatly speeded up by the **gastrocolic reflex,** which occurs when food enters the stomach and produces the desire for defecation. The process of defecation involves the coordinated action of muscles of the large intestine, abdominal muscles, diaphragm, and sphincter muscles of the anus. The act is partly voluntary and partly involuntary. The desire to defecate is induced by the distention of the rectum and the resulting stimulation of the nerves in its walls. Whenever the signal is ignored, the rectum adapts itself to the new size and the desire passes off temporarily. The fecal content is made up of the indigestible residue of food, bile pigments, secreted heavy metals, and bacteria.

Factors that regulate secretions and movements of digestive tract

The physiology of the digestive system centers around two important functions: **secretions** and **movements.** All glands in the alimentary canal must be stimulated to secrete their products. The action of the glands is controlled by the nervous system and by hormones. Salivary glands are controlled entirely by the nervous system. Sensory receptors, such as taste buds and olfactory receptors, carry impulses to the salivation center in the medulla which mediates impulses to the salivary glands. The salivary glands may also be influenced by the higher centers of the brain, such as thinking about or seeing food. The flow of gastric juice is regulated partly by a nervous mechanism and partly by the action of the hormone **gastrin** which is produced in the mucosa cells of the stomach. The hormone **secretin** stimulates the pancreas, but nervous impulses may also play a minor role. Intestinal juice is influenced by secretin and **enterocrinin** (a hormone), together with the action of the intrinsic nerves of the intestinal wall.

The most characteristic movements of the alimentary canal are those of **peristalsis** (several varieties) and **segmentation.** Peristaltic movements propel the food along the tract, but the segmental movements of the small intestine serve to divide and mix the food. Hormones and nerves influence the movements of the alimentary canal. **Enterogastrone,** produced in the duodenal mucosa, will slow gastric motility and decrease the secretion of gastric juice.

Absorption

Most foodstuffs are absorbed from the small intestine. In forms such as *Hydra* the food particles which are partly digested in the gastrovascular cavity are absorbed by the endodermal cells and are passed on to the other cells. Digestion in these animals is partially extracellular and partially intracellular. In Protozoa the food is digested in the food vacuoles and is then absorbed directly into the protoplasm.

In man, there is little absorption in the stomach. Some drugs and alcohol (in part) are absorbed there, which explains their quick action. **Villi** are mainly responsible for absorption, since they contain a network of blood and lymph capillaries which pick up the digested materials. These villi can twist and shorten, thus facilitating the process of absorption by propelling the flow of lymph and blood. Amino acids and simple sugars are absorbed directly into the blood, which delivers them to the liver before they are sent into the general circulation. Glycerol and fatty acids enter the lymph vessels. Since these lymph vessels eventually enter the thoracic duct, the fat also gets into the blood. In the large intestine most of the water is absorbed; this accounts for the solid nature of the feces. Bacterial decomposition products may also be absorbed. Some of these are toxic and odorous, but the liver usually detoxifies them.

Absorption is not simply a diffusion process, for it may occur sometimes when the substance being absorbed is in greater concentration in the blood than in the intestine. Some of the absorption can be explained on the basis of an active secretory process similar to the forces that operate in glandular secretion.

Fate of absorbed materials. Absorbed amino acids and glucose are carried by the hepatic portal system to the liver, where they are stored, changed into other forms, and released to the blood. Many of the amino acids are deaminized in the liver by the removal of the amino group (NH_2) which then combines with carbon dioxide to form urea, $CO(NH_2)_2$ a waste product of urine. The other part of the amino acid is converted into fat or sugar for energy purposes. Other amino acids are released by the liver to the cells of the body to repair or replace living protoplasm.

Glucose is converted to glycogen (animal starch) in the liver where it is stored to be released (as glucose) to the blood for the maintenance of the glucose level (0.1%). Some glucose combines with other substances to form a basic part of protoplasm, and some is also stored in the muscles as glycogen. Glucose is one of the most available sources of energy for muscular work and heat production.

Fat which enters the blood stream from the thoracic duct is changed into fat characteristic of the animal's body by rearrangement of the fatty acids. Some fats, in the form of lipids, enter into the structure of protoplasm, especially at cell surfaces, where they help form the nuclear and plasma membranes. Excess fat is stored in adipose tissues which are located in the connective tissues between muscles and skin, in mesenteries, and around various organs.

Nutritional aspects of the animal

A **food** may be defined as any substance which, when taken into the body, will furnish energy and materials for the structure and repair of tissues or has regulative action on body processes. The common classification of food includes **carbohydrates, proteins, fats, water, mineral salts,** and **vitamins.** The first three are required for energy and building materials, the latter three for building and regulative action. Although the needs of all animals for these substances are in general similar, they may have different ways of getting them. Some animals are exclusively **herbivorous** (rabbit), others are exclusively **carnivorous** (tiger), and still others are **omnivorous** (man). There are also differences in the amount and kind of food required. Rats do not need ascorbic acid since they make this vitamin in their own bodies, but man must include it in his diet. Water is acquired by animals in different ways. Aquatic animals take in copious amounts with their food; frogs, through their skin; and some forms make use of the water formed in the oxidation of their food. Some animals have an intense liking for salt (many herbivorous forms), but carnivores usually spurn it in their diets.

Energy requirements. The energy unit is the **kilocalorie;** this is the amount of heat necessary to raise 1 kilogram of water from 15° C. to 16° C. The caloric values of foods utilized in metabolism are as follows:

1 gram of carbohydrate	4.1 kg.-cal.
1 gram of fat	9.3 kg.-cal.
1 gram of protein	4.3 kg.-cal.

The daily expenditure of energy varies according to age, sex, weight, activity, and body proportions. To determine how much energy is required for various forms of activity, it is necessary to standardize the metabolic rate. This is done by first determining the **basal metabolic rate.** This rate for an adult male of average weight, relaxed and fasting, is about 1,600 kilocalories every twenty-four hours. As a result of many determinations, tables

618

have been prepared which give the normal basal metabolic rate for a given size, height, sex, and body area. The energy expended in a basal metabolic condition is for the working of the vital organs and for maintaining the body temperature.

Basal metabolism can be determined directly by measuring the heat given off while the subject is in a specially constructed insulated chamber, but the more common method is by **indirect calorimetry,** in which the oxygen consumption is measured over a short period of time. Since the heat and energy released depend upon the oxidation of food, their amounts can be calculated from the oxygen consumed. On the basis of oxygen consumed, it is found that every liter of O_2 will yield about 4.8 kilocalories of heat energy for the average diet. Any activity beyond that of basal metabolism will require additional kilocalories of energy. The requirements for energy will depend upon the kind of work in which one is engaged. Persons living a sedentary life use about 2,500 kilocalories daily; those engaged in heavy manual work, as many as 5,000 to 6,000 kilocalories daily.

Balanced diet. It is not enough to supply fuel foods—it is also necessary to furnish food components that will meet all the needs of the body. Any of the basic foods (proteins, carbohydrates, or fats) could supply the kilocalorie needs, but the individual could not thrive on such an unbalanced diet. The **balanced diet** takes into consideration all the metabolic requirements of the body—energy, growth, replacement, and physiological regulation. This must include energy or fuel food, mineral, green and yellow vegetables, roughage, vitamins, and water.

In the average American diet about two-thirds of the energy comes from carbohydrates and the other one-third from proteins and fats. Carbohydrates are widely used by most people because they are cheaper than other foods. Proteins are expensive foods and are restricted in the diet. Perhaps 50 grams of protein daily would meet the demands of the body, but the average American diet includes far more than this. The amino acids of proteins can be divided into two groups— essential amino acids, which the body cannot synthesize but must be supplied ready-made in the diet, and nonessential amino acids, which the body can make from any amino group of the diet. Whenever the body is making a particular protein, all the amino acids necessary for that protein must be present at the same time. This means that each meal must be balanced so far as proteins are concerned; the requirements of other food elements of the diet can be reckoned on a daily basis. A complete protein is one that contains all the essential amino acids, such as eggs, meat, and cheese. Some plant proteins are not complete.

The minerals required are **sodium chloride** for the blood and osmotic balance of the body, **iron** for the hemoglobin of the blood, **potassium** and **magnesium** for muscle contraction, **calcium** and **phosphorus** for the teeth and bones, and **iodine** for the hormone of the thyroid gland. As there is a steady loss of these salts from the body, they must be replaced in the food we eat. The chief source of sodium chloride is table salt; iron, meats and eggs; potassium and magnesium, meats and vegetables; calcium and phosphorus, milk and meat; and iodine, drinking water or iodized table salt. Water is necessary to the amount of at least 2,000 ml. daily.

Vitamins. Vitamins are somewhat simple compounds and are usually found in scanty amounts in foods, but they are absolutely essential to life. They are not sources of energy, but their lack from the diet causes pathological disturbances. Their chief functions are to regulate various bodily functions, at least in the higher animals. Just what role they perform in lower animals is largely unknown. Each vitamin must be present in a minimal amount to prevent deficiency diseases. Vitamins are widely scattered through a variety of foods, and most of their chemical structures have been worked out. Many are made synthetically and sold in the form of pills. If the diet is sufficiently varied and balanced, it will include the proper amounts of vitamins, but in restricted (reduction) diets and in the average diets of alcoholics, there may be a serious lack of them.

Methods of preparing foods may cause serious loss of vitamins. Refined flour and canned foods may be lacking in vitamins unless they are fortified. Cooking may destroy important vitamins, and some are discarded in pot liquor. Chemically, each vitamin is unrelated and more or less isolated from other vitamins. Perhaps the greatest advancement in knowledge about them is the part many of them play in enzyme systems of bodily metabolism.

Most plants and animals need vitamins, although the requirements are not the same for all animals. Some animals have the power to synthesize certain vitamins in their own bodies; others cannot. Many animals make vitamin C in their bodies. Insects seem to require only the B complex vitamins. This variation among animals may be due to evolutionary changes or mutations.

Instead of the letter designation so long used for vitamins, many are now called by their chemical names, if their chemical structures are known.

Vitamin A (fat-soluble, epithelium-protecting vitamin)

Source: Butter, eggs, milk, carotene of plants, cod-liver oil

Function: Maintenance of epithelial cells of skin, eye, and mucous membranes; regenerates visual purple of eye

Lack causes: Xerophthalmia, night blindness, retardation in growth

Prevalence of disorders: Among poorer classes, usually night blindness

Vitamin B complex (water-soluble)

1. Thiamine (B_1) (antineuritic)

    Source: Yeast, germ of cereals, egg yolk, liver, nuts, lean pork

    Function: Necessary for carbohydrate metabolism; acts as coenzyme to carboxylase in conversion of pyruvic acid to acetaldehyde

    Lack causes: Beriberi, loss of appetite, cessation of growth, polyneuritis in birds

    Prevalence of disorders: Common among people of rice-eating countries; uncommon in United States but may be found in alcoholics

2. Riboflavin (B_2 or G)

    Source: Green leaves, eggs, meat, cheese, milk, liver

    Function: Concerned with oxidation processes and intermediate metabolism of food; hydrogen acceptor and donator for cellular synthesis

    Lack causes: Stunted growth, inflammation at corners of mouth (cheilosis), dermatitis

    Prevalence of disorders: Fairly common in southern communities.

3. Niacin (nicotinic acid) (antipellagric)

    Source: Green leaves, egg yolk, wheat germ, liver, yeast

    Function: Constituent of certain coenzymes; essential to cellular functions

    Lack causes: Pellagra in man and pigs, blacktongue of dogs, degeneration of nerve cells

    Prevalence of disorders: Fairly common in the South

4. Pyridoxine (B_6)

    Source: Yeast, meat, eggs, nuts, cereals

    Function: Necessary in certain metabolic processes; as pyridoxal phosphate functions as coenzyme of some of transaminating enzymes

    Lack causes: Failure to grow, together with anemia and dermatitis, in experimental animals; may be necessary for man

    Prevalence of disorders: None known among man

5. Folic acid

    Source: Green leaves, soybeans, yeast, egg yolk

    Function: Essential for growth and formation of blood cells; necessary for certain metabolic processes

    Lack causes: Anemia and sprue in man, hemorrhage of kidneys, bone deformity in chickens

    Prevalence of disorders: Unknown

6. Pantothenic acid

    Source: Eggs, meat, sweet potatoes, cane molasses, milk

    Function: Forms coenzyme A of Krebs cycle metabolism; necessary for normal nerves and skin

    Lack causes: Dermatitis in chicks, graying of fur in black rats

    Prevalence of disorders: None known in man

7. Biotin (H)

    Source: Egg yolk, meat, molasses, fresh fruits, fresh vegetables, yeasts, cereal grains

Function: Forms coenzyme necessary for carbon dioxide utilization

Lack causes: Dermatitis in rats and chicks; egg-white injury

Prevalence of disorders: Few cases reported in man

8. Cyanocobalamin (B_{12})

Source: Milk, egg yolk, liver, oysters

Function: Extrinsic factor of antianemic factor for red blood cell formation (erythrocyte maturation factor)

Lack causes: Pernicious anemia, poor growth and wasting disease in some animals

Prevalence of disorders: Fairly common

Vitamin C (ascorbic acid) (antiscorbutic vitamin) (water-soluble)

Source: Citrus fruits, tomatoes, cabbage, spinach

Function: Formation of intercellular material and cement material between epithelial cells of capillary walls

Lack causes: Scurvy in man and guinea pig

Prevalence of disorders: Among some on restricted diets

Vitamin D (fat-soluble, antirachitic vitamin)

Source: Eggs, fish oils, beef fat, skin exposure to ultraviolet radiation; precursor in skin, ergosterol

Function: Regulates calcium and phosphorus metabolism

Lack causes: Rickets in young

Prevalence of disorders: Common in congested regions

Vitamin E (alpha tocopherol) (fat-soluble)

Source: Green leaves, vegetable fats, wheat germ, meats, eggs

Function: Nuclear growth and activity, necessary for differentiation in vertebrates

Lack causes: Sterility in some animals, death of embryos

Prevalence of disorders: Unknown, doubtful in human

Vitamin K (fat-soluble, antihemorrhagic vitamin)

Source: Green leaves, spinach, soybean oil, egg yolk, kale, liver

Function: Synthesis of prothrombin in liver, essential for blood clotting

Lack causes: Failure of blood to clot

Prevalence of disorders: Sometimes in newborn infants

CIRCULATORY SYSTEM

The primary purpose of the circulatory system is the transportation of materials throughout the animal body. It has taken on a large number of other functions as well. It serves to regulate the body temperature of warm-blooded animals. It helps regulate the water balance of the body, for the blood supplies water to the various tissues and in turn receives the excess water formed from metabolic processes. Its white corpuscles and antibody content have developed an effective mechanism for combating disease germs.

Blood is constantly on the move and is constantly changing as it gives up various products and picks up others. Blood is remarkably stable, however, in its component parts, for it has the adaptive power to adjust itself whenever any factor upsets its balance.

Historical background of the study of blood and lymph circulation

Before the time of William Harvey, the English physician, ideas about the circulation of blood were largely erroneous. Centuries before, Galen had taught that air enters the heart from the windpipe and that blood was able to pass from one ventricle to the other through pores in the septum which separated the two. He also believed that the blood flowed first in one direction and then in the other. In 1616 Harvey was able to demonstrate the main facts about blood circulation. He made use of a variety of animals for his experiments, including the little snake found in English meadows. By tying ligatures on arteries, he noticed that the region between the heart and the ligature swelled up. When veins were tied off, the swelling occurred beyond the ligature. When blood vessels were cut, blood flowed in arteries from the cut end nearest the heart; the reverse happened in veins. By means of such experiments, Harvey worked out a correct scheme of blood circulation, with the exception of the capillaries which he could not see because he lacked a microscope. It was not until 1628 that Harvey first published his account because of the opposition his results received from his contemporaries.

The Italian Marcello Malpighi was able to complete Harvey's work in 1661 by describing the capillaries in the tissues of the frog's lungs and pointing out their relations to the arteries and veins. He was able to do this by means of the simple lens of that day. Shortly afterward Leeuwenhoek was able to confirm Malpighi's work by observing capillaries in the tails of tadpoles. One of the best and simplest places to see capillaries is in the web of the frog's foot.

Gasparo Aselli, an Italian anatomist, first discovered the nature of lacteals in 1627. In a dog which had recently been fed and cut open, he noticed white cordlike bodies in the mesenteries of the intestine which he first mistook for nerves. When he pricked these cords with a scalpel, a milky fluid gushed out. It is now known that this fluid is largely fat which is carried after digestion to the thoracic duct. The thoracic duct and its relations to the lacteals was discovered by the Frenchman Jean Pecquet in 1647. These vessels are part of the lymphatic system which Thomas Bartholin, a Danish physician, first demonstrated in its general relations in 1653, when he made his investigations on dogs and executed criminals.

The first recorded demonstration of blood pressure was made in 1733 by Stephen Hales, an English clergyman. He tied a horse on its back, exposed the femoral artery in the thigh, and between two ligatures on the artery inserted a cannula in the form of a small brass pipe. To this pipe he fastened a glass tube nine feet long, which was held in an upright position. When he untied the ligatures on the artery the blood rose in the glass tube to a distance of more than eight feet and fluctuated up and down in accordance with the systolic and diastolic heartbeats. The weight of the column of blood indicated the actual blood pressure. Blood pressure is commonly expressed in mercury which is 13.6 times as heavy as water and is measured in millimeters. Hales' figures expressed in millimeters of mercury indicate that the pressure he measured in the horse was between 180 and 200 mm.

Plan of circulatory system

The plan of circulation in forms specialized enough to have a separate and distinct system is rather simple. It is made up of a system of channels, **blood vessels,** for carrying the fluid medium; a propulsive organ, the **heart,** which pumps the blood through the body; and a circulating medium, the **blood,** which is kept constantly on the move by the driving action of the heart. In addition, there is a similar cooperating system, the **lymphatic system,** the function of which is to return lymph to the blood. Lymph is formed from blood plasma that has filtered from the blood vessels but is unable to get back directly into the blood capillaries because of blood pressure. Lymph bathes the cells of the tissues directly and carries the digested foods and oxygen which the cells take as needed. In return, the cells lose to the lymph their waste substances, urea and carbon dioxide.

Open and closed circulatory systems

In higher forms, the circulatory system is a **closed** one in which the blood is confined to tubes throughout its course from the heart back to the heart. Among most invertebrates, part of the system is made up of well-developed blood vessels which pass from the heart to the body tissues; but there they open into spaces (**lacunae**) where the blood comes directly into contact with the cells. From these intercellular spaces blood returns to the heart. This latter arrangement is called an **open** system. A closed system keeps the blood moving rapidly through its various channels but requires an auxiliary lymphatic system where the fluid flow is slow and the tissue cells are bathed directly with the nutritive lymph. The closed system is a far more efficient system for animals of large size and active habits, for a complete circulation of blood occurs in a matter of minutes or less.

The circulatory system has penetrated to nearly every part of the body, but there are a few places where blood vessels do not go. These regions are the epidermis

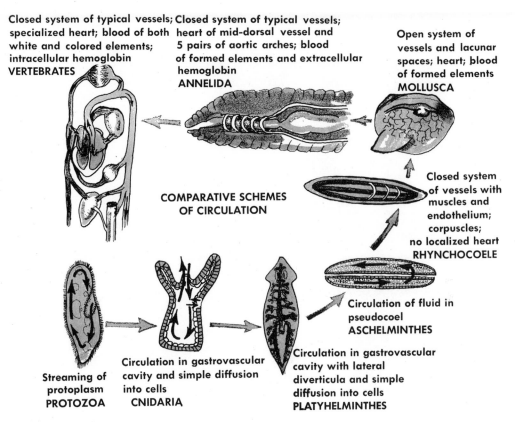

Figure 521. Comparative schemes of circulation among different animals.

Labels within figure:

Closed system of typical vessels; specialized heart; blood of both white and colored elements; intracellular hemoglobin
VERTEBRATES

Closed system of typical vessels; heart of mid-dorsal vessel and 5 pairs of aortic arches; blood of formed elements and extracellular hemoglobin
ANNELIDA

Open system of vessels and lacunar spaces; heart; blood of formed elements
MOLLUSCA

COMPARATIVE SCHEMES OF CIRCULATION

Closed system of vessels with muscles and endothelium; corpuscles; no localized heart
RHYNCHOCOELE

Circulation of fluid in pseudocoel
ASCHELMINTHES

Streaming of protoplasm
PROTOZOA

Circulation in gastrovascular cavity and simple diffusion into cells
CNIDARIA

Circulation in gastrovascular cavity with lateral diverticula and simple diffusion into cells
PLATYHELMINTHES

of the skin, cornea of the eye, cartilage tissue, enamel of the teeth, feathers, hair, and a few others. Nutritive fluids from blood vessels reach many of these through interstitial spaces by a process called **seepage**.

Circulation in invertebrates

In a protozoan, food products and oxygen are taken into the cell and distributed and the waste eliminated by diffusion. In more complicated animals, some cells are too far away to be in direct contact with food and oxygen, and some means had to be provided to carry these substances to them and to remove their metabolic wastes. In the sponges (Porifera) the extensive system of canals and internal cavity are sufficient to carry the food-laden water near enough to all the cells. Among coelenterates, the gastrovascular cavity serves a similar function, for all cells are bathed with fluid or else are close enough to profit from direct diffusion. Flatworms have a much-branched gastrovascular cavity which penetrates to most parts of the body. The development of a separate vascular system arose after a complete digestive system (tube-within-a-tube) evolved. Nemertean worms have a few blood vessels in which the blood is propelled by the "milking" action of the muscular walls of the vessels.

The heart as a definite propulsive organ appears in the mollusk, annelid, and arthropod. These highly developed invertebrates are provided with well-developed vascular systems, although some of them have the open, or lacunar, system (arthropods, mollusks). In the earthworm, in which a closed system is approached, the true heart is the dorsal blood vessel which forces the blood into the paired aortic arches (so-called "hearts"). The inverte-

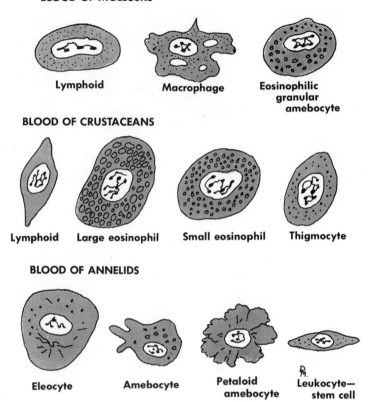

BLOOD OF MOLLUSKS

Lymphoid   Macrophage   Eosinophilic granular amebocyte

BLOOD OF CRUSTACEANS

Lymphoid   Large eosinophil   Small eosinophil   Thigmocyte

BLOOD OF ANNELIDS

Eleocyte   Amebocyte   Petaloid amebocyte   Leukocyte— stem cell

Figure 522. Types of blood cells in the blood of three invertebrate groups. Basic blood cell is leukocyte (white cell), but in some invertebrates prototypes of all vertebrate blood cells may be found, although they are not homologous to vertebrate blood cells. Most invertebrate respiratory pigments (hemoglobin or erythrocruorin, hemocyanin, etc.) are extracellular, not intracellular as in vertebrates. Some sea cucumbers have blood cells which carry respiratory pigments. Insect blood usually has no respiratory pigments.

brate heart is always located dorsal to the digestive tract.

The fluid media of invertebrates varies greatly (Figure 522). In some it is mostly water, with some nutriments, dissolved gases, and waste; in others it is more like the lymph of vertebrate animals, with a greater protein content and less water. Respiratory pigments for carrying oxygen, especially in the higher invertebrates, may also be found. There are at least four different kinds of respiratory pigments in invertebrates: (1) **erythrocruorin**, similar to hemoglobin which is found dissolved in the plasma and gives a reddish color to the blood (earthworms, midge larvae, and the smaller crusta-

ceans); (2) **hemocyanin**, which contains copper and is also carried dissolved in the blood (mollusks, lobsters, scorpion) to which it imparts a bluish color; (3) **chlorocruorin**, a greenish pigment similar to hemoglobin and carried dissolved in the plasma (certain polychaete worms); and (4) **hemerythrin**, a reddish pigment found in the corpuscles (certain annelids and polychaetes).

Circulation in vertebrates

Among vertebrates the circulatory systems are all provided with hearts, arteries, capillaries, and veins, with about the same plan of arrangement. The hearts of vertebrates have two, three, and four cham-

624

bers. In the evolution of the higher verte- brates from lower ones, the principal changes in circulation have involved the heart in the transformation from gill to lung breathing. These changes, thus, have been brought about as an adaptation from an aquatic to a terrestrial life. Embryologically the heart has developed from a tube which has become modified into a series of chambers. The fish heart consists of two main chambers, auricle and ventricle, arranged in tandem fashion. Fish have a **single-circuit** heart; that is, the blood passes through it only once in each complete circuit. Blood from veins passes through the **sinus venosus**, the re- ceiving chamber of the heart, to the **auricle**, then to the **ventricle** (the muscu- lar pumping chamber), and finally to the **conus arteriosus**. From here the blood is passed through the ventral aorta to the gills, to be oxygenated, and then through the dorsal aorta to all parts of the body. After passing through the capillary sys- tem of the various organs, the blood is returned by veins to the heart. In this circuit the blood has passed through two **capillary systems,** one in the gills and the other in the organ tissues.

In land forms a number of changes oc- curred in the heart and blood vessels. This change is correlated with the introduction of a new secondary shorter circuit by means of which the oxygenated blood from the lungs is returned directly to the heart before making a second circuit throughout the body. The first change in the evolution of the heart to meet this new plan was in lungfish and the cros- sopterygii in which the auricle is par- tially divided into a larger right and smal- ler left auricular chamber which receives blood from the swim bladder. The ven- tricle also shows the beginning of a divi- sion. The conus in these forms is also di- vided by a spiral septum in such a way that the arterial blood goes to the body and the venous to the swim bladder or lungs.

Amphibians and most reptiles have a three-chambered heart. A partition is formed down the middle of the auricle, dividing it into left and right portions. The sinus venosus now opens into the right auricle, and a vein from the lungs empties into the left auricle. Pulmonary arteries carry blood to the lungs. There is some mixing of aerated and nonaerated blood in the ventricle, so that this arrange- ment cannot be called a complete double circuit. In alligators and crocodiles the ventricle is also divided into left and right halves, and the four-chambered heart ap- pears for the first time. Birds and mam- mals have the four-chambered heart, and there are now two circuits, one through the lungs (**pulmonary**) and one through the body (**systemic**).

The course of the blood in this double- circuit arrangement may be summarized as follows: Starting with the left ventricle, the blood passes through the aorta and its many divisions to all parts of the body and then into the capillary bed within the tissues; veins collect the blood from the capillaries and carry it from there back to the right auricle of the heart. This cir- cuit from the left ventricle to the right auricle is the **systemic circulation.** From the right auricle the blood passes into the right ventricle, thence through the pul- monary artery to the lungs, where the gaseous exchange is made; then by a vein or veins the blood is carried to the left auricle and thence to the left ventricle. This short circuit from the right ventricle to the left auricle is the **pulmonary circu- lation.** In this complete circulation the blood has passed through the heart **twice.** In this plan, also, the right side of the heart handles oxygen-poor blood; the left side, freshly oxygenated blood.

In the four-chambered heart plan there is only one capillary bed in each circuit— the lungs in the pulmonary and the organ tissues in the systemic circuit. There is at least one marked exception to this prin- ciple in the systemic circuit, namely, the **hepatic portal system,** which collects blood from the stomach, pancreas, intes- tine, and spleen and conducts it to the liver. The blood in this system passes through a capillary bed in these visceral organs and is then collected by the portal vein which breaks up in the liver into sinusoids; the latter unite to form the hepatic veins. These hepatic veins then empty the blood into the inferior vena cava to the heart. All vertebrate classes, except mammals, have a **renal portal system** by which blood from the caudal regions of the body passes through a capillary network in the kidneys.

The advantages of the two-circuit plan over the one-circuit one are many. There is no mixing of the oxygen-rich blood and the oxygen-poor blood in the two-circuit scheme; the blood in the aorta contains relatively more oxygen; a higher metabolic rate is thus possible; and a resulting higher temperature can be maintained in the animal body.

Aortic arches (Figure 523). In the transition from water to land, there are also correlative changes in the aortic arches. In the embryos of all vertebrates there are six pairs of aortic arches which pass from the ventral aorta at the anterior end of the heart, run between the gill slits of the pharynx, and connect with the dorsal aorta. In this plan there is a pair of arches (blood vessels) for each pair of gills. When animals evolved lungs, only a single pair of blood vessels was necessary to supply them. In the course of evolutionary development some of these arches were lost and others underwent transformations. To understand the modifications which have taken place in these arches, they are numbered 1 to 6, beginning at the anterior end. The first two pairs are lost early, and arches 3 to 6 represent the ones found in adult fish. In consequence of the development of lungs, arch 3 on each side loses its connection with the dorsal aorta and becomes the carotid artery. Arch 5 disappears and arch 6 forms the pulmonary arteries to the lungs. Arch 4 remains as the only connection with the dorsal aorta. In higher amphibians and reptiles, this arch is paired; in birds, only the right arch persists; and in mammals, only the left.

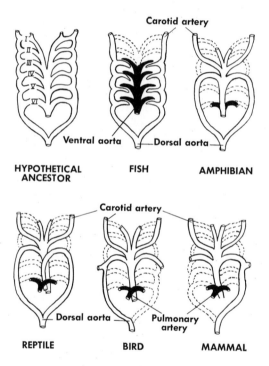

HYPOTHETICAL ANCESTOR **FISH** **AMPHIBIAN**

REPTILE **BIRD** **MAMMAL**

Figure 523. Fate of aortic arches among different classes of vertebrates (see text for description). Although prototypic condition in embryonic fish and tetrapods is considered to be six pairs of aortic arches, a greater number was probably found in primitive vertebrates. Some existing cyclostomes have as many as fifteen pairs. Since lungs, or their homologous forerunners (air bladders), are primitive, a pulmonary artery is thought to have arisen as a branch from sixth aortic arch even among placoderm fish, but such an artery is mostly absent among modern fish.

The heart and its physiology

The first mechanism for propelling the fluid blood is the contraction of the muscular walls of the blood vessels themselves. This "milking" action is the only kind of propulsion among animals such as the nemertean worms, earthworms, and some others. Mollusks and arthropods have more specialized hearts foreshadowing, in a fashion, the vertebrate heart. In these phyla the heart is a single structure divided into chambers and possessing valves to prevent backflow of blood. In the development of the heart the wall of the endocardial tube becomes the **endocardium** (lining membrane); the muscular wall which forms around the tube, the **myocardium** (cardiac muscle); and a thin

626

layer which develops around the outside of the heart, the **pericardium.**

The position of the vertebrate heart is ventral to the alimentary canal—just the opposite of the invertebrate heart which is dorsal. Birds have proportionately larger hearts than any other class of vertebrates. Small animals usually have larger hearts in proportion to their size than do the larger forms. The heart is also larger in wild animals than it is in domestic animals of the same size. The adult human heart weighs 9 to 11 ounces and is a little larger in males than in females.

The heart is really a complex network of cardiac muscle fibers which branch and fuse in most directions and planes. Because of this arrangement, the heart beats as a unit and obeys the **"all-or-none" law;** that is, if heart muscle beats at all, it does so to its maximum effect. The **refractory period,** or period of nonirritability and noncontractility, is very long in heart muscle. This prevents the heart from overworking. The heartbeat is rhythmic and automatic, but it can be influenced by nervous control, by temperature, and by certain salts in the blood plasma, as well as by certain hormones. Birds and mammals have four chambers, **two atria** and **two ventricles** (Figure 524). The valve between the right atrium and right ventricle is the **tricuspid;** that between

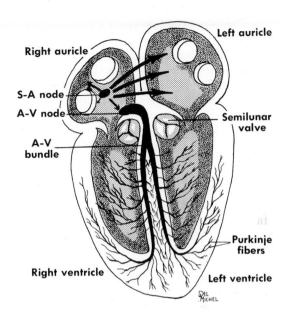

Figure 525. Scheme of neuromuscular mechanism of conduction in mammalian heart. Arrows indicate spread of waves of excitation. Sinus venosus of frog heart is present in mammalian heart as vestigial nodule in right auricle near entrance of large veins. This nodule is called sino-auricular node (S-A) and is pacemaker of heart. From this node wave of contraction spreads over auricles at rate of about 1 meter per second and then down to auriculoventricular (A-V) node and over the ventricles at 5 meters per second. The more rapid ventricular rate is made possible by His-Tawara (A-V) bundle and Purkinji fiber system which is a specialized myocardium for conducting impulses through heart septum. This produces a simultaneous contraction of ventricles to ensure efficient pumping of blood through semilunar valves at their location.

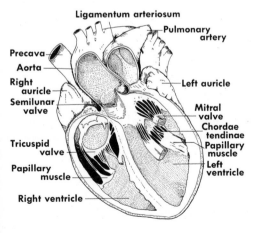

Figure 524. Internal structure of mammalian heart.

the left atrium and left ventricle, the **bicuspid.** Where the big arteries, the **pulmonary** from the right ventricle and the **aorta** from the left ventricle, leave the heart, there are found the **semilunar** valves. These valves are the only remnants of the conus arteriosus found in other classes of vertebrates. In the hearts of birds and mammals, the sinus venosus has been incorporated into the right atrium.

In the heart of man and some other mammals there is a special conducting tissue concerned with the instigation and regulation of the heartbeat (Figure 525). This specialized tissue, called **nodal tissue,** is necessary because of the functional separation of the atria from the ventricles, as there is no muscular connection between these chambers. To produce a functional stimulation of the atrial and ventricular beats, this nodal tissue conducts impulses so rapidly to the ventricles that all parts of them contract almost simultaneously. This special conducting tissue is made up of the **sino-atrial node (S-A node),** the pacemaker, in the right atrium; the **atrio-ventricular node (A-V node)** between the atria; and the Purkinje network of modified muscle fibers which pass to all parts of the ventricular walls. The nervous control of the heartbeat consists of two sets of fibers: (1) **sympathetic,** which accelerates it, and (2) **parasympathetic** (vagus), which slows it down. The pacemaker (S-A node) is regulated partly by these nerves and partly by such factors as the carbon dioxide of the blood and temperature changes.

Heart muscle has a unique blood supply. Capillaries, which ordinarily lie along the surface of other muscle fibers, actually penetrate into the fibers of heart muscle. This arrangement ensures a quick and efficient blood supply to an organ that must keep going. Heart muscle is also well supplied with sarcosomes, a kind of granule that may contain enzymes.

The cycle of heartbeat consists of a contraction, or **systole,** of the heart muscle followed by its relaxation, or **diastole.** The rate of heartbeat depends upon many factors, such as age, sex, fevers, metabolic rates, and others. Its normal rate is about 70 to 80 beats per minute. The atria contract first, followed by the contraction of the ventricles. During a part of the cycle all the chambers are in a relaxed condition. When the heart beats, characteristic sounds can be picked up by a stethoscope. They are supposed to be produced by the closure of the heart valves, the contraction of the ventricular muscles, and the closure of the semilunar valves. The heart muscle, when in action, produces **action currents** which can be picked up

and recorded by a sensitive **electrocardiograph.** Each beat produces a characteristic graph which reveals a great deal about the normal or abnormal functioning of the heart.

When an individual is resting, the normal heart pumps about 60 ml. of blood each beat; but at maximum output, it can increase this to 200 ml. each beat. During severe exercise, the rate may increase from 70 to more than 150 beats per minute. This increase is effected by several factors: (1) stretching the heart muscle by the distention of the chambers with blood (**law of the heart**); (2) increasing the carbon dioxide of the blood; (3) increasing the temperature which affects the pacemaker of the heart; (4) the **Bainbridge reflex,** or the stimulating effect of a large amount of blood in the right atrium; (5) hormones, such as adrenaline and thyroxin; and (6) the two sets of nerves, sympathetic and parasympathetic.

Physiological anatomy of blood vessels

In the vertebrate, such as man, blood passes through three types of blood vessels, **arteries, capillaries,** and **veins,** in a complete circulation. Arteries carry blood from the heart to the tissues; veins return blood from the tissues to the heart. Ordinarily, arteries carry aerated blood, but the pulmonary artery carries nonaerated blood; veins usually carry nonaerated blood, but the pulmonary veins carry aerated blood.

The structures among the different arteries and veins are correlated with their functions. All arteries and veins are typically made up of three coats, or layers (Figure 526): (1) an outer (**tunica externa**), composed mostly of connective tissue; (2) a middle (**tunica media**), composed of connective tissue and muscle; and (3) an inner (**tunica interna**), composed of connective tissue and endothelial lining. The connective tissue components enable the vessels to withstand pressure; the muscle regulates the amount of blood delivered to an organ; and the endothelium affords a smooth surface for

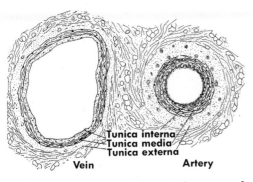

Figure 526. Cross-section of vein and corresponding artery.

the lumen in which the blood flows. Even the smallest arteries (arterioles) have all these coats, but they are thinner and have fewer components. The arteries, as they pass from the heart to the capillary bed, tend to shed parts of their coats until the **capillaries** have walls composed of little more than the endothelium. Capillaries effect the exchange of food and gases between the tissues and blood because the walls of other blood vessels are too thick for diffusion. Capillaries are found in enormous numbers, forming extensive networks in nearly all tissues. In muscle there are said to be more than 2,000 per square millimeter, or 1,250,000 per square inch. Their diameter rarely exceeds 10 microns, and, in some, the blood corpuscles literally have to squeeze through their lumens.

There are also other tiny channels which resemble capillaries. One type is the **sinusoids**, which are found in the spleen, suprarenal gland, liver, and bone marrow. Sinusoids have a large, irregular caliber and an incomplete lining of scattered cells which may be phagocytic (reticuloendothelial system). Sinusoids connect arterioles with venules or venules with venules. Another type is the **rete mirabile**, which is a plexus of capillaries found in the course of an arteriole or venule. A good example is the renal glomerulus where a network of capillaries connect an afferent arteriole with an efferent arteriole. The swim bladder of some fish also has a rete mirabile.

Veins have three coats also, but they differ in having thinner walls and no elastic connective tissue. A vein is about twice the cross-section of its corresponding artery. Veins, especially in the lower parts of the body, are provided with **valves** to prevent the backflow of blood.

The difference in blood flow in the various blood vessels depends upon the cross-sectional area of the blood vessels, the flow being inversely proportional to the cross-sectional area. All the blood has to pass through the aorta, which divides into smaller and still smaller arteries, until the smallest arteries discharge into the capillary network. Although these branches of the aorta are smaller than the aorta, their total cross-sectional area is much greater. The ratio between the cross-sectional area of the aorta and all the body capillaries is about 1 to 800. Most arteries have a rate of flow of 300 to 500 mm. per second; in the capillaries, the flow is from 0.5 to 1 mm. per second. The blood flow in the veins is about one-half that of corresponding arteries.

The flow from the heart into the aorta is intermittent, that is, pulsatile. This is due to the intermittent heartbeat with its systolic and diastolic rhythm. By the time the blood reaches the capillaries, it has become a steady flow (nonpulsatile). This steady flow in the capillaries is due to the stretch and elastic recoil of the arterial walls which keeps the blood moving. The alternating stretching and contraction of the arterial walls produced by the intermittent discharge of the blood from the heart into the aorta gives rise to the pressure **pulse**, which passes along the arterial wall at the rate of 5 to 8 meters per second. The frequency of the pulse is identical with the ventricular beat of the heart.

Blood pressure is the pressure against the walls of the blood vessels produced by the discharge of blood from the heart. It shows a marked gradient of pressure, being greatest in the arteries near the heart and dropping gradually in the more distant arteries, to decline markedly in the small arterioles and capillaries. In the veins the pressure drops still more, until it reaches the veins near the heart, where there may be a negative pressure (below atmospheric pressure). It is blood pressure that keeps the blood moving and keeps supplying the capillaries with a steady stream of blood. Several factors influence blood pressure, such as the blood output of the heart, the peripheral resistance offered by the arterioles and capillaries, the viscosity of the blood, the volume of blood, and the elasticity of the arteries. If the heart speeds up or there is an increase of the resistance of the blood vessels to blood flow, blood pressure will be elevated.

There are two phases of arterial blood pressure: **systolic** and **diastolic.** The difference between these two pressures is the **pulse pressure.** In man the systolic pressure is around 120 mm. of mercury; the diastolic, about 80 mm. of mercury. Blood pressure is taken by means of a device called the **sphygmomanometer,** and its measurement is a routine practice in medical diagnosis. Blood pressure plays an important role in the exchange of materials in the capillaries. Within the capillaries blood pressure is about 20 to 40 mm. This is the **filtration pressure.** As a contrary force, there is the osmotic pressure of the blood proteins which tends to move water into the capillaries. This osmotic pressure is around 20 to 30 mm. The difference between the filtration pressure and the osmotic pressure determines

the direction the water and its dissolved substances will go. If the filtration pressure is greater, the water will be forced out into the tissue spaces; if the osmotic pressure is the greater, water will enter the capillaries. There are conditions when one or the other of these two forces is dominant. Normally the water which passes out of the blood equals that which comes in.

Blood vessels are under the control of the **vasomotor system,** which has both constrictor (sympathetic) and dilator (parasympathetic) fibers. Whenever the vasoconstrictor center located in the medulla is stimulated, the arterioles and capillaries constrict and blanching occurs. On the other hand, stimulation of the dilator nerves causes the blood vessels to increase in diameter and flushing takes place.

Blood and its functions

The fluid medium, **blood,** is a liquid tissue composed of several kinds of cells (formed elements) and an intercellular fluid (plasma). The amount in man is 5 to 6 liters, about 7 or 8% of the body weight. It transports oxygen and food products to the tissues and removes carbon dioxide and other wastes, provides for the proper distribution of water throughout the body, equalizes and controls the body temperature, carries hormones from glands to their place of action, maintains

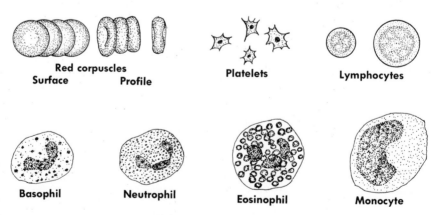

Red corpuscles
Surface   Profile

Platelets

Lymphocytes

Basophil   Neutrophil   Eosinophil   Monocyte

Figure 527. Formed elements of human blood.

630

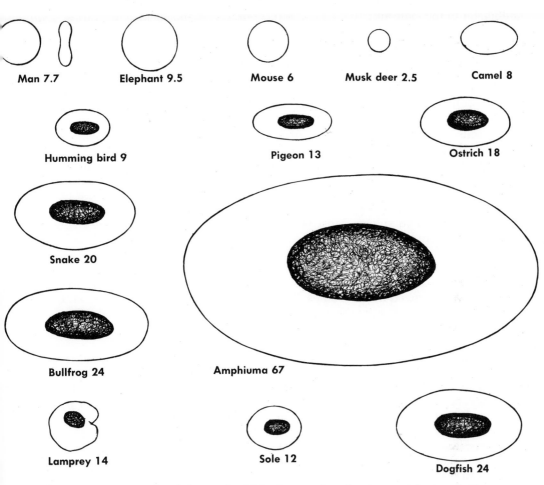

Figure 528. Comparative sizes and shapes of red blood corpuscles of various vertebrate animals. Number following name of each animal indicates the mean of the greatest diameter in microns. It will be seen that mammalian erythrocytes are all nonnucleated and are all flattened or biconcave discs except camels, which have ellipsoidal cells. All other vertebrate red blood corpuscles are nucleated. Only lamprey among vertebrates has an irregularly shaped corpuscle. (Modified from Orton and others.)

the acid or basic reaction of the body fluids, and defends the body against disease germs by its white cells and antibodies.

By volume, blood is 55% plasma and 45% formed elements (corpuscles). **Plasma** is more than 90% water and 8 to 10% solids. Plasma is a variable solution containing glucose, proteins, amino acids, fats, salts, enzymes, hormones, antibodies, and gases. It has some fairly stable constituents: plasma proteins (serum albumin, serum globulin, and fibrinogen),

about 7%; the inorganic salts (chlorides, sulfates, carbonates, etc.), 0.9%; and glucose, about 0.1%.

The formed elements of the blood are the **red blood corpuscles** (erythrocytes), **white blood corpuscles** (leukocytes), **platelets,** and cell fragments (Figure 527). Erythrocytes are nonnucleated biconcave discs 7 or 8 microns in diameter. They are made up of a stroma framework of protein, lecithin, and other substances and a red iron-bearing pigment, **hemoglobin.** They number about 5,500,000 per cubic millimeter in the male and about 5,000,000 per cubic millimeter in the female. Babies have more and the aged have fewer than these figures. Hemoglobin of the erythrocyte is specialized for carrying oxygen. Each 100 ml. of blood contains about 16 grams of hemoglobin, which is able to transport about 20 ml. of oxygen. Red blood cells are formed in red bone marrow, and there are many steps in their development before they are mature cells. Their life span, according to tracer experiments, appears to be about four months; they are destroyed by certain cells in the liver and spleen. Most of the iron is salvaged to be used over again, and other parts of the hemoglobin are converted into bile pigments. During every second of our existence, many millions of red cells are destroyed in our bodies. The red blood corpuscles vary in size and number among the different vertebrates (Figure 528).

The **white blood corpuscles**, or leukocytes, are much fewer in number than the red (5,000 to 10,000 per cubic millimeter) and are each provided with a nucleus but with no hemoglobin. The ratio of white cells to red cells is about 1 to 700. Many of them are larger than erythrocytes and have active ameboid movement. They can pass through the walls of the capillaries, which the red cells cannot do. Their different types and percentages are given as follows:

Nongranular
    Lymphocytes   20-25% of total white cells
    Monocytes   2- 6% of total white cells
Granulocytes
    Neutrophils   60-70% of total white cells
    Eosinophils   3- 4% of total white cells
    Basophils   0.5% of total white cells

The chief function of white blood cells is to defend the body against disease germs. Some of them (monocytes) have great power to engulf bacteria; in others this power is limited. The proportion of white cells of each type is obtained by a **differential white cell count.** The variations in this count have some significance in the diagnosis of certain diseases. The origin of the leukocytes varies. Lymphocytes are produced in the lymphoid tissues (lymph nodes, tonsils, spleen, etc.); monocytes, in the spleen and connective tissue; and the others, in red bone marrow. Their life span is unknown, but it is thought to be much shorter than that of the red corpuscles.

The other formed element of blood is the **platelet,** or thrombocyte. Platelets are tiny bodies about one-fourth the diameter of red corpuscles; they are colorless and nonnucleated. They originate in the bone marrow from giant cells (megakaryocytes). Their number shows considerable variation, being recorded as anywhere from 250,000 to 600,000 per cubic millimeter. They are supposed to be the source of thromboplastin, which initiates blood clotting. Lower vertebrates lack platelets but have spindle cells instead.

Coagulation of blood

Blood clotting is to prevent excessive loss of blood from the body. In some invertebrates, such as the crayfish and insects, loss of blood and body fluid is prevented by a **spasmic** contraction of the muscles in the walls of the blood vessels. Their blood pressure is very low and actually may be negative. Coagulation of blood is a function of the plasma. One of the constituents of blood proteins is the soluble **fibrinogen.** When tissue cells are damaged in a wound, a substance, **thromboplastin,** is liberated from disintegrated platelets and from the damaged tissue as well. Thromboplastin in the presence of calcium salts changes the inactive **prothrombin** in blood plasma to the active enzyme **thrombin** (thrombase). Thrombin then converts fibrinogen into fibrin. The mass of fibrin threads entangles the red blood corpuscles and the **clot** is formed. The clot later shrinks and squeezes out the **blood serum.** The clotting time in man is four to five minutes; in horses, it is longer.

Agitation, heat, and alum will hasten coagulation; cooling, leech extracts, heparin, and precipitation of the calcium salts will retard it. Persons who have the disease hemophilia have a very slow coagulation rate because of the stability of their platelets in an abnormal type of plasma.

The blocking of blood flow by an intravascular clot is called thrombosis, which is quite serious when it involves the blood vessels of the heart, brain, and other vital places. When the clot (thrombus) breaks away and is carried in the blood stream, it is an **embolus.** An internal clot can be initiated whenever thromboplastin is released by injuries to blood vessels and the breakdown of platelets through contact with rough, injured tissue.

Blood types

In blood transfusions the donor's blood is checked against the blood of the recipient. Blood differs chemically from person to person, and when two different (incompatible) bloods are mixed, **agglutination** is the result. The basis of these chemical differences is the presence in the red blood corpuscles of **agglutinogens (antigens)** A and B and, in the serum or plasma, **agglutinins (antibodies)** a and b. According to the way these antigens and antibodies are distributed, there are four main blood groups: O, A, B, and AB. Group O contains antibodies a and b but no antigens; group A, antibody b and antigen A; group B, antibody a and antigen B; group AB, antigens A and B but no antibodies. In these groups, normally no blood agglutinates itself because corresponding antigen and antibody, as, for example, A and a, or B and b, are not present together, for a is anti-A and b is anti-B. On the other hand, A is compatible with b and B is compatible with a. Each major group is also divided into subtypes, but transfusion reactions between blood of these subtypes are rare.

Although persons with type O blood are called universal donors and those with type AB, universal recipients, doctors in actual practice insist on giving blood of the same type as the patient's blood to prevent any possibility of incompatibility.

The red blood corpuscles also contain other agglutinogens, but there are no corresponding agglutinins in the plasma. These agglutinogens are called M and N, and all individuals have one or both of these. There are also other factors.

Blood groups are present in many other animals, such as dogs, cats, rabbits, chickens, and monkeys.

In blood transfusion practices, whole blood and blood plasma are commonly used. In blood banks, blood from several individuals of the same type is pooled and a preservative added. It is then put into storage in a refrigerator at about 4° to 6° C. Dried plasma is about as effective as whole blood for shock, although it is prepared without the red cells. For severe hemorrhage whole blood is best. For dried plasma, blood from many individuals of various types is used; thus the various agglutinins are diluted and pooled, the red cells removed by centrifuging, and the plasma made into a powder by freezing and drying. By adding an equal amount of distilled water, the plasma is made ready for use. Dried plasma is much easier to use than whole blood, for it keeps

Table 7 Standard blood groups (white persons, United States)

Blood group	Antigens in red corpuscles	Antibodies in serum	Can give blood to	Can receive blood from	Frequency (%)
O	None	a, b	All	O	45
A	A	b	A, AB	O, A	42
B	B	a	B, AB	O, B	10
AB	AB	None	AB	All	3

longer, requires no typing, and is easily transported.

Rh factor

In 1940 there was discovered in the red blood corpuscles a new factor called the Rh factor, named after the Rhesus monkeys in which it was first found. In the white race about 85% of individuals have the factor (positive) and the other 15% do not (negative). It was found also that Rh-positive and Rh-negative bloods are incompatible and that shock and even death may follow their mixing when Rh-positive blood is introduced into an Rh-negative person who has had a previous transfusion of Rh-positive blood. The Rh factor is inherited as a dominant; this accounts for a peculiar and often fatal form of anemia of the newborn called **erythroblastosis fetalis.** If the father is Rh positive, the mother Rh negative, and the fetus Rh positive (by inheriting the factor from the father), blood from the fetus may pass through defects in the placenta into the mother's blood. The fetal blood will stimulate the formation of Rh-positive antibodies in the blood of the mother. These antibodies then may diffuse back into the fetal circulation and produce agglutination and destruction of the fetal red blood cells. With a first pregnancy this effect may be slight, but a subsequent pregnancy may cause a build-up of these antibodies. The life of the first child may be threatened if the mother has had at some time previously a transfusion of Rh-positive blood. Testing for the Rh factor is as important as testing for the major blood types. If this testing is done in advance on the parents, the danger to the child's life can be prevented in most cases by methods known to medical science.

Lymphatic system (Figure 529)

The lymphatic system is an accessory blood system, and its main function is to correct certain omissions of the major circulatory system. When the filtration pressure of the blood capillaries filters out the liquid part of plasma into the spaces among the tissues' cells, there is formed

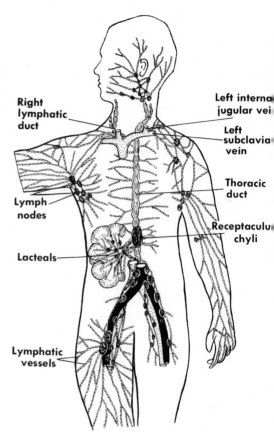

Figure 529. Diagram of lymphatic system.

lymph, a clear, colorless fluid. Lymph is about the same as plasma, minus a great deal of its proteins whose molecules are too large to diffuse through the capillary walls. All the cells of the body are bathed in **tissue fluid,** which returns to the circulation in two ways: (1) by entering into the venous ends of the capillaries where the osmotic pressure of the blood proteins exceeds the filtration pressure and (2) by means of the lymph capillaries and lymph vessels. Lymph contains no red cells, but it does contain white cells. There is less calcium and phosphorus in lymph than there is in blood. Lymph has the power to coagulate slowly.

Lymph vessels carry lymph only toward the heart. They are made up of the **peripheral lymph capillaries,** which are tiny vessels closed at one end, **larger lymph vessels,** provided with numerous

634

valves, and the large left **thoracic duct,** which enters the left subclavian vein in the neck region. Along the course of the lymph vessels are the **lymph nodes,** which filter out bacteria and other substances and produce lymphocytes. Lymph is kept flowing in the vessels by the squeezing action of adjacent muscles and inspiratory movements of the chest cavity. The valves prevent its backflow. Its movements are very sluggish, and in spite of the wide extent of this system, only about 2,000 ml. per day are discharged into the subclavian vein.

In some lower animals, such as the frog, there are special lymph hearts which propel the lymph forward; these are absent in man.

RESPIRATORY SYSTEM

The most common source of energy is oxidation, the union of oxygen with other elements. Energy is bound up in food and must be released to be available for use. It must be changed from a potential form to a kinetic form. A few animals are able to live in the absence of free oxygen (anaerobic), but they are able to get the necessary oxygen from the metabolism of carbohydrates and fats in their own bodies. Some of these anaerobic animals are worms and arthropods that live in the muck at the bottom of deep lakes; others are intestinal parasites.

The ultimate source of all energy is the sun; plants, with the aid of solar energy and the green pigment **chlorophyll** are able to make sugars from carbon dioxide and water. These sugars are converted into starches, fat, and proteins, which animals use as food. When these foods are changed back into glucose, they are then ready to be acted upon by the oxygen. Oxygen combines with the carbon of the glucose molecule to form carbon dioxide and water; during this process, energy which held the molecules together is released. This reaction, in an abbreviated form, may be expressed thus:

$$C_6H_{12}O_6 + 6\ O_2 \rightarrow 6\ CO_2 + 6\ H_2O + \text{Energy}$$
Glucose   Oxygen   Carbon   Water
                      dioxide

Many separate reactions, each controlled by enzymes, are required for the whole process (see cellular metabolism, page 66). The ratio of the volume of CO_2 given off to the O_2 consumed is called the **respiratory quotient** (RQ). In the above reaction the respiratory quotient is 1.0 (6 O_2-6 CO_2). It varies with different foods. With fats the respiratory quotient is about 0.7; with proteins, about 0.8; and with the average mixed diet, about 0.85. The respiratory quotient is an index of the kind of metabolism that is taking place in the body, for the nearer it is to 1.0 the more carbohydrates are being metabolized in the body at that particular time.

Land animals get oxygen from the air which is about one-fifth oxygen; most aquatic animals use the dissolved oxygen of the water in which they live. The process of taking in oxygen and giving off carbon dioxide is called **respiration.** There are two kinds of respiration, **direct** and **indirect.** Direct respiration is the exchange of oxygen and carbon dioxide between the cells of the organism and the surrounding environment. **Indirect respiration** makes use of a specialized structure in which gaseous exchange is made and involves two phases, external and internal respiration. **External respiration** includes the exchange of gases between the external environment and the blood; **internal respiration** is the exchange between the blood stream and the body cells. In animals that have direct respiration, both external and internal respiration are merged (Protozoa and Coelenterata).

Respiration in invertebrates

Protozoa, sponges, coelenterates, and many worms have a direct diffusion of gases between the organism and the environment. Gaseous exchange in most annelid worms is made through a moist skin well provided with blood vessels. Some echinoderms make use of the finger-like **dermal branchiae** (papulae), evaginations from the coelomic cavity, as well as the tube feet. **Gills** are common in aquatic invertebrates. They are thin fila-

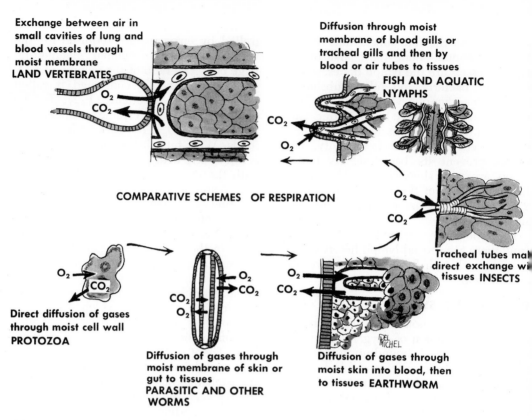

Figure 530. Comparative schemes of respiration among animals.

ments covered with an epidermal membrane and are provided with blood vessels. Some are simple in structure (marine annelids) and others are more complicated (arthropods and mollusks). The most efficient respiratory apparatus in any animal is the **tracheal system** found in insects—oxygen is delivered to the tissue cells directly by a ramifying system of small tubes (tracheae). Sea cucumbers have the odd **respiratory tree**, which fills with water drawn in and out of the cloaca.

Respiration in vertebrates

The various devices employed by vertebrates for respiration may be divided into three types: (1) direct surfaces, such as skin and pharyngeal regions, (2) gills, and (3) lungs.

Amphibians make use of the first type, for their skin allows gases to diffuse easily through it into blood vessels. Most amphibians also possess either gills or lungs, but some salamanders have neither and rely entirely upon their skin and pharyngeal region which is highly vascularized. This is the case with the members of family Plethodontidae, or lungless salamanders. Some fish (mudhoppers and eels) also absorb O_2 through the skin.

Most aquatic vertebrates have gills, either external or internal. In the cyclostomes, water passes in and out of the gill openings and bathes the gill filaments in the gill pouches. The gaseous exchange is made between the water and the gill filaments. In the elasmobranchs, water enters through the mouth or spiracle and passes out the various gill slits. Bony fish have an operculum which covers the gills in the common gill chamber; water enters through the mouth and passes over the gills and out through the opening of the perculum. Some larval forms have gills which are replaced by lungs in the adult.

Land vertebrates have developed **lungs,** which are internal cavities into which air is drawn (Figure 531). The exchange of oxygen and carbon dioxide is made between the air cavities and the blood capillaries which line the cavities. Dipnoi, or lungfish, use their swim bladders for lungs during the dry season of their habitats and thus may be considered transition forms. In lower amphibians lungs are sim-

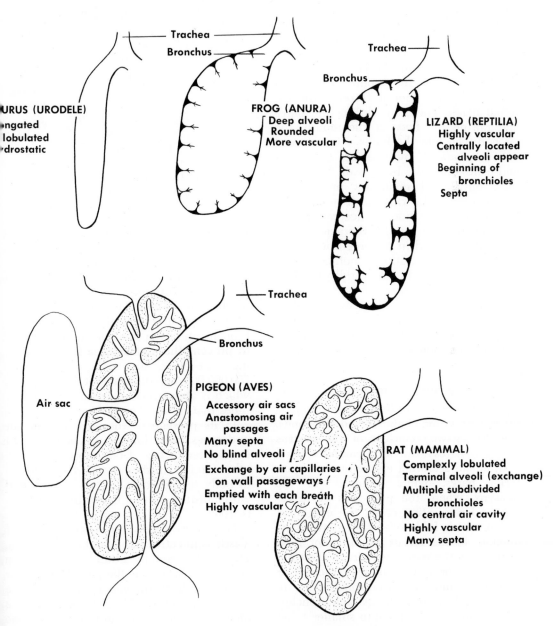

Trachea

Bronchus

URUS (URODELE)
ongated
lobulated
drostatic

FROG (ANURA)
Deep alveoli
Rounded
More vascular

Trachea

Bronchus

LIZARD (REPTILIA)
Highly vascular
Centrally located
    alveoli appear
Beginning of
    bronchioles
Septa

Trachea

Bronchus

Air sac

PIGEON (AVES)

Accessory air sacs
Anastomosing air
    passages
Many septa
No blind alveoli

Exchange by air capillaries
    on wall passageways
Emptied with each breath
Highly vascular

RAT (MAMMAL)

Complexly lobulated
Terminal alveoli (exchange)
Multiple subdivided
    bronchioles
No central air cavity
Highly vascular
Many septa

Figure 531. Diagram of internal structures of lungs among vertebrate groups. In general, evolutionary trend has been from simple sacs with little exchange surface between blood and air spaces to complex, lobulated structures of complex divisions and extensive exchange surfaces.

Digestive, circulatory, respiratory, excretory systems 637

ple, baglike affairs lined with capillaries; in higher forms their inner surfaces have many folds and corrugations with minute pockets (air sacs) where the gaseous exchange with the blood is made. Many lungs are also subdivided into lobes and lobules for increasing the respiratory surface.

One of the main problems of lung-breathing forms is getting air into and out of the lungs. Frogs take air in (inspiration) by closing the jaws and lowering the floor of the mouth; this sucks the air into the mouth through the external nares. Then, by closing the nares and raising the floor of the mouth, the air is driven into the lungs. Air is forced out (expiration) by opening the nares and contracting the body wall. Most reptiles, birds, and mammals breathe by movements of the ribs; such movements increase in inspiration, or decrease in expiration, the size of the thoracic cavity. Air is thus sucked in or forced out. Birds also employ an additional method in flying. Since their ribs are rigidly fixed to secure anchorage for their pectoral muscles, their lungs are filled and emptied by the action of the pectoral muscles during the process of flying and by the alternate expansion and contraction of their air sacs.

Respiratory system in man

In man, the respiratory system is made up of certain air channels and the lungs. The passageway consists of the nostrils (external nares); the **nasal chamber,** lined with mucus-secreting epithelium; the **posterior nares,** which connect to the **pharynx,** where the pathways of digestion and respiration cross; the **epiglottis,** a flap which folds over the **glottis** (the opening to the larynx) to prevent food from going the wrong way in swallowing; the **larynx,** or voice box; the **trachea,** or windpipe; and the two **bronchi,** one to each lung. Within the lungs each bronchus divides and subdivides into smaller tubes (**bronchioles**) which lead to the air sacs and **alveoli.** The walls of the latter are thin and moist to facilitate the exchange

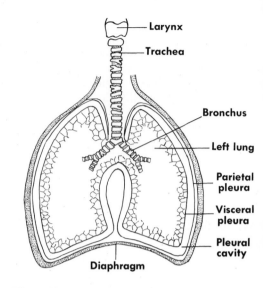

Figure 532. Diagram of thorax and its relation to respiratory system in man.

of gases between the air sacs and the adjacent blood capillaries. Air passageways are lined with mucus-secreting and ciliated epithelium and play an important role in conditioning the air before it reaches the alveoli. There are partial cartilage rings in the walls of the trachea, bronchi, and even some of the bronchioles to prevent these structures from collapsing. The lungs are made up of some 750,000,000 alveoli, the total surface of which is about 100 square meters, or fifty times that of the skin surface.

In its passage to the air sacs, the air undergoes three important changes: (1) It is filtered free from most dust and other foreign substances. (2) It is warmed to body temperature. (3) It is saturated with moisture, so that its relative humidity is 100%.

The lungs consist of a great deal of elastic connective tissue and some muscle. They are covered by a thin layer of smooth epithelium known as the **pleura.** A similar layer also lines the inner surface of the walls of the chest. The two layers of the pleura are in contact and slide over one another as the lungs expand and contract. A small amount of pleural fluid for lubrication is found between the pleural layers.

638

Between the two sheets of pleura is the **pleural cavity,** a partial vacuum. The chest cavity is closed off and does not communicate with the outside. It is bounded behind by the spine and back muscles, on the sides by the ribs, and in front by ribs and the breastbone. The diaphragm, a dome-shaped partition, forms the floor of the chest cavity and separates it from the abdomen.

Mechanism of breathing. The chest cavity is an air-tight chamber, and, as a result of the potential vacuum in the pleural space and the air pressure in the alveoli, the elastic lungs are held tightly against the chest wall. The volume of the lungs is thus increased or decreased in accordance with the size and shape of the chest cavity. In **inspiration,** when the ribs are elevated and the diaphragm contracted and flattened, the chest cavity is enlarged. This increase in the volume of the chest cavity (and lungs) causes the air pressure in the lungs to fall below atmospheric pressure, and air passes through the air passageways to the air sacs to equalize the pressure. **Expiration** is a less active process than inspiration. When their muscles relax, the ribs and diaphragm return to their original position and the chest cavity size is decreased. The distended, elastic lungs then contract and force the air out.

In ordinary quiet breathing (eupnea), an individual breathes in with each breath about 500 ml. of air. Of this amount, only 350 ml. reach the lung alveoli; the other 150 ml. are left in the air passages, the so-called "dead space," where no gaseous exchange can take place. This dead space air is the first to be pushed out with the next expiration. Likewise, the last 150 ml.

of air to be expelled from the air sacs remain in the passageway and will be the first to enter the alveoli at the next inspiration.

The 500 ml. of air breathed in and out at each breath are called the **tidal air.** After a normal inspiration, it is possible by deep and forcible inspiration to take in about 1,500 ml. more (**complemental air**); after expelling the tidal air, it is possible with forcible expiration to expel about 1,500 ml. more (**supplemental air**). After the deepest possible expiration, about 1,000 ml. of air remain in the lung (**residual air**). The **vital capacity** is the amount of air one can breathe in and expel with the greatest possible effort. It is somewhere around 3,500 ml. for the average person, although physically trained persons have a greater vital capacity than this. The vital capacity is equal to the sum of the tidal, complemental, and supplemental airs. The rate of quiet respiration in men is about 15 or 16 times per minute; for women and children it is about 20 times per minute. The rate at birth is much higher. Exercise and other factors increase the rate.

Composition of inspired, expired, and alveolar airs. The composition of expired and alveolar airs is not identical. Alveolar air contains less oxygen and more carbon dioxide than the air that leaves the lungs. Inspired air has the composition of atmospheric air. The variations in the three kinds of air are shown in Table 8.

Expired air is really a mixture of alveolar and inspired airs. The carbon dioxide in expired air is a little less than the oxygen taken into the blood, for some of the oxygen is given off in the form of water.

Gaseous exchange in lungs. The diffu-

Table 8 Variation in three kinds of air

	Inspired air (vol. %)	Expired air (vol. %)	Alveolar air (vol. %)
Oxygen	20.96	16.3	14.2
Carbon dioxide	0.04	4.0	5.5
Nitrogen	79.00	79.7	80.3

sion of gases, both in internal as well as external respiration, takes place in accordance with the laws of physical diffusion, that is, the gases pass from regions of high pressure to those of low pressure. The pressure of a gas refers to the partial pressure that gas exerts in a mixture of gases. If the atmospheric pressure at sea level is 760 mm. of mercury, the partial pressure of O_2 will be 21% (percentage of O_2 in air) of 760, or 159 mm. The alveolar membrane (epithelium) is thin and offers little resistance to the passage of gases. However, this membrane must be kept moist, for oxygen is dissolved in this film and then passes through the membrane. With respect to oxygen, the concentration of oxygen in the lung alevoli is greater (101 mm. mercury pressure) than it is in the venous blood of the lung capillaries (40 mm. mercury pressure). Oxygen then naturally diffuses into the capillaries. In a similar manner, the carbon dioxide in the blood of the lung capillaries has a higher concentration (46 mm. mercury) than has this same gas in the lung alveoli (40 mm. mercury), so that carbon dioxide diffuses from the blood into the alveoli. Thus in the diffusion of both these gases there is a marked diffusion gradient which determines the direction of their flow.

These gases behave in a similar manner when the exchange occurs between the blood and tissues (internal respiration). Here the concentration of oxygen in the blood (100 mm. mercury pressure) is greater than the concentration of oxygen in the tissues (0 to 30 mm. mercury pressure), and the carbon dioxide concentration in the tissues (45 to 68 mm. mercury pressure) is greater than that in blood (40 mm. mercury pressure). The gases in each case will go from a high to a low concentration.

Transport of gases in blood. Oxygen is carried in the plasma and the red blood corpuscles. A small amount is carried in solution in the plasma. The red pigment hemoglobin is well adapted for carrying the major part of the oxygen. The respiratory pigment hemoglobin is a complex protein made up of **hematin** (5%), con-

taining iron and giving the red color to blood, and **globin** (95%), a colorless protein. Each gram of hemoglobin can combine with about 1.3 ml. of oxygen. Each 100 ml. of blood in the normal man contains about 16 grams of hemoglobin; in the normal woman, about 14 grams. The amount of oxygen that will combine with hemoglobin depends upon the tension of the gas in the alveoli; at 101 mm. mercury pressure the arterial blood is about 97% saturated; at lesser tensions smaller amounts of O_2 will combine with the blood. When oxygen passes from the lung alveoli into the lung capillaries, it diffuses into the red cells and unites with hemoglobin to form oxyhemoglobin in accordance with this reaction:

$$\text{Hemoglobin} + \text{Oxygen} \rightleftarrows \text{Oxyhemoglobin}$$

The reaction is reversible, depending upon the pressure concentrations of the gas at a particular region. In the lungs the reaction goes to the right, because of the differences in pressure already described; in the tissues the reaction goes to the left releasing oxygen. The color of blood depends upon oxyhemoglobin and hemoglobin. Arterial blood is bright scarlet because of oxyhemoglobin; venous blood is purplish red because of hemoglobin.

Although carbon dioxide is converted into carbonic acid when it diffuses into the blood, it is transported in the blood in three ways: (1) about 5% of it is carried in solution in the plasma as carbonic acid (H_2CO_3); (2) 10% is carried in combination with the amino groups ($-NH_2$) of the hemoglobin; and (3) the other 85% is carried in the form of sodium or potassium bicarbonates in both the plasma and red blood cells. Thus carbon dioxide relies on the blood salts for most of its transportation. An important enzyme, **carbonic anhydrase**, present in the blood, plays an important role in the conversion of carbon dioxide into carbonic acid in the tissue capillaries and in the conversion of carbonic acid back to carbon dioxide in the lung capillaries. This process in tissues involves the chloride shift, or the passage of chloride ions from the plasma nto the red blood corpuscles, to balance he bicarbonate ions that have passed in he reverse direction, thus maintaining an acid-base equilibrium of pH 7.4 for the blood. In the lungs the chloride shift s reversed.

The oxygen capacity of each 100 ml. of human blood is about 20 ml., which is he amount found in arterial blood—a percentage saturation of about 97%. Each 100 ml. of venous blood contains about 12 ml. of oxygen, or 60% saturation. The utilization coefficient is the fractional amount of oxygen which the hemoglobin gives up as it passes through the tissue capillaries. Under normal conditions the value of the utilization coefficient is about 27%. During strenuous exercise its value may reach 77%. The amount of carbon dioxide carried by the blood has a wider fluctuation, since each 100 ml. of blood carries from 30 to 60 ml. of carbon dioxide.

Cellular respiration and oxidation. The ultimate aim of all respiratory activities is the cellular oxidations which involve the combination of oxygen with food or metabolic products and the release of energy thereby. (See discussion on cellular metabolism, page 66.)

Factors that control respiration. Respiration must adjust itself to the varying needs of the body for oxygen. The body in active states needs more oxygen and must give off more carbon dioxide than it does when it is resting. Respiration is essentially involuntary and automatic, but it is influenced and controlled voluntarily within limits. Normally, inspiration and expiration follow each other in rhythmic fashion and both are basically muscular in action. For the perfect coordination of the muscles and other structures involved in respiration, a nervous regulating mechanism is necessary. The center of this nervous mechanism is the **respiratory center** located in the medulla oblongata and connected with both afferent and efferent nerves. This nerve center may be a complex of separate inspiratory and expiratory centers lying close together. Although largely automatic, the center is influenced by (1) voluntary nervous control, (2)

nervous reflex factors, and (3) chemical factors within itself and within the blood.

To produce the normal alternation of inspiration and expiration, sensory nerves in the lungs are stimulated when the lungs are stretched (inspiration) and send impulses to the center, which is inhibited. Then expiration follows. Voluntarily, one can hold his breath for a time and also change the depth and rate of breathing. Many afferent nerves from various parts of the body connect with the respiratory center and influence it. Thus severe pain will accelerate the rate of breathing, and inhaling irritating gases will inhibit it.

The chemical regulation of breathing centers mainly around carbon dioxide. A slight rise of carbon dioxide (0.2%) in the alveoli will double the rate of respiration; a fall of 0.2% will decrease rate of breathing. These changes in the alveolar carbon dioxide are reflected in the blood by diffusion. This indicates that the respiratory center is very sensitive to changes in the carbon dioxide of the blood. Ventilating the lungs by rapid breathing will reduce the alveolar carbon dioxide. The individual has no desire to breathe until the carbon dioxide of the blood builds up and, by diffusion, raises the level of the gas in the alveoli. Another way of stating this is that one breathes just often enough to keep the carbon dioxide of the alveoli at a constant level. In ordinary quiet breathing, about 250 to 300 ml. of carbon dioxide are produced each minute by the body tissues. By way of the blood, this carbon dioxide reaches the alveoli and will diffuse into the alveoli until its concentration will be equal in both blood and alveoli. Exercise will step up the production of carbon dioxide, which leads to faster breathing.

Another method of influencing the respiratory center is the stimulation of the chemoreceptors in the aortic arch and the carotid sinus bodies by high carbon dioxide or low oxygen concentrations in the blood. The nervous impulses so aroused will pass to the respiratory center and increase its activity.

EXCRETORY SYSTEM

Waste products are universal products of metabolic processes and must be removed from the organism or some of them may poison the cells of the body. Other wastes may not be toxic, but they are useless and get in the way and must be removed. One of the duties of the blood is to pick up these wastes and carry them to the excretory system, whence they are discharged from the body. Some, such as **carbon dioxide** and **water,** are formed by the various oxidative processes; others, such as **nitrogenous waste** (urea, purine bodies, etc.), arise from the breakdown of protein. Although toxic in excess quantities, some waste substances (for example, carbon dioxide) are useful in regulating certain physiological processes, such as those of respiration. Water, a highly useful substance, is a waste when present in excess. One of the main functions of the excretory system is to maintain a constant internal environment for the cells, getting rid of substances in harmful quantities and conserving those that are helpful for normal functioning.

Students often confuse the true waste substances of the body with the refuse discharged in the feces from the alimentary canal. A true waste is a result of body metabolism, whereas the feces are mainly indigestible material rejected by the intestinal tract as unsuitable for food and have never been a part of the metabolic process.

Excretion in invertebrates

Excretion in Protozoa is simply a matter of diffusion through the cell membrane into the surrounding medium; the contractile vacuole may also help excrete. Essentially the same plan of excretion is employed by the sponges and coelenterates, in which the waste is either diffused through the epidermal cells or else into the canals and gastrovascular cavity by the endodermal cells. In the flatworms there are definite excretory organs, the **flame cells** (protonephridia), which are

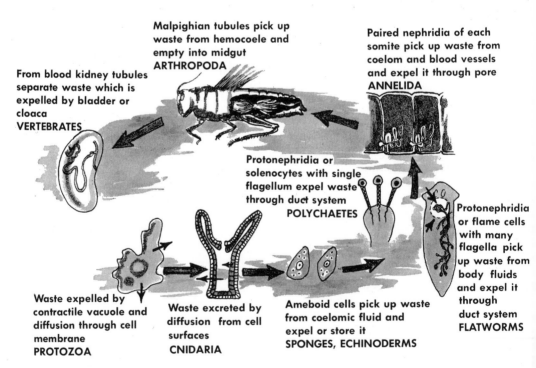

**Malpighian tubules pick up waste from hemocoele and empty into midgut
ARTHROPODA**

**Paired nephridia of each somite pick up waste from coelom and blood vessels and expel it through pore
ANNELIDA**

**From blood kidney tubules separate waste which is expelled by bladder or cloaca
VERTEBRATES**

**Protonephridia or solenocytes with single flagellum expel waste through duct system
POLYCHAETES**

**Protonephridia or flame cells with many flagella pick up waste from body fluids and expel it through duct system
FLATWORMS**

**Waste expelled by contractile vacuole and diffusion through cell membrane
PROTOZOA**

**Waste excreted by diffusion from cell surfaces
CNIDARIA**

**Ameboid cells pick up waste from coelomic fluid and expel or store it
SPONGES, ECHINODERMS**

Figure 533. Comparative mechanisms of excretion among different animals.

connected to a branched system of tubes that discharge the waste to the outside. Some invertebrates (echinoderms and others) make use of phagocytic cells, amebocytes, which engulf waste and carry it to the body surface for disposal or for storage. In the earthworm there is a pair of nephridia (metanephridia) for each segment. Insects have many blind **Malpighian tubules** which pick up, by diffusion, waste substances from the body cavity and pass them into the digestive tract. In other arthropods, especially the crustaceans, excretory glands similar to the nephridia of earthworms are found. Mollusks have one or two pairs of nephridia that drain waste from the coelom and the blood.

Excretion in vertebrates

In vertebrates the following organs are concerned with ridding the body of wastes: (1) skin (water, salts, carbon dioxide), (2) lungs (carbon dioxide and water), (3) liver (constituents of bile, bile pigments, etc.), (4) alimentary canal (certain salts, calcium, iron, magnesium, and fats), and (5) kidneys (urine and its constituents). The urinary system, made up of the kidneys and accessory organs, performs the main burden of taking care of the body waste. With the exception of the lungs, the other organs mentioned handle a relatively small amount of waste.

The urinary system is similar in all vertebrate animals (Figure 534). It is composed of two **kidneys**, which are compact organs located toward the posterior part of the body. From each kidney a **ureter**, or excretory duct, carries the urine posteriorly. In elasmobranchs, amphibians, reptiles, and birds, these ureters open directly into the cloaca, which is provided with a **urinary bladder** in some, but not all, forms. In most mammals the ureters are attached to the bladder, which discharges to the outside by a single duct, the **urethra**. Although the various kidneys in vertebrates are essentially specialized for removing waste from the body, they are not all homologous organs. The evolution of the urinary system in many forms has been closely interrelated with the reproductive system, so that the two systems share some common structures. Together they are often referred to as the **urogenital system**.

Histological structure of man's kidney

The paired **kidneys** in man are bean shaped, and each weighs about 4 ounces. They are located just below the stomach, one on each side of the mid-dorsal line, and rest upon the back muscles.

Inside, each kidney is made up of an outer zone, the **cortex**, and an inner zone, the **medulla**. In addition, there is a great deal of connective tissue and a rich vascular supply. The uriniferous tubules are called **nephrons** (Figure 535). Each nephron, or excretory unit, is made up of a Malpighian body, or **renal corpuscle**, and a much-convoluted **tubule**. A renal corpuscle is composed of a tuft of blood capillaries (glomerulus) surrounded by a double-walled sac (Bowman's capsule). The tubule also has a rich supply of blood

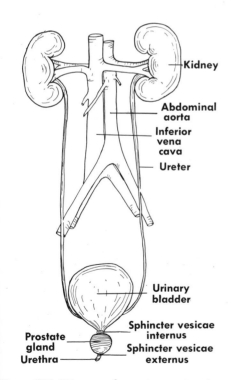

Kidney

Abdominal aorta

Inferior vena cava

Ureter

Urinary bladder

Prostate gland

Urethra

Sphincter vesicae internus

Sphincter vesicae externus

Figure 534. Diagram of excretory system in man.

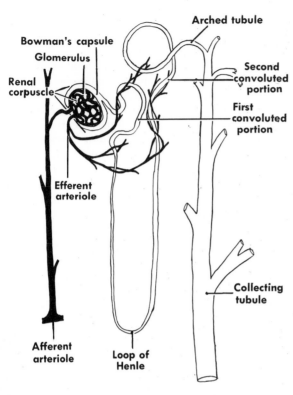

Bowman's capsule

Glomerulus

Renal corpuscle

Arched tubule

Second convoluted portion

First convoluted portion

Efferent arteriole

Collecting tubule

Afferent arteriole

Loop of Henle

Figure 535. Diagram of nephron.

capillaries and joins onto a collecting tubule which also receives from many other nephrons, so that a relatively few collecting tubules take care of the many nephrons of the kidney. Each renal corpuscle is about 0.2 mm. in diameter; its tubule is about 40 to 50 mm. long. There are about a million nephrons in each kidney, and the total surface area of the glomeruli is upward of 2 square meters. The blood flow to the kidneys is very great, being about twice the weight of the kidneys per minute. There are no excretory nerves to the kidneys, but the sympathetic and parasympathetic fibers control the blood supply.

Mechanism of urine formation

The problem of the mechanism involved has been a challenge to physiologists for more than a hundred years. The theory that is now generally accepted by physiologists is the one proposed by Cushny,

or a modification of it. All waste is brought to the nephrons by the blood, for in higher forms nephrons have no connection with the coelomic cavity, as they do in lower vertebrates. The function of the nephrons is to remove or separate the waste from the blood and discharge it into an independent series of channels for its final removal from the body.

The actual formation of urine involves three processes: **filtration, reabsorption,** and **augmentation.** All these steps take place before **urine** reaches the form in which it is eliminated from the body. Briefly, this means that a certain fluid with waste is separated from the blood, into the kidney tubules, that certain substances in this fluid are then returned to the blood by selective absorption, and that finally other substances are added to the fluid before it is actually urine.

Filtration. In the renal corpuscles blood fluids (excluding proteins and formed elements) are filtered out of the capillaries and into the neck of Bowman's capsule and tubule. This filtered substance is called the **capsular filtrate.** It consists of water, salts, sugar, urea, uric acid, and some other substances. This process of filtration is produced by the force of excess blood pressure in the glomerular capillaries over the osmotic pressure of the blood colloids. This effective filtration pressure is equivalent to about 40 mm. mercury pressure and is sufficient to filter out a small fraction (about 1%) of the blood plasma which passes through the glomerulus. There are so many glomeruli involved in a single kidney that the amount filtered averages about 120 ml. per minute, or 170 liters daily. The interesting experiments of Professor A. N. Richards have done much to clear up the nature of the capsular filtrate. By ingenious methods, he was able to obtain samples of the capsular filtrate and analyze it. He found that it was a protein-free plasma filtrate, that it contained the other constituents of plasma in the same concentration as plasma, and that it was alkaline in reaction. He also found that the 2,000 glomeruli of a frog's kidney produced about 4 to 16 ml. of cap ular filtrate per hour; this is several times the amount of urine formed in the same time.

Reabsorption. The second step in the process of urine formation takes place in the tubular part of the nephron. This tubule is made up of straight and convoluted portions, provided with blood capillary networks which are furnished with blood from the blood vessel that leaves the glomerulus. As the capsular filtrate passes down the tubule, many substances in it are differentially reabsorbed into the blood of the capillary network which surrounds the tubule. About 99% of this capsular filtrate is so absorbed and taken back into the blood. In this way, many waste substances are greatly concentrated compared with their condition in the capsular fluid. Some substances are completely removed from the filtrate and taken back into the blood. This selective reabsorption depends upon the nature of the substances and the needs of the body. Some (water and glucose) are reabsorbed in large amounts and are called **high-threshold** substances; others (urea, uric acid, and certain salts) are partly absorbed and partly excreted, the **low-threshold** substances; and still others (sulfates and creatinine) are normally not reabsorbed at all, the **nonthreshold** substances. Explanations of this selective absorption are hazy, for the simple laws of diffusion cannot be made to apply to much of it. In part, at least, it may be an active secretory process which involves the expenditure of energy.

Augmentation. A few substances may be added to the formation of urine by tubular secretion. Artificially injected dyes, such as phenol red, are apparently secreted by the tubules as well as by the glomeruli. In forms such as the toadfish there are no glomeruli at all, and the entire nephrons consist of only the tubular part, yet they have no difficulty in secreting the normal constituents of urine. Birds and reptiles also have tubular secretion of uric acid. In man and other mammals, tubular secretion appears to be of little importance. After reaching the collecting tubules, urine undergoes no further changes in its composition, with the exception of epithelial cells, mucus, etc., which it may acquire in the ureters, bladder, and urethra.

Evolution of kidney nephron. The extensive work of Professor Homer W. Smith on the kidney has revealed a fascinating account of evolutionary trends in the functional unit—the nephron—of vertebrate kidneys. The early chordate kidney started out as a segmented structure which ran the length of the coelomic cavity. Each body segment was provided with a pair of kidney tubules, each of which opened at one end into the coelom by a nephrostome and at the other end either to the outside, separately, or into a common longitudinal tube or groove. These primitive tubules also served to carry off the gametes which were shed into the coelom by the gonads. Such a kidney functions to wash out the waste of the coelomic fluid. Because of their fresh-water origin and the high concentration of salts within their bodies, fish were faced with the problem of getting rid of excess water that continually entered their bodies because of this diffusion gradient.

A filtering device, such as a glomerulus (a tuft of capillaries), was an excellent device for ridding the blood of water. At first the glomerulus simply protruded into the coelom and there discharged its glomerular filtrate, but later it was inserted into the kidney tubule. The nephrostome in time disappeared, so that the whole burden of excretion was thrown upon the glomeruli, as it is in higher vertebrates. When many fresh-water fish took up their existence in the sea, their problem now was to prevent undue loss of water, because the higher concentration of salts in the sea tended to draw water out of their bodies. Thus marine bony fish have tended to lose their glomeruli and depend entirely upon the tubule to remove their waste. Some have succeeded (the aglomerular fish); others have not been in salt water long enough to do this.

Composition and amount of urine excreted

The average amount of urine excreted daily is around 1,500 ml., but many factors influence its output one way or the other. If large quantities of fluid are ingested, the amount of urine will reflect this increase. Also, if the individual perspires freely, the total quantity of urine will be markedly cut down. The kind of food also influences the amount. Salty foods will cause an increase, for the excess salt must be eliminated. Diseases, such as diabetes, will cause a copious flow of urine to take care of the dissolved solids (sugar) in the blood. Certain forms of nephritis (inflammation of the kidneys) may cause a scanty flow if the glomeruli are involved; if the tubules are involved, the volume may be greater.

In the composition of urine, water naturally makes up the greater proportion of it (about 1,200 ml. daily). Of the other constituents, urea composes about 30 grams daily; uric acid, 0.5 gram; creatinine, 1 gram; various salts, 27 grams; and some others in small amounts. The color is due to a pigment—**urochrome.** The reaction of urine is usually on the acid side (pH 6) but varies with the diet. Proteins will produce an acid urine; vegetables and most fruits, an alkaline urine.

Substances that increase the flow of urine above normal are called **diuretics.** The common diuretics are water, salt water, tea, and coffee. These produce their action by increasing the glomerular filtrate, by decreasing tubular reabsorption, and by activating quiescent capillaries.

Regulative action of kidneys

In addition to getting rid of the waste, the urinary system performs other important functions. One of these is the elimination of foreign substances, such as drugs, toxins, and other things for which the body has no use, from the blood. By excreting excessively acid or alkaline substances, the pH of the blood can be maintained in a constant condition. The osmotic pressure of the blood, as well as its volume, is taken care of by the urinary system. Whenever the blood pressure drops, as from loss of blood, the filtration pressure in the glomeruli is lessened; thus less fluid is filtered and the body fluids are conserved thereby.

Mechanism of voiding urine

Urine is excreted continuously by the kidneys into the pelves of the kidneys but is carried down the ureters in peristaltic waves (one to five per minute) to the urinary bladder. As the bladder fills, its muscular walls distend to accommodate the excess urine. Ordinarily the bladder holds about a pint; but persistent filling may increase its capacity. As the walls of the bladder are distended, certain sensory nerve endings there are stimulated and reflexes are set up which lead to the desire for urination, or micturition. These reflex centers are located in the sacral region of the spinal cord and in the brain. The urethra is provided with two sphincter valves: the **internal vesical sphincter** and the **external vesical sphincter.** The former is composed of smooth muscle and is involuntary in its action; the latter is of striped muscle and voluntary. When certain reflexes occur, the involuntary sphincter opens automatically, but the voluntary one remains closed until conscious volition opens it.

ANNOTATED REFERENCES

Andresen, P. H. 1952. The Human Blood Groups. Springfield, Ill., Charles C Thomas, Publisher. *An up-to-date and authoritative account of this much-studied subject.*

Bullock, T. H. (editor). 1957. Physiological Triggers. Washington, American Physiological Society. *The trigger concept stresses the release of energy in a biological system by the application of an increment of energy beyond a certain critical point, such as the activation of an egg by a spermatozoan and the initiation of a muscle contraction or a nerve impulse.*

Cannon, W. B. 1939. The Wisdom of the Body, rev. ed. New York, W. W. Norton & Co., Inc. *In this work a great American physiologist shows how the human body retains a constant condition in spite of disturbing influences, a principle he calls homeostasis.*

Carter, G. S. 1951. A General Zoology of the Invertebrates, ed. 3. London, Sidgwick & Jackson. *More interest is shown in the invertebrates now than formerly. Although this work is not a textbook on all aspects of the invertebrates, it stresses the physiology and general biological principles of the group. It attempts to integrate the invertebrates into the broad synthesis of biology.*

Cott, H. B. 1957. Adaptive Coloration in Animals. London, Methuen & Co., Ltd. *This important monograph demonstrates in convincing fashion the role of color adaptation in the animal kingdom. The author points out three important classes of adaptive coloration—concealment, advertisement, and disguise. Each of these classes has many patterns according to circumstances.*

Diggs, L. W., D. Sturm, and A. Bell. 1956. The Morphology of Human Blood Cells. Philadelphia, W. B. Saunders Co. *This is an atlas of the morphology of normal and pathological human blood cells. Many of the illustrations are in color. It will give the student some idea of the complexity of the blood tissue and how difficult is its study. There is a good chapter on the making of blood smears and the methods for staining them.*

Drinker, C. K., and J. M. Yoffey. 1941. Lymphatics, Lymph, and Lymphoid Tissue. Cambridge, Harvard University Press. *A thorough and comprehensive work on a difficult subject.*

Edney, E. B. 1957. The Water Relations of Terrestrial Arthropods. Cambridge, Cambridge University Press. *Discusses the ways by which arthropods meet the problems of water economy in their environment. For conserving water, arthropods have devised adaptations which involve the three main potential sources of water loss—excretion, transpiration through the integument, and loss from respiratory surfaces.*

Evans, E. A., Jr. (editor). 1942. The Biological Action of the Vitamins. Chicago, University of Chicago Press.

Gemmill, C. L. 1943. Physiology in Aviation. Springfield, Ill., Charles C Thomas, Publisher. *The practical aspects of respiration at high altitudes and the physiological adjustments of the body under such conditions.*

Gerard, R. W. (editor). 1952. Food for Life. Chicago, University of Chicago Press. *The latest concepts of the role of foods in the body.*

Guyton, A. C. 1956. Textbook of Medical Physiology. Philadelphia, W. B. Saunders Co. *Although written primarily with the medical student in mind, this textbook of physiology has much value to all students of physiology. The concepts are presented with great fullness and clearness. Of especial interest to zoologists are the discussions on extracellular and interstitial fluids, the acid-base balance of the body fluids, enzymatic transfer of energy from foodstuffs, and radiation and nuclear physics. It is an excellent reference work for all students of zoology.*

Harrow, B. 1950. One Family: Vitamins, Enzymes, Hormones. Minneapolis, Burgess Publishing Co. *This little book gives an excellent appraisal of the present-day concept of the interrelationships among these three important substances.*

Krogh, A. 1941. The Comparative Physiology of Respiratory Mechanisms. Philadelphia, University of Pennsylvania Press. *A fine comparative account of the structural and functional aspects of respiration by an outstanding authority.*

Menkin, V. 1940. Dynamics of Inflammation. New York, The Macmillan Co. *A great deal of the physiology of circulation is described in a classical pathological condition.*

Ramsay, J. A. 1952. A Physiological Approach to the Lower Animals. Cambridge, Cambridge University Press.

Schechter, V. 1959. Invertebrate Zoology. Englewood Cliffs, N. J., Prentice-Hall, Inc. *A textbook built around certain types of the various invertebrate groups. This work affords good supplementary reading for the beginning student of zoology, for it is not too detailed and the illustrations are clear and easy to understand.*

Smith, H. W. 1951. The Kidney. New York, Oxford University Press. *One of the best technical treatises on the structure and function of the vertebrate kidney. Suitable only for the advanced student.*

Wolf, A. V. 1958. Thirst. Physiology of the Urge to Drink and Problems of Water Lack. Springfield, Ill., Charles C Thomas, Publisher. *A comprehensive review of the many problems associated with fluid balance, the regulation of fluid volume, and the various theories to account for thirst. A highly valuable treatise by a great authority.*

chapter 31

Nervous and sensory systems

Nearly every form of activity in the body requires coordination and cooperation of some kind. To integrate body units into a functioning whole and to pick up information about the body's external and internal environment, most animals have some form of **nervous system** with its closely allied **sensory system** (sense organs).

NERVOUS SYSTEM*

The origin of the nervous system is based upon one of the fundamental principles of protoplasm—irritability. Each cell responds to stimulation in a manner characteristic of that type of cell. But certain cells have become highly specialized for receiving stimuli and for conducting impulses to various part of the body. Through evolutionary changes, these cells have become the most complex of all body systems—the nervous system. In some animals the endocrine system is also used for coordination. However, the nervous system has wider and more direct control of body functions than the endocrine system.

Nervous mechanisms among invertebrates

Nervous structures are largely absent in protozoans. The one cell receives the impulse and carries it to other parts of the cell. Even in some protozoans, however, some regions may be more sensitive to stimuli. The **neuromotor apparatus** of paramecia represents a structure for coordinating the beating of the cilia in response to stimuli. Few metazoan groups

---

*Refer to Chapter 5, Principles 4 and 23.

are without a nervous system of some form. Simple forms have a relatively simple system; complex ones have a more specialized arrangement of receptors and nervous elements for detecting minute stimuli and for conducting impulses to effectors. The lowest metazoans, sponges have a very restricted nervous system, although they do appear to have a primitive type. In the **nerve net** of coelenterates the bipolar or multipolar nerve cells (**proto neurons**) may be separated from each other by synaptic junctions but form an extensive network which is found in and under the ectoderm all over the body. An impulse starting in one part of this net will be conducted in all directions, since the synapse is not restricted to one-way transmission. There are no differentiated sensory, motor, or connector components in the strict meaning of those terms. Branches of the nerve net connect to receptors in the epidermis and to the epitheliomuscular cells. Most responses are generalized, although a few localized responses and reflexes are evident, such a the movement of a tentacle independently of the others. Such a type of nervous system is retained among higher animals in the form of nerve plexuses where such generalized movements as peristalsis are involved.

Flatworms are provided with two anterior **ganglia** of nerve cells from which two main nerve trunks run posteriorly with lateral branches extending to the various parts of the body, thus beginning a central and peripheral differentiation This is the first appearance of the **linea** type of nervous system, which is more de

648

veloped in higher invertebrates. Higher invertebrates have a more centralized nervous system with the two longitudinal nerve cords fused (although still recognizable) and many ganglia present. The earthworm has a well-developed nervous system consisting of sensory and motor neurons, nerve cords, and fibers. At the anterior end, the ventral nerve cord divides and passes upward around the digestive tract to join the bilobed brain. In each segment the double nerve cord bears a double ganglion, each with two pairs of nerves. Arthropods have a system similar to that of the earthworm, except that the ganglia are larger and the sense organs better developed. Many arthropods have both compound and simple eyes, as well as statocysts, or organs of equilibrium. Mollusks have a system of three pairs of ganglia; one pair near the mouth, another pair at the base of the foot, and one pair in the viscera. The ganglia are joined by connectives. The mollusks also have a number of sense organs which are especially well developed in the cephalopods. Among the echinoderms the nervous system is radially arranged.

The nerve cord in all invertebrates is ventral to the alimentary canal and is solid. This arrangement is in marked contrast to the nerve cord of vertebrates, which is dorsal to the digestive system, single, and hollow.

Nervous system of vertebrates

In vertebrates the nerve tissue is massed in the head region, so that these forms have, as a rule, a brain much larger than the other part of the cord. In lower vertebrates this difference is not marked, but higher in the vertebrate kingdom the

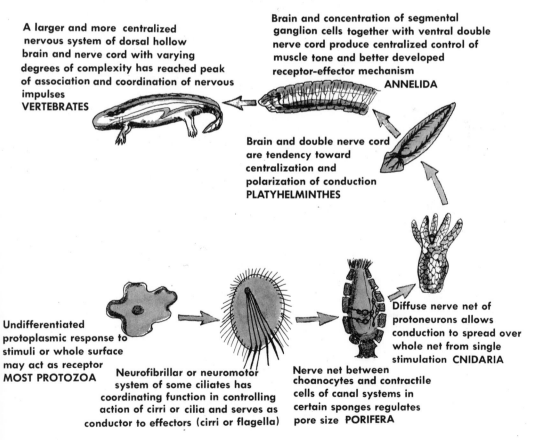

A larger and more centralized nervous system of dorsal hollow brain and nerve cord with varying degrees of complexity has reached peak of association and coordination of nervous impulses VERTEBRATES

Brain and concentration of segmental ganglion cells together with ventral double nerve cord produce centralized control of muscle tone and better developed receptor-effector mechanism ANNELIDA

Brain and double nerve cord are tendency toward centralization and polarization of conduction PLATYHELMINTHES

Undifferentiated protoplasmic response to stimuli or whole surface may act as receptor MOST PROTOZOA

Neurofibrillar or neuromotor system of some ciliates has coordinating function in controlling action of cirri or cilia and serves as conductor to effectors (cirri or flagella)

Nerve net between choanocytes and contractile cells of canal systems in certain sponges regulates pore size PORIFERA

Diffuse nerve net of protoneurons allows conduction to spread over whole net from single stimulation CNIDARIA

Figure 536. How nervous system has evolved.

brain increases in size, reaching its maximum in mammals, especially man, in which it may be larger than all the rest of the nervous system. Along with this enlargement has come an increase in complexity, bringing better patterns of coordination, integration, and intelligence. The physiology of the system has kept pace with its growth and development.

Neuron as structural unit

The basic cells that make up a nervous system are called **neurons**. A neuron is a nerve cell body and all its processes (Figure 27). The nerve cell body contains a nucleus and certain typical cytoplasmic structures, such as Nissl bodies, neurofibrils, etc. The processes include several **dendrites**, which carry impulses toward the cell body, and a single **axon**, which carries impulses away. The axons are usually covered with a medullary sheath which in turn is enclosed by the neurilemma. The latter is important in the regeneration of cut nerves. Neurons are commonly divided into three types—**motor, sensory,** and **association** or **connector.** The dendrites of sensory neurons are connected to a **receptor,** and their axons, to other neurons; associators are connected only to other neurons; and motor neurons are connected by their axons to an **effector. Nerves** are actually made up of many nerve processes—axons or dendrites or both—bound together with connective tissue. The cell bodies of these bundles of nerves are located either in **ganglia** or somewhere in the central nervous system (brain or spinal cord).

Reflex arc as functional unit

Neurons work in groups called **reflex arcs** (Figure 537). There must be at least two neurons in a reflex arc, but usually there are more. The parts of a typical reflex arc consist of (1) a **receptor,** a sense organ in the skin, muscle, or other organ; (2) an **afferent,** or sensory, neuron, which carries the impulse toward the central system; (3) a **nerve center,** where synaptic junctions are made between the sensory neurons and the association neurons; (4)

the **efferent,** or motor, neuron, which makes synaptic junction with the association neuron; and (5) the **effector** by which the animal responds to its environmental changes. Effectors may be grouped as follows: (a) muscles and glands, in most animals; (b) cilia and flagella, also of wide occurrence; (c) nematocysts, mainly restricted to the coelenterates; (d) electric organs, in certain fish; (e) luminous organs, in many groups; and (f) chromatophores, represented in both invertebrates and vertebrates. If only two neurons are involved, the afferent neuron makes a direct synapse with the efferent neuron and the association component is omitted.

The conducting pathways of reflex arcs may be far more complex than the one mentioned. Association neurons may connect afferent and efferent neurons on the same side of the spinal cord, connect them on opposite sides of the cord, or connect them on different levels of the spinal cord, either on the same or opposite sides. Complex reflex acts involve many neurons. In some cases the association neuron carries the arc through the spinal cord; in others it carries the reflex up the cord to the brain and back again to the efferent neuron. In almost any reflex act a number of reflex arcs are involved. For instance, a single afferent neuron may make synaptic junctions with many efferent neurons. In a similar way an efferent neuron may receive impulses from many afferent neurons. In this latter case the efferent neuron is referred to as the **final common path.**

A **reflex act** is the response to a stimulus carried over a reflex arc. It is **involuntary** and may involve the cerebrospinal or the autonomic nervous divisions of the nervous system. Many of the vital processes of the body, such as breathing, heartbeat, diameter of blood vessels, sweat glands, and others, are reflex actions. Some reflex acts are inherited and innate; others are acquired through learning processes (conditioned).

The point at which two neurons are in contact is called a **synapse,** or synaptic junction. There are different forms of syn-

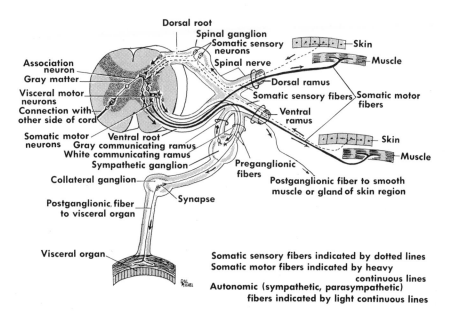

Labels on figure:
Dorsal root
Spinal ganglion
Somatic sensory neurons
Spinal nerve
Skin
Association neuron
Muscle
Gray matter
Dorsal ramus
Visceral motor neurons
Somatic sensory fibers
Somatic motor fibers
Connection with other side of cord
Ventral ramus
Somatic motor neurons
Gray communicating ramus
Skin
White communicating ramus
Muscle
Sympathetic ganglion
Preganglionic fibers
Collateral ganglion
Postganglionic fiber to smooth muscle or gland of skin region
Postganglionic, fiber to visceral organ
Synapse
Visceral organ

Somatic sensory fibers indicated by dotted lines
Somatic motor fibers indicated by heavy continuous lines
Autonomic (sympathetic, parasympathetic) fibers indicated by light continuous lines

Figure 537. Diagram of cross-section of nerve cord and related ganglia in higher vertebrates, showing functional components of spinal and autonomic nerves. Dorsal ramus supplies fibers only to certain muscles and skin of back. Ventral ramus, on the other hand, supplies fibers to skin and musculature of lateral and ventral parts of body and also forms networks or plexuses (brachial and lumbosacral) from which nerves to the forelimbs and hind limbs arise. On this account it is customary to regard ventral ramus nerves as spinal nerves and to ignore dorsal ramus. Spinal nerves in general are segmentally arranged, one pair to each segment of spinal cord. Each spinal nerve joins spinal cord by two roots. Usually dorsal root has only sensory or afferent fibers, ventral root only motor or efferent fibers. Sensory neurons have their cell bodies in spinal ganglion; motor neurons have their cell bodies in spinal cord. Thus each spinal nerve has somatic afferent fibers which carry impulses from sense organs of skin and striped muscle-tendon and somatic efferent fibers which carry impulses to the striped muscles. Autonomic nervous system (sympathetic and parasympathetic divisions) arises from rami of spinal nerves and supplies nerves to smooth muscle, cardiac muscle, and glands. It is also called visceral nervous system because it deals with the viscera over which we have little control (involuntary). Visceral motor components (sensory ones are commonly ignored) differ from somatic motor ones by having two-neuron chains. First neuron of chain is preganglionic neuron which has its cell body in cord and is myelinated; second neuron is postganglionic neuron, has its cell body in a ganglion, and is nonmedullated. Autonomic conduction is carried by two types of preganglionic fibers. One type makes synaptic junction in sympathetic ganglion and passes its impulses to postganglionic fiber which innervates muscles and glands of skin region; other type passes through sympathetic ganglion and makes synaptic junction in collateral ganglion with postganglionic fiber which relays the impulse to visceral organs.

aptic junctions in the body, but they are not in anatomical connection, although they are in functional connection with each other. Two thin surface membranes form the barrier at the junction. There is a gap between the branched ends of the axon and the branched ends of the dendrite. The synapse has the power to allow some impulses to pass and to block others.

Conduction of the impulse is slowed in its passage over the synaptic junction and is always unidirectional, that is, from afferent to efferent neurons, never in the reverse direction. It is very susceptible to fatigue, drugs, and other abnormal states. One theory accounts for the passage of the impulse over the synapse by the formation of a chemical substance, **neuro-**

humor, that forms a bridge over which the impulse can pass. The nature of this neurohumor is not known. In the autonomic system two neurohumors, acetylcholine and sympathin, have been identified, but whether or not an excitatory hormone is found at the synapse has never been convincingly demonstrated.

Stages in development of nervous system

The early formation of the nervous system is briefly discussed in Chapter 33, Principles of Development. The basic vertebrate plan is a dorsal longitudinal hollow nerve cord which runs from head to tail. At the anterior end, this cord expands to form a series of vesicles, at first three and later five in number. The three-part brain is made up of prosencephalon, mesencephalon, and rhomben-

cephalon. Each of these divisions, in order, is associated with an important sense organ, nose, eye, and ear with lateral line. Each division in time develops into a major differentiation of the brain, cerebral hemispheres, midbrain (roof), and cerebellum, respectively. The prosencephalon and rhombencephalon each divide again to form the five-part brain characteristic of the adults of all vertebrates. The five-part brain now includes the telencephalon, diencephalon, mesencephalon, metencephalon, and myelencephalon. From these divisions the different functional brain structures arise.

Central nervous system. The central nervous system is composed of the brain and spinal cord.

SPINAL CORD. The spinal cord varies in size with different vertebrates. In the average man, it is about 18 inches long, extending only to the level of the first lumbar vertebra. The cord is protected by three layers of **meninges** (Figure 539)—the **dura mater, arachnoid,** and **pia mater.** Spaces between these protective layers contain cerebrospinal fluid which forms a protective cushion.

In cross-section the cord shows two zones—an inner H-shaped one of gray matter, made up of nerve cell bodies (Figures 540 and 541), and an outer zone of white matter, made up of nerve bundles of axons and dendrites. The gray matter contains association neurons and the cell bodies of motor neurons. Just outside the cord on each side of the dorsal region are the **dorsal root ganglia,** which contain the cell bodies of the sensory neurons. The gray matter of the cord is divided into two posterior and two anterior horns.

The white matter of the cord is made up of bundles of nerves of similar functions, the **ascending tracts,** carrying impulses to the brain, and the **descending tracts,** carrying impulses away from the brain. The sensory (ascending) tracts are located mainly in the dorsal part of the cord; the motor (descending) tracts are found ventrally and laterally in the cord. In whatever tract they are located, the fibers somewhere in their course cross over

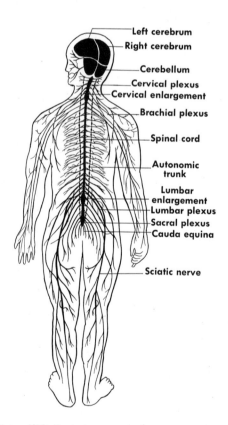

Left cerebrum
Right cerebrum
Cerebellum
Cervical plexus
Cervical enlargement
Brachial plexus
Spinal cord
Autonomic trunk
Lumbar enlargement
Lumbar plexus
Sacral plexus
Cauda equina
Sciatic nerve

Figure 538. Posterior aspect of nervous system in man.

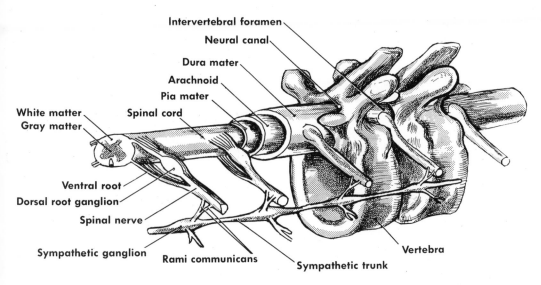

Intervertebral foramen
Neural canal
Dura mater
Arachnoid
Pia mater
White matter
Gray matter
Spinal cord
Ventral root
Dorsal root ganglion
Spinal nerve
Sympathetic ganglion
Rami communicans
Sympathetic trunk
Vertebra

Figure 539. Spinal cord and meninges with relation to spinal nerves, sympathetic system, and vertebrae. The three coats of meninges have been partly cut away to expose spinal cord. Only two vertebrae are shown in position. (After several sources.)

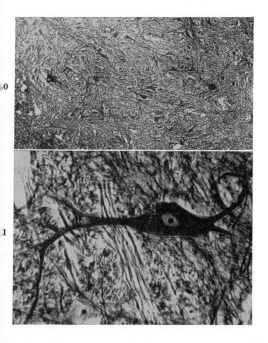

Figure 540. Gray matter of spinal cord, showing distribution of nerve cell bodies. Nerve cells are darkish irregular bodies.

Figure 541. Neuron from gray matter of spinal cord as seen under higher magnification. (Courtesy J. W. Bamberger.)

from one side of the cord to the other, the sensory fibers crossing at a higher level than the motor fibers.

BRAIN. The brain in vertebrates shows an evolution from the linear arrangement in lower forms (fish and amphibians) to the much-folded and enlarged brain found in higher vertebrates (birds and mammals). The brain is really the enlarged anterior end of the spinal cord. The ratio between the weight of the brain and spinal cord affords a fair criterion of an animal's intelligence. In fish and amphibians this ratio is about 1:1, in man the ratio is 55:1, or the brain is fifty-five times as heavy as the spinal cord. The average human brain weight is from 1,200 to 1,400 grams, but there are many variations.

The evolutionary trend has been to develop a dominant brain. This development has been correlated with better integration and better mastery over the environment. So-called lower forms have persisted and have adjusted admirably to their restricted environments, but their nervous equipment has denied them a more varied environment. The brain of vertebrates has steadily advanced, with a better sensory reception and a better nerv-

Nervous and sensory systems 653

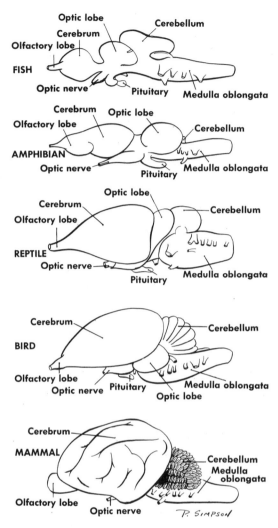

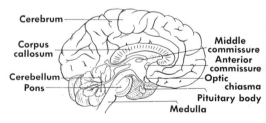

Optic lobe
Cerebrum
Cerebellum
Olfactory lobe
FISH
Optic nerve   Pituitary   Medulla oblongata

Cerebrum   Optic lobe
Olfactory lobe
Cerebellum
AMPHIBIAN
Optic nerve   Medulla oblongata
Pituitary

Optic lobe
Cerebrum
Olfactory lobe
Cerebellum
REPTILE
Optic nerve
Pituitary   Medulla oblongata

Cerebrum
Cerebellum
BIRD
Olfactory lobe
Optic nerve   Pituitary   Medulla oblongata
Optic lobe

Cerebrum
MAMMAL
Cerebellum
Medulla oblongata
Olfactory lobe
Optic nerve   *P. SIMPSON*

Figure 542. Comparative structure of principal brain divisions in different vertebrate groups—fish, amphibian, reptile, bird, and mammal. Note progressive enlargement of cerebrum in higher groups. Stubs of certain cranial nerves are shown.

tiles, but in mammals an additional formation (neopallium) is added on to the archipallium and exceeds in size and importance the remainder of the central nervous system.

The brain is made up of both white and gray matter, arranged in reverse of that found in the spinal cord, for the brain has the gray matter on the outside. (In fish and amphibians the brain mainly retains the spinal cord arrangement.) Most of the gray matter, consisting of nerve cell bodies and some fibers, is found in the much-convoluted **cortex.** In the deeper parts of the brain, the white matter, of nerve fibers, connects the cortex with lower centers of the brain and spinal cord or connects one part of the cortex with another. Also in deeper portions of the brain are collections of nerve cell bodies (gray matter) which provide synaptic junctions between the neurons of the higher centers and those of lower centers.

The six main regions of the brain are the medulla oblongata, pons, midbrain, thalamus, cerebrum, and cerebellum (Figure 543). The **medulla** is the most posterior and lies next to the spinal cord. It is really a conical continuation of the spinal cord. The central canal in the medulla is enlarged to form the fourth ventricle, and directly above it is the **cerebellum.** Cerebrospinal fluid passes from the ventricle through pores to the spaces in the meninges. The gray matter of the medulla includes **nerve centers,** which control many vital processes, such as heartbeat respiration, vasomotor control, deglutition (swallowing), and others. The medulla serves as the origin of many cranial

ous adjustment for meeting a complex environment. The pallium, or cerebral cortex, has shown the greatest evolutionary advancement. In fish and most amphibians the pallium (roof of the telencephalon) is almost nonexistent, consisting only of a thin layer (the archipallium) chiefly concerned with smell. This region represented mainly by olfactory lobes in higher vertebrates was instrumental in food finding. A rudimentary pallium is found in rep-

Cerebrum
Corpus callosum
Cerebellum
Pons
Middle commissure
Anterior commissure
Optic chiasma
Pituitary body
Medulla

Figure 543. Median section through brain of mammal, showing left cerebral hemisphere and principal divisions of brain.

nerves. The white matter of the medulla consists mainly of nerve tracts which connect higher centers of the brain with the spinal cord.

The **pons** lies between the medulla and the midbrain. It is made up of a thick bundle of fibers which carry impulses from one hemisphere of the cerebellum to the other.

Between the pons and the thalamus and in front of the cerebellum lies the **midbrain.** Its **cerebral aqueduct** connects the third and fourth ventricles. In its gray matter are the nuclei of the third and fourth cranial nerves and reflex centers for muscle tone. The white matter consists of ascending and descending tracts which go to the thalamus and cerebrum. On the upper side of the midbrain are the rounded **optic lobes,** serving as centers for visual and auditory reflexes.

The **thalamus** above the midbrain contains masses of gray matter surrounded by the cerebral hemispheres on each side. The thalamus is the relay center for the sensory tracts from the spinal cord. Here synapses are made with neurons which pass to the various sensory areas of the cerebrum. Centers for the sensations of pain, temperature, and touch are supposedly located in the thalamus. Near the thalamus in the floor (hypothalamus) of the third ventricle are centers which regulate body temperature, water balance, sleep, and a few other body functions. On the lateral side of each thalamus there is a triangular mass of gray matter, the **corpus striatum,** connected by fibers to the thalamus and to the cerebrum, cerebellum, and spinal cord. It may control muscle tone.

The largest division of the brain is the **cerebrum,** which is concerned with learned behavior, in contrast to the automatic behavior in the other divisions. It forms the most anterior part of the brain and, in man and most mammals, overlies most of the other parts of the brain. It is incompletely divided into two hemispheres by a longitudinal fissure. The outer **cerebral cortex** is much folded and is made up of gray matter. The uplifted folds are called

gyri; the depressions, **sulci.** Deeper fissures divide the brain into regions. Within the hemispheres are the first and second ventricles. Both gray and white matter are found in the cerebrum. The cortex contains many billions of neurons and their synaptic junctions with other neurons. In the deeper parts of the cerebral hemispheres are other masses of gray matter which function as centers or relay stations for neurons running to or from the cortex. The white matter, which consists of nerve fiber tracts, lies deeper in the cerebrum. These fibers connect one region of a hemisphere with another region of the same hemisphere (**association fibers**), one hemisphere with the other hemisphere (**transverse** or **commissural fibers**), and the cerebrum with lower centers (**projection fibers**).

To a certain extent there is localization of function in the cerebrum (Figure 544). This knowledge has been obtained by direct experimentation, such as by the removal of parts of the brain, by checking of the locations of brain lesions, and by the sensations experienced by patients during operations, etc. It has been possible to locate the visual center (back of cerebrum), center for hearing (side of brain or temporal lobe), the motor area which controls the skeletal muscle (anterior to central sulcus), and the area for skin sensations of heat, cold, and touch (posterior to the central sulcus). Large regions of the frontal lobe of the brain are the "silent areas," or **association areas.** These regions are not directly connected

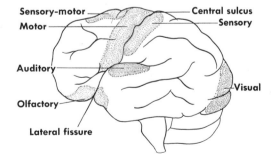

Figure 544. Diagram showing cerebral localization of function in left cerebrum.

to sense organs or muscles and are for the higher faculties of memory, reasoning, and learning.

The degree of development of the cerebrum determines the level of the animal in the evolutionary scale of life. Only forms which have well-developed cerebral cortices are able to learn and modify their behavior by experience. Vital reflex centers and life can be sustained without a cortex, but there can be no learning and no analyses of sensations or stimuli. In such cases the organism is only an automaton.

The **cerebellum**, lying beneath the posterior part of the cerebrum, consists of two hemispheres and a central portion called the vermis. In man, it is deeply folded and is composed of nerve cell bodies. Among its cells are the large, much-branched **Purkinje cells.** The white fiber tracts lie deeper in the cerebellum. The chief function of the cerebellum is regulation of muscular coordination. Its primary purpose is to coordinate the actions of the various muscles in a voluntary response.

Electrical changes in brain. In the living state, the brain is accompanied by electrical changes. The recordings of these changes are commonly referred to as **brain waves.** The instrument used for these recordings is called an **electroencephalograph.** When electrodes are attached to different parts of the scalp, this delicate instrument records the activity of the underlying cerebral cortex. These brain waves vary with the activity of the nerve cells. The brain is active awake or asleep. A very active brain will produce a large number of waves in a given time; a sluggish brain has fewer waves. Patterns of brain waves vary with mental disturbances; those for certain pathological lesions, such as epilepsy and brain tumor, are rather characteristic and useful in diagnosis.

Peripheral nervous system. This system is made up of the paired cranial nerves which run to and from the brain and the paired spinal nerves which run to and from the spinal cord. They consist of

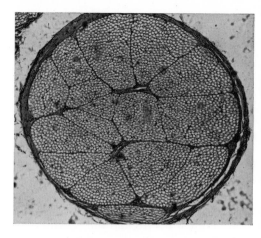

Figure 545. Cross-section of nerve trunk, showing cut ends of nerve fibers (small white circles). Such a trunk may be made up of thousands of fibers. Both afferent and efferent fibers represented.

bundles of axons and dendrites and connect with the receptors and effectors in the body.

CRANIAL NERVES. In the higher vertebrates, including the man, there are 12 pairs of cranial nerves. They are primarily concerned with the sense organs, glands, and muscles of the head and are more specialized than spinal nerves. Some are purely sensory (olfactory, optic, and auditory); some are mainly, if not entirely, motor (oculomotor, trochlear, abducens, spinal accessory, and hypoglossal); and the others are mixed with both sensory and motor neurons (trigeminal, facial, glossopharyngeal, and vagus). The majority arise from or near the medulla. Some of the cranial nerves bear autonomic nerve fibers, especially in the facial and vagus. For convenience the various cranial nerves are also designated by the Roman numerals I to XII, as well as by specific names. The numbering begins at the anterior end of the brain and proceeds posteriorly. In 1895, another sensory cranial nerve (nervus terminalis) was found running from the olfactory membrane to the olfactory lobe of the brain in all vertebrates except birds.

SPINAL NERVES. The spinal nerves contain both sensory and motor components in approximately equal numbers. In higher vertebrates and man there are 31 pairs: cervical, 8 pairs; thoracic, 12 pairs; lumbar, 5 pairs; sacral, 5 pairs; and caudal, 1 pair. Each nerve has two roots by which it is connected to the spinal cord. All the sensory fibers enter the cord by the dorsal root, and all the motor fibers leave the cord by the ventral root. The nerve cell bodies of motor neurons are located in the ventral horns of the gray zone of the spinal cord; the sensory nerve cell bodies are in the dorsal spinal ganglia just outside the cord. Near the junction of the two roots, the spinal nerve divides into a small dorsal branch (ramus), which supplies structures in the back; a larger ventral branch, which supplies structures in the sides and front of the trunk and in the appendages; and an autonomic branch, which supplies structures in the viscera. To supply a large area of the body, the ventral rami of several spinal nerves may join to form a network (plexus). These are the **cervical, brachial,** and **lumbosacral plexuses.**

Autonomic nervous system. The autonomic nerves govern the involuntary functions of the body which do not ordinarily affect consciousness. The cerebrum has no direct control over these nerves; thus one cannot by volition stimulate or inhibit their action. Autonomic nerves control the movements of the alimentary canal and heart, the contraction of the smooth muscle of the blood vessels, urinary bladder, iris of eye, etc., and the secretions of various glands. Although these nerves have both sensory and motor components, the former are considered of minor importance and are ignored by many authorities. The efferent, or motor, nerves of this system arise from small nerve cells located at different levels from the midbrain to the sacral region of the spinal cord. After issuing from the central nervous system, these fibers make synaptic junctions in ganglia, which may lie close to the spinal cord or in the organs innervated.

There are thus at least two neurons in an autonomic efferent connection—a **preganglionic** fiber, which has its nerve cell body in the central system, and a **postganglionic** fiber, whose nerve cell body is located in the ganglion (Figure 537). Sub-

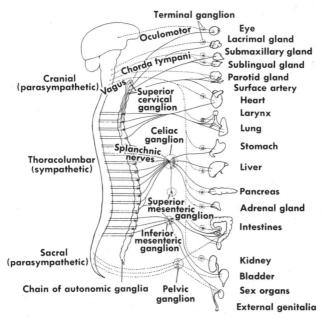

Figure 546. Diagram of autonomic nervous system in mammals. Parasympathetic fibers are indicated by dotted lines; sympathetic fibers, by continuous lines.

divisions of the autonomic system are (1) the **parasympathetic,** which is centered partly in the brain and partly in the lower end of the spinal cord (craniosacral outflow), and (2) the **sympathetic,** which is centered in the middle part of the spinal cord (thoracolumbar outflow). Most organs in the body are innervated by both sympathetic and parasympathetic fibers, and their actions are antagonistic. If one speeds up an activity, the other will slow it down. However, neither kind of nerve is exclusively excitatory or inhibitory. Parasympathetic fibers inhibit heartbeat but will excite peristaltic movement of the intestine; sympathetic fibers will increase heartbeat but slow down peristaltic movement.

The **parasympathetic** system consists of nerves, some of which emerge from the brain by certain cranial nerves and others from the pelvic region of the spinal cord by certain spinal nerves. In this division the preganglionic fiber is very long, for the ganglion where it makes synaptic junction is located near or in the organ innervated. On this account the postganglionic fiber is very short. Parasympathetic fibers **excite** the stomach and intestine, urinary bladder, bronchi, constrictor of iris, salivary glands, and coronary arteries. They **inhibit** the heart, intestinal sphincters, and sphincter of the urinary bladder.

In the **sympathetic** division the nerve cell bodies are located in the thoracic and upper lumbar areas of the spinal cord. Their preganglionic fibers pass out through the ventral roots of the spinal nerves, separate from these, and go to the sympathetic ganglia which are paired and form a chain on each side of the spinal column. In these ganglia the axons of the preganglionic fibers synapse with the postganglionic fibers which connect the ganglia with one another. Some of the postganglionic fibers run through spinal nerves to the limbs and body wall where they innervate the blood vessels of the skin, the smooth muscles of the hair, the sweat glands, etc.; and some run to the abdominal organs as the splanchnic nerves. The cell bodies of the latter fibers are located

in **prevertebral ganglia** along the aorta. Some of the sympathetic fibers lack a myelin sheath and are known as gray fibers. Sympathetic fibers **excite** the heart, blood vessels, sphincters of the intestines, urinary bladder, dilator muscles of the iris, and others. They **inhibit** the stomach, intestine, bronchial muscles, and coronary arterioles.

An enzyme of the blood, cholinesterase, checks undue spreading of the stimulation by acetylcholine. All preganglionic fibers, whether sympathetic or parasympathetic, release acetylcholine at the synapse for stimulating the ganglion cells. At the terminations of the postganglionic fibers on the organs, however, the parasympathetic fibers secrete acetylcholine, and the sympathetic fibers give off two neurohumors (epinephrine and norepinephrine). These chemical substances produce characteristic physiological reactions. Since there is some physiological overlapping of sympathetic and parasympathetic fibers, it is now customary to describe nerve fibers as either adrenergic (epinephrine effect) or cholinergic (acetylcholine effect).

The plexuses of Auerbach and Meissner, which are found in the walls of the digestive tract, are often included in the autonomic nervous system. They correspond in a way to the nerve net of invertebrates. It is thought by some that the ganglia of these plexuses represent the outlying ganglionic cells for the vagus nerve and that they are involved in certain reflexes of the alimentary canal.

Nature of nerve impulse

The **nerve impulse** is that physicochemical change in the nerve fiber membrane which is aroused by a stimulus and is carried along the nerve fiber to its termination. It may or may not produce excitation in a tissue or organ, depending upon its strength or the condition of the tissue to which the stimulus is delivered. A **stimulus** is an environmental change which produces an alteration in an irritable tissue. In the case of the nerve impulse, the alteration is produced in the nerve fiber, or in a receptor, which transmits the change to the nerve. Stimuli may be in the form of electrical, thermal, chemical, and mechanical changes. The nature of the nerve impulse has been extensively studied since its rate was first determined by Helmholtz a hundred years ago, but much is still to be discovered about its nature. Superficially, the impulse resembles an electric current, but it travels much more slowly than electricity (speed of light) and it cannot be conducted by a dead nerve as electric current can. It is commonly referred to as an electrochemical disturbance in the nerve fiber. It is a self-propagated disturbance and gets the energy for its transmission locally along the nerve fiber. A strong stimulus will not cause the impulse to travel faster than one induced by a feeble impulse, if the latter is of minimum intensity. All impulses are alike, whether they are conducted in motor, sensory, or association fibers. The impulse can be influenced by the condition of the nerve fiber and by such agencies as drugs. In such cases the impulse may be retarded or blocked entirely.

The **rate** of the nerve impulse is faster in some animals than in others. Nerve fibers with large diameters have faster rates than those with small. The rate is slower in nerve fibers which lack a myelin sheath. In some nerves in man it travels about 121 meters per second; in corresponding nerves of the frog its rate is only 30 meters per second. In the autonomic nerve fibers of man it travels about 10 meters per second.

Nerve fibers can transmit impulses in either direction. How far the impulse will travel will depend upon the nearest synaptic junction, which permits transmission in only one direction—from afferent to efferent neurons.

The transmission of the nerve impulse is a metabolic process, involving the consumption of oxygen and the giving off of carbon dioxide. Heat is also produced, but the amounts of each of these three factors —heat, oxygen, and carbon dioxide—are very small.

The nerve impulse is considered to be a surface phenomenon of the membrane surrounding each nerve fiber—the **membrane theory** of nervous conduction. According to this theory, the nerve membrane in a resting condition (not conducting an impulse) is in a polarized state with positive chemical ions on its outside and negative chemical ions on its inside. To prevent the positive and negative ions from coming together and neutralizing each other, the membrane, whch is impermeable to them, keeps the ions apart. Whenever a stimulus is applied to a nerve, the membrane at the point becomes permeable; thus the two kinds of ions can pass through the membrane and neutralize each other. This depolarization then spreads to adjacent regions and the neutralization of the ions occurs there. In this way the wave of depolarization (and neutralization) could move along the nerve fiber to its terminal.

Wherever the nerve impulse is passing, that point is electric negative to the inactive nerve fiber, as determined by galvanometers. This is called the **action potenial,** or **wave of negativity.** As the impulse passes forward, the depolarized region immediately behind it becomes polarized again and restored to its inactive state. This recovery requres a short amount of time, during which a second stimulus cannot be transmitted over that fiber. This very brief interval is called the **refractory** period and lasts from 0.001 to 0.005 second. Much experimental evidence has supported this theory, and artificial models have been cleverly designed to mimic the behavior of the nerve impulse and have helped to understand the phenomenon.

SENSE ORGANS

Specialized receptors, or **sense organs,** have been developed for detection of delicate environmental changes. These are made up of cells which are unusually sensitive to certain types of stimuli. A sense organ is stimulated by stimuli of low threshold intensity which are not strong enough to affect protoplasm or a nerve fiber directly.

Unspecialized sensitivity of general protoplasm and no localized regions of sensitivity, or else whole external surface may act as receptor (ameba)

Eyespot with lens for concentrating light on light-absorbing pigment—example of definite receptor (dinoflagellate)

Eyespot representing light-sensitive region shielded by a pigment, which makes light effective from 1 direction (euglena)

Light-absorbing pigment in front of light-sensitive cells (planaria)

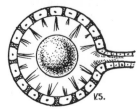

Statocyst is a common organ for perception of gravity; differentiation of perception depending on sensory hairs which are stimulated by statolith (pecten)

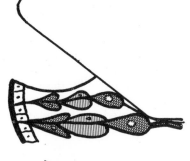

Tympanic membrane vibrates and transmits sound waves to scolophores which make up sensory part of auditory organ (insects)

Tactile sense organs often modified hairs (crustaceans)

Figure 547. Comparison of invertebrate

Vertebrates with a variety of sensory receptors, such as those of general sensibility (touch, pressure, pain, and temperature), and those of special sensibility (smell, taste, sight, hearing, and balancing); some organs of general sense are:

Free sensory nerve endings in epithelium for pain reception.

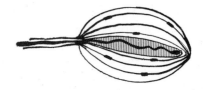

Pacinian corpuscle in superficial and deep parts of body for pressure reception

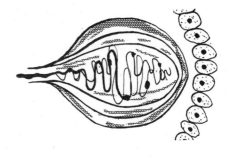

Meissner's corpuscle in dermal papillae of skin for light touch perception

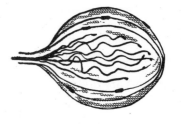

Krause's corpuscle in skin and mucous membrane for cold reception

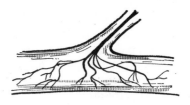

Neurotendinous spindles of tendon-muscle junctions for proprioception of position and tension of muscles

and vertebrate sense organs.

Receptors are specific for stimuli of a certain type and will not respond to other types. Thus the eye is specialized for picking up light rays but is not affected by sound waves. Receptors are in direct contact with the environment and receive and transmit impressions of what is going on in the environment.

Sense organs are specialized parts of the sensory nerve fibers. Since all nerve impulses are qualitatively the same, the real perception of sensation is done in the brain. Sense organs have a hookup with localized regions of the brain, and any impulse that comes to this part of the brain is interpreted in a definite way. For instance, whatever comes over the optic nerve is interpreted in terms of light sensation. The picture one gets of his environment must necessarily be imperfect, for many forms of stimuli cannot be picked up by the sense organs, or the sense organs may fail to register sensations because of the lack of attention or the presence of fatigue.

Classification of receptors

Receptors are classified on the basis of their location. Those near the external surface are called **exteroceptors** and are stimulated by changes in the external environment. Internal parts of the body are provided with **interoceptors**, which pick up stimuli from the internal organs. Muscles, tendons, and joints have **proprioceptors**, which are sensitive to changes in the tension of muscles and enable the organism to be aware of position and movement. These last are responsible for the so-called kinesthetic sense.

Receptors are divided into several types. Some have no specialized capsules around them and are merely **free nerve endings**. They often have small enlargements, or terminal varicosities, on their branches. Some form little knots of fiber networks. Many of them are concerned with the senses of **pain** and **heat** (end organs of Ruffini). Most receptors have some form of capsule around them and are thus called encapsulated. Because of their shape, they are also referred to as sense

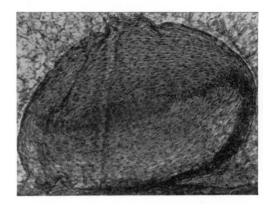

Figure 548. Pacinian corpuscle for pressure reception; from mesentery of cat. (Courtesy J. W. Bamberger.)

corpuscles. They lie in the connective tissues and include the Meissner's touch corpuscles, the end bulbs of Krause (cold), and the Pacinian corpuscles (pressure) (Figure 548). Many of these receptors are confined to regions close to the body surface and belong to the **cutaneous receptors**.

The chemical senses, taste and smell, and the highly specialized senses, sight and hearing, may be considered in a class of their own and deserve separate accounts.

Sense organs among invertebrates

In protozoans there are no special receptors unless the eyespot (stigma) of some forms be so considered. In the one-celled forms the stimuli strike the protoplasmic mass directly. There are no special sensory cells in sponges, but the cells react directly to stimuli. Coelenterates have many sensory cells scattered through the epidermis, especially on the tentacles and around the mouth. These cells are connected to the nerve network, which is connected to the epitheliomuscular cells of the epidermis. They are really tactile receptors. There are also found in this group eyespots sensitive to light, statocysts for equilibration, and sense pits as chemoreceptors. Flatworms have eyespots for light detection and chemoreceptors for taste and smell. Roundworms are provided with tactile receptors but with little else. Among the annelid worms, sense organs are much better developed and are found in the epidermis for touch, taste, and light perception. In some annelids (polychaetes) sense organs assume definite forms. Sense organs in mollusks and arthropods have attained their greatest development in the invertebrates. Statocysts for equilibration, tactile receptors, and chemoreceptors are common. Arthropods have both simple and compound eyes; among the cephalopods the eye is not unlike that of vertebrates, except that it has a different origin.

Chemical receptors

The chemical senses are taste and smell which are stimulated by specific chemical substances in liquid or gaseous form. These primitive receptors have a wide distribution among the lower vertebrates, where they may be found all over the body. In higher vertebrates they are localized. **Taste buds** (Figure 549) in higher forms are found on the tongue and in the mucous membrane of the mouth cavity, pharynx, and larynx. A taste bud consists of a few sensitive cells surrounded by supporting cells and is provided with a small external pore through which the slender tips of the sensory cells project. The basal ends of the sensory cells contact nerve endings from cranial nerves.

The four basic taste sensations—sour, salt, bitter, and sweet—are each due to a different kind of taste bud. The tastes for salt and sweet are found mainly at the tip of the tongue, bitter at the base of the tongue, and sour along the sides of the tongue. Taste buds are more numerous in ruminants (mammals that chew the cud) than in man. They tend to degenerate with age, for the child has more buds widely distributed over the mouth. The ability to distinguish certain tastes varies among people. This is especially the case with phenylthiocarbamide; the ability to taste this chemical is definitely inherited.

Sense organs of **smell** are found in specialized mucous membrane located high in the nasal cavity and called the olfactory

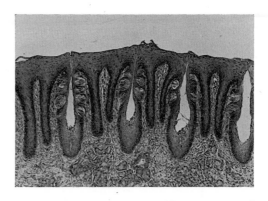

Figure 549. Taste buds in rabbit tongue. Buds are little oval bodies lined up on each side of slitlike recesses. (Courtesy J. W. Bamberger.)

epithelium. Gases must be dissolved in a fluid to be smelled; therefore the nasal cavity must be moist. The sensory cells with projecting hairs are scattered singly through the olfactory epithelium. Their basal ends are connected to fibers of the olfactory cranial nerve which runs to one of the olfactory lobes. In lower vertebrates the olfactory centers are very well developed. The sensitivity to certain odors is delicate. The human nose can detect 1/25,000,000 of one milligram of the odoriferous principle of the skunk. Since taste and smell are stimulated by chemicals in solution, their sensations may be confused, so that the taste of food is dependent to a great extent upon odors that reach the olfactory membrane through the throat. Many substances are tasted when they are being swallowed. All the various forms of taste, other than the four basic ones (sweet, sour, bitter, salt), are really due to the flavors' reaching the sense of smell in this manner.

The ear

The ear is a specialized receptor for detecting sound waves in the surrounding air (Figure 550). Another sense, equilibration, is also associated with the ears of all vertebrate animals. Among the invertebrates, only certain insects have any kind of sound receptors. In its evolution the ear was at first associated more with equi-

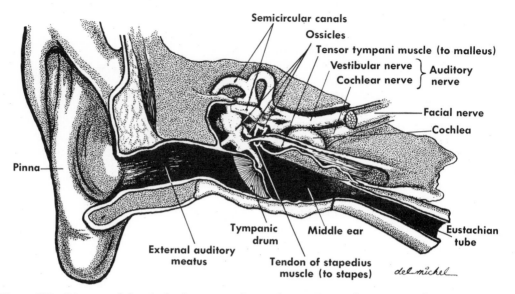

Figure 550. Diagram of longitudinal section of ear of man. Note the two muscles, tensor tympani and stapedius. Very loud noises cause these muscles to contract by reflex, thus stretching tympanic membrane and oval window and preventing damaging effect of loud, low-pitched sounds.

librium than with hearing. Hearing sense is found only in the internal ear, which is the only part of the ear in many of the lower vertebrates; the middle and the external ears were added in later evolutionary developments. In fish the lateral-line organs, specialized for the detection of water currents, take the place of hearing organs. The internal ear is considered to be a development of part of the lateral-line system. Some fish apparently can transmit sound from their swim bladders by the Weberian ossicles (series of small bones) to some part of the inner ear for they lack a cochlea.

The ear found in higher vertebrates is made up of three parts: (1) the **inner ear,** which contains the essential organs of hearing and equilibrium and is present in all vertebrates; (2) the **middle ear,** an air-filled chamber with one or more ossicles for conducting sound waves to the inner ear, present in amphibians and higher vertebrates only (Figure 551); and (3) the **outer ear,** which collects the sound waves and conducts them to the tympanic membrane lying next to the middle ear, present only in reptiles, birds, and mammals but best developed in the latter.

Structure and function of different parts of ear. In higher vertebrates the ear is typically made up of three parts—an outer ear for collection of sound waves, a middle ear for their transmission, and an inner ear specialized for sensory reception.

OUTER EAR. The outer, or external, ear of higher vertebrates is made up of two parts: (1) the **pinna,** or skin-covered flap of elastic cartilage and muscles, and (2) the **auditory canal.** In man, the pinna serves some function in collecting sound waves; in many other mammals, such as the rabbit and cat, the pinna is freely movable and so is more effective. The auditory canal extends inward in an oblique direction so as to prevent hard objects from striking the tympanic membrane directly. Its walls are lined with hair and wax-secreting glands as a protection against the entrance of foreign objects.

MIDDLE EAR. The middle ear is separated from the external ear by the eardrum, or tympanic membrane, which consists of a stretched connective tissue membrane. Within the air-filled middle ear a chain of

664

three tiny ossicles, **malleus, incus,** and **stapes,** conduct the sound waves across the middle ear. This chain of bones is so arranged that the malleus (hammer) is in contact with the eardrum and the stapes (stirrup) is in contact with the oval window membrane of the inner ear. When sound waves strike the tympanic membrane, its vibrations are transmitted by the chain of ossicles to the inner ear. To increase the tension of the tympanic membrane for delicate sounds or to counteract undue displacement of the membrane, a muscle (tensor tympani) is inserted on the malleus. Contraction of this muscle pulls the malleus and the tympanic membrane inward. A similar muscle (stapedius) is fastened to the stapes and controls the tension of the fluid in the internal ear. The middle ear communicates

with the pharynx by means of the Eustachian tube, which regulates the air pressure in the middle ear. Both the Eustachian tube and the middle ear are lined with mucous membrane and are subject to invasion by disease germs from the throat region.

INNER EAR. The inner ear consists essentially of two labyrinths, one within the other. The inner one is called the **membranous labyrinth** and is a closed ectodermal sac filled with the fluid, **endolymph.** The part involved with hearing (**cochlea**) is coiled like a snail's shell, making two and a half turns. Surrounding the membranous labyrinth is the **bony labyrinth,** which is a hollowed-out part of the temporal bone and conforms to the shape and contours of the membranous labyrinth. In the space between the two

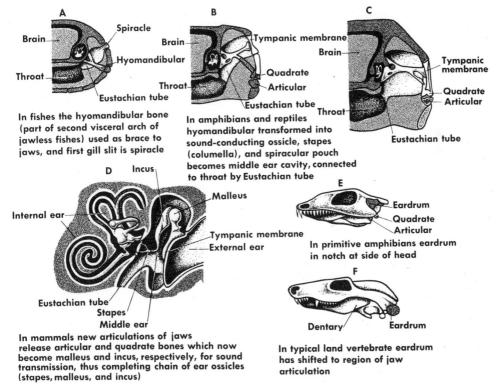

Figure 551. Diagram to show evolution of middle ear and auditory ossicles. Diagrammatic sections are made through otic region at level of ear and hind end of jaw of **A,** fish; **B,** primitive amphibian; **C,** reptile; **D,** mammal. **E** and **F** are side views of skull of ancient amphibian and land vertebrate. (Redrawn from Romer: The Vertebrate Story, University of Chicago Press.)

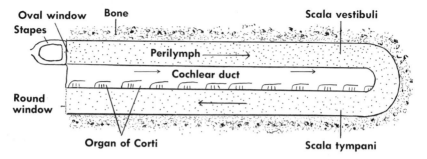

Figure 552. Diagram of cochlea straightened out to show pathway of vibrations through scala vestibuli (vestibular canal) and scala tympani (tympanic canal).

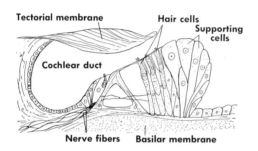

Figure 553. Diagram of cross-section of organ of Corti.

labyrinths, perilymph, a fluid similar to endolymph, is found.

The cochlea is divided into three longitudinal canals which are separated from each other by thin membranes (Figures 550 and 552). These canals become progressively smaller from the base of the cochlea to the apex. One of these canals is called the **vestibular canal;** its base is closed by the oval window. The **tympanic canal,** which is in communication with the vestibular canal at the tip of the cochlea, has its base closed by the round window. Between these two canals is the **cochlear canal,** which contains the organ of hearing, the **organ of Corti** (Figure 553). The latter organ is made up of fine rows of hair cells which run lengthwise from the base to the tip of the cochlea. There are at least 24,000 of these hair cells in the human ear, each cell with many hairs projecting into the endolymph of the cochlear canal and each connected with neurons of the auditory nerve. The hair cells rest upon the **basilar mem-**

brane, which separates the tympanic and cochlear canals, and are covered over by the tectorial membrane found directly above them. The basilar membrane is composed of transverse connective tissue fibers which vary in length at different levels of the cochlea.

In hearing a sound, sound waves are picked up by the external ear and transmitted through the auditory canal to the tympanic membrane, which is caused to vibrate. These vibrations are conducted by the chain of ear ossicles to the oval window, which transmits the vibrations to the fluid in the vestibular and tympanic canals. The vibrations of the endolymph cause the basilar membrane, with its hair cells, to vibrate so that the latter rub against the tectorial membrane. This stimulation of the hair cells causes them to initiate nerve impulses in the fibers of the auditory nerve, with which they are connected.

To produce discrimination in the pitch of different sounds, it is thought that sounds of different vibration frequencies stimulate different hair cells. Since the fibers of the basilar membrane are shortest at the base and longest at the apex, high notes will cause the shorter fibers to vibrate; low notes will stimulate the longer fibers nearer the apex. Whichever fibers are set in vibration, the particular hair cells in that region will be stimulated. Those impulses which are carried by certain fibers of the auditory nerve are interpreted by the hearing center as particular tones. The **loudness** of a tone depends upon the number of hair cells stimulated, whereas the **timbre,** or quality, of a tone is produced by the pattern of the hair cells stimulated by sympathetic vibration. This latter characteristic of tone enables one to distinguish between different human voices and different musical instruments, even though the notes in each case be of the same pitch and loudness.

Sense of equilibrium. Closely connected to the inner ear and forming a part of it are two small sacs, the **saccule** and **utricle,** and three **semicircular canals.** Like the cochlea, they are filled with endolymph. They are concerned with the sense of balance and rotation. They are well developed in all vertebrates, and in some lower forms they represent about all there is of the internal ear, for the cochlea is absent in fish. They are innervated by the nonacoustic branch of the auditory nerve. The utricle and saccule are hollow sacs lined with sensitive hairs and contain small stones, **otoliths,** of calcium carbonate. Whatever way the head is tipped, certain hair cells are stimulated; these are interpreted in a certain way with reference to position.

The three semicircular canals are at right angles to each other, one in each plane of space. They are filled with fluid, and at the opening of each canal into the utricle there is a bulblike enlargement, the **ampulla,** which contains hair cells but no otoliths. Whenever the fluid moves, these hair cells are stimulated. Rotating the head will cause a lag, due to inertia, in certain of these ampullae. This lag produces consciousness of movement. Since the three canals of each internal ear are in different planes, any kind of movement will stimulate at least one of the ampullae.

The eye

The earliest eyes in the animal kingdom are the eyespots of invertebrates. These spots may be only a small differentiated mass in a cell, or they may consist of several light-sensitive cells clustered together, with some pigment to direct the light to the sensitive cells. Such eyespots record different intensities of light, so that the organism can distinguish between light and dark and can determine the source of light. In the blind earthworms there are photoreceptors which are sensitive to light and enable the worm to avoid strong light. Arthropods have compound, or mosaic, eyes composed of many visual units (ommatidia), each being provided with a kind of lens and light-sensitive cells. Such eyes do not form a simple image but a mosaic one made up of separate images contributed by the numerous visual units. This eye is well suited for picking up motion, for the images registered by some of the ommatidia are quickly shifted to other ommatidia by the slightest movement of the object, thereby producing an exaggerated effect. Some of the cephalopods (squid and octopus) have well-developed skin eyes with cornea, lens, anterior and posterior chambers, and rod-bearing retina.

The eye of vertebrates (Figure 554) is of the camera type, with a light-tight chamber containing the lens system at the front end which focuses the picture of objects on the sensitive retina at the back.

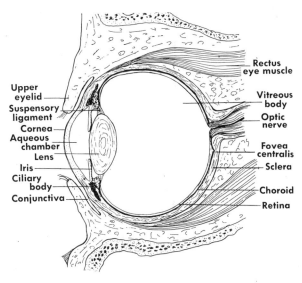

Figure 554. Diagram of section through eye of vertebrate.

In forming an image, the lens and accessory structures make use of the same laws of optics as a camera. That is why the wearing of glasses is able to correct defects in our lens system.

The eyeball is more or less spherical and is composed of three layers: (1) the outer white **sclerotic** coat, which is composed of tough connective tissue for support and protection; (2) the middle **choroid** coat, which contains blood vessels for nourishment; and (3) the inner **retinal** coat, which contains the light-sensitive units. The anterior part of the sclerotic coat is transparent, forming the **cornea,** for the admission of light. A circular curtain, the **iris,** a modification of the choroid coat, regulates the size of the light opening, the **pupil.** Just behind the iris is the **lens,** a modification of the ectoderm of the skin. The lens is a transparent, elastic ball which bends the rays and focuses them on the retina. In land vertebrates the cornea also bends the rays and the lens can adjust the focus for near and far objects. Between the cornea and the lens is the outer chamber filled with the watery **aqueous humor;** between the lens and the retina is the much larger inner chamber, filled with the viscous **vitreous humor.** Surrounding the margin of the lens and holding it in place is the **suspensory ligament,** which in turn is attached to the **ciliary body.** In front of the ciliary body is the **ciliary muscle,** a ring of radiating muscle fibers attached to the suspensory ligament. This muscle, with the ligament, makes possible the stretching and relaxing of the lens for close or distant vision (accommodation).

The **retina** (Figure 555), the sensory part of the eye, is only a partial coat, for it does not extend over the front region of the eye. It is made up of the photoreceptors, **rods** and **cones,** which in the human eye number about 125,000,000 rods and 7,000,000 cones. Cones are primarily concerned with light vision; rods, with dim or colorless vision. Back of the retina is the pigmented layer of cells which absorbs extra light rays and produces a dark interior. The retina is actually made

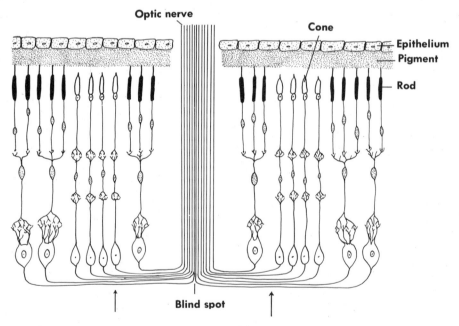

Figure 555. Diagram of section through retina. Arrows indicate direction of light rays. Note that light rays to reach the sensitive cells at back of retina must pass through many layers of neurons.

up of three sets of neurons in series with each other: (1) photoreceptors, or the rods and cones, (2) intermediate neurons, and (3) ganglionic neurons whose axons form the optic nerve. At the point where the fibers leave the eyeball to form the optic nerve there are no rods or cones (the blind spot). The light rays must pass through these layers of neurons to reach the rods and cones.

The **fovea centralis,** the region of keenest vision, is located in the center of the retina, in direct line with the center of the lens and cornea and contains only cones. In other regions of the retina, the cones and rods have an unequal distribution, for at the peripheral parts of the retina only rods are found. This is why one can see better at night by looking out of the corners of his eyes, for the rods, adapted for dim vision, are brought into use. Rods contain a sensitive substance known as **visual purple (rhodopsin),** which is a compound of vitamin A and a protein. Light falling on the rods transforms (bleaches) visual purple into visual yellow, which stimulates the rods. In the dark the color of visual purple returns. This reversible bleaching and regeneration goes on all the time in the eye. **Visual violet (iodopsin)** is found in cones, but less is known about it. The decomposition of photosensitive pigments with the formation of products which stimulate the receptor cells of the retina is known as the **photochemical theory** (Hecht).

The power to accommodate for close vision decreases with age. At rest, the lens is kept stretched and flattened by the tension of the suspensory ligament and the eye is focused for distant vision. When the ciliary muscles are contracted, their pull relieves the tension of the ligament by decreasing the distance between the ciliary body and the lens, so that the lens is free to assume a spherical shape for close vision. Thus focusing on a distant object is not a muscular act, but focusing on a near one is. The lens becomes less elastic with age, and the power to accommodate for near vision is lessened. This loss of power to accommodate is called **presbyopia.** Bifocal glasses, with one part for distant vision and another for close vision, are often worn to overcome this handicap.

The eye must also accommodate or adapt itself to differences in light intensity, as well as to differences in distance of the objects to be seen. To regulate the amount of light that enters the eye, the iris can increase or decrease the size of the pupil. The iris is composed of two sets of muscles, circular muscles, which can contract or decrease the size of the pupil, and radial muscles, whose contraction dilates the pupil. These muscles are under the control of the autonomic nervous system, and changes in the size of the pupil are not instantaneous, for when one steps from a darkened room (where the pupils are dilated) into bright sunlight, the eyes are dazzled and painful until the pupils decrease. The iris is also responsible for the color of the eyes. If little pigment is present, the color is blue; other colors—green, hazel, brown—are due to larger amounts of pigment.

Some variations among eyes of vertebrates. Among vertebrates there are two kinds of vision, day vision and night vision. With day vision, forms stand out sharply, and details of structure, as well as delicate shades of color, are distinguished. With night vision, things are perceived in outline with only vague details, and color is absent. This difference between the two types of vision forms the basis for the nocturnal and diurnal habits of animals. Man may be said to have both day vision and night vision, for he possesses both rods and cones in considerable numbers. However, many animals have only one type of vision. Chickens have only day vision; this explains why they go to roost so early. Owls and flying squirrels are active only at night. Usually those animals that are active at night have large numbers of rods and few cones; diurnal forms, on the other hand, have mostly cones. However, there are a number of variations in this respect. Diurnal lizards have no rods, but crocodiles have many rods in their retinas. Some nocturnal snakes have few or no cones but plenty of rods. The retinas of most birds consist mainly of cones.

Color vision is based upon three photo-pigments (in the cones) for absorbing red, green, and violet colors. Color vision is found in certain insects, many fish, reptiles, diurnal birds, and a few mammals (mostly primates).

ANNOTATED REFERENCES

Bard, P. 1956. Physiology in Modern Medicine, ed. 10. St. Louis, The C. V. Mosby Co. *The section on the nervous system is especially well written in this outstanding medical physiology.*

Brodie, B. B., and A. D. Bass (editors). 1959. Evolution of Nervous Control From Primitive Organisms to Man. Washington, American Association for the Advancement of Science. *A symposium. This comparative study takes the logical approach that the roots of human nervous integration are found in the behavior of lower forms.*

Cold Spring Harbor Symposia on Quantitative Biology. Vol. XVII. 1952. The Neuron. Cold Spring Harbor, The Biological Laboratory. *This symposium by many specialists represents the last word on the concept of the neuron. For the advanced student.*

Detwiler, S. R. 1943. Vertebrate Photoreceptors. New York, The Macmillan Co. *A technical account of the structure and function of the retina of vertebrates. Mainly for the advanced student.*

Eccles, J. C. 1957. The Physiology of Nerve Cells. Baltimore, The Johns Hopkins Press. *A summary of the present status of certain concepts of nervous integration, including the architecture of the neuron and the transmitter substances of the central nervous system.*

Gardner, E. 1947. Fundamentals of Neurology. Philadelphia, W. B. Saunders Co. *A concise and accurate discussion of the subject. One of the best works on neurology for the beginning student.*

Geldard, F. A. 1953. The Human Senses. New York, John Wiley & Sons, Inc. *A summary of the latest theories on sense perception.*

Pfeiffer, J. 1955. The Human Brain. New York, Harper & Brothers. *A popular account of the mechanism of the brain and how it operates in daily life. It can serve as a good introduction to the study of the more intricate and complicated integrations of the nervous system.*

Sherrington, C. S. 1947. The Integrative Action of the Nervous System, rev. ed. New Haven, Yale University Press. *A classical work on the structural and functional plan of the nervous system. The basic concepts of neurophysiology laid down in this work have been little altered since its publication.*

Thruelsen, R., and J. Kobler (editors). 1959. Adventures of the Mind. New York, Alfred A. Knopf, Inc. *An appraisal of the significant ideas and advances in knowledge of the present era by competent authorities from many disciplines. A stimulating book for the zoology student.*

chapter 32

Reproductive and endocrine systems

There is a logical reason for considering the reproductive and endocrine systems together. Nearly all the principal endocrine glands influence sex and reproduction in some way and in turn they are influenced by the reproductive organs. Various endocrine glands are concerned with every step of the reproductive cycle, including the development and implantation of the fertilized egg, the maintenance of pregnancy, and the development of the mammary glands. Our growing knowledge of the role of hormones in reproduction has been put to practical use with the administration of hormones for the correction of sexual abnormalities and maladjustments.

HISTORICAL BACKGROUND OF SPONTANEOUS GENERATION*

Spontaneous generation, or **abiogenesis,** is the belief that life can originate without pre-existing life or from inorganic matter. This is in contrast to **biogenesis,** the theory that life always originates from previous life. A belief in spontaneous generation was natural before man had developed the basic concepts of cause and effect or before he had mastered the valuable scientific procedure of controlled experiment. Aristotle himself believed in spontaneous generation, at least for certain groups of animals, and most biologists considered him 'the supreme authority.

*Refer to Chapter 5, Principle 7.

The belief in abiogenesis often assumed grotesque forms, such as frogs arising from mud, mice from putrefied matter, insects from dew, etc. Before the advent of the microscope, belief that small organisms came out of nonliving matter was the only viewpoint one could take. If a beaker of blood were left standing open for a few days, it would teem with maggots, even though no flies were visible. It was quite natural that no association was made between the maggots and the flies.

Francesco Redi, an Italian physician, in 1668 exposed meat in jars, some of which were uncovered and others covered with parchment and wire gauze. The meat in all three kinds of vessels spoiled, but only the open vessels had maggots, and he noticed that flies were constantly entering and leaving these vessels. He concluded that if flies had no access to the meat, no worms would be found there. On the other hand, John T. Needham, an English Catholic priest, boiled mutton broth and put it in containers corked and closely sealed and found after a few days the medium was swarming with microscopic organisms (1748). He concluded that spontaneous generation was real, for he thought that he had killed all living organisms by boiling the broth and that he had excluded the access of others by the precautions he took in sealing the tubes. However, an Italian investigator, Lazaro Spallanzani (1767), was critical of Needham's experiments and conducted experiments which led to a telling blow against the theory of abiogenesis. He thoroughly boiled extracts of vegetables and meat, placed these extracts in clean vessels, and sealed the necks of the flasks hermetically in flame. He then immersed the sealed flasks in boiling water for several minutes to make sure that all germs were destroyed. As controls he left some tubes open to the air. At the end of two days he found the open flasks swarming with organisms; the others contained none. However, this experiment did not settle the issue, for the advocates of spontaneous generation maintained that air, which Spallanzani had excluded, was necessary for the production of new organisms or that the method he used had destroyed the vegetative power of the medium. When oxygen was discovered (1774), the opponents of Spallanzani seized upon this as the vital principle which he had destroyed in his experiments.

Pasteur (1861) answered the objection of a lack of air by introducing fermentable material into a flask with a long S-shaped neck which was opened to the air. The flask and its contents were then boiled for a long time. Afterward the flask was cooled and left undisturbed. No fermentation occurred, for all organisms that entered the open end were deposited on the floor of the neck and did not reach the flask contents. When the neck of the flask was cut off, the organisms in the air could fall directly on the fermentable mass and fermentation occurred within it in a short time. The conclusion which Pasteur drew from this experiment was that if suitable precautions were taken to keep out the germs and their reproductive elements (eggs, spores, etc.), no fermentation or putrefaction could take place.

REPRODUCTIVE SYSTEM*

Reproduction makes possible the continuity of the race. Without such provision the race would become extinct in one generation. Although the earliest forms of

------

*Refer to Chapter 5, Principle 8.

life undoubtedly came from nonliving substance, there is no convincing evidence that such is occurring today.

The importance of reproduction is shown in the physical and physiological activities necessary to ensure the fertilization of the eggs, the many methods of breeding, and the different devices for taking care of the offspring during its development. Much of the animal's life is focused upon the varied aspects of sex and reproduction, morphological as well as physiological. Morphologically, the secondary sex characters, such as the mane of the lion, the gorgeous colors of male birds, the size and strength of the bull and the male fur seal, are due to certain aspects of reproduction. Physiologically, patterns of behavior have evolved because of the basic urge for reproduction. Many of the altruistic instincts of man and other animals have developed from the care that is bestowed upon the helpless young and the provisions that are made to ensure their survival.

There are two main types of reproduction, **asexual** and **sexual**. The asexual involves only one parent and no special organs or cells. Sexual reproduction involves, as a rule, two parents, each of which contributes one gamete or special cell to a union known as the zygote. Variant forms of sexual reproduction are the union of nuclei in the paramecium and the development of the egg without fertilization in parthenogenesis. There are usually two kinds of gametes, the **ovum** (egg) and the **spermatozoan.** Eggs are produced by the female, are nonmotile, and contain a great amount of yolk. Sperm are formed by the male, are motile, and are relatively small. The union of egg and spermatozoan is called **fertilization,** and the fused cell so formed is known as the **zygote,** which develops into a new individual.

Sexual reproduction is of universal occurrence among all higher forms and has certain biological advantages and disadvantages over the asexual method. One of its advantages is that the characteristics of two organisms can combine and varia-

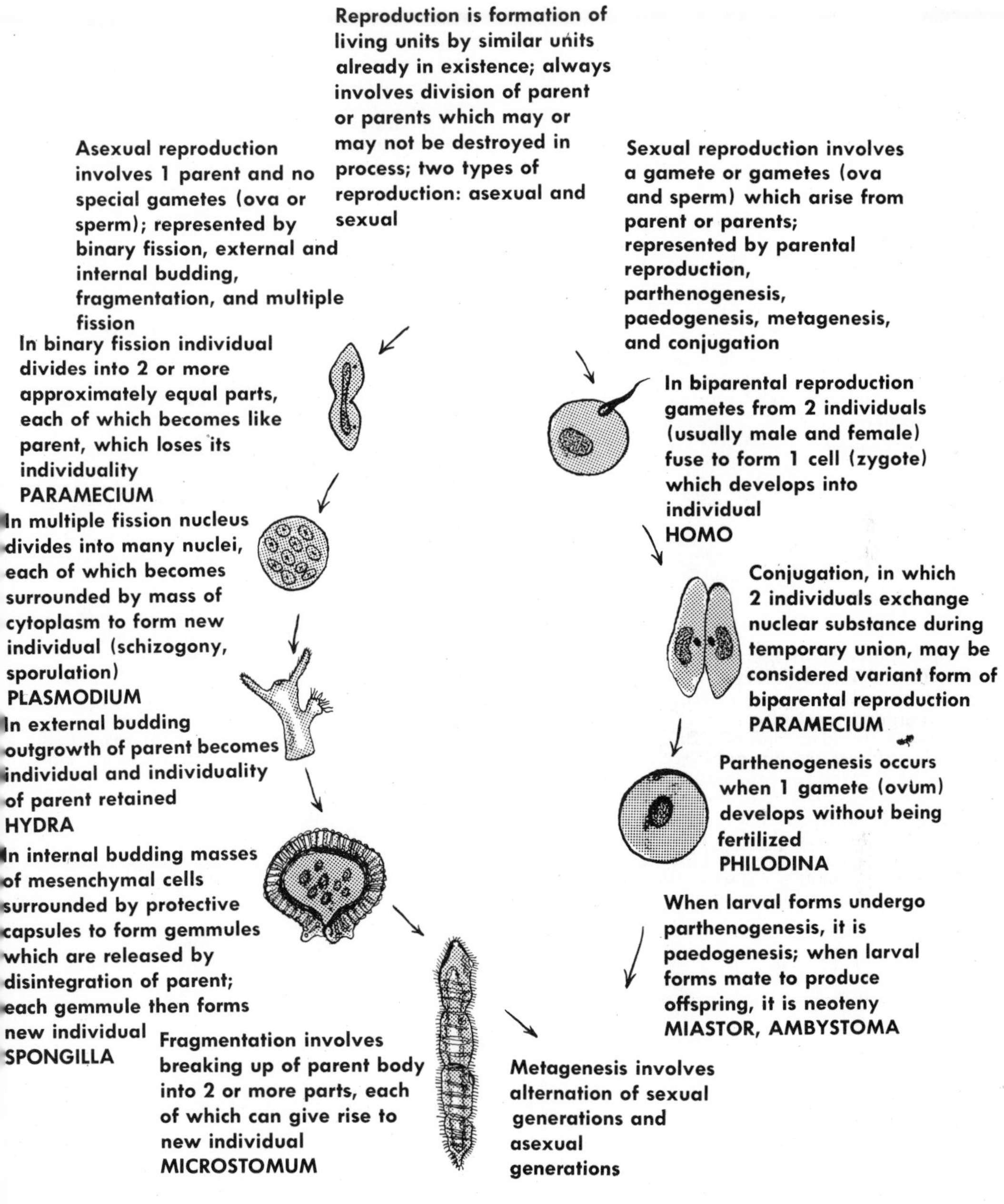

Reproduction is formation of living units by similar units already in existence; always involves division of parent or parents which may or may not be destroyed in process; two types of reproduction: asexual and sexual

Asexual reproduction involves 1 parent and no special gametes (ova or sperm); represented by binary fission, external and internal budding, fragmentation, and multiple fission

In binary fission individual divides into 2 or more approximately equal parts, each of which becomes like parent, which loses its individuality
PARAMECIUM

In multiple fission nucleus divides into many nuclei, each of which becomes surrounded by mass of cytoplasm to form new individual (schizogony, sporulation)
PLASMODIUM

In external budding outgrowth of parent becomes individual and individuality of parent retained
HYDRA

In internal budding masses of mesenchymal cells surrounded by protective capsules to form gemmules which are released by disintegration of parent; each gemmule then forms new individual
SPONGILLA

Fragmentation involves breaking up of parent body into 2 or more parts, each of which can give rise to new individual
MICROSTOMUM

Sexual reproduction involves a gamete or gametes (ova and sperm) which arise from parent or parents; represented by parental reproduction, parthenogenesis, paedogenesis, metagenesis, and conjugation

In biparental reproduction gametes from 2 individuals (usually male and female) fuse to form 1 cell (zygote) which develops into individual
HOMO

Conjugation, in which 2 individuals exchange nuclear substance during temporary union, may be considered variant form of biparental reproduction
PARAMECIUM

Parthenogenesis occurs when 1 gamete (ovum) develops without being fertilized
PHILODINA

When larval forms undergo parthenogenesis, it is paedogenesis; when larval forms mate to produce offspring, it is neoteny
MIASTOR, AMBYSTOMA

Metagenesis involves alternation of sexual generations and asexual generations

Figure 556. Types of reproduction.

tions can be multiplied. This affords evolution a greater variety of forms to pick from in natural selection. Recombination of characters makes possible wider and more diversified evolution. The chief disadvantages of the sexual method are

the hazards involved in the meeting of eggs and sperm and the possibilities of unfavorable growing conditions. Elaborate devices must be produced to ensure fertilization and to take care of the offspring.

Reproductive and endocrine systems 673

SPERM

Function of testis to produce sperm in its seminiferous tubules and sex hormones in its interstitial tissue; in lower species (fishes and salamanders) seminiferous tubules short, lobulated structures and all developing sperm cells in 1 part of tubule tend to be approximately at same stage of development.

In higher species (including frog and man) seminiferous tubules are long and their walls contain sperm cells in various stages of development

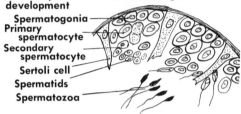

Spermatogonia
Primary spermatocyte
Secondary spermatocyte
Sertoli cell
Spermatids
Spermatozoa

In final maturing of sperm, testes of vertebrates may be divided into 2 types In 1 type (certain fishes, salamanders, and frogs) anterior part of sperm duct does not form convoluted epididymis, and sperm mature and are stored in testis; this type of testis best suited for seasonal activity when sperm discharged at one time. In other type (higher vertebrates) sperm become physiologically functional only in convoluted epididymis where they are also stored; this type best adapted for more or less continuous reproduction

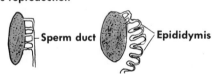

Sperm duct — — Epididymis

OVA

Ova formed in ovaries which vary among different vertebrate classes; 2 ovaries of frog saccular because interiors represented by large lymph spaces; each ovarian sac consists of 2 membranes, theca externa and theca interna; between these, young ova in various stages of development; each ovum surrounded by follicle cells (for nourishment) which are left behind when mature egg discharged into body cavity through rupture in theca membranes

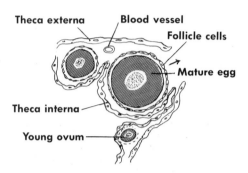

Theca externa — Blood vessel
Follicle cells
Mature egg
Theca interna
Young ovum

In mammalian ovary developing egg with its surrounding cells called Graafian follicle. As egg or ovum enlarges, split appears between outer and inner layers of cells and follicular cavity formed; this cavity filled with liquor folliculi which contains hormone estrogen; when mature follicle ruptures, freed egg surrounded with fuzzy coat of follicle cells

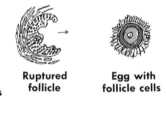

Ruptured follicle
Egg with follicle cells

Figure 557. Comparison of male and female gamete formation in vertebrates.

Asexual reproduction

Asexual reproduction is found only among the simpler forms of life, such as protozoans, coelenterates, bryozoans, and a few others. It is absent among the higher invertebrates (mollusks and arthropods) and all vertebrates. Even in phyla in which it occurs, most of the members employ the sexual method. Asexual reproduction ensures rapid increase in numbers where the differentiation of the organism has not advanced to the point of forming highly specialized gametes.

The forms of asexual reproduction are fission, budding (both internal and external), fragmentation, and sporulation. **Fission** is common among protozoans and to a limited extent among metazoans. In this method the body of the parent is divided into two approximately equal parts, each of which grows into an individual similar to the parent. Fission may be

674

either transverse or longitudinal. **Budding** is an unequal division of the organism. The new individual arises as an outgrowth (bud) from the parent. This bud develops organs like that of the parent and then usually detaches itself. If the bud is formed on the surface of the parent, it is an external bud, but in some cases internal buds, or **gemmules**, are produced. Gemmules are collections of many cells surrounded by a dense covering in the body wall. When the body of the parent disintegrates, each gemmule gives rise to a new individual. External budding is common in the hydra and internal budding in the fresh-water sponges. Bryozoans also have a form of internal bud called statoblast. **Fragmentation** is a method in which an organism breaks into two or more parts, each capable of becoming a complete animal. This method is found among the Platyhelminthes, Nemertinea, and Echinodermata. **Sporulation** is a method of multiple fission in which many cells are formed and enclosed together in a cystlike structure. Sporulation occurs in a number of protozoan forms.

Sexual reproduction

Sexual reproduction is the general rule in the animal kingdom. It is a process involving a gamete or gametes. **Conjugation** among protozoans comes under this method, for two individuals fuse together temporarily and exchange micronuclear material. Other forms of sexual reproduction occur in protozoans, in which there is a union between two special cells. These cells may be alike (**isogametes**) or they may be different (**anisogametes**). Usually the difference is one of size between the gametes, but in certain cases one kind of gamete may be motile and the other nonmotile. In some cases it is difficult to distinguish sex, for although two parents are involved, they cannot be designated as male and female. Work by Sonneborn and others on certain distinctive strains of paramecia would indicate the beginning of sex distinctions, for the members of some strains will not conjugate among themselves but only with those of another strain.

Among metazoans, some individuals can be called **male** and others **female**. Organs

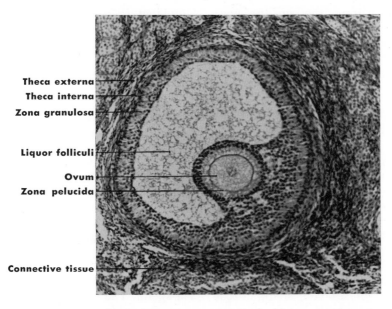

Theca externa
Theca interna
Zona granulosa

Liquor folliculi

Ovum
Zona pelucida

Connective tissue

Figure 558. Enlarged view of Graafian follicle, showing ovum or egg in position. Follicle is nearing maturity and is about ready to rupture and discharge egg. In human ovary usually only one ovum ruptures each four weeks during active life of ovary. (Courtesy J. W. Bamberger.)

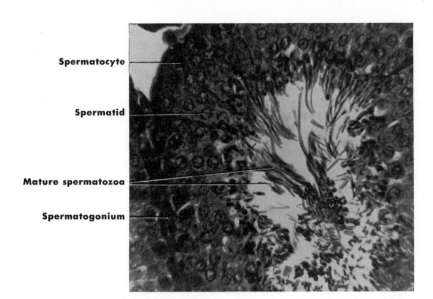

Spermatocyte

Spermatid

Mature spermatozoa

Spermatogonium

Figure 559. Section through testis of rat, showing seminiferous tubule with different stages of sperm formation. Mature sperm are nearest fluid-filled center of tubule; between them and outermost part of tubular wall are various stages of sperm formation. In rat, each spermatogonium has 42 chromosomes, but by meiosis this number is reduced to 21 in each sperm. Corresponding figures for human being would be 46 and 23. (Courtesy J. W. Bamberger.)

that produce the germ cells are known as **gonads.** The gonad which produces the sperm is called the **testis** (Figure 559) and that which forms the egg, the **ovary** (Figure 558). The gonads represent the **primary sex organs,** the only sex organs found in certain groups of animals. Most metazoans, however, have various **accessory sex organs.** In the primary sex organs the sex cells undergo many complicated changes during their development, the details of which are described in a later section. In our present discussion we shall point out the various types of sexual reproduction—biparental reproduction, parthenogenesis, paedogenesis, and hermaphroditism.

Biparental reproduction. The common method of sexual reproduction involves two separate and distinct individuals, male and female. Each of these has its own reproductive system and produces only one kind of sex cell, spermatozoan or ovum, but never both. Nearly all vertebrates and many invertebrates have separate sexes, and such a condition is called **dioecious.**

Parthenogenesis. This is a modification of sexual reproduction in which an unfertilized egg develops into a complete individual. It is found in rotifers, plant lice, certain ants, bees, and crustaceans. Usually parthenogenesis occurs for several generations and is followed by a biparental generation in which the egg is fertilized. In some cases parthenogenesis appears to be the only form of reproduction. The queen bee is fertilized only once by a male (drone). She stores the sperm in her seminal receptacles and as she lays her eggs she can either fertilize the eggs or allow them to pass unfertilized. The fertilized eggs become females (queens or workers); the unfertilized eggs become males (drones).

Artificial parthenogenesis was discovered in 1900. Eggs that normally are fertilized can be artificially induced to develop without fertilization or the presence of sperm. The agents employed are dilute organic acids, hypertonic salt solutions, and mechanical pricking with a needle. Eggs of certain invertebrates, such as those of the sea urchin, were first used,

676

but later vertebrate eggs were successfully induced to develop without fertilization. Many frogs of both sexes were developed beyond metamorphosis. Rarely do such forms complete development and they are usually smaller than normal ones. In recent years even a mammal (rabbit) has resulted from a stimulated unfertilized egg.

Paedogenesis. Parthenogenesis among larval forms is called **paedogenesis.** It is known to occur in *Miastor* (a gallfly) in which eggs produced by immature forms develop parthenogenetically into other larvae. Whenever larval forms mate and produce fertile eggs, the condition is called **neoteny.** The most striking example of this is the tiger salamander *(Ambystoma tigrinum)* which in certain parts of its range is found to mate in a larval (axolotl) form. Such larvae can be transformed into adults under certain conditions.

Hermaphroditism. Animals that have both male and female organs in the same individual are called hermaphrodites and the condition is called **hermaphroditism.** In contrast to the dioecious state of separate sexes, hermaphroditism is called **monoecious.** Many lower animals (flatworms, hydra) are hermaphroditic. Most of them do not reproduce by self-fertilization, but the individuals exchange germ cells with each other in cross-fertilization. The earthworm ensures that its eggs are fertilized by the copulating mate, as well as vice versa. Another way of preventing self-fertilization is by developing the sex products at different times. In some monoecious forms the sperm are formed first and the eggs later (**protandry**), but this condition may be reversed (**protogyny**). However, some hermaphrodites have regular self-fertilization, such as tapeworms and certain snails.

Reproductive systems in invertebrates and vertebrates

The basic plan of the reproductive systems is similar in all animals. Many structural differences are found among the ac-cessory sex organs, depending upon the habits of the animals, their methods of fertilizing their eggs, their care of the young, etc. Many invertebrates have reproductive systems as complex as those of vertebrates, as shown by flatworms, snails, earthworms, and others. There are often complicated accessory sex organs, such as reproductive ducts, penis, seminal vesicles, yolk glands, uterus, seminal receptacles, genital chambers, etc. In vertebrate animals the reproductive and excretory systems are often referred to as the **urogenital system** because of their close connection. This association is very striking in their embryonic development and their use of common ducts. The male urogenital system usually has a more intimate connection than has the female. This is the case with those forms (some fish and amphibians) that have an opisthonephros kidney. In these the **Wolffian duct** which drains the opisthonephros also serves as the sperm duct. In male reptiles, birds, and mammals in which there is a metanephric kidney with its own independent duct (**ureter**) to carry away waste, the Wolffian duct is exclusively a sperm duct (**vas deferens**). In all of these forms, with the exception of mammals higher than monotremes, the ducts open into a **cloaca.** In higher mammals there is no cloaca, but the urogenital system has an opening separate from the anal opening. The **oviduct** of the female is an independent duct which, however, does open into the cloaca in forms that have a cloaca.

The plan of the reproductive system in vertebrates includes (1) **gonads,** which produce the sperm and eggs; (2) **ducts,** to transport the gametes; (3) **special organs,** for transferring and receiving gametes; (4) **accessory glands** (exocrine and endocrine), to provide secretions necessary for the reproductive process; and (5) **organs** for storage before and after fertilization. This plan is modified among the various vertebrates, and some of the items may be lacking altogether.

Male reproductive system. The male reproductive system in man (Figure 560)

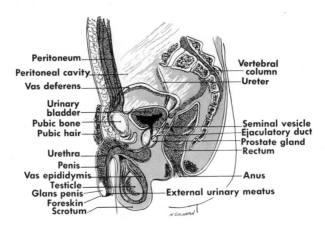

Figure 560. Diagram of median section of male reproductive system in man, showing relations to adjacent structures.

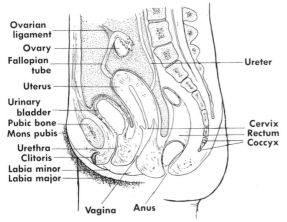

Figure 561. Diagram of median section of human female reproductive system, showing its relation to adjacent structures.

includes testes, vasa efferentia, vas deferens, penis, and glands.

TESTES (TESTICLES). The testes are paired and are responsible for the production and development of the sperm. Each testis is made up of about 500 **seminiferous tubules,** which produce the sperm, and the **interstitial** tissue, lying among the tubules, which produces the male sex hormone (testosterone). The two testes are housed in the scrotal sac, which hangs down as an appendage of the body. The scrotum acts as a thermoregulator for protecting the sperm against high tempera-

tures. Sperm apparently will not form at body temperatures, although they are able to do so in elephants and birds (with very high temperatures). In some mammals (many rodents) the testes are retained within the body cavity except during the breeding season, when they descend through the inguinal canals into the scrotal sacs.

VASA EFFERENTIA. Vasa efferentia are small tubes connecting the seminiferous tubules to a coiled **vas epididymis** (one for each testis) which serves for the storage of the sperm.

VAS DEFERENS. This tube is a continuation of the epididymis and runs to the urethra which it joins opposite its mate from the other testis. From this point the urethra serves to carry both sperm and urinary products.

PENIS. The penis is the external intromittent organ through which the urethra runs. The penis contains erectile tissue for distention during the copulatory act.

GLANDS. There are at least three pairs of exocrine glands (those with ducts) which open into the reproductive channels. Fluid secreted by these glands furnishes food to the sperm, lubricates the passageways of the sperm and counteracts the acidity of the urine, so that the sperm will not be harmed. The first of these glands is the **seminal vesicle,** which opens into each vas deferens before it meets the urethra. Next are the **prostate glands,** which are really a single fused gland in man; it secretes into the urethra. Near the base of the penis lies the third pair of glands, **Cowper's glands,** which also discharge into the urethra. The secretions of these glands form a part of the seminal discharge.

Female reproductive system. The female reproductive system (Figure 561) contains ovaries, oviduct, uterus, vagina, and vulva.

OVARIES. The ovaries are paired and are contained within the abdominal cavity, where they are held in position by ligaments. Each ovary is about as large as an

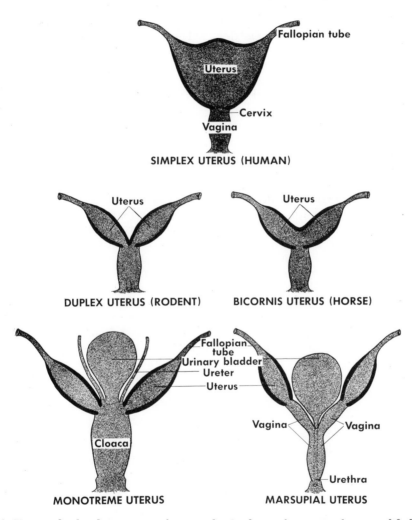

Figure 562. Uteri and related structures of mammals. Oviducts of a mammal are modified to form a uterus for development of the young and a vagina for reception of male penis. Most primitive condition is found in monotremes which lack a vagina but have a cloaca. They are the only mammals that lay eggs. Marsupials have a double vagina and uterus because their oviducts are only partially fused at the bases. Placental mammals, on the other hand, have a single fused vagina with uteri in progressive stages of fusion. In some (rodents) the uterus is two horned or duplex; in others (artiodactyles) the bases of oviducts are partly fused and form bicornis (bicornate) type; in a few (primates) the uterus is a single median cavity (simplex). In carnivores and some others there is an intermediate type (not shown) in which two uteri are united at their posterior ends with a single cervical opening (bipartite uterus).

almond and contains many thousands of developing eggs (ova). Each egg develops within a Graafian follicle that enlarges and finally ruptures to release the mature egg (Figure 558). During the fertile period of the woman about thirteen eggs mature each year, and usually the ovaries may alternate in releasing an egg. Since the female is fertile for only some thirty years, only about 400 eggs have a chance to reach maturity; the others degenerate and are absorbed.

OVIDUCT (FALLOPIAN TUBE). These egg-carrying tubes are not closely attached to the ovaries but have funnel-shaped ostia for receiving the eggs when they emerge from the ovary. The oviduct is lined with cilia for propelling the egg in its course. The two ducts open into the upper corners of the uterus, or womb.

UTERUS. The uterus is specialized for housing the embryo during the nine months of its intrauterine existence. It is provided with thick muscular walls, many blood vessels, and a specialized lining, the endometrium. The uterus varies with different mammals. It was originally paired but tends to fuse in higher forms. The different types are illustrated in Figure 562.

VAGINA. This large muscular tube runs from the uterus to the outside of the body. It is adapted for receiving the male's penis and for serving as the birth canal during the expulsion of the fetus from the uterus. Where the vagina and uterus meet, the uterus projects down into the vagina to form the cervix.

VULVA. The vulva refers to the external genitalia and includes two folds of skin covered with hair, the labia majora; a smaller pair of folds within the labia majora, the labia minora; a small erectile organ, the clitoris, at anterior junction of the labia minora; and a fleshy elevation above the labia majora, the mons veneris. The opening into the vagina is the vestibule which is normally closed in the virgin state by a membrane, the hymen.

Homology of sex organs

There is a correspondence between the organs of the reproductive systems of the two sexes. For every structure in the male system, there is a homologous one in the female. This does not mean they have the same functions in the two sexes, for the various organs of the two sexes perform functions peculiar to each sex. Although homologous structures may be well developed in both sexes, many of them are functional in one sex and their homologues in the other may be vestigial and nonfunctional. To understand this sex organ homology, it is necessary to observe the way in which the reproductive systems have arisen in embryonic development. Although sex is probably determined at the time of fertilization, it is not until many weeks later that the distinct sex characters associated with one or the other sex are recognized. Before this time

Table 9 Organ homologies of male and female systems

Male	Indifferent stage of embryo	Female
Testis	Genital ridge	Ovary
Vas deferens	Wolffian duct	Vestigial
Epididymis	Wolffian body	Vestigial
Appendix of testis	Müllerian duct	Uterus, vagina, Fallopian tube
Penis	Genital tubercle	Clitoris
Glans penis		Glans clitoris
Anal surface of penis	Genital folds	Labia minora
Scrotum	Genital swellings	Labia majora

the external genitalia of the two sexes cannot be distinguished. The hormonal interpretation of sex shows how slight the differences are between the two sexes. The animal is a chemical hermaphrodite and bears the possibilities of becoming either sex, depending upon the balance of the sex hormones.

Some of the chief homologies of the male and female reproductive systems are shown in Table 9.

Origin of reproductive cells

Protoplasm is commonly divided into two types, **somatoplasm** and **germ plasm.** The body cells are made up of somatoplasm and are called **somatic cells;** reproductive cells are formed of germ plasm and are called **germ cells.** All the somatic cells die with the individual. The germ plasm is continuous from generation to generation, whereas the somatoplasm is formed anew at each generation. At the present time this continuity is recognized as residing in the chromosomes and so the chromatin material of the nucleus is considered to be the germ plasm and the cell cytoplasm the somatoplasm. The distinction, however, between somatic and germ cells, as mentioned in another section, is not absolutely rigid.

In many animals the germ cells are set apart very early in the development of the egg. This is the case with certain invertebrates, such as *Miastor* and *Sagitta*, in which it is possible to distinguish a certain region of the egg (zygote) which is going to give rise to the germ cells later on. In higher forms the germ cells are recognized at much later stages. Both germ cells and somatic cells have come from the same one-celled zygote but have differentiated in different ways. Somatic cells have undergone a greater differentiation, for they have a greater variety of functions to perform. Germ cells are specialized for the process of fertilization, for initiating the process of cleavage and development, and for the nourishment of the embryo.

Gametogenesis (Figure 563). Quite early, then, in the life of the organism germ cells are differentiated from the somatic cells. The earliest germ cells recognizable are called **primordial germ cells.** These multiply and migrate to the site of the gonads. When the gonads develop, these primordial germ cells are incorporated within them. In higher forms, birds and mammals, it appears that all future germ cells arise from the germinal epithelium of the gonads. In the gonads these early germ cells remain quiescent until the organism reaches sexual maturity. In man, this time of sexual maturity is called **puberty.** The germ cells undergo a series of transformations called **gametogenesis,** or the formation of the mature gametes. The first step in this transformation is a rapid multiplication of the cells by ordinary mitotic division (see pages 60 to 66). In the ovary these dividing cells are called **oögonia;** in the testis they are **spermatogonia.** Both oögonia and spermatogonia have the same number of chromosomes as the somatic cells; that is, the diploid number (2n). In man, this number is 46 divided into 23 pairs. In each pair, one chromosome has come from the female parent and one from the male. The members of a pair are called **homologous chromosomes.** In the final differentiation of the sex cells, half of the chromosomes are going to be lost to each cell, so that the mature gametes have only one member of each homologous pair, or a **haploid** (n) number of chromosomes. In man, each egg and each sperm has 23 chromosomes.

The process of gametogenesis, or maturation of the germ cells, involves a change not found in ordinary mitosis—that is, a reduction of the chromosomes. This nuclear change is called **meiosis** and should be carefully distinguished from mitosis. In ordinary mitosis each of the two daughter cells receives exactly the same number and kind of chromosomes. The chief function of mitosis is to multiply the number of cells (or individuals in Protozoa). In contrast to mitosis, meiosis is concerned with nuclear reorganization and genetic reassortment. In meiosis there are two nuclear divisions, known as the first and second maturation

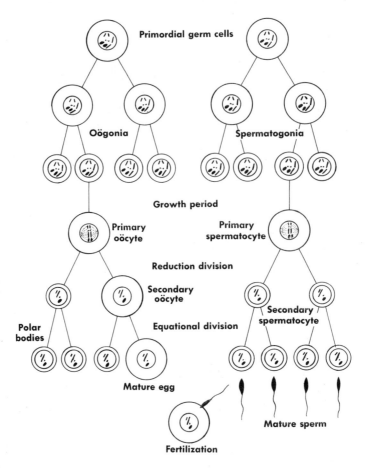

Figure 563. Process of gametogenesis, or formation of germ cells. Oögenesis shown on left, spermatogenesis on right.

divisions, each of which is different from ordinary mitosis.

Although the same essential processes are involved in the maturation of both sperm and eggs, there are some minor differences. Gametogenesis in the testis is called **spermatogenesis** and in the ovary, **oögenesis.**

Spermatogenesis (Figure 563). Spermatogenesis occurs in the walls of the many seminiferous tubules of the testis (Figure 559). These tubules contain the differentiating sex cells which are arranged to form a stratified layer about five to eight cells deep. The outermost layers are made up of spermatogonia which have increased in number by ordinary mitosis. Each spermatogonium increases in size and be-

comes a **primary spermatocyte.** Before the primary spermatocyte undergoes the first maturation division, its chromosomes come together in homologous pairs (**synapsis**). Each pair of homologous chromosomes is made up of one paternal and one maternal chromosome. After synapsis, each member of the chromosome pair appears doubled either by the formation of a new chromosome from the nucleus or by a splitting of each homologous chromosome into two **chromatids.** As a result each pair of homologous chromosomes appears as a bundle of four components called a **tetrad.** There are as many tetrads as there are haploid number of chromosomes (twenty-three in man).

These chromosomes, at first elongated

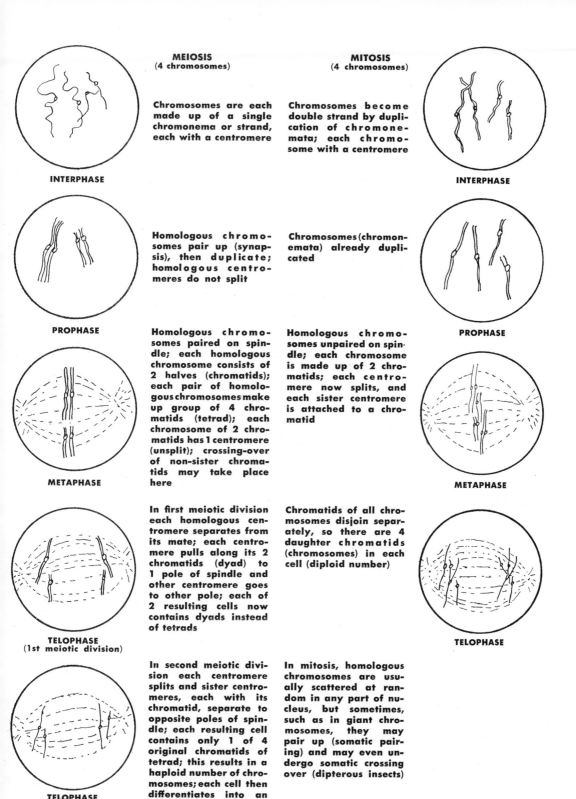

MEIOSIS (4 chromosomes) | **MITOSIS** (4 chromosomes)

INTERPHASE

Chromosomes are each made up of a single chromonema or strand, each with a centromere

Chromosomes become double strand by duplication of chromonemata; each chromosome with a centromere

INTERPHASE

PROPHASE

Homologous chromosomes pair up (synapsis), then duplicate; homologous centromeres do not split

Chromosomes (chromonemata) already duplicated

PROPHASE

METAPHASE

Homologous chromosomes paired on spindle; each homologous chromosome consists of 2 halves (chromatids); each pair of homologous chromosomes make up group of 4 chromatids (tetrad); each chromosome of 2 chromatids has 1 centromere (unsplit); crossing-over of non-sister chromatids may take place here

Homologous chromosomes unpaired on spindle; each chromosome is made up of 2 chromatids; each centromere now splits, and each sister centromere is attached to a chromatid

METAPHASE

TELOPHASE (1st meiotic division)

In first meiotic division each homologous centromere separates from its mate; each centromere pulls along its 2 chromatids (dyad) to 1 pole of spindle and other centromere goes to other pole; each of 2 resulting cells now contains dyads instead of tetrads

Chromatids of all chromosomes disjoin separately, so there are 4 daughter chromatids (chromosomes) in each cell (diploid number)

TELOPHASE

TELOPHASE (2nd meiotic division)

In second meiotic division each centromere splits and sister centromeres, each with its chromatid, separate to opposite poles of spindle; each resulting cell contains only 1 of 4 original chromatids of tetrad; this results in a haploid number of chromosomes; each cell then differentiates into an egg or a spermatozoan

In mitosis, homologous chromosomes are usually scattered at random in any part of nucleus, but sometimes, such as in giant chromosomes, they may pair up (somatic pairing) and may even undergo somatic crossing over (dipterous insects)

Figure 564. Chromosome cycle in meiosis and mitosis of a cell with four chromosomes, as in *Ascaris*. Intervening stages between the first and second meiotic divisions are not shown.

and threadlike, now shorten and thicken. In the meantime a spindle is formed between the centrioles, and when the nuclear membrane is dissolved, the tetrads line up around the equator of the spindle. When metaphase occurs the maternal and paternal members of a pair, or the homologous mates, separate, but the double chromosomes do not. At anaphase this separation is completed, so that each homologous member and its double (called a **dyad**) move to one pole and the other double chromosome (dyad) to the other pole. How the different tetrads divide depends on the way they are placed on the spindle. On some spindles all the maternal pairs may face toward one pole and all the paternal toward the other, or they may be mixed. One of the resulting daughter cells (**secondary spermatocytes**) of this division might have all maternal dyads and the other all paternal dyads, or each daughter could have part paternal and part maternal dyads. This division is called the **reduction division** because the two homologous chromosomes, which came together to form a pair in synapsis, have separated from each other.

The second maturation division (equational division) occurs usually just after the first without the intervention of a resting period. It differs from ordinary mitosis in that the chromosomes are haploid in number and the chromatids may differ genetically (in case of crossing-over, etc.) from their original condition. A new spindle is formed in each cell at right angles to the spindle of the first division and the haploid number of dyads are arranged on its equator. The ensuing division results in a separation of the members of the dyads, so that one member (chromatid) goes to one pole and the other to the other pole. The resulting cells are called **spermatids**, and each contains the haploid number (twenty-three) of chromosomes. A spermatid may have all maternal, all paternal, or both maternal and paternal chromosomes in varying proportions. Without further divisions the spermatids are transformed into mature sperm by losing a great deal of cytoplasm, by con-

densing the nucleus into a head, and by forming a whiplike tail.

It will be seen from following the divisions of meiosis that each primary spermatocyte gives rise to four functional sperm, each with the haploid number of chromosomes.

Oögenesis (Figure 563). The early germ cells in the ovary are called oögonia, which increase in number by ordinary mitosis. Each oögonium contains the diploid number of chromosomes. In the human being, after puberty, typically one of these oögonia develops each menstrual month into a functional egg. After the oögonia cease to increase in number, they grow in size and become **primary oöcytes.** Before the first meiotic division, the chromosomes in each primary oöcyte meet in pairs, paternal and maternal homologues, just as in spermatogenesis. They also form tetrads and dyads which behave as in spermatogenesis. When the first maturation (reduction) division occurs, the cytoplasm, however, is divided very unequally. One of the two daughter cells, the **secondary oöcyte,** is large and receives most of the cytoplasm; the other is very small and is called the **first polar body** (polocyte). Each of these daughter cells, however, has received half the nuclear material or chromosomes.

In the second (equational) meiotic division, the secondary oöcyte divides into a large **oötid** and a small polar body. If the first polar body also divides in this division, which sometimes happens, there will be three polar bodies and one oötid. The oötid grows into a functional ovum; the polar bodies disintegrate, for they are nonfunctional. The formation of the nonfunctional polar bodies is necessary to enable the egg to get rid of excess chromosomes, and the unequal cytoplasmic division makes possible a large cell with sufficient yolk for the development of the young. Thus the mature ovum has the haploid number of chromosomes the same as the sperm. However, each primary oöcyte gives rise to only **one** functional gamete instead of four as in spermatogenesis.

Gametes of various animals. Sperm among animals show a greater diversity of form than do ova. A typical spermatozoan is made up of a head, a middle piece, and an elongated tail for locomotion. The head consists of the nucleus containing the chromosomes for heredity and an acrosome for puncturing the egg in fertilization. The total length of the human sperm is 50 to 70 microns. Some toads have sperm which exceed 2 mm. (2,000 microns) in length. Most sperm, however, are microscopic in size. Some invertebrates have sperm which vary from the typical form. *Ascaris* has a short conical-shaped one without a tail, and the crayfish has one with radially arranged prongs. All sperm are able to swim in a fluid medium.

Ova are oval or spherical in shape and are nonmotile. Usually they contain a great deal of yolk (deuteroplasm) for the nourishment of the young. Mammals' eggs are very small (not more than 0.25 mm.) because the young receive nourishment from the mother. On the other hand, the eggs of some birds and sharks are very large, to supply nutritive material for the developing young before hatching. Some eggs (reptiles and birds) also contain a great deal of albumin which also serves for nourishment. Most eggs are provided with some form of protective coating. This may be in the form of a calcified shell (birds), leathery parchment (reptiles), or albuminous coats (amphibians).

The number of sperm in all animals is greatly in excess of the eggs of corresponding females. The number of eggs produced is related to the chances of the young to hatch and reach maturity. This explains the enormous number of eggs produced by certain fish as compared with the small number produced by mammals.

Fertilization (syngamy)

The formation of a **zygote** by the union of a spermatozoan and an ovum is called **fertilization.** This process restores the original diploid number of chromosomes char-

acteristic of the species, stimulates the zygote to cleavage and development, and combines the hereditary characteristics of both male and female parents. The haploid egg or sperm nucleus is called a **pronucleus.** The union of the sperm and egg pronuclei occurs after the egg is mature. In *Ascaris* the spermatozoan enters the egg before the first maturation division is finished; in the frog and some others, between the formation of the first and second polar body; and in some, after maturation is completed. Sometimes the entire spermatozoan enters the egg, but often the tail is left outside and only the head and a few other structures enter. The male head (pronucleus) absorbs materials from the cytoplasm of the egg and increases to a size similar to that of the egg pronucleus. The two pronuclei meet and the first cleavage division takes place soon after.

If the egg has a shell at the time of fertilization, there is a special pore through which the spermatozoan enters; in other eggs it may enter anywhere. Usually only one sperm enters an egg, for a **fertilization membrane** formed at this time may prevent others from coming in, although the physiological state of the egg cytoplasm may be the real barrier. In the fertilization of some eggs (e.g., sea urchin) when the spermatozoan approaches the egg its tip gives rise to an acrosomal filament by which the spermatozoan is attached to the egg. Cortical changes (cortical reaction) in the outer layer of the egg then occur, such as the formation of a funnel-shaped cone around the acrosomal filament, the disappearance of cortical granules, and the formation of the fertilization membrane. This cortical reaction appears to be necessary for the initiation of development. There is evidence that the egg has in its gelatinous coat a substance called **fertilizin,** which, combining with a substance (antifertilizin) on the sperm, causes the latter to clump together and stick to the surface of the egg. Mammalian sperm are also known to produce an enzyme, **hyaluronidase,** which dissolves away the glue (hyaluronic acid) holding the follicle cells together, so that the spermatozoan can enter and fertilize the egg.

Polyspermy (entrance of more than one sperm) occurs in birds and some others, but only one spermatozoan fuses with the egg pronucleus in such cases. The development of the egg may be induced by certain physical and chemical agents (artificial parthenogenesis), as pointed out in a previous section.

When the egg and spermatozoan come together to form the zygote, the diploid number of chromosomes is restored and there is no doubling of the chromosome number which would be the case if the gametes had the somatic (diploid) number of chromosomes. The reduction division of gametogenesis ensures a continuity of chromosome number from one generation to another.

Types of fertilization. Fertilization is accomplished in one of two ways: (1) by discharging the gametes directly into the water and allowing the germ cells to come together by chance (**external fertilization**) or (2) by discharging the sperm into special cavities of the female so that fertilization occurs there (**internal fertilization**). External fertilization is common among aquatic forms, for the water affords an excellent medium for the locomotion of the motile sperm to the eggs. In this type there are devices employed to ensure fertilization. Some aquatic animals (lamprey, horned dace) make a nest in the form of a depression in the sand and shed their gametes there where they are close together. Others (frogs, toads) extrude their eggs and sperm when the male is clasping the female, so that the gametes have an excellent chance of meeting.

In **internal fertilization** the eggs and sperm are thrown so close together that fertilization is inevitable. This is the type practiced by land forms (and also by some aquatic animals), for external fertilization would expose the delicate germ cells to the air and there would be lacking the fluid medium which is required for all fertilization. Animals vary with respect to the methods they employ in

the transfer of the sperm to the female cavities. Some of the male salamanders deposit on leaves or other objects packets of sperm (spermatophores) which the female picks up with the cloaca. Usually those forms that have internal fertilization have special copulatory organs (penis, claspers, etc.) for transferring the sperm into the female vagina or cloaca.

Breeding habits of animals

The breeding habits of animals vary with different forms. These differences are correlated with methods for fertilization, with kinds of habitats, with the structure of the reproductive systems, with the prenatal care of the young, and with seasonal and physiological changes in animals. Bats mate in the fall and the sperm is stored in the female till the following spring before fertilization occurs. The queen honeybee stores up enough sperm from the drone on one nuptial flight to fertilize all the eggs she lays during her lifetime. Salmon spend most of their lives in the sea but spawn far up inland rivers in fresh water. Eels grow to maturity in freshwater streams but migrate to the sea to spawn. Many animals provide nests of various sorts to take care of the young (birds, some fish). Others have cases for the eggs (insects and spiders). Some female animals carry the eggs attached to the body or to the appendages (crayfish, certain amphibians). Brood pouches for the eggs are provided by such forms as the mussel, the sea horse (a fish), and many others. Social insects (bees and ants) have huge colonial nests organized on a complex scale. Mammals are retained in the uterus of the female during early development and later are nourished by the milk from the mammary glands.

Animals may be divided into three classes on the basis of the methods they employ to nourish their young. Those animals that lay their eggs outside the body for development are called **oviparous.** In such cases the eggs may be fertilized inside or outside the body. Some animals retain their eggs in the body (in the oviduct) while they develop, but the embryo derives its sole nourishment from the egg and not from the mother. These are called **ovoviviparous.** In the third type, the egg develops in the uterus, but the embryo early in its development forms an intimate relationship with the walls of the uterus and derives its nourishment directly from food furnished by the mother. Such a type is called **viviparous.** In both of the last two types the young are born alive. Examples of oviparity are found among many invertebrates and vertebrates. All birds are of this type. Ovoviviparity is common among certain fish, lizards, and a few of the snakes. Viviparity is confined mostly to the mammals.

ENDOCRINE SYSTEM

The physiological mechanism of the body is under the control of two systems, nervous and hormonal. Nervous coordination is rapid, for its messages are sent over its extensive network of nerves with the speed of the nervous impulse. In contrast, the hormones produced by the endocrine glands are carried in the blood at a slower pace and their effects are usually longer lasting. A **hormone,** therefore, may be defined as the specific product of an endocrine gland or specialized tissue secreted into the blood which carries it to some part of the body where it produces a definite physiological effect. This effect may be either excitatory or inhibitory in its action. Some hormones, also, have a widespread action on many tissues and organs. This control involves chiefly a catalytic influence on the tissue metabolism of the target organ. There are also chemical coordinators other than hormones, such as carbon dioxide and other metabolites. Such substances are often called parahormones. Although all hormones are organic substances, some are more complex than others.

The chemical structure of many is well known and many are made synthetically. Knowledge about this system is fairly recent, mostly within the last sixty years. The science of its study is called **endocrinology,** which has been put on an ex-

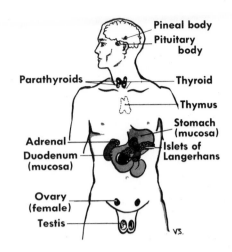

Figure 565. Diagram of human body, showing location of principal endocrine glands. Both male and female represented.

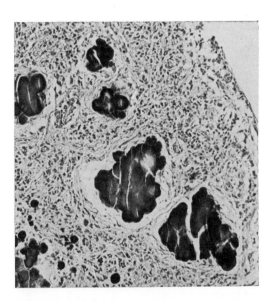

Figure 566. Section of pineal gland with brain sand. These calciferous incrustations are abundant in old glands.

perimental basis. The importance of its study was early recognized because of its application to various medical problems. Upsets in the balance of endocrine activities, hormonal imbalance, are responsible for various functional diseases.

Much of our knowledge about endo-

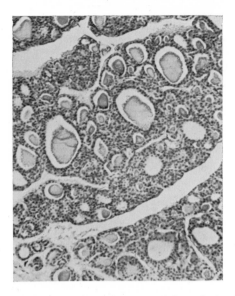

Figure 567. Histological section of thyroid gland, showing follicles filled with colloid. (Courtesy W. Bamberger.)

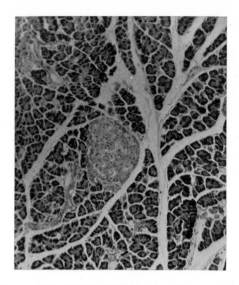

Figure 569. Histological section of mammalian pancreas, showing one large (center) and some smaller islets of Langerhans. (Courtesy J. W. Bamberger.)

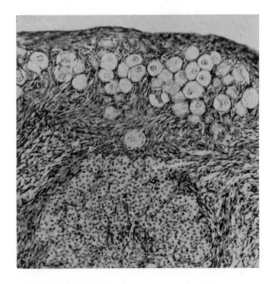

Figure 568. Section of cat ovary, showing corpus luteum (large, rounded mass of light-colored cells in lower center). (Courtesy J. W. Bamberger.)

crinology has been acquired in the following ways:

1. Removing the glands in young and adults and observing any functional or structural disturbances which may arise

2. Grafting the glands or parts of them into animals of different ages

3. Observing the effects of clinical diseases associated with defect in particular glands

4. Injecting extracts of glands or hormones into animals and noting what happens

5. Replacing an excised or diseased gland with glandular extracts and hormones to compensate for the normal loss of hormonal influence

Historical background of hormones

Although the action of chemical substances in certain physiological processes of the body had long been suspected, it was not until 1902 that two English physiologists, William M. Bayliss and Ernest H. Starling, demonstrated the presence and action of an internal secretion. They were interested in determining how the pancreas secreted its digestive juice into the small intestine at the proper time of the digestive process. In an anesthetized dog they tied off a section of the small intestine beyond the duodenum (the part of the intestine next to the stomach) and removed all nerves leading to this tied-off loop, which retained its blood vessels intact. The injection of hydrochloric acid into the blood had no effect upon the secretion of pancreatic juice, but when these two investigators introduced 0.4% hydrochloric acid into the intestinal loop, a well-marked flow of pancreatic juice into the duodenum occurred through the pancreatic duct. When they scraped off some of the mucous membrane lining of the intestine and mixed it with acid, they found that the injection of this extract into the blood caused an abundant flow of pancreatic juice. They concluded that when the partly digested and slightly acid food from the stomach arrives in the small intestine, the hydrochloric acid reacts with something in the mucous lining to produce **secretin,** a small protein, which, carried in the blood stream, stimulates the pancreas to secrete.

In 1889 Von Mering and Minkowski discovered that surgical removal of the pancreas of dogs caused severe symptoms of diabetes and resulted in the animals' death within a few weeks. Many attempts were made to isolate the diabetes-preventive factor in the pancreas, but all were unsuccessful because powerful protein-splitting digestive enzymes produced in the pancreas destroyed the hormone during the extraction procedures. Then in 1920, Dr. Frederick Banting, a young Canadian physician, discovered in the literature that when the pancreatic duct was ligated, the pancreatic cells which secrete the digestive enzymes degenerated but the islets of Langerhans, where insulin is formed, were undisturbed. In collaboration with his former teacher, Professor J. J. R. Macleod, and with Dr. C. H. Best, and with the use of improved surgical techniques, Banting was able to isolate insulin from duct-ligated glands of dogs. The accomplishment meant that millions of diabetics, who prior to the discovery could expect to live no more than a few years at best, could now look forward to nearly normal lives. In 1923 Banting and Macleod were awarded the Nobel Prize.

Plan of hormone regulation

The two types of glands in the animal body are the exocrine and the endocrine. **Exocrine** glands are provided with ducts for discharging their secretions onto a free surface. **Endocrine** glands are ductless and their products are discharged and carried in the blood all over the body, but the hormones are picked out by some specific organ on which they exert a physiological effect. Endocrine glands are similar to the exocrine, although their cells are usually arranged in cords or plates with abundant blood sinusoids. The ductless glands derive their antecedents from the blood and transform them into their characteristic hormones, which are stored in cells or follicles until they are delivered back to the blood.

Secretin and other hormones of the alimentary canal are produced in the duodenal mucosa, which cannot be considered an endocrine gland in the strict meaning of the term. Some glands, such as the pancreas, have both exocrine and endocrine functions. The exocrine part elaborates the important digestive secretion, pancreatic juice, and the endocrine furnishes insulin for carbohydrate metabolism.

The chemical substances called hormones act in very small quantities. Their total mass makes up only a small proportion of the organism. Their general mechanisms of action are slow and long drawn out, although there are some exceptions to this principle; epinephrine acts with considerable speed because it is under direct autonomic nervous control; the slower hormones are secreted in response to hormonal stimulation.

The various hormones overlap each other in their actions. Their interrelations represent one of the most difficult problems in endocrinology. Removal of one kind of endocrine gland often affects other kinds, and some of the hormones are unable to function without the aid of others. Glands such as the adenohypophysis (anterior pituitary) influence practically every other endocrine gland in the body. This may indicate an evolutionary significance in hormonal integration similar to the dominance of the cerebral cortex over the nervous system.

On the basis of their control and influence over physiological processes, hormones may be divided into four categories: (1) hormones concerned with metabolism, (2) hormones of digestion, (3) hormones that regulate growth and development, and (4) hormones that control reproduction.

Endocrine glands in invertebrates

Although most of our knowledge about hormones has been acquired from vertebrates, much information about invertebrate endocrine glands has been obtained in recent years. There is reason to believe that hormones have an equally important role among these simpler forms.

In general, it is difficult to homologize the invertebrate endocrine glands with those in vertebrates, but many hormonal functions are analogous in the two groups. Most endocrine investigations among the invertebrates has been made in the arthropods, especially in crustaceans and insects. The chromatophores or pigment cells of shrimp and crabs are definitely known to be controlled by hormones from the sinus gland in the eyestalk or in regions close to the brain. When the eyestalk (and sinus gland) is removed or sinus gland extracts are injected, the effects on bodily coloration vary with different crustaceans; some darken and others pale under the experimental conditions. Migration or shifting of the retinal pigments of the arthropod compound eye for light adjustments is controlled by a hormone from the sinus gland. Ecdysis, or molting, in crustaceans and insects is also regulated by sinus gland extracts. The rather complicated process of insect metamorphosis (from larva to adult) involves a precise functioning of hormones from the brain and the corpus allatum of the head region. There is some evidence that secondary sex characteristics among invertebrates are under hormonal control. When parasitic castration by the parasite *Sacculina* occurs in male crayfish, sexual changes toward femaleness are known to occur.

Endocrine glands in vertebrates

Hormones of pituitary gland (hypophysis). The **pituitary gland,** or **hypophysis,** produces many hormones which influence many parts of the body. For this reason it is often called the "master gland of the body." It is well protected, for it lies between the roof of the mouth and the floor of the brain in a depression of the sphenoid bone. The weight of the pituitary gland in man is about 0.5 gram. The pituitary is a duplex gland of double embryonic origin. The anterior lobe and intermediate part come from a pouch on the roof of the mouth; the posterior lobe arises from the brain. The anterior lobe makes up about three-fourths of the entire gland.

According to functional organization the pituitary body is classified into the **adenohypophysis,** or portions that come from the mouth region, and the **neurohypophysis,** or portion from the brain. The **hypothalamus** of the brain controls the secretion of the tropic hormones of the pituitary. It controls the secretions of the adenohypophysis through a hypophyseal portal system and the secretions of the neurohypophysis by direct nervous connections. The hypothalamus itself is controlled through nerves from higher nerve centers.

Except for the adrenal medulla the **neurohypophysis** (posterior lobe) is the only gland receiving direct nervous connections. The hormones are formed in the lower hypothalamus and travel down nerves to be stored in the neurohypophysis. An extract from the entire lobe is known as **Pituitrin,** which is made up of more than one fraction. Two of these are **Pitocin (oxytocin),** which contracts smooth muscle, especially of the uterus, and **Pitressin (vasopressin),** which constricts the smooth muscle of the gastrointestinal tract, urinary bladder, gallbladder, and arterioles. Pitressin is also responsible for the antidiuretic effect of the posterior lobe since it stimulates the

690

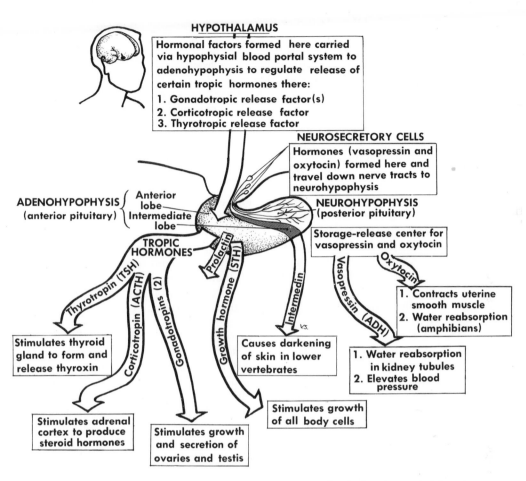

HYPOTHALAMUS

Hormonal factors formed here carried via hypophysial blood portal system to adenohypophysis to regulate release of certain tropic hormones there:

1. Gonadotropic release factor(s)
2. Corticotropic release factor
3. Thyrotropic release factor

NEUROSECRETORY CELLS

Hormones (vasopressin and oxytocin) formed here and travel down nerve tracts to neurohypophysis

ADENOHYPOPHYSIS (anterior pituitary) { Anterior lobe — Intermediate lobe —

NEUROHYPOPHYSIS (posterior pituitary)

Storage-release center for vasopressin and oxytocin

TROPIC HORMONES

Thyrotropin (TSH) · Corticotropin (ACTH) · Gonadotropins (2) · Prolactin · Growth hormone (STH) · Intermedin · Vasopressin (ADH) · Oxytocin

1. Contracts uterine smooth muscle
2. Water reabsorption (amphibians)

Stimulates thyroid gland to form and release thyroxin

Causes darkening of skin in lower vertebrates

1. Water reabsorption in kidney tubules
2. Elevates blood pressure

Stimulates adrenal cortex to produce steroid hormones

Stimulates growth and secretion of ovaries and testis

Stimulates growth of all body cells

Figure 570. Diagram of relations of hypothalamus to pituitary gland, showing varied functions and relations of complex. (Courtesy C. P. Hickman, Jr.)

resorption of water in the renal tubules and reduces the volume of urine excreted. When vasopressin is deficient, diabetes insipidus occurs, in which an excessive amount of urine is excreted.

The **adenohypophysis** (anterior lobe) produces several hormones, all of which are small proteins. One of these is the growth hormone (**somatotropin, STH**). Others stimulate the gonads (**gonadotropins**), the adrenal cortex (**adrenocorticotropin** or **ACTH**), the thyroid gland (**thyrotropin, TSH**), and the mammary glands (**prolactin**). The diabetogenic hormone is also produced here. Another hormone, **intermedin,** is produced in the intermediate part, or, in animals that lack

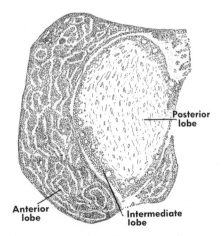

Posterior lobe

Anterior lobe

Intermediate lobe

Figure 571. Histological section of pituitary gland.

this part, in the anterior lobe. This hormone is of doubtful entity in man, but in many vertebrates it stimulates the expansion of the melanophores (pigmented cells) in the adjustment of body coloration to environmental conditions.

The **hypothalamus** elaborates three important tropic hormones—**gonadotropic release factor, corticotropic release factor,** and **thyrotropic release factor**—which are carried by the hypophyseal portal system or by the general circulation to the adenohypophysis, causing it to release its various tropic hormones. In return, these tropic hormones react back (**feedback**) and influence the functions of the nervous system. Thus this plan involves a three-stage hormonal system—releasing factors from the hypothalamus regulate tropic hormones from the adenohypophysis, which in turn regulate the hormone secretions of the respective target glands (gonads, thyroid, etc.). This mechanism of feedback, whereby a target organ can influence its own production positively or negatively by sending back information to an early stage in its synthetic pathway, is not clear in all instances, but it is thought that whenever a feedback occurs it is mediated through the nervous system and reaches the pituitary by way of the hypothalamus. Apparently some pituitary hormones are not subject to feedback control and are secreted independently of the central nervous system. This general scheme shows that parts of the nervous system function as specialized endocrine organs.

Hormones of metabolism. Hormones that affect the metabolic activity of the individual are secreted by the thyroid, parathyroid, pancreas, and adrenal cortex.

THYROID HORMONE (THYROXIN). The thyroid is a double gland, with a lobe on each side of the trachea at the base of the larynx. The lobes may be joined by a connection, the isthmus. Embryologically, the thyroid starts out as an exocrine gland, secreting through the thyroglossal duct into the mouth; this duct is later lost. The thyroid is the largest of all the endocrine organs, weighing from 20 to 30

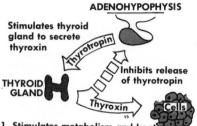

Figure 572. Diagram of relation between thyroxin and thyrotropin.

grams in the human being. The secreting part of the gland consists of tiny spheres (follicles) lined with cuboidal epithelium (Figure 567). These follicles are filled with a colloid, which contains the thyroid hormone **thyroxin.** Its primary function is to regulate the metabolism of the body. A second and more universal function is the regulation of growth, development, and maturation. In lower vertebrates (amphibians) it is necessary for metamorphosis. Hyperfunction of the gland speeds up the metabolic rate; hypofunction slows it down. Since iodine is the principal constituent of thyroxin, deficiency of this chemical in water or food will often produce disturbances in the gland. **Myxedema,** a disease characterized by a low metabolic rate and puffy skin, is caused by the secretion of too little thyroxin and represents a hypothyroid condition. Another hypothyroid condition, **endemic colloid goiter,** is caused by a deficiency of iodine in the diet and may result in a greatly enlarged thyroid gland. When hypothyroidism is present from birth, the condition is known as **cretinism.** Such children are stunted and of low intelligence. Administration of iodine or thyroxin is used in the treatment of hypothyroid conditions. Iodized salt is an effective preventive of endemic colloid goiter.

Hyperthyroidism involves an overactive gland and is characterized by a slight swelling of the gland and the production of a great amount of thyroxin. This causes a high metabolic rate, and it is often called

692

toxic goiter. Other effects may be increase in blood pressure and heart rate, tremors and irritability, and protrusion of the eyeballs. Major treatments now used are (1) surgical removal, (2) use of drugs which inhibit thyroxin, and (3) administration of large doses of radioactive iodine which destroys most of the thyroid cells.

Iodine makes up about 65% of thyroxin, as indicated in the following structural formula:

$$HO- \hexagon -O- \hexagon \overset{I}{\underset{I}{}} - \overset{\overset{H}{|}}{\underset{\underset{H}{|}}{C}} - \overset{\overset{NH_2}{|}}{\underset{\underset{H}{|}}{C}} - COOH$$

Thyroxin

Nearly 1 mg. of iodine is required in our diets each week to supply normal quantities of thyroxin. When stored in the follicles, thyroxin is combined with a globulin to form thyroglobulin which releases thyroxin when the latter passes into the blood.

PARATHYROID HORMONE (PARATHORMONE). Four **parathyroid** glands, all small, are located on the posterior surface of the lateral lobes of the thyroid gland. The hormone-secreting tissue is made up of cords of epitheloid cells closely related to the blood capillaries. The hormone is called **parathormone.** It is a small protein (molecular weight 20,000) whose main function is to regulate the level of blood calcium and phosphorus. These two minerals are necessary for bone growth, for osmotic balance, and for muscle contraction. Deficiency of parathormone decreases blood level of calcium and leads to convulsions and tetany. This sometimes occurs in children. Treatment consists of the injection or feeding of calcium or the injection of the hormone. Hyperparathyroidism is produced by tumors on the glands and causes the calcium to be withdrawn from the bones, thus producing a high blood level of calcium. Under such conditions the bones may become soft and porous or have only localized areas of calcification. Vitamin D promotes the rate of calcium absorption from the intestine. From Figure 573 it will be noted that bone cells withdraw calcium and phosphate from the blood for the production of bone, whereas parathormone draws the minerals from the bones. These two actions are antagonistic and tend to balance each other.

INSULIN FROM ISLET CELLS OF PANCREAS. The pancreas is both an exocrine and an endocrine gland. The exocrine portion produces the digestive secretion, pancreatic juice. The **endocrine** part of the gland consists of the small islets of **Langerhans** which are very numerous and vary greatly in size (Figure 569). They are made up of at least three different kinds of cells, alpha, beta, and delta cells. It is thought that the **beta cells** produce the hormone **insulin,** which is of great importance in the metabolism of fats and carbohydrates. Deficiency of insulin leads to excess sugar in the blood which is excreted in the urine. The hormone appears to be necessary for the storage of glucose as glycogen in the liver and for the oxidation of glucose. Many metabolic disturbances are brought about in **diabetes mellitus,** the disease caused by a lack of insulin. Much urine is excreted, the individual loses weight, and there is an accumulation of incompletely oxidized ketone bodies from fat oxidation. These latter substances are toxic and eventually lead to the death of the patient. The injection of insulin since its discovery in 1922 is very effective and removes all the symptoms for a short time. But repeated injections are necessary, for insulin

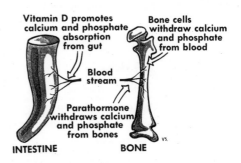

Figure 573. Diagram showing relation of parathormone (parathyrin) to calcium metabolism. Two hormones may be involved—one regulating excretion of phosphorus and the other deposition of calcium in tissues.

does not cure diabetes permanently. Too much insulin will produce convulsions by sweeping the sugar out of the blood. Another hormone, glucagon or the hyperglycemic factor, is produced by the alpha cells and possibly other tissues and causes a breakdown of liver glycogen into glucose.

ADRENAL CORTICAL HORMONES. The adrenal or suparenal gland is a double endocrine organ, being made up of a **cortex** and a **medulla.** Each of these has its own internal secretions, and each has developed differently embryologically. The adrenal cortex has arisen from the same origin (mesodermal) as that of the sex glands; the medulla has an ectodermal origin similar to that of the postganglionic fiber cells of the sympathetic nervous system.

The adrenal cortex is absolutely essential to life; when it is completely removed, most animals will live only a week or two. The cortex has several hormones and it ranks next to the anterior pituitary in endocrine importance. Structurally, the cortex is made up of parallel and looped cords of cells with numerous blood capillaries.

All the adrenocortical hormones are steroid compounds and all are structurally similar. They can be divided into three groups: (1) **glucocorticoids,** such as **cortisone** and **hydrocortisone,** which regulate food metabolism (glucose, proteins, and fats); (2) **mineralocorticoids,** such as **aldosterone** and **desoxycorticosterone,** which control the reabsorption of sodium by kidney tubules as well as the regulation of other salts; and (3) **sex hormones,** which have **androgenic** (chiefly) and **estrogenic** effects to a minor extent. All these hormones are controlled by the corticotropin hormone of the adenohypophysis.

A typical steroid structure may be illustrated by aldosterone:

$$\text{Aldosterone}$$

In Addison's disease, the adrenal cortex degenerates, resulting in a complicated syndrome of altered fluid balance and a bronze pigmentation of the skin. In hyperfunction of the adrenal cortex, a condition which sometimes arises from tumors, male children may become sexually mature precociously, and females take on masculine characters, such as a beard, deep voice, and oversized clitoris.

ADRENAL MEDULLA HORMONES. The cells of the adrenal medulla form the central core of the adrenal gland. Sympathetic fibers secrete at their terminals the hormones **epinephrine** (**Adrenalin**) and **norepinephrine** (**noradrenalin**). Epinephrine is one of the few hormones whose rate of secretion is affected by nervous stimulation. The general action of this hormone centers around emergency functions of the body, such as those of fear, fight, flight, rage, and work. During emotional states epinephrine is secreted in great amounts. Specifically, the hormone causes a rise in blood pressure, increase in heart rate, increase in blood sugar, inhibition of the gastrointestinal tract, decrease in liver glycogen, and hastening of blood coagulation. **Norepinephrine** of the adrenal medulla has a similar effect but has a wider vasoconstrictor influence. Most of these effects can also be produced by stimulating the sympathetic nervous

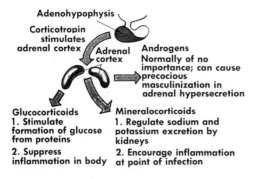

Figure 574. Diagram showing relations of adrenocortical hormones and their functions.

694

system. Epinephrine is one of the simplest hormones known and can be produced synthetically.

Hormones of digestion. Certain hormones influence the secretion and motility of the gastrointestinal tract.

HORMONES OF GASTROINTESTINAL MUCOSA. Several hormones are associated with the activities of the digestive tract. All of these hormones are produced in the mucosa lining. One of these is **gastrin**, produced in the pyloric wall. When food enters the stomach gastrin stimulates the gastric glands to secrete gastric juices. The active principle of this hormone appears to be histamine. The intestinal mucosa produces three hormones which are active in some phase of the digestive process. **Secretion** is formed when acid chyme from the stomach enters the upper intestine; it stimulates the secretion of pancreatic juice. **Cholecystokinin** is liberated from the intestinal mucosa by fatty foods and causes the gallbladder to empty. **Enterogastrone** is also liberated in the small intestine by fatty foods, and when carried by the blood to the stomach it slows down the motility of the stomach. No deficiency diseases have been associated with the undersecretion of the gastrointestinal hormones, and some endocrinologists consider them of minor importance.

Hormones of growth and development. Every step in normal growth and development depends upon one or many hormones.

PITUITARY GROWTH HORMONE. Somato-tropin, **STH,** from the anterior lobe of the pituitary, has a controlling influence over the rate of growth. In excess it produces **gigantism** in the young, so that the period of skeletal and tissue growth is extended beyond the normal period. If this hormone is produced in excess after the person has completed his normal growth, **acromegaly** results. In this condition the bones are greatly thickened and the hands and feet are enlarged. Deficiency of the hormone causes **dwarfism** and the young mature as midgets. The growth hormone also has an "anti-insulin" effect, since it increases blood sugar.

Most of the major hormones influence growth and development in some manner. Deficiency in the production of thyroxin, insulin, adrenocortical hormones, parathormone, or sex hormones may cause stunted growth or improper development.

Hormones that control reproduction. Some male and female organs are endocrine-forming as well as gamete-forming (cytogenic) glands.

MALE SEX HORMONE. Reproduction is a process which involves the coordinated action of many hormones. Those hormones that promote male characteristics are called **androgens;** those that promote female characteristics are **estrogens.** The primary sex organs, testes and ovaries, not only produce sperm and eggs but they also serve as sources for important sex hormones which are concerned with the regulation and control of reproduction. The male sex hormone is called **testosterone** and is produced by the **interstitial**

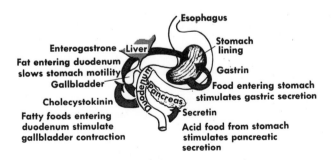

Esophagus
Enterogastrone Liver
Fat entering duodenum slows stomach motility
Gallbladder
Cholecystokinin
Fatty foods entering duodenum stimulate gallbladder contraction
Pancreas
Duodenum
Stomach lining
Gastrin
Food entering stomach stimulates gastric secretion
Secretin
Acid food from stomach stimulates pancreatic secretion

Figure 575. Diagram of actions of gastrointestinal hormones. Under each hormone the stimulus for its secretion and the specific action of the hormone are indicated.

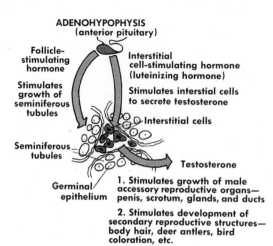

ADENOHYPOPHYSIS
(anterior pituitary)

Follicle-stimulating hormone

Interstitial cell-stimulating hormone (luteinizing hormone)

Stimulates growth of seminiferous tubules

Stimulates interstial cells to secrete testosterone

Interstitial cells

Seminiferous tubules

Germinal epithelium

Testosterone

1. Stimulates growth of male accessory reproductive organs— penis, scrotum, glands, and ducts

2. Stimulates development of secondary reproductive structures— body hair, deer antlers, bird coloration, etc.

Figure 576. Diagram showing hormonal relations and functions of testosterone.

cells (Leydig) located between the seminiferous tubules which produce the sperm. Interstitial cells are not present during childhood but are found in the infant and after puberty. The production of testosterone is stimulated by such gonadotropins as the luteinizing (or the interstitial cell-stimulating) hormone. Testosterone is responsible for the secondary male sex characteristics, such as the beard on the face and the distribution of hair on the body, the character of the voice, and the distribution of fat pads. It is also concerned with the growth and development of the accessory sex characters, penis, seminal vesicle, and prostate gland. When injected into a female the latter often develops secondary male sex characteristics. Testosterone is also responsible for the sex urge and for sexual behavior. Estrogens are also produced by the sustentacular cells (Sertoli) of the seminiferous tubules.

Castration, or the removal of the testes, has long been practiced on domestic animals. Such animals usually become fatter and more docile. If castration is performed on the young animal, the secondary sex characteristics and the accessory sex organs fail to develop; if performed on adults, they undergo retrograde changes. Castration in man (**eunuchism**) will cause the boy's voice to remain high pitched.

Such a castrate is neutral toward sex (without sex desire); if castration is done after puberty, sex urge and potency may remain, although reduced in intensity.

In the condition in which the testes fail to descend into the scrotal sac from the abdominal cavity (**cryptorchidism**), the higher temperature there destroys the sperm and the individual is sterile. However, the interstitial cells are not affected by the higher temperature and the male hormone is produced.

FEMALE SEX HORMONES. Two important hormones are involved in the cyclic sex changes of the female. One of these is **estradiol** (estrogen), which is produced by the cells of the developing Graafian follicles of the ovary. One or more of these follicles enlarge each lunar month, burst open through fluid pressure, and release an ovum, or egg, by the process of **ovulation.** The egg passes into the oviduct where it may be fertilized if sperm are present or else it goes on to the uterus where it degenerates. In the ruptured follicle the follicular cells increase and fill up the cavity left by the egg and follicular fluid. These cells are yellowish in color and the structure they form is called the yellow body, or **corpus luteum,** which lasts only two to three weeks if the egg is unfertilized but throughout the first half of pregnancy if the egg is fertilized. This corpus luteum forms the second female hormone, **progesterone.**

The combined action of these two hormones accounts mainly for the reproductive cycle in the female. Estradiol, for instance, is responsible for the sex changes at puberty, the development of the accessory sex organs, the development of the secondary sex characters (breasts, pubic hair, voice quality, etc.), the initiation of the growth changes in the endometrium, vagina, and other organs, and the production of **estrus,** or heat. Progesterone carries on the growth of the endometrium, makes possible the implantation of the fertilized egg in the uterine wall, and stimulates the development of the mammary glands. Just as testosterone is produced by females as well as males, so the two

696

female sex hormones are also found in the male. The chief commercial source of estradiol is the urine of stallions, male horses. The same hormone has also been obtained from sources outside the animal body, for example, from pussy willows. Another female sex hormone, **relaxin,** is produced by the corpus luteum and causes the pelvic ligaments to relax in childbirth.

Estrus cycle. The females of all mammals, with the possible exception of human beings, show certain cyclic or rhythmic changes in the intensity of the sex urge. Sexual reception at its height, is called **estrus,** or heat, and usually the female will receive the male only during this period. Most mammals have only one estrus period each year, although there are several exceptions. Cats and dogs usually have two each year, whereas rabbits and rats have many. Estrus is closely correlated with the ripening and discharge of the ova. Some animals, such as the cat and rabbit, will ovulate only following copulation; others have spontaneous ovulation. Changes in the uterine lining occur in anticipation of the implantation of a fertilized ovum or ova and involve a thickening of the lining (endometrium) and an increase in the uterine glands and blood vessels. If fertilization of the egg does not occur, these changes revert to their original state. In this estrus cycle all stages are governed by the interplay of the female sex hormones and those of the anterior pituitary gland. The relation of these hormones to each other and to the

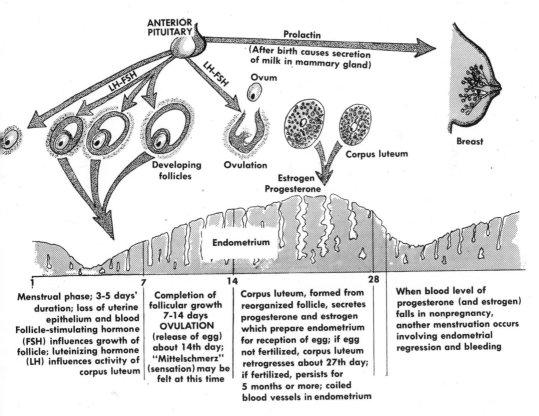

| Menstrual phase; 3-5 days' duration; loss of uterine epithelium and blood Follicle-stimulating hormone (FSH) influences growth of follicle; luteinizing activity of corpus luteum | Completion of follicular growth 7-14 days OVULATION (release of egg) about 14th day; "Mittelschmerz" (sensation) may be felt at this time | Corpus luteum, formed from reorganized follicle, secretes progesterone and estrogen which prepare endometrium for reception of egg; if egg not fertilized, corpus luteum retrogresses about 27th day; if fertilized, persists for 5 months or more; coiled blood vessels in endometrium | When blood level of progesterone (and estrogen) falls in nonpregnancy, another menstruation occurs involving endometrial regression and bleeding |

Figure 577. Diagram of reproductive cycle in human female, showing hormonal-ovarian-endometrial relationships. It will be noted that endometrium undergoes cyclical chain of events (thickness, congestion, etc.) under influence of hormones from ovary—estradiol (estrogen) and progestin (progesterone)—and from pituitary gland—FSH and LH. Another hormone, prolactin, stimulates secretion of milk.

rhythmic changes can best be shown by the menstrual cycle in the human being.

Menstrual cycle. In primate animals, the estrus cycle is largely replaced by periods of bleeding, called **menstruation.** This period on the average occurs every twenty-eight days (in the human being), but it is far from regular. The actual menstrual, or bleeding, periods are of three to five days' duration. Menstruation is the sloughing off of the thickened endometrium which has been developed under the influence of the female sex hormones. If the egg is fertilized and implanted, menstruation does not occur. The initiation of the menstrual flow is due to a marked decline in the hormones progesterone and estra-diol. Ovulation occurs about fourteen day after the beginning of the menstrual pe riod. Following is a summary of the event that occur during a menstrual cycle and the relation of the various hormones to these events.

Just after the menses flow, most of the endometrium has been sloughed off and only a thin lining is left. By means of a gonadotropic hormone (the **follicle-stimu lating hormone,** or **FSH**) from the anterior pituitary, a follicle in the ovary is stimulated to grow. Then the follicular cells secrete estradiol which causes a thickening of the uterine lining but does not cause ovulation. This latter process appears to be due to a balance between the

Table 10. Important endocrine glands and their hormones

Gland	Hormone	Function
Gastric mucosa of stomach	Gastrin	Stimulates secretion of gastric juice
Intestinal mucosa of duodenum	Secretin Enterogastrone Cholecystokinin	Stimulates secretion of pancreatic juice Decreases motility and secretion of stomach Causes gallbladder to contract
Thyroid	Thyroxin (primary) Triiodothyronine	Controls rate of metabolism, growth, and maturation Similar to thyroxin but more rapid in action
Parathyroid	Parathormone	Regulates calcium and phosphorus metabolism
Islets of Langerhans of pancreas	Insulin Glucagon	Controls metabolism of glucose Controls glycogen breakdown in liver
Adrenal cortex	Glucocorticoids (hydrocortisone, cortisone) Mineralocorticoids (androsterone, desoxycorticosterone) Androgens (androsterone and others similar to testosterone)	Control food metabolism, suppress inflammation Control salt and water excretion, promote inflammation Mimic action of testosterone
Adrenal medulla	Epinephrine (adrenin, Adrenalin) Norepinephrine	Raises blood pressure, increases sugar of blood, increases heart rate, mimics action of sympathetic nerves

onadotropic hormones of the pituitary. Estradiol has an inhibitory action on FSH, so that no other follicles are developed. When ovulation occurs, the corpus luteum is formed in the ruptured follicle and becomes the source of the other female sex hormone, progesterone. The corpus luteum is also formed under the stimulating action of hormones from the anterior pituitary, the **luteinizing hormone (LH)** and **luteotropin (LTH) (prolactin)**. Progesterone continues the preparation of the uterine lining as well as the growth of the mammary glands. If the egg is not implanted in the uterine wall, the corpus luteum disappears and its hormone is no longer secreted. Since the endome-trium depends upon progesterone for its maintenance, when this hormone ceases to be secreted the disintegration of the uterine lining with its characteristic flow begins.

The **placenta** must also be considered an endocrine organ. Actually, during the latter part of pregnancy most of the progesterone comes from it because the corpus luteum is decreasing. Estradiol and progesterone are responsible mainly for the development of the mammary glands during the period of pregnancy. Lactation (milk secretion) is the result of another hormone, luteotropin or LTH (prolactin), from the anterior pituitary. This hormone is assisted by those adrenal cortex

Table 10–Cont'd

Gland	Hormone	Function
Adenohypophysis (anterior pituitary)	Growth stimulator (STH)	Regulates somatic cell growth
	Follicle stimulator (FSH)	Regulates growth of follicles in female, spermatogenesis in male
	Interstitial stimulating hormone (ICSH)	Same as FSH
	Luteinizing (LH)	Forms corpus luteum, interstitial cells
	Prolactin (LTH)	Stimulates lactation after alveolar growth; stimulates secretion of corpus luteum hormones
	Thyrotropic (TSH)	Controls thyroid gland
	Adrenocorticotropic (ACTH)	Controls adrenal cortex
	Intermedin	Chromatophore expansion in lower vertebrates
Neurohypophysis (posterior pituitary)	Vasopressin (Pitressin, anti-diuretic hormone, ADH)	Stimulates smooth muscle, elevates blood pressure, decreases volume of urine
	Oxytocin (Pitocin)	Contracts uterine muscle
Testis (interstitial tissue)	Testosterone (primary) Androsterone	Controls secondary sex characteristics
Ovary (follicles) Placenta Testis (interstitial)	Estradiol (estrone, estrogen)	Controls secondary sex characteristics, menstrual cycle, mammary glands
Ovary (corpus luteum)	Progesterone	Regulates menses, mammary glands, pregnancy
Placenta	Chorionic gonadotropin	Regulates growth of corpus luteum during pregnancy
	Relaxin	Relaxes pelvic ligaments at labor

Reproductive and endocrine systems   699

hormones that regulate carbohydrate metabolism. Milk is not secreted during pregnancy because the female sex hormones inhibit the production of prolactin by the pituitary; when the level of the sex hormones falls, prolactin has an opportunity to act. The secretion of prolactin is also increased through nervous stimulation when the nipple is manipulated by sucking. During lactation the follicle-stimulating hormone of the pituitary is inhibited by prolactin, so that follicle production and ovulation do not usually occur.

Other possible endocrine organs. Other organs are strongly suspected of having some hormonal function, although so far the evidence is not entirely conclusive.

THYMUS. The thymus is a large mass of lymphoid tissue located in the upper part of the chest and covering the great vessels at the base of the heart. It reaches its maximum size during the second year of life, when it may weigh about 12 grams. After puberty it regresses, so that it is very small in later life. The organ contains lobules of lymphatic tissue which are separated by fibrous connective tissue. Lymphatic nodules and germinal centers, however, are absent, but it is divided into cortex and medulla regions. Because of its age changes, attempts have been made to find a hormone that affects sexual maturity, but nothing convincing so far has been revealed about its endocrine nature.

PINEAL GLAND. This small organ is located on the upper surface of the brain between the two halves of the cerebral cortex and in front of the mid-brain. It contains connective tissue, certain characteristic cells, and nerve fibers. In older individuals it contains the interesting brain sand (Figure 566) (**corpora arenacea**) which is composed of concretions of mineral salts. The pineal gland has no known function but has been suspected of secreting a hormone influencing sex.

ANNOTATED REFERENCES

Bullough, W. S. 1951. Vertebrate Sexual Cycles. London, Methuen & Co., Ltd.

Burrows, H. 1949. Biological Action of Sex Hormones, ed. 2. Cambridge, Cambridge University Press. *A very complete and advanced account of the actions of the various sex hormones.*

Carlisle, D. B., and Knowles, F. 1959. Endocrine Control in Crustaceans, Cambridge Monographs in Experimental Biology. London, Cambridge University Press.

Carlson, A. J., and V. Johnson. 1948. The Machinery of the Body, ed. 3. Chicago, University of Chicago Press. *A good, clear statement of the main features of endocrinology. Especially good for the beginning student of zoology.*

Corner, G. W. 1942. The Hormones in Human Reproduction. Princeton, Princeton University Press. *The influence of the sex hormones on the reproductive cycle is written in a very fascinating style. Can be easily understood by those who have had little zoology.*

De Kruif, P. 1945. The Male Hormone. New York, Harcourt, Brace & Co., Inc. *Traces the development of our knowledge of the hormone and the possibilities of its clinical application.*

Gorbman, A. (editor). 1959. Comparative Endocrinology. New York, John Wiley & Sons, Inc. *This work is based upon an important symposium on comparative endocrinology held at Columbia University in 1958. It is an up-to-date account of the work of many active investigators in this rapidly growing field of research.*

Hall, P. F. 1959. The Functions of the Endocrine Glands, Philadelphia, W. B. Saunders Co. *An account of our present knowledge about the physiology of endocrinology. It is not as heavy as some other works in this field but is concise and to the point. It is recommended to the advanced undergraduate student.*

Hanstrom, B. 1939. Hormones in Invertebrates. New York, Oxford University Press. *One of the few works devoted to invertebrate hormones. Gives a full summary of the work done in this field up to the time of its publication.*

Turner, C. D. 1955. General Endocrinology, ed. 2. Philadelphia, W. B. Saunders Co. *This work presents an excellent and concise summary of the main principles of endocrinology.*

Walter, H. E. 1939. Biology of the Vertebrates, rev. ed. New York, The Macmillan Co. *The reproductive systems in the different classes of vertebrates are well covered in this text.*

Windel, W. F. 1940. Physiology of the Fetus. Philadelphia, W. B. Saunders Co. *One of the most thorough accounts dealing with the fetus during its physiological development.*

Part Four

Origin and relationship of animals

chapter 33

Principles of development

In Chapter 4 a brief survey of embryological development was described. This chapter is concerned with some of the special aspects of development in the higher groups (amniotes) as well as an account of some concepts in experimental embryology. Certain embryological facts and theories should be studied by the student in order to gain a comprehensive knowledge of the organism as a whole. At this point it would be well for the student to review briefly the main points of embryological development in Chapter 4.

HISTORICAL BACKGROUND OF EMBRYOLOGY

The development of the living organism is one of the most marvellous phenomena in nature. How a one-cell fertilized egg is able to develop into a complete animal usually within a relatively short time has challenged investigators in nearly every field of biological thought. Aristotle made extensive studies on the development of animals, and his description of the chick in the hen's egg has considerable accuracy. His belief that development was a gradual building up was somewhat in line with present-day concepts. The modern study of embryology really started in the early seventeenth century when the revival of learning was making itself felt in nearly all spheres of human activity and thought. In 1600 Fabricius of Aquapendente, an Italian, published the first embryological treatise. His description of the hen's egg and the development of the chick has much of interest but contains the erroneous belief that the various parts of the organism appeared much sooner than is actually the case.

The idea of many early biological students was that the young animal was preformed in the egg and development was an unfolding and growth of a miniature animal which they claimed could be seen in germ cells. This **preformation theory** was advocated by many naturalist-philosophers of the seventeenth and eighteenth centuries, notably by Bonnet and Haller. This idea, however, was opposed by many able contemporary biologists. William Harvey, the great student of blood circulation, who published a treatise on embryology in his old age, was against the preformation theory, and his famous dictum, *ex ovo omnia* (all from the egg), was a fruitful concept for all future embryologists. The preformation theory, however, received its death blow in 1759 when the German Caspar Friedrich Wolff plainly showed that there were no little animals or plants in germ cells, but only undifferentiated tissue which gradually developed into germ layers and organs. His theory was called **epigenesis** (origin upon). This view is nearer the truth than preformation but errs in assuming that the formative substance which gives rise to the embryo is undifferentiated. It is now known that there are certain substances in germ cells which are predes-

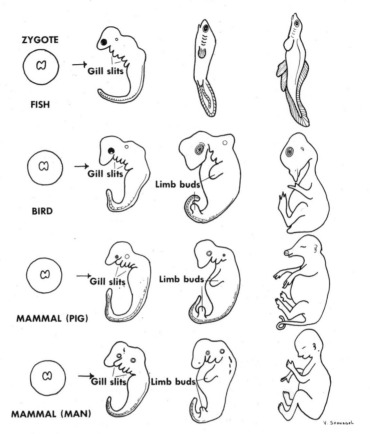

ZYGOTE

FISH

→ Gill slits

BIRD

→ Gill slits

Limb buds

MAMMAL (PIG)

→ Gill slits

Limb buds

MAMMAL (MAN)

→ Gill slits

Limb buds

V. SPRANGEL

Figure 578. Comparative series of four vertebrate embryos, showing comparable stages of development. It will be noted that early stages of all four series look very much alike. Distinctive characteristics show up in later stages. Because of this pattern of similarity Haeckel formulated his Biogenetic Law which stated that "ontogeny (development of the individual) recapitulates phylogeny (evolutionary history of a group.)" In its extreme form this view is no longer held, for all stages of ontogeny are modified in evolution. Von Baer's view that embryonic stages of a higher form are like embryonic stages of lower animals but not like the adults of those animals is considered to be more accurate.

tined to guide the development of parts and are, in a restricted sense, preformed.

The discovery of the small mammalian egg by Karl Ernst von Baer in 1827 represents a great landmark in embryology. The eggs of the other classes of vertebrates as well as those of most invertebrates are large enough to be easily seen. In contrast, the mammalian egg is very small and microscopic, and its discovery brought the reproductive process of mammals in line with other animals. No other embryologist contributed as much to this field as did von Baer, for he established the germ layer theory, made embryology

comparative, discovered the notochord, and developed the **biogenetic law**, which states that the embryos of higher and lower forms tend to resemble each other more closely the farther one goes back in their development (Figure 578). He gave the study of embryology an impetus which has led to the development of one of the greatest divisions of zoology.

EMBRYOLOGY OF AMNIOTES*

Embryos that develop into land animals, such as reptiles, birds, and mam-

*Refer to Chapter 5, Principle 20.

704

mals (**amniotes,** or those that develop an amnion), are provided with **extraembryonic membranes.** These membranes are the yolk sac, amnion, allantois, and chorion. Of these, only the yolk sac is present in other vertebrates (fish and amphibians). These membranes, which are not a definite part of the developing embryo, afford a sort of aquarium for the embryo so that it may develop as its fish ancestors did before an aquatic life was abandoned for a land existence.

The **yolk sac,** a protruding outgrowth of the primitive gut, encloses the yolk mass. It is connected by a yolk stalk to the gut and is lined with endoderm and covered with mesoderm. Endodermal cells digest the yolk material, and the mesodermal blood capillaries absorb the digested material and carry it to the growing embryo. When the embryo hatches, the degenerating yolk sac is absorbed in the body cavity. Although best developed in the reptiles and birds, some of the sharks have large yolk sacs.

The **chorion** and **amnion** develop at the same time in reptiles and birds. A combined fold of ectoderm and mesoderm (the head of the amnion fold) appears at the anterior end and gradually extends backward over the surface of the embryo. A similar fold (the tail fold) appears posteriorly in the embryo, meets and fuses with the head fold. Lateral folds of the amnion extend above and below the embryo and finally fuse over the top of the embryo, thus enclosing the amniotic chamber. The outer double layer is the chorion and the inner double layer is the amnion. Between the chorion and the amnion is the extraembryonic space. The amniotic cavity becomes filled with fluid and contains the developing embryo. The mesodermal muscle cells of the amnion contract rhythmically; this rocks the embryo in the amniotic fluid and prevents its adhesion to the surrounding wall.

The **allantois** grows out as a tube from the ventral wall of the hind gut and is formed in about the same way as the urinary bladder of amphibians. As it grows, its free end expands into the space between the amnion and yolk sac internally and the chorion externally. It fuses with the chorion to form the chorioallantoic membrane. This has been a favorite experimental site for the growth and differentiation of isolated parts of the developing embryo. Its mesoderm is supplied with blood vessels which pick up oxygen that diffuses through the porous shell and gives off carbon dioxide in the opposite direction. Its function is primarily one of respiration, but some nitrogenous waste is also excreted into its cavity.

Reptiles and birds. The large amount of yolk in the eggs of reptiles and birds offers so much resistance to cell cleavage that the latter is confined only to the surface layer (**partial cleavage**). In such cases the yolk is a continuous mass. In the fertilized hen's egg (Figure 580) the white albuminous matter and the shell are envelopes which surround the yolk or true zygote. The nucleus and its chromosomes are found in the small **germinal disc** on top of the yolk. Two spiral cords (**chalazae**) at the blunt and narrow ends of the egg represent the twisted dense mucin fibers of albumin formed by the rotation of the egg through the oviduct. When cleavage is initiated the nucleus in the germinal disc divides repeatedly by meroblastic cleavage, cell

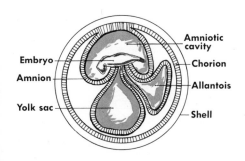

Figure 579. Amniote egg in an early stage of development, showing embryonic membranes. This type of egg made a land existence possible, for it is protected against drying out by a tough shell, embryonic membranes, and fluids which surround the embryo. Other adaptive features of this egg are gaseous exchange (O_2, CO_2) through porous shell and yolk nourishment for growing embryo until it hatches.

Principles of development 705

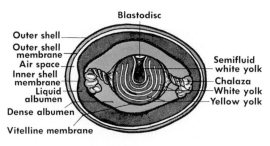

Blastodisc

Outer shell
Outer shell membrane
Air space
Inner shell membrane
Liquid albumen
Dense albumen
Vitelline membrane

Semifluid white yolk
Chalaza
White yolk
Yellow yolk

Figure 580. Longitudinal section of bird's egg. Adaptive structures of egg are as follows: (1) Limy shell is minutely porous for gas exchange and its double membrane lining encloses an air bubble for the young embryo. (2) Yolk is anchored by twisted cords of albumin (chalazae) and enclosed in a sac (vitelline membrane). (3) Blastodisc which gives rise to the embryo always turns uppermost to be nearest incubating bird and external air. (4) Lighter, semifluid yolk is collected nearest developing embryo for nourishment. (5) Albumin suspends egg and furnishes aqueous environment for it. Yolk is ovarian egg; albumin, shell membranes, and limy shell are secreted by wall of oviduct and by shell gland and are added as coatings to yolk. Such a telolecithal (megalecithal) egg restricts early cleavage stages to blastodisc (meroblastic cleavage).

membranes are formed, and a plate of cells result (**blastodisc**) on top of the yolk mass, which is eventually used up in the nourishment of the embryo. When the center of the germinal disc pulls away from the yolk, a cavity is formed, the **blastocoele.** This stage corresponds to the blastula of other types of development and is called a **blastoderm. A blastopore** is also formed. The separation of the blastoderm into a superficial layer (**ectoderm**) and a deeper layer (**endoderm**) takes place by a process of delamination. A thickening of the ectoderm and endoderm occurs at the posterior part of the blastoderm to form the **primitive streak,** which is homologous to the dorsal lip of the blastopore of lower forms. It also marks the longitudinal axis of the future embryo. At the anterior end of the primitive streak there is formed a node which lays down the **notochord. Mesoderm** is formed as a sheet of cells between the ectoderm and the endoderm at either side of the notochord. The mesoderm typically splits into

two sheets which grow between the ectoderm and endoderm; one of these sheets is attached to the outer ectoderm and the other to the inner endoderm. The space between the two sheets is the **coelomic cavity.** On each side of the notochord somites or segments appear in the mesoderm; from these the main muscles of the trunk develop. Above the notochord the ectoderm thickens to form the **neural plate** which later develops into the neural tube and finally the brain and spinal cord. Only the central part of the blastoderm develops into the embryo; the other portion develops into the four extraembryonic membranes described above. Most other aspects of reptilian and bird development are similar to those of the mammal to be described later.

EARLY DEVELOPMENT OF HUMAN EGG

The monotremes have eggs that resemble those of birds, because they con-

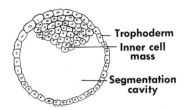

Trophoderm
Inner cell mass
Segmentation cavity

Figure 581. Morula stage. Trophoderm becomes the chorion; inner cell mass gives rise to embryo and other fetal membranes.

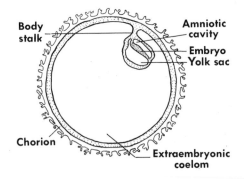

Body stalk
Amniotic cavity
Embryo
Yolk sac
Chorion
Extraembryonic coelom

Figure 582. Early embryonic stage in man, showing amniotic cavity and yolk sac.

706

tain much yolk and are laid externally. Other mammals have very small eggs (human egg is only 0.2 mm. in diameter) which contain very little yolk. The early cleavage of the human egg results in a spherical group of cells (**morula** stage) which becomes divided into two parts, an outer layer of cells, and an inner mass of cells attached to the outer layer. The outer part develops into the chorion which is concerned with the nourishment of the embryo from the maternal wall of the uterus; the inner cell mass gives rise to the embryo and the other fetal membranes.

The formation of a gastrula from the inner cell mass is similar to that of other mammals, but, unlike other vertebrates, there is no blastopore. Two cavities arise in this inner cell mass. The upper one is the **amniotic cavity** lined with ectoderm, and the lower is the **yolk sac** and the primitive gut lined with endoderm. Between the two cavities the embryo arises as a flat, two-layered plate (the embryonic disc). As development proceeds, the posterior end of the embryo becomes connected to the chorion by the **body stalk** (Figure 582). After the gastrula stage the human embryo, as well as that of other mammals, undergoes a development similar to that of birds during its early embryology. Gill slits or depressions are plainly visible at an early stage but probably do not break through into the pharynx.

PLACENTA AND UMBILICAL CORD

The embryo of mammals differs from that of reptiles and birds in having little or no food in the yolk sac for its nourishment and in having in its place a special device, the **placenta,** for obtaining its food from the mother (Figure 583). The placenta is formed by processes, or **villi,** of the chorion embedded in the uterine wall close to the maternal blood vessels. These villi and the tissues of the uterus where they are embedded form the combined structure known as the placenta. The placenta, therefore, has both an embryonic and a maternal part. Connecting the placenta with the ventral surface of the

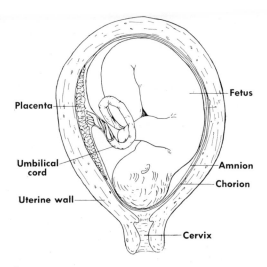

Figure 583. Human fetus just prior to birth. Note discoidal placenta, in contrast to diffuse and zonary types shown in Figures 584 and 585.

embryo's abdomen is the soft flexible **umbilical cord,** which encloses two arteries and a vein for carrying materials to and from the embryo. There is no direct connection between the embryonic and maternal circulations, for there is no mixing of the bloods of the two, although the embryo's blood circulates in the chorionic villi in close contact with the mother's blood in the maternal part of the placenta. The relationship between the two is purely an osmotic one and all substances must diffuse through a membrane which separates the two systems. The placenta grows in size as the embryo develops; in the human at birth it is about 7 inches in diameter and a little more than 1 inch thick.

The form of the placenta varies with different mammals. In man and rodents its shape is dislike (discoidal); in hogs (Figure 584) and cattle it is called a **diffuse** placenta because the villi are scattered; and in cats and other carnivores the placenta is in the form of a band and is called **zonary** (Figure 585). At the time of birth the embryonic part of the placenta is expelled either with the young or shortly thereafter as the "afterbirth." Some mammals eat the placenta after the birth of their young.

Principles of development 707

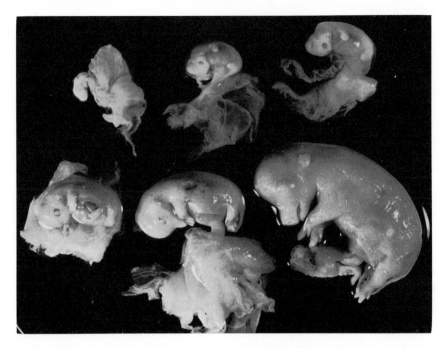

Figure 584. Stages in embryonic development of pig. Stages range from 9 mm. (upper left) to 45 mm. (lower right). Pig has diffuse type of placenta.

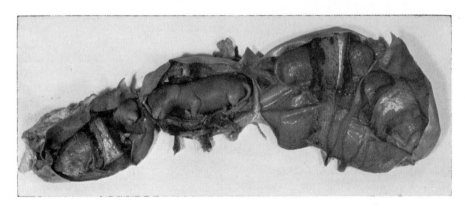

Figure 585. Uterus of dog opened up to expose litter of four pups. Zonary placenta, which is a band around the body, is well shown. Three pups are still wholly or partially enclosed in their amniotic sacs; one has been exposed to show its umbilical cord.

DEVELOPMENT OF SYSTEMS AND ORGANS IN AMNIOTES

The **nervous system** is one of the first to form. Shortly after gastrulation the ectoderm thickens over the notochord to from a **neural plate**. The center of this plate becomes depressed by the more rapid growth of cells along its margin and the plate becomes a neural groove (Figure 586). Then the outer ridges or folds come together at the top to form the hollow neural tube. The anterior end of this tube enlarges to form the brain, while the posterior part becomes the spinal cord. Nerve cells and nerves originate from the walls of the tube or from the neural crest along the sides.

Most of the **endoskeleton** arises as os-

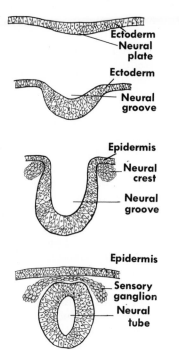

Figure 586. Development of neural tube from neural plate of ectoderm (cross-section).

folding of the body wall (Figure 588). The ends of the tube open to the exterior and are lined with ectoderm, whereas the rest of the tube is lined with endoderm. The **lungs, liver,** and **pancreas** arise from the foregut. At the anterior end of the body crevices appear which in early verte-

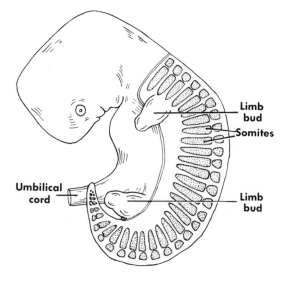

Figure 587. Diagram of embryo, showing muscle somites.

sification of cartilage, but some of the cranial bones come from membrane. In man, some bones begin their ossification as early as the end of the second month of prenatal life. Large bones may have several centers of ossification, which is not complete until long after birth. In frogs the notochord buds off from the roof of the archenteron, but in amniotes it arises from the anterior end of the primitive streak. The **skin** has a double origin, the epidermis coming from ectoderm and the dermis or corium from the mesoderm.

Most **muscles** arise from the mesoderm along each side of the spinal cord (Figure 587). This mesoderm divides into a linear series of somites (thirty-eight in man) which by splitting, fusion, and migration become the muscles of the body and axial parts of the skeleton. The **limbs** begin as buds from the side of the body. Projections of the limb buds develop into digits.

The **alimentary canal** is early folded off from the yolk sac by the growth and

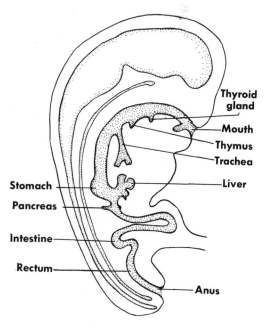

Figures 588. Derivatives of alimentary canal.

brates, such as fish, open directly into the pharyngeal part of the digestive system. These are the **gill clefts** associated with the gills of gill-breathing forms. In man, these cervices never break through to form gill clefts, but they do suggest a fish stage in his ancestry. The transformation of the pharyngeal region in the land vertebrates is an interesting evolution. Since these forms breath by means of lungs instead of gills, the gill pouches develop into other structures. The Eustachian tube, for instance, comes from a remnant of the first gill pouch, whereas the palatine tonsils, the parathyroid, and the thymus come from certain of the other pouches.

The **heart, blood vessels,** and **red blood cells** are formed from the mesoderm. In its early condition the human heart is similar to the heart of lower vertebrates. Two tubes fuse for a part of their length into a single tube which divides into two cavities, the auricle and the ventricle. Later each of these subdivides, forming two auricles and two ventricles. This type of heart is characteristic of birds, mammals, and some of the reptiles.

The **urinary bladder** varies a great deal among the vertebrates, for in some it is entirely absent. In some fish the bladder is formed by the fusion of the lower parts of the Wolffian ducts and a part of the cloaca. In other vertebrates it arises from the ventral wall of the cloaca. In higher vertebrates the base of the allantois helps in the formation of the bladder.

Both **testes** and **ovaries** of the **reproductive** system develop from the genital ridge, along the dorsal ridge of the coelom. The male cells, or sperm, develop in special seminiferous tubules of the testes, but the ova, or eggs, of the ovaries develop in special follicles and must break through the ovarian walls when mature. The higher vertebrates use Wolffian or mesonephric ducts to carry the sperm and Müllerian ducts to carry the eggs.

BIRTH OR PARTURITION

During the period of pregnancy the placenta gradually takes over most of the functions of regulating the growth and development of the uterus and the embryo (fetus). As an endocrine gland it secretes estradiol and progesterone, which are secreted by the ovaries and corpus luteum in the early periods of pregnancy. The placenta also assumes the function of the pituitary in secreting a chorionic gonadotropin hormone which now performs the role of the LH and FSH pituitary hormones which cease their secretions about the second month of pregnancy. This gonadotropin hormone of the placenta maintains the corpus luteum so that it may secrete progesterone and estradiol necessary for the attachment of the placenta. In the later stages of pregnancy, the placenta can manage affairs without either the corpus luteum or pituitary.

What stimulates birth? Why does not pregnancy continue indefinitely? What factors produce the onset of labor (the rhythmic contractions of the uterus)? So far, no satisfactory answer can be given to these questions. The real mechanism for parturition seems to reside in the uterus and placenta. Various theories have been proposed. Since the uterine-placental relationship is dependent mainly upon the estradiol-progesterone ratio, it may be that labor is initiated by a high concentration of estradiol and a low concentration of progesterone. But mammals vary in their reactions to sex hormones. As a usual thing, progesterone cuts down uterine contractions and estradiol speeds them up. Injections of the latter hormone will cause abortion in mice but not in the human being. The mechanical effect of uterine muscle stretching (by the increased size of the fetus) may be a stimulus for labor.

The first major signs of labor or the beginning of parturition are the so-called labor pains which are caused by the rhythmic contractions of the uterine musculature. These are usually slight at first and at intervals of fifteen to thirty minutes. They gradually become more intense, longer in duration, and more frequent. They may last anywhere from six to twenty-four hours, usually longer with the first child. The object of these contractions is to expel the child from the uterus and birth canal to the outside. Childbirth occurs in three stages. In the first stage the neck (cervix) or opening of the uterus into the vagina is enlarged by the pressure of the child in its bag of amniotic fluid which may be ruptured at this time; in the second stage the child is forced out of the uterus and through the vagina to the outside; and in the third stage the placenta, or afterbirth, is expelled from the mother's body. After birth, the umbilical cord that connects the child to the placenta is clamped off and cut. Usually within ten minutes after the baby is born the placenta is expelled from mother's body.

PROBLEM OF DIFFERENTIATION

Differentiation in biology is the formation, localization, and modification of cells, tissues, and organs in function and structure during the course of development. It is the biggest problem in biology and only a little is known about its fundamental nature. Most of the higher organisms originate from a fertilized egg cell (zygote) which has the potentiality to form an organism consisting of billions of cells with an infinite complexity of structures and function. Life thus begins as a single cell which by successive cell divisions (cleavage) forms cells of many different kinds and functions in the make-up of a complex individual. Some of the daughter cells in cleavage are destined to form muscle, others brain, and so on throughout the whole range of bodily structures. Can this differentiation be explained? For a long time, embryologists were content to describe comparatively the embryological histories of different animals, and a vast amount of accurate information about the development of animals resulted. But it was soon apparent to thoughtful investigators that mere description did not explain the underlying problems of development and that an experimental and analytical approach was necessary. From this new viewpoint there arose the science of experimental zoology

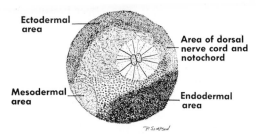

Figure 589. Organization of recently fertilized egg of *Amphioxus*, showing organ-forming areas which, when egg develops, will give rise to differentiations indicated on drawing. In cytoplasm of many chordate eggs there is found a basic organization of definite areas which are predestined to develop into certain organs. Although these organization areas are visible, many morphogenetic organization patterns are invisible and their exact location in egg before development can only be guessed. It has been assumed that real morphological ground substance of egg consists of enzymes, hormones, and other regulative materials. (After Conklin.)

which has been in the forefront of biological investigation for many years. Many able investigators have been active in this field, but two who have spearheaded causal embryology deserve special mention—W. Roux and H. Spemann. Experimental embryology emphasizes methods for artificially modifying normal development by such means as separating early cleavage blastomeres, by subjecting eggs and embryos to various external factors (temperature, chemicals), by transplanting grafts from one region of an embryo to another, by fusing eggs and embryos together, and by many other ways.

Modern embryologists have sought a middle ground between the theories of preformation and epigenesis as previously described. Results indicate that neither the egg nor spermatozoan can be considered homogeneous and lacking in organization, but also they cannot be thought of as containing the embryos in miniature form. The germ cells are highly differentiated and possessed of certain potentialities localized more or less in the zygote, which develops under the influence of both external and internal factors. Descriptive embryology shows that certain structures in their earliest beginnings (anlagen or primordia) can be located or mapped in certain regions of the egg, and the exact organs they are going to give rise to can be followed with great accuracy.

Eggs of different species vary in their organization both before and after fertilization. It has been shown experimentally that, in certain forms, the blastomeres when separated from each other in early cleavage stages will each develop into a complete individual, whereas undisturbed they stay together and produce only one individual. In the frog's egg, for instance, if one of the blastomeres in the two-cell stage is killed by a hot needle, the intact blastomere will give rise to half an embryo; but when the two intact blastomeres are separated, each will form a whole embryo. In some eggs this power of separate blastomeres to form a complete embryo is possessed up to the 4-cell stage. Such a condition is called **in-determinate** cleavage and is found in the regulative eggs of echinoderms, jellyfish, *Amphioxus*, and others. On the other hand, there are eggs whose blastomeres when separated will give rise to only that part of the embryo which each blastomere would form in an intact egg. In such a case one may get a half or a quarter or some other part of an embryo, depending upon the blastomeres that have been separated. This is called **determinate** cleavage or mosaic development. Examples of this type are the eggs of annelids, mollusks, ctenophores, and a few others.

The explanation behind these two types of cleavage and development seems to lie in the time of differentiation and organization of the egg. In those forms in which each of the early blastomeres will give rise to a complete embryo, or in which the blastomeres are totipotent, the formative substance is scattered through the egg and each blastomere receives a portion of all material necessary for a complete organism. Hoerstadius has shown, however, that this formative substance is of two types, both of which must be pres-

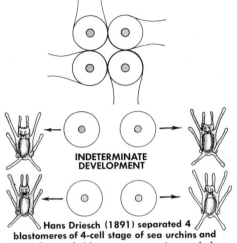

INDETERMINATE DEVELOPMENT

Hans Driesch (1891) separated 4 blastomeres of 4-cell stage of sea urchins and found that each blastomere gave rise to whole pluteus larva; early cleavage stages of other forms, including man, will behave in similar manner; such is called indeterminate development

DETERMINATE DEVELOPMENT

When 2 left blastomeres of 4-cell stage of Styela (tunicate) larva are killed with hot needle, right blastomeres will form only half of larva; early cleavage stages of annelids and mollusks similar; each cell can produce only specific part of whole organism; this is called mosaic (determinate) development

Figure 590. Determinate (mosaic) and indeterminate cleavage.

ent for a blastomere to form an entire embryo. Thus the regulative power of these eggs have restrictions. In the determinate cleavage type the material is organized and localized so early that each blastomere receives a portion which is qualitatively different from that received by the others. It has been possible in some cases to map out the organization of some eggs (mosaic) to show that certain parts of the egg will give rise to only certain parts of the embryo. In this way certain regions can be determined in blastula and early gastrula stages that are presumptive for specific structures, such as the germ layers, notochord, and nervous system. From the evidence of identical twins, man apparently has the indeterminate type of cleavage, for identical twins come from the same zygote.

ROLE OF ORGANIZERS AND EMBRYONIC INDUCTORS

A method helpful in explaining the differentiation and development of the embryo is furnished by **embryonic induction.** Embryonic induction is a process by which a developing structure (inductor) stimulates another structure to become a specific differentiation. Induction is mediated by chemicals called evocators. It has been demonstrated by numerous investigators during the last two or three decades that when certain groups of cells are transplanted from their normal position to some other parts of the body of the early developing embryo, they are profoundly altered in the new positions. In other words, the fate of these cells can be changed by placing them in a different location. Presumptive skin cells transplanted to a region of the brain to take the place of brain cells which have been removed become nerve cells rather than skin cells. These changes occur only when the transplantation is made during the early gastrula stage; if made later, the transplanted cells will remain the same. In early transplantation the region determines the nature of the growth, but older transplanted cells have already been determined and therefore do not change.

When pieces from the dorsal lip of the blastopore of the gastrula are transplanted beneath the ectoderm of another gastrula, a second embryo may be made to develop on the side of the host embryo. The dorsal lip of the blastopore is known to be a center of organization (organizer) and is responsible for the formation of the brain, spinal cord, and notochord. There are many centers of organization in a developing embryo. Source centers such as the dorsal lip of the blastopore are known as **primary organizers** because they are concerned with the establishment of the basic axial organs of brain, spinal cord, etc. A secondary organizer is the optic vesicle which, trans-

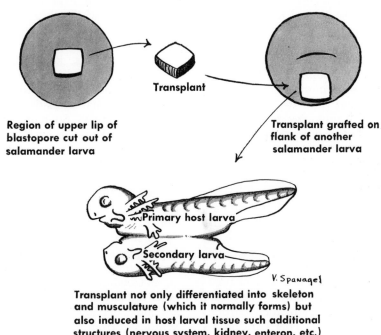

Transplant

Region of upper lip of blastopore cut out of salamander larva

Transplant grafted on flank of another salamander larva

Primary host larva

Secondary larva

V. Spanagel

Transplant not only differentiated into skeleton and musculature (which it normally forms) but also induced in host larval tissue such additional structures (nervous system, kidney, enteron, etc.) necessary to form whole secondary embryo

Figure 591. Spemann's famous organizer experiment.

planted to some region of the body other than the eye, will induce the formation of a lens in tissue that is normally destined for other roles. Many chemical substances (nucleoproteins, steroids, various acids) will cause induction and there is some evidence to show that inductors can exert their influence on the reacting tissue at a distance by means of diffusible substances.

SOME ASPECTS OF DIFFERENTIATION AND SPECIALIZATION*

Differentiation is determined by both external and internal factors. Most embryologists believe that internal activities exert the greater influence on morphogenesis. The belief commonly held is that the nuclei of an organism appear to be genetically uniform and that differentiation is a cytoplasmic phenomenon. According to this view the different cytoplasms can activate or inhibit the gene systems of the nuclei by chemical agents, so that only certain genes can exert an influence within a particular morphogenetic field. However, in recent years there is some evidence (Briggs and King) to show that nuclei are not all the same, and their differences may play a part in determination or differentiation. There is much evidence that the developing embryo is divided into areas or morphogenetic fields which are different from each other with respect to their potencies to determine particular body structures (limbs, tail, heart, etc.). Each field has the power of self-differentiation and possesses all the requirements for specific specialization. In the early embryo, there is considerable regulative power and flexibility in the morphogenetic fields, so that the organ primordia may undergo considerable alteration, such as duplication, under certain conditions. Later, the fields become rigidly fixed and lose their power of regulation. In their differentiation, cells are restricted by the potency of their particular morphogenetic field. There are no intermediate possibilities, for they must de-

*Refer to Chapter 5, Principles 10 and 11.

714

velop into bone, muscle, nerve, etc. or abnormal modifications thereof.

As a general rule, the hereditary pattern of the induced structure expresses itself in the character of the induced organ and not that of the inductor. Thus, in Schotte's famous experiment in which he transplanted a small piece of flank skin of a frog embryo to the mouth region of a salamander embryo, he obtained the mouth character of a frog, although the presumptive flank skin was induced to become mouth tissue by the salamander inductor. In this case the induced cells from the frog followed their own genetic equipment. This method of differentiation is sometimes called the feedback theory because the character of the induced structure is controlled by the chemical feedback of its own genes.

Some external or environmental factors are very effective in producing cellular differentiation. Thus a single median or cyclopia eye will result when an embryo is exposed during a sensitive period to a solution of lithium salts. Another striking example is the experiment of Fell and Mallanby in which they exposed the epidermis of a chick embryo to vitamin A. Under normal conditions chick embryo epidermis forms keratinized squamous epithelium, but exposure to vitamin A converted it into ciliated, mucus-producing epithelium characteristic of the respiratory passageways. Such experiments might be explained on the basis that some cells and tissues have many synthetic codes and that certain environmental factors will activate one code and suppress others. In the vitamin A experiment it is interesting to note that the process is reversible, for the ciliated, mucus-secreting epithelium is converted back into the normal squamous type when placed into a normal medium. Many such alterations do not change the essential nature of the cells but are merely modulations.

Some striking experiments of tissue synthesis from dissociated cells throw some light on the intrinsic nature of differentiation. The classic experiment of Wilson, who dissociated sponge cells by

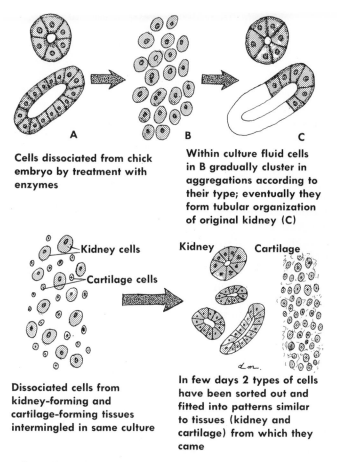

A

Cells dissociated from chick
embryo by treatment with
enzymes

B

Within culture fluid cells
in B gradually cluster in
aggregations according to
their type; eventually they
form tubular organization
of original kidney (C)

C

Kidney cells

Cartilage cells

Kidney   Cartilage

Dissociated cells from
kidney-forming and
cartilage-forming tissues
intermingled in same culture

In few days 2 types of cells
have been sorted out and
fitted into patterns similar
to tissues (kidney and
cartilage) from which they
came

Figure 592. Tissue synthesis from dissociated cells. Such experiments in time may make possible restoration of lost cells from vital organs by simple process of injecting suitable cell suspensions. Student should recall pioneer work of H. V. Wilson on regeneration of marine sponges.

pressing live sponges through finely woven cloth and found that the cells collected together later to form complete sponges, has instigated many other similar experiments with such highly developed organisms as the amphibian, chick, and mouse embryos (Figure 592). By separating with enzymes or other means the cells of a morphogenetic field, which is destined to form a specialized organ, such as kidney, wing bud, etc., it was found that these cells when cultured in a suitable medium would assemble together to form an organized organ like the original one. If cells from different organs are mixed together, the cells would selectively regroup themselves according to type and form the tissues from which they came, kidney cells forming kidneys, cartilage cells forming cartilage, etc. Something in the cells causes similar cells to associate together and dissimilar cells to separate.

How do the cells of a particular organ all differentiate at the same time? Some light on this problem has been thrown by recent electron microscope observations on germinal epithelium. Clusters of spermatids, for instance, are found joined together by intercellular connections or cytoplasmic bridges. These bridges are different from the connecting strands of spindle apparatus remnants in that the former contain the cytoplasmic elements of the regular cell. It is thought that this protoplasmic continuity represents open communication between the cells and is responsible for the synchronous coordination of differentiation within a particular group of spermatids. Similar bridges have been reported in clusters of cnidoblasts in the hydra.

REGENERATION

Problems of regeneration. One interesting aspect of experimental embryology is regeneration. Regeneration is the normal response of organisms to replace lost structures by cellular multiplication and differentiation. Most animals possess this power to a greater or lesser extent. The higher the animal in the scale of life, the more restricted this power is. Many lower forms, however, have this capacity to a marked degree. We have already seen that pieces of the flatworm, planaria, are each able to produce complete flatworms. In higher forms the capacity for regeneration is shown by the formation of new tissue during wound healing. But there are many other examples in the body, for cells of various tissues, such as blood and skin, are being lost and replaced all the time.

All animals are in a state of dynamic equilibrium throughout their life span. The chief difference between the lower and higher organisms in this respect is that the former retain more of the embryonic organization in their adult stages. This ability is extremely marked in the flatworms and coelenterates but is lessened in vertebrates. Vertebrates themselves show remarkable variations in regeneration. For instance, if the limb of a young salamander is amputated, a new limb will grow out from the cut stump in the course of a few weeks. This replacement will also include everything that was lost. Where a frog's limb is cut off, the skin heals over the cut stump without regeneration of the lost part. If all the skeletal parts of a salamander's limb are removed, but leaving all the other muscles, connective tissue, nerves, blood

vessels, etc., in place, a normal limb will regenerate, with all the missing bones replaced in normal position. When the limb of a larval salamander is amputated, at the end of the cut stump a region of small cells called the **blastema** is formed. This blastema is apparently formed from dedifferentiated cells from skin, muscle, and bone which are found in that region. When the blastema has assumed a certain size, it begins the differentiation of the various tissues which go to make up the limb.

In these cases of regeneration the presence of nerves seems to be indispensable for the regeneration processes. If the nerves that supply a limb are cut before amputation, no regeneration will occur. In addition, when the nerve supply is lacking, complete regression of the limb will take place and it is resorbed, so that no blastema is formed. If a blastema is allowed to form before the nerves are cut, regeneration will continue and a new limb is formed. Here the blastema is the controlling factor and no nervous control is necessary. If nerves are allowed to grow back into the limb during the period of degeneration, growth and differentiation will be resumed, which again shows the influence of nervous control.

Recent work indicates that the capacity of a limb to regenerate depends upon the number of nerve fibers that run to it. If the number of nerves running to the limb of a salamander is reduced artificially, there will be no regeneration. In adult frogs it has been possible by operation to shift to an amputated forelimb the peripheral end of the sciatic nerve and its branches which run to the hind limb, thereby increasing the number of nerves in the forelimb. In such a case the amputated frog forelimb will regenerate. This experiment might indicate that regeneration of limbs in higher forms is lost because their nerve supplies are inadequate and that a certain minimum number is required for regeneration. This principle of regeneration presents a striking contrast to embryonic development in which the evidence indicates that nervous innervation plays little or no role in the differentiation of organs. When nerves are prevented from entering the limb buds of amphibian and chick embryos, the buds differentiate into limbs in a normal manner.

When a frog's limb is cut off, the wound normally heals over without the formation of a blastema and consequently no regeneration. If the wound is prevented from healing by the application of a salt solution, a blastema is formed at the cut surface and a completely new limb will form. In a salamander, if the whole skin is pulled over the cut surface of the amputated stump, no regeneration occurs, because apparently the presence of the skin blocks the formation of the blastema. The salt solution in the case of the frog limb prevents the migration of the skin over the wound surface so that a blastema has a chance to perform. These results would indicate that the power of regeneration of lost parts, apparently absent in some animals, is actually present but is halted by normal healing.

One aspect of regeneration that has received considerable attention is that of **axial gradients.** According to this theory, there is a metabolic differential from the head to tail region. The head has the higher metabolic rate and more or less dominates the rest of the body where the metabolic rate is lower. These gradients have thrown some interesting light upon regeneration, for the higher the metabolic rate, the more sensitive that region is to poisons. Abnormalities may be induced more easily in the head region than in posterior regions. Where they are located in the gradient determines the fate of the embryonic cells to a great extent. Gradients also help to explain how environmental conditions influence the development of organisms.

GROWTH*

Biological growth is a complex physiological process. It is a fundamental characteristic of protoplasmic systems and ex-

---

*Refer to Chapter 5, Principle 11.

presses itself in a hereditary pattern more or less specific for each kind of animal. It is not easy to define growth, for a mere increase in size may not be true growth. The accumulation of excess fat is not considered growth, for such a condition may be temporary. True growth involves a permanent increase in volume, especially during the stages of the development. Growth is mainly a synthesis of protein substances throughout the cell, a process known as **intussusception.** This process can take place only when the cells are supplied with materials beyond their needs of metabolism. Anything additional can thus be used to construct new molecules. During the development period of the life cycle, both increase in cell numbers and increase in cell size play a part in growth.

Growth is not necessarily restricted to protoplasmic increase, however, for it is possible to have growth by the differentiation of nonliving substances, such as the extracellular fibers in connective tissue. In bone, for instance, there are many nonliving materials outside the bone-forming cells which are relatively undifferentiated. But cells can undergo differentiation within themselves, such as those of muscle and nerve, and the more they are differentiated, the more they lose the capacity for growth. This may be one of the reasons why undifferentiated primitive tissues, connective and epithelial, are affected with abnormal growths (cancer) and why the differentiated muscle and nerve cells are free from it.

As complex animals get older, the growth rate slows down and may finally cease altogether. Growth curves have been worked out for many organisms. This may be done in various ways, but one common method is to plot weight against time. Many factors influence these curves. If animals are well nourished and develop under ideal conditions, the growth curve rises steeply almost in a straight line, but organisms developing under poor environmental conditions will give growth curves more or less S shaped (Figure 593). What causes growth to decrease

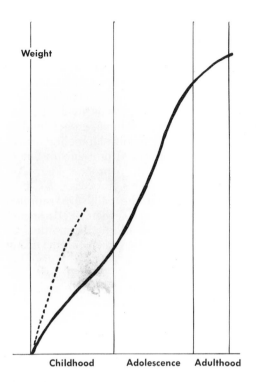

Weight

Childhood   Adolescence   Adulthood

Figure 593. Growth curve. Under ideal conditions, curve will follow dotted line.

as the animal grows older? One reason is that more and more of the body becomes differentiated into nonliving substance, such as fibers, sheaths, and mineral deposits, which do not grow. Another reason is that when cells become highly specialized, they cease to grow. The animal tends to reach a condition of adult stability or equilibrium. In aging, the body tissues may actually shrink (negative growth). These changes will all be expressed in the growth curve.

AGING AND DEATH

Aging and death are the terminal stages of the life cycle. Aging refers to the decline which occurs after the organism has reached the peak of its activity. This period naturally varies with different kinds of animals and also with different individuals. Animals with a short life span will be undergoing the aging process while animals that live longer are still in the flush of activity. Likewise, the decline

shows a great variation among individuals of the same species. Some men are as old at 50 as others are at 70. The problem of aging has been studied in many animals with emphasis upon what occurs in individual cells and tissues of the organism as it declines. Do all animals exhibit aging? Professor Woodruff of Yale University carried one strain of paramecia through thousands of generations from 1907 to 1943 and found that they could multiply indefinitely by fission alone without conjugation and showed no evidence of decline. He found, however, that nuclear reorganization did occur periodically in these protozoans. Other strains of protozoans, however, do exhibit changes of senescence and old age. Among the metazoans practically all forms studied have shown some signs of aging. Both anatomical and physiological changes occur but not all organs and tissues show equal degrees of decline. Degenerative changes in the heart and vascular system are important because of their effect on the life span.

The problem of old age has a practical importance in human populations as an increasing proportion of our population reaches old age. Many studies recently published indicate a great interest in the science of aging, or **geriatrics.**

Death may be considered the terminal sequence of the degenerative changes of old age. Death of the organism involves the death of cells, but not all of the cells die at once. Many cells of the body continue to live after the animal has been pronounced dead by certain conventional signs we associate with death. Among protozoans that reproduce by fission, death in the ordinary sense does not occur, since the body is shared by the daughter cells resulting from the division. Life spans are usually considered more or less definite for most species of animals, but it is very difficult to state with accuracy just how long these life spans are. Even in the case of man whose life span is better known than that of any other animal only general averages can be given. The average life expectancy has increased

718

in man from about 50 years to around 70 years in the past half century and further increases are expected under better medical and hygienic conditions. However, there is little indication that the upper limit of the life span of man has increased. So many factors influence the span in all animals that exact figures cannot be given in most cases. Natural death resulting from the degenerative changes of aging rarely occurs in animals other than man, for the debility produced by senescence makes them an easy prey for their enemies. Death, however, considered from any standpoint is a definite part of the hereditary pattern of animals. Specifically, death from whatever cause is due to the failure of one of the following: heart, blood, and nervous system. Death must occur whenever the vascular system fails to deliver oxygen, vitamins, hormones, and other vital substances. Failure of the nervous system may affect vital centers and quickly result in death.

Derivation of basic terminology

allantois (Gr. *allas*, a sausage, + *eidos*, resemblance).

amnion (Gr. *amnion*, bowl for sacrificial blood).

anlage (Gr. *anlage*, foundation).

archenteron (Gr. *arch*, primitive, + *enteron*, intestine).

blastocoele (Gr. *blastos*, germ, + *koilos*, hollow).

blastomere (Gr. *blastos*, germ, + *meros*, part).

blastopore (Gr. *blastos*, germ, + *porus*, a pore).

blastula (Gr. *blastos*, germ, + L. *ula*, diminutive suffix).

centrolecithal (Gr. *kentron*, center, + *lekithos*, yolk).

chorion (Gr. *chorion*, membrane).

cleavage (AS. *cleofian*, to cut).

embryology (Gr. *embryon*, embryo, + *logos*, science).

epigenesis (Gr. *epi*, upon, + *genesis*, origin).

gastrula (Gr. *gaster*, stomach, + L. *ula*, diminutive suffix).

holoblastic (Gr. *holos*, whole, + *blastos*, germ).

isolecithal (Gr. *isos*, equal, + *lekithos*, yolk).

meroblastic (Gr. *meros*, part, + *blastos*, germ).

morula (L. *morus*, mulberry, + *ula*, diminutive).

otocyst (Gr. *otos*, ear, + *kystis*, bladder).

placenta (Gr. *plakous*, a flat cake).

telolecithal (Gr. *telos*, end, + *lekithos*, yolk).

umbilical (L. *umbilicus*, the navel).

zygote (Gr. *zygotos*, yolked).

ANNOTATED REFERENCES

Barth, L. G. 1949. Embryology. New York, The Dryden Press. *A good concise account of the fundamental principles of development.*

Bonner, J. T. 1958. The Evolution of Development. Cambridge, Cambridge University Press. *An evolutionary approach to development and how it helps explain the mechanisms of the developmental process.*

Gilbert, M. S. 1939. Biography of the Unborn. Baltimore, Williams & Wilkins Co. *A brief yet fascinating summary of the main events that is rapidly becoming a classic in elementary human embryology. Can be read by all beginning biology students with profit.*

Huettner, A. F. 1948. Fundamentals of Comparative Embryology of the Vertebrates, ed. 2. New York, The Macmillan Co. *An excellent text with clear and revealing illustrations.*

Lillie, F. R. 1952. The Development of the Chick, ed. 3 (revised by H. L. Hamilton), New York, Henry Holt & Co., Inc. *This American classic has often been considered a model of embryological presentation.*

McElroy, W. D., and H. B. Glass. 1958. A Symposium on the Chemical Basis of Development. Baltimore, The Johns Hopkins Press. *This work is based on a symposium held in 1958 and attempts to throw some light on growth and differentiation—one of the most difficult problems in biology.*

Mintz, B. (editor). 1958. Environmental Influences on Prenatal Development. Chicago, University of Chicago Press.

Morgan, T. H. 1934. Embryology and Genetics. New York, Columbia University Press. *The bearing of genetics on the problems of development is treated in a masterly fashion by a great authority.*

Needham, J. 1942. Biochemistry and Morphogenesis. Cambridge, Cambridge University Press. *An authoritative and highly technical discussion of the biochemical aspects of morphology.*

Nelsen, O. E. 1953. Comparative Embryology of the Vertebrates. New York, The Blakiston Co. *This treatise is a comprehensive study of the comparative morphology of the vertebrates and protochordates, the only one so far written by an American. Although it treats the subject from a morphological point of view, there is also an enormous amount of information from the related fields of cytology, histology, etc. The tendency of the author to crowd his illustrations together for economy* of space has detracted somewhat from the general merits of the work.

Rugh, R. 1948. Experimental Embryology. A Manual of Techniques and Procedures. Minneapolis, Burgess Publishing Co. *Emphasizes the practical procedures in embryological work. A good book for all students of embryology.*

Spemann, H. 1938. Embryonic Development and Induction. New Haven, Yale University Press. *An authoritative work by a pioneer in this aspect of embryology. Suitable for the advanced student.*

Thornton, C. S. (editor). 1959. Regeneration in Vertebrates. Chicago, University of Chicago Press.

Waddington, C. H. 1956. Principles of Embryology. New York, The Macmillan Co. *This treatise is for the advanced student and re-search worker and is written by a famous English embryologist and geneticist. The author assumes some preliminary acquaintance with introductory embryology on the part of the student and devotes a great part of his discussion to an explanation of the experimental approach to the subject. This lack of pure description is reflected in the scanty illustrations in the book. A fine bibliography of experimental embryology is included.*

Watterson, R. L. (editor). 1959. Endocrines in Development. Chicago, University of Chicago Press. *A symposium on the influence of hormones on growth and development.*

Windle, W. F. 1940. Physiology of the Fetus. Philadelphia, W. B. Saunders Co. *Stresses the physiological aspects of prenatal life.*

chapter 34

Principles of inheritance

MEANING OF HEREDITY*

It was recognized long ago that heredity was one of the great stabilizing agencies in nature. In spite of dissimilarities between offspring and parents in a particular generation, there was a sameness that ran from generation to generation through the same type of plant or animal. Cattle were always cattle, dogs were always dogs, and never did they change into something else. But variations appeared, and some were inherited and others disappeared with the generation in which they arose. The real causes behind these variations, as well as those responsible for all hereditary factors, were of course unknown until the laws of genetics were worked out. These inherited characteristics, which may be like or unlike those of the parents, we now know to be due to the segregation of hereditary factors, and those that are not inherited, to be caused by environmental conditions.

Children are not duplicates of their parents. Some of their characteristics show resemblances to one or both parents, but they also demonstrate many not found in either parent. What is actually inherited by an offspring from its parents is a certain type of germinal organization (**genes**) which under the influence of environmental factors differentiates into the physical characteristics as we see them. While development is orderly and progressive, many unpredictable environmental factors can alter the general outcome. The mechanism for the orderly distribution of the germinal substance

through individual development and successive generations is now well known. We know, too, that heredity can be changed by altering the germ cells, either by changing the genic constitution or by rearranging chromosome organization.

The inheritance of any characteristic depends upon the interaction of many genes. This interaction is often complex, although the individual genes may behave as though they are independent of one another. There is a germinal basis for every characteristic that appears in the development of the organism, such as stature, color of eyes and hair, and intellectual capacity. The germinal organization sets the potential bounds of these and all other characteristics, but environmental factors of food, disease, etc. may greatly affect the physical expression of the characteristics so that their potentialities are never fully realized. The organism simply inherits the genes; how they express themselves depends upon the environment under which they develop.

The pattern of heredity naturally depends upon whether reproduction is unisexual or bisexual. In a unisexual organism, only one parent is involved, as in binary fission or sporulation. Unless there is mutation or other genetic variation, the offspring and parent are genetically alike. But in bisexual reproduction, two sets of genes are pooled together in the zygote and the offspring shares genetic potentialities of both parents and can produce combinations of traits unlike either parent. Mutation also may play a part here in the alteration of genes.

---

*Refer to Chapter 5, Principles 10 and 21.

CYTOLOGICAL BACKGROUND OF HEREDITY

Heredity is a protoplasmic continuity between parents and offspring. In bisexual animals the gametes are responsible for establishing this continuity. It is therefore important to understand the nature of this mechanism whereby the hereditary transmission is made between parent and offspring. Certain parts of the cell must represent the physical basis for inheritance. The basic laws of genetics were first worked out without much understanding of the physical mechanism which formed the real explanation of the whole process. Experiments and observations were made from visible traits. There could be no real scientific explanation of genetic principles until a study had been made of the germ cells and their behavior. This was really a case of working backward from certain visible results of inheritance to the mechanism responsible for such results. Considerable progress had already been made in cytology, or the science of cells, particularly germ cells, by the time the chief laws of genetics were announced. The problem was to link together the two fields of study, the behavior of the germ cells and the products of inheritance. The nuclei of sex cells were early suspected of furnishing the real answer to the mechanism. This applied especially to certain constituents of the nuclei, the chromosomes, for they appeared to be the only entities passed on in equal quantities from parents to offspring.

When the rediscovery of Mendel's laws was announced in 1900 (a date which may be considered the beginning of modern genetics), the time was ripe to demonstrate the parallelism which existed between these fundamental laws of inheritance and the cytological behavior of the chromosomes. In a series of brilliant experiments by Boveri, Sutton, McClung, and Wilson, the mechanism of heredity was definitely assigned to the chromosomes. Since that time geneticists have been busy establishing the chromosome theory of heredity. The next problem was

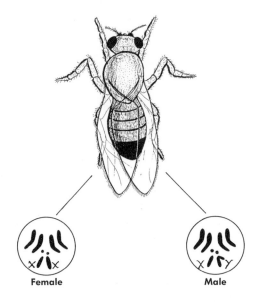

Figure 594. Diagram of fruit fly (*Drosophila melanogaster*) and diploid set of chromosomes of each sex. Sex chromosomes X and Y are marked. Males have three black bands on abdomen, which is rounded at tip; females have five black bands, with pointed abdomen. Many genetic concepts have been developed from extensive investigations on this now classical animal.

to find how chromosomes affected the hereditary pattern. This study led to an analysis of the chromosome structure and the idea of the gene as the physical basis of hereditary traits. The outstanding work of Thomas Hunt Morgan and his colleagues on the fruit fly (*Drosophila*) led to the mapping of chromosomes in which the location of genes was more or less definitely determined. Out of all this work there developed a new science, that of **cytogenetics.** In recent years the chromosome has been studied with renewed interest, as new techniques developed, with the main objective of finding and demonstrating the actual physical units or genes and their nature. Some recent developments along this line will come out in the following discussion.

Nature of chromosome

The important role played by chromosomes in heredity and development, their

722

Figure 595. Diploid chromosomes of *Drosophila*.

individualized structure, and the precision with which they are distributed at mitosis have made them of primary interest ever since cells were studied in detail. The fact that they contain the factors which control the hereditary pattern make them of especial interest to geneticists. Every aspect of their chemical and physical make-up is being closely scrutinized. Perhaps more has been learned about them in the past two decades than in all previous times, partly because of better techniques and partly because of more intensive study.

Chromosomes differ a great deal among the different organisms, although for a particular form they have in general a definite size and shape in each stage of their cycle (Figure 595). Fixatives may alter them to some extent, and in certain stages of mitosis they are more clearly seen than in others. In the metaphase and anaphase stages their general morphology shows up most distinctly, whereas in other stages they appear as fine chromatin threads. Whatever their appearance, they are distinct structural entities and retain their individuality throughout all stages of the cell cycle. Each chromosome is made up typically of an elongated body consisting of a matrix and a central, spiral thread called a **chromonema** which bears beadlike enlargements, the **chromomeres.** The chromomeres were first though to be identical with the **genes,** the chief hereditary factors, but many cytologists have more recently adopted the view that a chromomere may contain more than one gene, and some genes apparently are not associated with chromomeres at all. The various chromomeres appear in regular and constant patterns in a particular chromosome.

Chromosomes constant for a species

Each somatic cell in a given organism contains the same number of chromosomes. Somatic chromosomes of diploid organisms are found in pairs, the members of each pair being alike in size, in position of spindle attachment, and in bearing genes relating to the same hereditary characters. In each homologous pair of chromosomes, one has come from the father and the other from the mother. The number of chromosomes found in the various species of animals varies. The lowest diploid number in the cell of any organism is 2, which is found in certain roundworms; the largest number (300 or more) is found in some protozoa. In most forms the number is between 12 and 40, the most common diploid number being 24. Naturally, many forms wholly unrelated have the same number of chromosomes and so the number is without significance, for the nature of the genes is what differentiates different species of animals. In man the number is 46. Some chromosomes are as small as 0.25 micron in length and (with the exception of salivary chromosomes) some are as long as 50 microns. Within the haploid set of chromosomes of most species there are considerable differences in size and shape. In man, most chromosomes are 4 to 6 microns in length.

Mature germ cells have only one-half as many chromosomes as somatic cells. Only one member of each homologous pair of chromosomes is found in a mature, functional gamete.

Significance of reduction division

In each body or somatic cell there is a pair of genes (except sex-linked genes) for each trait, one gene from each parent. Since these genes are in paired, homologous chromosomes, when these chromosomes separate at the reduction division of meiosis the homologous genes must also separate, one gene going to each of the germ cells produced. Thus at the end of the maturation process each mature gamete (egg or sperm) contains one gene of every pair or a single set of every

Principles of inheritance 723

kind of gene instead of two genes for each character as is the case in somatic cells. The haploid number of chromosomes found in the germ cells does not consist of just any half of the diploid somatic number but must include one of the members of each homologous pair of chromosomes. A particular germ cell does not necessarily contain all the chromosomes from one or the other parent of the individual producing that germ cell. It is a matter of chance in the reduction division whether the paternal chromosome of a homologous pair goes to one daughter cell or the other, and the same is true of the maternal chromosome.

The real significance of the reduction division for explaining the principles of heredity lies mainly in the segregation of the chromosomes and consequently the genes which the chromosomes carry. We have seen that there are two genes for each trait that develops in the individual, but in the mature germ cells there is only one gene for a trait. Of course, when the zygote is formed at fertilization the homologous pairs of chromosomes (and genes) will be restored. It will be seen later that the factors of the genetical laws behave in a similar manner and were arrived at before the cytological explanation was forthcoming.

Salivary gland chromosomes

Details about the structure of chromosomes have been difficult to obtain because of their small size in most animals. Since most chromosomes are only a few microns in length, and each one bears many genes, little hope was held for discovering the real nature of the physical units of heredity. About 1934 Professor Painter of the University of Texas and some German investigators independently discovered in the salivary glands of the larvae of *Drosophila* and other flies chromosomes many times as large as those of the ordinary somatic or germinal chromosomes of these forms. Actually, these giant chromosomes had been discovered as early as 1881 by the Italian cytologist Balbiani in the larval forms of the midge fly, *Chirono-*

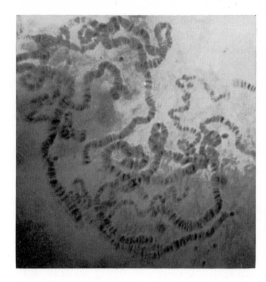

Figure 596. Chromosomes from salivary gland of larval fruit fly, *Drosophila*. These are among largest chromosomes found in animal cells. Bands of nucleoproteins may be loci of genes. Such chromosomes are sometimes called polytene because they appear to be made up of many chromonemata. These chromosomes are not confined to salivary glands but are also known to occur in other organs, such as gut and Malpighian tubules of most dipteran insects. Technique for their study is simply to crush salivary glands between cover glass and slide in drop of acetocarmine so that chromosomes are set free from nuclei and are spread out as shown in photograph. (Courtesy General Biological Supply House, Chicago.)

mus, but their real meaning was not detected until they were rediscovered. Their rediscovery marked a new era in the development of cytogenetics, for they afforded much new information about the structure and nature of chromosomes.

The salivary glands of the larval flies are a pair of club-shaped bodies attached to the pharynx and each is made up of about 100 cells. Each gland has attached to it a fat body which helps identify the gland. When the glands are stained with acetocarmine, the chromosomes can be seen more or less coiled up within the cells. When the cell membrane is disintegrated, the chromosomes are scattered out and can be easily studied. The giant chromosomes are elongated, ribbonlike bodies about 100 to 200 times longer than the ordinary chromosome (Figure 596). In some flies they lie separated from each other; in *Drosophila* they are attached to a dark mass called the **chromocenter.**

What are these chromosomes and what do they show? The chromosomes are really somatic prophase chromosomes with the homologous chromosomes closely paired throughout their length. Such a pairing of somatic chromosomes is unusual, for such a feature is commonly restricted to meiosis. In favorable preparations these double chromosomes appear as six single strands instead of four because two pairs are attached to the chromocenter by their centers, thus producing four arms, and the other two pairs are connected to the chromocenter by their ends. One of their most striking characteristics is the transverse bands with which they are made. Another feature is the number of chromonemata they possess. In the ordinary somatic chromosome there may be only one or two of these gene strings, but in the salivary gland chromosome there may be between 512 and 1,024 (*Drosophila*). This indicates that the chromonemata may have divided many times without being accompanied by the division of the whole chromosome; hence they are often called **polytene** chromosomes. A polytene chromosome may be considered a typical mitotic chromosome that has uncoiled and undergone many repeated duplications which have remained together in the same nucleus.

The transverse bands appear to be made up of chromatic granules, the chromomeres. These bands result from the lateral apposition of the chromomeres on the adjacent fibrils or chromonemata. More than 6,000 of these bands have been found on the three large chromosomes of *Drosophila*. Of great genetical significance is the fact that the bands form a pattern that is constant for a given chromosome and that the bands in one chromosome are identical with those in the homologous mate. On the basis of differences in the

bands it is possible to make out different regions of the various chromosomes and to assign the basis of certain characters to particular regions of the chromosomes. In this way it has been possible to construct chromosome maps. Some investigators think the bands represent the actual genes, but this view is not held by the majority of cytologists. It is not yet apparent whether the genes are located within the bands or in the regions between the bands. One interesting bit of information regarding these bands is that whenever flies are altered by radiation or x-rays, some of the bands in the giant chromosomes of their larvae are often missing. This would indicate that the bands have some relation to the genes.

The even larger lampbrush chromosomes found in the oöcytes of many vertebrates and some invertebrates are characterized by loops extending laterally which give them the appearance of a brush. These chromosomes each appear to be composed of two chromatids which form loops (gene loci) when they are active but are coiled up within a chromomere when at rest. Both salivary and lampbrush chromosomes may shed more light on the genetic relations of genes in the course of future investigations.

THE GENE THEORY

The term **gene** was given by Johannsen in 1909 to the hereditary factors of Mendel (1865). Genes represent the material bases or chemical entities which are responsible for the hereditary pattern of an organism. No one perhaps has seen a definite gene and much is yet to be discovered about the nature of genes; yet by much investigation, direct and indirect, a great deal has been learned about them. It is known that they belong to chromosomes and go wherever chromosomes go. By long, patient genetical experiments their relative positions (loci) on the chromosomes have been mapped in many cases. Evidence indicates that they are arranged in linear order on the chromosome like beads on a string and in some cases (salivary gland chromosomes) are assigned to definite bands. Since chromosomes are few and genes are many in number, each chromosome must contain many genes (linkage group). It is not known how many genes there are in an organism. Estimates of 10,000 (*Drosophila*) to 90,000 (man) have been made.

Each zygote of sexual reproduction has two sets (diploid) of homologous chromosomes, one set from each parent; in other words, there are two of each kind of chromosomes, one from the father and the other from the mother. When the gametes are formed in meiosis, disjunction of the homologous chromosomes occurs, so that each germ cell receives one or the other of the pair at random. Since the genes are a part of the chromosomes, their distribution will parallel that of the chromosomes. All the genes of a particular homologous chromosome, or **linkage group** will go at meiosis into one gamete and all the genes of the other homologous mate will go into another gamete. If each gene occupies a specific locus in a specific chromosome, all the genes occupying this locus in a given pair of homologous chromosomes are called **alleles.** Just as members of a homologous pair of chromosomes are derived from separate parents, so does each member of a pair of alleles come from a different parent. In some cases a set of alleles may contain more than two members (maybe as many as twenty) and such sets are called multiple alleles. But, normally, only two alleles for any one hereditary character may occur in a somatic cell and only one in a gamete.

The two members of a homologous pair of chromosomes often exchange corresponding segments or blocks of genes. Such is called **crossing-over.** There is visible evidence of this physical exchange, for at the beginning of the first meiotic division the two members of each pair of chromosomes come into side-by-side contact (synapsis) and become twisted. When they separate they have exchanged parts. Naturally, the genes on the traded portions will be exchanged also. The new

combinations so found are as stable as the original ones. Linkage groups are also altered by such rearrangements as the linear reversal of gene sequence in the **reversal of a chromosome segment,** by the shifting of a chromosome segment to another part of the same chromosome **(translocation),** by **polyploid changes** in chromosome number, etc.

Although genes can reproduce themselves exactly for many generations, they do occasionally undergo abrupt changes called **mutations.*** A mutation involves a change in the chemical arrangement of a gene so that there is a difference in the structure and action of a gene which may result in a new character. In such cases the mutant gene now faithfully reproduces itself just as before. The natural mutation rate, which varies with different animals, is slow but can be speeded up artificially by such agents as radiation, which is cumulative in its effect, by temperature, by certain chemicals, and by other environmental agents. Mutations are called **random** because they are unpredictable and because they are unrelated to the needs of the organism, but some mutations are favored by tissue and environmental conditions. Many mutant genes are actually harmful because they may replace adaptive genes which have evolved in the long evolution of the organism. However, a minority of mutant genes are advantageous and have great significance in evolution. Some mutant genes are dominant genetically, but more are recessive and their effects are masked by normal dominant alleles. Mutation may be a reversible process, and the difference between the mutation of a gene in one direction and its mutation rate in the reverse direction is called its **mutation pressure.** Such reverse mutations indicate that true mutations are not gene losses. Gene mutations may occur in one direction more frequently than in others, and thus certain mutant alleles are far more common than others. Most mutations ordinarily occur in one gene at a time

---

*Refer to Chapter 5, Principle 22.

and thus are called **point mutations.** In the long evolution of any organism, all the genes it carries have had time to mutate and all its present genes are really mutants.

There is some evidence that some genetic variability is the result of self-duplicating, hereditary units in the cytoplasm. Such units are called **plasma-genes** and are apparently transmitted only by the cytoplasm. Two examples of this type of cytoplasmic inheritance are plant plastids and the "kappa" (killer) substances of *Paramecium*. In some cases the plasmagenes depend upon the nuclear genes for their reproduction and maintenance. Plasmagenes can mutate and produce definite characters. They also have Mendelian patterns of genetical behavior, but some are distributed more or less at random to daughter cells at cell division. Their exact role in the over-all hereditary pattern of organisms is still obscure.

Genes perform a unique role in cellular economy. As the chief functional unit of genetical material, they determine the basic architecture of every cell, the nature and life of the cell, the specific protein syntheses, the enzyme formation, the self-reproduction of the cell, and, directly or indirectly, the entire metabolic function of the cell. By their property to mutate, to be assorted and shuffled around in different combinations, genes have become the basis for our modern interpretation of evolution. Genes are molecular patterns which can maintain their identities for many generations, can be self-duplicated in each generation, and can control cell processes by allowing their specificities to be copied. Genes thus have the properties of controlling protein specificities, of determining the specificities of new genes, and, by changing their own specificities (mutation), furnishing the materials for evolutionary advancements and adaptations. Specifically, genes are able to store information which they can transmit as needed for a basic pattern of life and its maintenance. What things the gene can do, or its varied properties, are intimately associated with its chemical structure. The nature of the gene substance has been the subject of intense biological investigation during the past decade. It is now known that genes, like chromosomes, are made up chiefly of nucleoproteins which consist of nucleic acids and proteins (histones and protamines). Life as we know it really began with the first formation of nucleoproteins, because they have the properties of self-duplication and specificity. Nucleoproteins so far as known are the only molecules with the power of self-duplication.

The evidence indicates that the nucleic acid components are the essential parts which display the properties of genes, because (1) the constant amount of nucleic acid for each chromosome set of a given organism, (2) the transfer of the donor's genetic traits when a donor's nucleus is transplanted into a recipient cell, and (3) the ability of nucleic acid extracts from one kind of bacteria to produce hereditary transformation in another type of bacteria.

The nucleic acids are each chemically made up of a purine or pyrimidine base, a sugar, and phosphoric acid. On the basis of the kind of sugar (desoxyribose or ribose), the nucleic acids are divided into two main groups: **desoxyribonucleic acid (DNA)** and **ribonucleic acid (RNA).** DNA occurs only in the nucleus where it is the major structural component of genes; RNA is found throughout the cell, being especially abundant in nucleoli and in the cytoplasm. The nucleic acids may be broken down chemically or enzymatically into **nucleotides.** A nucleic acid molecule thus is made up of many nucleotides joined to form long chains. Each nucleotide consists of phosphoric acid, either desoxyribose or ribose sugar, and a pyrimidine or purine base. The purine units are adenine and guanine; the pyrimidines are cytosine, thymine, and uracil. Five kinds of nucleotides are recognized on the basis of these purines and pyrimidines: (1) adenine-sugar-phosphate, (2) guanine-sugar-phosphate, (3) cytosine-sugar-phosphate, (4) thymine-sugar-phosphate, and (5) uracil-sugar-phosphate.

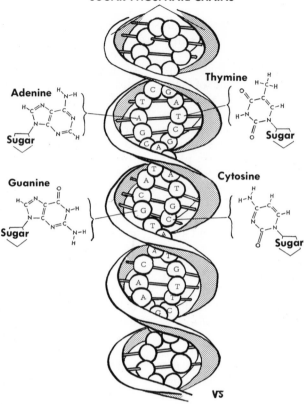

SUGAR-PHOSPHATE CHAINS

Adenine

Sugar

Guanine

Sugar

Thymine

Sugar

Cytosine

Sugar

VS

Figure 597. Structure of DNA (desoxyribose nucleic acid) molecule. Evidence at present indicates that molecule is formed by two interlocking helixes or chains of nucleotides. Each nucleotide is made up of a desoxyribose sugar attached to a phosphoric acid molecule on one side and to a nitrogenous base on another side. Bases are of four kinds: adenine (**A**), cytosine (**C**), guanine (**G**), and thymine (**T**). It will be noted that adenine is always paired with thymine and guanine with cytosine. This pairing is necessary because in every pair only a large base and a small one will fill the space available between the parallel sugar-phosphate chains. Apparently the nucleotides occur in a great variety of sequences, so that long double chains contain many combinations which confer specificity on a given DNA molecule, just as many words are formed out of a few letters of the alphabet. Since each spiral thread is complement of the other, this structure of DNA molecule provides basis for duplication, for either spiral chain can serve as a template on which a missing part of other spiral can reconstruct itself. Various sections (genes?) of the long molecule may also serve as pattern codes for enzymes, proteins, and other kinds of molecules so necessary for living cell.

The DNA molecule has the first four of these nucleotides; the RNA has the first three and the last one. Although the phosphate-sugar part of the long chain of nucleotides is regular, the base attached to the sugar is not always the same and the order of these bases is irregular and varies from one section to another of the nucleic acid molecule. Depending upon the proportion and sequence of the nucleotides there is an almost unlimited variety of nucleic acids. The evidence at present indicates that the nucleic acid of genes is DNA and that it is arranged in a double chain of nucleotides. In the single chain the nucleotides are so united that the phosphate group of one molecule is linked to the sugar molecule of the

728

next. These two chains or threads run parallel to each other and are held together by hydrogen bonds between bases. The pairing of these bases is very specific. Adenine of one chain always pairs with thymine in the other, and guanine in one chain always with cytosine in the other. A given base may occur at any location in either chain, but when present in one its partner base in the other chain is specifically determined. Each chain is thus the exact complement of the other.

According to the Watson-Crick model, the DNA molecule consists of two complementary polynucleotide chains helically wound around a central axis. In this arrangement the phosphate and sugar groups are on the outside of the central axis, the bases inside and connected to each other by hydrogen bonds. The functionally different genes for each organism are made possible by the varied arrangements of the four nucleotides. Such base pair sequences can provide a large number of coded pieces of information much as the amino acids of proteins can account for their specificity of action. A gene may be regarded as a segment of a DNA molecule and its chief function is to serve as templates for coded information which directly or indirectly control the nature of proteins and the varied metabolic processes of the cell. But those sections that serve as templates vary in size and length, and thus the gene cannot be considered a fixed part of a chromosome but only a functional unit. One way this information could be conveyed is for the DNA of a gene to act as a template for the formation of RNA, which in the microsomes or elsewhere could in turn serve as the template for protein syntheses. In certain viruses only RNA is found, and genetic information must be carried by this nucleic acid. With the use of radioactive tracers it has been found that, in replication, each new chromosome is made up of one-half old material and one-half newly synthesized material. In terms of DNA, this is explained by the separation of the two complementary threads of the helix, with each thread in turn reforming a complementary thread by the template method for a new partner from raw materials of the cytoplasm. Mutation could be explained by the failure of the gene in self-copying or a change in chemical arrangement so that different genetic information is given out.

The exact role of the other nucleic acid, RNA, is obscure, but it has been suggested that it is formed in the chromosomes, obtains its specifications from the genes, and is stored temporarily in the nucleoli. Later, it is transferred to the microsomes (fine particles scattered through the cytoplasm) where most protein synthesis occurs under the direction of RNA. According to this unproved scheme the specificity of the DNA gene is passed by way of RNA to the cell proteins as the latter are synthesized in the microsomes.

Viruses and bacteria have been helpful tools in understanding the nature of genetic materials and the mechanism of heredity. In the typical virus the DNA core is surrounded by a protein coat in the form of a capsule. When a virus enters a cell to reproduce, only the DNA core enters; the protein coat remains outside. In the phenomenon of transformation, extracts of the DNA core from one strain of bacteria may be transferred to a second strain of bacteria which incorporates some of the DNA material into its own genetic system. The recipient cells, as a result, produce new characters. A similar phenomenon is transduction, in which a bacteriophage (bacterial parasite) can transfer DNA from one host to another. The bacteriophage does this by disintegrating one kind of bacterium, picking up some of the DNA of the host bacterium, and transferring this genetic material to the next host of another strain. The latter may acquire new traits by this method. Groups of linked genes and not single genes appear to be transferred by this process. Both transformation and transduction represent a type of non-Mendelian heredity, for sexual fusion of the bacterial cells is not involved.

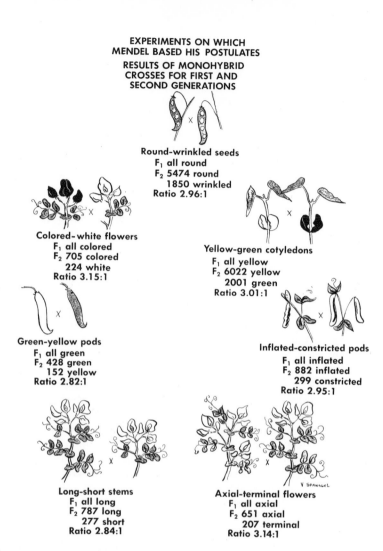

EXPERIMENTS ON WHICH MENDEL BASED HIS POSTULATES

RESULTS OF MONOHYBRID CROSSES FOR FIRST AND SECOND GENERATIONS

Round-wrinkled seeds
F_1 all round
F_2 5474 round
1850 wrinkled
Ratio 2.96:1

Colored-white flowers
F_1 all colored
F_2 705 colored
224 white
Ratio 3.15:1

Yellow-green cotyledons
F_1 all yellow
F_2 6022 yellow
2001 green
Ratio 3.01:1

Green-yellow pods
F_1 all green
F_2 428 green
152 yellow
Ratio 2.82:1

Inflated-constricted pods
F_1 all inflated
F_2 882 inflated
299 constricted
Ratio 2.95:1

Long-short stems
F_1 all long
F_2 787 long
277 short
Ratio 2.84:1

Axial-terminal flowers
F_1 all axial
F_2 651 axial
207 terminal
Ratio 3.14:1

Figure 598. Seven experiments of Mendel.

MENDEL'S INVESTIGATIONS

The first man to formulate the cardinal principles of heredity was Gregor Johann Mendel (1822-1884), who was connected with the Augustinian Monastery at Bruenn, Moravia, then a part of Austria, later a part of Czechoslovakia. In the small monastery garden he conducted his experiments upon hybridization which resulted in two clear-cut laws that bear his name. In the conduction of these experiments from 1856 to 1864 he examined with great care and accuracy many thousands of plants. He worked with several kinds of plants, but his classical observations were made on the garden pea. In the first place, there were several distinct varieties of these plants which always bred true, because gardeners over a long period by careful selection had produced pure strains. For example, some varieties were definitely dwarf and others were tall. A second reason for selecting peas was that they are self-fertilizing, but they are also capable of cross-fertilization as well. To simplify his problem he chose single characters and those that were sharply contrasted. Mere quantitative and intermeliate characters he carefully avoided. Mendel selected seven pairs of these contrasting characters, such as tall plants and dwarf plants, smooth seeds and wrinkled seeds, green cotyledons and yellow cotyledons, inflated pods and constricted pods, yellow pods and green pods, axial position of flowers and terminal position of flowers, and transparent seed coats and brown seed coats. Mendel crossed a plant having one of these characters with one having the contrasting character. He did this by removing the stamens from a flower, so that self-fertilization could not occur, and then on the stigma of this flower he placed the pollen from the flower of another plant which had the contrasting character. He then prevented the experimental flowers from being pollinated from other sources, such as wind and insects. When the cross-fertilized flower bore seeds, he noted the kind of plants (hybrids) they produced when planted. His next step was to cross these hybrids among themselves and to see what happened. He made careful counts of his plants, repeated his experiments, and worked out certain ratios.

Among other experiments, Mendel crossed pure tall plants with pure dwarf plants and found that the hybrids (F_1 or first filial generation) thus produced were all tall, just as tall as the tall parent which was involved in the cross. This result he found was always obtained whether the tall plant furnished the male germ cells or the female germ cells. Next, he crossed two of these hybrid tall plants together. From this cross he raised several hundred plants and found that both tall plants and dwarf plants were represented among them. He also noted that none of this generation (F_2 or second filial generation) were intermediate in size; they were either as tall or as short as the parents in the original cross. When he counted the actual number of tall and dwarf plants in the F_2 generation he found there were three times as many tall plants as dwarf ones, or a ratio of 3:1. His next step was to self-pollinate the plants in the F_2 generation, that is, the stigma of a flower was fertilized by the pollen of the same flower. The results showed that self-pollinated F_2 dwarf plants produced only dwarf plants, whereas one-third of the F_2 tall plants produced tall and the other two-thirds produced both tall and dwarf in the ratio of 3:1, just as the F_1 plants had done. This experiment showed that the dwarf plants were pure, for they at all times gave rise to short plants when self-pollinated; the tall plants contained both pure tall and hybrid tall. It also demonstrated that, although the dwarf character disappeared in the F_1 plants which were all tall, the character for dwarfness appeared in the F_2.

MENDEL'S LAWS

From the results of these and other experiments, Mendel formulated certain postulates. Mendel knew nothing about the cytological background of heredity, for chromosomes and genes were unknown to him. Instead of using the term genes as we do today, he called his inheritance units factors. He reasoned that the factors for tallness and dwarfness were units which did not blend when they were together. The F_1 generation contained both these units or factors but when these plants formed their germ cells, the factors separated out, so that each germ cell had only one factor. In a pure plant both factors were alike; in a hybrid they were different. He concluded that individual germ cells are always pure with respect to a pair of contrasting factors, even though the germ cells are formed from hybrids in which the contrasting characters are mixed. This idea formed the basis for his first principle, the **Law of Segregation**, which states that whenever two factors are brought together in a hybrid, when that hybrid forms its germ cells the factors segregate into separate gametes and each germ cell is pure with respect to that character. Thus, in the gametes of the F_1 plants, half of the germ cells will bear the factor for tallness and half for dwarfness; no germ cell will contain both factors.

In the crosses involving the factors for

tallness and dwarfness, in which the resulting hybrids were tall, Mendel called the tall factor **dominant** and the short **recessive.** Similarly, the other pairs of characters which he studied showed dominance and recessiveness. Thus, when plants with yellow unripe pods were crossed with green unripe pods, the hybrids all contained yellow pods. In the F_2 generation the expected ratio of 3 yellow to 1 green was obtained. Whenever a dominant factor (gene) is present, the recessive one cannot produce an effect. The recessive factor will show up only when both factors are recessive, or, in other words, a pure condition.

The law of segregation deals only with one pair of contrasting characters. Mendel also ascertained what would happen when a cross is made between plants differing in two pairs of contrasting characters. Thus, when a tall plant with the yellow type of pod was crossed with a dwarf plant bearing green pods, the F_1 generation was all tall and yellow, for these factors are dominant. When the F_1 hybrids were crossed with each other, the result was 9 tall and yellow, 3 tall and green, 3 dwarf and yellow, and 1 dwarf and green. In this experiment each factor separated independently of the other and showed up in new combinations. This is Mendel's second law, or the **Law of Independent Assortment,** which states that whenever two or more pairs of contrasting characters are brought together in a hybrid, the factors of different pairs segregate independently of one another. Rarely do two organisms differ in only one pair of contrasting characters; nearly always they differ in many. The second law of Mendel therefore deals with two or more pairs of contrasting characters.

Crosses involving more than two pairs of characters result in still more complicated ratios of types of offspring. However, it is usually convenient to work with just one pair of contrasting characters, for each pair may be considered by itself. It may be stated here that Mendel's second law is true only when the factors for the different pairs of characters are

located on different pairs of chromosomes. It happened that all seven pairs of characters Mendel worked with were on different pairs of chromosomes, but since his laws became known many pairs of characters have been found on the same chromosome, which alters the original Mendelian ratios. This modification does not detract, however, from the basic significance of his great laws.

Although Mendel published his observations on the principles of heredity in The Proceedings of the Society of Natural Science of Bruenn in 1866, his experiments attracted no attention and apparently were forgotten. In 1900 three investigators, De Vries in Holland, Tschermak in Austria, and Correns in Germany independently rediscovered his laws but found that the obscure priest had already published them thirty-four years before.

EXPLANATION OF MENDELIAN RATIOS

In representing his crosses Mendel used letters as symbols. For dominant characters he employed capitals and for recessives, corresponding small letters. Thus the factors or genes for pure tall plants might be represented by TT, the pure recessive by tt, and the hybrid of the two plants by Tt. In diagram form one of Mendel's original crosses (tall plant and dwarf plant) could be represented in this manner:

	(tall)	(dwarf)
Parents	TT	× tt
Gametes	all T	all t
F_1	Tt	
	(hybrid tall)	
Crossing hybrids	Tt	× Tt
Gametes	T,t	T,t
F_2	TT Tt tT tt	
	(3 tall to 1 dwarf)	

It is convenient in most Mendelian crosses to use the checkerboard method devised by Punnett for representing the various combinations resulting from a cross. Thus, in the previous F_2 cross the following scheme would apply.

Eggs

	T	t
T	TT (pure tall)	Tt (hybrid tall)
t	Tt (hybrid tall)	tt (pure dwarf)

(Sperm labels the left side)

Ratio: 3 tall, 1 dwarf

Mendel's experiment involving two pairs of contrasting characters instead of one pair may be demonstrated in the following diagram.

In the cross between tall and dwarf it will be noted that there are two types of visible characters, **tall** and **dwarf**. These are called **phenotypes**. On the basis of

genetic formulas there are three hereditary types, TT, Tt, and tt. These are called **genotypes**. In the cross involving two pairs of contrasting characters (**tall yellow and dwarf green**) there are in the F_2 generation four phenotypes: **tall yellow, tall green, dwarf yellow,** and **dwarf green.** The genotypes are nine in number: $TTYY$, $TTYy$, $TtYY$, $TtYy$, $TTyy$, $Ttyy$, $ttYY$, $ttYy$, and $ttyy$. The F_2 ratios in any cross involving more than one pair of contrasting pairs can be found by combining the ratios in the cross of one pair of factors. Thus the genotypes will be $(3)^n$ and the phenotypes $(3:1)^n$. To illustrate, in a cross of two pairs of factors the phenotypes will be in the ratio of $(3:1)^2 = 9:3:3:1$. The genotypes in such a cross will be $(3)^2 = 9$. If three pairs of characters are involved, the phenotypes will be $(3:1)^3 = 27:9:9:9:3:3:3:1$. The genotypes will be $(3)^3 = 27$. Thus it is seen that the numerical ratio of the various

	(tall, yellow)		(dwarf, green)
Parents	TTYY	×	ttyy
Gametes	all TY		all ty
F¹		TtYy	
		(hybrid tall, hybrid yellow)	
Crossing hybrids	TtYy	×	TtYy
Gametes	TY, Ty, tY, ty		TY, Ty, tY, ty
F²		(see checkerboard)	

	TY	Ty	tY	ty
TY	TTYY pure tall pure yellow	TTYy pure tall hybrid yellow	TtYY hybrid tall pure yellow	TtYy hybrid tall hybrid yellow
Ty	TTYy pure tall hybrid yellow	TTyy pure tall pure green	TtYy hybrid tall hybrid yellow	Ttyy hybrid tall pure green
tY	TtYY hybrid tall pure yellow	TtYy hybrid tall hybrid yellow	ttYY pure dwarf pure yellow	ttYy pure dwarf hybrid yellow
ty	TtYy hybrid tall hybrid yellow	Ttyy hybrid tall pure green	ttYy pure dwarf hybrid yellow	ttyy pure dwarf pure green

Ratio: 9 tall yellow, 3 tall green. 3 dwarf yellow, 1 dwarf green.

phenotypes is a power of the binomial $(3 + 1)^n$ whose exponent (n) equals the number of pairs of heterozygous genes in F_2. This is true only when one member of each pair of genes is dominant. By experience, then, one may determine the ratios of phenotypes in a cross without using the checkerboard. In a dihybrid (9:3:3:1 ratio), for instance, it will be seen that those phenotypes which make up the dominants of each pair will be 9/16 of the whole F_2; each of the 3/16 phenotypes will consist of one dominant and one recessive; and the 1/16 phenotype will consist of the two recessives.

LAWS OF PROBABILITY

When Mendel worked out the ratios for his various crosses, they were approximations and not certainties. In his 3 to 1 ratio of tall and short plants, for instance, the resulting phenotypes did not come out exactly 3 tall to 1 short. All genetical experiments are based on probability; that is, the outcome of the events is uncertain and there is an element of chance in the final results. Probability values are measures of expectations. Probabilities are expressed in fractions, or it is always a number between 0 and 1. This probability number (p) is found by dividing the number (m) of favorable cases (i.e., a certain event) by the total number (n) of possible outcomes: $p = \dfrac{m}{n}$

When there are two possible outcomes, such as in tossing a coin, the chance of getting heads is $p = \frac{1}{2}$, or one chance in two.

The more often a particular event occurs, the more closely will the number of favorable cases approach the number predicted by the p value. Probability predictions are often unreliable when there are only a few occurrences.

The probability of independent events occurring together involves the **Product Rule,** which is simply the product of their individual probabilities. When two coins are tossed together, the probability of getting two heads is $\frac{1}{2} \times \frac{1}{2} = \frac{1}{4}$, or 1 chance in 4. Here, again, this prediction is

most likely to occur if the coins are tossed a sufficient number of times.

The ratios of inheritance in a monohybrid cross of dominant and recessive genes can be explained by the Product Rule. In the gametes of the hybrids the sperm may carry either the dominant or the recessive gene; the same applies to the eggs. The probability that the sperm carries the dominant is $\frac{1}{2}$ and the probability of an egg carrying the dominant is also $\frac{1}{2}$. The probability of a zygote obtaining two dominant genes is $\frac{1}{2} \times \frac{1}{2}$, or $\frac{1}{4}$. Thus 25% of the offspring will probably be pure dominants. The same principle applies to the recessive gene which will be pure for 25% of the offspring. The heterozygous gene combinations will be found by the sum of the two possible combinations—a sperm with a dominant gene and an egg with a recessive gene, and a sperm with a recessive gene and an egg with a dominant gene—which yields 50% heterozygotes. Thus we have the 1:2:1 ratio.

TERMINOLOGY OF GENETICS

Genetics in common with other branches of science has built up its own terminology. Some of the terms first proposed by Mendel have been replaced by those which seem more suitable in the light of present-day knowledge. These terms are all important to the student of heredity for they are essential in understanding the analyses of genetic problems. Whenever a cross involves only one pair of contrasting characters, it is called a **mono hybrid;** when the cross has two pairs, it is a **dihybrid;** when the cross has three pairs, it is a **trihybrid;** and when it has more than three pairs, it is a **polyhybrid.** Characters which show in the F_1 are **dominant,** those which are hidden are **recessive.** When a dominant always shows up in the phenotype it is said to have **complete dominance;** when it sometimes fails to manifest itself it is called **incomplete dominance.** When two characters form a contrasting pair, they are called **alleles** or **allelomorphs.** The term factor which Mendel used so widely is replaced by gene. A **zygote** is the union of two gametes; whenever the two members of a pair of genes are alike in a zygote, the latter is **homozygous** for that particular character; when the genes are unlike for a given character, the zygote is **heterozygous**. A **hybrid**, for instance, is a heterozygote, and a **pure** character is a homozygote.

ADVANCES IN GENETICS SINCE MENDEL'S LAWS REDISCOVERED

The rediscovery of Mendel's laws in 1900 served as an enormous stimulus to the study of genetics. The basic contribution of Mendel was that hereditary characters behave as units. His principles have been abundantly verified by many investigators. Since his time, however, it has been necessary to modify and extend some of his conclusions. It has been found that his laws are not so simple and direct as he first proposed them. Many of the modifications advanced, however, served all the more to strengthen Mendel's concepts. It has already been pointed out that the principle of Independent Assortment applies only when the pairs of contrasting genes are in different chromosomes. Since his time the phenomena of linkage and crossing-over make necessary a modification of the law. The principles of dominance and recessiveness are no longer stressed as much as formerly, for they are not well marked in many crosses. The idea of unit character is no longer thought of as Mendel thought of it, for it is now known that many factors may enter into the development of a particular character. Adult characters as such are not found in germ cells, but only differentiation determines which cells cause a character to express itself in a certain way.

Although many significant investigations have been made in genetics since 1900, none have been more fruitful than those performed by Professor Thomas Hunt Morgan and his colleagues on the fruit fly, *Drosophila*. This little fly, which is much smaller than the common house fly, is found on decaying fruit. It is ideal for genetical experimentation because it produces so many generations within a few weeks. Morgan started his work on these forms about 1910, and now the heredity of no animal is better known than this common fly. Many of its characters are easily recognized and followed, and several striking mutations have helped explain the more intricate mechanism of heredity. As many as 500 genes have been mapped on its four pairs of chromosomes. The principles of linkage and crossing-over have also been best explained in this form. In addition, the salivary gland chromosomes, which have yielded so much information about the nature of the gene, were also first discovered in this fly.

One of the greatest advancements in understanding the physical basis of heredity made since Mendel's laws were known is the parallelism between these laws and the behavior of the chromosomes (and genes) during the processes of maturation and fertilization. The Sutton-Boveri hypothesis has already been described earlier in this chapter. It may be regarded as the one basic concept of biology, for Morgan's great work, as well as the more recent work on the salivary gland chromosome, has given striking confirmation of the principle.

THE TESTCROSS

The dominant characters in the offspring of a cross are all of the same phenotypes whether they are homozygous or heterozygous. For instance, in Mendel's experiment of tall and dwarf characters, it is impossible to determine the genetic constitution of the tall plants of the F_2 generation by mere inspection of the tall plants. Three-fourths of this generation are tall, but which of them are heterozygous recessive dwarf? The test is to cross the F_2 generation (dominant hybrids) with pure recessives. If the tall plant is homozygous, all the plants in such a testcross will be tall, thus:

TT (tall) $\times$ tt (dwarf)
Tt (hybrid tall)

If, on the other hand, the tall plant is

heterozygous, the offspring will be half tall and half dwarf, thus:

$$Tt \times tt$$
Tt (tall) or tt (dwarf)

The **testcross** is often used in modern genetics for the analysis of the genetic constitution of the offspring as well as for a quick way to make homozygous desirable stocks of animals and plants.

INCOMPLETE DOMINANCE

A cross that always shows the heterozygotes as distinguished from the pure dominants is afforded by the four-o'clock flower *(Mirabilis)* (Figure 599), discovered since Mendel's time. Whenever a red-flowered variety is crossed with a white-flowered variety, the hybrid (F_1), instead of being red or white according to whichever is dominant, is actually intermediate between the two and is *pink*. Thus the homozygotes are either red or white, but the heterozygotes are pink. The testcross is therefore unnecessary to determine the nature of the genotype.

In the F_2 generation, when pink flowers are crossed with pink flowers, one-fourth will be red, one-half pink, and one-fourth white.

This cross may be represented in this fashion:

	(red flower)	(white flower)
Parents	RR	rr
Gametes	R,R	r,r
F_1		Rr
		(all pink)
Crossing hybrids	Rr $\times$	Rr
Gametes	R,r	R,r
F_2	RR Rr	rR rr
	(red) (pink)	(pink) (white)

In this kind of cross neither of the genes demonstrates complete dominance; therefore, the heterozygote is a blending of both red and white characters. A similar phenomenon is found in the Blue Andalusian fowl in which a cross between black and white varieties produces a hybrid blue. In a cross between red and white cattle a roan hybrid is obtained. In both these cases of fowl and cattle a

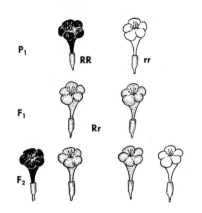

Figure 599. Cross between red and white four-o'clock flowers. Red and white are homozygous, pink is heterozygous (stippled).

heterozygote always gives rise to blue or roan, respectively.

PENETRANCE AND EXPRESSIVITY

Penetrance refers to the percentage frequency with which a gene manifests phenotypic effect. If a dominant gene or a recessive gene in a homozygous state always produces a detectable effect, it is said to have **complete penetrance.** If dominant or homozygous recessive genes fail to show phenotypic expression in every case, it is called **incomplete** or **reduced penetrance.** Environmental factors may be responsible for the degree of penetrance, for some genes may be more sensitive to such influences than are other genes. The genotype responsible for diabetes mellitus, for instance, may be present but the disease does not always occur because of reduced penetrance. All of Mendel's experiments apparently had 100% penetrance.

The phenotypic variation in the expression of a gene is known as **expressivity.** For instance, a heritable allergy may cause more severe symptoms in one person than in another. Environmental factors may cause different degrees in the appearance of a phenotype. Other genes in the hereditary constitution of one may also modify the expression of a trait. What is inherited is a certain genotype, but how it is expressed phenotypically is determined by environmental and other factors.

SOME SPECIAL FORMS OF HEREDITY

The types of crosses already described are simple in that the characters involved are due to the action of a single gene, but many cases are known in which the characters are the result of two or more genes. At first these more complex cases were thought to be non-Mendelian, for they often produce unusual ratios. Most of these crosses, however, are now considered to be merely modifications of the Mendelian expectations and do not invalidate the basic laws of Mendel. Mendel probably did not appreciate the real significance of the genotype as contrasted with the visible character, the phenotype. We now know that many different genotypes may be expressed as a single phenotype.

It is also known that many genes have more than a single effect. A gene for eye color, for instance, may be the ultimate cause for eye color, yet at the same time it may be responsible for influencing the development of other characters as well. Also, many unlike genes may occupy the same locus on a chromosome, but not, of course, all at one time. Thus more than two alternative characters may effect the same character. Such genes are called **multiple alleles** or factors. In the fruit fly (*Drosophila*) there are 18 alleles for eye color alone. Not more than two of these genes can be in any one individual and only one in a gamete. What is the reason for multiple alleles? The answer is that all genes can mutate in several different ways if given time and thus can give rise to several alternative conditions. In this way, many alleles for a particular locus on a chromosome may have evolved and added to the genetic pool of a population. Although it cannot be proved, it is thought that all genes present in an organism are mutants. In some cases dominance is lacking between two members of a set of multiple alleles, but usually one is dominant over the other. In *Drosophila*, the gene for red eye color (wild type) is dominant over all other alleles of the eye color series; the gene for white eye is recessive to all the others.

Some of these unusual cases of inheritance are described in the following discussions on supplementary, complementary, cumulative, and lethal factors and pseudoalleles.

Supplementary factors. The variety of comb forms found in chickens illustrates the action of supplementary genes (Figure 600). The common forms of comb are *rose, pea, walnut,* and *single.* Of these, the pea comb and the rose comb are dominant to the single comb. For instance, when a pea comb is crossed with a single comb, all the F_1 are pea and the F_2 shows a ratio of 3 pea to 1 single. When the two dominants, pea and rose, are crossed with each other, an entirely new kind of comb, walnut, is found in the F_1 generation. Each of these genes supplements the other in the production of a kind of comb different from each of the dominants. In the F_2 generation the ratio is 9 walnut, 3 rose, 3 pea, and 1 single. The walnut comb cannot thus be considered a unit character but is merely the phenotype's expression of pea and rose when they act together.

Inspection of the ratio reveals that two pairs of genes are involved. If P represents the gene for the pea comb and p its

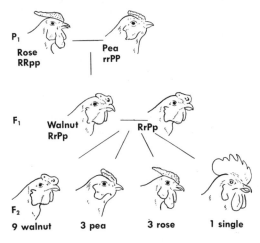

Figure 600. Heredity of comb forms in chickens.

recessive allelomorph and if R represents the gene for the rose comb and r its recessive allelomorph, then the pea comb formula would be PPrr and the one for rose comb, ppRR. Any individual having both dominant genes has a walnut comb. When no dominant gene is present, the comb is single. The cross may be diagramed as follows:

Parents   PPrr   ×   ppRR
            (pea comb)   (rose comb)
Gametes   all Pr   all pR
F₁   PpRr   ×   PpRr
                    (walnut)   (walnut)
Gametes   PR, Pr, pR, pr × PR, Pr, pR, pr

By the checkerboard method the F_2 will show 9 walnut, 3 pea, 3 rose, and 1 single. It will be seen that genotypes with the combinations of PR will give walnut phenotypes; those with P, pea; those with R, rose; and those lacking in both P and R, single.

Complementary factors. When two genes will produce a visible effect together, but each alone will show no visible effect, they are referred to as **complementary genes.** Some varieties of sweet peas can be used to illustrate this kind of cross. When two white-flowered varieties of these are crossed, the F_1 will show all colored (reddish or purplish) flowers. When these F_1 are self-fertilized, the F_2 will show a phenotypic ratio of 9 colored to 7 white flowers. This is really a ratio of 9:3:3:1 because the last three groups cannot be distinguished phenotypically. The explanation lies in the fact that in one of the white varieties of flowers there is a gene (C) for a colorless color base (chromogen) and in the other white variety a gene (E) for an enzyme which can change chromogen into a color. Only when chromogen and the enzyme are brought together is a colored flower produced. The cross may be diagramed in this way:

Parents   CCee   ×   ccEE
            (white)   (white)
Gametes   all Ce   all cE
F₁   CcEe   ×   CcEe
                    (colored)   (colored)
Gametes   CE, Ce, cE, ce   CE, Ce, cE, ce

By the checkerboard method, the F_2 phenotypes will be as follows:

9 colored (CCEE, CCEe, CeEE, or CcEe)—both chromogen and enzyme
7 { 3 white (CCee, or Ccee)—only chromogen
    3 white (ccEE, or ccEe)—only enzyme
    1 white (ccee)—no chromogen or enzyme

Cumulative factors. Whenever several sets of alleles produce a cumulative effect on the same character, they are called **multiple genes** or factors. Several characteristics in man are influenced by multiple genes. In such cases the characters instead of being sharply marked off show continuous variation between two extremes. This is what is called **blending** or **quantitative inheritance.** In this kind of inheritance the children are more or less intermediate between the two parents. The best illustration of such a type is the degree of pigmentation in crosses between the Negro and the white race. The cumulative genes in such crosses have a quantitative expression. A pure-blooded Negro has two pairs of genes on separate chromosomes for pigmentation (AABB). On the other hand, a pure-blooded white will have the genes (aabb) for nonblack. In a mating between a homozygous Negro and a homozygous white, the mulatto (AaBb) will have a skin color intermediate between the black parent and the white. The genes for pigmentation in the cross show incomplete dominance. When such mulattoes are crossed (F_2), the children will show a variety of skin color depending upon the number of genes for pigmentation they inherit. Their skin color will range all the way from pure black (AABB) through dark brown (AABb or AaBB), half-colored (AAbb or AaBb or aaBB), light brown (Aabb or aaBb) to pure white (aabb). In the F_2 there will be the possibility of a child resembling the skin color of either grandparent, and the others will show intermediate grades. It is thus possible for parents heterozygous for skin color to produce children with darker colors and also with lighter colors than themselves.

738

The relationships can be seen in the following diagram:

Parents   AABB   ×   aabb
          (black)   (white)
Gametes   AB   ab
F₁   AaBb   ×   AaBb
                 (mulatto)   (mulatto)
Gametes   AB, Ab, aB, ab   AB, Ab, aB, ab

By the checkerboard method, the F_2 will show this ratio:

1 pure black (AABB)
4 dark brown (AABb or aABB)
6 half-colored mulattoes (AaBb, AAbb, or aaBB)
4 light brown (Aabb, aaBb)
1 pure white (aabb)

The student should realize that when the term pure white is used in a cross involving mulattoes, it refers solely to skin color and not to other characteristics, for other racial characteristics are inherited independently. Thus, in such a cross an individual may have pure white color (no genes for black) but could have other Negro characteristics.

Although skin color appears to depend upon the distribution of two pairs of genes, there are many other traits in human inheritance which involve more than two pairs. These more complicated cases result in more varied ratios than in the simpler cases. When there are so many genes involved in the production of traits, the latter often take the form of distribution curves. One such trait is stature in man where between a few extremely short and tall individuals there are many in between these extremes.

Pseudoalleles. Some genes which have similar phenotypic effects may be so closely linked together that they are often considered as multiple alleles. Instead of being a single locus with multiple alleles, there are two or more closely linked loci with genes acting on the same trait. Such genes are called **pseudoalleles,** or **duplicate genes.** The only way in which a geneticist can be sure that pseudoalleles exist is by crossing-over, which is very rare because the genes are so close together. It is thought that

pseudoalleles arose in the course of evolution as duplications of original genes and became slightly different in function by mutation. The fact that pseudoalleles act in a similar way indicates a common origin. The problem of pseudoalleles is complicated, and much investigation must be done to clarify it. The condition has been described in fruit flies and corn and affords some insight into the intricate evolution and nature of the gene.

Lethal factors. A lethal gene is one which, when present in a homozygous condition, will cause the death of the offspring. These have been found in both plants and animals, but the classical case is that found in mice. It has been known for a long time that the yellow race of the house mouse (*Mus musculus*) is heterozygous. Whenever two yellow mice are bred together, the progeny are always 2 yellow to 1 nonyellow. In such a case the expected ratio should be 1 pure yellow, 2 hybrid yellow, and 1 pure nonyellow. Examination of the pregnant yellow females shows that the homozygous yellow always dies as an embryo, which accounts for the unusual ratio of 2:1. What causes the lethal condition is not known. Some lethals bring about death in the early stages of the embryo, others in later stages. Some human defects are supposed to be caused by them. Although many lethal genes are recessive and produce their effects only when they are homozygous, there are other lethal genes that are dominant, causing nonlethal effects when heterozygous and lethal effects when homozygous. The creeper fowl, for instance, has very short legs in the heterozygous state; when homozygous, the chicks die before hatching.

SEX DETERMINATION

Before 1902 the cause of sex was variously ascribed to many different external and internal influences. Many of these early beliefs seem ridiculous to modern geneticists in the light of what is now known about sex determination. The first really scientific clue to its cause was discovered in 1902 by McClung, who found that in some species of bugs *(Hemiptera)* two kinds of sperm were formed in equal numbers. One kind contained among its regular set of chromosomes a so-called accessory chromosome which was lacking in the other kind of sperm. Since all the eggs of these species had the same number of haploid chromosomes, half the sperm would have the same number of chromosomes as the eggs and half of them would have one chromosome less. When an egg is fertilized by a spermatozoan carrying the accessory (sex) chromosome, the resulting offspring is a female; when fertilized by the spermatozoan without an accessory chromosome, the offspring is a male. There are, therefore, two kinds of chromosomes in every cell: X chromosomes determine sex (and sex-linked traits) and **autosomes** determine the other bodily traits. The particular type of sex determination just described is often called the XX-XO type, which indicates that the females have two X chromosomes and the male only one X chromosome (the O stands for its absence).

Later, other types of sex determination were discovered. In man and many other forms, there are the same number of chromosomes in each sex, but the sex chromosomes (XX) are alike in the female but unlike (XY) in the male. Hence the human egg contains 22 autosomes + 1 X chromosome; the sperm are of two kinds: half will carry 22 autosomes + 1 X and half will bear 22 autosomes + 1 Y. The Y chromosomes in such cases are diminutive. At fertilization, when two X chromosomes come together, the offspring will be a girl; when XY, it will be a boy.

A third type of sex determination is found in birds, moths, and butterflies in which the male has 2 X (or sometimes called ZZ) chromosomes and the female an X and Y (or ZW). In this latter case the male is homozygous for sex and the female is heterozygous.

Whether or not sex in animals is solely determined by the sex chromosomes may well be doubted, notably in the case of *Drosophila*. In this form certain intersexes have been found which suggest that auto-

somes may play a part in the development of sex. Due to irregularity (**nondisjunction**) in meiosis it is possible for a fly to have an extra set of autosomes in addition to the regular set. The female fly normally has 6 autosomes (expressed as 2 A) plus 2 X chromosomes. If a fly has 3 A plus 2 X, instead of being a female as expected from the sex chromosomes' composition, it actually is an intermediate between male and female. The extra autosomes have upset the genic balance, indicating that sex is determined by a quantitative relation between the X chromosomes and the autosomes. Also, through irregularities of meiotic divisions it is possible for a female to have a chromosome complex of 2 A plus 3 X, in which case she is called a **super female.** A **super male,** on the other hand, has 3 A plus 1 X. In both these cases the sex characteristics are exaggerated toward femaleness or maleness, respectively. These experiments also show that the X chromosomes carry more genes for femaleness and the autosomes more genes for maleness. These abnormalities in sex determination do not invalidate the various types of sex determination described earlier in this section when there is a normal genic balance between the autosomes and the sex chromosomes.

Sex ratios in certain forms can also be influenced by environmental forces. When toad eggs are partially dried out, the proportion of females over males is thereby increased, and variations in diet are also known to upset the ratio between the sexes of some animals.

An interesting abnormality of sex is illustrated by the so-called **gynandromorphs** or **sex mosaics.** In such cases one part of the body shows male and the other female characteristics. It is due to the irregular distribution or loss of sex chromosomes during early development. Thus a zygote with 2 X chromosomes could lose one of the X's from one of the early blastomeres and all the descendants of that cell would have male characteristics; the 2 X cells would be female. Such abnormalities are found in insects in which the sex characteristics of the cell depend mainly upon the sex chromosomes. They are also excellent examples for the confirmation of the chromosomal determination of sex.

SEX-LINKED INHERITANCE

Sex-linked inheritance refers to the carrying of genes by the X chromosomes for body characters which have nothing to do with sex. The sex chromosomes in addition to determining sex in an organism also have genes for other body traits, and because of this the inheritance of these characters are linked with that of sex. The X chromosome is known to contain many such genes, the Y chromosome only a few regardless of its small size. Such sex-linked traits are not always limited to one sex but may be transmitted from the mother to her male offspring or from the father to his female offspring. One of the examples of a sex-linked character was discovered by Morgan in *Drosophila* (Figure 601). The normal eye color of this fly is red, but mutations for white eye do occur. The genes for eye color are known to be carried in the X chromosome. If a white-eyed male and a red-eyed female are crossed, all the F_1's are red eyed, for this trait is dominant. If these F_1's are interbred, all the females of F_2's will have red eyes and half the males will have red eyes and the other half white eyes. No white-eyed females are found in this generation; only the males have the recessive character (white eyes). The gene for white-eyed, being recessive, should appear only in a homozygous condition. However, since the male has only one X chromosome (the Y does not carry a gene for eye color), white eyes will appear whenever the X chromosome carries the gene for this trait. If the reciprocal cross is made in which the females are white-eyed and the males red-eyed, all the F_1 females are red-eyed and all the males white-eyed. This is called **crisscross inheritance**. If these F_1's are interbred, the F_2 will show equal numbers of red-eyed and white-eyed males and females.

If the allele for red-eyed is represented

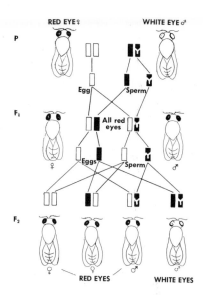

Figure 601. Sex-linkage in fruit fly, *Drosophila,* involving cross between homozygous red-eyed female and homozygous white-eyed male. Red eye color is dominant to white eye color. Genes for red eyes (black) and white eyes (white) are carried by sex chromosomes. Y chromosome (white) carries no genes for eye color. Reciprocal cross of homozygous white-eyed female and red-eyed male will give in F_1 generation white-eyed males and red-eyed females. In F_2 there will be equal numbers of red-eyed females, white-eyed females, red-eyed males, and white-eyed males.

by R and white-eyed by r, the following diagrams will show how this eye color inheritance works:

Parents	RR (red ♀)		X	rY (white ♂)	
F_1		Rr (red ♀)	X	RY (red ♂)	
Gametes		R,r		R,Y	
F_2	RR	RY		rY	rR
	red ♀	red ♂		white ♂	red ♀

Reciprocal cross

Parents	rr (white ♀)		X	RY (red ♂)	
F_1		rR (red ♀)	X	rY (white ♂)	
Gametes		r,R		r,Y	
F_2	rr		rY	Rr	RY
	white ♀		white ♂	red ♀	red ♂

Many sex-linked genes are known in man, such as bleeder's disease (hemophilia), night blindness, and color blindness. The latter is often used as one of the most striking cases of sex-linked inheritance in man. The particular form of color blindness involved is called Daltonism, or the inability to distinguish between red and green. The defect is recessive and requires both genes with the defect in the female but only one defective gene in the male to procure a visible defect. If the defective allele is represented by an asterisk (*), the following diagram will show the inheritance pattern:

Cross between color-blind male (X*Y) and homozygous normal female (XX)

	X*Y	×	XX	
F₁	X*X	×	XY	(all normal)
Gametes	X*,X		X,Y	
F₂	X*X, X*Y, XX, XY			
	(X*Y, color-blind individual)			

It will be seen from this cross that the color-blind father will transmit the defect to his daughters (who do not show it because each has only one defective gene), but these daughters transmit the defect to one-half their sons (who show it because a sex-linked recessive gene in the male has a visible effect).

LINKAGE AND CROSSING-OVER

As has been pointed out previously, all of the pairs of contrasting characters Mendel worked with were in different or nonhomologous chromosomes. This fact formed the basis for his principle of random assortment. But the study of heredity since the discovery of his laws reveals that many traits are inherited together. Since the number of chromosomes in any animal is relatively few compared to the number of traits, it is evident that each chromosome bears many genes. All the genes contained in a chromosome tend to be inherited together and are therefore said to be **linked.** The sex-linked phenomena described in the previous section are examples of linkage; genes borne on chromosomes other than sex chromosomes form **autosomal linkage.** Genes, therefore, occur in linkage groups and there should be as many linkage groups as there are chromosomes. In *Drosophila*, in

which this principle has been worked out most extensively, there are four linkage groups that correspond to the four pairs of chromosomes found in these flies. Small chromosomes have small linkage groups and large chromosomes have large groups. Five hundred genes have been mapped in the fruit fly and all these are distributed among the four pairs.

Linkage alters the expected Mendelian ratios which are based on the free assortment. Linkage was first discovered in 1906 by Bateson and Punnett in sweet peas, when it was found that sweet peas with purple flowers had elongated pollen grains and those with red flowers had round pollen grains. How the Mendelian ratios can be altered by linkage can best be illustrated by one of Morgan's experiments on *Drosophila*. When a wild-type fly with gray body and long wings is crossed with a fly bearing two recessive mutant characters of black body and vestigial wings, the dihybrids (F₁) all have gray bodies and long wings. If a male of one of the F₁'s is testcrossed with a female with a black body and vestigial wings, the flies are all gray-long and black-vestigial. If there had been free assortment, that is, if the various characters had been carried on different chromosomes, the expected offspring would have been represented by four types of flies: gray-long, gray-vestigial, black-long, and black-vestigial. However, in this case gray-long and black-vestigial had entered the dihybrid cross together and stayed together, or linked.

Linkage, however, is usually only partial, for it is broken up frequently by what is known as **crossing-over.** In this phenomenon the characters usually separate with a certain frequency. How often two genes break their linkage, or their percentage of crossing-over, varies with different genes. In some cases this percentage of crossing-over is only 1% or less; with others it may be nearly 50%. The explanation for crossing-over lies in the synapsis of homologus chromosomes during the maturation division when the two chromosomes sometimes become inter-

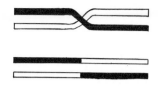

Figure 602. Diagram showing simple case of crossing-over between two chromatids of homologous chromosomes. Block of genes shown in black is thus transferred to white and vice versa.

twined and, before separating from each other, exchange homologous portions of the chromosomes (and the genes they bear) (Figure 602).

Cytological proof for crossing-over was demonstrated by Stern in 1931. By using strains of fruit flies which had distinctive X chromosomes formed by translocation (in which a portion of one chromosome abnormally becomes attached to another chromosome), he followed certain sex-linked traits and chromosomal configurations through crosses. He was thus able to demonstrate that there was an actual visible exchange of chromosomal segments that agreed with genetical results. If the genes are arranged in a linear order on the chromosomes, the closer any two linked genes are, the less chance there is that they will break their linkage and go to different chromosomes; the greater the distance between any two genes, the more likely they will separate from each other. This crossing-over thus makes possible new combinations of linked genes.

Crossing-over makes possible the construction of chromosome maps and proof that the genes lie in a linear order on the chromosomes. To illustrate how this is done one may take a hypothetical case of three genes (A, B, and C) on the same chromosome. In the determination of their comparative linear position on the chromosome it will first be necessary to find the crossing-over value between any two of these genes. If A and B have a crossing-over of 2% and B and C of 8%, then the crossing-over percentage between A and C should be either the sum (2 + 8) or the difference (8 − 2). If it is 10%, B lies between A and C; if 6%, A is be-

tween B and C. By laborious genetical experiments over many years the famed chromosome maps in *Drosophila* were worked out in this manner. Cytological investigation on the giant chromosomes since these maps were made tend to prove the correctness of the linear order, if not the actual position, of the genes on the chromosomes. There is no evidence of crossing-over occurring in the giant chromosomes themselves.

THE GENE AND MUTATION

Among the variations that appear in the make-up of animals there are both hereditary and nonhereditary kinds. Nonhereditary variations are due to environmental changes, such as nutrition, light, heat, and other factors which operate during the development of the animal. Such fluctuating variations occur in all animals and are not hereditary. The hereditary variations are due to changes in the genes or chromosomes and are referred to as **mutations.** Ordinarily, genes are very stable, but they are molecules and are subject to change under the influence of many kinds of factors. Some changes arise spontaneously, and others can be induced by artificial agencies. Undoubtedly many more mutations occur than are actually seen, but most of them are recessive and produce visible effects only when they are homozygous. Mutations happen in both somatic and germinal tissue, but only the latter ones are transmitted sexually. Moreover, many mutant genes are concerned with abnormalities or other defects and thus have little significance in the evolutionary development of animals. Others, however, have proved quite useful, such as hornless Hereford cattle. Also, the rate of mutation varies greatly in various animals and for different genes. Many genes are far more mutable than others. The gene for eye color in the fruit fly has at least 18 mutant forms which are variants of the normal red eye. Mutations to white and to vermilion eyes have occurred many times. The spontaneous mutation rate in *Drosophila* has been estimated to be from 1 in 100,000 to 1 in several billion per gene per generation. A mutation involves a change in a gene, not an actual loss of a gene. This is proved by the fact that a mutant gene may revert back to the original gene. Similar mutations, known as **parallel mutations,** may also occur in closely related species of animals. One significant fact about gene mutations is that usually only one gene mutates at a time; mass mutations are very rare.

In the past twenty-five years or so many mutations have been induced by artificial methods, such as x-rays, radium, temperature. By such means it has been possible to increase the mutation rate more than a hundredfold. Many mutations so induced were similar to those which arose spontaneously and were heritable. Some of them were also lethal and harmful. These induced mutations were first discovered in *Drosophila* by Muller, but they have since been produced in bacteria, yeasts, and other forms.

CHROMOSOMAL CHANGES

The term mutation is usually restricted to alteration within the gene itself, but there are also other heritable variations associated with chromosomal changes. These are often referred to as chromosomal aberrations and involve variations in the number, structure, and arrangement of chromosomes. These are usually gross changes in the chromosomes and affect many genes at one time. The main types of chromosomal changes are loss of a part of a chromosome (**deletion**), shifting of a part of a chromosome over to another chromosome (**duplication**), rearrangement of parts of a chromosome so that a block of genes is **inverted** (**inversion**), and the gaining of a whole set or sets of chromosomes (**polyploidy**). This latter term refers to those conditions in which there are more than the diploid number, so that triploids, tetraploids, and even higher combinations are formed. Although most of such cases are found in plants, they are not unknown among animals, particularly some amphibians.

HYBRID VIGOR

Hybrid vigor, or **heterosis,** refers to the greater vitality and vigor manifested by the hybrids produced by crossing individuals of two pure races which differ from each other in a number of genes. Such hybrids are often bigger and more vigorous than either parent. What actually happens is that such crosses may bring together dominant genes for vigor in the hybrid, provided each of the pure line races carries a vigor gene lacking in the other. In this way it is conceivable that the hybrid may contain homozygous dominant vigor genes which would account for its more desirable traits. There is also the possibility that some genes in the heterozygous condition in the hybrid might produce more vigor than genes in the homozygous state found in the inbred race. Hybrid vigor, however, tends to be lost in succeeding generations when hybrids are crossed, for the desirable dominant genes may segregate out again and the undesirable recessives would again make their effects visible.

There are many examples of hybrid vigor in both plants and animals. Among the former is the valuable hybrid corn which enabled the farmers of the United States to greatly increase their corn yield; among animals one of the best examples is the mule, which is the hybrid between a jackass and a mare and is stronger and sturdier than either parent. To overcome the infertility of inbred lines in hybrid corn production, the **double cross** method is employed. Four inbred lines (A, B, C, D) are intercrossed in pairs (A-B, C-D). The hybrids of these two crosses (AB and CD) are then crossed to produce the commercial seed of the farmer.

Many studies have been made on hybrid vigor in man. A study of history usually shows that great civilizations are preceded by a mixing of races. Race crossing, even among subgroups of one race, often results in exceptional vitality and vigor. Mulattoes in proportion to their number far exceed the pure Negro in achievements. The flowering of Greek culture a few centuries before the Christian era has been shown to be due to a preliminary close inbreeding of many independent political units, thus producing many types of gene pools, followed by a recombination of these genes in crosses (hybrid vigor) when political barriers were broken down in the later, larger city units. Close inbreeding in the human race usually results in reduced vitality, many defective traits, and a pronounced sterility of the stock.

CYTOPLASMIC INHERITANCE

All the genetical behavior so far considered has stressed the importance of the nuclear elements (chromosomes and genes) as the bearers of heredity. Does the cytoplasm bear any hereditary factors? Of course, the effects of the gene are carried out in the cytoplasm, such as growth, development, secretion, enzymatic action, etc., but are there self-duplicating genetic units in the cytoplasm itself? Evidence for cytoplasmic inheritance is often sought in reciprocal cross differences (i.e., whether or not the genetic type is introduced into a cross by the father or the mother), because the egg (maternal contribution) contains most of the cytoplasm of the new organism, and the phenotype of the latter should follow that of the mother. A few cases of cytoplasmic inheritance seem well established. One of these is the chlorophyll-bearing plastids in the cytoplasm of certain plants. These are self-duplicating bodies and some of them are always maternal in character regardless of the kind introduced by the pollen in the cross.

Mention has already been made in Chapter 6, Phylum Protozoa, of the kappa substance in the cytoplasm of certain strains of paramecia. This kappa substance produces paramecin which can kill sensitive strains containing no kappa substance. When individuals of killer clones conjugate with members of sensitive strains, the latter will become killers only when they receive some cytoplasm in the exchange, indicating that the cytoplasm carries the plasmagenes which such cytoplasmic bodies are called. Kappa particles have many of the characteristics of genes, for they are self-duplicating and contain DNA. However, it has been shown that the maintenance of the kappa substance is actually dependent upon a nuclear gene. Thus, in some cases at least, there is an interrelationship between plasmagenes and nuclear genes and some geneticists consider the former as replicas of nuclear genes which are released into cytoplasm. Plasmagenes have many resemblances to viruses, such as self-duplication, cytoplasmic location, and capability of transmissible mutations, but they do not cause diseases in the cells in which they are found. The demonstration of plasmagenes bids to shed some light upon the difficult problem of developmental differentiation.

chapter 35

Applied genetics; human heredity

PRACTICAL APPLICATION OF GENETICS

Although genetics as a science has developed within the last fifty years, many of the practical applications of heredity extend as far back as the dawn of civilization itself. The improvement of domestic plants and animals has interested man ever since he could think and reason on such matters. Has the discovery of the precise way by which the laws of heredity work helped him to make additional progress? Genetics as a pure science has had a tremendous influence on students of biology since Mendel's laws were rediscovered. It is not amiss for the zoology student to look at a few of the ways by which man has been able to use the principles of hereditary formulas to his own advantage.

Methods of increasing productivity in plants and animals. Plant and animal breeders have two main objectives: to produce strains that give greater productivity and to produce those that are pure in their pedigree. The latter enables the breeder to control and predict the outcome of his crosses. Purity of strains does not solve all the problems of the geneticist, however, as witness the striking case of hybrid vigor. One of the first problems facing the breeder is to distinguish between environmental and heritable characters in the forms with which he works. This is not always easy, for most characters can be influenced by environmental factors. Desirable hereditary qualities are carefully selected and propagated by breeding. Much effort is made to use pure lines in order to control the desired qualities. Plant geneticists make use of hybridization between different strains of plants which will cross and often get desirable characters this way. Often the production of pure lines is for the purpose of crossing with other strains in order to take advantage of hybrid vigor, a practice used by both plant and animal breeders. Practical application of Mendel's laws are freely used and form the basis for most plant and animal experiments, greatly simplifying the work in comparison with methods before Mendel's time. The testcross, for instance, is a common procedure in getting homozygous stocks.

The alert breeder takes advantage of new combinations and variations produced by crossing different strains, by mutations, and by crossovers. A planned selection program must always be worked out and carefully followed, and the real work for successful results often rests upon this program.

Hybrid varieties. The production of hybrid corn was one of the great triumphs of genetics. In the thirty years since it was introduced, the yield of corn per acre has been increased 25 to 50%. Pure lines of corn were found to be of low fertility and gave scanty yields. When these pure strains were crossed, the hybrids showed a remarkable increase in both fertility and general yield. Only the seed of the first generation following a cross can be used, for later generation seed tends to produce segregation of undesirable traits as explained under hybrid vigor, page 744. This makes it necessary for the farmer to buy his seed each season. The principle of first-generation hybrids has been applied successfully to other plants, such as squash, pine trees, and cucumbers. It will probably be more extensively used as more is known about it.

Progeny selection. Selection, an effective tool in the hands of the breeder, may be done by **phenotypic selection** or by **progeny selection.** The first is based upon the appearance of the desired trait or traits in the individual. This method has obvious disadvantages, for the phenotypic appearance of the animal or plant is not necessarily an indication of its genotype. For this reason, prize-winning stock may not transmit desirable traits to its offspring. Progeny selection, however, is based upon selecting those individuals which produce desirable offspring, so that the genotype is the chief basis of selection. Many great successes have been scored this way, such as high milk-producing cattle, poultry with higher yield of eggs, desirable strains of tobacco, etc.

Disease-resistant strains. By careful selection and breeding, plant breeders produce varieties that do not become infected by common plant diseases. In this way it has been possible to develop wheat that is resistant to rust and corn to smut. However, many disease germs mutate, and some of the mutants may be able to attack plants that were formerly disease resistant. Constant vigilance is necessary to spot these changes and to introduce a new resistant gene into the genetic constitution of the stock.

Detection and control of lethal genes. Many cases of lethal genes, or genes that destroy the individual, are known among stock breeders. Some of these produce visible effects in the offspring, such as the peculiar "bulldog" calf (so-called because of its facial appearance) and the creeper fowl with unusually short appendages,

and may not kill until a late stage of development, but others may destroy early without noticeable effects in the offspring. Some lethal genes produce their effects only in the homozygous condition and others when they are heterozygous. In the first case their detection is not always easy, for as long as the lethal gene is carried along with a normal one no harm is done. But there is always the possibility, especially in close inbreeding, that two lethal genes will be brought together. Stock breeders can by trial matings find these lethals and exclude such animals from breeding. Some plants are also known to bear hidden lethal genes.

Polyploidy. Although the diploid number of chromosomes is characteristic, we have seen that there are cases in which there are three or more of each kind of chromosome in an organism (**polyploidy**). Such aberrant conditions arise through a duplication of the chromosome complement by nondisjunction in the reduction division of maturation. Such polyploids differ in characters from the original parent stock. Many such polyploids have been experimentally produced, such as tulips, roses, fruit trees, tomatoes, and even cotton, and represent an improvement over the original stock. In cases where polyploids cannot breed true, as in triploids, they may be propagated asexually.

Application of biochemical genetics. Another practical application of an unusual form is the use of molds, such as *Neurospora*, in determining the presence of certain vitamins and amino acids. When these molds are irradiated, some of their genes may be made to mutate so that they lose the power to synthesize specific vitamins and amino acids. Apparently this failure to synthesize is due to the loss of certain enzymes. Each enzyme is dependent upon a single gene and when this gene mutates its enzyme suffers as a result. Strains of mold that lack the power to synthesize a particular amino acid will not grow in a medium deficient in this specific amino acid. It is thus possible to determine whether or not a culture contains or lacks specific vitamins or amino acids by ascertaining its ability to support certain such strains of mold.

HUMAN HEREDITY

The study of human inheritance is one of the most difficult fields in genetics. Experimental breeding, the key to most genetic studies, is impractical. It is also difficult to study man's heredity from a cytogenetical viewpoint because of the many chromosomes (forty-six) which he possesses as compared with simpler forms. Moreover, man is a relatively slow-breeding animal, he is largely heterozygous in his hereditary make-up, and he is influenced in his development to a greater extent by an extremely complicated and varied environment. In spite of these handicaps, however, a great deal of information is known about his heredity. There is every reason to suppose that man follows the same principles of genetics as those of other organisms. In his hereditary pattern there should be the same application of dominance and recessiveness, free assortment and linkage, multiple factors, sex-linked genes, etc. Many studies of human inheritance have stressed congenital defects because such traits can easily be followed through many generations and are easily recognized. Many of these defects are dominant, and their visible effects are not hidden as are recessive traits. Naturally much of the information about human inheritance is fragmentary and some of it is conflicting, but significant achievements are being made in the field.

Some wrong ideas

A subject of such common interest as human heredity has naturally built up many concepts regarding the transmission of family traits from parents to children. Some of these ideas have a certain basis of fact behind them, but many are altogether erroneous. One of the chief reasons for this confusion is that all individuals are the product of both heredity and environment, and it is in many cases extremely difficult to distinguish between the relative influences of these two factors or to state which of them is the more important for making the individual what he is.

One common misconception is that of the inheritance of acquired characters. The belief that certain changes in the body of the parent can be transmitted directly to children appeals to many. Indeed, most persons instinctively incline toward such a belief because superficially it seems so logical. However, all sound investigation of the germ plasm and its working is against this widespread idea. Scientific analyses reveal that for something to be inherited it must involve the germ plasm itself; mere changes in the body, whether structurally, intellectually, or culturally, cannot be transmitted in a hereditary way as such. Our germ cells are relatively stable, and although the genes they bear can and do change sometimes, such alterations are not induced by changes in the somatic cells.

Another false notion is the belief that maternal impressions during pregnancy can influence the developing fetus. The only way the mother can influence her developing offspring is through nutrition and certain chemical changes in her blood involving drugs or diseases. The child thus can suffer from a poor intrauterine existence, but this is not inheritance. This factor of nutrition is probably responsible for the fact that a child born to a mother toward the close of her child-bearing period may be more weakly than those born earlier.

The theory of **telegony** persists among many, especially stock breeders. This is the belief that if a female is bred to successive males, the influence of the first male may show up in the offspring of successive males. There is no scientific confirmation for this idea, for only one sperm is needed to fertilize the egg and all others die at the time of mating.

Many erroneous ideas are also held about the appearance of more characteristics (**prepotency**) of one parent than the other in a particular child. This may be due to the fact that one parent may

748

have more dominant genes, or at least more obvious ones, than the other parent. There are some curious beliefs regarding the determination of sex, such as the belief that the children will be of a sex opposite to the stronger and more forceful personality of the two parents, or that the acid state of the vagina at conception results in a girl, or alkaline, a boy. Actually, the sex of each child is determined at the time of fertilization (conception) and is determined by the kind of sperm (X or Y) the male contributes to the union.

How information is acquired

Most of our knowledge of human inheritance has come from the observation and statistical study of family pedigrees and a comparison with the conditions in experimental organisms. Mere observations and statistics based upon them have definite limitations, for the study of several generations should be involved to make them reliable, and information about previous family histories is not always available or reliable. Since the development of any individual is dependent upon both heredity and environment, it is often necessary to select groups for hereditary study that have similar environmental conditions. This poses many difficulties. The patterns of human inheritance are often confusing, for human offspring are relatively few and there are no pure lines, so it has not always been easy to apply the principles of genetics to man in the same detail as in some other forms.

Roles of heredity and environment

If the human organism is the product of both heredity and environment, which is the more important factor? This question has been asked many times, but no outright answer can be given at present. Even the naive know that no kind of environment can transform a monkey into a human being. Each kind of animal has something that makes it different from all other kinds, and this something we refer to as as heredity. At conception a certain hereditary potentiality is given the zygote,

but how this potentially expresses itself is influenced by the environment. The genes determine the general pattern of development, but at every step of the way these genes must interact with environmental factors. Although the genic constitution within the nucleus remains essentially the same in all cells and tissues, the cytoplasm undergoes various changes under the joint influence of genes on the one hand and a constantly changing environment on the other. Both these factors are, therefore, important in the realization of the individual's possibilities. The germinal elements in their expression must have the influence of environmental stimuli, or else remain undeveloped.

Of the two factors, heredity is relatively constant and stable, whereas the environment is constantly changing. Although one may think at first that the early environment of the fetus developing in the mother's uterus is more or less similar in most cases, this is far from being the case. During its intrauterine existence the important factor of nutrition is operating as well as numerous hormones from the mother's body. Here there are interactions between the genes of the embryo and the environment of the uterus. After birth, additional factors, including complex social ones, have a marked effect in the final molding of the individual character. Genes direct the general course of development, but their potentiality can be expressed or suppressed by the environment. Perhaps the best way of appraising the relative importance of heredity and environment is to consider them complementary in the development of individual characters.

Experiments have been made to determine the relative influence of environment and heredity on lower animals. These experiments involve keeping certain factors constant while varying others. Results are not always conclusive because of the complicated factors involved. Such work is restricted in the case of man, but attempts have been made to determine the relative influence of heredity and environment on identical twins. Identical twins come from one egg and have the same set of genes, so their hereditary patterns are alike. What differences they manifest in their expressed characters should therefore be due to environment. Some studies have been made on twins which have been reared in different homes and under different social and other environmental conditions from a very early age. Such twins show a remarkable similarity in height, weight, and other physical characteristics. However, their mental traits, I.Q., and general intelligence may show some differences. Many cultural aspects of their characters, too, may vary according to the different social environments under which they have been reared. Conclusions drawn from such investigations indicate that hereditary factors dominate in influencing the general development and personality of the individual, although environment, such as education, does have a bearing upon the general intelligence level of the individual.

Hair and eye color

The color of hair seems to be determined by several genes or several pairs of modifying factors, at least in certain cases. Often the pigmentation of hair and eye color are correlated, for the darker shades of hair are usually accompanied by darker eyes. In general, blond hair is recessive to the darker shades, but the presence of varying shades of blond and dark hair indicates a blending effect or the interaction of more than one pair of genes. Red hair is recessive to the other shades of hair. One may be homozygous for red genes and have a darkish shade of red hair color because of the presence of genes for darker hair.

The color of the eyes is due to the presence and location of pigment in the iris. If the pigment is on the back of the iris, the eyes are blue; if the pigment is on both back and front of the iris, the eyes are of the darker shades. If pigment is lacking altogether (albinism) the eyes are pinkish because of the blood vessels. The pigment is actually dark and produces the varying eye colors by the reflection of light. Blue eyes are recessive to the other eye shades, and when the parents are blue-eyed the children are normally blue-eyed. Blue-eyed children may appear also if the parents are heterozygous for the darker eye colors. The manner in which eye color is inherited indicates that there are many kinds of genes, all variant forms of the gene for dark color, which furnish the many varieties of eye color. These genes behave in a simple Mendelian way in their hereditary expression as shown by the dominance of the darker over the lighter shades. In exceptional cases, environmental factors may upset the normal expectation by preventing the full expression of eye pigment, so that homozygous dark-eyed parents could have a blue-eyed child.

Blood group inheritance

The inheritance of blood groups follows Mendel's laws. This inheritance is based upon three genes or allelomorphs, I^a, I^b, and i. I^a and I^b are antigens and dominant and never appear in a child's blood unless present in at least one of the parents; i represents no antigen and is recessive to the antigens. Neither I^a nor I^b is dominant to each other, but each is dominant to i. The relationships of the blood groups and genotypes are as follows:

Blood groups	O	A	B	AB
Genotypes	ii	I^aI^a or I^ai	I^bI^b or I^bi	I^aI^b

From a study of these genotypes and their possible combinations between parents and offspring, it will be seen that if both parents belong to group O a child must also belong to group O. On the other hand, if one parent belongs to group A and the other to B, the child could belong to any one of the four groups. The various possibilities of inheritance are shown in Table 11.

This pattern of heredity has some practical applications in medicolegal cases involving disputed parentage. From the possibilities given in Table 11 it is seen

750

Table II Inheritance of blood groups

Parent groups	Possible children groups	Impossible children groups
O × O	O	A, B, AB
O × A	O, A	B, AB
O × B	O, B	A, AB
A × A	O, A	B, AB
A × B	O, A, B, AB	None
B × B	O, B	A, AB
O × AB	A, B	O, AB
A × AB	A, B, AB	O
B × AB	A, B, AB	O
AB × AB	A, B, AB	O

that if a child in question has group A and the supposed parents group O, it is obvious that the child could not belong to them. On the other hand, if the parents belong to groups A and B, the blood tests would prove nothing, for the parents could have children of all groups.

Evolutionists have laid much stress upon the geographical distribution of blood groups among the various racial populations. Perhaps no human trait has been more extensively studied than has blood grouping. The frequencies of the blood groups O, A, B, and AB have been tabulated by investigators for most races all over the world, although data are scanty and incomplete in many instances. Among the interesting facts revealed by these studies is the absence of the allele B in the American Indians and Australian aborigines, the high frequency of B in Asia and India and its decline in Western Europe, and the high frequency of group O in Ireland and Iceland. The distribution of the Rh factor also shows a varied pattern. Reasons for these varied distributions are obscure, but some explanations have been advanced, such as genetic drift involving small populations, natural selection, migration and mixing of races, and others.

Inheritance of Rh factor

As stated in a former section, about 85% of American people possess a domin-

ant gene called **Rh,** which causes the formation of a special antigen in the blood. The remaining 15% have the recessive allele **rh** which cannot produce this antigen. Investigations have disclosed that there are many other alleles at this locus, thus greatly increasing the possible blood groups. Thus there are several kinds of Rh-positive and Rh-negative persons. At present at least eight different alleles are found in the series designated as R^1, R^2, R^0, R^z, r', r'', r^y, r. The capital letters indicate those alleles that give an Rh-positive reaction; the small letters stand for the Rh-negative ones. Although all of these subtypes are inherited and produce antigens, it appears that the allele Rh^0 is mainly responsible for the clinical cases of erythroblastosis fetalis. The genetics of all these subtypes becomes involved, when one considers all their possible combinations. They represent one of the most extensive groups of multiple alleles known. Other antigens are caused by factors independent of Rh, such as the so-called Kell antigen produced by an uncommon dominant gene which, in incompatibility cases, can cause serious hemolytic diseases.

Other antigens that do not react to form antibodies and are of no clinical significance are the M and N antigens. No allele for the absence of these antigens has been found. All persons are typed as M, N, or MN. In their inheritance pattern, two M-type parents will produce only M children; two N-type parents only N children; and types M and N parents will give all these types of children in the ratio of 1M:2MN:1N.

Inheritance of mental characteristics

Mental traits, both good and bad, are known to be inherited, although because of environmental influences it is not always possible to appraise them genetically. Heredity is in general responsible for the basic patterns of intelligence and mental deficiencies, although environmental factors can and do influence the development of intellectual capacities. Intelligence is not a single hereditary unit; apparently many different genes are responsible for its expression. The field of inheritance affords many examples of both outstanding abilities and mental defects being handed down through long family histories. With all due respect to environmental factors, one is forced to conclude that hereditary factors have played a major part in the determination of these intellectual strengths or weaknesses. The best kind of environment in the world cannot make a superior intelligence out of one who has inherited a moron potentiality, and, conversely, superior hereditary abilities may always remain mediocre unless stimulated by favorable environmental factors. Identical twins, for instance, with exactly the same genes for intelligence may show considerable difference in their I.Q.'s when reared under different advantages of education and culture.

Many defective genes are recessive and their effects are masked unless they are homozygous. This appears to be the case with feeblemindedness. There are several million feebleminded persons in the United States, but only a small per cent have come from feebleminded parents. The great majority of them are born of parents heterozygous for this trait. Such parents may be in all particulars normal for intelligence and carry the recessive gene for feeblemindedness. Pure lines in human stock are practically unknown, for different stocks have crossed in nearly every conceivable manner, and thus the human germ plasm is largely heterozygous. Recessive genes are therefore hidden and **may** continue so until they become homozygous. That is why the sterilization of feebleminded persons to **prevent them** from reproducing their kind would eliminate only part of such defectives.

The inheritance of special abilities, such as that of music, has been thoroughly investigated, and the evidence indicates that talents for music may have a constitutional basis. The hereditary pattern, however, is very complex and probably involves a number of genes. It is not always possible to distinguish between the influences of heredity and environment in musical families, for children in such homes are brought up under the influence of music, which tends to develop talents that might otherwise be hidden. Special talents of this kind may be to a considerable extent independent of general intelligence, for some individuals of marked ability along some lines may have a low I.Q.

Should first cousins be allowed to marry?

If some defective genes are recessive, there is a greater possibility that the marriage of near relatives, such as first cousins, would bring these genes together in a homozygous condition so that they could express themselves in a visible way. It is logical that descendents from a near common ancestor are going to share his genes. The more remote the relationship, the less is this possibility. There is a great deal of evidence that inbreeding does intensify many kinds of defects, such as feeblemindedness, congenital deafness, and albinism. For this reason, in most states marriage of first cousins is prohibited. Of course, inheritance can work both ways, for good as well as for bad. Inbreeding does not create hereditary defects but tends to create a homozygous condition of genes, beneficial as well as defective ones. If there should be desirable genes in a family stock, marriage between cousins should bring these traits together and produce superior children. Many great English families, including that of Charles Darwin, bear out the truth of this statement. Laws, however, are made with reference to the prevention of undesirable traits instead of the promotion of favorable ones.

Inheritance of twinning

There are two types of twins, fraternal and identical. **Fraternal** twins, which are four or five times as common as identical ones, result from the independent fertilization of separate ova by separate sperm. They are simply conceived and born together, and genetically they have the same likenesses and differences as ordinary brothers and sisters. They may be of the same or opposite sex. **Identical** twins come from a single zygote which has split during its early stages. They have the same genetical constitution and are always of the same sex. Identical twins show a remarkable similarity in their general characters, both physical and mental. When the halves of the zygote fail to separate completely, Siamese twins are the result.

The inheritance of twinning is very complex, but there seems to be no doubt but that there is a hereditary basis for many cases of twins. This hereditary tendency is found in domestic animals as well as in man. Sheep, especially, exhibit strains of twinning. Environmental factors may play a part in the production of multiple births, but what they are is largely unknown. Both father and mother seem to influence the heredity of twinning. It is not too difficult to see how the father could induce the formation of identical twins, for something about his sperm might cause the zygote to split. It is more difficult to see how he could cause fraternal twins. Some biologists suggest that the female releases two eggs at ovulation, of which only one is normally fertilized. But if the sperm are unusually virile, both eggs could be fertilized. More puzzling still is the fact that older parents tend to have more twins than younger ones. There are also racial variations. Negroes have more twins than whites, but most Mongolian peoples have fewer than whites. There is also the possibility that the prenatal mortality rate of twins is much higher than that of single conceptions, which would make a difference in the ratios.

Inheritance of certain physical traits in man

The analysis of human inheritance is more complicated than it is in simpler forms, for it is impossible to deal with man's heredity in a simple Mendelian ratio. Information about his heredity must be acquired by inspection and analysis of family life histories, or pedigrees. Such a plan involves the formation of hypotheses to explain hereditary expression and careful checking of these hypotheses to determine whether they apply to the data obtained. The inheritance of many abnormal characters has been stressed in family pedigrees, because they are easily followed.

Following are some of the more common traits:

Dominant	Recessive
Curly hair	Straight hair
Dark hair	Light hair
Nonred hair	Red hair
Dark skin color	Light skin color
Hairy body	Normal hair
Skin pigmentation	Albinism (no pigment)
Brown eyes	Blue or gray eyes
Hazel eyes	Blue or gray eyes
Ichthyosis (scaly skin)	Normal skin
Near or farsightedness	Normal vision
Hereditary cataract	Normal vision
Astigmatism	Normal vision
Glaucoma	Normal vision
Normal hearing	Deaf-mutism
Normal color vision	Color blindness
Normal blood clotting	Hemophilia
Broad lips	Thin lips
Large eyes	Small eyes
Long eyelashes	Short eyelashes
Short stature	Tall stature
Polydactylism (extra fingers or toes)	Normal number of digits
Brachydactylism (short digits)	Normal length of digits
Syndactylism (webbed digits)	Normal digits
Normal muscles	Progressive muscular atrophy
Hypertension	Normal blood pressure
Diabetes insipidus	Normal excretory system
Enlarged colon	Normal colon
Tasters (of certain substances)	Nontasters
Huntington's chorea	Normal
Normal mentality	Schizophrenia
Nervous temperament	Phlegmatic temperament
Average intellect	Very great or very small
Normal intellect	Feeblemindedness
Migraine headache	Normal

Application of genetics to medical problems

Medical men are realizing more and more that the hereditary pattern of people has an important bearing on clinical problems. This new science of **medical genetics** has accumulated a great deal of information about family histories which has proved helpful in the prevention and diagnosis of diseases. Doctors now take family histories as a routine procedure and often find data that are useful. Disease germs are not carried through genes from one generation to another, but many authorities have found marked susceptibility to a particular disease running through families. Much practical information about human heredity has been employed in the case of married couples and the possibility of undesirable traits appearing among their children.

Some of these bad traits have already been pointed out, such as color blindness, Rh factor, deaf-mutism, etc. Certain susceptibilities to cancer are inherited in both man and other animals. Children of parents who carry abnormal traits should be watched as they develop. For instance, hemolytic icterus, a condition in which the spleen is enlarged, is inherited as a dominant gene and about half of the offspring of a parent carrying this gene should be expected to have the defect. When such is known, it is the duty of the physician to check the suspected children frequently and detect the disorder in time to remove the spleen before serious damage is done. Some forms of hypertension have a hereditary basis, and children of such a parent should be trained to conform to conditions which will not aggravate the malady. It is possible for doctors to facilitate their diagnosis of obscure diseases by knowing whether the family and near relatives carry susceptibilities to them.

Many of our great universities have heredity clinics, such as California, Michigan, Ohio State, Oklahoma, Texas, Minnesota, and Tulane, where expertly trained geneticists give counseling and information on problems of heredity.

Influence of radiation upon human heredity

Radiation and radioactive substances, such as x-rays, radium rays, and ultraviolet light, greatly increase the mutation rate of the gene. Most of these gene mutations are lethal and either destroy or else produce abnormalities of various types in the offspring of animals exposed under certain conditions to irradiation. Since the development and use of the atomic bomb in modern warfare, geneticists have been concerned about the possible genetic effect these could have upon man. The explosion of an atom bomb releases large amounts of ionizing radiations which differ in their ability to penetrate tissues. Many other factors affect the amount of damage radiation can do, such as the intensity and duration of exposure, whether the exposure occurs immediately after the explosion or later, and so on.

In the light of the fierce controversy which is raging over the possible effects of radiation in an atomic age, it may suffice to summarize certain generalizations which the data seem to substantiate:

1. All life is constantly exposed to high-energy radiations. Some of this radiation comes from natural sources, such as cosmic rays from outer space, radioactive elements (radium, thorium, radioactive isotopes of potassium), and atomic disintegration within the organism; some comes from the technological use of radioactive substances in medicine and industry (x-rays, radium treatment, mustard gas); and some from the fallout of the explosion of atomic bombs.

2. High-energy radiations are definitely known to increase the rate of mutation in every organism tested.

3. Most mutations are harmful to the organism whether they are natural mutants or artificial ones induced by man.

4. Mutations do not as a rule occur in more than one gene at a time, for a mutation is highly localized and may involve only one gene locus when the latter is struck by a quantum of radiation.

5. Radiations may affect any cell in the body, but only those changes that are

produced in sex cells can be transmitted to the offspring.

6. Sensitivity to radiation effects vary from species to species. Mice are far more sensitive than fruit flies.

7. An atomic fallout occurs when atom bombs are exploded and refers to the unstable and radioactive isotopes of many elements which are hurled high into the air and carried about the earth by the winds, eventually settling down to earth upon a large or small area, depending upon circumstances. Some radioactive elements may settle out quickly and others may remain aloft for years.

8. Genetic radiations from whatever source are insidious in that their effects are cumulative. Small exposures add up, and what really counts in the long run is the total amount of radiation one is exposed to during one's reproductive life. The rate of delivery of the radiation is of no consequence; the genetic effect is the same for low or high rate.

9. Some of the radioactive elements released in an atom bomb explosion decompose very slowly and have half-lives of many years, such as strontium 90 (half life, 28 years). This means that the body may be exposed to these isotopes for a long time and can absorb a large amount of them.

10. The danger of radioactive substances is far greater to future generations than to present ones because of the genetic implications referred to above.

11. In addition to genetic effects of radiation, there are also physiological or somatic effects. Some somatic effects are leukemia, cancer, and a syndrome of radiation illness, depending upon the amount of exposure. Body tissues of rapidly dividing cells are especially prone to damage. If the exposure has not been excessive, many somatic effects may be healed by therapeutic measures, but healing does not apply to genetic damages.

Improvement of human race

The scientific improvement of the human race is called **eugenics.** Many or-

ganizations all over the world have been formed with the objective of promoting a superior stock of people such as has been done with domestic animals and plants. Even before the laws of heredity were formulated, educators, sociologists, and others had pointed out the necessity of controlling or eradicating undesirable strains of human inheritance. They reasoned that if man was able to improve his domestic animals, why should not the same principles applied to his own inheritance promote desirable traits for the advancement of society as a whole. Such notorious families as the Jukes and Kallikaks (probably fictitious) have been used as examples of how degeneracy and social misfits are carried by inferior stocks. On the other hand, such families as the Darwins in England and the Edwards in America have been used to illustrate the beneficial effects of good heredity. However, it is impossible to direct, control, and select the desirable human traits and eliminate the undesirable ones in the manner of animal and plant breeders. To obtain pure lines of good traits in man, as with other animals, it would be necessary to practice continued selection over many generations. Moreover, man is a huge mixture of so many traits, both good and bad, that the task of selecting all good ones and eliminating poor ones would not be practical.

A large part of our population carries defective genes. The mental and physical capacity of millions of Americans is below normal and many of these people constitute a serious burden upon society for their maintenance. Of course, not all physical and mental conditions are hereditary; some are due to environmental causes, such as diseases, injuries, etc. Subnormal people reveal only a part of the defective traits found in a population. Many defective genes are recessive and are carried by individuals who have normal phenotypes. Because of this, abnormal individuals are continually cropping out from the normal population as defective genes become homozygous. As we have seen, a large percentage of feeblemindedness is found in children born to normal parents.

Trained geneticists view with a critical eye many of the programs advocated by eugenists. The great emphasis upon family pedigrees is considered unwarranted in the light of possible environmental factors. Many geneticists claim that had the so-called degenerate stocks been provided with better social conditions, their showing would have been vastly improved. There is also the possibility that many eugenists have been influenced by racial or national prejudice in advocating their eugenic objectives. Some of them are inclined to draw sharp lines of distinction between what they call superior and inferior races. Their belief is that hybrid races are in general inferior and that race intermixture should be discouraged. Geneticists, on the other hand, are prone to recognize desirable traits in all races and believe that racial mixtures may have an invigorating influence. Hybrid vigor probably applies in man's case the same as it does with domestic stock and plants. Man's hereditary pattern is so complex that many undesirable genes are linked up with good ones, even in the best of stocks.

The eugenic movement, however, has helped institute some methods for control. Many states have sterilization laws for such defectives as feebleminded persons, imbeciles, and persons with certain forms of insanity. These statutes, however, are broad in their interpretation and make little attempt to distinguish between hereditary and environmental causes, and only a few states have made use of these laws to any extent. There is still much popular feeling against enforcing them.

On the constructive side, engenists have advocated a greater birth rate among the upper and desirable stocks of people. There is no doubt that the lower socioeconomic groups have a higher birth rate, but whether there are marked genetical differences between the different levels of society is not known with certainty. Tests of intellectual abilities so far devised are not able to distinguish between native abilities of individuals who are of different socioeconomic levels. These tests too frequently take into consideration the environmental factors which influence the expression of mental traits, and these factors favor those of the higher social and economic classes. Therefore, under the present setup there seems to be a tendency for a drop in the average I.Q. among Americans from generation to generation. This decline, however, may be due largely to environmental conditions and not to a widespread increase in mediocre genes.

Review questions on heredity

1. What is the meaning of the following terms: allele, heterozygous, dominance, recessive, hybrid, phenotype, testcross, genotype, homozygous.
2. What is the difference between the haploid and diploid number of chromosomes? Are their numbers the same in all organisms?
3. How many chromosomes are in a human spermatozoan? In a human ovum? In a human zygote?
4. Do all the mature germ cells of a particular animal have the same number of chromosomes? What are some exceptions to this?
5. What is the difference between mitosis and meiosis?
6. Why are tetrads absent in mitosis? Why are tetrads present in meiosis?
7. What is meant by the pairing of the chromosomes?
8. What part of meiosis is important in heredity? Show reasons by diagram.
9. How many kinds of gametes can an animal with 3 pairs of chromosomes produce? If an animal having the formula Bb should produce 50 gametes, how many of these gametes should have the formula B? How many b? How many Bb?
10. How many kinds of gametes can be produced by an individual of genotype A/a B/b C/C D/d e/e F/F?
11. What is the evidence that chromosomes carry the materials for inheritance?
12. What is a polar body? Can it be fertilized? Why?
13. What evidence can you present that the genes are located on chromosomes?
14. What are the chief differences between plasmagenes and nuclear genes? In what ways are they alike?
15. Why are the chromosomes of the zygote in

pairs? What is the source of each member of a pair?

16. What are the maturation divisions? How many are there and how do they differ? Why is the second maturation division not the same as ordinary mitosis?

17. How many sperm come from 100 primary spermatocytes? How many sperm come from 100 secondary spermatocytes? How many eggs come from 100 primary oöcytes? How many eggs come from 100 secondary oöcytes?

18. A mare (38 chromosomes) crossed with a jackass (66 chromosomes) produces a mule. How many chromosomes does the mule have? From the behavior of homologous chromosomes in meiosis, why is the mule usually sterile?

19. Are all genes found on chromosomes? Explain.

20. What are autosomes? Do the two sexes differ as to their autosomes?

21. Have genes been seen? Give evidence for and against.

22. What are multiple genes? How may they affect phenotype ratios?

23. What are giant chromosomes? What significance do they have for cytogenetics?

24. In cytoplasmic inheritance would the offspring resemble the father or mother? Why?

25. What are the advantages of bisexual reproduction over asexual reproduction?

26. Explain Mendel's two laws.

27. Why is the testcross so important in genetical experiments?

28. How would you determine whether some rose-combed fowls are heterozygous? (Rose comb is dominant over single comb.)

29. Explain heterosis. Why is hybrid vigor lost when organisms are bred together for a number of generations?

30. Can hereditary characteristics of an organism be altered in any other way than by altering the genes?

31. Why do not animals of identical genotypes show identical phenotypes?

32. If tall peas are dominant over dwarf peas, what would be the appearance of the F_1 plants? If the hybrids of the F_1 are self-fertilized, what would be the appearance of the F_2?

33. What is a sex hormone? What do these symbols mean: XX and XY?

34. Can you give a reason why more human eggs are fertilized by Y sperm than by X sperm?

35. Explain the different types of sex determina-

tion. Give an example of a nongenetic control of sex determination.

36. Fatherless rabbits produced by artificial parthenogenesis are always of what sex?

37. Does an earthworm have sex chromosomes? Why?

38. In man, which sex determines the sex of the offspring? In birds, which sex determines the sex of the offspring?

39. How is sex determined in a form like *Bonellia*?

40. Many other things besides chromosomes influence or determine sexual characteristics. Explain.

41. If a frog is produced by artificial parthenogenesis would it have a haploid or diploid number of chromosomes? Explain.

42. Can a man be homozygous for a sex-linked character? From what parent does a male receive his sex-linked genes?

43. If red-green color blindness is a recessive sex-linked character, can a man with normal vision transmit it? Can a color-blind man transmit this defect to his sons?

44. If a woman of normal vision whose father was color-blind marries a color-blind man, what will be the vision probability of their children?

45. A few mutant traits are always transmitted directly from fathers to sons and are never found in women. On what chromosomes would such a gene be?

46. What are dizygotic twins? Monozygotic twins? How do these two different types of twins differ in genetic constitution?

47. What is partial or incomplete dominance? Give and explain two examples.

48. Why should the same disease be more severe when inherited as a recessive than when inherited as a dominant?

49. What offspring can be expected by crossing two pink four-o'clock flowers?

50. If the gene from brown eyes is dominant over that for blue eyes, what could be expected in the offspring of a blue-eyed man and a brown-eyed woman whose mother was blue-eyed.

51. Could a homozygous brown-eyed man married to a blue-eyed woman have a blue-eyed daughter?

52. If the gene for diabetes mellitus has a penetrance of 10% and 100 individuals in a community are homozygous for this gene, how many are likely to have the disease?

53. On the basis of gene penetrance how would you explain "skipping a generation"?

54. A single gene for baldness in man is dom-

inant whereas two genes for baldness are necessary to produce the condition in women. If a nonbald woman whose mother was bald marries a nonbald man, what is the probability of baldness among the children?

55. If two parents had genotypes AaBb and aabb, what genotypes among the offspring would be possible?

56. If two parents are each heterozygous for a recessive gene for feeblemindedness and have a feebleminded child, what is the probability that the next child will be feebleminded?

57. What would be the blood groups of the offspring in the following crosses: OO × BO, AA × BB, AO × AB.

58. If a mother belongs to group O and her child has group A, to what blood groups can the father not belong?

59. Two parents are each heterozygous for a recessive gene for albinism. If they have four children, what is the possibility that three will be normal and one an albino?

60. In shorthorn cattle matings between white animals and red produce a roan color. Explain this type of inheritance.

61. If two roan shorthorns are mated, what is the probability that the calf will be a red cow? A roan bull? A white bull?

62. If man has 46 chromosomes in his somatic cells, how many linkage groups does he have?

63. If you were to map the location of the following genes from their cross-over values, where would you place them:

    A–D 5 units
    C–B 12 units
    D–C 8 units
    A–C 13 units
    D–B 20 units

64. The pea Mendel worked with has 7 pairs of chromosomes. Mendel performed his classical experiments with 7 pairs of contrasting characters. How do you explain his failure to find linkage?

65. Why is the hereditary basis of mental traits more difficult to establish than the hereditary basis of physical traits?

66. Why is it so difficult to map the chromosomes in man?

67. Why does crossing-over occur in blocks of genes? Show by diagram.

68. If an animal has 24 linkage groups in its somatic cells, how many chromosomes does it have?

69. In cocker spaniels black color is dominant

to red. In a cross between two black spaniels, the litter showed two black and two red. What is the genotype of each parent?

70. Certain forms of diabetes are inherited as a recessive allele. If two nondiabetic individuals have a diabetic child, what is the probability that their next child will be diabetic?

71. In *Drosophila*, gray body is dominant over ebony, and straight wing is dominant over curved. If a gray-curved female is crossed with an ebony-straight male, what different phenotypes will this cross produce in the F_2 and in what ratio?

72. Skin color in man appears to be affected by two pairs of alleles, A and B for black color and a and b for light color. The phenotype will depend upon the number of capital letters there are in the genotype, thus AABB = black; AABb or AaBB = dark; AaBb or AAbb or aaBB = mulatto; Aabb or aaBb = chocolate; and aabb = white. What is the probability of each phenotype in a cross of two heterozygous mulattoes? Of two homozygous mulattoes?

73. In cats, the genotype BB is yellow color, the genotype bb is black color, and Bb is tortoise-shell color. The genes B and b are sex-linked. What types of offspring are to be expected in a cross between a tortoise-shell female and a black male?

74. Is it possible for black parents to have white-skinned children? For two mulattoes? Can two mulattoes have black-skinned children?

75. Is it possible for two normal parents to have a feebleminded child? Explain.

76. What is a lethal gene? Why is it impossible to produce a homozygous yellow mouse?

77. Would selection be easier in a self-fertilized crop such as wheat or in a cross-fertilized crop such as maize? Why?

78. What is meant by a mutation? What happens to a somatic mutation when the organism dies? How may a recessive mutation produce a visible effect? What factors affect the mutation rate?

79. How has the study of identical twins given information about relative roles of heredity and environment?

ANNOTATED REFERENCES

Cold Spring Harbor Symposia on Quantitative Biology, vol. 24. 1959. Genetics and Twentieth Century Darwinism. Cold Spring Harbor, L. I. *In line with the fine traditions of the others in this series, this symposium gives* an up-to-date appraisal of the mechanisms of the evolutionary processes as developed from the study of population genetics, ecology, paleontology, and other disciplines.

Conklin, E. G. 1929. Heredity and Environment, ed. 5. Princeton, Princeton University Press. *A classic in this field. Emphasizes the relative influence of heredity and environment in the development and evolution of animals.*

Dunn, L. C. 1951. Genetics in the 20th Century. New York, The Macmillan Co. *A fine appraisal of the development of genetics since the rediscovery of Mendal's laws. Written by numerous specialists in the field of heredity.*

1957. Effect of Radiation on Human Heredity. Geneva, World Health Organization. *This report is made up of papers presented by certain members of WHO. The investigators well realize the imperfect nature of our present state of knowledge, and sweeping conclusions cannot be made. Much remains to be done in determining the relative frequency of spontaneous and induced mutations, a critical point in the study.*

Falconer, D. S. 1960. Introduction to Quantitative Genetics. New York, The Ronald Press Co. *The application of statistics to the study of populations, gene frequency, variations, and other concepts of genetics.*

Gates, R. R. 1946. Human Genetics, 2 vols. New York, The Macmillan Co. *A comprehensive summary of human genetics and one of the best reference works on the subject. Some parts are difficult for beginning students.*

Goldschmidt, R. B. 1952. Understanding Heredity. New York, John Wiley & Sons, Inc. *An authoritative, yet concise account of the fundamental principles of genetics. An excellent treatise for the beginning biology student.*

Jepsen, G. L., E. Mayr, and G. G. Simpson. 1949. Genetics, Paleontology, and Evolution. Princeton, Princeton University Press. *This comprehensive work gives a good summary of the three fields and of their interrelationships.*

Lerner, I. M. 1958. The Genetic Basis of Selection. New York, John Wiley & Sons, Inc. *This monograph deals entirely with genetic selection and is perhaps the only one of its kind so far published. It analyzes and appraises the latest concepts of selection in Mendelian populations, the problems of selection pressure, and the limits of selection.*

Muller, H. J., C. C. Little, and L. H. Snyder. 1947. Genetics, Medicine, and Man. Ithaca, Cornell University Press. *An appraisal of the relations of genetics to medicine by three eminent authorities in the field.*

Peters, J. A. (editor). 1959. Classic Papers in Genetics. Englewood Cliffs, N.J., Prentice-Hall, Inc. *Here are the principal landmarks in the development of the science of genetics. All students of heredity should be familiar with these classical papers.*

Riley, H. P. 1948. Introduction to Genetics and Cytogenetics. New York, John Wiley & Sons, Inc. *A readable text in the relatively new field of cytogenetics. Can be understood by the beginning student.*

Scheinfeld, A. 1950. The New You and Heredity, ed. 2. Philadelphia, J. B. Lippincott Co. *A popular yet accurate account of human heredity. One of the best works for the beginning zoology student.*

Sinnot, E. W., and L. G. Dunn. 1957. Principles of Genetics, ed. 4. New York, McGraw-Hill Book Co., Inc. *An excellent textbook of the fundamental principles of genetics. For the advanced student.*

Snyder, L. H. 1951. The Principles of Heredity. Boston, D. C. Heath & Co. *The practical application of genetics to man's welfare is given considerable attention in this excellent text.*

Srb, A. M. and R. D. Owen. 1952. General Genetics. San Francisco, W. H. Freeman & Co. *An excellent and comprehensive text in this widely studied field. Some of the discussions are too advanced for beginning students of heredity.*

Stern, C. 1949. Principles of Human Genetics. San Francisco, W. H. Freeman & Co. *An up-to-date account of human heredity and its implications.*

Waddington, C. H. 1939. An Introduction to Modern Genetics. London, George Allen & Unwin Ltd. *Treats the subject of genetics in a thorough and often technical manner. The cytological background of genetics is stressed.*

Waddington, C. H. 1957. The Strategy of the Gene. New York, The Macmillan Co. *A work for the serious student on the deeper aspects of development. It is an attempt to explain the nature of genic action and the way in which living systems operate.*

Wallace, B., and T. Dobzhansky. 1959. Radiation, Genes and Man. New York, Henry Holt & Co. *The potential danger of atomic energy to man's genetic heritage is vividly pointed out in this revealing work by two eminent geneticists.*

Zamenhof, S. 1959. The Chemistry of Heredity. Springfield, Ill., Charles C Thomas, Publisher. *A popular explanation of the mechanism of heredity in the light of recent investigation on the nature of heredity determinants.*

Applied genetics; human heredity   759

chapter **36**

The record of fossils (paleontology)

Paleontology is the science of ancient life as revealed by the study of fossil forms. The forms that exist today had ancestors which lived millions of years ago in the dim geological eras, and some of them left fossil records. This study shows how animals have arisen in the past and how they have become diversified. It reveals what organisms were dominant in certain geological ages and how they flourished and became extinct. It embraces an ecological study of animal life, for throughout the study of paleontology the student sees how the evolution of animal and plant life is correlated with the development and changes in the earth's crust. The fossils tell us much about the climatic conditions, the nature of the earth's topography, and the distribution of animals and plants with relation to the evolution of the earth's surface.

The fossil record is far from complete. There are many "missing links" in the phylogeny of every group of animals which have left fossil records. Many extensive groups of the past left no records at all. Scavengers, bacteria, soil, weather, and other disintegrating forces quickly destroy all evidences of most dead animals, especially soft-bodied organisms. The hard bones and teeth of vertebrate animals have afforded the best fossil evidences of the past. Invertebrate animals that have shells or other hard structures have left fair records. Most of the fossils found have been formed in dry dust or volcanic deposits, in peat bogs, in dry sandy regions, in cold regions where the bodies became quickly frozen, in muck at the bottom of lakes and oceans, and in asphalt pits such as that of the famed tar pits of Rancho La Brea in Los Angeles, California.

WHAT IS A FOSSIL?

In its broadest sense, a fossil is any evidence of past life. The ideal fossil, perhaps, would be the entire remains of an organism, but most fossils are only parts of animals or plants or they may be no part of the organism at all. They may be simply impressions, footprints, feather imprints, or some other forms of evidence that reveals something of their past existence. From this standpoint, fossils may be briefly classified as entire remains, actual hard parts, petrification, molds and casts, and coprolite.

Entire remains. Entire remains are illustrated by the mammoths which have been preserved in the frozen tundras of Siberia and the insects found in amber of certain European regions.

Actual hard parts. Teeth, bones, even entire skeletons have come down from the past, such as the skeletons of the saber-toothed cat and ground sloth of the La Brea tar pits.

Petrification. This type of fossil involves a replacement of the hard parts (skeleton), and sometimes the soft tissues, by minerals (silica is one of the best) which are infiltrated by water seepage. In some cases the original constituents of the bones are retained. Ground water heavily loaded with minerals and carbonic acid brings about this hardening process. Such a method of fossil formation often preserves the utmost details of outline, contour, and even microscopic structures. Even details of nerves and blood vessels were found in the ostracoderms discovered in Spitzbergen and elsewhere. Many invertebrates, such as those of Mollusca, as well as the petrified trees of the Petrified Forest of Arizona, are also striking examples.

Molds and casts. Whenever the hard parts of an animal are dissolved away by water, a cavity may be left showing the original shape, which is known as a **mold**. Minerals may infiltrate into and fill up this cavity to show only the external features and form a **cast**. Neither molds nor casts represent parts of living things. Many tracks and impressions were made by animals and plants in soft mud which later hardened sufficiently to keep their shape (molds). Later, new material filled the impressions, hardened, and formed casts. These molds and casts can be separated from each other at their lines of junction.

Coprolite (fossil excrement). Fossil dung often reveals much about the kinds of animals and plants which serve as food for contemporary animals. Fossil pellets have also been useful this way.

WHERE ARE FOSSILS FOUND?

Fossils may be found in any part of the world, although certain regions, because of ideal conditions for their formation, may have a greater abundance than others. Few places have been more favorable for fossil collections than the tar pits of Rancho La Brea in Hancock Park, Los Angeles. These had their origin as petroleum springs where the evaporation of the more volatile constituents of the oil left tar residues which served as traps for animals that were attracted to the water pools. Many predators came to to the pools to prey upon those that came

for water and were themselves trapped in the treacherous asphalt. When these pits were examined some years ago, hundreds of well-preserved fossils of many kinds of mammals and birds, both recent and extinct forms, were found. These include elephants, bears, sloths, saber-toothed cats, horses, vultures, and others. Visitors to the County Museum can see some of the wonderful collections made from these rather small, modest-looking tar pits. Fossils rarely are found in such extensive groups but are usually picked up singly here and there by accident. Limestone quarries and caves may yield rich finds in fossils as well as places buried under volcanic ash.

HOW DO PALEONTOLOGISTS ESTIMATE AGE OF FOSSILS?

One of the most useful methods for determining the age of geological formations and fossils is radioactivity. Radioactive elements are transformed into other elements at certain rates independent of pressure and temperature. Uranium^{238}, for instance, is slowly changed into lead^{206} at a rate of 1/2 gram of lead for each gram of uranium in a period of 4.5 billion years. The ratio of lead^{206} to the amount of uranium^{238} in a sample of rock formation should give a fair estimate of the age of the stratum from which the specimen was taken. Another radioactive substance, thorium, can be used in a similar manner. However, radioactive materials are not found in all rocks and some of them may be dissolved away by underground water.

For fossils not over 30,000 years of age, the radiocarbon method of Libby is very accurate. Radioactive carbon^{14} (an isotope), formed by the neutrons in the upper atmosphere under the influence of cosmic rays, is absorbed in constant amounts by all living (organic) materials (but not after death). The one-half life of this isotope is 5,560 years, i.e., one-half of it will disintegrate in that time, one-half of the remainder in the next 5,560 years, and so on. By comparing the amount of C^{14} in a fossil specimen with the amount it should have contained when

The record of fossils (paleontology) 761

alive, it is possible to arrive at a very accurate determination of its age.

Other methods of dating geological time or determining the relative age of fossils are also known. In recent years the potassium-argon method offers great promise in the precise dating of sedimentary rocks. When the radioactive isotope of potassium disintegrates it forms argon^{40} (12%) and calcium (88%). By knowing the amount of argon emitted from each unit of potassium in a unit time, it has been possible to estimate the age of rocks. As they age, fossil bones pick up fluorine, and thus it has been possible to arrive at the comparative age of bones by determining the amount of fluorine they contain. It was this interesting method that exposed the Piltdown man hoax a few years ago.

SIGNIFICANCE OF FOSSILS*

As a general rule the older the fossil, the deeper it is located in the earth's surface. Most fossils are laid down in deposits which become stratified and, if undisturbed, the older strata are the deeper, lower ones. However, strata are not always found in such regularity, for in many regions they have buckled and arched under pressure, so that older strata may be shifted over more recent ones. Since various fossils are correlated with certain strata, the former often serve as a means of correlating the strata of different regions. A common method of fossil formation is the burial of animals under the sediment deposited by large bodies of water. The finding of aquatic fossils on mountains indicates that the mountains were once under water. Our great western plains once formed the basin of a great inland sea, so that many marine fossils have been found there. The presence of tropical plant fossils in Greenland indicates that this region was not as rigorous and cold as it is now.

Differences between fossils and the structures of present-day organisms gave Charles Darwin the first indication of the

---

*Refer to Chapter 5, Principle 16.

fact of evolution. The study of fossils also brings out in a striking way the evolutionary sequence of animal groups. Certain fossils are characteristic of certain strata, and if they are not found in early geological strata, it may indicate that they arose since the early strata were laid down. Such studies show that animal life first appeared long after the earth's history had its beginning. Of course, soft-bodied forms could have lived before fossils were formed and thus left no vestiges of their past history, but all the evidence from hard parts, which are found to some extent in nearly all groups of animals, indicates rather clearly the phylogeny of most phyla of animals.

Some of the "missing links" are well shown by borderline forms which serve to connect one group of animals with another. In this way it has been possible to find relationships of animals which otherwise could only be guessed at. For instance, the birdlike reptilian fossils show unmistakably the affinities of birds and reptiles, and crossopterygian fish may indicate a link between fish and amphibians. Paleontology also shows us the diversification of species within each group. The earliest phyla to appear have living representatives today, but the present-day forms usually differ from the ancient ones in both structures and a much greater variety of species within the group. Some fossil histories are so complete that it is possible to trace the phylogeny of some organisms from one geological period to another, such as that of the elephant and the horse. Knowledge of fossils and their relation to the sequence of rock strata is also of practical importance in discovering mineral and oil deposits.

GEOLOGICAL ERAS AND CORRELATED FOSSIL RECORD

The earth's crust has witnessed many striking revolutions. In some regions of the earth these changes have taken the form of mountain elevations, emergence of large areas from the sea, sinking of areas into the sea, and marked climatic changes. All these geological changes in-

Figure 603. Representative fossils, **A**, Fossil arthropod, *Eurypterus*, which was abundant during upper Silurian period; related to modern scorpions. **B**, Some worm tubes. **C**, Bryozoan. **D**, Trilobite, related to king crab of today and one of the most abundant of arthropod fossils. **E**, Cephalopod; chambered nautilus of today is little changed from this ancient fossil. **F**, Coral. **G**, Gastropod. **H**, Coelenterate strobila.

volved changes in the distribution of animals and plants. On the basis of these revolutions and resulting contrasts, geologists divide the history of the earth's crust into eras, periods, and epochs. There is first the division into five **eras** within which there were striking changes in the history of the earth's crust involving the elevation and sinking of continents, the invasion of the sea by the land, and the invasion of the land by the sea. In this way each era is subdivided into **periods.** Periods in turn were subdivided into **epochs.** These various divisions of the geological time scale are closely correlated with the fossils they bear. (See Table 2, page 31.)

A simplified version of the geological time scale with the characteristic animal life for the various periods is presented.

Archaeozoic era. This, the longest of the eras, is supposed to have lasted at least 2,000,000,000 years from the time the earth's crust had reached a solid state. During this era volcanic formations and upheavels and bucklings of the surface crust made enormous changes in the earth's surface. Most of its rocks are igneous (molten) so that most of the fossil record was destroyed. A few vestiges of plant life are found and the unicellular forms are supposed to have arisen during this time.

Proterozoic era. This era, about half as long as the preceding one, is characterized by deposits and extensive glaciation. Ice sheets extended close to the equator, and limy deposits indicate the existence of unicellular plants. There are evidences of jellyfish, sponges, arthropods, and some others in this era.

Paleozoic era. This era of about 350,000,000 years' duration witnessed the appearance of a great outburst of animal life, represented by members of every phylum in the animal kingdom and by most of the classes as well. Its seven major periods can be grouped according to the animals which were dominant and most characteristic of a particular group.

CAMBRIAN AND ORDOVICIAN PERIODS. This is the **age of the higher invertebrates,** es-

pecially the shelled forms. The rocks of these periods are rich in fossil brachiopods and trilobites (Figure 603, *D*). All phyla except chordates are found in the Cambrian period, and chordates are represented in the Ordovician period in the form of the ostracoderms, but the ancestors of these must have existed before Many of the formations of these periods show well-preserved specimens of jellyfish, echinoderms, sponges, gastropods, cephalopods, and annelid worms. A shale found in British Columbia is one of the richest sources of fossils of the Cambrian period and includes the forms already mentioned as well as the connecting link between the annelids and arthropods which may be considered the counterpart of the modern *Peripatus.* Geologically during these two periods the continental land masses were gradually being submerged with water and relatively little dry land was available.

SILURIAN AND DEVONIAN PERIODS. These two periods represent what is known as the **age of fishes.** During this time the land masses which had largely been covered with water began to rise, and land plants, such as ferns, and air-breathing animals appeared. Some fossil fish are found in the Silurian period, but far more are present in the succeeding Devonian period. The brachiopods reached their peak during these periods, but the trilobites began to fade from the scene. Among other common fossils of this time are sponges, corals, snails, and the peculiar eurypterids (Figure 603, *A*). The ostracoderms already mentioned were jawless fish, but during the Devonian period the first jawed fish, the placoderms, arose These fish were provided with paired fins (often more than two pairs) and bore armored plates. The cartilaginous fish the sharks, and the bony fish also appeared in the fresh water during this period, and many of them later migrated to the ocean Among the bony fish, one type, the lobe finned fish, was the ancestor of the land vertebrate and was supposed to be extinct long ago until a single living specimen was found off the coast of Africa in 1938

Near the end of the Devonian period the first land vertebrate, the amphibian, in the form of the labyrinthodont appeared.

MISSISSIPPIAN, PENNSYLVANIAN, AND PERMIAN PERIODS. These three last periods of the Paleozoic era represent what is known as the **age of amphibians.** The first two of these periods are commonly combined into the Carboniferous period because many of our coal deposits were laid down during this time. Many swamps with luxuriant vegetation, ferns, horsetails, etc. were characteristic of the land and formed the source of the coal. Many amphibians, mainly armored, were common, as well as mollusks, crinoids, and insects. The Permian period is noted for its reptilian fossils, provided with enormous dorsal spines. Some of these fossils were borderline forms of both amphibian and reptilian characters, indicating the relationship between the two groups. Some of the reptiles of this period, the pelycosaurs and therapsids, had some mammalian features, especially of the skull and teeth, and are supposed to be the direct ancestors of the mammals.

Mesozoic era. Because of the great development of the reptiles, this era is known as the **age of reptiles.** They included among others the famed dinosaurs, the ichthyosaurs, and the pterodactyls or flying reptiles. Many were of enormous size, especially the dinosaurs, some of which were 60 to 90 feet long and weighed 50 tons. One of the most characteristic invertebrates of the early part of the era was the ammonite, which belongs to the cephalopod group of the mollusks. The first birds also appeared during the Jurassic period, and one of their fossils, Archaeopteryx (Figure 323), had both reptilian and bird characteristics. In the Triassic period, which was the first period of the era, true mammals appeared for the first time, although they played a very minor role alongside the huge reptiles. The Mesozoic era lasted about 150,000,000 years, and its chief geological development was the elevation of a large part of the continental areas above water and the formation of many great mountain ranges. Climate during the era varied from dry and warm to moist and warm.

Cenozoic era. The evolution of the mammals occurred mainly during this era and hence it is called the **age of mammals.** Actually, this era saw also the great development of birds and insects, but mammals represented its most striking feature. The era is commonly divided into two periods, the Tertiary and Quaternary. This era started about 75,000,000 years ago and includes present geological time. There are five epochs in the Tertiary period: Paleocene, Eocene, Oligocene, Miocene, and Pliocene. Differentiation of these epochs is made mainly on the basis of the kind of fossils, for their geological formations are much the same. It was during the early periods of this era that the great Rocky Mountains and other ranges were formed. Climatic conditions also varied a great deal in the various epochs.

The earliest mammal fossils were laid down in the Triassic and may have been represented by the monotremes or egg-laying mammals. Modern representatives of these primitive mammals are the platypus and the spiny anteater. Late in the Mesozoic era there arose the marsupials which brought forth their young alive but retained them for some time in the mother's abdominal pouch. Some of these primitive members, such as the opossum, are now little changed from these early forms. The higher placental forms originated from a small insectivoral form which lived in the trees. Fossil forms of these have been found in the rock formations of the Cretaceous period of the Mesozoic era.

The real development of the mammals and their multiple evolutionary branching occurred during the Tertiary period (Figure 604). Evolutionary tendencies were the larger size of the brain and the differentiation of their teeth and feet. Changes in structures were closely correlated with differences in food habits and habitats. The sudden appearance of many of these mammals no doubt indicates a long and varied history before they left fossil forms.

Figure 604. Mammal, *Brontotherium*, rhinoceros-like animal that flourished during late Eocene and Oligocene times. (Courtesy Chicago Natural History Museum.)

Figure 605. Mammoths. These have been found frozen in Siberia in a good state of preservation. (Courtesy Chicago Natural History Museum.)

The Quaternary period is divided into the Pleistocene and Recent epochs. The two epochs together make up more than a million years of the earth's history, of which the Recent epoch constitutes the last 25,000 years. Geologically, there were some marked changes in the earth's surface during the Quaternary period. Immense glacial sheets advanced and receded four times during the period. The Great Lakes of North America were formed, and there were also many changes in water-land relations. Animal life of the Quaternary period was quite similar to that of the present. Some of the noted forms which flourished during that period, but later became extinct, were the saber-toothed cat, the mammoth (Figure 605), and the ground sloth. Some of these have been found in an excellent state of preservation in the Rancho La Brea tar pits.

FOSSIL RECORD AS EVIDENCE OF EVOLUTION

Paleontology is supposed to give substantial support to the theory of evolution, for the fossil record indicates that species change continuously. Those fossils of a particular geological era or period showed enough likeness to and difference from those of other eras and periods to conclusively prove genetic continuity. From the standpoint of the special creation idea of the origin of life, it was assumed that all life was destroyed from time to time to be followed by a new creation of organisms somewhat different from the preceding ones. This theory has been discredited by all scientific geologists, for it was discovered that extinction of the various forms of life did not occur simultaneously and that some forms have undergone far more marked changes than others through the long geological past.

766

The fossil record is far from complete. Some animals are not fossilized at all; others that do form fossils have left very incomplete records. The more complete the fossil of a particular organism is, the better the evidence for its evolutionary line of descent. Paleontology has afforded evidences for tracing the phylogeny of a number of groups of animals, but none more convincing than those for three great groups, the cephalopods, the horse, and the elephant. Fossil records for these have been found in such abundance and the evolutionary trends of their major morphological features can be traced with such thoroughness that paleontologists are practically content to rest their evidence on these alone.

EVOLUTION OF CEPHALOPODS

The Mollusca represents the second most extensive group in the animal kingdom. They were well established by the Cambrian period, which is often referred to as the **age of the shelled higher invertebrates.** The most advanced class of the Mollusca is Cephalopoda, which includes the octopuses, the squids, and others. The shelled cephalopods are represented today by only one genus, the chambered *Nautilus*. This form lives in one chamber of a coiled shell, the other chambers of the shell being divided from each other by partitions. Each chamber corresponds to a stage in the growth of the animal, and the animal lives in the most recently secreted chamber with the exception of a stalk that extends backward through the others. As the animal grows, it moves forward into the wider part of the shell and secretes a partition or septum behind it.

Nautilus represents the last of a group which dominated the oceans in the late Cambrian and early Ordovician periods. Closely related to the *Nautilus* were the now extinct ammonites. Morphologically, the course of their evolution was marked by changes in two structural features, the shape of the shell and the sutures where the septa formed their lines of junction. The straight shell gradually became coiled in a flat spiral form as represented by the present *Nautilus*. On the other hand, the sutures which were mostly straight at first gradually became bent, wavy, and highly angular. The fossil record reveals a regular sequence in the evolutionary pattern of these two structures, one type of pattern being succeeded by another type. This evolution from a straight to a coiled shell and from straight to bent and crooked sutures demonstrates a remarkable example of straight-line evolution and used to be made much of by paleontologists.

EVOLUTION OF ELEPHANTS

The elephant group and their relatives represent a second example of a fossil record which is complete enough to show evolutionary changes throughout a long period of time. This group stressed two morphological features in particular, a prehensile proboscis and teeth. They originated in Africa and gradually spread to the other continents, Europe, Asia, North and South America. From the primitive proboscidean stock there arose many side branches, for they cannot all be placed in a direct line of descent. One of the earliest of these elephant-like animals, *Moeritherium,* has been traced to the Upper Eocene and early Oligocene epochs of Egypt. Its fossils reveal that it was only about 2 feet in height, with a long head and a flexible elongated snout with the nasal opening well toward the top (Figure 606). Its dentition showed some of the characteristics of later proboscidean forms, for the second incisors were enlarged to form tusks and there were indications of ridges on the molar teeth.

Although many different types of elephant-like fossils have been discovered, it has been difficult to arrange them in definite sequences. There may have been several lines of descent running more or less parallel with each other (adaptive radiation). One of these extinct lines is the mastodon from which the modern elephant is supposed to be an indirect descendant. Mastodons were long jawed with four tusks. Some of them were the size

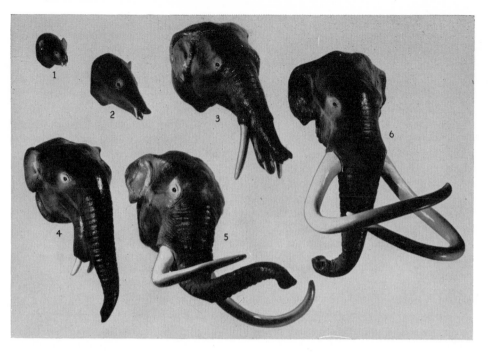

Figure 606. Restoration of heads of fossil elephant-like animals. **1,** *Moeritherium.* **2,** *Palaeo-mastodon.* **3,** *Trilophodon.* **4,** *Dinotherium.* **5,** *Mastodon.* **6,** *Elephas.* (Courtesy Ward's Natural Science Establishment, Inc., Rochester, N. Y.)

of present-day elephants. During the Miocene they spread from Africa over Asia, Europe, and North America. They had simpler and more numerous teeth than those of the later elephants. The most primitive of the mastodons was *Palaeomastodon* of the Lower Oligocene epoch. So extensive has been elephant evolution that authorities recognize 350 species, of which only two survive at the present day.

The main features of the evolutionary trends were the shortening of the lower jaw, the development of a high, short skull with the molar teeth for grinding, and heavy tusks. Some, such as the mammoth (Figure 605), developed long curved tusks. The mammoths which had a wide distribution survived until recently in Siberia and a few other countries where their carcasses have been found well preserved in the ice. One of these *(Elephas imperator)* grew to be 13 to 14 feet tall. The two existing species are the African elephant *(Loxodonta)* and the Asiatic

form *(Elephas)*. There are a number of differences between these two species with respect to ears, molar teeth, tusks, and shape of head. Just how they may be related and from what ancestry they have come is not known with certainty.

EVOLUTION OF THE HORSE

The fossil record affords us no more convincing or more complete evolutionary line of descent than that of the horse. The evolution of this form which covers many millions of years extends back to the Eocene period, and much of it took place in North America. This record seems to indicate that its evolution proceeded in a definite direction but there were undoubtedly many side branches where the forms showed many variations from the main line of descent. Some of these became extinct through the operation of natural selection. In the evolution of the horse the morphological changes of the limbs and teeth were of primary importance, along with a progressive increase in size of most of the types in the direct line of descent.

The first member of the horse phylogeny is considered to be *Hyracotherium*, about the size of a small dog. Its forefeet had four digits and a splint (Figure 607); the hind limb had three well-developed toes and two splints which represented the first and fifth toes. The teeth, 44 in number, had short crowns and long roots, and the teeth in the cheek were specialized to some extent for grinding, since their upper surfaces possessed conical cusps which tended to fuse. The habitat of this form was mostly forest underbrush on which it grazed. The middle Eocene was represented by *Orohippus*, which had a further development of molarlike teeth.

The next type in the line of descent was *Mesohippus* which flourished in the Oligocene epoch. This animal was taller than the others and had three digits on each foot. Of the three toes, the middle one was larger and better developed than the others. The cheek teeth especially tended to have their cusps united into ridges. *Miohippus*, which was also found in the Oligocene, was larger but definitely of the three-toed type. These horses as well as *Hyracotherium* were browsing forms.

The Miocene epoch was represented by two types, *Parahippus* and *Merychippus*, the latter arising in direct line from the former. *Merychippus* is considered the direct ancestor of the later horses. They were three toed, but the lateral toes were high above the ground. Thus the weight of the body was thrown upon the middle toe. The teeth were definitely high crowned, and the molar pattern was adapted as a flat grinding surface with sharp ridges of enamel. The evidence indicates that *Merychippus* was associated with grass feeding. It also had a larger skull and heavier lower jaws than the preceding forms. This horse was between 3 and 4 feet high at the shoulders. *Merychippus* gave rise to a number of horse

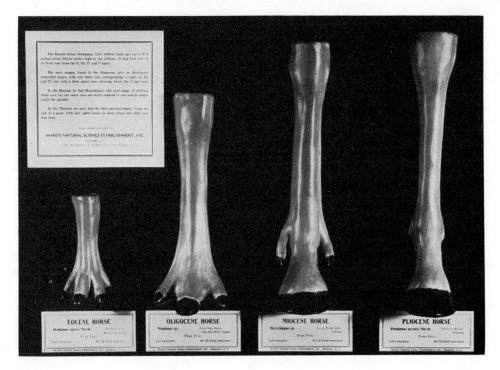

Figure 607. Evolution of forefoot of horse as revealed by fossil record. (Courtesy Ward's Natural Science Establishment, Inc., Rochester, N. Y.)

The record of fossils (paleontology) 769

types, most of which became extinct by the end of the Tertiary period. One of these which persisted into the Pleistocene was *Pliohippus*. This type was the first one-toed horse, for the lateral toes had disappeared.

From *Pliohippus* the genus *Equus,* or modern horse, arose. *Equus* is supposed to have arisen in the Pleistocene epoch. It arose in North America and spread to most of the other continents. In time they came to be about 60 inches or more in height at the shoulders. They have only one toe on each foot, but the two splint bones are evidences of the former lateral toes. By the end of the Pleistocene the horse had become extinct in North America, but migrant forms persisted in Eurasia to become the ancestors of the present-day horse. One or two wild types are still found in central Asia. After the discovery of America by Columbus, the horse was reintroduced by the early Spanish colonists and many escaped to become wild on the great plains of our west and the pampas of South America.

It is impossible to appreciate the full significance of the horse's evolution without at the same time taking into consideration the geological changes that went along with it. The development of this great animal from a small foxlike form was closely associated with the geological development from a hilly, forested country to the great plains of the west. The horse thus in its evolution represents a close parallelism between the development of an adaptive structural pattern on the one hand and a great geological development of the earth's surface on the other.

ANNOTATED REFERENCES

Boule, M., and H. V. Vallois. 1957. Fossil Men. New York, The Dryden Press. *A revealing account of man's past history and keen appraisals of the many discoveries in the field of human paleontology.*

Camp, C. L., and G. D. Hanna. 1937. Methods in Paleontology. Berkeley, University of California Press. *Good descriptions of the collection and preparations of fossils.*

Gregory, W. K. 1951. Evolution Emerging. A Survey of Changing Patterns From Primeval Life to Man. New York, The Macmillan Co. *This excellent work by a student of evolution emphasizes the major evolutionary trends in the emergence of animal life, but considerable attention is given to fossils and their significance throughout the work. Suitable for the specialist only.*

Moore, R. C. 1956. Introduction to Historical Geology, ed. 2. New York, McGraw-Hill Book Co., Inc. *Much stress is given to fossils and their formation. There is a great deal of interest in this work for the beginning student.*

Moore, R. C., C. G. Lalicker, and A. G. Fischer. 1952. Invertebrate Fossils. New York, McGraw-Hill Book Co., Inc. *An extremely well-balanced textbook with abundant and revealing illustrations. Every group has a concise list of definitions which are very helpful in understanding the discussions of the different forms. There is an excellent chapter on the way fossils are formed and preserved.*

Place, R. 1957. Finding Fossil Man. New York, Philosophical Library. *Although not a technical discussion of man's early origin, all zoology students will find this little book very informative and interesting. The style of writing is popular, and the photographs and line drawings add much to the explanation of man's evolution.*

Romer, A. S. 1950. Vertebrate Paleontology, ed. 2. Chicago, University of Chicago Press. *An advanced text and one of the best in the field. Of great interest to all students of fossils.*

Simpson, G. G. 1953. Life of the Past. New Haven, Yale University Press. *One of the best works on fossils for the beginning student. In a clearly written manner the author surveys the formation of fossils, their meaning, and how they fit into the evolutionary plan.*

Stirton, R. A. 1959. Time, Life and Man. The Fossil Record. New York, John Wiley & Sons, Inc. *An up-to-date account of paleontology, its methods, and its principles. Among its many interesting chapters, the student will find especially revealing the ones dealing with the history of paleontology, the relation of the Foraminifera to oil deposits, and prehistoric men.*

Symposium (many authors). 1950. Origin and Evolution of Man. Cold Spring Harbor Symposia on Quantitative Bilogy, vol. XV. Cold Spring Harbor, The Biological Laboratory. *While this excellent symposium stresses the latest evidence of man's ancestry, much attention is also given to fossil records and their* interpretation. *A work for the advanced student.*

Watson, D. M. S. 1951. Paleontology and Modern Biology. New Haven, Yale University Press. *The value of paleontology in the study of evolution cannot be overemphasized and no one is better qualified to discuss this rela-* tionship than the greatest of English paleontologists.

Zittel, K. von. 1893. Handbuch der Palaeontologie. *This excellent summary of the fossil record up to the time it was published has exerted an enormous influence on the development of paleontology everywhere.*

chapter 37

Principles of variation
and organic evolution

ORIGIN OF LIFE*

Many theories about the origin of the earth and the other planets of the solar system have been proposed, but none are entirely satisfactory. There has been an unusual amount of speculation on these matters in recent years and right now the dust-cloud hypothesis seems to hold the limelight. According to this theory planets and stars were originally formed from great collections of submicroscopic particles and gases floating in space and rotating around the sun. Under the influence of gravity large, dense masses of this interstellar dust were gradually condensed and coalesced into planetary nuclei. In time these nuclei picked up other material and grew in size and compactness. These masses which formed the earth and the other planets had at first a very high temperature not unlike that of the sun and were in the gaseous state. When separated as an isolated body, the earth mass began to cool by radiation of heat into space, became molten, and solidified at the surface to form a solid crust. Relatively this cooling-off process was fairly rapid, for it is thought that the temperature of the surface reached its present condition within 25,000 years. Because of the great heat, at first only a thick layer of superheated steam covered the earth. As this steam cooled it condensed to form water, which fell to the

earth as rain, and as the earth cooled the water remained to form the oceans. For a long time the earth's atmosphere contained little free oxygen, which was combined as water and as oxides. The atmosphere consisted of water vapor, carbon and nitrogen compounds such as ammonia, and possibly certain gases (methane, hydrogen, etc.). Gradually the seas acquired many kinds of salt carried there by the leaching action of the surface streams.

Most of the other planets at present have atmospheres of this type with temperatures too hot or too cold to support life as we know it. The atmosphere of Mars has both oxygen and water as well as carbon dioxide and could possibly support life. By means of the spectroscope it has been possible to analyze partially the atmospheres of other planets. Their atmospheres undoubtedly have changed since the formation of the solar system but not to the same extent as that of the earth. During these early stages of the cooling-off process the earth's mass was gradually assuming a condition similar to what it is today. Free oxygen was first formed by photochemical and ionization processes from molecules of oxides of carbon and nitrogen—and later by the photosynthesis of living organisms. Because the lighter atoms tended to move away from the center of the mass more rapidly than the heavier atoms, a condition of layers occurred, so that the earth

---

*Refer to Chapter 5, Principle 7.

had a core of high density with an outer covering of lighter materials. The outermost part consisted of the land surface, water, ice, and an atmosphere of gases. To reach a stage suitable for the support of life must have required hundreds of millions of years in the earth's history.

When and how did life originate? Only speculations can be given for an answer to this problem. The only direct evidence we have are the fossil life of the past and the laboratory demonstration of synthetic reactions for the creation of complex molecules, such as certain amino acids. It is generally agreed by most biologists that life came from nonliving substances. The belief that life may have come to this earth in the form of spores from some other planet is simply "passing the buck," and it is highly improbable that such a source could survive the unfavorable conditions of interplanetary space travelling. There is no real evidence that spontaneous generation occurs today, for it seems that the conditions under which life first arose (probably two to three billion years ago) are no longer in existence. In whatever way life originated there is no reason for thinking that it was an event that occurred only once or in one place but that the conditions for its synthesis must have been widespread.

As a prerequisite for the origin of life it was necessary first to have complex organic substances such as amino acids and their linkages (polypeptids). Organic molecules can be formed from inorganic ones in the laboratory. In 1953 Urey and Miller showed that the amino acids, alanine, glycine, and some others, could be produced by circulating a mixture of water vapor, ammonia, methane, and hydrogen past an electric discharge for a few days. In this experiment the electric spark was supposed to simulate the action of lightning in the formation of the first organic compounds. All of these prerequisites for life were thought to be present in the early evolution of the earth's atmosphere. Although the likelihood of forming organic molecules is highly improbable, nevertheless there were so many

possibilities with the staggering number of atoms and molecules which existed that some of them by chance could and probably did form such combinations. In time, complex substances such as carbohydrates and amino acids were formed in the sea by the reaction and aggregation of molecules. In this way molecular structures of increasing size and complexity arose.

The crucial point occurred when colloidal combinations of molecules acquired a self-duplicating property, for now they could multiply and compete for their components. Natural selection could now operate, for a favored variant might be able to catalyze reactions better than others and acquire the ability to form additional molecules faster. Selection would also favor those molecules which could break down other molecules and weave the constituents into their own patterns. This might be considered the beginning of predation. This earliest autocatalytic structure might have the properties of our present-day concept of the gene or that of a virus. Both these entities have similar chemical structures (nucleoproteins), can duplicate themselves, and can undergo mutation. Both the gene and virus have a molecular pattern of organization rather than colloidal phases as shown by the crystallization of certain viruses. These primordial living units had to rely upon their environment for molecules with which they built their structures; hence they were **heterotrophs**. As such they could survive only as long as there were organic molecules in the sea. However, by natural selection some evolved to the stage of being able to make their own molecules by chemosynthesis or photosynthesis (**autotrophs**). Symbiotic associations of nucleoproteins, each with a specific function to perform in the synthesis of necessary components, would be favored by natural selection. Such a symbiotic system might represent the first distinction between genes and cytoplasm.

Another advance in the evolution of life was the organization of the genes into linear threads or chromosomes, which made possible precise duplicating mechanisms for mitosis and meiosis. This afforded great genetic variation due to recombinations and mutations within a population and set the stage for the evolutionary entity of species. From now on evolutionary progress in both unicellular and multicellular forms displayed almost infinite potentialities, especially in biparentally reproducing individuals.

MEANING OF EVOLUTION*

It is evident that animals and plants as we see them present an immense variety of different forms, ranging all the way from those of small size and low degree of complexity to those of large size and complicated structure. Moreover, organisms are found in nearly every kind of habitat that will support life at all and manifest every conceivable kind of adaptation to their surroundings. The thinking person must often ask himself whence and how came this abundance of life? Have these different species always existed this way? Are some more closely related than others? Is there a similar basic pattern throughout all life? What is the basis for grouping animals into certain taxonomic units? These and similar questions have posed real problems to scientists for centuries. One of the most important contributions of biology is the principle of evolution, which attempts to answer these questions.

Evolution is the doctrine that modern organisms have attained their diversity of form and behavior through hereditary modifications of pre-existing lines of common ancestors. It means that all organisms are related to each other because of common descent, or that all organic life can be traced back to relatively simple common ancestral groups. It also implies the genetic changes populations undergo in their descent from ancestral populations. Basically, evolution is the change in the relative frequency of genes. This theory rejects the old traditional belief of the origin of life as expressed in the

book of Genesis. Organic evolution is only one aspect of the larger view that the entire earth has undergone an amazing evolution of its own. The evolutionary principle has profoundly influenced every field of human thought and, one may add, no principle has been more disturbing to persons at certain stages of thinking. On the other hand, the grand concept of evolution arouses in all thoughtful individuals a feeling of awe and wonder, and one of inspiration, at the great drama that has and is unfolding before their eyes.

Evolution is more than a change in the form and function of organisms; it is rather a change in their whole, integrated life as a part of nature. Evolution must account for all the conditions of life. That is why the population is the natural form of existence of all organisms. The evolution of any particular organism always involves its complex interrelations with the fellow members of its population and with its total environment. It is impossible to appreciate the concept of species—a focal point in all evolutionary theories—without understanding the mutual relations of organisms to one another in their natural population groups. The basic principle of evolution must, therefore, emphasize two vital points: (1) how the genotype changes and operates to perform its action in the body and (2) how the conditions of the environment influence the adjustments of an organism, its preservation, its variations, and its life history. The environment is thus the directive force in the evolutionary process. How the organism responds depends upon its genotype or gene pool, its mutant genes, and its gene combinations. The adaptive value of the genotype must depend upon the environment in which a species lives.

The study of evolution is a definite branch—perhaps the most important branch—of biological science. Its problems must be treated in accordance with the principles of any empirical science, that is, studied by observation and experiment. However, evolutionary study has certain limitations in this respect, for

---

*Refer to Chapter 5, Principle 18.

evolution is an extremely slow process; most of it has occurred in the remote past and much of it must remain in the stage of a hypothesis because it is not easily testable in practice. The fossil record represents the most clear-cut and verifiable evidence that the evolutionary process has occurred, and population genetics also affords a certain amount of direct testable experiments of the process.

The student may well ask at this point the questions: Does evolution have a definite goal? What is the purpose of evolution anyway? Much of the evolutionary process does appear to be directional and shows specialization and advancement along certain definite lines. Many groups, especially vertebrates, show definite trends toward better organization patterns by which the animal is capable of a more efficient life and is more independent of the environment. All successful evolution is progressive. Change in the same direction may continue for long periods of time, as shown by the horse and many other forms. It is a popular belief that man has been the ultimate goal—the pinnacle toward which the evolutionary process has been pointed. But there is no evidence for such a view. Evolution has had many directions and many of them have been successful in a biological sense. Man enjoys a superior position because he has evolved a type of genotype which enables him to profit from the transmission of cultural development. As Professor J. S. Huxley emphasizes, human evolution tends to become conscious and self-directing. But about the only purpose the student can see in this vast panorama of evolution is that organisms are striving for preservation and survival by means of more efficient adaptations. Man, along with other organisms, has been the outcome of the same forces of natural selection and environmental opportunity. Blessed with favorable mutant genes and gene combinations in his genotype, he has met the challenge of the environment with a greater degree of educability than have other species.

Evolution is a continuous process and is taking place today. It is a very slow process but some striking evolutionary changes have taken place within historic times. Once it occurs, evolution seems to be irreversible except for small, minor reversals. A new pattern is always a modification of one that has existed. Many striking patterns of animal life, such as the dinosaurs, have been lost irretrievably.

Many viewpoints and hypotheses have been proposed to account for the evolutionary process, but within recent years there has been a fruitful attempt to converge or synthesize these various points of view into one unified and consistent picture of the whole process. Instead of many different processes, it is now thought a single mechanism is involved in explaining evolution. This approximation of the various viewpoints is often referred to as the **Modern Synthesis of Evolution.**

In the over-all picture of evolution one may discern three important stages: (1) a period of evolution in which many different basic chemical patterns were evolved in the inorganic world, from which organic forms later arose; (2) the origin of the living systems from the non-living through the gradual development and transformation of self-duplicating units into more complex units; and (3) the establishment of the organic systems as we know them from the fossil record and from existing forms. It is with the last stage that we are most concerned in our discussion of evolution.

The evolution of almost any group of animals in general follows a basic course or pattern. There is first the emergence of a complex of adaptations which are exploited in diverse ways by adaptive radiation into various ecological niches, if these are available (opportunism). Within each of these lines more or less directional progress occurs, with alternate stages of advancement and stability, and in some cases there is enough diversification within a line for the formation of taxonomic units of the rank of species or higher. In time and on rare occasions new adaptive complexes of further improvement may emerge in some or all of the original adaptive lines and a new cycle is initiated, upsetting the stable phases of no essential change. This process in a group may continue indefinitely or it may be cut short by extinction. Within the various groups there has been an enormous diversity of rate, directness, stability, progress in complexity, and number of branches of phyletic lines.

Nearly every branch of biology, as well as other sciences, has made contributions to our understanding of evolution, but the recent outlook has greatly emphasized the roles of genetics and ecology. The importance of the genotype and its composition explains the emphasis on genetics; the role of the environment in directing the course of evolution explains the emphasis on ecology. Evolutionary study involves direct experiments of breeding and artificial mutations, observation of biogeographic and ecological factors of distribution, morphological similarity of patterns and adaptations to different ways of life, a study of the fossil sequences in their relations to each other, and the statistical transformation of populations in terms of gene and chromosomal frequencies. It should be possible to demonstrate the elements of the evolutionary processes at the present day.

In an analysis of the modern synthesis of evolutionary processes, the following major causes are given priority rating— mutation rate, natural selection, chance or random genetic drift, and isolation and population structure.

Mutation rate. Mutation rate is the chance, random change of hereditary mechanisms. This and the subsequent reshuffling of the genes into various new combinations by bisexual reproduction makes possible structural differences in populations. Gene mutations occur by chance in an unpredictable manner, but their rate can often be predicted. Mutations provide the basis for hereditary variations.

Natural selection. Natural selection is the real basic external factor that molds the development of a species. Selection determines which mutant genes survive and which ones are eliminated. It molds the genes into a coordinated whole, and although it cannot originate new characters, it can determine what sets of genes can be of immediate biological usefulness to the species. It can produce rapid evolutionary transformation or it can stabilize the evolutionary trend.

Chance or random genetic drift. In small populations, random fluctuations or changes in gene frequency may have an important bearing on evolutionary trends. Some genes may be entirely lost and others may be greatly increased in frequency because certain mutant genes may not be included in gametes in the process of meiosis, or they may not be present at all or present with a greater frequency than they were in the original larger population. Close interbreeding in such populations would tend to make heterozygous genic pairs homozygous.

Isolation and population structure. This factor refers to those conditions in which groups of organisms are prevented from interbreeding or are divided into subunits with limited cross-migration. This results in evolutionary divergence, for an isolated population would not share its mutant genes with others and would develop its own unique evolution. This process could lead to the formation of a new species in each of the isolated groups by this chance accumulation of mutations.

How these four basic factors operate in the evolutionary process may be made clear by selecting a hypothetical species population of great extent and following it through its possible evolutionary fate. Suppose this population is found in a wide geographical area and exhibits the characteristics of a **cline,** that is, there is a gradual, continuous, gradient change in the members of the population because of of adjustments to local conditions which show considerable variations in different parts of the cline. Thus, in certain parts of the cline climate conditions may be hot, in others cold; weather may vary from extreme moisture in some parts to very dry in others, etc.

Within a cline the species will be divided into smaller units of population (demes) which are more or less isolated from each other in accordance with the different habitats found within the range of a cline. The members of a deme may breed freely with each other but usually not with the members of other demes. Each deme more or less can develop an evolution of its own, for small hereditary differences (mutations) which occur in demes may be, to some extent, unique, and thus each deme in time becomes different from other demes. Natural selection will operate to select the better-adapted characters in each case and their possessors will increase in frequency. In most cases the variations or mutations are small and quantitative in effect (micromutations), but some may have larger effects (macromutations). Some of the mutations may confer only small advantages at first, but reshuffling of the genes at meiosis and further recombinations may increase their effects. Recessive mutants will spread slowly, dominant ones more rapidly. If the environmental conditions remain fairly stable, there is a slow successional evolution within the deme; readaptation to changing conditions, however, speeds up the evolutionary rate.

The demes within a cline will not all have the same fate. Some of them may come together (if interbreeding can occur) and fuse; others may differentiate far enough to prevent interbreeding and form true species. Whenever two demes fuse, each contributes its pool of genes to the future offspring, which thus acquire advantageous genes of both demes. Still other demes may become extinct in a large cline. Other degrees of demes may be found in a large species population. Adjacent demes may intergrade into each other. A common pattern of demes consists of many subspecies formed by divergent evolution in partially isolated demes. The time factor may cause these subspecies to differentiate into true species. Because of the smallness of some of the demes, genetic drift can operate to produce a marked differential in gene frequency. In this way chance may determine whether or not certain genes will be emphasized or neglected. It will thus be seen that whenever a population is subdivided into small subunits there is a strong possibility that there may be a rapid evolutionary process of a divergent nature with results favorable to the formation of new species.

EARLY HISTORY OF EVOLUTIONARY IDEA

Although the development of the evolutionary theory has occurred chiefly during the past hundred or so years, many thinking men long before this time had ideas about the evolving of the various forms of life from one another. Some of the early Greek philosophers, Thales, Epicurus, Empedocles, and Aristotle, who lived from 500 to 300 B.C., thought a great deal on the evolution and the development of the different types of organisms. Many of their ideas were very crude in the light of present-day information, for they lacked the necessary data to test their observations. Their viewpoint was that all animal life had its origin by special creation or by spontaneous generation. Many puzzling problems were posed by the discovery of fossils which had remarkable resemblances to present-day forms and yet at the same time showed considerable differences. This evidence of former life was explained largely by the theory of catastrophism, which was the idea that animal life had suffered total destruction at times by some form of catastrophe and had been replaced by forms somewhat different from the previously existing ones.

Among modern zoologists who thought seriously about the idea of evolution was the French naturalist Buffon (1707-1788) who stressed the influence of environment upon the modifications of animal types. In 1745 Maupertuis, a French philosopher, described many of the concepts of variation and the diversity of animal life. Another French zoologist, Lamarck (1744-1829), put his ideas into a more concrete form and elaborated a

Principles of variation and organic evolution 777

theory to account for the evolutionary changes of animal life by use and disuse of organs. Although the basic idea of his theory is no longer considered seriously by most biologists, the influence of Lamarck did stimulate serious thought about evolution. Erasmus Darwin (1731-1802), the grandfather of Charles Darwin, recognized that the various forms of organisms arose from each other and stressed the response of the animal to environmental changes as the basis for its modifications.

One development that helped foster sound thinking along evolutionary lines was the science of geology in the early nineteenth century. The geologist Sir Charles Lyell (1797-1875), in his *Principles of Geology* (1830), elaborated the theory of **uniformitarianism,** which stated that the causes that produced changes in the earth's surface in the past are the same that operate upon the earth's surface at present. Such forces over a long period of time could account for all the observed changes, including the formation of fossil-bearing rocks, and did not require catastrophes for an explanation of the geological process. This concept of geology showed conclusively that the earth's age must be reckoned with in millions of years rather than in thousands. Charles Darwin was greatly stimulated by this important geological work and was aided greatly by it in his own thinking on the processes of organic evolution.

No one has done more to stimulate interest and study in the field of evolution than the great Englishman Charles Darwin (1809-1882). His name, or rather his theory, is almost a synonym for evolution itself. Although the theory he proposed is now known to have many flaws, so forcibly did he present his ideas and his array of carefully collected scientific data that no one before or since can really challenge his pre-eminence in this field. He was thus the first to give a clear-cut idea of how evolution may have operated. Although the theory of natural selection was not entirely original with Darwin, no one else had proposed it with such clarity or supported it with such forcible argu-

ments. *The Origin of Species,* published in 1859, has influenced biologists of every race and country, and many have extended the concept of organic evolution by valuable information. Darwin's theory and the many modifications of it will be mentioned later in this section.

EVIDENCES FOR EVOLUTION

About the fact of evolution there is almost universal agreement among scientists. On what evidences do they base this conviction? It is difficult to state exactly what line or lines of evidence are most responsible for the belief that species do change. Such beliefs usually do not come full blown, but only gradually, and subconscious ideas gleaned from many sources influence their development. Darwin emphasized the importance of his fossil studies in South America and the geographical distribution of animals on oceanic islands, such as the Galápagos, in influencing his early belief in the theory.

Most of the evidences of evolution are obtained from paleontology (already discussed in Chapter 36) and from the biological disciplines of comparative anatomy, embryology, physiology, taxonomy, geographical distribution, and experimental biology. Paleontology is the historical record and, in some respects, the most direct and convincing of all lines of evidence. Fossils are often associated with strata of sedimentary rocks which, arranged in chronological sequence, give a clue to the age and changes in the fossils. The simplest animal forms belong to the oldest fossil-bearing rocks and more complicated forms in more recent strata.

Comparative anatomy

Animals can be arranged in groups whose morphological patterns are quite similar. The principle of homology, you recall, refers to structurally similar organs which become adapted for different environmental conditions, such as the wing of a bird and the forelimb of a mammal. Homologous organs may show many modifications among the various animal groups. Vestigial or useless and degenerate

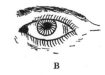
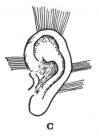

A   B   C

Figure 608. Certain vestigial organs in man. **A,** Vermiform appendix. **B,** Nictitating membrane in corner of eye, remnant of a functional structure in lower forms. **C,** Extrinsic muscles of ear, largely nonfunctional in man.

organs are common in most vertebrate forms, such as the vermiform appendix, nictitating membrane of the eye, the extrinsic muscles of the ear, and many others. These examples suggest that animals have become adapted to different environments so that structures are variously modified (adaptive radiation) or have become useless altogether.

Embryology

Embryology reveals a transition in structures from one stage to another in the development of a single individual. The biogenetic law states that an individual during its development passes through stages similar to its ancestors. This postulate can only be an approximation, for no embryo is precisely like an ancestral form. Many embryonic characters are peculiar (cenogenetic) and are not found in the adult, such as the yolk sac, and fetal membranes. But the sequence of morphological patterns of the circulatory system and the kidneys, for example, which pass through the transition stages of fish, amphibian, and reptile in the development of a mammal, must be considered remnants of ancestral conditions and afford clues about the nature of mammalian ancestors. Genetically, the reason for this sequence lies in the appearance of new genes by mutation in the evolution of higher from lower forms.

Physiology and biochemistry

Physiological processes of digestion, circulation, respiration, excretion, nervous,

and others are very much the same in all animals, with only minor modifications. The chemical and physiological fluids are also much the same. The hormones from one kind of animal will produce about the same reactions in all other kinds. Blood tests by the antigen-antibody reaction which will produce a precipitation among the members of a closely related group but scanty or none in that of others may be used to show degrees of relationship between different animals. The physiological action of enzymes in all kinds of animals shows a remarkable similarity. Trypsin and amylase, two important digestive enzymes, have been found in practically all animal phyla. All animals are related in their metabolic processes and share similar cellular and protoplasmic structures.

Classification

The present-day interpretation of taxonomy is based upon the degree of natural relationship. The concept of evolution assumes that the various taxonomic categories have arisen by modification of species. Early life was represented by only a few species, perhaps by only one. Modifications within these early species built up a slow accumulation of different characteristics which resulted in the divergence found among the different groups of animals today. Evolution has in its course proceeded from the taxonomic groups of the lower ranks (species, genera, families) to the higher ranks (orders, classes, phyla). Thus, within the animal

Principles of variation and organic evolution   779

kingdom the resemblance becomes more detailed as the lower taxonomic units are approached. Many intermediate organisms linking one group with another have been found among both living and fossil forms.

Geographical distribution

Whenever a new species arises by mutation in a center of origin, it tends to spread out until it is prevented by a barrier of some kind. The higher taxonomic units, such as families, orders, and classes, occupy larger areas than the lower ranks of species and genera. Evolution would explain this on the basis that the higher taxonomic ranks are older, have had a longer time for dispersal, and have had time to break up. Discontinuous distribution, where closely related animals are far apart, can often be explained by the fossil record in the gap between the groups of animals. The camel family, for instance, is represented by the true camels in Asia and the llamas in South America. However, the fossil record indicates that camels may have had their true center of origin in North America, spreading to the other regions. Thus a continuous range became discontinuous. Animals long isolated from each other also tend to show great differences from each other, such as those in Australia and oceanic islands in contrast to those that are near the mainland (continental).

Experimental biology

By carefully selecting and preserving desirable qualities, man has been able to produce the numerous varieties of plants and animals found in the world today. Although these varieties cannot be considered separate species, they are known to come from common ancestors and may give an inkling of what could be done by nature in the wild. Experimental induction of mutant forms by x-rays, radiation, etc. indicates ways by which speciation may occur in nature.

Within recent years one of the most striking evidences for evolution is the rapid, man-influenced evolution of certain viruses, bacteria, and insects. Confronted with antibiotics and insecticides, these forms have evolved and are evolving within short periods resistance to these drugs. These organisms have short generations, amazing reproduction, and high mutation rates. Such evolution is observable and its mechanism can be verified.

THEORIES TO ACCOUNT FOR METHODS OF EVOLUTION

In a field that lends itself to so many different interpretations, we should expect to find many theories. Many theories have some elements of truth in them but the mistake, common enough in any field of inquiry, of considering a few logical and demonstrated facts as being the whole picture, is characteristic of most of them. The background of training of the biologist often has an important bearing on the theory of evolution he espouses. The paleontologist, for instance, leans strongly toward the orthogenetical interpretation of evolutionary mechanisms; the cytogeneticist, on the other hand, stresses the importance of gene transformations and behavior in mutational changes.

Although no one theory adequately explains the mechanism of evolution, biologists are gradually getting a clearer comprehension of the over-all picture of evolution. Many fields of biological study have made contributions toward its understanding. The difficulty of testing experimentally is a serious disadvantage to any line of scientific inquiry and explains the relative slowness in working out the mechanism of organic evolution.

Inheritance of acquired characters

One of the earliest evolutionary theories proposed was the one by Jean Baptiste de Lamarck (1744-1829), a French biologist. This theory is named after him and is commonly known as **Lamarckianism.** He first published his theory in full in his *Philosophic Zoologique* (1809). His theory was based upon the concept of the use and disuse of organs in the adaptation of animals to their environment. His belief was that whenever such an adaptation arose, it was definitely inherited from generation to generation, the inheritance of acquired characters. In other words, environmentally induced characteristics are transferred to genetic mechanisms. According to Lamarck, new organs and transformations arose in response to the demands of the environment. The size of an organ depended upon its use and disuse, and in this way he tried to account for vestigial organs. The limbless condition, for instance, of the snake he would explain by the handicap of legs in crawling through dense vegetation and thus the loss of the legs through disuse. On the other hand, he would explain the long neck of the giraffe by its habit of reaching up into trees to browse. There is little or no evidence for Lamarck's theory, and it has never received much support from biologists.

The effects of use and disuse are restricted mainly to somatic tissues but genetics does not give support to the transmission of somatic characters. Certain features of the theory are attractive to many who have not studied its limitations. As a great evolutionist once said, "Everyone is instinctively a Lamarckian until he knows better." Many experiments have been performed to demonstrate the validity of the theory, but none are convincing. There can be no permanent change unless the germ cells themselves are altered, and experiments have shown conclusively that they are subject to little or no effect from the somatic or body cells and the environment. In all justice to the Lamarckians it may be said that some of the experiments which have been performed to disprove the theory, such as amputation of tails, changed environmental conditions, etc., are quite naive, for they neither prove nor disprove any theory. Evolution is a slow process involving thousands of years, and experiments conducted over a relatively few generations have no significance.

Natural selection theory of Darwin

The first real mechanical explanation of evolution was the one proposed by Charles Darwin in his work, *The Origin of Species,* published in 1859. Another English scientist, Alfred Russell Wallace (1823-1913), should receive some credit for this theory of **natural selection.** Both Darwin and Wallace had arrived at the main conclusions of this theory independently, but the publication of *The Origin of Species* the year after Wallace had announced his conclusions in a brief essay really clinched Darwin's position and prestige.

Darwin's early training had afforded him an opportunity to accumulate data for his theory. As a young man he had spent five years (1831-1836) as a naturalist on board the *Beagle,* a vessel that had been commissioned to make oceanographic charts for the British admiralty. This vessel in the course of its voyage around the world spent much time in the harbors and coastal waters of South America and adjacent regions, and Darwin had ample time to make extensive collections and studies of the flora and fauna of those regions. He kept a detailed journal of his observations on the animal and plant life, an account which he later published. When he returned to England he brought out a number of scientific papers based on the collections and observations he had made on this extensive voyage.

The idea of natural selection did not occur to him for some time after he had returned. Many of his observations on the trip had been very puzzling to him, especially the great diversity of animal and plant life and its manner of distribution. He was especially puzzled over the fossils he found in Patagonia and elsewhere, for he noted the similarities and dissimilarities of these to existing forms of life. The bird life of the Galápagos Islands also intrigued him. When the idea of natural selection dawned on him, he spent the next twenty years accumulating data from all fields of biology to prove or disprove his theory. He made many experiments to test this and that point of natural selection and he evaluated all his work with a careful, scientific appraisal. Darwin, incidentally, obtained some of his clues for this theory from the *Essay on Population* by Malthus, especially the part on competition among people in an overpopulated world. Essentially, most of the concepts of the theory of natural selection were worked out by Darwin himself. So much evidence was brought forth and so forcible were the arguments advanced for natural selection by Darwin in his book, that one may safely say that a new era in thinking, not only in organic evolution but in many related fields as well, dates from the publication of the book.

The essential steps in the theory of natural selection as advanced by Darwin include nature of variation, great rate of increase among offspring, struggle for survival, natural selection and variation, survival of the fittest, and formation of new species.

Nature of variation. No two individuals are exactly alike. There are variations in size, coloration, physiology, habits, and other characteristics. Darwin did not know the causes of these variations and was not always able to distinguish between those that were heritable and those that were not. Only the heritable ones are important in evolution, since those caused by environmental factors of temperature, food, etc. are not passed on to succeeding generations. He laid stress upon artificial selection in domestic animals and plants and the role it played in the production of breeds and races of livestock and plants. He observed that man had been able to do this by carefully selecting and breeding those individuals with the desired modifications. Darwin thought that this idea of selective breeding under human planning and control could also be produced by agencies operating in the wild state. These agencies he sought to explain in his theory.

Great rate of increase among offspring. In every generation the young are far more numerous than the parents. Even in a slow-breeding form, such as the elephant, if all the offspring lived and produced offspring in turn, in a few hundred years the earth could not hold the elephants. Most of the offspring perish, for the population of most species remains fairly constant under natural conditions. Few animals or plants ever have the opportunity to increase within their theoretical possibilities. Placed in locations more favorable for their natural rate of increase they may multiply with enormous rapidity, such as the rabbit in Australia. Usually natural checks of food, enemies, diseases, etc. keep the populations within bounds.

Struggle for survival. If more individuals are born than can survive, there must be a severe struggle for existence among them. This competition for food, shelter, breeding places, and other environmental factors results in the elimination of those which are not favorably suited to meet these requirements. There are many factors involved in this struggle for existence, many of them obscure and difficult to demonstrate.

Natural selection and variation. Individuals of the same species tend to be different through variations. Some of these variations make it easier for their possessors to survive in this struggle for existence; other variations are a handicap and result in the elimination of the unfit.

Survival of the fittest. Out of the struggle for existence there results the survival of the fittest. Natural selection, therefore, determines that those individuals which have favorable variations will survive and will have a chance to breed and transmit their characteristics to their offspring. The less fit will naturally die without reproducing themselves. This process will operate anew on each succeeding generation so that the organisms will gradually become better and better adapted to their environment. With a change in the environment there must also occur a change in those characters which have survival value, or else the animal will be eliminated by the new conditions.

Formation of new species. How does this result in new species? According to Darwin, whenever two parts of an animal or plant population are each faced with slightly different environmental conditions, they would diverge from each other and in the course of time become different enough from each other to form separate species. In this way two or more species may arise from a single ancestral species. Also a group of animals, through adaptation to a changed environment, may become different enough from their ancestors to be a separate species. In a similar manner, greater divergencies could arise in time and lead to the higher taxonomic ranks of genera, families, etc.

What happens to characters when they are nonadaptive or indifferent? Variations which are neither useful nor harmful will not be affected by natural selection and may be transmitted to succeeding generations as fluctuating variations. This explains many variations which have no significance from an evolutionary viewpoint.

Appraisal of theory of natural selection. Although Darwin's theory of natural selection has given in general a logical and satisfactory explanation of evolution, many parts of his theory have to be changed in the light of biological knowledge and interpretation. Two weaknesses in his theory centered around the concepts of variation and inheritance. Darwin made little effort to distinguish between variations induced by the environment (physical or chemical) and those which involved alterations of the germ plasm or the chromosomal material. It is now known that many of the types of variations Darwin stressed are noninheritable and can have no significance in evolution. Only variations arising from changes in the genes (mutations) are inherited and furnish the material on which natural selection can act.

It will be recalled that the mechanism of genetics was not appreciated until 1900, long after Darwin's death. Darwin referred to sudden and radical variations as "sports" and considered them of little importance in evolution. Modern biology now considers mutations as the cornerstone of the evolutionary concept. Darwin overemphasized the role of natural selection and failed to note its limitations. He thought that selection could operate indefinitely in promoting the development of a desirable variation. It is now known

that when the population becomes homozygous for the genes of a particular trait, natural selection can no longer operate, as shown from experiments in pure lines. Additional genic changes (mutations) must occur before selection can continue.

Darwin did not appreciate the real nature of isolation in the differentiation of new species. There are really two types of isolation involved, **geographical** and **genetical.** Darwin appreciated the fact that groups of animals cut off from each other by natural barriers such as mountains, deserts, and water were often quite different from each other. He noticed this in the Galápagos Islands and elsewhere. This geographical isolation accounts for the existence of many different species and subspecies of animals in rather small regions which are broken up effectively by natural barriers, so that each taxonomic group has a chance to develop independently of the others. A small oceanic island, such as St. Helena, with many valleys separated by high mountains has many species of snails which are effectively isolated from each other. The explanation for this is that whenever a group of individuals in the range of a given species are in slightly different environments, mutations which may arise within a particular group may enable that group to diverge from the others. If the groups are separated from each other long enough, they may become distinct species.

There may be several kinds of barriers that prevent interbreeding. The geographical ones which have been mentioned are often effective this way. But there are also cases in which mutations may occur in a species and result in a group of organisms that are infertile with the parent stock. This **genetic isolation** is as effective in isolating separate species as are the geographical ones. Although infertility is not always used as a criterion in distinguishing between species, there is no doubt that when two groups of animals are infertile with each other they are distinct species.

Ecological isolation may be due to differences in habitats and ecological niches which may tend to keep groups of animals away from each other during the breeding season. Or two groups of animals may actually intermingle but because of a seasonal variation in their breeding habits are effectively isolated from each other.

Natural selection seems to play its most important role in the later stages of the evolutionary process. It does not explain the origin of mutations which give a group of animals its unique characteristics. Natural selection may determine what mutations are adaptive and have survival merit. It operates upon the whole organism and not merely upon individual traits, so that a particular trait in a successful species may be highly nonadaptive yet not sufficiently injurious to upset the survival of the species. However, if the environment changes or the animal moves to a new environment, traits formerly of no use may now prove to be highly advantageous. Thus it is possible for an animal to be adapted in some way long before it actually meets an environment to which it is best suited. This theory of **preadaptation** may have played an important role in the evolutionary process. Ecologically, preadaptation may account for the remarkable way some animals have flourished in new surroundings.

Orthogenesis

Orthogenesis is the inherent tendency for a group of animals to continue to change in a definite direction. This is often referred to as **straight-line evolution,** and the idea involved is that certain structural changes once started may continue without deviation for an indefinite period unless checked by extinction. Some authorities have described such an evolutionary process as oriented evolution. Paleontology furnishes many classical examples, such as that of the horse already described, where certain structural trends, such as the increased size, the reduction in the number of toes, and the increased differentiation of the teeth, are very marked. In the case of the horse, the evolutionary trend has proved highly adap-

tive, but in others no such advantage is seen.

The theory of orthogenesis occupies a unique position in evolutionary study. The theory does not explain the underlying cause for the evolutionary change along a particular line. The theory also is connected with the idea of the irreversibility of evolution, or the view that an animal does not return toward a former condition. Blum, in his illuminating book, *Time's Arrow and Evolution,* has stressed this viewpoint of the irreversibility of evolution through the operation of the second law of thermodynamics which in some cases permits no exercise of natural selection in altering the direction of evolution. But this author shies away from the implication of an extraphysical force which early advocates of orthogenesis had in mind and thinks the term orthogenesis should be avoided altogether.

The random mutation of genes has undoubtedly produced many patterns, some of which have been eliminated by natural selection, leaving those that do have adaptive advantages. The sequence of the adaptive patterns gives the impression of direction and orientation, even though there have been many irregularities in the process. Paleontologists do not stress orthogenesis with all its implications as much as they formerly did, for they now recognize that most examples of it do not have direct, unbranched lines, but that there have been many side branches which have been eliminated by natural selection.

Mutation*

Little was known in Darwin's time about the behavior of chromosomes and their bearing on heredity. Soon after the principles of Mendelism were rediscovered in 1900 the parallelism between the chromosomal behavior and Mendelian segregation was worked out. It was some years later before the real significance of cytogenetics to the problems of evolution

---

*Refer to Chapter 5, Principle 22.

was appreciated. Hugo de Vries, a Dutch botanist, had stressed the importance of **mutations** in the evolutionary process. Working with the evening primrose, he had found certain types of this plant differing materially from the original wild plant and, more important, he found that these aberrant forms bred true thereafter. De Vries explained these mutant forms mainly on the basis of a recombination of chromosomes, but, since his time, stress has been laid upon genetic transformations. Mutations, as now understood, refer to sudden random changes in genes and chromosomes due to errors in self-copying, but it is precisely these errors that make evolutionary progress possible.

The work of Morgan and his colleagues in working out the theory of linkage of genes, the mapping of chromosomes, nondisjunction of chromosomes, etc. laid the basis for the modern understanding of the hereditary mechanism. The experimental production of mutations through radiation, x-rays, etc. and the discovery of the giant chromosomes in the salivary glands of certain larval insects have added to this understanding.

Natural selection is an important factor in evolution, but its chief role operates in a much later stage of evolution than Darwin had assigned it. Before a new species can evolve, there must be both mutation and natural selection. Mutations furnish many possibilities, natural selection determines which of them have survival merit, and the environment imposes a screening process which passes the fit and eliminates the unfit. Mutations are constantly producing new allelomorphs on which natural selection works.

Nature of mutations. Mutations may be harmful, beneficial, or neutral in their action. Perhaps the majority are harmful, because most animals are already adapted and any new change would likely be disadvantageous, but some are distinctly beneficial. In *Drosophila,* in which they have been studied extensively, it has been found that the same mutation occurs with a certain frequency. Thus the red-eyed wild type can be expected to mutate to

the white-eyed type ever so often. Moreover the white-eyed type undergoes mutation, either changing back to the original red eyes or else to one of the other eye color allelomorphs. Mutant characters tend to be recessive in their hereditary patterns and may show up as a phenotype only when they are homozygous; when paired with normal or original allelomorphs, they usually show no effect. Some mutant characters are lethal, but here this action is expressed, as a usual thing, only in the homozygous condition. Since mutations ordinarily occur at random, it is not possible to predict the nature or time of their appearance. Nor is it possible to see a concerted action of mutants along a particular direction, for the genes appear to mutate independently of each other.

Mutations can also be divided into those that produce small changes (micromutations) and those that produce large changes (macromutations). Evolutionary changes produced by the action of the former are referred to as **microevolution;** those produced by the latter, as **macroevolution.** The great majority of evolutionists now favor small mutations as the more important in causing evolution. In this way they can also explain the many intermediate forms (races, subspecies, etc.) between the parent species and the new one. Those who hold to macroevolution explain such intermediate forms as being only geographical varieties of basic species (produced by big changes) that do not lead to definite taxonomic units. Some striking changes due to large mutations are the tailless manx cat and the bandy-legged Ancon sheep.

Most mutations are destined to a very short existence, for competition in nature quickly eliminates them. There are cases, however, in which mutations may be harmful to an animal under one set of environmental conditions and decidedly helpful under a different set of conditions. If the environment should happen to change at about the same time as favorable mutations appear, then there could be adaptations along special lines and within restricted limits. Such an opportunism of evolution may help explain the evolution of the horse; otherwise it is very difficult to see how the unidirectional and highly specialized nature of its adaptation could occur except through a balance between changing environment and the adaptive mutations of the animal. For the environment to change without a simultaneous appearance of the right mutations would have little or no significance for evolution. The physical world has in its history provided many opportunities for animals with the right mutations, as evidenced by the numerous forms found in the animal kingdom today.

Types of mutations. There are two main types of mutations, gene mutations and chromosome mutations. A **gene mutation** is a chemical or physical change of a gene resulting in a visible alteration of the original character. Although the actual change in the gene is largely unknown, it is thought to be a rearrangement of the atoms making up the protein molecules of the gene. Such changes cannot be detected under the microscope, for there are no visible alterations in the chromosomes bearing the genes in question. Many of this type of mutation have been found in *Drosophila* and other forms. Most gene mutations are point mutations, i.e., the physical or chemical change of one gene.

Chromosome mutations involve either chromosome rearrangement during meiosis or an alteration in the number of chromosomes. The rearrangement of the chromosomes may involve inversion of the linear order of the genes, the deletion of blocks of genes, translocation of portions of chromosomes in which a part of one chromosome becomes attached to another nonhomologous chromosome, and some other irregular procedures. Such changes are usually detectable and often produce phenotypic changes which are inherited in the regular Mendelian manner. Increase in number of chromosomes usually involves the formation of extra sets of chromosomes, sometimes a doubling or tripling of the diploid set, resulting in the condition called **polyploidy.**

Polyploids are usually characterized by a larger size than the parent stock. Such mutations are far more common in plants than in animals. Among roses, for instance, there are found species with 14, 28, 42, and 56 diploid chromosomes, although the basic parent rose is thought to be one with 14 chromosomes. Such duplication of chromosome sets is due to an upsetting of the meiotic process, so that through omission of the reduction division, germ cells are formed with the diploid number of chromosomes instead of the normal haploid number. Experimentally, polyploidy may be induced by the drug colchicine which prevents the division of cells but does not interfere with the duplication of the chromosomes. This results in gametes with the diploid number of chromosomes.

This variability gives natural selection something to work on in the production of a new species, for natural selection can eliminate the unfit characters and allow the adaptable ones to survive. Such variations come and go, dependent upon such factors as the size of populations, degree of segregation and isolation, etc. Many mutant characters, therefore, never have a chance to become persistent characters in a population.

Causes and frequency of mutations. Different genes possess different frequencies of mutation rates, for some genes are more stable than others. Mutation is also a reversible process and cases of back mutation are well known. Gene A, for instance, may mutate to gene a, and gene a may mutate back to gene A. This reversibility must be taken into account in mutation equilibrium, and the difference between the mutation rate in one direction and the mutation rate in the reverse direction constitutes **mutation pressure,** which is usually of a low magnitude. Mutation frequencies are best known in the fruit fly, *Drosophila,* and the corn plant. In corn, some genes are known to mutate much more frequently than others. Some plants may be expected to produce 10% of their offspring with at least one mutant gene. The widely known

786

Drosophila is supposed to produce at least one new mutation in every 200 or so flies. Many mutations are not detected and estimates of their frequency are in many cases only guesses. Certain genes are also known to increase the mutation rate of other genes in the same organism.

So far as the causes of natural mutations are concerned, very little is known about the matter. Many mutations which were first found in laboratory stocks are now known to occur in the wild state. This contradicts the belief once common that most mutations happen under the influence of laboratory conditions. It is true that both gene and chromosome mutations can be produced artificially by the influence of x-rays, ultraviolet rays, chemicals, temperature, and other agencies. It has been suggested that cosmic rays may be responsible for the appearance of mutations in wild populations. There is also the possibility that spontaneous mutations may be caused by metabolic influences on the unstable genic molecules.

RATES OF EVOLUTION

Evolution has not always proceeded at the same rate among different types of organisms or within different geological periods. Some groups of animals, such as the brachiopods, have undergone relatively little change since early geological times. Others, such as the primates, have evolved rapidly. Evolution appears to be most rapid when a new species first appears and then slows down in the later development of the group. The nature of the geological periods has had an important bearing on the rate of evolution. When there are geological changes in surface, temperature, and water distribution, only those animals that have suitable variations for natural selection to operate upon can adapt to these changes. On the other hand, periods of geological uniformity and stability have usually been periods of slow evolutionary progress. Stability of environmental conditions is not conducive to rapid evolution of any form. The type of animal group is correlated to some

extent with the rate of structural change and diversification. In general, vertebrates have tended to evolve faster than invertebrates, although there are some exceptions to this rule. We have seen that the opossum has changed little since the late Cretaceous period. Evolution seems to advance by spurts and rarely does it proceed in a steady, uniform manner.

Evolutionary rates have been computed for some taxonomic units. Such estimates show that it takes about 500,000 to 1,000,000 years for a new species to evolve among birds and mammals, 20,000 to 50,000 years for a subspecies in the same groups. Paleontology has given some revealing data on evolution rates. The horse required 45 to 50 million years to evolve to its present state and passed through some eight genera. Thus about 6 million years were required, on the average, for each genus. Some species, no doubt, have evolved faster than these rates; fossil records can neither affirm nor deny estimates about the evolutionary rate in most instances.

EVOLUTION AND ADAPTATION

The major aim of evolution is the adaptation of the animal to the environment. From whatever standpoint animals are viewed, they have adaptations of some kind, or else they could not have existed. The strongest point of Darwin's theory is the explanation natural selection affords for the presence of adaptations. In the past, emphasis has been placed on structural adaptations, for they were more obvious and apparently easier to explain. In time more attention has been given to physiological adaptations, for they were found to be as important as the structural ones when once they were worked out. No animal is perfectly adapted to its environment; in every case adaptation is a relative thing. There seem to be many characteristics, both anatomical and physiological, which do their possessors little actual benefit. It is difficult to see how natural selection could operate effectively on some of the minute changes which distinguish certain species from each other.

Adaptability must be taken as a whole. The life of any organism is complex and consists of many stages. To fail in one of these stages, regardless of how well adapted it is to the others, means failure for that animal. Its success is determined by the sum total of all its adaptations. This means that some of its adaptations may be highly favorable, others may be highly unfavorable, still others may actually be a handicap, but in the over-all result the animal manages to survive. This is why many so-called adaptations are now viewed with a critical eye. Among the adaptations which have come in for a close scrutiny are **protective coloration** and **sexual selection.**

Coloration is widespread throughout the animal kingdom and apparently serves many purposes, camouflage being one of the most common. In protective coloration, the organism blends into its environment, so that it can escape detection by enemies. A common example is the dark dorsal and lighter ventral side of fish and many birds. Their color blends with the sky to a potential enemy viewing them from underneath, and, viewed from above, the darker shades blend with the darker shades and regions below. Many types of concealment blend the animal into its background; frogs and lizards have the added advantage of changing their color to suit their background. One of the most striking cases of protective camouflage is the *Kallima* butterfly which has a remarkable resemblance to a leaf with venation, imitation holes, and leaf-coloration patterns. For predators, concealing coloration enables them to approach their prey undetected. **Mimicry** adaptation is common among many forms where harmless animals have found survival value by imitating other species which are well equipped with defensive or offensive weapons. Thus harmless snakes may have a resemblance to venomous ones, and some flies look very much like bees. There are also many examples of **warning** coloration which advertises the presence of a well-protected animal, such as the white stripes of the skunk and the brilliant colors of the poisonous coral snake.

These adaptive resemblances, whether of protection, warning, or mimicry, have been subjected to experiments with the idea of determining their selective value. Conclusions from these experiments are often conflicting. Some biologists have gone so far as to deny the selective value of color altogether. The extensive investigations of McAtee on the stomach contents of birds indicated that protectively as well as nonprotectively colored insects were eaten by birds without discrimination but the relative abundance of the protected and unprotected forms in nature must be carefully considered in such experiments. Other experiments seem to indicate that color patterns do play some useful role in survival selection. It has been suggested that some animals which are not protectively colored to the human eye are so protected when viewed by the type of vision of their enemies. Many experiments have also been performed where predators had an opportunity to choose among prey bearing concealing, warning, or other color devices, and the results indicated that these color patterns do have selective value. These and other experiments emphasize the point that sweeping denunciations of the coloration concept are not warranted.

Darwin's idea of **sexual selection** has been more bitterly criticized than any other aspect of his natural selection theory. Darwin believed that the conspicuous patterns of pigmentation in the males of many species of birds could be accounted for on the basis that the females tend to select those males with the most brilliant colors and most ornamental devices. In this way only those males so attractively equipped would have a chance to leave descendants. Darwin also suggested that such structures as antlers and spurs could be accounted for by sexual selection. Stronger males in this respect could win out over less favored rivals, but often the female will select the vanquished. Sexual selection usually implies that there are more males than females or that polygamy is generally practiced. Polygamy is found among certain groups, such as the fur seals, but with them the females have no choice in the matter, for the strongest and most aggressive male simply takes over a number of females for his harem and fiercely defends them against the weaker males. Experiments to determine the role of ornamentation in the selection of their mates by females have not given very conclusive results, for courtship display may not occur until after pairing. So many factors are involved that it is difficult to state just what part sexual selection does play. It is generally agreed, however, that Darwin overemphasized its importance.

MODERN SYNTHESIS OF EVOLUTION (NEO-DARWINISM)

Our present interpretation of evolutionary processes began to take form about 1930. In the first thirty years of the present century there was gradually accumulated a great factual amount of information about the chromosomal and genic theory of heredity, the way Mendelian heredity operated, and a more fundamental understanding of the mutation theory. All these branches of investigation had become more or less unified into what we now call cytogenetics. Under the influence of a brilliant group of biological thinkers, such as J. S. Huxley, R. A. Fisher, and J. B. S. Haldane in England, and Sewall Wright, H. J. Muller, and T. Dobzhansky in America, there has been a fruitful attempt to unify all the various theories and ideas of evolution into one underlying mechanism of organic evolution. The new outlook on evolutionary causes has pinpointed the genotype and its behavior in the organism as the focal point for understanding how evolution operates. Evolution has thus been found to be mainly a sequence of genic changes. These workers and many others have shown that changes in the genotype (mutations) with the recombination of genes through biparental reproduction under the influence of natural selection over long periods of time can operate to pro-

duce evolution as we see it around us. How the major causes operate together to produce evolution has already been briefly summarized in a former section.

It remains to examine these evolutionary factors more in detail.

Population genetics and evolutionary processes

Evolution implies changes in the hereditary characteristics, and it is generally agreed that the best conditions for evolutionary changes occur in large populations which are broken up into small subdivisions. The population must be considered the natural form of existence of all species. Moreover, the materials with which evolution works are the genetic variations produced by mutation and recombination of genes. This is especially true of biparental populations in which the normal mechanisms, aside from mutations, of recombinations can operate to produce great variation. The gene pool of large populations must be enormous, for at observed mutation rates many mutant alleles can be expected at all gene loci. In some cases more than forty alleles of the same gene have been demonstrated. Suppose there are two alleles present, A and a. Among the individuals of the population there will be three possible genotypes: AA, Aa, aa. When there are three alleles present, there are six possible genotypes. Increasing the number of alleles increases the possible genotypes. The reshuffling of genes at the reduction division of meiosis makes possible combinations of a gene at one locus with any of several others at other loci.

Changes in uniparental populations occur by the addition and elimination of a mutation; in biparental populations the mutant gene may combine with all existing combinations and thus double the types. With only 10 alleles at each of 100 loci, the number of mating combinations would be 10^{100}. Genetic differences must, therefore, exist among the individuals of biparental populations. The student has seen in the discussion on genetics the many genotypes and phenotypes that can be produced when only a few pairs of genes are involved, but when an organism has thousands of pairs the amount of diversity is staggering. Even though many genes are found together on a single chromosome and tend to stay together in inheritance, this linkage is often broken by crossing-over. If no new mutations occurred the shuffling of the old genes would produce an inconceivably great number of combinations. But this is not the whole story, for genes exert different influences in the presence of other genes. Gene A may act differently in the presence of gene B than it does in the presence of gene C. The diversity produced by this interaction and the addition of new mutations now and then adds to the complication of population genetics. If this diversity is possible in a single population, suppose two different populations with different genes should mix by interbreeding. It is easy to see that many more combinations of genes and their phenotypic expression would occur. All this means that populations have enormous possibilities for variation.

What does this signify for evolution? It has already been stated that genetic variation produced in whatever manner is the material on which natural selection works to produce evolution. Natural selection does this by favoring beneficial variations and eliminating those which are not useful to the organism. Selective advantages of this type represents a very slow process, but on a geological time scale they can bring about striking evolutionary changes represented by the various taxonomic units (species, genera, etc.), adaptive radiation groups, and the various kinds of adaptations. It must be stressed, however, that natural selection works on combinations of genic variations on the whole animal and not on single hereditary characteristics. The organism that possesses the most beneficial combination of characteristics or "hand of cards" is going to be selected over one not so favored. This concept helps explain some of those puzzling instances in which an animal may have certain characteristics that can be of no advantage to it or actually be harmful but in the overall picture it has a winning combination. In this way population genetics can create pools of variations on which natural selection can work to produce evolutionary change.

Why are most mutations recessive? If mutations represent the material for evolutionary change, would not dominant mutants be the most important in evolutionary processes? Why are most mutations recessive? In *Drosophila* only about 7% of the 600 or so mutant genes are dominant. Not all of the answers to these questions are known. We do know that the character of each organ in an organism is controlled by many genes, not by a single gene. The genotype or all the genes of an animal or plant controls the character of each organ. This interaction of genes or mutants on each other may be complex. One may inhibit the action of another or one may have no effect without the other, etc. Dominance and recessiveness can be altered in this manner also. Ordinarily, a recessive gene would express itself only in a homozygous condition which might require many generations, but there is some evidence to indicate, however, that new mutations may not be completely recessive and may make their presence felt at once in a heterozygous condition. It is thus possible that a heterozygous condition may give natural selection an opportunity to exercise its effect, for good or bad, over the homozygous condition. It is also possible for natural selection to change recessive genes into dominant ones, for it could spread more rapidly as a dominant.

Why are not recessive genes lost from the population? In an interbreeding population why does not the dominant gene gradually supplant the recessive one? It is a common belief that a character dependent upon a dominant gene will increase in proportion because of its dominance. This, however, is not the case, for there is a tendency for genes to remain in equilibrium generation after generation. In this way a dominant gene will not change in frequency with respect to its allele. This important principle is based upon a basic law of population genetics called the Hardy-Weinberg equilibrium. According to this law gene frequencies and genotype ratios in large biparental populations will reach an equilibrium in one generation and will remain constant thereafter unless disturbed by new mutations, by natural selection, or by genetic drift (chance). The rule does not operate in small populations. A rare gene, according to this principle, will not disappear merely because it is rare. That is why certain rare traits, such as albinism, persist for endless generations. It is thus seen that variation is retained even though evolutionary processes are not in active operation. Whatever changes occur in a population, gene flow from other populations, mutations, and natural selection, involve the establishment of a new equilibrium with respect to the gene pool, and this new balance will be maintained until upset by disturbing factors.

The Hardy-Weinberg formula is a logical consequence of Mendel's first law of segregation and is really the tendency toward equilibrium inherent in Mendelian heredity. Select a pair of alleles, such as T and t. Represent the proportion of T genes by p and the proportion of t genes by q. Therefore, $p + q = 1$, since the genes must be either T or t. By knowing either p or q, it is possible to calculate the other. Of the male gametes formed, p will contain T and q will contain t, and the same will apply to the female gametes. (See checkerboard.) As we know from Mendel's Law, there will be three possible genotypic individuals, TT, Tt, and tt, in the population. By expanding to the second power, the algebraic formula $(p + q)$ will be $(p + q)^2 = p^2 + 2pq + q^2$, in which the proportion of TT genotypes will be represented by p^2, Tt by $2pq$, and tt by q^2. Recall the 1:2:1 ratio of a Mendelian monohybrid. The homozygotes TT and tt will produce only T and t gametes, whereas the heterozygotes Tt will produce equal numbers of T and t gametes.

In the gene pool the frequencies of the T and t gametes will be as follows:

$$T = p^2 + \tfrac{1}{2}(2pq) = p^2 + pq = p(p + q) = p$$
$$t = q^2 + \tfrac{1}{2}(2pq) = q^2 + pq = q(q + p) = q$$

In all random mating the gene frequencies of p and q will remain constant in sexually reproducing populations (subject to sampling errors). It will be seen that the formula $p^2 + 2pq + q^2$ is the algebraic formula of the checkerboard diagram, and thus the formula can be used for calculating expectations without the aid of the checkerboard.

To illustrate how the Hardy-Weinberg formula applies, suppose a gene pool of a population consisted of 60% T genes and 40% t genes. Thus:

$$p = \text{frequency of } T \ (60\% \text{ or } 0.6)$$
$$q = \text{frequency of } t \ (40\% \text{ or } 0.4)$$

Substituting numerical values of gene frequency in the following:

$$p^2 + 2pq + q^2$$
$$(0.36 + 0.48 + 0.16)$$
$$TT \qquad Tt \qquad tt$$

The proportions of the various genotypes will be 36% pure dominants, 48% heterozygotes, and 16% pure recessives. The phenotypes, however, will be 84% (36 + 48) dominants and 16% recessives.

On the other hand, suppose 4% of a population is made up of a certain recessive trait, then:

$$q^2 = 4\% \text{ or } .04$$
$$q = \sqrt{.04} = 0.2 \text{ or } 20\%.$$

Thus 20% of the genes are recessive. Even though a recessive trait may be quite rare, it is amazing how common a recessive gene may be in a population. Only 1 person in 20,000 is an albino (a recessive trait); yet by the above formula, it is found that 1 person in every 70 carries the gene or is heterozygous for albinism.

HOW CHANCE OPERATES TO UPSET THE EQULIBRIUM OF GENES IN A POPULATION. The Hardy-Weinberg equilibrium can be disturbed, as already stated, by mutation, by selection, and by chance or genetic drift. The term **genetic drift** (Wright) refers to changes in gene frequency resulting from purely random sampling fluctuations. By such means a new mutant gene may be able to spread through a small population until it becomes homozygous in all the organisms of a population (random fixation) or it may be lost altogether from a population (random extinction). Such a condition naturally would upset the gene frequency equilibrium mentioned in the previous section. It also affords a means by which small, isolated populations can originate characteristics which are of no use to the individuals of that population, such as the small differences between subspecies and even species. It has also been suggested that genetic drift may result in a new species being formed or else contributing to the gene pool of the large, ancestral population under certain conditions.

How does the principle apply? Suppose a few individuals at random became isolated from a large general population. This could happen by some freakish accident of physical conditions, such as a flood carrying a small group of field mice to a remote habitat where they would have no opportunity to mix with the general population, or a disease epidemic could wipe out most of a population and produce the same effect. Suppose that in the general population individuals would be represented by both homozygotes, **TT** for example, and heterozygotes, **Tt**. It might be possible for the small, isolated group to be made up only of **TT** individuals and the **t** gene would be lost altogether, or the reverse could happen. Also, when only a small number of offspring are produced, certain genes may, by sampling errors, be included in the germ cells and others not represented. It is possible in this way for heterozygous genes to become homozygous. In this way the new group may in time have gene pools quite different from the ancestral population.

We should note also that most breeding populations of animals are usually small. Most large and widespread populations are divided into more or less isolated groups by physical barriers of some kind. The home areas even of animals that can get around are amazingly small in many instances. A mere stream may be effective in separating two breeding populations. Thus chance could lead to the presence or absence of genes without being directed at first by natural selection. In the long run, however. whether or not the trait has adaptive significance will depend upon natural selection.

Genetic drift has been assigned the cause of the frequency of certain human traits, such as blood groups. Among some American Indian tribes it is known that group B, for instance, is far rarer than it is among other races and may be due to small isolated mating units.

How effective genetic drift is in the evolutionary process is a controversial subject, and there are many who deny its importance. But it is generally agreed that in bisexually reproducing species evolution proceeds more rapidly when a population is broken up into isolated or partially isolated breeding communities, and the smaller the population the greater will be the importance of genetic drift.

What is natural selection? The concept of natural selection was Darwin's great contribution to evolution and is a key factor in most if not all theories of evolution. Most of us think of natural selection as the struggle for existence, survival of the fit, brutal competition, etc. But other factors which are less related to struggle and competition and which play a part in the natural selection concept are the ability to produce large numbers of viable offspring, ability to resist disease, speed of development, mutual cooperation, and others. In accordance with the evolutionary opportunity of an environment in which an organism is living, natural selection can stabilize, direct, or disrupt the whole evolutionary process of a particular form. Natural selection is a blind force without purpose and has often been called noncreative. But the newer evolutionary synthesis assigns it to a creative role, for natural selection can ensure the continuance of a favorable allele and the elimination of an unfit allele and can

792

mold all the chromosomes and their genes into an integrated whole. The material on which natural selection works to produce this result is the failure of genes to copy themselves precisely, or mutations. Natural selection represents all the forces which ensure that organisms possessing a favorable genetic constitution will leave more descendants than those which do not have a favorable genetic setup, or, in other words, it is nonrandom reproduction.

Examples of speciation. Speciation refers to the splitting of one species into two or more other species. It implies the formation of two or more populations which do not exchange genes. Mutations, recombinations of genes, selection, and isolation operating together produce genetic diversification which is the essence of species formation. Although there may be several patterns in the diversification of organisms, it is thought that the sequence of geographical isolation, morphological differences (mutations, etc.), and conditions which prevent future fusion of groups represents one of the most important and effective patterns of evolutionary progress. It is clear that whenever distinct forms interbreed, their genotypes will intermix and any differences between them will be lost. Any effective evolutionary pattern must prevent this interbreeding so that each group (species) can profit from its own independent evolution. Evolution seems to be most rapid when a group of organisms are presented with a new environment with many unoccupied ecological niches of low competition and predation. By adaptive radiation many new types can evolve to fill these niches

A striking illustration of isolation and adaptive radiation is afforded by Darwin's finches of the Galápagos Islands. These islands are found about 600 miles west of the South American mainland (Ecuador) and attracted the attention of Darwin when he visited them about 1835 during his famous voyage on the *Beagle*. Darwin was struck by the unusual animal and plant life on these islands as contrasted with that on the nearest mainland of South America. These volcanic islands have never had land connections with the mainland and such life as is found there had to be by accidental immigration. Darwin was particularly interested in the bird life of the islands, especially the finches.

In 1947 the English ecologist, Lack, published a book on these finches which has served to renew interest in their evolutionary development. All the different species of finches (family Geospizidae) found on these islands are supposed to have descended from a South American finch which reached the island. Their most interesting adaptive structures are their different beak modifications which permit them to exploit the food resources of the various ecological habitats. The ancestral finch was probably a ground feeder, but as competition increased in this habitat, finches evolved that were adapted (or radiated out) to utilize food in other ecological niches unavailable to the ancestral form. The ground feeders have thick, conical beaks for seed, the cactus ground finch has a long, curved beak for the nectar of cactus flowers, the vegetarian tree finch has a parrotlike beak for buds and fruit, and the woodpecker finch has a long, stout beak (and an improvised spine) for probing into bark. Some of the finches are vegetarian and some are insectivorous. Altogether, some fourteen species (and some subgenera) of finches have evolved from the ancestral finch which first reached the islands. Moreover, each island of the group, because of geographical isolation, has had an effect on the evolution of the various species, although most of the islands have the same type of ecological habitats.

An example of speciation in the making is the common laboratory frog, *Rana pipiens*. For years herpetologists have puzzled over the status of this frog which ranges from northern Canada to Panama and from the Atlantic coast to the edge of the Pacific states. Is it one species or is it divided into subspecies? Individuals from adjacent localities, such as those from

New England and New Jersey, or those from Florida and Louisiana, can be crossed successfully and yield normal and viable embryos. Also, a frog of this species from New Jersey can be crossed with one from Louisiana and will produce normal embryos. But crosses between individuals from widely separated localities, such as a cross between one from Wisconsin and one from Florida, will produce abnormal and nonviable embryos. Evidently the genetic differences between the northern and southern forms are great enough to prevent normal hybrid development. Selection has produced different developmental physiologies in these types of frogs. Those in the north are adapted for rapid growth at low temperature; those in the south, for slow growth at high temperatures. This genetical difference is sufficient, if one ignores the individuals from adjacent localities, to produce at least two distinct species, the northern form and the southern form. They certainly meet the chief criterion of separate species in not being able to interbreed.

Species populations or their subdivisions, separated from each other by natural barriers and thus occupying different territories, are called **allopatric.** Two or more species or populations inhabiting the same geographical range are called **sympatric.** Allopatric and sympatric populations may show different degrees of isolation. It is easy to see that effective barriers will produce complete isolation and prevent interbreeding between separate groups, so that evolution may proceed in the isolated group without interference with other groups. In sympatric populations isolation may be seasonal (breeding at different times of the year) or behavioral (incompatibility of mating reactions); these are as effective as the geographical one.

IS IT POSSIBLE TO OBSERVE EVOLUTION IN ACTION TODAY?

Darwin in his time could not point to a single visible example of evolution in action. Some of his opponents were quick to point out that this lack was a major

weakness in his arguments. However, in England during his lifetime, a striking case of evolution was actually taking place in nature, before his eyes, had his attention been directed to it. Such an example is industrial melanism in moths. Within the last century, certain moths, such as the peppered moth (*Biston*), has undergone a coloration change from a light (*B. betularia*) to a dark melanic form (*B. carbonaria*). This moth is active at night and rests on the trunks of trees during the day. The light form is especially well adapted to rest on the background of lichen-encrusted trees where it is largely invisible. In the industrial regions of England, however, there has been a change of tree trunk backgrounds of light to darker ones because of the pollution from the fallout of smoke particles. Such pollution kills the light-colored lichens and blackens the vegetation. Against a dark background, light-colored moths are conspicuous and fall prey to predator birds. Natural selection would therefore, in the course of time, largely eliminate the moth, as numerous experiments have shown. However, by mutation the light-colored moth has given rise to a dark-colored melanic form which has a much better survival rate under such surroundings. Within a period of years in polluted areas, the dark species (*B. carbonaria*) has, to a great extent, replaced the light species (*B. betularia*). The mutation for industrial melanism appears to be controlled by a single dominant gene which is also known to occur in natural environments (not due to pollution) where a dark color is a distinct advantage. Thus by mutation and natural selection a moth of a wholly different color and physiological nature has emerged to confirm Darwin's mechanism of the evolution of a new species from another species.

SOME EVOLUTIONARY GENERALIZATIONS

In evolution there are several generalizations which reveal certain trends in the evolutionary process. There are some exceptions to these rules, but they do reveal many interesting aspects which the student of evolution might overlook. Some of these, such as Gloger's, Bergmann's, and Allen's rules, represent geographical variation gradients correlated with adaptive morphological structures and are the result of mutation and selection.

Dollo's law. Dollo's law applies to the irreversibility of evolution and was first stated by a paleontologist, Dollo. Recently the principle has been greatly emphasized by the American evolutionist Blum. Although minor reversals, such as back mutations, may occur, there is no evidence to indicate that evolution is other than a one-way process.

Cope's law. This principle states that during the course of evolution there is a tendency for animals to increase in size until they become extinct. It was formulated by the American paleontologist Cope and is based upon the over-all increase in complexity of most evolutionary lines. The present horse, for instance, evolved from a much smaller animal.

Gloger's rule. In the Northern Hemisphere, most species of birds and mammals living in a north-south range tend to be lighter colored (less melanin) in the north than races of the same species living in humid, warm climates. Darker colors are usually associated with greater humidities, and this factor, as well as tem-

In closely related species of warm-blooded animals, larger members inhabit colder climates (Bergmann's rule)

King penguin—south to 55° (subantarctic)
Body length 40 inches

Magellan penguin—south to 52°
Body length 28 inches

Humbolt penguin—
west coast of South America
Body length 20 inches

P. SIMPSON

Figure 609. Bergmann's rule as illustrated by three of seventeen species of penguins. The emperor penguin, even larger than the king penguin, is restricted mainly to Antarctic continent. Rule is based upon principle that a large body has a smaller surface in proportion to mass (weight) than a small body and so is better able to maintain its heat. Other birds and mammals verify rule, for larger members are found in colder parts of their range, whether in Northern or Southern Hemisphere.

perature, may play a part in the application of the rule.

Bergmann's rule. According to this principle endothermal animals are usually larger in the colder parts and smaller in the warm parts of their range. It is based upon the physiological principle that a large body is correlated with a relatively smaller body surface and thus can conserve its heat better. There are many striking examples of this rule. Penguins are much larger on the Antarctic continent than they are on the islands of the coast of South America; bears are larger in Alaska than they are in the United States; and hares are much larger in Russia than they are in central Europe. There are some exceptions, however, to the rule.

Allen's rule. Most races of mammals and birds in cold regions have relatively shorter extremities than races of the same species from warmer regions. Arctic hares and foxes, for instance, have much shorter ears than closely related southern species of those animals. The rule has some experimental verification, for mice reared at high temperatures have relatively longer ears and feet than those developed at lower temperatures. This is an adaptation against loss of heat and the possibility of freezing in cold climates. There is about a 25% exception to this rule.

Jordan's rule. This rule states that closly related species or subspecies are not found in the same range but in adjacent ones separated by some barrier. This generalization is verification of the role of geographical isolation in the evolution of species. There are some exceptions to the rule, for some closely related forms may be found in the same region but, due to ecological or other isolation, do not interbreed.

Gause's rule. Two species with identical ecological relations cannot occupy indefinitely the same ecological niche in the same habitat. Usually one species exterminates or drives out the other. If the species have sparse populations, it is possible for the two groups to share similar ecological niches, or one species could occupy peripheral regions and the other central areas of the same general habitat (centrifugal speciation).

EVOLUTION OF MAN

Man is a product of evolution and shares with other animals the evolutionary process. Evidence for his lowly origin is found in many parts of his body. Throughout his development he shows similarities to other lower forms. Many of the structures of his organs are homologous with those found in other vertebrate animals, and the many vestigial organs he possesses are good evidence that he originated from forms where these structures were definitely functional. His embryonic development is essentially the same as that of other mammals. The gill slit depressions, multiple aortic arches, and the sequence of kidneys in the human embryo are just a few of the many structural features man shares with the embryos of other mammals as well as most other vertebrates. Many types of fossil man have been discovered. Although the record is far from complete, the discovery of these early fossil men reveals a great deal about man's early ancestry. The fossil record is the most impressive evidence of any animal's evolution. Human paleontology in the last seventy-five years has grown into an important branch of the great paleontological record of animal life.

The common misconception that man has arisen directly from the higher apes should be corrected, for there is no good evidence that such is the case. This erroneous idea no doubt arose over a wrong interpretation of man's origin as described by the early evolutionists, Darwin and Haeckel, in particular. Man and the higher apes have each had their own evolution, for the idea held by most evolutionists is that man and the apes have diverged from a common ancestor. This common simian ancestor, however, undoubtedly had monkeylike characteristics, and, strictly speaking, there is nothing gained for human dignity by merely shifting man's early ancestry directly from the anthropoid apes to a much more primitive form.

Man's closest relatives—the primates

Man belongs to the order of mammals called the primates. This order includes three suborders—Lemuroidea, Tarsioidea, and Anthropoidea—as mentioned in the section on mammals. The earliest primate fossils ever discovered were those of lemurs and tarsioids, which have been found back as far as the Paleocene period in Europe and North America. The tarsioids are mostly extinct and are represented today by a single surviving species (Tarsius), an animal about the size of a squirrel found in the East Indies. In some respects the tarsioids are more primitive than the lemurs, but their larger, overlapping cerebrum and better-developed placenta place them nearer to the anthropoids than to the lemurs. Both the lemurs and tarsioids were probably derived from the tree shrews or insectivores which represent the base of the mammalian stock.

The anthropoids have come, it is thought, from the tarsioids. The suborder Anthropoidea includes monkeys, apes, and man. This group retains the primitive five-toed limb and shows specialization for an arboreal existence. They differ from other mammals chiefly by their larger, more complicated brain, by tear ducts opening into the optic sockets, and by their higher development of sight which is characterized by the eyes being directed forward with true stereoscopic vision. The power to grasp is made possible in most cases by the divergent thumb (hallux) which is opposable to the other digits. The suborder Anthropoidea is divided into two subdivisions—the Platyrrhinii (flat noses), or New World monkeys, and the Catarrhinii (narrow noses), or Old World monkeys. Both New and Old World monkeys originated from the tarsioids, although each group evolved separately. The animal which seems to be in direct line of ancestry of the Old World monkeys, anthropoid apes, and man is the fossil form Parapithecus, which has been found in the Lower Oligocene rocks of Egypt. From this form the Old World monkeys diverged in one direction and the higher anthropoids in another. These early ancestors of the primates were small animals, but later in the Miocene period much larger ones evolved. Although there are many gaps in a knowledge of the ancestors of the higher apes and man, Dryopithecus, a fossil ape of the Miocene period, appears to fit best the requirements of a common ancestor of the group.

The animals which are closest to man in structure and physiology are the anthropoid apes belonging to the family Simiidae. These include the gibbon, the orangutan, the chimpanzee, and the gorilla. They differ from the Old World monkeys in lacking tails, cheek pouches, and (with few exceptions) ischial callosities; in having longer arms than legs, opposable thumbs in both hands and feet, vermiform appendices, and larger brains (some with 600 ml. capacity) similar to the pattern and organization of that of man. Their common posture is mostly semierect, often walking on all fours rather than as bipeds. In the past thirty years many fossils of manlike apes have been found in South Africa in Pleistocene cave deposits. They have features that resemble those of man and are thought to be descended from a stage just preceding that of the ancestor of man. These will be discussed later.

Record of human evolution

The differences between man and the higher apes (family Pongidae) are considered sufficient to place him in a family of his own, Hominidae. These differences are relatively few in number but are important in an evolutionary sense. Among the chief anatomical differences may be mentioned the following human characteristics: erect posture, legs longer than arms, well-developed spinal curvature, great toe not opposable, a brain of 1,200 to 1,500 ml. capacity. There are also other minor differences, such as the reduction of body hair, a nose with bridge and tip, jutting chin, and rolled-out lips. In some respects man has features similar to certain apes; in others he resembles other apes more. In general, man probably resembles the gorilla more than he does any other ape, especially in his limbs and brain. Only the orangutan has the same number of ribs as man. There is no aspect of human anatomy that is not also present in the apes, and differences between them is a difference in proportion of parts correlated with differences in type of life (terrestrial or arboreal). Some of these structural differences between man and the apes are less striking in some fossil human types which more or less tend to fill the anatomical gap between the two groups.

That man has come from primate ancestors there is not the least doubt among paleontologists. The best evidence indicates that the human line of descent diverged from that of the ape line near the stage represented by *Dryopithecus* somewhere in the late Miocene period. By the early Pleistocene, man was well represented and was developing several types.

The fossil record of man's evolution is incomplete like that of every other animal. In many cases fossil men have been found along with tools and other implements of culture which afford good evidence of the cultural advancement of that particular type of man. In other cases the fossils and cultural evidences are unassociated. Fossil apes have been found with many human characteristics, but all of them lack the large brain characteristic of man. The known history of man is restricted to the Pleistocene onward. No certain fossils of man are found before that time. This was a period of succession of rapid changes in the climate of the earth. Great ice sheets moved down from the Arctic regions and spread over a large part of North America and Europe. These glacial periods reshaped the land over which they moved and changed the fauna and flora of the regions affected. Between the ice ages (four in number) the climate became warmer and the ice receded toward the North Pole. Along with the re-

cession of the ice sheets the flora and fauna moved northward also.

The relative scarcity of early fossil man may be attributed in part to his failure to bury his dead, perhaps allowing wild animals to dispose of them. Preservation of his skeletons must have been a rare affair and took place when death happened by accident in quicksand or other formation that would ensure their preservation. Now and then some of his skeletons were found in cave deposits. The chief criteria used in distinguishing fossil men from fossil apes were associations of man with certain cultural advancements as well as anatomical differences, such as the larger cranium, the type of pelvis, leg bones, and teeth and jaws. Fossil men found to date must give an incomplete picture of man's early origin. Just how they are related to modern man is not clear. We should expect that the distinct human characteristics did not arise all at once but came gradually. This means that there should be intermediate forms between the apes and man, with both apelike and human qualities. A number of human stocks are recognized by paleontologists among the various fossils which have come to light. However, it is doubtful if more than one manlike species was in existence at any one time, but any one species may have had many variant types. There is considerable diversity of opinion as to the relationships of these various stocks to each other and to modern man.

Some of the better-known fossil ape men are described in the following account. It will be noted that some of them are placed in the same genus (*Homo*) as that of modern man; others are placed in separate genera.

Java man (Pithecanthropus erectus) (Figure 610). One of the most famous ape men is the so-called Java man, discovered in Eastern Java by the Dutchman Dubois in 1891. In many ways this primitive creature bridges the gap between man and the higher apes. It had a brain capacity of up to 900 ml. and is thus intermediate between the 1,200 to 1,500 ml. of modern man and the 600 ml. of the gorilla,

Figure 610. Restoration of prehistoric men. Left to right: Java man, Neanderthal man, and Cro-Magnon man. (Courtesy Dr. J. H. McGregor.)

and his brain had certain human features. Since this early discovery other specimens of this type have been found. *Pithecanthropus* walked semierect and had massive jaws, projecting face, and heavy ridges over the eyes. His teeth were large, but his canines were not developed to the same extent as those of the apes. He apparently flourished around the middle Pleistocene 500,000 years ago.

Peking man (Sinanthropus pekinensis). In 1927, Dr. Davidson Black, an American doctor connected with the Peking Medical School, found some human teeth near Peking, China, and from their morphological character established a new species of man, *Sinanthropus pekinensis.* Later, in this same region, many skulls and other fragments of skeletons were found belonging to this type of fossil man. Intensive study of these fossils reveals that *Sinanthropus* was closely related to *Pithecanthropus,* and the two types probably existed at the same time. The skulls of *Sinanthropus* reveal very primitive apelike characters, such as great length, sharply receding forehead, and heavy brow ridges. The jaws are massive, and there is little or no chin present. The brain capacity is somewhat greater than that of the Java man, being about 1,050 ml. on the average, although its range overlaps that of modern man. The teeth and leg bones of the Peking man are also different

from those of the Java ape man. So similar are *Sinanthropus* and *Pithecanthropus* that many authorities consider them identical races or else two races of the same species.

Piltdown man (Eoanthropus). The fragments of a supposed primitive man were discovered at Piltdown, Sussex, England, around 1912-1915. This man was named *Eoanthropus* and was placed in direct line with the main evolution of modern man. Recent evidence has shown that the Piltdown man is not primitive at all but that the fragments represent a mixture of an ape and modern man and was a cleverly designed hoax.

Neanderthal man (Homo neanderthalensis) (Figure 610). This was the first primitive human fossil found. In 1856 the first specimen was uncovered near Düsseldorf, Germany, but many other skeletons have been discovered since in various parts of Europe and Africa. Since so many skeletons of this type are known, a very complete knowledge of its characteristics is available. The Neanderthal man was a powerfully built individual, a little more than 5 feet tall, and walked in a slightly stooped position. His brain case was as large as that of modern man, and although the forehead was low, the occipital region of the brain was greatly expanded. The face projected but had more human than apelike characteristics. The skull was pro-

Principles of variation and organic evolution   799

vided with large brow ridges, the jaws were massive and powerful, and the canine teeth small. Neanderthal man flourished around 100,000 to 200,000 years ago and became extinct at a later date. Some authorities think this man descended from the Heidelberg man. He lived in caves and had developed a crude culture, called the Mousterian, or a type of Stone Age culture.

In 1939 an important series of human fossils was found in caves at Mount Carmel in Palestine. They were supposed to have lived about the same time as the Neanderthal man, which they resemble in much of their structure. They may represent a hybrid between the Neanderthal man and a more modern race which lived mainly in Africa.

Heidelberg man (Homo heidelbergensis). The evidence for the existence of the Heidelberg man rests on an almost perfect human jaw discovered in a sand pit in 1907 near Heidelberg, Germany. It was found in a deposit from the first interglacial stage of the Lower Pleistocene more than 500,000 years ago and thus may be regarded as the oldest human fossil. The jaw is large and powerful and exceeds that of any other known primitive man. The pattern of tooth arrangement is more human than apelike, and the canines do not project above the others. The jaw resembles that of the Neanderthal man who is supposed to be a descendant of the Heidelberg man.

Rhodesian man (Homo rhodesiensis). In South Africa around 1921 there was discovered a human fossil which has been called the Rhodesian man. The remains consisted of an almost perfect skull and a few other skeletal parts. The skull is characterized by enormous eyebrow ridges, a low forehead, and a low vaulted crown. Its cranial capacity was about 1,300 ml. The humanlike teeth were badly decayed, which is unusual among primitive men. The relationship of this man is unknown, but some think he originated from a common stem with *Pithecanthropus.*

African man-apes. In 1925 the discovery of a fossil brain cast of an immature anthropoid ape by Professor Raymond Dart of South Africa threw additional light upon the gap between man and the ape. Later, Professor Robert Bloom of the same region found the cranial cast of an adult manlike ape which he considered to be a different species from the one discovered by Dart. Dart gave the name of *Australopithecus africanus* to his fossil; Bloom called his *Plesianthropus transvaalensis.* Other types of man-ape fossils have been found in the same region by the same investigators. These fossils apparently date from the late Pliocene to the lower Pleistocene ages. These man-apes walked in an erect or semierect posture, and the volume of their brain casts varied from 440 ml. to 600 or 700 ml. Thus their cranial capacities overlapped the range of the chimpanzee and gorilla (300 to 650 ml.).

Paleontologists are far from agreed on the relationships of these man-apes to man. They appear to be closer to man than any other ape fossils ever found, but most authorities do not consider them ancestors of man. The prevailing view appears to be that these man-apes and man both diverged from a common ancestral ape stock. The fact that some of the man-ape characters were human and some distinctly apelike affords a great deal of significance. They must be regarded as the earliest type with distinct manlike characteristics and may have lived as long as 1,000,000 years ago. They seem to represent a blend of the families Hominidae and Pongidae. They come closer than any form yet discovered to having the anatomical structures expected in a "missing link."

Giant fossil men. One of the most puzzling discoveries of early fossil men was that of *Meganthropus* and *Gigantopithecus* found in Java and China (1935-1939). These forms were reconstructed largely from fragments of the lower jaw and a few teeth. Both the jaw and teeth are considerably larger than those of any human fossil so far discovered, but they seem to have more human than ape characteristics. Authorities disagree as to the position of these fossils. Some think they are definitely manlike and others think they are apelike in structural features. Of all the fossil men, the evidence seems to indicate they are nearest like *Australopithecus*. One telling criticism about these giant fossils has been made by many paleontologists, and that is that giant teeth do not necessarily mean that they belong to a giant. The early primates are known to have had much larger jaws and teeth than those living today. There is also the suggestion that these fossil giants could have been the result of gigantism, an abnormality associated with hormone imbalance.

Nutcracker man (Zinjanthropus boisei). The most recent discovery of a fossil man was made by Dr. and Mrs. L.S.B. Leakey in 1959 in the Olduvai Gorge, Tanganyika, Africa. The fossil consisted of a skull with a massive lower jaw and strong, well-formed molars; hence the popular name, "nutcracker man." The skull shows many definitely manlike characters (e.g., nuchal crest for attachment of neck muscles) and may be considered in direct line of human ancestry. It is more advanced than *Australopithecus* to which it seems to be related. The skull dates from the lower Pleistocene more than 600,000 years ago. Its culture probably represents the oldest stone toolmaker ever found. A complete appraisal of this interesting find has not yet been made.

Emergence of modern man (Homo sapiens). Modern man (*Homo sapiens*) suddenly appeared in Europe more than 75,000 years ago, but from what source is unknown. Nothing is known about his immediate ancestors. There is some evidence to indicate that these men were contemporaries of the Neanderthal man and may have hastened the extinction of the latter. Any relationship modern man may have to the Neanderthal type must be one of common descent and not by direct descent. There is reason to believe, according to some, that the human stock early split into a number of branches of descent, of which *Homo sapiens* became one and the aforementioned ape-men became other lines. These branches of human evolutionary development undoubtedly existed side by side in many instances. The discoveries in the Middle Pleistocene deposits of the Galley Hill and Swanscombe human fossils in England, both of which belong to *Homo sapiens* in spite of many apelike characters, would indicate that modern man as we know him existed far earlier than some of the primitive apemen, such as the Neanderthal man.

The Neanderthal man was replaced before the end of the last ice age by the Cro-Magnon race in Europe (Figure 610). This race represented the modern type of man, for they had a high forehead, no eyebrow ridges, prominent chin, and a brain capacity as large or larger than present-day man. The so-called Cro-Magnon race was not homogeneous but was a mixture of peoples which showed considerable physical variations in different localities. Some of the physical differences may have been due to the interbreeding of the original Cro-Magnon race with conquered people. Many authorities believe that the Cro-Magnon man was the direct ancestor of the modern Europeans and that some of them still survive in a relatively pure state. There is, however, a great deal of uncertainty about the exact relationships of the Cro-Magnon man and the extent to which he has mixed with other races. Their culture (Aurignacian) was considerably more advanced than the Mousterian culture of the Neanderthal man, for the Cro-Magnons left artistic paintings and carvings in their caves as well as other evidences of a superior culture.

Remains of other fossils of *Homo sapiens* have been found in South Africa and elsewhere. Fossils of primitive men in America have all been of the modern type, for most of the skeletons discovered are similar to the modern Indian. It appears that man reached America only after the retreat of the last ice age, probably within the last 20,000 years.

In summary, it may be stated in accordance with some anthropologists that all the present races of man have descended through such types as the Galley Hill and Cro-Magnon with the possibility of some admixture of such primitive types as the Neanderthal man.

Summary of man's evolution. Primates probably arose at the beginning of the Paleocene from small tree-shrewlike animals and diverged into two main branches —lemuroids and tarsioids. From the latter, anthropoid apes developed. Adaptive radiation proceeded rapidly during the late Oligocene and early Miocene. It is thought that the family Hominidae sprang from a closely allied group of Miocene apes. According to Le Gros Clark, a noted authority on human evolution, ·the sequence of human fossils as displayed by a graded morphological series, so far as the record is clear, would be *Australopithecus, Pithecanthropus, Homo,* in that order. This sequence or series may also represent the ancestor-descendant genera.

Man today (Figure 611). How has present-day man changed in a morphological way from the primitive men mentioned in the previous accounts? During the million or so years man has existed on earth, he has undergone striking changes in some respects and in others he has not changed much from his primitive ancestors. In the first place he has not increased much in bulk or stature; actually he is of slighter build and less massive than some of his forebears. He has become fully erect and his neck is relatively slender as compared with the apelike and other primitive men. His brain capacity is larger than the early primitive men such as *Pithecanthropus* and *Sinanthropus* but not much greater than some of the others. The forehead is more vertical and the supraorbital ridges have greatly decreased. There has also been a great reduction in the size of the jaw which is also correlated with a reduction in the size and complexity of the teeth. His feet also have become better adapted for walking. In general, man has undergone a change from a strong, heavy physique with jaws adapted for tearing and chewing food to a slighter build adapted for greater skill and dexterity correlated with a much higher intelligence.

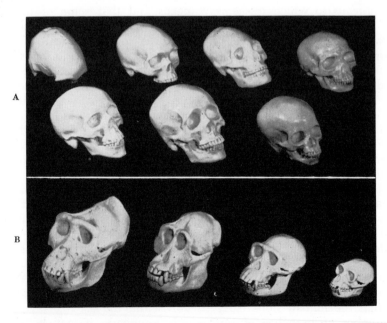

Figure 611. Comparison of skulls of living races of man with those of living simians. **A,** Seven living races of man. **B,** Four living simians. (Courtesy Ward's Natural Science Establishment, Inc., Rochester, N. Y.)

What is the basis of man's diversity? There are many stocks of people scattered over the earth. These changes are not only reflected in physical differences but also in social and cultural conditions. The biological species of man has followed the same principles of environmental adaptations as that of other animals. Each interbreeding group has produced a particular genotype which is suited for a certain kind of environment. In addition, the range of genotypes within a group has permitted the various human populations to modify their phenotypes for a variety of environmental conditions when the necessity arises. Man thus has a much wider range of adaptability than other animals. Mankind on this basis is divided into many populations of diverse genetical and phenotypical structures in accordance with their adaptations to their environments. Authorities do not agree on the number of human groups or races. A **race** may be defined as a population which differs from other populations in the frequency of certain genes in its gene pool. The members of a race share certain morphological and physiological features because of common descent.

In common practice, the human species is divided into three major races or groups: **Negroid, Mongoloid,** and **Caucasoid.** The Negroids are usually characterized by wooly or kinky hair, flat noses, dark skins, and thick lips; the Mongoloids by stiff, straight hair, flattened faces, and yellowish brown skin; and the Caucasoids by smooth or wavy hair, pale skins, and narrow, long noses. There are many subdivisions under each of these races and some intermediate groups which are difficult to assign. Therefore anthropologists have often broken up the groups further and further to include all possibilities. Some have recommended a thirty-race classification. But most races are in a state of flux because intermarriage has often occurred and is occurring. It is almost impossible to speak of pure races as far as man is concerned because of hybridization.

Along with his morphological evolution man has also undergone a cultural evolution. Many of the primitive men described are known to be associated with certain cultural levels from the tools, implements, and other objects found in the same deposits with their fossils. Thus we have the Lower Paleolithic culture of the Java man, the Mousterian culture of the Neanderthal man, the Upper Paleolithic culture of the Cro-Magnon man, and the Neolithic (New Stone Age) of the oldest Egyptian and other peoples at the dawn of history.

FUTURE OF EVOLUTION

Has evolution run its course? Is evolution occurring at the present time? What is expected to be its trend in the future? These and other questions are no doubt in the mind of the inquiring student of biology. Some authorities seriously believe that evolution has largely spent itself and little evolutionary progress is to be expected in the future. They argue that because of the great abundance of life and its infinite variety of adaptations, practically all niches of the environment have been filled. This assumes to a certain extent that the environment is relatively stable and that there are no new environmental niches to be filled. Most evolutionists do not agree but maintain that evolution is going on and will continue long into the future. Evolution is far from exhausting all possibilities. It seems to be an inherent quality of protoplasm to mutate and this, coupled with a constantly changing environment, means that equilibrium between the two factors is a remote possibility. Potentialities for adaptive radiation are present in most if not all groups of animals.

Man is a product of evolution and has been subjected to the same evolutionary laws as other animals. As man, he has been on earth about 600,000 years or more. During this time he has split into relatively few species; at present there is only one. Rarely was there more than one species of man on earth at any one time. He has retained a remarkable unity. Human evolution, however, is occurring today, for many racial groups are fusing and others are disappearing. There is plenty of evidence to show that human genes are mutating today. Man's evolution is slow—of the nature of microevolution. In many important respects, man possesses a uniqueness not found in other animals. He has abstract thought, a symbolic language, and a culture of learned behavior. Man has the power to adapt his environment to his own hereditary constitution; other organisms must alter their genes to fit their environment in order to survive. Man in the future may have the power to control consciously by radiation or other means the mutation of his genes. One of his biggest problems is to detect his bad genes which are often recessive and hidden among heterozygotes. Some progress has been made in detecting hemoglobin abnormalities by electrophoresis. Certain mutagenic effects may be counteracted by chemical means. In the future man is going to be less a product of natural selection.

Some think man has reached the end of his physical evolution—that all advances in the future will be along the lines of social and cultural evolution. Others regard man as being on the road to degeneracy because he protects the unfit and allows them to reproduce, in some cases much faster than the more desirable strains of our populations. Still others picture the future evolution of man as being along mental lines, with a weakening of his physical capacities. Such views hold that future man will depend almost entirely upon his wits for making his adjustments. His physical appearance will undergo some changes, such as the appearance of more refined features, smaller bones, more efficient sensory organs (at least in those necessary for a machine age), and smaller teeth (with the loss of the wisdom teeth). Not much increase in brain capacity will occur, although it should increase greatly in efficiency and organization. Of course, certain other anatomical as well as physiological alterations should be expected, such as a further reduction in body hair, a shortening per-

haps of the intestines, the loss of certain muscles (some are already on the way out), a greater body metabolism, and a greater susceptibility to old-age diseases. A longer life expectancy should result from medical science advances.

ANNOTATED REFERENCES

Anfinsen, C. B. 1959. The Molecular Basis of Evolution. New York, John Wiley & Sons, Inc. *Molecular biology is the liviest subject in the biological sciences and this work attempts to pinpoint the evolutionary process insofar as genetics and protein chemistry reveal it.*

Barnett, S. A. (editor). 1958. A Century of Darwin. Cambridge, Harvard University Press. *Another work in commemoration of the centennial year of Darwin's publication of the Origin of Species. It is made up of chapters contributed by eminent American and English authorities on the various aspects of Darwin's contributions to biology.*

Bates, M., and P. S. Humphrey. 1956. The Darwin Reader. New York, Charles Scribner's Sons. *This is made up of generous portions of Darwin's principal works and is a fine introduction for one who wishes to become acquainted with the works of the great master.*

Berrill, N. J. 1955. Man's Emerging Mind. New York, Dodd, Mead & Co. *In this thought-provoking book, a biologist makes an appraisal of himself in relation to the world around him. He thinks man still has possibilities of future brain improvement by refined differentiation of the brain he at present possesses; it is mainly a matter of exploiting the capacities of our existing state.*

Blum, H. F. 1951. Time's Arrow and Evolution. Princeton, Princeton University Press. *A work for the serious student on certain implications of evolution.*

Carpenter, G. D. H. 1933. Mimicry. London, Methuen & Co., Ltd. *A classical work on a subject of perennial interest—and also of perennial controversy.*

Conklin, E. G. 1943. Man: Real and Ideal. New York, Charles Scribner's Sons. *The author believes that there is no evidence that man has advanced in intellectual capacities since ancient time but that his future progress will be along the lines of cooperation and organization of social forces for his own welfare. Although evolution has taken many directions and has regressed as well as progressed, he thinks that there has been no permanent* retreat in the evolution of man's intellect, reason, and ethics.

Count, E. W. (editor). 1950. This Is Race. New York, Henry Schuman, Inc., Publishers. *A comprehensive anthology dealing with many aspects of the different human races. A work of great interest to all students of anthropology and of the evolution of mankind.*

De Chardin, P. T. 1959. The Phenomenon of Man. New York, Harper & Brothers. *An evaluation of man's evolutionary position. Much of its thesis is in line with that of Sir Julian Huxley (writer of introduction to this work) who has long stressed the unique aspects of man's evolution in the biological world.*

Dobzhansky, T. 1941. Genetics and the Origin of Species, ed. 2. New York, Columbia University Press. *A treatise showing the bearing of modern genetic interpretation upon the problems of evolution. A work for the advanced student.*

Dobzhansky, T. 1955. Evolution, Genetics, and Man. New York, John Wiley & Sons, Inc. *There is perhaps no better book in its field than this one. It is written by one of the foremost students of evolution in relation to genetics, and the up-to-date presentation will appeal to all serious students in this field. The material is written in an easy style and can be comprehended by one with only an elementary knowledge of biology.*

Dodson, E. O. 1952. A Textbook of Evolution. Philadelphia, W. B. Saunders Co. *An up-to-date and clearly written text on evolution. The beginning student of zoology can read much of it with great profit.*

Dunn, L. C. 1959. Heredity and Evolution in Human Populations. Cambridge, Harvard University Press. *A great evolutionist appraises the human race in the light of modern genetic and evolutionary factors. Among other things he considers that radiation factors may pose great problems in mutation rates among human populations. But he also believes that man has the possibility of controlling the mutation rate in the future.*

Eiseley, L. 1958. Darwin's Century. Evolution and the Men Who Discovered It. New York, Doubleday & Co. *An excellent background of the evolutionary theory and the many conflicts between the divergent views of scholars in this field during the nineteenth century.*

Florkin, M. (editor). 1960. Aspects of the Origin of Life. New York, Pergamon Press. *A series of papers by many eminent authorities on the basic problems of the origin and development of life.*

Glass, B., O. Temkin, and W. L. Straus, Jr. (editors). 1959. Forerunners of Darwin: 1745-1859. Baltimore, The Johns Hopkins Press. *All scientific concepts have an extensive background and this work rightly assigns some credit for Darwin's great theory to some of the minds which had been thinking along similar lines long before Darwin arrived at his basic conclusions. Among some of these forerunners were Maupertuis, Buffon, Kant, Lyell, Malthus, and Lamarck.*

Hardin, G. 1959. Nature and Man's Fate. New York, Rinehart & Co., Inc. *An excellent appraisal of man in relation to our present concept of evolutionary progress. Written in a lucid and popular style, this book is excellent supplementary reading for the general zoology student.*

Hill, W. C. 1957. Man as an Animal. London, Huchinson & Co., Ltd. *This little book stresses the animal nature of man and his position in the animal kingdom. Man differs from other animals merely in certain quanitative respects rather than in any basic qualitative features. The evolutionary emergence of man from the lower primates is presented with great clearness.*

Hooton, E. A. 1949. Up From the Ape. New York, The Macmillan Co. *A fine study of the background of human evolution.*

Huxley, J. 1942. Evolution: the Modern Synthesis. New York, Harper & Brothers. *The modern interpretation of evolutionary advancement by one of the foremost students in the field. For the advanced student.*

Huxley, T. H. 1859. Darwin on the Origin of Species. The Times (London), Dec. 26, 1859. *This famous review of Darwin's epoch-making work was published a few weeks after The Origin of Species came from the press. It was unsigned, but, as Darwin surmised, there was only one man in all of England who could have written it, and Huxley was quickly identified as the author.*

Irvine, W. 1955. Apes, Angels, and Victorians. New York, McGraw-Hill Book Co., Inc. *Darwin published his great work, The Origin of Species, just a hundred years ago (1859). By skillfully combining history and biography, the author has given a vivid account of this "intellectual holocaust" which revolved around the theory of evolution when it was first announced and for many years thereafter.*

Keith, A. 1947. Evolution and Ethics. New York, G. P. Putnam's Sons. *A discussion by a great anthropologist of man's evolutionary course with relation to man's ethical development.*

Keith, A. 1949. A New Theory of Human Evolution. New York, Philosophical Library. *The* author emphasizes the importance of isolation through differences in mentality as being responsible for the evolutionary transformation of man from the lower primates.

Lack, D. 1947. Darwin's Finches. Cambridge, Cambridge University Press. *Adaptive radiation is a highly interesting subject in evolutionary development, but no example has ever been found that illustrates this principle better than these finches Darwin studied in the early development of his evolutionary theory.*

Le Gros Clark, W. E. 1960. The Antecedents of Man, Chicago, Quadrangle Books. *This noted authority explains the evolution of man by first tracing the extensive background of the primate order. The chapter on the evolutionary radiations of the primates is especially revealing.*

McKinley, G. M. 1956. Evolution: The Ages and Tomorrow. New York, The Ronald Press Co. *The author discusses man's relation to the evolutionary process and how evolution has affected man's outlook on life and its problems. He believes that there is a definite purpose in the over-all picture of the universe. The beginning student in zoology will derive much profit from this book.*

Meggers, B. J. (editor). 1959. Evolution and Anthropology: A Centennial Appraisal. Washington, The Anthropological Society of Washington. *A series of papers by eminent authorities on the relations of the evolutionary theory to current problems in anthropology. This work is a good example of how far-reaching the concept of evolution has been in its influence on man's thinking in many disciplines.*

Moody, P. A. 1953. Introduction to Evolution. New York, Harper & Brothers. *There is no better introduction to evolution for the beginning student than this work. The last chapter entitled "An Open Letter to Students" is a sound appraisal of some of the implications of evolution on the religious adjustments of students.*

Persons, S. (editor). 1950. Evolutionary Thought in America. New Haven, Yale University Press.

Simpson, G. G. 1951. Horses. New York, Oxford University Press. *A comprehensive account of the interesting evolution of the horse.*

Simpson, G. G. 1953. The Major Features of Evolution. New York, Columbia University Press. *This is one of the most up-to-date accounts of evolution, written by one of the best authorities in the field.*

Spuhler, J. N. (editor). 1958. Natural Selection in Man. Detroit, Wayne State University Press. *Man is becoming more and more the subject of investigation from an evolutionary viewpoint, and these four papers are added evidence of this tendency.*

1953. Symposia of the Society for Experimental Biology, Number VII: Evolution. New York, Academic Press. *This volume contains the papers delivered at a symposium at Oxford in 1952. They are by British authorities mainly and cover many concepts in the field of evolution. Among the many interesting papers in the volume, the one on "Regressive Evolution in Cave Animals" is especially revealing. Unfortunately the volume is not indexed.*

Tax, S., and C. Callender (editors). 1960. Evolution After Darwin. Vol. I: The Evolution of Life; Vol. II: The Evolution of Man; Vol. III: Issues in Evolution. Chicago, The University of Chicago Press. *A collection of the papers given at the Darwin Centennial held at the University of Chicago in November, 1959. A monumental tribute to the great evolutionist and an epoch-making appraisal of evolution as it is understood at present.*

Wendt, H. 1959. The Road to Man. New York, Doubleday & Co., Inc. *A popular and interesting presentation of many animal groups and their relations to man. It is excellent reading for a beginning student in zoology.*

Wheeler, L. R. 1947. Harmony of Nature. A Study in Co-operation for Existence. London, Edward Arnold & Co. *This little work stresses the important principle of mutual cooperation in the struggle for existence and shows how it may be made to apply to man's political and social life. It is interesting reading for zoology students.*

Willmer, E. N. 1960. Cytology and Evolution. New York, Academic Press. *The author presents a revealing picture of evolutionary cytology in the light of present-day physical and chemical techniques.*

Part Five

Adaptive and environmental relations of animals

Relation of animals to their environment (ecology)*

Ecology is the science that deals with the interrelations between organisms and their environment. No animal can live apart from various physical and biological forces to which it must continually make adjustments. These forces influence its characteristics, its behavior patterns, and its distribution. Although as a science ecology is somewhat new, man has always been interested in natural history. From this beginning ecology has developed into a complex study of all the physical, biological, and climatic influences of the environment upon the animal. Ecology emphasizes the reciprocal relation between the organism and the environment and shows how each influences the other. Both the animal and its surroundings are in a continuous state of change, requiring continuous adjustment. Ecology is primarily concerned with the external environmental forces on the entire organism in contrast to the physiological sciences that deal with the interactions of the internal environment of cells and tissues. This distinction is not always sharp, for many ecological aspects involve the internal environment as well and many physiological studies involve the response of the entire organism to environmental factors. However, broadly speaking, the external environment refers to anything that is not a basic constituent of the body's organization.

*Refer to Chapter 5, Principles 13, 14, 15, and 27.

Ecology, which is both a descriptive and an experimental science, makes use of many other sciences. The techniques of physics, chemistry, geology, paleontology, limnology, and mathematics, as well as the life sciences of botany, zoology, and physiology, are used in understanding the broad concept of environment. Depending upon what aspect of ecology is stressed, its study is often subdivided into individual ecology, community ecology, population ecology, plant or animal ecology, insect ecology, and many others. This kind of classification is for convenience and reflects the complexity and specialized nature of this field of investigation.

BASIC REQUIREMENTS FOR EXISTENCE

For life to exist there are certain basic requirements which make up what is known as the fitness of the environment. These essentials are suitable and available **food,** a place to live (**shelter**), and suitable conditions for **reproduction.** To meet these requirements organisms are provided with adaptive structures of both form and function. If one requirement is lacking, the organism suffers even though the others are ideal. These basic needs vary; most plants require chlorophyll for photosynthesis, but animals get their food in a different way. Each animal is adapted for a particular combination of factors of food, shelter, and reproduction. An anteater would starve in the midst of plenty if there were no ant hills. A shelter may be suitable for some but not others. Favorable climate, weather, food, and shelter conditions are necessary for reproduction, a critical period in the life cycle. Basic needs may vary with different stages in a life cycle. Dormant animals need no food; a caterpillar's needs differ from those of an adult insect; amphibian young often require an aquatic habitat, whereas the adults may live on land.

These three requirements—nutrition, shelter, and reproduction—interact with each other as well as with other environmental factors to control the existence of an organism. The amount of available food often determines breeding activity. Many animals need special breeding places in which to raise their young. Meadowlarks nest in meadows and grasslands, not in forests or tilled fields. The food habits of some animals destroy the shelters of others. A flock of goats will clean out the shrubbery of a waste field and thus destroy the nesting sites of birds and meadow mice. Competition in meeting these requirements is found within the same species or between different species. The struggle for survival among these members includes competition for space, food, shelter, mates, etc. This intense competition of many complex relations is called the **web of life.**

Many of the constantly changing conditions are caused by organisms in their struggle for these basic necessities. Then the organisms must adjust to the new conditions in order to survive. The ability of an organism to adjust readily to unfavorable conditions is called **vagility.** Many animals can adapt to a new food when their preference is unavailable. Grass-eating animals will often browse on shrubbery during severe winters. This adaptability, which may be considered an adaptation, is often the deciding factor in survival.

ENVIRONMENTAL FACTORS OF ECOLOGY

The nature of an organism is largely determined by the interaction of its heredity and environment. Heredity furnishes in the genes a basic type of germ plasm organization. But how these genes express themselves in the structure and functioning of an animal is conditioned by environmental factors. These include both the nonliving **physical** factors (temperature, moisture, light, etc.) and the living or **biotic** factors (other organisms). The environment, then, includes every external object or factor that influences the organism and determines its total economy in the general scheme. To meet basic requirements and to make successful adjustments, organisms react toward their environment in characteristic ways, either seeking favorable positions in the environment, thus tending to avoid detrimental situations, or being able to adjust physiologically, within their genetic limits, to adverse environmental factors.

How organisms are influenced by these physical and biotic factors is determined largely by the **law of tolerance.** This law deals with the quantitative and qualitative amounts of factors which affect the distribution of organisms. The range of distribution of each species is determined by its range of tolerance to the variations in each factor. Animals vary greatly in range of tolerance. To describe a species with a narrow range of tolerance for a particular factor we use the prefix **steno-;** for those with a wide range the prefix, **eury-.** The terms **stenothermal** and **eurythermal** refer to temperature tolerance. A species will be most restricted by the factor for which it has the narrowest range of tolerance; those with the widest range for the most factors are likely to have the widest distribution.

Any factor that limits the range of a species or an individual may be known as a **limiting factor.** Temperature is a limiting factor for the polar bear whose thick insulation of fur and fat make temperatures above freezing unsuitable. (The presence of polars bears in zoos is, of course an unnatural distributional pattern.)

PHYSICAL FACTORS

Temperature. Temperature is an important factor in the animal's environment. Warm-blooded (homoiothermal or endothermal) animals are more independent of temperature changes than cold-blooded (poikilothermal or ectothermal) animals, although even endothermal animals are restricted in their activities and food supplies by temperature extremes. Usually cold-blooded forms have body temperatures not much higher than that of their surroundings, although some active forms such as insects may have higher temperatures. Some forms can help regulate the body temperature to some extent by fanning their wings to create air currents and increase evaporation or by living massed together as the bees do to conserve heat.

Many animals have an optimum temperature at which their body processes work best. For some protozoans this is between 24° and 28° C. Other forms have a wider range, usually with a lower limit of just above freezing and an upper limit of around 42° C. However, an actual upper and lower thermal level is difficult to define because the temperature at which a degree of lethality occurs depends on duration of exposure, thermal history of the animal, nutrition, etc. Every ectothermous animal has a certain range of temperature within which it can exist and function; stenothermal animals have a very narrow range of temperature tolerance and have restricted distribution whereas eurythermal animals are more widely distributed. An increase in temperature speeds up body metabolism, so that cold-blooded animals which are quite sluggish during cold spells become more active as the temperature rises. Fluctuating temperatures will sometimes speed up metabolism faster than constant temperatures. The eggs of certain arthropods develop faster at optimum temperatures after they have been subjected to cold temperatures for part of their existence.

Temperature helps determine the habits of animals. Many warm-blooded animals **hibernate** during winter months. Cold-blooded forms may retire deep underground or to other snug places to pass the winter. In some of the lower forms, the adults die at the approach of winter and the species is maintained by larval forms or by eggs. Prolonged freezing or excessive heat is highly destructive to cold-blooded forms.

Habitats of animals are greatly influenced by temperature. A number of factors operate here, for temperature may determine the availability of food as well as other things. Herbivorous forms are restricted by the amounts of grass and leaves available. Deer feed high on the mountains during the summer months but in winter retreat to the valleys where they find better shelters and more food. Birds that live upon insects are forced to go elsewhere when their food is destroyed by cold weather. Temperature also plays a part in the rearing of the young and the hatching of eggs. Some eggs will not develop unless the temperature is fairly high.

Temperature changes are also known to effect structural changes. The common fruit fly, *Drosphila,* may in certain cases undergo structural modifications at high temperatures. The vestigial wings of one of the mutants will develop into normal wings at high temperatures. Evolutionary changes in the same fly may be induced by temperature. Some of the changes induced by radiation in fruit flies can to some extent be duplicated by temperature effects. Color patterns in many insects can be induced or altered by regulating the temperature under which they develop. Many of the differences in the color phases of animals of the same species living in different environments may be thus explained.

Effective temperature for body comfort is a relative matter; it is affected by the amount of moisture (relative humidity) and the evaporating power of the air. A dry atmosphere at a certain temperature is not as uncomfortable as the same temperature in a humid air of high relative humidity and low evaporation.

Light. Light is an environmental factor toward which most animals react in a characteristic way. Many low forms express this reaction in the form of tropisms or taxes, either moving toward the light (positively phototactic) or away from it (negatively phototactic). These tropic responses are fairly simple, but there are many complicated factors in the reactions of animals to light. The effect of different intensities and wave lengths of light varies greatly for different animals. Visible light represents only a small fraction of the radiation from the sun. Within the visible spectrum, heat energy is more common at the red end (longer rays) and photochemical influences are greater at the violet end (shorter rays). Those animals that are positively phototactic usually collect near the blue end of the spectrum when they have a choice; negatively phototactic forms collect at the red end.

Since plants depend upon photosynthesis, which requires light, their distribution affects animal life, for directly or indirectly animals depend upon plants as their ultimate source of food. Plankton, which is composed of small plants and animals in surface waters, is restricted to the upper strata of water because light rays cannot penetrate deeply. Only about 0.1% of light reaches a region 600 feet below the surface of most marine waters, and this depth is usually considered the lower level of the population gradient of plant life. The distribution of plants at the surface and at the margins of bodies of water determines the range of many aquatic animals. Certain regions of land, especially in northern climates, may lack sufficient light to support an extensive flora, thus affecting the distribution of animals there.

The color of animals is also influenced by light conditions. Pigment cells (melanophores) are affected by the amount of light that enters the eye in many of the lower vertebrates. Nerve impulses aroused in the eye cause a contraction of the pigment cells and a lighter color in the animal; less light causes expansion of the pigment cells and a darker color. Many animals, such as flatfish, show this color adaptation to dark and light backgrounds.

Photoperiodicity, or the effect of light on the physiology and activities of organisms, is marked in some animals. A certain amount of light is necessary to activate the gonads and determine the breeding season in many forms. Ferrets and starlings become sexually active with lengthening days and can be induced to breed out of season when exposed experimentally to a great amount of light. It is thought that the seasonal northward migration of birds may be induced by the stimulation of their gonads by the greater light associated with longer days in the spring; the southward migration is caused by the regression of their glands by shorter days. In many other ways animals (and plants) are influenced by the length of the daylight (photoperiod), such as the diapause (resting period) in arthropods, excretion and other physiological functions of animals, the seasonal coat changes of birds and mammals, and the growth of trees. These seasonal responses may be controlled by a photoreaction involving the anterior pituitary and certain hormones. Both day and night lengths may determine the response, but little is known of these factors. The filarial worm (*Wuchereria bancrofti*) lives by day in the deeper blood vessels but by night in skin vessels where they can be picked up by mosquitoes.

Aside from color, structural changes may occur in some animals through the effect of light. Shull has shown that certain strains of aphids (plant lice) may be made to develop wings by exposing them alternately to light and darkness. Short periods of darkness followed by continuous light produced wingless forms.

Hydrogen ion concentration. The concentration of hydrogen ions is thought to have a limited importance in the distribution of animals. Although some animals prefer alkaline surroundings and others acid ones, many forms can endure a wide range of pH concentration. Tapeworms can live in concentrations of pH 4 to pH 11, or very acid to very alkaline. Some protozoans are limited to a very narrow alkaline medium whereas others, such as

812

certain species of *Euglena,* live and flourish in water which varies from pH 2 to pH 8. Some mosquito larvae are normally found in water with a pH of less than 5 and will not live in an alkaline medium. The pH of water has a very limited importance in the distribution of fish, which seem able to adjust to a wide range. Animals with calcium carbonate shells, such as clams, may be more sensitive to acid media, because their shells are corroded by acids. Water with a pH of 6 or less contains few mollusks. The factors that regulate the hydrogen ion concentration of the water are numerous and complicated. Some of these are carbon dioxide and carbonates; and these factors, rather than the hydrogen ions, may be responsible for an animal's reactions in a particular medium. At present, hydrogen ion concentration seems of minor importance in the general distribution of animal life.

Substratum and water. The **substratum** is the medium on or in which an animal lives, such as the soil, air, water, and bod-

ies of other animals. Many of the structural adaptations of animals are determined by the type of substratum. The wings of bats, insects, and birds are fitted for the air; the streamline form of fish and whales for the water; the digging feet of moles and other mammals for the earth; and the hooks and suckers of parasites for the host. Many animals spend their entire life suspended in water; others spend a great deal of time in the air. Most organisms are found on a hard substratum on the land, at the bottom of a body of water, in the hole of a tree, etc. Such a physical substratum affords them support and attachment, a variety of ecological habitats, and desirable chemical relations. Many small forms, such as water striders, whirligig beetles, various larvae, and pulmonate snails, make use of the surface film of water either in locomotion or for clinging.

The soil supports an enormous population of animals; some are fairly large, but the great majority of them are small

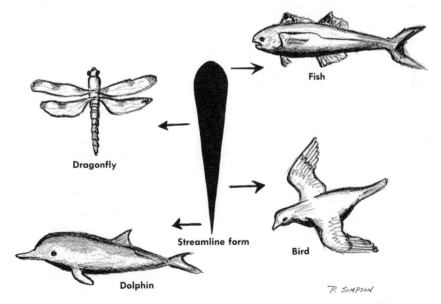

Figure 612. Streamline form. This is one of most successful body forms for rapid locomotion through air and water. It is an elongated tapering form, somewhat rounded anteriorly and tapering posteriorly, and with its greatest diameter a short distance from anterior end. As animal moves through water, for instance, body anteriorly offers resistance, but return force of water against longer tapering posterior part more than offsets force used in pushing water aside in front and so aids locomotion. Same advantages accrue when body is stationary against moving water.

Relation of animals to their environment (ecology) 813

NATURE'S 4 EXPERIMENTS IN FLYING

Butterfly (arthropod)

Pterodactyl (reptile) (extinct)

Bat (mammal)

Duck (bird)

Figure 613. Of the four groups of animals which experimented with flying, only reptiles, as a group, gave it up entirely.

forms, such as nematodes, crustaceans, insects, protozoans, and bacteria. The nature of the soil influences the distribution of the forms found in it. Earthworms, for instance, are common in soil rich in humus and are scarce or absent in sandy soils with little vegetable matter. Whether the soil is acid or alkaline seems to make little difference to them if they have abundant food. Land snails are more common on soils rich in calcium because they need this mineral for their shells. The same is true of other animals, such as deer, which depend upon calcium for their antlers and bony skeleton. Many chemicals (cobalt, fluorine, iodine) in trace amounts in the soil are important to animals.

The most common soil habitat is the burrow. Animals have evolved interesting adaptations for burrowing. Moles and

mole crickets have shovel-like appendages and broad, sturdy bodies. Earthworms secrete mucus to line their burrows. One of the most interesting burrows is made by the trap-door spider, which lines its burrow with silk and conceals the entrance with a trap door which it pops open to seize its prey (Figure 194). Many forms live under stones and other objects on the surface of the soil. Termites and ants build mounds of soil in which they make tunneled passageways. Sometimes these mounds are elevated far above the surface and may consist of excavated material and excreta cemented together with their salivary secretions.

Most forms that live in the soil make their own burrows, but some utilize those made by others. Many snakes, burrowing owls, American rabbits, and even insects take over abandoned burrows made by rodents or other forms. Many animals merely take advantage of natural crevices between rocks and debris.

A large part of any animal is water, for protoplasm consists of 70 to 92% water. Within the bodies of all animals chemical and physiological processes involve water in some form. All animals must preserve a proper water balance. The conservation of water is naturally more acute in terrestrial forms, for they are constantly in danger of desiccation. Most animals cannot lose more than one-third of their water and live, but some can undergo considerable desiccation and still survive. Protozoans secrete a cyst around themselves to prevent excessive desiccation; roundworms and rotifers may lose much water and then revive when placed in moist conditions. Water is a limiting factor for life in the desert. Many desert animals have thick, horny skins to prevent evaporation. During prolonged dry spells, some undergo **aestivation,** burrowing deep in the soil and remaining dormant until the wet season comes again. Breathing systems such as the tracheal systems of insects and the internal lungs of snails help cut down the amount of water evaporated. The dry feces of birds and reptiles is another water-saving device. Nocturnal habits of many animals expose them to lower temperature and lower relative humidity; during the day, they remain under cover most of the time.

Water requirements are correlated with the kind of animal, its habitat, kind of food, etc. Many animals get most of the water they need from their food, especially such animals as jackrabbits, mountain goats, and certain mice. Carnivorous animals may get their water supplies from the blood of their prey. Water supplies play a vital role in the distribution of many animals, for in tropical countries some do not stray far from water holes. This determines the distribution of other animals which prey upon those that must have water.

Water has unique properties as a medium for animal life. It contains many salts and other substances which organisms use for the structure and functioning of their bodies. Organisms also must work out favorable water balances between their internal and external environments, as pointed out in a previous section. The salinity of marine water is rather constant in all oceans, being about 3.5%; the salinity of fresh water varies greatly, although its salts may be limiting factors in many instances. Some salt lakes may have a salinity of 25 to 30% which greatly restricts the life in them. The freezing point of sea water is about $-1.9°C$. which is an advantage to animals in colder regions. Water is heaviest at 4° C., so that ice at 0° C. can float; thus deep lakes and ponds do not have permanent ice on their bottoms. Although shallow lakes in high altitudes do remain frozen to the bottom in the winter, life can survive there. Water also has a very high heat capacity which makes for a constancy in temperature during most of the year. Water makes up 71% of the earth's surface and represents the most extensive medium for animal life.

An important water relation is the relative humidity of the air. Animals in rain forests live only where the air is almost saturated with moisture (high humidity); desert forms live where the air is extremely dry (low humidity). There seems to be an optimum humidity for most animals which are uncomfortable under other conditions. Amphibians are especially sensitive to humidity changes, and their distribution and activity are affected by humidity factors. The calls of tree frogs at night are correlated with the relative humidity around them. Humidity and temperature have an important bearing on the distribution of animals in forest regions. Forests are important as shelters, food supplies, and hiding places, for the relative humidity is higher and evaporation much lower than in open fields.

Wind and general weather conditions. Air-borne eggs, spores, and adults (insects and snails) are often taken long distances by strong currents of air. Such forms may suddenly spring up in regions where they were not previously found.

Ballooning spiders are carried on their gossamer threads to locations far away. So powerful are wind currents that animal life may be transported from continents to islands and other lands hundreds of miles away.

To offset the effect of wind currents animals have sought shelters and habitats free from wind influences. Where wind currents are prevalent, birds place their nests in sheltered places. Insects and other forms on wind-swept regions take advantage of cover to prevent being swept away. Many such insects are wingless; this may be adaptive, for wingless animals might stand less chance of being blown away. Forests afford many habitats which are protected against the force of winds. Wind is also an agency of erosion. In our western states, the wind has shifted and carried away the top soil for great distances, producing the well-known "dust bowl" of the west.

Animals in temperate climates face many fluctuating weather conditions which are largely unknown in tropical countries. Seasonal changes influence habits and distribution and cause animals to make great changes in their reactions in order to survive. Many of the physical factors, temperature, light, etc., already mentioned, are correlated with seasonal changes in weather. Some animals in the temperate zones can undergo enormous ranges in physical factors and still survive, such as temperatures far below zero. Many, however, are killed near the freezing point of water, but the races are preserved by spores, eggs, and larval forms which can withstand such rigorous conditions. The hazards of winter are met by animals in various ways. Many migrate; others hibernate. Fur-bearing animals of many kinds, as well as some birds, remain active in cold weather because of their fur and feathers. Food habits of animals may change in winter. Insect-eating birds, for instance, may select seeds, nuts, and buds to supplement their rations. Food chains in winter differ greatly from those in summer.

Shelters and breeding places. An animal, to survive in a particular habitat, must have a suitable place of protection. Many animals, such as fish, squids, deer, and antelopes are endowed with speed to keep out of the way of predators. Such animals make limited use of shelters, but others have to depend upon protected retreats where they can hide from danger. Some animals have special devices for staying within their habitats. In rapid streams, where there is danger of being dislodged and washed away, some animals are flat for creeping under stones, others have suckers for attachment, and still others live in firmly attached cases. Vegetation creates shelter for both land and aquatic animals. Forest areas, grasslands, and shrubbery contain a variety of habitats for terrestrial animals; aquatic plants serve as cover for small fish, snails, crustaceans, and other forms. In many instances proper cover is a limiting factor.

Breeding places are important; many animals are restricted to certain areas where their young can be reared or their eggs hatched. The destruction of forests has brought a decline of large birds of prey, because the birds have been unable to find suitable nesting sites. The disappearance of sandy beaches due to the growth of aquatic vegetation affects fish that require sandy bottoms in which to spawn. Salamanders are scarce in regions that lack streams or pools in which their young may be hatched and reared.

Other physical factors. Aquatic animals which live at great depths in water are subjected to enormous pressure (more than 14 pounds per square inch for each 33 feet of depth). Many vertebrates and invertebrates do live at such depths because their internal pressure is the same as the external pressure. Forms which normally do not live at high water pressures can withstand high pressures, so that the latter is chiefly a limiting factor only when it is extreme. Fish without swim bladders are less sensitive to deep pressure than those with swim bladders, because of gas tension complications; and most invertebrates are more resistant to pressure than vertebrates. Many marine animals (eurybathic) have wide vertical ranges, making diurnal movements of great amplitude, and can adjust themselves to a wide range of pressures.

Atmospheric pressure decreases with increased altitude and influences breathing, circulation, and general activity, but the ecological significance of such pressure is not yet understood. At high altitudes, many other factors (temperature, humidity, wind, etc.) may be limiting factors.

Dissolved oxygen is a limiting factor in the distribution of aquatic organisms. Animal life may be lacking from the bottoms of deep bodies of water (Black Sea) where no dissolved oxygen is found. However, some deeper waters of the sea may have more oxygen than regions near the surface, because of the currents of sinking cold water from the polar seas. A certain amount of free oxygen must be available for aerobic animals; a few organisms, such as certain bacteria, protozoa, parasites, and other small invertebrates, can live without oxygen. Lakes at high altitudes (Andes) cannot dissolve enough oxygen to support fish life. Atmospheric oxygen can thus be considered a limiting factor, for at altitudes of 18,000 to 20,000 feet, the barometric pressure is less than one-half that at sea level, and the absolute amount (but not the percentage) of oxygen is correspondingly reduced. For man, and possibly for some other animals, oxygen requirements at high altitudes cannot be met by the oxygen available.

BIOTIC FACTORS

Nutrition. Because most animals require specific types of food, much animal behavior is focused upon food getting. The presence of an animal in a particular region is determined to a great extent by the available food. Many animals such as man have a varied diet and can use the food that happens to be convenient (**omnivores**). Other animals are plant feeders (**herbivores**) or flesh feeders (**carnivores**). Within each of these main types there are numerous subdivisions. Thus the beaver lives upon the bark of willows and aspens, the crossbill lives upon pine cones, aphids suck plant juice, leeches suck blood, and the king cobra feeds upon other snakes. Animals restricted to seasonal foods are sometimes forced either to starve or to migrate to more favorable regions. Aquatic animals depend less upon vegetation than do terrestrial ones, for water plants are restricted to limited regions, such as the shore lines, shallow bottoms, and surface plankton.

The interrelations between animals in their food getting furnish interesting **food chains.** Because plant life is the most abundant food in most localities, herbivorous animals form the basis of the animal community. These in turn serve as food for certain carnivorous forms which also may serve as food for larger predators. Eventually in this food cycle an animal is found that does not serve as food for another animal. In a food chain the successive animals involved usually are larger in size but fewer in numbers. In other words, animals at the end of a food chain are large and few, and usually one or two of them dominate a definite region, jealously keeping out all other members of that species. Many food chains could be used as examples. In a forest, for instance, there are many small insects, a lesser number of spiders and carnivorous insects which prey upon the small insects, still fewer small birds which live on the spiders and carnivorous insects, and finally one or two hawks which live upon the birds. Such an arrangement of populations in the food chain of a community is called a **food pyramid;** each successive level of the pyramid shows an increase in size and a decrease in numbers of animals. Food chains may be more complex than the one cited or may be very short, as, for example, the whale, which lives mainly upon plankton which forms the base of that particular pyramid. In every food chain plants form the basic energy for the chain. On account of this pyramid arrangement one could expect very few large predatory animals within any region, for such a large pyramid of ani-

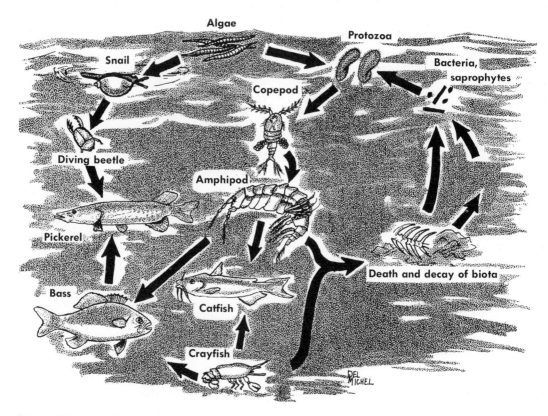

Figure 614. Some interrelationships between food chains or webs of a pond. Arrows point from prey to consumer. Chains have many side branches and are not always in linear order.

mals is required to support them. Only one grizzly bear can be found on the average of each 40 square miles of its territory; and in India, tigers are few in number for the same reason.

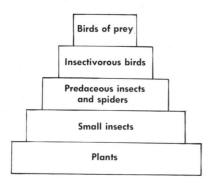

Figure 615. Simple food pyramid. Size of boxes does not correspond to relative abundance of forms. Many food pyramids are far more complicated than this one.

Another quantitative way of expressing the population of a step in a food chain is through the concept of the **biomass.** Biomass refers to the weight of a species population per unit of area. For instance, Juday (1938) found in a Wisconsin lake that there were 209 pounds of carp per acre (biomass). The biomass of a community would be the sum of the biomasses of the many species which make up the steps of the food pyramid. This might be called a **pyramid of biomass.** However, total biomasses obtained by sampling methods are not always reliable. So far, no complete biomass for a community has been obtained.

Many authorities have pointed out the importance of food size in the arrangement of a community. Carnivorous animals, for instance, are unable to kill animals above a certain size, and many cannot live on forms below a certain size, for they cannot eat enough to furnish them the necessary amount of energy. A lion, for example, could not catch enough mice under ordinary circumstances to satisfy its food requirements. Elton showed that the tsetse fly (*Glossina palpalis*) can suck up the blood of only those animals whose blood corpuscles do not exceed 18 microns in diameter. Man by his ingenuity overcomes this handicap and masters any food, regardless of size.

Competition for food is of concern in any animal community. This applies to animals of the same or of different species which live on the same type of food. Grasshoppers, for instance, may eat up grasslands so that the latter are unable to support other herbivorous animals (including domestic animals). Some animals are able to change to a food they ordinarily do not eat. The fox, when pressed by winter scarcity, can subsist on dried-up berries and grapes. Many animals adjust their food requirements to the seasonal abundance of various types of food. Animals with a wide range of food habits are better fitted for survival. The robin is a good example, for its diet includes seasonal items, such as cherries, raspberries, and other small fruits, in addition to insects and earthworms which form its staple diet.

Other biotic factors. In addition to food relations, other biotic factors play a part in the structure of an animal community. These involve social life within a group, cannibalism, mutual assistance, symbiotic relations, mating habits, predatory and parasitic relations, commensalism, mutual dependence of plants and animals, and others. These factors determine behavior patterns within animal communities and may be as important as any other factors.

Many animals are solitary in their habits, but others live together in colonies. Various degrees of social life are found among animals, from those that simply band together with no real division of labor (schools of fish and flocks of birds) to those that have worked out complicated patterns of social organization and division of labor (bees, termites, and ants). Many predators (grizzly bears, mountain lions, tigers, hawks, and owls) tend toward a solitary life and are rarely found together except for mating purposes. Many birds may be more or less solitary most of the year but quite gregarious during their migrations. Snakes are mainly solitary but hibernate together in numbers.

Many cases of **symbiotic relationship** could be mentioned, such as the small fish that obtains shelter in the cloaca of certain sea cucumbers or the flagellates that live in the gut of the termite and make its digestion possible. Ants use the secretions of aphids for food and in return give protection and shelter to the aphids. The ant slave maker, *Polyergus*, raids the colonies of other species of ants and carries away their larvae to be reared as slaves in its own colony. **Parasitism** is another common type of symbiosis.

Eat and be eaten is almost a universal rule in the animal kingdom. Most of the animals in a food chain are **predators,** preying upon other animals. **Cannibalism** (eating members of one's own species) is not unusual among animals, both low and high. It is common among insects, especially ants and termites.

Some of the relations between plants and animals are beneficial to both. Many plants depend upon insects for transferring their pollen. This is a mutual relation, for insects use nectar or pollen from the blossoms and carry pollen to other blossoms as they make their rounds. The classical case of the delicately adjusted reciprocal relation between the insect and the plant in pollination is shown by the yucca moth and the yucca plant of the southwestern states. This moth collects some pollen from one plant and carries it to another where it lays its eggs in the ovary of the yucca; after depositing an egg, the moth climbs to the top of the pistil and inserts the pollen into a stigmatic tube. This process is repeated for each egg laid (usually six). Each egg in its development requires a fertilized ovule, but enough ovules are left unmolested by the developing larvae to ensure seed for the plant. This relationship is essential to the perpetuation of the yucca plant.

PHYSIOLOGICAL ADAPTATION*

All living organisms are constantly undergoing reactions with their environment. In order to survive, every organism must make adjustments and regulations which promote constancy in its bodily states (homeostasis). Basically every phase of ecology is concerned with that physiological response by which the organism is able, in ways favorable to itself, to meet the conditions of existence. The ability of a living system to make favorable adjustments to environmental relations is called adaptation. Organisms can make all kinds of adaptive adjustments. Some adaptations are induced by the environment and others are genetically determined. Some are very rapid, such as those our sense organs make to changes in light conditions, and others are relatively slow (acclimatization). If many generations are required for favorable adjustments to be made there is the possibility that natural selection of gene mutations may be involved.

Much investigation is currently under way in the field of adaptive physiological changes in individual organisms to such factors as light, temperature, salinity of water, and other factors mentioned earlier in this chapter. Many living systems, for instance, have considerable ability to become acclimatized gradually to temperatures above and below what they normally endure. What at first was lethal temperature is now much higher or lower after a period of acclimatization. Animals naturally vary with respect to acclimatization. Dogs and cats can withstand much higher temperatures than can rabbits and rats; tropical forms under high temperature conditions can survive longer than can temperate ones. Such reactions have an important bearing on the distribution and other ecological relations of animals. How are such physiological regulations brought about? How are compensatory responses induced in the body of the organism? The mechanism by which this is done poses a problem of the first magnitude to all physiological ecologists, for the answers are still largely unknown. It has been suggested that the nervous system involving communication pathways, transformations in enzymatic systems and other cellular mechanisms, morphological changes, etc. are involved in some way.

ANIMAL POPULATIONS*

The term population is defined by some ecologists as a group of organisms of the same species which live at a given time in a particular area. Others broaden the term to include similar species. Genetically, the members of a population share in a common gene pool. A population has its own characteristics, such as population density, birth rate, death rate, reproductive potential, age distribution, population pressure, population cycles, growth, and so on. In a broad sense the study of population is the study of biology with all of its implications. Ecological units, such as communities, are made up of complex population groups and cannot be understood without a study of the interrelations of populations. Populations must adjust to the environment the same as individuals, although their environmental relations are far more complex. A population may live in a continuous small or large area; but the term does not usually include local populations of the same species which are isolated from one another.

Studies of animal populations in most habitats often reveal a large number of different species as well as of individuals in each species. In general, the small forms are most numerous. An acre of rich humus soil may contain several hundred thousand earthworms and many million nematode worms. A quart of rich plankton water may have more than one million protozoans and other small forms. The number of insects of all kinds found on an acre of lush meadow in midsummer often reaches millions of individuals. On

*Refer to Chapter 5, Principles 25 and 26.

*Refer to Chapter 5, Principle 17.

the other hand, there may be only two or three birds per acre and only one or two foxes per several hundred acres. Animals at the top of the food pyramid, having few or no enemies, often regulate their numbers by arbitrarily dividing their territory and keeping out all other members of their species. This avoids competition for food, nesting sites, and shelters.

The population of any species at a given time and place depends upon its birth rate and its mortality or death rate. If more organisms are born than die, the species will increase. Shifting of members of a species from one habitat into an adjacent one (migration, etc.) would affect the local abundance of that species but not the general population of the species involved.

The **biotic potential** rate of increase for all animals is very great, and, if unchecked, the members of any species could quickly overrun the world. The biotic potential rate is the innate capacity of a population to increase under optimal surroundings and stable age ratios. The factors responsible for keeping the population in check are called the **environmental resistance,** and they include density, competition, mortality rates, and others. Naturally, small forms have a faster birth rate than large organisms, but even slow-breeding ones quickly build up populations if conditions are favorable.

The success of a population is reflected in its **density,** which is the number of individuals per unit area or volume. Ecological studies are always concerned with changes in population density and the reasons for these changes. The unit of area used in measuring density varies. For small forms such as plankton, estimates may be made from forms found in a liter of water; for larger animals the acre or square mile may be the unit. The complete count of individuals in an area is called a **census.** Usually counts are made on sample plots, from which estimates are made. Small mammals, such as mice and chipmunks, may be trapped in live traps, tagged by clipping toes or ears, and then released. A recent method em-ploys radioactive tagging by which it has been possible experimentally to trace and recover small animals in the field with a Geiger-Müller counter. Suppose 100 animals are caught and tagged, and at a later date another lot of animals is caught in the same way on the same area. In the second sample the number of tagged animals is noted. If the second sample showed 5 tagged animals among 100 caught, then the total population (X) would be $100/X = 5/100$, or $X = 2,000$. This assumes that animals caught in the first sample are just as likely to be caught in the second sample. If sample plots are carefully selected and possible sources of error carefully checked, this random sampling method of estimating the population density of the entire area is considered fairly reliable. It is important in these estimates to make sure that the entire area covered is suitable as a habitat for the organisms being studied.

All populations undergo what is called **population dynamics,** which refers to the quantitative variations of growth, reproductive rates, mortality rates, fluctuations in numbers, age distribution, etc. The characteristic growth of a population is represented by a **population growth curve.** This is the mathematical expression of the growth of a population from its early beginning until it arrives at some stabilizing level of density. Such a curve or graph is produced by plotting the num-

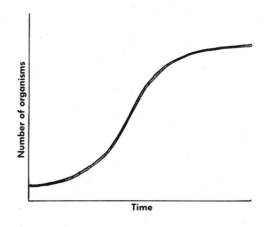

Figure 616. Population growth curve.

ber of animals, or its logarithm, against the time factor. In the beginning, if there is no serious competition with other species and enemies and there is plenty of food, the population grows at about the rate of its potential increase and the curve grows steeply upward. Such curves, however, are rarely realized except for brief periods, because of the entering factors of competition, crowding, and increased mortality rates. These growth curves are very similar for all types and sizes of organisms. One usually starts out with a **lag phase**, because it takes time for the few individuals to find each other and start mating. Then it proceeds at a rapid rate, so that a **logarithmic phase** of growth occurs when the population tends to double with each generation, and the curve is fairly straight. But because of more competition for food, losses to enemies, fewer places to live, and greater mortality rate, the growth rate slows down or levels off into the **stationary phase.**

The logistic theory of population growth seems to be restricted to the population growth of animals with simple life histories, such as many kinds of protozoans, but does not apply closely to those animals which have complex life histories (many insects). Many complicated factors of an ecological nature may greatly alter the conditions which produce the generalized logistic curve as described originally by Verhulst. There is a tendency for every population to reach a number at which it becomes stabilized (saturation level) with the resources of its environment. There is reason to believe that human populations will experience the same type of growth curve and eventually become stabilized. Human populations are now growing very rapidly because of better health facilities and increased food resources, although in certain countries the birth rate and death rate are almost in equilibrium because of limiting factors.

The **birth rate** (natality) is the average number of offspring produced per unit of time. The theoretical or maximum birth rate is the potential rate of reproduction which could be produced under ideal con-

ditions. This is never realized because not all females are equally fertile, many eggs do not hatch, not all the larvae survive, and for many other reasons. **Mortality rate** is the opposite of birth rate and is measured by the number of organisms that die per unit time. **Minimum mortality** refers to those that die from old age. The actual mortality rate, however, is far different from the minimum one, for as the population increases, the mortality rate increases. Survival curves (made by plotting number of survivors against total life span) vary among different species. Among many small organisms the mortality rate is very high early in life; others, such as man, have a higher survival rate at most levels. Man is unique in being able to change his life expectancy through better medical and other practices. Both birth rates and mortality rates are influenced by the **age distribution** of a population. Age at which animals can reproduce varies. Asexual forms begin to multiply quite early; many sexual forms (insects, etc.) attain sexual maturity a few days after hatching; others may not become mature for several months or years. Reproductive capacity is usually highest in middle-age groups. Rapidly growing populations have many young members; stationary populations have a more even age distribution. The relative distribution of age groups in a population indicates trends toward stability or otherwise.

Fluctuation in members occurs in all animal populations. Some of these fluctuations are very irregular; others show only slight variations over long periods of time. Some annual seasonal changes are to be expected. There are more birds in early summer than at other times because of the crop of recently hatched members. Later, many of these birds are destroyed by the hazards of the environment, such as **population pressure.** Examples of cycle populations are the lemmings of the northern zones which become so abundant every three or four years that they migrate to the sea and drown; the snowshoe hares of Canada which have approximately a ten-year cycle of abundance (there is a close parallelism in cyclic abundance of the lynx which feeds on the hare); and meadow mice which usually show a four-year cycle of abundance. There are many other cyclic examples, such as the muskrat, salmon, ruffed grouse, and locusts. Irregular fluctuations are especially common in insects. Grasshoppers may appear suddenly in enormous numbers, but at other times they are very scarce. No satisfactory theory as yet accounts for cyclic fluctuations, although sunspots and climatic cycles have been suggested. Some irregular fluctuations can be explained by weather and climate changes. Temperature, rainfall, severe cold, etc. have marked influences on populations. The great "dust bowl" of 1933-1936 must have affected every aspect of life in the stricken area.

The so-called **population turnover** refers to the movement of individuals into and out of populations and is caused by birth, death, and immigration into and emigration out of a given population. Some species have rapid turnovers, especially those that live only a single season or have more than one generation a year. However, even in species that live much longer the turnover rate per year may be 70% or more.

BIOTIC COMMUNITIES

The community concept stresses the idea of a natural assemblage of plants and animals which are bound together by their requirement of the same environmental factors. Whenever organisms are found together in a community they share the same physical factors and they react to them in a similar way. Communities may be widely separated, but if the environmental factors are the same, similar kinds of animals will be found in them. Thus in any brook rapids community certain characteristic animals are likely to be found. There will, of course, be exceptions.

A **major community** is the smallest ecological unit that is self-sustaining and self-regulating. It is made up of innumerable smaller **minor communities** that are not altogether self-sustaining. Forests and ponds are major communities; decaying logs and ant hills are minor communities. Members of a major community are relatively independent of other communities, provided they receive radiant energy from the sun. These members will show a similarity in their physiological make-up, behavior, and mode of life. Communities do not have exact limits but tend to overlap each other. Animals frequently shift from one community to another because of seasonal or other variations. Some spend the day in one and the night in another. A larger functional unit is the **ecosystem** which includes the nonliving environment as well as the living organisms.

Stratification is the division of the community into definite horizontal or vertical strata. A forest community, for instance, has marked strata, each occupied by certain animals. There are animals that live on the forest floor, others on shrubbery and low vegetation, and still others in the tree tops. Many forms shift from one stratum to another, especially in a diurnal manner. Many of the adjustments and requirements of a particular stratum are very similar in forests widely separated from each other in many parts of the world. The animals that occupy such similar strata, although geographically separated, are called **ecological equivalents.** The pronghorn antelope of North America and the zebra of South Africa are equivalents.

Between two distinct communities there may be an intermediate transitional zone. This is called an **ecotone,** or tension zone. An example would be the marginal region between a forest and a pasture or open land.

Food relations are a basic aspect of all communities. In a self-sufficient community they follow a certain sequence. **Producer organisms,** such as green plants, make their own food; **primary consumers,** such as insects, larvae, and various other arthropods, feed upon plants; **secondary consumers,** such as carnivores, live upon the primary consumers, etc. Other organisms such as bacteria are called **decom-**

poser organisms, for they break down the dead organisms into simpler substances which can then be used by plants.

In every community some plants and animals exert a dominant influence because of their numbers, activities, and other reasons. Generally those organisms with the largest biomasses within their levels of feeding interrelations are the ones that exert a controlling interest. In land communities, plants are usually the **dominants,** and some communities are named from their dominant vegetation, such as beech-maple woods. In the ecological cycle of a community the removal of a dominant usually causes serious disturbances.

A basic characteristic of community organization is **periodicity.** This refers to rhythmic patterns of organisms in their search for mates, food, and shelter. Some community periodicities are correlated with the daily rhythms of day and night, some are seasonal, and others represent tidal or lunar events. Periodic activities include the diurnal and nocturnal faunas which are specialized for day and night activities, respectively; seasonal cycles of growth, mating periods, hibernation, migration, etc.; and activities of swarming spawning, etc. which are correlated with the lunar and tidal periodicity. There are also various intermediate activities such as those which occur during the crepuscular period (twilight). Because of this community periodicity more ecological habitats are available and more ecological relationships are established.

ECOLOGICAL NICHE

The special place an organism has in a community with relation to its food and enemies is called an **ecological niche.** In every community there are herbivorous animals of several types, some of which feed upon one kind of plant and others upon other plants. There are also in every community different types of carnivores which prey upon different species of animals. Similar niches in different communities are occupied by forms which have similar food habits or similar enemies, although the species involved may be different in each case. For example, there is the niche in wooded regions occupied by hawks and owls which prey upon field mice and shrews, but in regions close to homes this niche is taken over by cats. In this respect the birds of prey and cats occupy the same niche. The arctic fox and the African hyena are other examples. Both are scavengers; the arctic fox eats what the polar bear leaves; the African hyena eats leavings from the lion. Elton, the English ecologist who elaborated the concept of the ecological niche, has described many such niches in animal communities. The concept of the ecological niche greatly aids the student in understanding the complicated nature of animal community organization. It also shows the similarity in pattern of the various types of communities.

ECOLOGICAL SUCCESSION

Communities are not static but are continually changing according to well-defined laws. This process, called biotic or **ecological succession,** may be brought about by physiographic factors such as the erosion of hills and mountains down to a base level, the filling up of lakes and streams, the rise and fall of the earth's surface, etc. Another factor of ecological change is the influence of plant and animal life upon the substratum. All organisms die, decay, and become a part of the substratum; vegetation invades ponds and lakes; regions of the earth's surface become grasslands, forests, or deserts according to physical factors of temperature and rainfall. These changes are often regular and directional and may be predicted. Communities are succeeded by other communities until a fairly stable end product is attained. Such a sequence of communities is called a **sere** and involves early pioneer communities, transient communities, and finally a **climax community** which is more or less balanced with its environment.

The sequence of plants follows in a certain order during the evolution of a habitat. For instance, a small lake begins as a

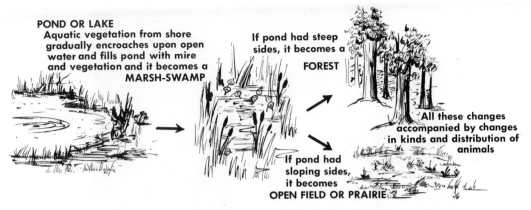

Figure 617. Ecological succession in a pond or lake.

clear body of water with sandy bottom and shores more or less free from vegetation. As soil is washed into the lake by the surrounding streams, mud and vegetable muck gradually replace the sandy bottom. Vegetation grows up along the sides of the lake and begins a slow migration into the lake as the latter fills up. A bog or marsh results in the places where plants become rank. At first this plant life is typical of aquatic or semi-aquatic habitats, consisting of filamentous algae on the surface and later of rooted plants, such as *Elodea,* bulrushes, and cat-tails. As the water recedes and the shore becomes firm, the marshy plants are succeeded by shrubs and trees such as alders and larches, and later beeches and maples. Eventually, when the lake disappears as such, it may be replaced by a forest, especially if its sides and slopes are steep; if the sides have gentle slopes, a grassy region may replace the site of the lake. The terminal forest or grassland is a climax community (Figure 617).

Along with the succession of plants there will be a corresponding ecological succession in the types of animal communities. In its beginning a lake may contain fish which use the gravelly or sandy bottoms for spawning. When the bottoms are replaced by muck, these fish will be replaced by others which spawn in aquatic vegetation. Eventually, no fish may be able to live in the habitat; but other forms, such as snails, crayfish, many kinds

of insects, and birds, are able to live in the swampy, boggy community. As the community becomes a forest or grassland, there will be other successions of animal life.

Ecological succession can be demonstrated in the laboratory in a hay infusion culture of protozoans and other simple forms. The maximum populations of the different forms usually appear in an order such as this: flagellates, free-swimming ciliates, stalked ciliates, and, finally, Sarcodina. Among each of these there is a period of growth, a period of dominance, and then one of decline, usually with some overlapping and persistence of species. The causes of these sequences are complex. Many species are dependent upon the presence of other species. Paramecia seem to depend upon the presence of hypotrich ciliates, or at least their excreta, in order to flourish. Another factor is hydrogen ion concentration. Certain flagellates can endure wide ranges of hydrogen ions; various ciliates are restricted to narrow ones.

In general, it may be stated that communities in their development and evolution tend to go from a state of instability to one of stability or climax. The term stability, however, must be used in a relative sense, for changes are inevitable.

KINDS OF HABITAT

Habitats tend to be rather sharply defined from each other, each with its own

Relation of animals to their environment (ecology) 825

Figure 618. Woodland pond affords excellent shelter and breeding places for many forms, such as amphibians, reptiles, and insects. (Courtesy Charles Alender.)

set of physical and biotic factors. Transition zones between them are not common. An abundance of different habitats may be found in a small region if there is a diversity of physicochemical and other factors. A small lake or pond (Figure 618) may have littoral or open water, cove, sandy or pebbly bottom, bulrush or other vegetation, drift, and other kinds of habitats. Within the relatively short range of a high mountain there are many life zones, each of which may correspond to the latitudinal zones. The small altitudinal life zones of the mountain are similar to the large latitudinal zones of the earth's surface with respect to vegetation and, to some extent, to the distribution of animal life. On the other hand, there may be extensive regions, such as the surface of the open sea or a sandy desert, where there is no such diversity of habitats, because ecological conditions are more or less uniform throughout its extent.

The animals which are distributed among the various habitats may be classified into two groups: (1) exclusive, or those that are not found outside a particular habitat (Figure 626), and (2) characteristic, or those that are not confined to one habitat but also occur in others. Examples of the first are crossbills, which, on account of their peculiar adaptation, are confined to the coniferous forests, and, of the second class, such forms as rabbits, which roam both woods and open fields.

Fresh-water streams

Fresh-water habitats are usually divided into those that are found in **running water** and those found in **standing water**. Fresh-water streams naturally belong to the first type. They range from tiny intermittent brooks to rivers. Smaller streams are either intermittent ones which flow only at certain seasons or spring-fed streams which usually flow all the time. Larger, permanent streams include the swift brooks and the rivers and have reached the level of permanent ground water. Water found in streams differs from marine water in having smaller volume, greater variations in temperature, lesser mineral content, greater light penetration, greater suspended material content, and greater plant growth. Many of the forms found in such habitats have organs of attachment, such as suckers and

Figure 619. Brook rapids habitat contains many different forms which have special adaptations for withstanding strong water currents.

modified appendages, streamlined body shapes for withstanding currents, or shapes adapted for creeping under stones. Various kinds of habitats are found in all streams. Some are found in the swiftly flowing regions where there may be rapids or cataracts, others are in pools of sluggish waters. Usually the types of animals found in the two regions vary. In rapids (Figure 619) the most characteristic forms are the black fly larvae *(Simulium)*, caddis worms *(Hydropsyche)*, snails *(Goniobasis)*, darters of several species, water penny larvae (Figure 620), miller's-thumbs, and stone fly nymphs. All these forms have characteristic behavior patterns such as positive rheotaxis, high oxygen requirements, and low temperature toleration. In the pool habitats of streams are found various minnows, mussels, certain snails, dragonfly nymphs (Figure 225), mayfly larvae, crayfish, flatworms, leeches, and water striders (Figure 621). Many of the forms which dwell here partially bury themselves in the sandy or mucky bottoms.

Some of the larger streams and rivers may have considerable plankton, but this plankton has gotten into the rivers from

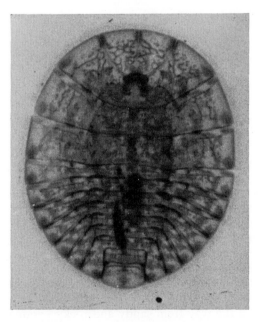

Figure 620. Water penny, larva of riffle beetle, *Psephenus.* This flat larva is adapted for clinging to lower surfaces of stones in swift brooks. (Size, ⅓ inch.)

lakes and backwaters and is not developed from the rivers, for their currents are too swift.

Figure 621. Group of forms found in quiet pools of brooks. This shows water strider, *Gerris,* small crustacean, *Asellus,* in upper center, head of horsefly larva in lower left, and water snail in lower center.

The study of fresh waters in all their aspects is called **limnology.**

Ponds

Ponds usually have an abundance of animal life, for their conditions are more or less ideal for animal existence (Figure 618). Unlike the streams, ponds have feeble currents or none at all. They vary, depending upon their age and location. Most ponds contain a great deal of vegetation which tends to increase with the age of the pond. Many of them have very little open water in the center, for the vegetation, both rooted and floating types, has largely taken over. As ponds fill up, the higher plants become progressively more common. The bottoms of ponds vary all the way from sandy and rocky (young ponds) to deep mucky ones (old ponds). The water varies in depth from a few inches to 8 to 10 feet, although some may be deeper. Ponds are too shallow to be stratified, for the force of the wind is usually sufficient to keep the entire mass of water in circulation. Because of this, the gases (oxygen, carbon dioxide) are uniformly distributed through the water and the temperature is fairly uniform.

Animal communities of ponds are usually similar to those of bays in larger bodies of water (lakes). The large amount of vegetation and plant decomposition products affords an excellent habitat for many forms. Among the common forms found are varieties of snails and mussels, larvae of flies (Figures 225 and 622), beetles, caddis flies, dragonflies, many kinds of crustaceans, midge larvae, and many species of frogs. Most of these live on the bottom or among the submerged vegetation and are called the **benthos.** Many swimming forms, called **nekton,** are also found in ponds and include many varieties of fish, turtles, water bugs, and beetles. Muskrats (Figure 484) are usually found in the larger ponds where they make their characteristic houses. Because of the abundance of food, many birds are usually found in and around ponds. These include herons, killdeers, ducks, grebes, and blackbirds. Most ponds also have plankton composed of microscopic plants and animals, such as protozoans, crusta-

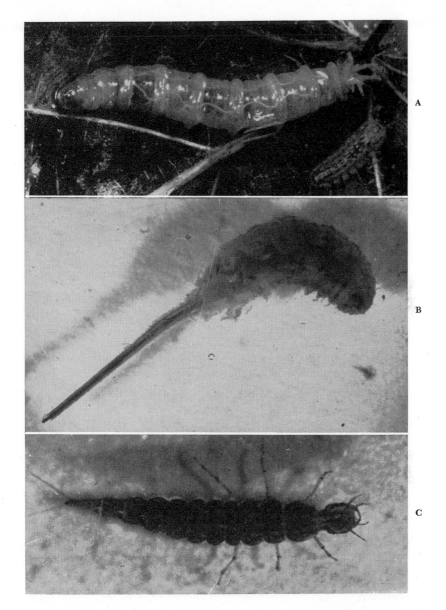

Figure 622. Group of larval forms commonly found in ponds. **A,** Horsefly larva found in decaying debris along bank. Besides it is small crustacean, *Asellus*. **B,** Rat-tailed maggot, *Tubifera*. This larva lives in water and gets its air when submerged by means of its caudal respiratory tube ("rat-tail") which is in sections like a telescope and can be extended to four times the length of body. **C,** Larval form of *Dytiscus*, giant diving beetle (shown in Figure 250). Larva is equally as savage and predaceous as adult. These were all found in tiny midwestern woodland pond in early March.

ceans, worms, rotifers, diatoms, and algae. Plankton floats on or near the surface and is shifted about passively by the winds.

Forms that live in ponds ordinarily require less oxygen than those found in streams or rapids (Figure 623).

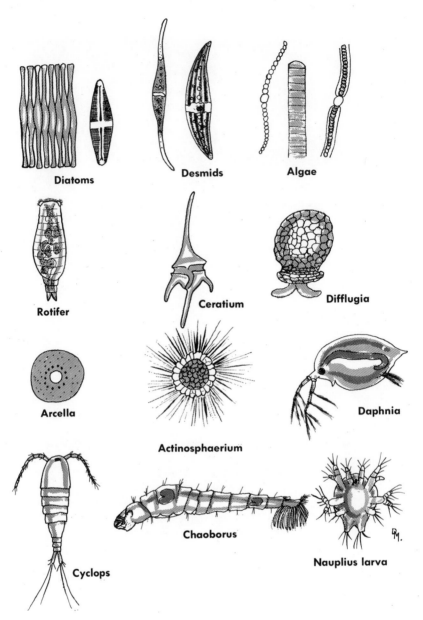

Diatoms

Desmids

Algae

Rotifer

Ceratium

Difflugia

Arcella

Actinosphaerium

Daphnia

Cyclops

Chaoborus

Nauplius larva

Figure 623. Some typical forms found in pond plankton.

Lakes

The distinction between lakes and ponds is not sharply defined. Lakes are usually distinguished from ponds by having continuous and permanent water in their centers and by having some sandy shores. Lakes vary with respect to vegetation and other factors. Most of them have bays where there may be aquatic vegetation similar to that of ponds. The bottoms of lakes depend to a great extent on exposure to winds. Where waves are common, the bottoms are usually sandy, but protected areas may contain a great deal of deposited bottom muck. Sizes vary from oceanlike bodies of water to those only a few acres in extent. Naturally, there are differences associated with their size.

830

There is less surface of water in proportion to the total volume of water in a lake than there is in a pond, for lakes are deeper. The depths vary too. In large lakes, such as the Great Lakes of America, the depth rarely exceeds 500 meters; in moderate-sized lakes the depth is much less. Many factors, therefore, influence the ecological nature of a lake. Oxygen is scarcer in the deeper regions where there is little circulation. Light penetration depends upon the sediment in water. Most of the light is absorbed by the first meter of surface water, and little penetrates beyond a few meters. One factor of great importance is temperature. Water in lakes tends to become stratified, and only the surface layers are stirred up by wind action during the summer. Within this surface layer of water, usually about 10 meters deep in medium-sized lakes, the temperature is very uniform (about 20° to 25° C.). Below this the water becomes much colder (reaching 4° to 5° C. at the bottom) and is poorly oxygenated and stagnant. This level between the surface layer of uniform temperature and that stratum where the temperature falls rapidly is called the **thermocline.** In other words, the waters above the thermocline are agitated; below it they are still. The thermocline is shallow at midsummer and deeper in early autumn. In the autumn, when the surface water is colder, the wind agitates the water from surface to bottom and the thermocline disappears so that the temperature is about uniform throughout. In winter the surface water may freeze (0° C.), but the bottom remains at 4° to 5° C. Water at the latter temperature is heavier than ice, which accounts for the fact that ice remains at the surface. As the surface waters become warmer in the spring, there occurs another complete overturn through wind action. In early summer the thermocline is established again.

The thermocline is important ecologically, for it establishes the division between two animal communities. Several habitats are found in lakes, such as **terrigenous bottoms,** where the water is shallow and vegetation is absent; **cove,** which has a great deal of vegetation (emergent, submerged, and floating); and **open water,** which may contain some floating plants, especially algae. Characteristic organisms are found in each. Snails, caddis worms, and May fly nymphs are found in the terrigenous bottom habitat; bryozoans, small crustaceans, snails, and some insects in the cove habitat; and plankton and nekton (fish, turtles, and insects) in the open waters. The animals that live on the bottom (the **benthos**) are restricted to those that require no light and little or no oxygen (a few annelid worms, bivalves, and midge larvae).

Terrestrial

Land habitats are more varied than those of the water, because there are more variable conditions on land. Physical differences in the air are expressed in such factors as humidity, temperature, pressure, and winds to which air-dwelling forms must adapt themselves, as well as types of soils and vegetation. Variations from profuse rainfall to none at all; topographical differences of mountains, plains, hills, and valleys; climatic differences from arctic conditions to those of the tropics; temperature variations from those in hot deserts to those of high altitudes and polar zones; and air and sunlight differences from those of daily variations to great storms—all these factors have influenced animal life and have been responsible for directing its evolutionary development.

Land forms have become specially adapted for living in the soil (subterranean), on the open ground, on the forest floor, in vegetation, and in the air. Although more species of animals live on land than in water, there are fewer phyla among terrestrial forms. The chief land organisms are the mammals, birds, reptiles, amphibians, worms, protozoans, and arthropods.

Land habitats are classified on the basis of soil relations, climatic conditions, plant associations, and animal relations. Some of the more important habitats in North

Figure 624. Group of common land snails, largely various species of *Polygyra*, found on forest floor.

625 626

Figure 625. Habitat of shelving and drift rock—excellent habitat for many species of salamanders and lizards.

Figure 626. Tree hole habitat. Some arthropods found here are never or rarely found elsewhere. One of these groups is pselaphid beetles.

America will be considered here, together with a few of their characteristic animals.

Subterranean. This refers to regions within the soil or under the land surface. It includes such habitats as holes and crevices in or between rocks (Figure 625), burrows in the soil, and caves and

832

caverns. Many animals spend at least a part of their lives in the soil. Larval forms of many insects develop there. Ants, nematodes, earthworms, moles, and shrews either have their homes in the soil or spend a part of their time there. For abundance of forms, no other ecological habitat can compare with the soil. Most cave animals originated on the surface and were adapted for existence in caves before they entered them. Caves are unique in having uniform darkness, high humidity, no green plants, and no rain or snow. Meager food supply restricts the number of animals living there. Cave animals are usually small, have little or no pigment, and have degenerate sense organs. Many are totally blind. Most true cave animals illustrate regressive evolution in that selection puts a premium on loss of internal stability, low basal metabolism, and low food requirements. Common examples of cave animals are springtails, mites, small crustaceans, fish, salamanders, and snails.

BIOMES

Biotic communities may also be aggregated into **biomes** which are the largest ecological units. In a biome the climax vegetation is of a uniform type, although many species of plants may be included. Each biome is the product of physical factors, such as the nature of the substratum, the amount of rainfall, light, temperature, etc. They are distributed over the surface of the earth as broad belts from the equator to the poles and each may or may not be continuous. Within each biome are many major communities. Biomes are not always sharply marked off from each other; there are often intermediate zones. Some six important terrestrial biomes are recognized: desert, grassland, equatorial forest, deciduous forest, coniferous forest, and tundra. This succession of biomes from the tropics to the poles may also be found in condensed form on the vertical zones of a high mountain. The various oceans make up the so-called marine biome which contains a single major community, the marine com-munity, which may be subdivided into a number of minor communities.

Marine

To call the sea a single biome is perhaps too simple a description. The oceans have so many diversified physical and chemical conditions that innumerable habitats are found in them. Animals here have undergone striking evolutionary developments. Life came from the sea, and all the ancestors of present-day forms have had some connection with it.

The conditions of marine existence are many. Salt water makes up about 70% of the earth's surface. The average depth of the sea is about 10,000 feet, but there are much deeper regions and along the shores its depth may grade down to a few feet. Its average salt content is about 3.5%, which makes its density greater than fresh water but not so great as protoplasm, for the animal body will sink in it. Its pressure in the great depths may reach a thousand atmospheres; yet animals live there and are not crushed, for their own body fluids have the same pressure. Mechanical disturbances in the forms of waves, tides, and currents have profound effects upon the animal life.

The movement of the sea is one of the most important features of marine ecology. Besides tides and surface wave action, the sea is in continuous circulation. The major surface currents of oceans have been worked out, although they are not rigidly fixed and variations are always occurring. Their causes and mechanics are complicated and pose problems for the science of oceanography. In general, they are due to prevailing trade winds, caused by temperature differences between poles and equator, and to the rotation of the earth, which can give rise to movements in the deep layers of the ocean as well as near the surface. The icecaps at the poles, particularly the South Pole, form glaciers which eventually melt in the sea and produce a cold but light current of dilute salt water that flows away toward the equator. A similar current of cooled water under the surface layer sinks and flows along the ocean floor also toward the equator. Other currents of water flow toward the poles between the other two currents to take the place of the displaced waters. Off-shore winds push coastal waters away, and their place is taken by the upwelling of water from below. This upwelling brings to the surface water rich in phosphates and nitrates which influence the distribution of plankton.

The temperature of sea water varies with location and with the seasons. In the arctic regions it may go to below 0° C.; in the tropics the surface water may exceed 30° C. These regions may have a relatively uniform temperature the year round, but in the temperate zones there are seasonal variations in the temperature of surface waters which are more pronounced in land-locked bodies of the sea. Deep regions of the sea always contain cold water. The penetration of light is restricted mainly to the upper 50 to 60 meters, although it can be detected at greater depths. Oxygen varies in different parts of the sea. Where deep waters obtain their oxygen supply from cold currents from the polar regions (which can absorb more oxygen than warm water), the concentration of oxygen may be greater than at intermediate depths. Bottom drifts of such cold water may extend long distances. In deep sea water where there is no such replacement, there is a total absence of oxygen. Stagnated water with much hydrogen sulfide is found in many isolated bays and gulfs and supports few or no animals. Surface and shore waters contain a great deal of oxygen. Plant life is restricted to certain regions. The surface layers contain plankton; sheltered regions may contain plants where they can take root; and seaweeds are found floating about in most seas.

Differences in environmental conditions have produced corresponding differences in the adaptations of marine animals. The animals that inhabit the sea may be divided into two main groups: pelagic and benthonic.

Pelagic group. The pelagic group includes (1) the **plankton,** small organisms (protozoans, crustaceans, mollusks, worms, etc.) which float on the surface of the water; and (2) the **nekton,** composed of animals that swim by their own movements (fish, squids, turtles, whales, seals, birds, etc.)

Benthonic group. The benthonic group includes the bottom-dwelling forms or those that cannot swim about continuously and need some support. This group can be subdivided according to the zones in which they are found: (1) **Littoral,** or lighted zone. This is the shore region between the tidelines that is alternately exposed to air and water at each tide cycle. These forms are subjected to high oxygen content and much wave disturbance. In this region originated the ancestors of all aquatic fauna, both fresh water and salt water. It contains a very rich animal life, both in species and numbers of individuals. Some are adapted for crawling (worms, echinoderms, mollusks), some are adapted for burrowing (worms, mollusks), and some are attached, or **sessile** (crinoids, bryozoans, corals). (2) **Neritic** zone, which lies below tide water on the continental shelf and has a depth of 500 to 600 feet. There is some wave action here, and the water is well oxygenated. Many forms, including fish, echinoderms, and protozoans, are found in this habitat. (3) **Bathyal** zone, which is a stratum of the deeper water from the neritic region down to 5,000 or more feet. It contains small crustaceans, arrowworms, medusae, and fish. Many of the animals in this region have luminescent organs, for this is a dark zone. (4) **Abyssal** zone, or deeper parts of the oceans. The water is always cold and there is total darkness. Oxygen is scarce or absent, and only a few deep-sea forms are found—certain specialized fish and crustaceans. Many of these are provided with light organs.

Tundra. The tundra is characteristic of severe, cold climates, especially that of the treeless arctic regions and high mountain tops. Plant life must adapt itself to a short growing season of about 60 days and to a soil that remains frozen for most of the year. Most tundra regions are covered with bogs, marshes, ponds, and a spongy mat of decayed vegetation, although high tundras may be covered only with lichens and grasses. In spite of the thin soil and short growing season, the vegetation of dwarf woody plants, grasses, sedges, and lichens may be quite profuse. The plants of the alpine tundra of high mountains, such as the Rockies and Sierra Nevadas, may differ from the arctic tundra in some respects. Characteristic animals of the arctic tundra are the lemming, caribou, musk ox, arctic fox, arctic hare, ptarmigan, and (during the summer) many migratory birds.

Grasslands. This biome includes prairies and open fields and has a wide distribution. It is subjected to all the variations of temperature in the temperate zones, from freezing to extremely hot temperatures. It undergoes all the vicissitudes of seasonal climatic factors of wind, rain, and snow. The animals that occupy this region vary with different localities. On the western prairies there will be jack rabbits, antelope, wolves, coyotes, skunks, gophers, prairie chickens, and insects. In the eastern parts of the country, some of these will be replaced by other forms.

Desert. Deserts are extremely arid regions where permanent or temporary flowing water is absent. The yearly amount of water is widely fluctuating, but when rain does come, it may do so with a terrific downpour. The skies are usually unclouded; the temperature becomes very hot during the day but cools off at night. There is some scattered vegetation which quickly revives after a rain. Some of the most characteristic plants are the cacti.

Desert faunas are varied and mostly active at night, so as to avoid the heat of the day. Most of them show adaptive coloration and the power of rapid locomotion. To conserve water they have physiological devices for passing dry excretions. To the casual visitor the desert fauna may seem somewhat scanty, but actually the desert possesses representatives of many animal groups. Mammals found there include the white-tailed deer, peccary, cottontails, jack rabbit, kangaroo rat, pocket mouse, ground squirrel, badger, gray fox, skunk, and others. Birds include migrants and those that are quite typical to desert life, such as the road runner, cactus wren, turkey vulture, cactus woodpecker, burrowing owl, Gambel's quail, raven, hummingbird, and flicker. Reptiles are numerous, such as the horned lizard, Gila monster, race runner, collared lizard, chuckwalla, coral snake, rattlesnake, and bull snake. A few species of toads are also common. Arthropods include a great variety of scorpions, spiders, centipedes, and insects.

Coniferous forests (taiga). These are the forests of evergreens—pines, firs, and spruces—found in various areas of the North American continent. They may occur in mountains or flat country. They bear leaves the year around and afford more cover than deciduous forests. They are often subject to fires which influence the animal habitats. Conditions within such forests depend upon their location. On mountains and in northern regions they undergo severe winters with much snowfall; in southern regions they have milder conditions. A great deal of food—berries, nuts, and cones—is found in evergreen forests, and there is also a great variety of animal life. In the north there are martens, lynxes, foxes, moose, bears, many birds, some reptiles, amphibians, and many insects. Southern coniferous forests lack some of these forms but have more snakes, lizards, and amphibians. Many of these undergo extensive seasonal migrations.

Deciduous forests. Deciduous forests are more common east of the Mississippi river, and their distribution depends upon moisture, soil, and temperature. The trees shed their leaves in the fall, leaving them bleak during the winter, especially in northern climates. There may be some low underbrush and vines. Some of these forests have scattered evergreen trees. They possess a varied animal life, including many burrowing forms. Among characteristic fauna of these forests are the deer, fox, bear, beaver, squirrel, flying squirrel, raccoon, skunk, wildcat, rattlesnake, copperhead, and various songbirds, birds of prey, and amphibians. Insects and other invertebrates are common since decaying logs afford excellent shelters for them.

Tropical rain forests. Tropical rain forests are found in Central America. Vegetation is luxuriant and varied. The trees are mainly broad-leaved evergreens; also there are many vines. These forests have a copious rainfall and a constant high humidity. Because of their density, they have a reduced illumination. The forests are divided ecologically into a vertical series of strata, each of which is occupied by characteristic animals. These strata include the forest floor, the shrubs, small trees, lower tree tops, and the upper forest canopy. The enormous amount of life found here is represented by monkeys, amphibians, insects, snails, leeches, centipedes, scorpions, termites, ants, reptiles, and birds.

FOOD CYCLE*

Animals are stores of potential energy which they transform into kinetic energy to be used in their life processes. All energy utilized by animals is derived ultimately from the sun. Plants utilize radiant energy from sunlight and the chlorophyll in their cells to produce carbohydrates from carbon dioxide and water. Plants can also form proteins and fats. Animals, with few exceptions, do not have this power and depend upon the plants as sources for the basic food substances. Animals that do not live directly on plants live upon animals that do; therefore, all their potential energy can be traced back to a plant origin.

In this energy cycle of transfer and transformation the laws of thermodynamics apply. When a plant transforms light into the potential energy of food by the process of photosynthesis, energy is being transformed into another form without being destroyed (First Law of Thermodynamics), but when this plant food

*Refer to Chapter 5, Principle 14.

is utilized or consumed by other organisms, although there is no loss in total energy, there is a decrease in amount of useful energy, for some energy is degraded or lost as heat in a dispersed form (Second Law of Thermodynamics). Thus, in every step in a food chain or pyramid there is a certain loss in useful energy. When the sun's energy is exhausted there will be no further photosynthesis and no more life.

All plants in their metabolism require certain elements, such as carbon, oxygen, nitrogen, hydrogen, and, to a lesser extent, potassium, magnesium, calcium, sulfur, iron, and a few others. All these are derived from the environment, where they are present in the air, soil, rock, or water. Animals require about the same elements, most of which they get from the plants. When plants and animals die, and their bodies decay, or when organic substances are burned or oxidized, these elements are released and returned to the environment. Bacteria fulfill a useful role in decomposing the body wastes and the bodies of dead animals and plants. The elements which are involved in these processes, therefore, pass through cycles which involve relations to the environment, to plants, and to animals. Three or four of these important cycles will be pointed out here.

Carbon cycle (Figure 627). Both animals and plants respire and give off carbon dioxide to the air. More is released in the bacterial decomposition of organic substances, such as dead plants and animals. Although the percentage of carbon dioxide in air is relatively small (0.04%) as compared with the other gases of air, this small amount is of great importance in nature's economy. Living green plants take carbon dioxide from the air or water and by **photosynthesis**, with the help of sunlight, carbohydrates are formed. This process is complicated but in a simple form may be expressed thus:

$$6 \text{ H}_2\text{O} + 6 \text{ CO}_2 \rightarrow \text{C}_6\text{H}_{12}\text{O}_6 + 6 \text{ O}_2$$

Carbon dioxide   Sugar   Oxygen

Carbohydrates thus formed, together

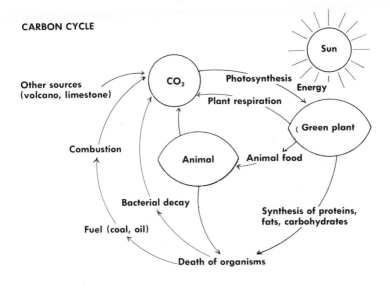

CARBON CYCLE

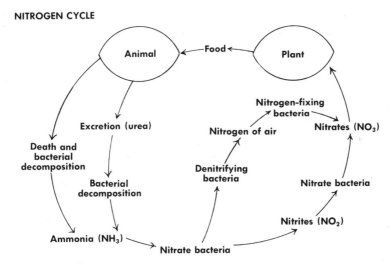

NITROGEN CYCLE

Figure 627. Carbon and nitrogen cycles.

with proteins and fats, compose the tissues of plants. Animals eat the plants and the carbon compounds become a part of animal tissue. Carnivorous animals get their carbon by eating herbivorous forms. In either case a certain amount of carbon dioxide is given off to the air in breathing (this also occurs in plants), and when the animal dies, a great deal of the gas is released to the air by bacterial decomposition. This cycle is called the carbon cycle. The importance of carbon in the organic world cannot be overestimated; for of all

the chemical elements, it is the one which enters into the greatest number of chemical combinations.

Oxygen cycle. Animals get their oxygen from the air or from oxygen which is dissolved in water and utilize it in their oxidative reactions. They return it to their surroundings in the form of carbon dioxide (CO_2) or water (H_2O). Plants also give off some oxygen in photosynthesis as seen in the foregoing formula. Plants use some oxygen in their own respiration. In the interesting relationship between plants and animals in the plankton life of surface waters, the floral part of these populations gives off the oxygen necessary for the life of the faunal portion and determines the distribution of the latter. Light is the determining factor in the distribution of the plant life of plankton.

Nitrogen cycle (Figure 627). Atmospheric nitrogen (78% of air) can be utilized directly only by nitrogen-fixing bacteria which are found in the soil or in the root nodules of leguminous plants. These nitrogen-fixing bacteria combine nitrogen into nitrates (NO_3), and plants form proteins from these nitrates. When animals eat plants, the proteins of the latter are converted into animal proteins. In animal metabolism, nitrogenous waste (urea, etc.) is formed from the breakdown of proteins and is excreted. In the soil or water certain bacteria convert this waste into ammonia and into nitrites; other bacteria (nitrifying) change the nitrites into nitrates. Whenever plants and animals die and undergo bacterial decomposition, their proteins are converted into ammonium compounds.

Mineral cycle. Many inorganic substances are necessary for plant and animal metabolism. Usually the amount of these constituents is small and varies with different kinds of living things. Among these, phosphorus is one of the most important. It is found in the soil and water in the form of phosphoric oxides. It is taken up by plants, is passed on to the animals, and is eventually returned to the soil or water in the form of excreta or upon the decay of their bodies.

ECOLOGY AND CONSERVATION

Most aspects of ecological study are related to the principles of conservation. Conservation may be defined as the most efficient and most beneficial utilization of natural resources (soil, forests, water, wildlife, minerals, etc.). This is a logical relation, for the basis of ecology is the ecosystem or the combination of the biotic community and the physical environment. A great conservationist, Aldo Leopold, once stated that the biotic pyramid is really a symbol of land and its uses as a circuit of energy which involves soil, plants, and animals. A study of ecology is necessary to understand these relations. Whenever a change occurs anywhere in this broad persistent circuit of energy, adjustments must be made to maintain a proper balance of nature.

Our natural resources are commonly divided into (1) the renewable, such as the biotic factors of flora and fauna and the physical factors of soil and water; and (2) the nonrenewable, such as minerals. The renewable resources form an intricate relationship and are closely tied together; one cannot be disturbed without disturbing the others. Able conservationists now believe that the wisest way to preserve renewable natural resources is to use them within the limits of continuous renewal. Good forest management, as many European countries have demonstrated, is to remove the less vigorous trees for timber and allow the others a chance for normal growth. Good game management involves regulated hunting seasons so that wildlife may stay within the bounds of food resources and optimum populations. In conservation planning it is not always the best policy to eliminate the inferior or less desirable plant or animal members of the ecosystem. Predators, for instance, have their place in the biotic pyramid.

In the final analysis, sound conservation is the best possible use of the available energy in an ecosystem. Without the biotic factors energy from the sun is mostly lost on our planet, for sunlight energy is stored by plants and passed in food chains and food webs around the ecosystem. Soil is dependent upon biotic factors which must be present or else there is the enormous problem of erosion waste.

Specifically, any adequate conservation program must include the natural resource background of soil, water, wildlife, vegetation, and natural topography. It should include the application of ecological principles to the integration of those environmental factors. It should include methods for the most efficient use of the land for a growing population. Definite controls must be worked out to limit the wastage of land erosion, fires, flood, and water pollution. Effective controls involving both biological and chemical methods must be employed to check insect pests, rodents, and disease-carrying animals. The program includes the dynamics of wildlife populations and the most efficient practices of hunting and fishing. Such a plan also provides recreational areas for the health and enjoyment of the people.

The ultimate success of a conservation program will depend mainly upon an efficient system of education which teaches basic ecological concepts throughout its curriculum. The development of this conservation attitude in the public will be slow and laborious. Leopold refers to this concept or attitude as a land ethic which he regards as a product of social evolution based upon intellectual and emotional processes and woven into the very pattern of the community's daily life.

Definitions of ecological terms

biomass The weight of a species population per unit of area. It is another quantitative way of expressing the density of the population of a link or step in a food chain.

biome The largest ecological unit, which consists mainly of a single climax type of vegetation. It is the product of specific factors of temperature, rainfall, etc. It is usually made up of many major communities and may be considered a major life zone of both plants and animals. Example: desert.

climax A state of dynamic equilibrium; a tendency toward stability in ecosystems; a culmination of the succession in the biota of a community. It may be a single climatic climax in equilibrium with the general climate, such as a beech-maple forest, or it may consist of several edaphic (local) climaxes which are controlled by local conditions of soil and water, such as the standing water sere of ponds and marshes.

community An assemblage of organisms which are associated together in a particular habitat in complex interrelationships of a self-sustaining and self-regulating nature. The members of a community have functional and structural adaptations for similar environmental conditions. Closely knit communities

are sometimes called biocoenoses. Example: brook rapids.

ecological equivalence Ecological types of the same requirements which are in similar but geographically separated environments. Ecological equivalents occupy the same ecological niche in similar communities and may or may not be closely related. Examples: pronghorn antelope (North America), zebra (South Africa).

ecological niche The status of an organism in a community with reference to its responses and behavior patterns. It includes food habits and other levels of activity with relation to other organisms in the association. Example: the arctic fox occupies the same ecological niche as the African hyena.

ecosystem An ecological unit consisting of both biotic communities and the nonliving (abiotic) environment which interact to produce a stable system. It is the largest functional unit in ecology. Examples: pond, forest.

ecotone An intermediate transitional zone between adjacent communities. Often called a tension zone because two distinct communities meet here. Example: margin of a forest with a pasture or open land.

food chain A relationship between groups or organisms of different trophic levels by which one group is eaten by another group, which in turn is consumed by others, etc. Instead of a linear arrangement, the relationship is more often expressed by many interrelations and cross-connections to form a **food web.**

habitat The place where an organism lives or where individuals of a population live and reproduce. It includes physical as well as biotic features.

sere The sequence or series of communities which develop in a given situation from the pioneer communities to the terminal climax during ecological succession. Example: transformation of a pond into a dry land area which involves many seral stages.

stratum A horizontal layer or division of a biological community or association which exhibits stratification of habitats. Example: a forest is made up of floor, shrubs and small trees, canopy, etc.

symbiosis The close association (host-guest) of two dissimilar organisms which live together for mutual or one-sided benefit. It includes mutualism, commensalism, and parasitism.

tolerance A principle that refers to the limits an environmental factor imposes upon an organism in order for it to exist. The range of tolerance may be wide or narrow.

vagility Ability to tolerate environmental varia-

Relation of animals to their environment (ecology) 839

tion or the ability to cross ecological barriers. Example: birds have high vagility, mollusks very low.

ANNOTATED REFERENCES

Ecology

Allee, W. C., A. E. Emerson, O. Park, T. Park, and K. P. Schmidt. 1949. Principles of Animal Ecology. Philadelphia, W. B. Saunders Co. *A comprehensive treatise. Nearly every aspect of the subject is covered in this masterly work.*

Andrewartha, H. G., and L. C. Birch. 1954. The Distribution and Abundance of Animals. Chicago, The University of Chicago Press. *An analysis of animal populations and the factors which influence their abundance and distribution. Both laboratory and natural populations are considered. The treatise is of value to all ecologists and to all serious students of animal life.*

Buchsbaum, R. 1958. The Life in the Sea. Condon Lectures. Eugene, Oregon, University of Oregon Press. *An excellent appraisal of man's exploration of the mysteries of the sea. Many fine illustrations.*

Buchsbaum, R., and M. Buchsbaum. 1957. Basic Ecology. Pittsburgh, The Boxwood Press. *For the general student of biology, the basic concepts of ecology are presented with accuracy and clarity. Students interested in this field should read this little book before studying the more comprehensive treatises.*

Cold Spring Harbor Symposia on Quantitative Biology. Vol. XXII. 1957. Population Studies: Animal Ecology and Demography. Cold Spring Harbor, The Biological Laboratory. *Eminent authorities from various disciplines present papers on the problems of human populations and attempt to integrate these problems in the light of general ecological concepts.*

Dice, L. R. 1952. Natural Communities. Ann Arbor, University of Michigan. *An excellent ecology text built around the community concept.*

Edmondson, W. T. (editor). 1959. Ward and Whipple's Fresh-Water Biology, ed. 2. New York, John Wiley & Sons, Inc. *This is a revision of the well-known work of Ward and Whipple published many years ago. The present edition is the work of many specialists and is a concise guide to the identification of the fauna and flora in the United States and Canada. A "must" for all zoologists.*

Elton, C. S. 1927. Animal Ecology. Sidgwick & Jackson, Ltd. *A concise statement of ecological principles, well organized for ready comprehension.*

Elton, C. S. 1958. The Ecology of Invasions by Animals and Plants. New York, John Wiley & Sons, Inc. *The noted ecologist points out with graphic clearness how the invasion of fauna and flora pests (which he terms "ecological explosions") has altered the face of the earth, affected the welfare of man and beast, and posed problems for man to solve.*

Hesse, R., W. C. Allee, and K. P. Schmidt. 1937. Ecological Animal Geography. New York, John Wiley & Sons, Inc.

Hutchinson, G. E. 1957. A Treatise on Limnology, vol. I. Geography, Physics, and Chemistry, New York, John Wiley & Sons, Inc. *This is the first of a projected two-volume work on the rapidly growing science of limnology. It is an ambitious work which appeals to a variety of professional workers, such as limnologists, general biologists, and oceanographers.*

Kevan, D. K. M. 1955. Soil Zoology. London, Butterworth's Scientific Publications. *This is one of the few monographs that deal exclusively with the forms found in the soil. Their economic relation, ecology, methods for their control, and methods for sampling their populations are all dealt with in a thorough manner.*

Morgan, A. H. 1939. Field Book of Animals in Winter. New York, G. P. Putnam's Sons. *Discusses how various groups of animals meet the problems of existence in the temperate zone.*

Neal, E. G. 1958. Woodland Ecology, ed. 2. Toronto, William Heinemann, Ltd. *This little book is an interesting study of a woodland community over a period of about four years. It emphasizes the woodland as a unit and shows the interrelationships between the animal and plant factors. A good introduction to the study of ecology and recommended for beginning students in zoology.*

Needham, J. G., and J. T. Lloyd. 1937. The Life of Inland Waters. Ithaca, Comstock Publishing Co.

Odum, E. P. 1959. Fundamentals of Ecology, ed. 2. Philadelphia, W. B. Saunders Co. *An up-to-date textbook in ecology with a description of the latest concepts and terms.*

Palmer, E. L. 1949. Fieldbook of Natural History. New York, McGraw-Hill Book Co., Inc. *Useful for field identification.*

Ruttner, F. 1953. Fundamentals of Limnology (translated by D. G. Frey and F. E. J. Fry). Toronto, University of Toronto Press.

840

A good basic treatise on the principles of limnology.

Shelford, V. E. 1913. Animal Communities in Temperate America. Chicago, University of Chicago Press. *A classical work in ecological study. Has had a profound influence on the direction of much ecological work.*

Simpson, G. G., A. Roe, and R. C. Lewontin. 1960. Quantitative Zoology, rev. ed. New York, Harcourt, Brace & Co. *A study of statistical principles dealing with distribution, the interpretation of numerical data, the quantitative treatment of sampling, and other problems of biometrics. This treatise is one of the best in the rapidly growing science of biometry.*

Marine biology

Bruun, A. F., and others (editors). 1956. The Galathea Deep Sea Expedition, 1950-1952. New York, The Macmillan Co. *This expedition was conducted in the traditions of the famed "Challenger" one of 1872. It was sponsored by the Danish and many important discoveries were made.*

Buzzati-Traverso, A. A. (editor). 1958. Perspectives in Marine Biology. Berkeley, University of California Press. *A symposium presented in 1956 on various phases of marine biology, such as underwater television, reef-building corals, biological clocks, ethology, species formation, fish migration, and many others.*

Colman, J. S. 1953. The Sea and Its Mysteries. London, G. Bell & Sons, Ltd. *Summarizes many important concepts of oceanography, such as the shape of the sea, its physical and chemical properties, life in the depths, tides and currents, etc. Students who wish to know more about these subjects should read the great work by Sverdrup, Johnson, and Fleming: The Oceans, Their Physics, Chemistry and General Biology.*

Davis, C. C. 1955. The Marine and Fresh-Water Plankton. East Lansing, Michigan State University Press. *A good introductory account of plankton, with good definitions of ecological concepts. Includes many keys and figures of plankton forms. An excellent account (with keys) of the protozoan part of plankton is given on pages 169 to 199.*

Hardy, A. C. 1956. The Open Sea. Its Natural History: The World of Plankton. Boston, Houghton Mifflin Co. *This fine work shows the role of Protozoa and other forms in the natural history of plankton. Good descriptions are given of the Radiolaria and other protozoans in Chapter 6. Beautiful color illustrations.*

Marshall, N. B. 1954. Aspects of Deep Sea Biology. New York, Philosophical Library. *There are interesting chapters on deep sea sound (in the limelight in recent years), ways of exploring the ocean, and the historical development of marine biology.*

Monkman, N. 1958. From Queensland to the Great Barrier Reef. Garden City, Doubleday & Co., Inc. *An interesting account of the life around coral reefs, including the Great Barrier Reef of Australia. The illustrations are photographs, many of which are in color.*

Moore, H. B. 1958. Marine Ecology. New York, John Wiley & Sons, Inc. *Stresses the ecology of the marine environment and summarizes the latest concepts in the complex interaction of the organism and its surroundings.*

Pearse, A. S. 1950. The Emigrations of Animals From the Sea. Dryden, N. Y., The Sherwood Press. *The author believes that by leaving the stability of the ocean for a relatively greater instability on land, animals have been stimulated to faster living and a more rapid and varied evolution. He believes that life originated in the ocean, probably in the littoral zones, and that all the major phyla had their origin there. However, early chordates, such as ostracoderms, and later the bony fish, may have had their origin in fresh water.*

Pettersson, H. 1954. The Ocean Floor. New Haven, Yale University Press. *The role the Foraminifera and Radiolaria have played in building up the sediment carpet of the ocean floor is vividly described in this little book. The author thinks the time of accumulation of deep-sea deposits to be two billion years and the rate of sedimentation of Globigerina ooze to be 0.4 inch in 1,000 years.*

Ricketts, E. F., and J. Calvin. 1952. Between Pacific Tides, ed. 3 (revised by J. W. Hedgpeth). Stanford, Stanford University Press. *In many ways this is a unique book of seashore life. It stresses the habits and habitats of the invertebrates of the Pacific coast. Illustrations are abundant and revealing. It includes an excellent systematic index and bibliography.*

Roughley, T. C. 1947. Wonders of the Great Barrier Reef. New York, Charles Scribner's Sons. *An account of the famous reef near Australia.*

Russell, F. S., and C. M. Yonge, 1936. The Seas. Our Knowledge of Life in the Sea and How It Is Gained. London and New York, Frederick Warne & Co., Ltd. *This book gives in popular style a good introduction to the science of oceanography. Many fine photographs and color plates.*

Smith, F. G. W. 1948. Atlantic Reef Corals. Miami, University of Miami Press. *This is an accurate but nontechnical account of the corals around Florida and the West Indies. Excellent plates of photographs of the various corals are given. An interesting and informative summary of the different theories of the manner of coral formation is clearly presented with explanatory illustrations.*

Smith, R. I., and others (editors). 1957. Intertidal Invertebrates of the Central California Coast. Berkeley, University of California Press. *Mainly taxonomic keys to the forms found in the intertidal zone.*

Yonge, C. M. 1949. The Sea Shore. London, Collins. *Of the many books about the sea shore, this one easily takes first rank. The superlative color illustrations are not the only attraction of this work; the descriptions of the coastal forms are clear and revealing. Gives attention to the ecological relations of the animal groups. The reading of this book will stimulate the most lethargic of zoology students.*

Conservation

Allen, D. L. 1954. Our Wildlife Legacy. New York, Funk & Wagnalls Co. *An interesting and provocative description of the way our wild life resources fit into a program of national conservation.*

Callison, C. H. (editor). 1957. America's Natural Resources. New York, The Ronald Press Co. *Each chapter in this small work has been written by a specialist and each author gives a brief summary of the main problems in his particular aspect of conservation. A good introduction to a study of this field; more comprehensive treatises can be followed up later.*

Carson, R. L. 1951. The Sea Around Us. New York, Oxford University Press. *A popular account of the sea and its influence upon animals, including man.*

Dasmann, R. F. 1959. Environmental Conservation. New York, John Wiley & Sons, Inc. *An ecological appraisal of conservation problems. To read this excellent book is to become a conservationist in spirit.*

Huth, H. 1957. Nature and the American: Three Centuries of Changing Attitude. Berkeley and Los Angeles, University of California Press. *Traces the development of the conservation movement. Shows how a love of natural scenery aroused an interest in the natural resources of America.*

Leopold, A. 1949. A Sand County Almanac. New York, Oxford University Press. *A great conservationist points out many of the problems which must be solved for any comprehensive conservation plan.*

Mountfort, G. 1958. Wild Paradise. The story of the Coto Donana Expeditions. Boston, Houghton Mifflin Co. *Coto Donana is a wild, unspoiled wilderness in the southwestern part of Spain and is noted for its many varieties of wild life.*

Ritchie, J. 1920. The Influence of Man on Animal Life in Scotland. Cambridge, Cambridge University Press. *This work has had a marked influence on conservation problems the world over, for the author has traced the influences of man upon the fauna of a restricted compass and has shown how this fauna has reacted to this influence. The treatise has served as a model for later similar works.*

Sears, P. B. 1935. Deserts on the March. Norman, Okla., University of Oklahoma Press. *An ecological interpretation of the causes of the "dust bowl" regions.*

Sears, P. B. 1957. The Ecology of Man. Condon Lectures. Eugene, University of Oregon Press. *The eminent ecologist shows how man can apply his vast biological knowledge to improving his ecological relationships.*

Thomas, Jr., W. L. (editor). 1956. Man's Role in Changing the Face of the Earth. Chicago, University of Chicago Press. *This ponderous volume is the outcome of a symposium of the Wenner-Gren Foundation of Anthropological Research. More than fifty eminent authorities contributed to the work which represents a far-flung picture of man's influence on the earth's resources and how this has affected man's cultural patterns.*

chapter 39

Distribution of animals (zoogeography)

It is evident from the preceding chapter that many factors and principles may affect the distribution of animals. A study of animal distribution may be approached from the standpoint of ecological principles, or of geological history, or of geographical range. Many branches of zoology, as well as allied sciences, contribute to the interpretation of why animals are located where they are. The factors responsible for animal distribution make up the science of **zoogeography.**

DEFINITION OF AN ANIMAL'S RANGE

The **range** of a species is the area that it occupies; in other words, the area of its **distribution.** A few animals are found over such an extensive range that they may be called cosmopoliton. Examples are the mussel *Mytilus* and the brine shrimp *Artemia.* Such forms either have adaptive structures for meeting the varied conditions of large areas or great powers of movement so that they can spread across natural barriers. Animals with wide ranges are called **eurytopic.** On the other hand, some animals are restricted to narrow boundaries (**stenotopic**) because of specialized adaptations or inability to overcome natural barriers. Birds can be expected to have much wider ranges than snails. Slow locomotion and feeble power to cross topographical barriers accounts for the local distribution of some species of snails which seem to be restricted to certain mountain areas and are found nowhere else. Animals which are on the verge of extinction (*Sphenodon*) or those which have newly arisen (certain moths in the industrial regions of England) also have restricted ranges.

There is usually a taxonomic correlation between animals and their range of distribution. Families and orders usually have larger ranges than genera, and genera have larger ranges than species. As a rule, members of a particular species or closely related species occupy **continuous** ranges, but there are exceptions. When the same taxonomic unit is found in different areas far apart it is said to have **discontinuous** or **disjunctive distribution.** The classical example of the latter is the strange arthropod *Peripatus,* which is found in both tropical America and tropical Africa, two widely separated areas. Closely related genera are found in Indo-Malay and Australia. Other examples are the opossum in North America and the marsupials of Australia, also the tapirs of Central and South America and those found in Asia. In all these cases there are no intermediate forms in between these remote regions.

PRESENT AND PAST DISTRIBUTION

The distribution of animals may not always have been what it is today. The evolutionary pattern has been one of increase in diversity which has resulted partly from the evolving of different ecological habits and partly from spreading into new environments. Fossil study reveals many examples of important groups of animals that flourished in early geological eras but became extinct within their early range. Such groups, however, often left descendants which had migrated to other regions and survived. There is the classic case of the camel family which apparently had its origin in the great plains of North America, where only their fossils are found now. One branch of the family is represented by the true camels of Asia and Africa and another branch by the llamas of South America. Both undoubtedly came from the North American forms but migrated before the latter became extinct.

The evidence indicates that population shifts over the earth have been common in the past just as they are at present. Just as the earth has undergone physical change, so has its animal life undergone changes both in the origin of new species and in their distribution. Many present-day species are widening their ranges, and fossils show the same tendency in the past. The distribution of today will not necessarily exist tomorrow. This succession of faunas involves evolution, adaptive radiation into new ecological niches, the spreading and extinction of dominant groups, and their replacement by other dominant animals. If a certain species drops out of an ecological niche, its place is usually taken by another. The present distribution of an animal may give little indication about its place of origin. Only when the history of a group is known, through fossil records and other means, is it possible to appraise its existing geographical distribution.

PLACE OF ORIGIN

Each species of animal apparently has originated in one particular place on earth, from which point it has spread through its present range into places where it is ecologically fitted. Usually the center from which it has spread is located within its present range, but there are many exceptions, such as the camel family. Distinct species found in the same general area are called **sympatric** species; those living in different geographical areas are called **allopatric.** Life is believed to have originated in the sea which has representatives of all the structural types of animal life. Yet evolution in the ocean is slow because isolation is rarely complete there because of the more or less uniform and constant conditions. On the other hand, terrestrial conditions favor a more varied and more rapid evolution. More than 90% of all animal species are found on land. Although fresh-water habitats are numerous and varied, little evolution occurs there because such isolation as they afford is too transitory for the transformation of species. Ponds and lakes fill up in a relatively short time and streams often change their courses. Only deep and ancient lakes such as Lake Baikal in Siberia are permanent and have distinctive faunas.

FACTORS RESPONSIBLE FOR DISPERSAL

When a species has originated in a certain place and has successfully gained a foothold, it will inevitably tend to spread out from this center of origin. As the individuals multiply the greater competition for food, shelter, and breeding places may cause spreading. Changes in environment may force them to move elsewhere, although most great groups have spread to gain favorable conditions, not to avoid unfavorable ones.

In the actual process of distribution two forces are at work: (1) the springing up of new species by mutation or other causes and (2) the development of the earth. These two factors must always be considered in explaining dispersal. For instance it is impossible to visualize the striking evolution of the horse without considering at the same time the correlation between its development and that of the earth in the region where the horse originated.

There are a number of factors that affect the dispersion and range of animals. One is the time during which the animal is spreading out from its center of origin. In general the older the species, the greater its range. There are, of course, some species too restricted to spread. *Sphenodon,* the New Zealand lizard, represents a very ancient species of reptiles, but its distribution at present is limited to two small islands. Natural barriers are also important factors. Great land masses once connected by land bridges which later disappeared, such as the Bering Strait between Asia and America, account for many examples of discontinuous distribution. Climatic changes, glacier movements, and the drying up of land once covered with water have produced profound alterations in distribution.

Another factor in the dispersal of animals is the opportunity they may have for transportation. Such opportunities may be afforded by wind, water currents, rafts, and so on. Small forms such as insects are often carried long distances by winds. Eggs of many forms, or even adults, are often carried by birds to distant regions. Some species have their own methods for dispersal, illustrated by the glochidia of the fresh-water clam. Barriers that cannot be crossed by gradual population expansion may now and then be crossed suddenly by what Simpson calls "sweepstakes" dispersal, i.e., by a remote fortuitous event. Remote oceanic islands, such as the state of Hawaii and St. Helena, were no doubt colonized this way. Wind, gales, and floating debris or rafts might serve as the agencies in such dispersals.

Distribution is a dynamic process present wherever animals are. New species are always originating. Evolution of animals must not be considered a process that has happened but one that is happening. From their centers of origin these new species are spreading out just as their predecessors dispersed in the past.

WHAT DETERMINES AN ANIMAL'S RANGE?

When one examines the ranges of various species one is struck by the fact that some occupy extensive territories and others are restricted to small areas. The correlation between range size and taxonomic rank has been pointed out. The problem, however, is more complicated when a group such as a species shows a great inequality in distribution. Of course, a species is not always found in all places suitable for it, because of its history or natural barriers or both. The polar bear may be absent from Antarctica because it has lacked the opportunity to get there. In the evolution of every species the interplay between its evolution and the development of its environment plays the determining role.

Just as there are ecological equivalents (that is, related or unrelated species in the same ecological niche), so there are also closely allied or unrelated groups which inhabit the same general territory (**geographical equivalents** or **syngeographs**). The widely distributed salamanders of the genus *Plethodon* of the eastern United States afford some examples of geographical equivalents. *P. glutinosus* and *P. cinereus* are so considered, for both groups in general have the same range, except that *P. glutinosus* extends farther south and *P. cinereus* farther north.

In some cases man has been responsible for the wide range of a species that might otherwise have been restricted. Examples are the introduction of the rabbit from England into Australia and the English sparrow into the United States. In both cases the alien forms were more successful than in their native country.

Whenever the same species is found in discontinuous regions there is always the possibility that it has arisen independently in the different areas. This is **convergent evolution** and could occur by the repetition of a mutation under similar environmental conditions in the different ranges. A more feasible reason in such cases is that the original range has been broken up by environmental changes, so that individuals of the same species became isolated.

SOME PHYSICAL AND BIOLOGICAL CONDITIONS OF ANIMAL RANGES

An analysis of any animal's range reveals many physical and biological factors which influence the type of life found within it. Most of these factors have been discussed in Chapter 38. They include such things as rainfall, snow, temperature, humidity, soil moisture, distribution of vegetation, and so on.

How these various physical and biological factors operate within a rather narrow range can be illustrated by a high mountain within a tropical region. Its range of **vertical climates** corresponds in a manner to the climates one would meet in passing from the tropics to the polar region. At the base of the mountain there would be the typical tropical climate with the physical and biological conditions characteristic of such a climate. A higher altitude would bring a warm, temperate climate with marked seasonal changes. Higher still is the cold temperate level with a decrease in temperature which is especially marked in winter. In this zone the vegetation begins to thin out, so that its upper limits mark the cessation of tree growth of any size. Farther up the mountain are regions which correspond to the frigid and arctic zones where vegetation is absent and where the weather conditions are rigorous the year round. Mt. Washington in New Hampshire shows this vertical arrangement of zones to a great extent, except for the tropical base.

Along with this vertical distribution there are corresponding distributions of animal life; the life in the vertical life zones corresponds to that found in the horizontal life zones at sea level. There are many exceptions. Polar bears, for instance, are not found in the vertical arctic zones of high mountains.

The concept of life zones is based mainly upon climate or temperature. Regions with the same effective temperatures (isotherms) coincide to some extent with the distributional boundaries of certain animals and plants. In general, as one goes from the tropics to the arctics there is a corresponding change in the vegetation and animals. This latitudinal distribution of zones and the life associated with the various zones is similar, as we have seen, to the vertical distribution on a high mountain. In North America, for instance, the principal zones in passing northward from the tropics would be Tropical, Lower Sonoran, Upper Sonoran, Transition, Canadian, Hudsonian, and Arctic. Each of these zones was supposed to be characterized by certain total quantities of heat, as well as mean temperatures which regulated and restricted the biotic conditions found within each zone.

This concept of life zones was formulated by Merriam in 1894 and has been widely used to explain distribution. But as more knowledge of ecological relations has been worked out, most authorities now consider that this idea of temperature relations is oversimplified and that temperature is only one of many factors (humidity, vegetation, soil, niches, etc.) that influence biotic distribution. Life zones are now based on the actual distribution of plants and animals, and in many classifications there is a marked overlapping of biome divisions with them. Among some of the more logical classifications is the one called Biotic Provinces (Dice). This classification divides North America into some twenty-nine biotic provinces, each of which represents a continuous geographical area and is characterized by certain ecological associations, climate, soil, and other factors.

MAJOR FAUNAL REALMS

On the basis of animal distribution, numerous regions over the earth have distinctive animal populations. These divisions indicate the influence of land masses and their geological history, as well as the corresponding evolutionary development of the various animal groups. These realms of distribution have developed and fluctuated during geological times. The higher vertebrates have been used mainly in working out these broad faunal realms. There are many complications in dividing the earth into such realms where all groups of animals are involved. Some animals have purely a local origin; others within the same realm show affinities with groups quite remote. To explain many of these discrepancies it has been necessary to assume various land connections or bridges for which there are no geological evidences. Such major faunal realms can thus have only a limited significance.

Sclater (1858) first proposed this scheme for birds, and later Wallace (1876) applied this pattern of distribution to vertebrates in general. There have been modifications of the plan by other workers, such as the one which grouped the six original regions into three major regions—Arctogaea (Holarctica, Ethiopian, and Oriental), Neogaea (Neotropical), and Notogaea (Australasian). Following is a discussion of the major zoogeographic realms and their faunas.

Continental

The continental plan of distribution is a horizontal one, but there may also be a similar vertical distribution. The six major regions are Australian, Neotropical, Ethiopian, Oriental, Palearctic, and Nearctic.

Australian. This realm includes Australia, New Zealand, and New Guinea and certain adjacent islands. Some of the most primitive mammals are found here, such as the monotremes (duckbills) and marsupials (kangaroo, Tasmanian wolf), but few placental mammals. Most of the birds are also different from those of other realms, such as the cassowary, emu, and brush turkey. The primitive lizard, *Sphenodon,* is found in New Zealand.

Neotropical. This includes South and Central America, part of Mexico, and the West Indies. Among its many animals are the llama, sloth, New World monkey, armadillo, anteater, vampire bat, anaconda, toucan, and rhea.

Ethiopian. This is made up of Africa south of the Sahara desert, Madagascar, and Arabia. It is the home of the higher apes, elephant, rhinoceros, lion, zebra, antelope, ostrich, secretary bird, and lungfish.

Oriental. This region includes Asia south of the Himalaya Mountains, India, Ceylon, Malay Peninsula, Southern China, Borneo, Sumatra, Java, and the Philippines. Its characteristic animals are the tiger, Indian elephant, certain apes, pheasant, jungle fowl, and king cobra.

Palearctic. This consists of Europe, Asia north of the Himalaya Mountains, Afghanistan, Iran, and North Africa. Its animals include the tiger, wild boar, camel, and hedgehog.

Nearctic. This includes North America as far south as southern Mexico. Its most typical animals are the wolf, bear, caribou, mountain goat, beaver, elk, bison, pronghorn, sewellel, lynx, eagle, and owl.

Island

Island distribution usually depends upon the nearness of the island to a continent. If near a continent it is called a continental island; if at a considerable distance, an oceanic island. Animals of continental islands are usually similar to those of the nearest great land mass. Oceanic islands (e.g., Madagascar, Galápagos) often have fauna more or less peculiar to them and usually lack types which cannot withstand sea water, such as amphibians and land mammals. Oceanic islands are so isolated that except for forms that can fly or swim, their faunas have evolved independently in the course of evolution. The birds and insects of such islands are often wingless. Distance from the nearest mainland is not always indicative of insularity. The direction of the winds and ocean currents, which often carry animals long distances, is one of the basic factors in determining the distribution of animals to islands.

Marine

In extent, the marine realm is the largest of all, for the sea makes up about 70% of the earth's surface. All phyla and most of the classes of animals are represented in it. The sea has characteristic zones, each with its own peculiar properties which attract certain species and discourage others. Tides and ocean currents play an important role in the distribution of animals there. Another factor is the vertical pressure of the water which increases nearly one-half pound to the equare inch for every foot of water depth. Heat and light are effective as agencies only in the few hundred feet of the upper surface of water. Yet many animals have become adjusted to the extremely high pressures, to a total absence of light, and to temperatures only slightly above freezing. Many of the marine life zones (tidal, pelagic, abyssal, etc.) have been discussed in the preceding chapter.

MIGRATION AND SPORADIC DISPERSAL

The term **migration** has been used with different meanings. Most authorities think of it as a regular to-and-fro movement between two regions, such as the periodic migration of birds, the seasonal return of shad fish to fresh-water streams, the regular return of salmon to fresh water from the sea, the vertical or altitudinal movements of deer or other mammals up and down mountains in spring and fall, and so on. Migration, or repeated movements between two regions, should be distinguished from the wandering movements of animals which result in the dispersal of the species. **Dispersal movements** are undirectional and one way and involve **emigration** from a given region and **immigration** into another region. Such phenomena results in a change of habitat. Many movements of this kind may occur fairly rapidly, but most of them involve long periods of time and cover long distances. Many examples of the latter are known in paleontology, such as the emigration of the camels from North America and the dispersal of North American forms into South America and the reverse. The usual reasons for this mass movement are the search for food, better conditions for rearing their young, escape from enemies, etc. How rapidly animals move depends upon their powers of locomotion. It is regulated usually by basic instincts which are aroused by temperature changes, hunger, functional state of the repro-

ductive organs, sense of direction, and location.

Sporadic, or irregular, dispersals are common among many forms. Mass movements of locusts occur in many parts of the world at irregular intervals, usually when they have increased to the point where all available food is consumed. In Africa in 1909 immense bodies of locusts flew in from the Libyan desert into Tunis and Algeria. They covered several hundred square miles of territory which they completely denuded of all living vegetation. Another classic example of mass movement is that of the lemming.

These sporadic movements play a minor role in extending the range of animals, for in most cases they are unable to maintain themselves in the new areas. On the other hand, there are authentic cases of the common Norway rat extending its range in just this way. Rats' powers of adaptability to new ranges may explain their rapid spread over extensive regions. Other agents of dispersion, such as wind, water currents, rafts, feet of birds, etc., appear to be more potent in the distribution of animals, especially small forms.

KRAKATAO AS EXAMPLE OF ANIMAL DISPERSION

Krakatao is a volcanic island off the Sundra Straits between Java and Sumatra in the East Indies. In 1883 this island was practically destroyed by one of the most terrific volcanic eruptions in modern times. Every living thing was reported to be destroyed, for what remained of the island was covered with many feet of hot volcanic ash. Several naturalists from the first have been interested in seeing when life would first appear there again. It thus served as an interesting case of animal distribution under direct observation. The position of the island between two great land masses and less than forty miles from the nearest land made it specially favored for receiving a new stock of plants and animals.

Vegetation was the first to appear on the island and in a matter of some years completely covered the island. The first animals to appear were flying forms—birds and bats. It took more than twenty years for the first strictly terrestrial animals to gain a foothold. Rats, snakes, and lizards became common there. Insects, centipedes, millipedes, and spiders, especially those that travel by gossamer threads, had become common by 1921. Some of these had reached the island by driftwood, by currents of water, and by wind. There are few species but many individuals on the island which may be due to the absence of natural enemies. Yet in spite of the favorable position of the island for receiving new animals, some forms have been slow in reaching the islands and many have not reached there at all. This may indicate how long oceanic islands, far from the mainland, have been in acquiring their flora and fauna.

LAKE BAIKAL AS EXAMPLE OF RESTRICTED DISPERSAL

The large Lake Baikal in eastern Siberia is the deepest lake in the world, being more than a mile deep in some places. It is famed for its characteristic fauna which is almost unique in the great number of peculiar or endemic species. Among certain groups up to 100% of the species are found nowhere else. Some groups, such as planarian worms, are represented by more species here than in all the rest of the world put together. Only groups such as protozoa and rotifers, which are easily transported from one region to another, are represented by non-endemic species to any extent. The distribution in the lake is also somewhat unique in that animal life is found at nearly all depths, perhaps because the water is well oxygenated throughout. All the evidence indicates that Lake Baikal has never had any connection with the sea but is strictly a fresh-water formation. Whence came its unique fauna? Long geographical speciation through isolation, for this lake is very ancient, might account for some species. But the prevailing opinion is that the fauna of this lake mainly represents species which have evolved elsewhere in many ecological habitats and have been washed into this lake by different river systems over long periods of time. Hence, the present fauna represents the accumulation and survival of ancient fresh-water organisms (relicts) which were widely distributed at one time but are now found only here. Other deep fresh-water lakes of ancient geological history, such as Tanganyika and Nyasa in East Africa, also have unique faunas for the same reasons.

ANNOTATED REFERENCES

Darlington, P. J. 1957. Zoogeography: The Geographical Distribution of Animals. New York, John Wiley & Sons, Inc. *This is an up-to-date book about animal distribution. It does not emphasize the ecological approach, although it draws heavily on ecology and evolution for an explanation of its basic principles. The work is extremely fascinating and informative. Excellent bibliographies are listed for most of the chapters. An outstanding work.*

Dice, L. R. 1943. The Biotic Provinces of North America. Ann Arbor, University of Michigan Press. *The author considers a biotic province as an extensive geographical area where the environment produced by climate, topography, and soil is sufficiently uniform to permit the development of characteristic types of ecologic associations. These are in the process of evolution and undergoing change; boundaries are also changing. He bases his classification mainly on the type of vegetation, because animals depend upon plants for food, shelter, and other reasons. Although any such classification is arbitrary, the author presents one with considerable logic based upon personal observations. He describes twenty-nine provinces.*

Hubbs, C. L. 1958. Zoogeography. Washington, American Association for the Advancement of Science. *This includes the papers presented at two symposia at Stanford and Indianapolis. Part I deals with the Origin and Affinities of the Land and Freshwater Fauna of Western North America, and Part II with the Geographic Distribution of Contemporary Organisms. Zoogeography is one of the most fascinating divisions of zoological study, and this volume does not detract from this interest.*

Jaeger, E. C. 1950. Our Desert Neighbors. Stanford, Stanford University Press. *This work is made up of short descriptions of the forms found in our western deserts and covers mam-*

mals, birds, and reptiles. *It will give the student some idea of the varied and interesting fauna to be found in a seemingly barren region.*

Kerr, J. G. 1950. A Naturalist in the Gran Chaco. Cambridge, Cambridge University Press. *El Gran Chaco is a region between Paraguay and Argentina and is the habitat of one of* the three existing lungfish (Lepidosiren). *This book is an interesting account of Kerr's quest for them in order to study their life histories.*

Simpson, G. G. 1953. Evolution and Geography. Eugene, Oregon State System of Higher Education. *An excellent appraisal of the main concepts of animal distribution by a great paleontologist.*

chapter 40

Some interesting and striking adaptations

NATURE OF ADAPTATIONS*

Nearly everything about an organism is an adaptation of some kind, for adaptations may be structural, physiological, or behavioral. Although we often are amazed at some gross spectacular adaptation of an unusual nature, the adaptive nature of bodily processes, such as the precision of chromosome behavior in mitosis, the interrelations of hormonal balance, the teamwork of enzymes in metabolic processes, the intricate pattern of nervous integration, and many others should elicit our wonder still more. The entire living system is adaptive throughout its organization. All adaptations from simple to complex have been due to the operation of natural selection on favorable mutations through long periods of time. By such processes, even the intricate mechanism of a sense organ, such as the eye, has been gradually evolved, provided each step of formation has conferred some advantage to the organism and resulted in differential reproductive success.

Adaptations may be classified in various ways. Narrow adaptations are associated with highly specialized and restricted habits, such as the tongue of an anteater. Broad adaptations are those shared with many other groups, such as hair and constant body temperature, which are found in all mammals as well as in anteaters. Evolutionary change and biological progress have been due mainly

*Refer to Chapter 5, Principles 12 and 25.

to improvements of adaptations. Nowhere is this principle illustrated better than in the evolution of the nervous system throughout the animal kingdom from lower forms to man. Such improvements have led to better knowledge of the environment and to better adjusted behavior.

Although animals have similar objectives in their living processes, they have different ways of attaining these ends. Often within the same group of animals and among closely related species there are strikingly different ways or adaptive methods for meeting the problems of life. Many of the adaptations described in this section are interesting not only because they are striking and somewhat unique in their patterns but also because many of them have been extensively studied by observational and experimental methods for the purpose of discovering their basic mechanisms.

MIGRATION

Birds. The phenomenon of bird migration has attracted the attention of man from the earliest times. Perhaps no phase of animal life has given rise to so many speculations regarding its nature, its causes, and its true meaning. Although it has been studied extensively and much data have been accumulated about it, migration is of perennial interest among all ornithologists. The widely practiced bird banding which has now been employed for many years has been a very useful tool in checking, with considerable precision, the movements of birds, thus eliminating much guesswork.

The term "migration" as used with refernce to birds signifies the regular seasonal shift birds make from one region to another. It does not mean the occupation of a new territory by birds so that they extend their ranges, although this may sometimes occur. For instance, there is the well-authenticated example of the mass migration of the crossbills from northern Europe into Ireland in the latter part of the nineteenth century, as a result of which many of them became permanent residents of Ireland.

Closely associated with migration is **homing,** which is the ability of an animal to return to a familiar region when the animal has been removed to some other region. Homing may depend to some extent upon topographical memory of landmarks, which could explain certain forms of migration. However, it could not explain the ability of some young birds to migrate without their parents to wholly unknown places.

Most bird migrations are **latitudinal,** that is, the birds move into the northern zones during the summer and return south for the winter. In the Southern Hemisphere, where the seasons are reversed, there is a similar but more restricted migration of certain forms. Some birds are permanent residents the year round; others shift from regions far in the Northern Hemisphere to those deep in the Southern Hemisphere. Some birds in mountainous regions undergo a regular **altitudinal** or vertical migration from the lower levels to higher ones in the summer and the reverse for the winter. Some birds move only short distances in the winter from their regular homes, often into the deep woods, and are back early in the spring. Food and climatic conditions are also known to cause sporadic and irregular migrations of birds, such as the appearance of the snowy owl, an arctic form, in regions south of the Canadian border.

What are the advantages of migration? No doubt, one of the principal advantages is that the bird can live in a favorable climate all the time. This not only ensures it an adequate supply of food but also provides the optimum conditions for the rearing of its young. Waterfowl can avoid frozen waters by retiring to the south. The shortened hours of daylight in northern climates would also restrict the ability of birds to get enough food. The factors of low temperatures and severe winter conditions are probably minor ones, for most birds are able to withstand such, if they have sufficient food. However, many birds leave their breeding grounds while food supplies are still abundant.

Migration has become so firmly established in the behavior of birds that it has long since become a hereditary instinct. Many theories have been proposed to account for the origin of migration but no one theory can explain all cases. One theory tries to account for the movement by assuming that birds spread over the Northern Hemisphere when the latter was warm and food conditions were favorable all through the year. When the glacial era came and forced the birds to go south for survival, they came back in the spring when the ice age receded, only to be forced south again in winter because of the sharp establishment of the winter and summer seasons. This led in time to the firm establishment of the habit. Another theory centers around the view that the ancestral home of birds was in the tropics and some went north to avoid congestion and competition during the breeding season. After raising their young, they then returned.

The annual stimulus for bird migration has been analyzed experimentally. Professor Rowan in Alberta, Canada, performed pioneer investigations on this problem as early as 1925. He kept juncos and crows in outdoor aviaries during the fall and winter at cold temperatures but exposed them to artificial lighting, thus simulating spring conditions. He concluded that this increased the exercise or wakefulness of the bird so that the gonads were stimulated to enlarge and undergo reproductive activity. When released, some of the birds tended to migrate northward in winter. Some bird species, however, will not react this way to light. It has been proposed in recent years that the migratory urge may be due to a favorable energy balance and improvement in metabolism because the increased photoperiod makes fewer demands on temperature regulation, thus releasing more energy for gonad activity.

The direction-finding or orientation of birds has been much investigated in the past decade, for a solution of this problem would get at the very heart of homing and migration. Griffin, who released gannets many miles from their nesting sites and followed their wanderings in an airplane, concluded that the birds wandered aimlessly or in circles at first until they picked up visual clues; then they headed straight for home. Such an explanation could hardly apply to a shearwater that was released in America after being removed from its home in Wales and was back home a few days later. Kramer in recent years has shown that starlings and pigeons can orient themselves by the sun's position. In specially covered cages provided with six windows, these birds were trained to find food in a definite compass direction at a certain time of day. When tested at another time of day when the sun's position had changed, they compensated for the sun's motion and immediately went to the right window by keeping track of the time of day. Although this interesting experiment does not explain nocturnal migration (very common among birds), some theories have been proposed to account for direction finding at night, Sauer, a German investigator, has recently advanced evidence that birds (warblers) could orient themselves in a particular geographical position in a planetarium when the stars coincided with the night sky in Germany. By changing the synthetic constellations about, the birds were able, with their amazing time sense, to take that direction which would enable them to reach the point normally taken when they start their migration. These experiments involving the apparent effect of visible celestial bodies on migration may explain the ability of shearwaters to return thousands of miles directly to their home.

Many species of migratory birds have well-established routes which they follow on schedule. Some use different routes in the fall and spring. Some of them complete their migratory routes in a very short time; this appears to be the case with certain aquatic species. Many, however, make the trip in a leisurely manner, often stopping here and there to feed. Some of the warblers are known to take fifty to sixty days to migrate from their winter quarters in Central America to their summer ones in Canada. Not all members of a species perform their migrations at the same time; there is a great deal of straggling, so that some members do not reach the summer breeding grounds until after others are well along with their nesting. Many of the smaller species migrate at night and feed by day; others migrate chiefly in the daytime; and many swimming and wading birds, either by day or night. The height at which they fly varies greatly. Some apparently keep fairly close to the earth, and others are known to fly as high as 4,000 to 5,000 feet. Many birds are known to follow landmarks, such as rivers and coast lines; but others do not hesitate to fly directly over large bodies of water in their routes. The routes of any two species rarely coincide, for there is almost infinite variety in the routes covered. Some birds have very wide migration lanes, and others, such as certain sandpipers, are restricted to very narrow ones, keeping well to the coast lines because of their food requirements. Since birds have a tendency to follow the major topographical features of the earth's surface, many of their routes are in a north-and-south direction; but there are many exceptions to this rule. Some species, including the scarlet tanager, have a wide breeding ground in the United States, but as they migrate in the fall, their migratory lines tend to converge toward their winter quarters in Central America.

Some species are known for their long-

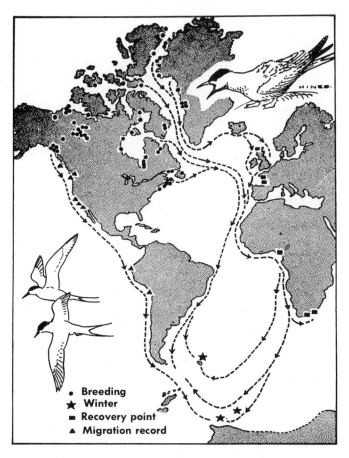

Figure 628. Map showing migration of arctic tern. Enormous route covered by this bird in one year is probably 25,000 miles. (From drawing by Robert W. Hines, U. S. Fish and Wildlife Service.)

distance migrations.. The arctic tern (Figure 628), for example, breeds north of the Arctic Circle and in winter is found in the antarctic regions, 11,000 miles away. This species is also known to take a circuitous route in migrations from North America, passing over to the coast lines of Europe and Africa and thence to their winter quarters. Other birds which breed in Alaska follow a more direct line down the Pacific coast of North and South America.

Some birds with restricted food habits are still very much of a mystery so far as their migration is concerned. Some hummingbirds in tropical America are known to feed solely on one flower which is in bloom only for a month during the year;

it is not known where they spend the rest of the year.

How precise are the arrivals of birds to their northern homes in the spring? This time of arrival varies greatly among different species. Some of their arrivals can only be predicted within a wide range. Other birds, such as the purple martin, catbirds, etc., return to a certain locality on almost the same day of the month each season. Records of catbirds kept in a certain eastern state reveal that the birds arrived in the particular locality about the middle of April and did not vary more than a day in a period of five years. Many observations also revealed that the same individual bird returns not only to the same locality but also to the same territory that it occupied in previous seasons.

Eels. One of the most remarkable achievements in the field of natural history in the first part of the present century was the solving of the mystery of the common eel. For centuries naturalists had been puzzled about the breeding and development of this queer fish. It was known that the adults spent most of their life in fresh-water streams in both North America and Europe, but where they spawned or where they underwent their development was not known until the patient work of Dr. Johannes Schmidt brought to light most of the facts in the case.

There are two common species of eels: the European form *(Anguilla vulgaris)* has a backbone of 114 vertebrae; the American species *(Anguilla rostrata)* has only 107 vertebrae in its backbone. (The number may vary slightly in each species.) The spawning grounds of both species are in the sea northeast of Puerto Rico, although in general the breeding grounds of the two species do not overlap. The eggs hatch into pelagic larval forms less than ¼ inch long and are called **lepto-cephalia.** The adults die immediately after spawning. A year later, the American species, now about 3 inches long, reach the American coasts where the females distribute themselves through the fresh-water streams and rivers; the males usually remain behind in the brackish waters near the coast. It takes from eight to fifteen years for them to grow to maturity. Eventually each female goes down the stream to the sea and joins a male; they go together to their breeding grounds. At this time they have changed their yellow color for a silver one, and their digestive system is undergoing degeneration. Their rate of travel through the sea is only about one-half mile an hour. It has been estimated that it takes them about one to two months to reach the place of spawning, although no adult eels have ever been taken in the open ocean. The European species has a much greater distance to travel, and its larval forms take three years to reach the European coast where the females also ascend the rivers and streams and the males remain behind near the coast. Eventually they, too, return across the Atlantic to the spawning grounds, although they are about six months on the voyage.

A recent theory suggests that both American and European eels belong to the same species and that the adult European forms all die before reaching the spawning grounds. All eggs are laid by American eels, but when hatched the larvae in the northern part of the spawning grounds will be carried by currents to Europe; those in the southern part will be carried toward the American coast. The larger number of vertebrae in the European eel could be explained on the basis of Jordan's law, which states that fish in colder waters have more vertebrae than those in warmer temperatures.

The larvae, or elvers, are flat, ribbon-like, and transparent, but by the time they ascend the fresh-water streams they have assumed the cylindrical shape of the adults. At maturity, the females are about 3 feet long; the males about 1½ feet. In their spawning grounds of the Sargasso Sea, the adults descend to depths of a thousand feet below the surface to spawn. Among the interesting and mysterious aspects of this strange migratory phenomenon is how the tiny elver without its parents is able to find its way across the sea, and why the elvers of the two species which are hatched in practically the same region do not mix to some extent. Yet each apparently reaches its respective home in America or Europe. Two other species of eels, *Anguilla japonica* and *Anguilla dieffenbachi,* are found in Japan and Australia, respectively.

Salmon. The salmon has a spawning habit the reverse of the common eel's, for the adult lives far out at sea and returns to the headwaters of streams to spawn. Both the Atlantic (one species) and Pacific (five species) forms have this practice, but there are some differences between the two. After spending three to four years at their feeding grounds at sea, the salmon return and ascend the fresh-water streams (Figure 629), both

Figure 629. Salmon jumping falls. (Courtesy Dr. George B. Kelez, U. S. Fish and Wildlife Service.)

sexes making the journey together. It has also been proved that they return to the identical spot in the stream where they originally grew up some years before. After spawning, the Pacific species die, but some of the Atlantic species survive, go out to sea again, and are able to spawn a second or third time. From the time they return to fresh water until they spawn, the salmon lives on its reserve food, which it has accumulated in its body in the form of fat. After hatching in the shallow gravel pits, the larval fish live for some time in the streams before going out to sea. Some species stay only a few weeks, but others may remain for months. Hoar found that young salmon could not return to the sea until their salt-secreting cells had developed. In the ocean they grow much faster because of abundant food there.

All sorts of theories have been proposed to account for the marvelous way in which salmon are able to return to the very place where they hatched. Some authorities think the fish have an extremely sensitive chemical sense that enables them to perform this feat. Another theory links the accelerated metabolism at spawning time with the need for more oxygen, which increases in amount the farther one ascends the headwaters of a stream. Still another idea stresses the importance of a carbon dioxide gradient in the water as being the determining factor. The research of Hasler and Larson favors very strongly the theory that the sense of smell is the determining factor in precision of homing, for different streams have different odors.

Butterflies. A number of the larger and stronger winged insects apparently are able to make long flights, such as the monarch butterfly (*Danaüs plexippus*) of North America. In early autumn immense swarms of these butterflies gather in the northern part of the United States and eastern Canada and make southward flights that may take them 2,000 miles or more to warmer regions, around the Gulf of Mexico and South America. Some of them are known to leave the mainland and journey as far as the Hawaiian Islands. Many observers have seen swarms of these butterflies far at sea. The northward flight in the spring is not so well known but appears to take place. The actual flight of these forms is not as directional as that of birds; they are carried more by wind currents; this may account for their sporadic appearance in places in which they ordinarily do not resort. Recent work (Tilden and Duncan) seems to indicate that most of the adult monarchs that drift southward in the fall have developed during the preceding summer. Those that go northward in the spring reproduce on milkweeds along the way and give rise to the fall migrants.

BREEDING BEHAVIOR

Animals exhibit an enormous amount of diversity in the care and development of their young. Some young are quite precocious at birth and need little attention from the parents; others have need of long prenatal and postnatal care. Breeding behavior is often involved and complicated, but there is no real correlation between the degree of the evolutionary level of an animal and the complexity of its breeding reactions. Breeding behavior also involves the interesting phases of courtship which have intrigued naturalists ever since natural history was first studied.

856

Many have tried to interpret the real meaning of the odd behavior many animals perform in the mating process. Birds, especially, often go through elaborate ceremonies which are intriguing to all students of animal behavior. The sexual selection theory that Darwin emphasized does not carry the weight it once did, according to modern interpretation. It is true that many birds do display marked sexual dimorphism in color which may be distinguished only during the breeding season. But many birds exhibit little or no sexual dimorphism, and the only way in which the opposite sex may be recognized is on the basis of behavior patterns which the sexes, particularly the males, show. Selection by the females, therefore, may be more a matter of choosing between those males that are vigorous in their courtship patterns and those that are less so.

In the animal kingdom, there are almost endless methods of caring for the eggs and young during their development. Among viviparous forms, the problem is solved in approximately the same way, but among those that lay their eggs (oviparous), many experiments have been tried. Perhaps no group shows more diversity than do the amphibians. Some of these devices may be correlated with the general problems of a group which are partly terrestrial and partly aquatic. At any rate, the ingenious methods they employ represent a most interesting and inexplicable aspect of animal behavior.

Most of these strange breeding behavior patterns are found in tropical amphibians. Some of their unique devices are concerned with keeping the eggs or young in bodily contact with the parents; others, with peculiar nesting sites. One of the most famous examples of the first type is the Surinam toad *(Pipa pipa)* found in northern South America (Figure 630). At the breeding season, the dorsal skin of the female becomes pitted with small cavities which are formed of skin pouches. There is also a rich blood supply running to this region. As the female lays her eggs, the oviduct protrudes in a bladderlike

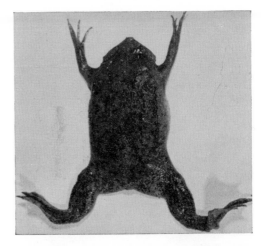

Figure 630. Live male Surinam toad, *Pipa*, native of South America. This toad grows to be 5 inches long and has a very flattened body and long webbed toes. Note peculiar triangular head. It is famous for its unique method of rearing its young. When female lays eggs they are passed upward by male onto back of mother, where eggs adhere and sink into little pits on glandular, soft-skinned back. Here they develop directly into young toads. (Courtesy Vancouver Public Aquarium, British Columbia.)

structure which is pushed back over the female's back by the belly of the male. By manipulating his body, the male forces out the eggs, spreads them over the female's back, and presses them into the small cavities. A lid of uncertain origin is then formed over each cavity, so that the eggs are completely enclosed. Complete metamorphosis occurs within these cavities, and eventually the female's back is covered with developing toads. When they leave the mother, they are tailless and do not enter the water. A similar, though in some ways quite different, method is employed by the marsupial frog *(Gastrotheca,* Figure 631). The female of this form is provided with a dorsal brood pouch formed from a fold of the skin and opening posteriorly. Into this sac the male shoves the eggs as they are laid. Here the eggs hatch and the larvae undergo considerable development before emerging.

Care and protection of the eggs and young are not confined to the female among the amphibians. A striking example

Figure 631. Female marsupial frog, *Gastrotheca* or *Nototrema*, with dorsal brood sac exposed to show eggs. Eggs as laid are pushed into pouch by male. The young hatch out as tadpoles and reach outside through narrow opening in sacral region of back. This frog is native to South America.

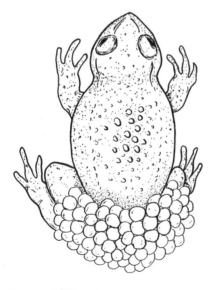

Figure 632. "Midwife" toad, *Alytes obstetricans.* Male carries cluster of eggs wrapped around his thighs.

is that of *Alytes obstetricans* (Figure 632). When the female lays the eggs, the male takes possession of them and entangles them around his hind legs. He stays in damp places near pools with his load of developing eggs; eventually the tadpoles emerge from the eggs and enter a convenient pool to complete their metamorphosis. The male of another species of tree frog, *Rhinoderma darwini*, found in southern South America, pushes the fertilized eggs down into his enlarged vocal sacs where they undergo complete transformation before being released as small frogs.

Amphibians also show adaptations in providing nesting devices for their young. One interesting example of this practice is demonstrated by a tree frog of Brazil (*Hyla faber*, Figure 633). This frog makes little craters or corrals out of the mud of shallow ponds. These little rings of mud have their rims projecting a short distance above the surface of the water, and in them the female frog lays her eggs. The tadpoles can thus develop without danger from enemies until they are large enough to hop over the barriers and fend for themselves. Another tree frog (*Hyla resinfictrix*) lines a cavity in a hollow tree with beeswax obtained from the combs of certain stingless bees and lays its eggs in this cavity when it is filled with rain water; there the young can develop relatively free from enemies. Many amphibians also make use of their copious mucus secretions to provide nests for their young. One of these (*Leptodactylus mystacinus*) stirs up a frothy mass of mucus and deposits it in cavities in the ground near streams. The tadpoles can undergo part of their growth in these improvised nests until they are ready to enter the water nearby. Other species of frogs place their frothy nests in broad leaves which are folded and gummed together into a pocket receptacle.

Fish as a group are commonly thought of as giving a minimum amount of care to their eggs and young during development. Most of them are content to ensure the fertilization of their eggs during spawning but bestow little attention on them. There are, however, some notable exceptions in which the young are guarded with great solicitude. One of the most interesting examples of this is the practice of the male stickleback (*Gasterosteus*, Figure 634), a small fresh-water fish of our northern lakes and ponds. This fish actually makes a nest of dead aquatic plants. To hold the rounded nest together, the male makes use of a secretion from his kidneys. The aggressive male by an elaborate courtship ritual induces sev-

Figure 633. Little mud crater made by tree frog, *Hyla faber*. Tadpoles hatch within this protective barrier and remain here until they mature. The nest, built entirely by the male, is about 12 inches in diameter and 4 to 6 inches in depth.

Figure 634. Nest of stickleback, *Gasterosteus*.

eral females to lay their eggs in the nest; and then he mounts guard, keeping away intruders in a fierce, pugnacious manner. The bowfin (*Amia calva*) of the great lakes of North America builds a less elaborate nest in an area which it makes among aquatic plants. When the eggs are laid, the male remains on guard until they hatch and then keeps the young fish with him for some time afterward. The method many amphibians employ—attaching the eggs to the body—is found in the New Guinea fish *Kuryus*. The male of this species entangles the mass of eggs on a hook-like process on top of his head, where the eggs are kept until they hatch. In the sea horse (*Hippocampus*) there is in the male a brood pouch in which the eggs are carried and in which they develop.

Some fish also display elaborate courtship and breeding ceremonies. The horned dace (*Semotilus atromaculatus*) may be taken as an example. This fish is a small minnow found in northern fresh-water streams. In the spring when they spawn, the males build pit nests in sand and gravel and assume a bright rosy red color on their ventral sides. In the course of their spawning, a number of males may fight over the possession of a single nest, and now and then two males undergo a peculiar ceremony. In this ceremony two males will swim away from the nest, side by side, nudging each other with their heads as they swim. This side-by-side journey keeps up until one of them gets ahead of the other; then they turn around quickly and head back for the nest. The same two males may put on this act repeatedly. How long they journey depends upon how quickly one courses ahead of the other. The real significance of such a ceremony is a matter of speculation.

LOCOMOTION

Certain groups of animals are indelibly stamped with a particular type of movement. Thus birds stand for flying, snakes for crawling, etc. But there are many forms that deviate from the methods we expect them to follow from their group relations. Such aberrant types are always of interest, for they indicate how adaptable animals are, and how they can vary to meet the conditions of existence.

One unusual method of locomotion is gliding. The forms that have this method nearly always use it to supplement another, more regular method. Thus flying squirrels have folds of skin which they can extend when volplaning from high in a tree to some lower level; they use their gliding ability mainly when they are seeking safety from possible danger. Animals that are adapted in this way can only employ gliding under restricted conditions. Ordinarily they can use this method only in traveling from a height to some lower level.

There are two other forms which are remarkable this way. One is the so-called flying lemur of the East Indies; it is adapted by having a large flat tail and a wide, thin membrane (parachute) formed of skin folds on each side of the body. When these devices are extended, this animal can glide swiftly from one tree to another with a minimum amount of climbing. The other example is the flying or gliding tree frog of Borneo, which has stressed a little different method of gliding. The body of this frog is less than 4 inches long, but the long toes of its limbs are united with exceptionally large webs. The entire surface of these webs exceeds twelve square inches; this gives the frog such buoyancy that it can glide considerable distances through the forest. To aid still more in its gliding, the animal inflates its body, a trick employed by many amphibians.

A certain species of spider found in Australia also makes use of the gliding method. This parachuting spider (*Saitis volans*) has lateral outgrowths of its abdomen which greatly increase its leaps in pursuit of prey. When not so engaged, the spider can bend these lateral plates downward along the sides of its body.

Some spiders use their spinning abilities in working out a unique method of locomotion. Young spiders climb to the top of a bush or other elevation and spin out of their spinnerets a few feet of thread which hardens on contact with the air. Whenever a breeze blows these threads taut, exerting a pull upon the legs, the spiders release their hold on their perches and allow the threads to carry them away in the breeze. They are carried, back downward, for considerable distances, or until the threads may catch on some object. If they wish to descend at any time while being carried along, the young spiders pull in the threads and gather them under their bodies with their feet. As the threads shorten, the body weight causes them to descend. How effective this aerial method is is shown by the observations of ballooning spiders far out at sea and in other remote places.

The ability to move on the surface film of water is found among a number of insects. The water strider is provided with two pairs of long hind limbs which, like the body, are covered with short hairs. These hairs form a matlike structure in which air is enmeshed, so that the insect is not wetted. In their rapid skating movements over the surface of still water, the middle pair of legs does the running while the hindmost pair is employed chiefly for steering. Whirligig beetles have relatively short legs, but the hind pairs are broad and paddle shaped, with a fringe of long, stiff hairs. The hindmost pair of legs is used mainly for propulsion by quick back thrusts. Most of their movements on the water surface are of an erratic, gyratory nature; this they perform with great dexterity. When alarmed, these animals quickly dive beneath the surface, carrying with them bubbles of air at the posterior ends of their bodies. Surface walking of another type is shown by a bird, the Mexican jacana (*Parra*). This form lives in tropical pools more or less covered with lily pads. The bird is provided with enormously elongated claws and toes which enable it to glide over the flat lily pads without sinking into the water. Such a queer adaptation imposes a severe limitation on its possessor, for in other kinds of habitats the bird is handicapped.

Fish have also worked out some queer methods of locomotion by the transformation of their fins and the development of certain other bodily structures. The flying fish, for example, have their pectoral fins greatly enlarged into winglike structures. With these, however, it is more a case of gliding than of flying, although they do vibrate their fins somewhat. The fish manages to leave the water by swimming rapidly near the surface; and as the body leaves the water, the pectoral fins are fully extended and the force of its initial impetus enables the fish to rise for some distance. It then glides for a few seconds before descending to the water. The distance it can travel in a single glide has been variously estimated from 100 to 1,000 feet, at a rate of forty miles an hour. When the flying fish put on this display of gliding, it is usually due to a frantic attempt to escape their enemies.

The interesting climbing perch (*Anabas*) of India has modified certain body structures for climbing out of the water and also for carrying on its respiration while on land. On its gill covers and elongated ventral fin are sharp spines. Using the gill cover spines for clinging to the bark and the ventral fin for pushing, the fish manages to climb out of water and up a nearby tree or limb. For breathing out of water, the fish is provided with a special chamber above the gill chamber.

FOOD GETTING

Unusual methods of procuring and manipulating food are found among most of the major groups of animals. Many have become highly specialized for living upon a particular kind of food and cannot adapt themselves to any other. Thus the anteater is restricted to a diet of ants by virtue of its elongated snout and cylindrical extensible tongue; the crossbill, chiefly to pine cones and seeds by its peculiar beak; and the termite to wood, by its symbiotic relationship with a flagellate protozoan.

It would be expected that a food such as blood would be the chief diet of many forms. Mosquitoes, leeches, and other forms are so specialized, but such an exclusive diet is hardly to be looked for among mammals. One mammal which does have this habit is the vampire bat. The vampires are restricted to two species (*Desmodus rufus* and *Diphylla ecaudata*) which are found in South America. Their adaptations for such a method of feeding are partly structural and partly behavior patterns. They seem to prey entirely upon warm-blooded animals, including man. They are strictly nocturnal in their habits and take advantage of sleeping animals. Those who have had the rare opportunity of observing them in their feeding habits state that the bats approach their victims with great stealth and usually manage to bite without detection.

The incision the bat makes with its sharp teeth is so small that the victim is rarely aware of the wound. As the blood oozes out, the vampire laps it up gently with pumping movements of its tongue, a constituent in its saliva keeping the blood from coagulating. The most common part of the human body in which they make their incisions is the undersurface of the toes, although they are known to make them in the tip of the nose, lobe of ear, or other exposed places. Vampire bats are highly selective in choosing their victims from a group. Some individuals are attacked night after night; others are never molested. The stomach of the bat is provided with a diverticulum or elastic pouch, which can enlarge to great proportions to accommodate the blood. Vampires are known to transmit paralytic rabies, as well as other diseases, among both domestic animals and man.

Eggs are favorite articles of diet for the members of many groups of animals such as snakes and lizards. Such a method of food getting is often wasteful, for the sharp teeth of a snake often break an egg as it is being swallowed and much of its contents run out of the mouth. The poisonous lizard, the Gila monster (*Heloderma*), first breaks the egg and then laps the contents off the ground. One snake in Africa, *Dasypeltis*, which, unlike other snakes, lives exclusively on eggs, has evolved certain structures for such an adaptation. In the first place, its teeth are few and short; thus they do not damage the egg as it is taken into the mouth. As the unbroken egg passes down the esophagus, it is broken by a second adaptation, the so-called spine teeth. These teeth are fashioned from about six long spines, which develop from the undersurface of the vertebrae in that particular region and project downward like pins through the esophageal wall into the lumen. When the egg reaches this point and comes to lie directly under these spines, a forceful contraction of the body wall and esophagus causes the teeth to rupture the egg. The contents of the egg then flow backward into the stomach and the empty shell is regurgitated into the mouth and expelled to the outside. There are some snakes, however, which manage to swallow eggs without breaking them until they are in the esophagus, where violent muscular contractions or digestive juices do the trick.

Methods for reaching prey at a distance are not unknown in the animal kingdom. Thus the strange wormlike form, *Peripatus*, is provided with a pair of oral papillae, each of which is connected with a slime gland. By squirting slime from these papillae, they can incapacitate insects several inches away, for the sticky slime adheres to anything with which it comes in contact. One of the strangest examples of this method is the javelin or archer fish *(Toxotes)*. This small fish is found in the fresh waters of the East Indies, and its favorite food is insects. Whenever it sees an insect resting on vegetation over the water, the fish aims his mouth at the prey and squirts a jet of water at it. This usually causes the insect to drop into the water, where it is quickly seized.

LIGHT PRODUCTION

The production of light by living organisms (bioluminescence) is widespread throughout the animal kingdom and nearly every phylum is represented. Its presence, however, is sporadic; and usually only scattered representatives are found within a particular phylum. There are more ex-

amples among the coelenterates than are found in any other phylum. Altogether, light production has been found in more than 300 genera. The forms which do possess it are largely marine or terrestrial, for no luminous fresh-water forms have yet been discovered, except an aquatic glow-worm. Many theories have been suggested as to its possible uses among animals. It may be for sex signalling, for kin recognition, for frightening enemies, for allurement, or for a lamp to guide the animal's movement. It is also possible that it has no significance for the organism, especially in those forms whose light is produced by symbiotic bacteria.

On the basis of light production, animals may be divided into two groups—those that produce their own light (self-luminous) and those whose light is produced by symbiotic bacteria. The self-luminous forms will emit light only when they are stimulated. This accounts for the luminescence of the sea at night when a boat is passing by. All this phosphorescence is due to small organisms which are disturbed by the boat or by other agitation. Many of the self-luminous organisms have rather complicated organs for the production of light. These light organs usually consist of a group of photogenic cells for producing the light, a transparent lens-like structure for directing the light, a layer of cells behind the photogenic tissue for reflecting the light, and, surrounding most of the organ, a pigmented layer of cells for shielding the animal's own tissues from the possibly injurious effects of its own light. The luminescence of this type of luminous animal is due to the interaction of two substances—**luciferin,** which is oxidized in the presence of an enzyme, **luciferase.** Oxygen is therefore necessary for light production also. It is now known that there are several different kinds of luciferins in different organisms, and some luciferins have been obtained in pure form. In the firefly the mechanism of light production also involves ATP and magnesium. The stimulation for light production may be merely mechanical, or nervous, as it appears to be in higher organisms. In those whose light is produced by symbiotic bacteria, light is given off continuously, although some of the forms have devices for concealing and showing the light intermittently. These bacteria may also be cultured by laboratory methods. Four or five classical examples of luminescence will give the student some idea of this interesting adaptation.

Among the protozoans, *Noctiluca* is the most striking example of bioluminescence. This flagellate is sphere shaped and about 1 mm. in diameter. It will give off light only when stimulated. Its luminescence originates from small granules scattered over the periphery and other parts of the cell. These animals will flash vividly whenever they are disturbed by a passing boat. They can also be stimulated by mechanical, chemical, and other agencies. Luciferin and luciferase cannot be demonstrated in these forms. In the absence of oxygen, *Noctiluca* will not produce light. *Noctiluca* often collect in enormous numbers at the surface of the sea; their display of color in the wake of a passing vessel on a dark night is wonderful to behold.

The famed glowworm (Figure 635) of literature is usually the wingless female of the lampyrid beetle *(Photinus)*, although some are larval forms. Most of them are terrestrial, although one or two live in fresh water. The luminous organs are found on the ventral side of the posterior segments. The light they emit is rather bluish green in appearance. Experiments show that the light rays are restricted to a very narrow range of the spectrum, as compared with other luminous animals, and that they give a very high degree of luminous efficiency. In the glowworm, perhaps more than in most luminous animals, the problem of producing light without heat is solved to a great extent. Its light, as well as that of all forms which have bioluminescence, is really "cold light."

The best known of all light-producing organisms is the firefly. These beetles have a wide distribution, and many genera and species are found. Most of them are tropical, but two genera are very common in temperate North America *(Lampyris* and *Photinus)*. These are the familiar "lightning bugs" known to everyone. The light organ of the male is located on the ventral surface of the posterior segments of the abdomen. It is made up of a dorsal mass of small cells (the reflector) and a ventral mass of large cells (the photogenic tissue). Many branches of the tracheal system pass into the organ and subdivide into tracheoles which are connected with tracheal end cells to ensure an ample supply of oxygen, so necessary for the light. The organ is also supplied with nerves which control the rhythmic flashing. The function of the reflector is to scatter the light produced by the photogenic cells. In the female the light organ is confined to a single abdominal segment. The flashing of fireflies is rhythmic and may be single or double, depending upon the species.

In the tropics, the synchronous flashing of fireflies is common; thousands of individuals flash together with great regularity. Often these displays are made in and around certain trees, where one of the insects may act as a pacemaker. The light is considered a mating signal in the American forms. During the day the fireflies lie hidden under vegetation, but they emerge at dusk. The males do most of the flying,

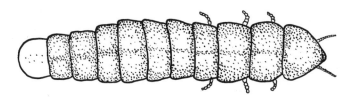

Figure 635. Glowworm. Luminous organs represented on last segment.

Some interesting and striking adaptations   863

for the females of some species are wingless or have very short wings and usually remain on the ground or on low vegetation. When the males flash, the females respond and they eventually find each other.

All the foregoing examples of bioluminescence are self-luminous. One of the most striking examples of luminous symbiosis is that of certain East Indian fish (*Photoblepharon* and *Anomalops*). In these forms, under each eye there are large luminous organs; these give off light continuously, day and night. The organs are made up of a series of tubes having an abundant supply of blood vessels. These tubes contain luminous bacteria which give off the light. Like the other type of light organ, these are sensitive to lack of oxygen and will quickly cease to give off light if the oxygen supply fails. Although the bacteria give off a continuous light, the fish can conceal the organ at will by drawing a fold of black tissue over it like an eyelid (or by some other device). This is an example of true symbiosis, for the fish is dependent upon the bacteria for light and the bacteria depend upon the fish for nourishment and shelter. Many other cases have been described in which luminous bacteria are considered the responsible agents for light production in animals.

ELECTRIC ORGANS

The power to produce strong electric shocks is much more restricted among animals than is light production, being restricted to two groups, teleosts and elasmobranchs. The actual forms which have this adaptation are the electric eels, *Electrophorus* and *Gymnotus;* the electric ray, *Torpedo;* the stargazer, *Astroscopus;* and the electric catfish, *Malapterurus.* The electric organs in all these forms are modified from skeletal muscles, with the possible exception of *Malapterurus*, in which they have developed from skin glands. The organs are composed of flattened plates arranged one above another like the alternating layers in a storage battery. Each plate, of which there are thousands, is innervated by a nerve fiber. In some forms more than 200 to 300 volts of electricity have been recorded. The position of the organs varies greatly with the different forms; this indicates that the various organs have arisen independently. Since active muscle normally generates some electricity, it is logical that such electric organs should have arisen from muscles. All the fish which have developed these organs are rather sluggish and frequent shallow water where they stun their prey by their electric shocks.

The most familiar example of an electric fish along the Atlantic coast is the *Torpedo,* or electric ray (Figure 636). In these forms, the organs are present, one on either side of the head, in the large, flat, expanded pectoral fins. One of the most interesting and also one of the most powerful of fish possessing electric batteries is the electric eel, *Electrophorus,* which is found in parts of Brazil, Venezuela, and other South American countries. It is an elongated, eel-like fish 3 to 7 feet long, with a continuous midventral fin extending from the head to a point near the tail. The electric organs in this fish are three pairs in number and occupy the greater part of the posterior body cavity, for the visceral organs are shoved forward to the region just behind the head. The paired organs are not of equal size; this may account for the ability of the animal to regulate the intensity of its shock. This form is the only electric fish capable of doing this.

It is thought that the largest of the paired organs delivers the largest shocks and the smallest organs, lesser ones. The reason advanced to explain this difference in degree of shock intensity is that the smaller shocks serve as a warning to possible enemies and the strong shocks are used for killing prey or enemies. The discharge is entirely according to the will of the fish, for sometimes it will shock when touched and will not at other times. It is not necessary for an animal to come into contact with the eel to receive a shock, for the electric discharge carries through the water. How effective these

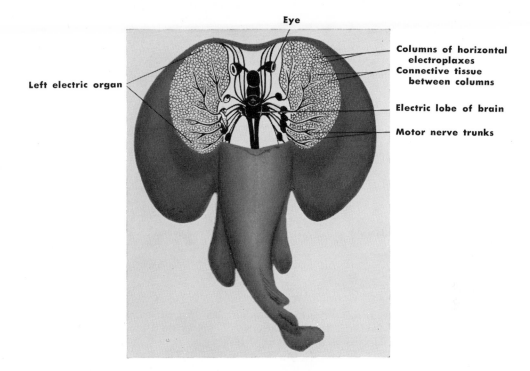

Eye

Columns of horizontal
electroplaxes

Connective tissue
between columns

Left electric organ

Electric lobe of brain

Motor nerve trunks

Figure 636. Electric ray, *Torpedo*, with electric organs uncovered from above. Electric organs are restricted to certain teleost and elasmobranch fish. Electric organs are all modified from striated muscle (with one possible exception). Organs are built up of disclike, multinucleated cells called electroplaxes or electroplates which are embedded in a jellylike substance and enclosed within connective tissue compartments. Each vertical column in electric ray is made up of a stack of electroplaxes piled on top of each other. Nerve fibers run to electroplaxes and blood capillaries course through jelly layer. In addition to defensive and offensive purposes, electric organs may be used for recognition among members of a species where other methods of communication are absent.

shocks are in killing animals is a matter of controversy. There seems to be authentic records of the death of men and horses killed by the larger electric eels. In general, most of the victims of the fish are paralyzed and eventually recover, except for those caught and eaten by the creature.

HOW HONEYBEES COMMUNICATE LOCATION OF FOOD

Among animal behavior patterns which have long puzzled biologists are the habits of the social insects. To understand the social organization of these organisms has been the object of able investigators in many lands, and many of their findings

have elicited wonder and amazement. Problems of comparative psychology have been posed by these experiments, for many of them seem to be beyond man's realm of knowledge and experience. Man has generally interpreted such behavior phenomena as complex instinctive reactions on the part of the insects without being able to analyze the factors involved in the process. It has long been suspected that the sensory mechanisms of insects are extremely baffling in comparison with man's sensory equipment. Among the most interesting of these complicated behavior patterns is the power many insects have of finding their directions and of communicating such to others. It seems as if

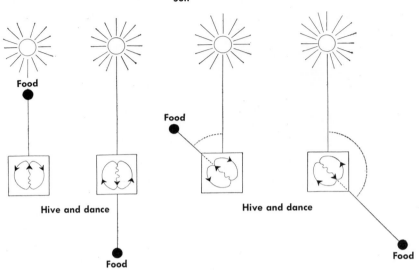

Figure 637. Wagging dance of honeybee to indicate direction of food sources far from hive. Four possible directions of food from hive and direction of appropriate dance in each case are given. Dance is usually conducted on vertical side of hive.

they had a kind of language for conveying information to each other.

One of the most striking behavior patterns is the ability of honeybees to inform others about the location of a source of food. The experiments conducted in recent years by Professor Karl von Frisch have given some clues to this interesting problem. By using glass observation hives and marked bees, he was able to observe with considerable accuracy just what occurs when bees report back to the hive the presence of a source of honey. Whenever a foraging bee finds a source of honey, she returns to the hive and performs a peculiar dancing movement which conveys to others in the hive in what direction and how far they must go in order to find the nectar. The pattern of this dance depends upon how far the food is from the hive. If the food is more than 100 meters away, she performs a characteristic waggle dance. This dance is roughly in the pattern of a figure of eight which she makes against the vertical side of the comb. In the performance of this act she waggles her abdomen from side to side in a characteristic manner.

She repeats this dance over and over, the number of dances decreasing per unit of time the farther away the source is. The direction of the food source is also indicated by the direction of the waggle dance in relation to the position of the sun. When the waggle dance is upward on the comb, the source of food is toward the sun. A waggle run downward on the comb indicates that the food is opposite to the position of the sun. If the food source is at an angle to the sun, the direction of the waggle dance is at a corresponding angle. During a dance other bees keep in contact with the scout bee with their antennae, and each performance results in several bees taking off in search of the food. When they return with the food they also perform the dance if there is still food there. When the source of food is less than 100 meters from the hive the pattern of dance is less complex. In this case the scout bee simply turns around in a circle first to the right and then to the left, a performance she repeats several times (Figure 638). She is able in this way to convey to the other bees the information to seek around the

866

Figure 638. Round dance of honeybee. Whenever food supply is within a hundred yards or so of the hive, scout bee circles first one way and then other to convey information of food source.

hive food of the same odor she bears. One other interesting phenomenon is the ability of bees to determine the direction of the sun when only a small area of the sky is visible. They seem to be able to do this by the pattern of polarization in the light from that part of the sky that is still visible. When the waggle dance is performed on a horizontal surface outside the hive, the bee goes through the dance in the actual direction of the food and not in relation to the sun.

STRESS OR ALARM REACTION AS ADAPTIVE RESPONSE

The complex nature of adaptations is well illustrated by the recent development of the concept of the way the animal body meets the stresses produced by its environment, the so-called **alarm reaction.** According to this view the organism has a general defense mechanism which is employed whenever it is subjected to the damaging action of drugs, poisons, severe cold and burns, and other stress agents. How do animals meet such conditions and what elements in the body are involved in the generalized reactions to them? The concept as now understood illustrates one of the primary adaptive features of animals in their struggle to survive. Moreover, the adaptation is a revealing example of the complicated interrelationships of the endocrine glands and their functional associations.

The man chiefly responsible for the main features of the concept as it now stands is Dr. Hans Selye of the Institute of Experimental Medicine and Surgery of the University of Montreal. This investigator has spent many years in determining the effects of stress agents on the animal body and the role hormones play in the complicated process. The research is far from completed and may lead eventually to a better understanding of the basic causes of the degenerative diseases, such as hardening of the arteries and heart failure. Such practical medical aspects are, of course, of great importance, but from a biological viewpoint the chief interest of the concept lies in its adaptive nature.

Whenever animals are subjected to stress agents in lethal dosages, autopsies always reveal certain characteristic changes in bodily organs, such as abnormal enlargement of the adrenal glands, decrease in size of the thymus, and the presence of bleeding ulcers in the stomach. Body fluids also show a decrease in sugar and chloride ions. According to those who have worked on the problem, there is a rather definite sequence of chain reactions in the alarm reaction. Acute stress from whatever cause instigates the anterior pituitary, probably through a neurohumoral mechanism (epinephrine) to secrete the hormone ACTH, which in turn stimulates the adrenal cortex to release the hormones desoxycorticosterone (DCA) and cortisone. Of these two hormones, desoxycorticosterone tends to keep the body fluids constant by regulating their salt content, and cortisone controls their sugar metabolism. In this way the animal is adapted to the stress condition. If the stress is continued, however, for a long time, this adaptive mechanism is broken down, and the organism, after passing through a resistance stage where it makes a recovery to the stress for a time, finally passes into a stage of exhaustion and dies. How long an animal is able to endure such stress depends to some extent upon the nature of the agent to which it is exposed, for some are much more severe than others. The whole mechanism is known as the **general adaptive syndrome** of the adrenal-pituitary axis.

ANNOTATED REFERENCES

Allen, G. M. 1939. Bats. Cambridge, Harvard University Press. *An interesting and authoritative account of bats and their adaptations.*

Andrews, R. C. 1951. Nature's Ways. New York, Crown Publishers. *An excellent description of some of the most striking adaptations in the animal kingdom. One of the best books for the beginner.*

Barrett, C. 1955. An Australian Animal Book, ed. 2. New York, Oxford University Press. *The unique fauna of Australia has always been a fascinating puzzle to zoologists and this work covers the many varied forms found in that strange continent. One of the most useful features of the book is the many excellent photographs of animals.*

Beebe, W. 1944. The Book of Naturalists. An Anthology of the Best Natural History. New York, Alfred A. Knopf, Inc. *One of the most interesting books of its kind, for it contains striking selections from the classics of natural history.*

Bertin, L. 1957. Eels: A Biological Study. New York, Philosophical Library, Inc. *Ever since the time of Aristotle, the puzzling migration of the fresh-water eel has intrigued biologists for two thousand years. Although Schmidt solved the main problem when he discovered its spawning grounds in the Sargasso Sea, there is still much to learn about the life cycle of this mysterious animal. This little work gives an excellent summary of what is known about its life cycle at present.*

Breland, O. P. 1957. Animal Friends and Foes. New York, Harper & Brothers. *A popular account of the ways animals affect man's welfare and also each other. The topic headings pose questions which are often asked by the layman (and sometimes by professional zoologists). General zoology students will find much of interest in the book.*

Carthy, J. D. 1956. Animal Navigation. New York, Charles Scribner's Sons. *Locomotion is one of the basic activities of most animals, and this popular work tries to explain how insects and birds especially get to new places and how they find their way back. The author does not believe that animals famed for reaching their target are provided with senses different from those of man but rather that their navigation can be explained in terms of a greater sensitivity to sources of stimuli already familiar to man.*

Devoe, A. 1951. This Fascinating Animal World. New York, McGraw-Hill Book Co., Inc. *This work attempts to answer the common questions which zoologists are confronted with in the field of natural history.*

Frisch, K. von. 1950. Bees. Their Vision, Chemical Senses, and Language. Ithaca, Cornell University Press. *A striking account of the classical experiments of this investigator in the determination of the ways bees convey information about food location.*

Harvey, E. N. 1952. Bioluminescence. New York, Academic Press, Inc. *The latest authoritative work on this fascinating subject.*

Johnson, F. H. (editor). 1955. The Luminescence of Biological Systems. Washington, American Association for the Advancement of Science. *This book represents the Proceedings of the Conference on Luminescence which was presented in California in 1954. It is an excellent summary of the physical, chemical, and biological factors involved in light production, together with the practical applications of certain aspects in industry. The introductory paper by Harvey, one of the most outstanding authorities in the field, is a good summary of the present status of our knowledge of luminescence.*

MacGinitie, G. E., and N. MacGinitie. 1949. Natural History of Marine Animals. New York, McGraw-Hill Book Co., Inc. *A good account of the marine forms along the California coast.*

Milne, L., and M. Milne. 1958. Paths Across the Earth. New York, Harper & Brothers. *In this nontechnical account of the travels of animals the authors have presented descriptions of how animals find their way around and the various theories used to explain how they do it.*

Noble, R. C. 1945. The Nature of the Beast. New York, Doubleday & Co., Inc. *This study of animal behavior gives many interesting examples of animal adaptations with respect to sex recognition, instinct, intelligence, etc.*

Pinner, E. 1953. Curious Creatures. New York, Philosophical Library, Inc. *Many curious adaptations are found in this interesting book. The illustrations are revealing.*

Prosser, C. L. (editor). 1958. Physiological Adaptation. Washington, American Physiological Society.

Schultz, L. P., and E. M. Stern. 1948. The Ways of Fishes. New York, D. Van Nostrand Co., Inc. *The beginner in zoology can acquire a great deal of information about fish and their adaptive ways from this book.*

Animal behavior patterns

chapter 41

SIGNIFICANCE OF BEHAVIOR

Every kind of organism has its characteristic pattern of response to changes in its environment. No organism can be understood without reference to its reactions to its surroundings. Even the simplest form has many responses often so complicated that no one has been able to puzzle out the stimulus-response processes involved. It may be relatively easy for a close observer to determine the external activities of a particular animal, but the correlated internal mechanisms are a different matter. A given behavior pattern may start in response to a definite external change or stimulus, or it may originate from internal stimuli. Many animals may initiate a behavior pattern without any apparent reason at all. A response may take place immediately after an animal is disturbed, or it may be delayed for a considerable time after the stimulation. Levels of organization also complicate the problem. It is obvious that a vertebrate animal has a greater complexity of nervous and other systems involved in behavior than that of many low forms of life. Most animals also have social responses of behavior as well as individual ones. Consequently there are many varied behavior patterns because of these differences. Anything that lives, moves, and has its being has some form of behavior, but the same can also be said of nonliving entities which have molecular patterns of action involving movements of atomic constituents. Larger components of the universe also show definite patterns of activity. A mechanistic viewpoint would say that there is a unity of behavior plan for both living and nonliving matter, but this has not yet been demonstrated.

Some may well question the viewpoint that animal behavior is a genuine science at the present time. Science implies conceptual schemes of general principles with wide applications, and it is very doubtful that the study of behavior has progressed this far. The vigorous controversies which our leading behavior students have over even the simplest type of behavior indicate how observations and experiments must be extended before general laws and principles can be formulated. This does not in the least detract from the impressive work which has been done or is being done in the field of behavior.

HISTORICAL BACKGROUND

Because of man's intimate association with animals at all cultural levels, he has been interested in the reactions of animals, at least in so far as they affect human welfare. Primitive people have not always distinguished sharply between themselves and other animals with regard to emotions, feelings, and understanding. According to the eminent American psychologist Schneirla, two views have developed regarding man's relations to the lower animals. One view emphasizes differences and ignores similarities between man and the so-called brute world; the other, which is more modern and is an outcome of evolutionary thought, analyzes in a comparative way both similarities and differences. In a strict scientific sense, Aristotle was one of the first to record descriptions of animal behavior in in which he set off rather sharply man's reasoning powers against that of lower animals. Roman writers, such as Pliny and Plutarch, also recorded observations on the intelligence of animals. In more modern times, Erasmus Darwin, Lamarck, Herbert Spencer, Charles Darwin, and many others made important observations on animal instincts and intelligence.

Significant behavior studies were made only when animal activities were analyzed in objective terms. Anecdotal and anthropomorphic methods (i.e., ascribing human attributes to other animals) were of little or no significance. Evolutionary development gave a great impetus to experimental testing and control methods of analyzing behavior. Two early investigations deserve special mention—the outstanding work of E. G. and G. W. Peckham on the instincts and habits of the solitary wasp and the work of C. O. Whitman on the behavior of pigeons. J. Loeb and C. Morgan did much to develop the study along the lines followed by present-day investigators. Morgan (1894) gave an important principle known as "Morgan's canon" which states that an animal's behavior pattern should be interpreted in terms of the simplest explanation that meets the facts involved. Loeb advanced his theory of forced movements (tropisms), or the reactions of an animal in response to a difference in stimulation on its two sides. Both these investigators tried to explain behavior, at least in part, on the basis of physicochemical principles. H. S. Jenning's theory of trial and error was in conflict with Loeb's tropism theory, and his study of the behavior of the lower organisms represents an important advance in this field. In the early part of the present century I. R. Pavlov demonstrated his famous conditional reflexes wherein he showed that basic physiological functions and behavior of an animal could be modified by associated experience.

But one of the most outstanding investigations was done by G. E. Coghill, who carefully traced throughout all stages of the developing vertebrate (salamander) embryo the emergence of correlated movements and nervous connections and thus laid the basis for a structural interpretation of behavior. He showed, among other things, how broad, general movements preceded the appearance of more specialized local reflexes because of the delay in the development of the nervous connections for the latter.

The marked revival of interest in animal behavior in recent years has been due mainly to the researches of two European investigators, K. Lorenz and N. Tinbergen. Their theory of instinctive and innate behavior has attracted attention everywhere because of their fresh outlook. In fact, they call their approach to behaviorism **ethology,** which is the comparative study of the physiological basis of the organism's reaction to stimuli and its adaptations to its environment. They have tried to explain innate behavior by investigating the stimuli which control it and by studying the animal's internal conditions which are organized for particular patterns. Their studies have greatly stimulated other competent workers, such as D. S. Lehrman, T. C. Schneirla, and W. H. Thorpe, to undertake similar investigations either in confirmation or in refutal of the theories Lorenz and Tinbergen have proposed. What these investigators did will be more apparent in the succeeding sections of this chapter.

METHODS OF STUDYING BEHAVIOR

Animal behavior is a difficult subject and its study requires techniques from many branches of science, such as neurology, genetics, physiology, ecology, embryology, and the physical sciences. It involves the activities of the whole organism with reference to the environment, so that animal sociology or group relations must also be understood. In any comparative study it is necessary to use the soundest methods available and check one against the other. Animal behavior work involves both laboratory experiments and field observations. Testing must conform to the standard scientific procedure of the control experiment in which conditions are kept as uniform as possible except in the one environmental factor (stimulus, etc.) which is being studied. So many variable factors may enter into behavior studies, such as age, physiological conditions, hormonal balance, insidious disturbances, individual difference of intelligence, and number of subjects studied, that one's conclusions are not valid enough for sweeping generalizations. The experimentalist must know the nature and normal responses of the animals being studied. A racoon, for instance, is far more adept in manipulating its forelimbs than a cat, and experiments that involve the use of this limb must therefore take this into account. An animal can organize its behavior capacities only within the range of its abilities.

Since the nervous system is mainly responsible for the coordination of behavior, many investigations have been conducted to determine the neurological basis of behavior. Several methods may be employed. Certain areas of the brain may be removed surgically or destroyed and the resulting functional deficiencies noted; electric stimulation of brain regions is effective in causing responses in muscles and other effectors; and it is possible to use the electroencephalogram (for detecting electric discharges) to find those parts of the nervous system which are functioning under a given condition. By such methods it has been possible to determine important nerve centers, such as the cocoon-spinning center (corpus pedunculatum) of caterpillars, the satiety center of mammals, motivation centers, and many others. Coghill's great work emphasized the parallelism between the emergence of behavior patterns and the growth of nervous connections. Such a study combined both a physiological method and a microanatomical method.

The greatest pitfall in all behavior studies is interpretation. Since it is impossible for man to be aware of the conscious or inward states of an animal, there is the tendency to attribute humanlike reasons for an animal's activities. There is the danger also of using analogous reasoning and making hasty generalizations on insufficient evidence. Morgan's canon of using the simplest explanation for explaining animal activity may at times be wrong, but it has often been neglected when it could have proved useful. When another animal does something humanlike in nature, it does not mean that the animal is thinking like a man. It is reacting in accordance with its own basic behavior patterns which in turn depend upon the organization and degree of complexity of its own nervous system. A bird thinks like a bird, a dog like a dog, and an anthropomorphic interpretation is unjustified in either case. Another pitfall is the ascribing of purpose to an animal's reactions. It is true that many of its behavior patterns are adaptive, but this does not mean that animals perform these acts with an understanding of the end result or with the ability to anticipate what the end is to be. Such an interpretation would involve human reasoning. A simpler explanation of reflexlike reactions would be more logical in many cases of animal behavior.

LEVELS OF NERVOUS ORGANIZATION

The behavior patterns of an animal largely depend upon its type of nervous system. Among all metazoan animals (even including the sponges) the organization of the nervous system is closely correlated with its sensory and motor systems. Complex behavior is restricted to highly organized nervous systems and superior sensory reception. It is only when the brain has advanced to the role of an organizing center that it can truly be thought of as regulating and controlling behavior organization.

The trend of evolution in the nervous system beyond the protists and sponges is centralization. From this standpoint most animals fall into one of three major types of nervous systems—nerve net of coelenterates, nervous systems with beginnings of brains, and centralized nervous systems.

Nerve net of coelenterates. There is very little centralization in this type, for a reaction to a stimulus may spread over the entire net and cause the animal to act as a whole. This diffused type of conduction does allow some coordination, for a slight stimulus may cause only a single tentacle to react, whereas stronger ones may involve other tentacles or even the entire body.

Nervous systems with beginnings of brains. There are several kinds of this type of nervous system. Mollusks have paired masses of ganglia located in the head, foot, and viscera which are interconnected by nerves. In the cephalopods there is a definite concentration of ganglia in the head. Nematodes and nemerteans have ganglia in the head region with usually several longitudinal nerves. Planarians, with two longitudinal nerves running from paired ganglia (brain) in the head, have rather complex behavioral reactions and can be taught simple processes. The evolution of the nervous system in higher forms may be considered a modification and an elaboration of the planarian plan.

Centralized nervous systems. This type consists of a brain, or aggregation of ganglia in the head, from which runs a centralized nerve cord or cords (with ganglia) and includes the higher invertebrates (annelids and arthropods) and the vertebrates. There is a wide diversity of centralization and coordination in a range from earthworm to mammal, but it is in such a type that we find the highest development of nervous coordination and behavior patterns.

In summary, it may be stated that the evolutionary trends which promote the capacity for organized behavior of increasing complexity are (1) the development of centralized control by means of concentrating the nerve cells (neurons) in dominant ganglia (brains) and in ganglia on or near a few nerve cords; (2) the differentiation of various kinds of neurons of more or less polarity (carrying impulses in one direction only), such as afferent, efferent, and association neurons, which are arranged to form a mechanism of coordination (reflex arc); (3) the variety and richness of nerve pathways, connections, and associations which make

an organization suitable for precision and variation of specialized behavior; and (4) the development of the sensory capacities which depend upon many sense organs of great complexity, sensitivity, and range of response.

SIMPLE BEHAVIOR PATTERNS (TROPISMS AND TAXES)

The simplest form of organized behavior is one in which a specific stimulus gives rise to a specific response. This type belongs to what is called inherited behavior patterns and is best represented perhaps by the **tropisms** of plants and the **taxes** of animals. It is true that early embryos and perhaps sponges have a form of organized responses because they have poorly developed nervous systems or none at all. (Irritability you may recall is a property of all protoplasmic systems.) Plants illustrate this specific stimulus-response behavior, or tropism, for most of their behavior patterns are tropistic responses. A tropism, which literally means a "turning," refers to the bending movements of plants brought about by differences in the stimulation of the two sides of an organ (stem, root, etc.). Tropisms involve two aspects: a definite direction caused by a difference in stimulation intensity and a rigid hereditary pattern not subject to modification. Tropisms take their name from the stimulus involved, such as phototropism (light), geotropism (gravity), etc.

The term **taxis** is now employed for freely swimming organisms and is used by zoologists to describe the movements of forms, such as protozoans. Description of the various forms of taxes is given in Chapter 6, Phylum Protozoa.

In the early part of the century J. Loeb and his school tried to interpret all animal behavior, whether low or high, on the basis of tropisms (taxes). He attempted to show that the differences in stimulation intensity on the two sides of an animal toward light, current, etc. caused the animal to orient itself toward or away from the source. Specifically, he explained the orientation of multicellular animals to light as being due to differences in muscular movements brought about by a faster contraction of the less illuminated side (or eyes) so that the animal curves toward the source of light (forced movement). When the light intensity is the same on both eyes the animal goes in a straight direction.

Loeb's theory has met with opposition from many sources. H. S. Jennings, in his now classical book, *The Behavior of the Lower Organisms*, proposed a trial-and-error explanation in place of the tropistic theory. This is really a stimulus-response theory, for Jennings found that most environmental changes will produce a response. The avoiding reaction of paramecium is due not to unequal stimulation of its two sides but to a fixed orientation pattern which enables the animal to find a favorable escape channel. (See Chapter 6, Phylum Protozoa.) All organisms have the capacity for several different responses to the same external stimulus. As Jennings showed, a ciliate like *Stentor* will react in a highly variable way to a constant stimulus such as carmine particles or ink—it will turn to one side, reversing its cilia, and finally retire into its protective tube. When *Stentor* emerges again from its tube and is subjected to the same stimuli it contracts again into its tube immediately as though it remembered its previous experience. Another valid objection to Loeb's theory is that the exhibition of a response pattern may be delayed until the animal has attained a certain degree of maturity. Its responses, therefore, at one stage of the life cycle may be different from that at another.

HEREDITY AND BEHAVIOR

Behavior patterns are the result of the interaction between hereditary factors and the environment. No behavior pattern is found as such in the zygote. It must develop out of certain potentialities (or genes) which physiological influences act upon and limit at each stage of development. The so-called inheritance of behavior thus falls into line with the modern concept of genetics that genes and somatic expression are not in a direct relationship. Behavior patterns involve many factors such as nervous integration, hormone balance, and muscular coordination. Many genes must therefore be responsible for even the simplest activity of an animal. It is often difficult to determine whether heredity or learning experience is most involved.

Some types of activity are pretty definitely triggered. Each species of bird builds its typical nest without being taught; the parasitic cowbird raised in a warbler's nest never tries to mate with a warbler but only with its own kind; a spider weaves its web without learned modification; a stickleback fish always performs its courtship ritual the same way; and so forth. The influence of hereditary factors seem to be much more pronounced in lower than in higher animals. Many of the basic patterns of adaptive behavior in them do not seem to change much but are rigidly stereotyped. It must not be forgotten that the sensory, muscular, and other mechanisms that limit and define behavior can be controlled or affected by heredity. Behavior patterns can also be influenced by the kind of endocrine system an animal inherits. Certain forms of dwarfism are caused by a mutant gene which produces an underactive pituitary gland. The pituitary is known to control growth.

Some behavior traits of vertebrates segregate in accordance with Mendelian heredity. In a cross between the wild gray rat and the docile white rat the progeny will be of the dominant, wild, savage type. Other cases of cross-breeding involving behavior traits show the same effect, but it is not always possible to rule out environmental effects. Much more work in this field needs to be done before definite generalizations can be made.

TAXONOMY AND BEHAVIOR

In recent years emphasis has been placed upon the relationship between behavior patterns and taxonomic units at all levels. Evolutionary relationships are clearly expressed by behavior similarities and differences which are correlated with taxonomic subdivisions. It is thus possible to study species differences on the basis of behavior characteristics. H. S. Barber was able to separate many species of fireflies on the basis of differences in characteristic flashes emitted by flies of different populations. Most revealing of all was the work of B. B. Fulton on field crickets in which he found four different populations (supposedly one species) which would not interbreed (a behavior trait) in the laboratory, thus indicating the divergence and formation of four new species. Behavior patterns of *Drosophila* have also been shown to conform to the accepted taxonomy of the various species, and in some cases taxonomic revision has been made on a behavior basis. When knowledge about behavior is extended its importance as a taxonomic tool will be more apparent, for the study of behavior is more complicated than morphological study.

WHAT IS AN INSTINCT?

The concept of the term instinct has undergone some changes among animal behaviorists in recent times. It formerly meant any form of innate behavior that arose independently of the animal's environment, that was distinct from learned behavior, and that followed an inherited pattern of definite responses. At one time there was thought to be a sharp line between instinct and learned experience, and any action of an organism was either instinctive or learned. The chief problem was to determine which explanation was the right one. In the evolutionary process instinct was supposed to be the primitive plan of behavior patterns; intelligence and the learning process came later. Psychologists at present believe that most behavior must be interpreted in terms of both innate traits and learning. Few behaviorists are willing to concede that a particular activity is wholly instinctive or is wholly learned.

Some behaviorists rightly argue that behavior cannot be inherited through the genes of the chromosomes but must de-

velop under the influence of environment. Certain types of behavior, it is true, can be modified more than other types. Nest building among birds is unlearned, yet older robins build better nests than younger robins (Allee). Some birds reared away from their parents will still sing the song characteristic of their species; other kinds of birds when raised with members of another species will sing the song of that species rather than their own.

Lorenz and Tinbergen, the well-known European investigators, have stressed instinctive behavior as a stereotyped action which follows a definite pattern of expression. They believe that there are at least three components involved in an instinct. First, there is an **appetitive behavior,** which may be regarded as a build-up of readiness for the instinctive act. An appetite for the act is generated in the organism, so that it gets into a situation in which the instinct can be released. The animal is very restless until the instinct is released. This phase is goal directed, concerned only with the actual performance of the act. Second, an **innate releasing mechanism** is activated. This may be due to something in the environment or to an inner bodily condition. It refers to the removal of any inhibition for the performance of the instinctive behavior. Third, the **final consummatory act,** which might be considered the relief of the animal's tension by the actual discharge of the activity. This pattern of instinctive behavior might be illustrated simply by the reactions of a hungry young bird in a nest when something is waved before it. The bird is in a condition for response (appetitive); the movement of the object activates the release mechanism; and the lunge and gaping that follow is the consummatory act.

This theory has been subjected to critical analysis by able American behavior students who believe that some of its concepts are too preconceived and lack experimental verification and that it is based too much on preformed, inherited behavior.

Perhaps in our present state of knowledge the best way to regard an instinct is that it is concerned with activities which depend mainly or wholly upon an animal's organic equipment in reaction with the environment, with learning playing a minor role or else being entirely absent in the process.

INSTINCTIVE BEHAVIOR PATTERNS

An instinct is usually considered to differ from a taxis or tropism in being more complicated and involving more separate phases in the performance of the act. However, the two types of behavior may overlap. Both involve reflex action, but a taxis or tropism is less flexible and is based more upon a rigidly inherited plan. Another way of expressing the difference is to state that a taxis is more innate, is based more upon a specific neural mechanism, and is less modifiable in its expression. In studying any instinctive behavior it is necessary to determine the stimuli which control the behavior, to appraise the internal conditions which prepare the organism for the reaction, and to seek out the neural mechanism responsible for the integration of the whole basic pattern of behavior. To merely state that such and such an act is due to instinct does not explain anything. No instinctive action can be explained without knowing the organic circumstances under which it occurs and the role environment has played. The organic factors that may be involved in instincts are the sensory equipment, endocrine system, neuromuscular system, and others. Another important influence on instinctive behavior is maturation or the development of behavior patterns as correlated with the age and growth of animals. The innate behavior of young animals for a particular act may be quite different from that of an adult, as Coghill so well demonstrated. To a certain extent this can be explained by the development of new types of connection in the nervous mechanism.

Most instincts are adaptive in nature and can contribute much to the success of a group, as shown by the arthropods in which innate behavior of great variety predominates over learning. However, one cannot attribute purpose in their performance, for instincts are triggered by definite stimuli and will occur when certain stimuli act upon an inherited organic equipment, producing thereby a more or less predictable outcome. In some cases the act may be far from adaptive. The life cycle of the schistosome cercariae, which produce swimmer's itch in man, is terminated by the death of the cercariae when they penetrate man's skin.

Striking examples of automatic behavior as represented by clear-cut cases of instincts are perhaps best shown by the web spinning of spiders, the communication of honeybees, and the cocoon spinning of caterpillars. The animal involved performs its act with mechanical regularity step by step. Each stage of performance seems to serve as a stimulus for the succeeding stage. How the inherited organic factors of instincts require environmental influences for a characteristic behavior to appear is demonstrated by the experiment of D. Lack on the European robin. He discovered that a male robin during its breeding season and when holding its territory will attack even a bundle of red feathers (which simulate the red breast of an actual male robin) but will do so only under the conditions mentioned. The same experiment also shows the effect of what is called "sign stimuli," for Lack found that a tuft of red feathers would provoke an attack, whereas a stuffed young robin with a brown breast would not. In this case the red breast is the effective stimulus. A somewhat similar case of sign stimuli is the reaction of the herring gull chicks. These chicks beg food by pecking at the tip of the parent's beak where there is a little red spot. When this spot is painted out or painted some other color there is no releasing stimulus, and the chicks are confused.

MOTIVATION AND BEHAVIOR

Why do animals perform characteristic patterns of activity? What is the motive behind their behavior? Why do they act at all? A simple answer for many forms of activity is the stimulus-response theory which may involve some change in the environment. But not all behavior can be answered as simply as this, for some are related to internal conditions which are not easy to appraise. One of the basic principles of life is the maintenance of stable internal conditions (recall the principle of homeostasis). Hunger, for instance, is accompanied by a low blood glucose level, an imbalance of fluids, and so on. Such internal changes stimulate characteristic behavior patterns. All levels of animal organization seem to be affected by hunger. A hungry hydra will behave differently from a satiated one. It is very difficult to understand many of the complex mechanisms of internal stimulation, for they vary greatly.

The basic motivating force behind most behavior is a reward or punishment factor. Animals perform acts which either give them pleasure or else prevent pain or unpleasant conditions. They make their adjustments to these conditions perhaps wholly unconscious of the end results (this certainly would be true of the lower forms). This concept, as the student can see, is in line with the maintenance of internal stability as already described. The appetitive phase of instincts which Lorenz and Tinbergen stressed is supposed to furnish the chief source of motivation. According to their theory animals actively seek out those stimuli which trigger their instinctive acts. Failure to find such outlets is supposed to create intense emotion in animals.

A clearer understanding of these instinctive acts is furnished by the rather modern concept of **biological drives**. A biological drive may be defined as a motive for stabilizing the organism. Each type of drive is supposed to arise from physiological conditions which have compelling demands for adjustments. Examples of such drives are hunger, which arises from the nervous impulses of an empty, contracting stomach; thirst, which may be due to sensations from a drying pharyngeal mucosa; and sex, which is caused by a release of hormones from sex glands. All of these upset internal stability, and restoration of this stability is a reward or motive. Most drives are also characterized by rhythm patterns in which the drive fluctuates up and down in a periodic manner, such as the estrous cycle of the female mammal. Some drives are not as clear-cut, but a certain nervous pattern has to be satisfied, as, for instance, the weaving of a net by a spider.

In recent years great strides have been made in locating brain centers associated with motivation of particular kinds. W. R. Hess, a Swiss psychologist, was able to fasten fine metal electrodes into specific parts of the brain (by inserting them through the skull), and when the wound healed, the ordinary activities of an animal (rat) could be studied by giving electric shocks through these electrodes. By such means it has been possible to explore the brain and locate specific seats of emotions, such as pleasure, pain, sex, eating, satiety, etc. For instance, when an electrode was placed in a certain part of the hypothalamus and a rat had learned to stimulate itself by manipulating a lever (as in a Skinner box), it would press upon the lever with great frequency. The conclusion was that this particular spot was a pleasure center. Other regions have been found where stimulation is avoided by the experimental animal. Evidence from these and other experiments indicates that the hypothalamus is the chief center for many sensations and is where various drives lie. Whatever action is found here, however, is controlled and influenced by the higher centers of the cerebral cortex. The consummatory phase of an act, the way in which motivation is expressed, is controlled by the cerebral cortex.

REFLEX ACTION

A simple reflex act (reflex arc or circuit) is a ready-made behavior response in which a specialized receptor, when stimulated, transmits impulses to a specialized motor cell that arouses an effector (muscle or gland) to act. Most reflexes, at least in the higher forms, are more involved and include an association neuron, and the impulse must pass through a number of synapses. A reflex act may or may not involve a conscious sensation. Reflex acts are built into the body mechanism and control the automatic working of the internal organs. They may also be involved in general behavior patterns of higher animals. Reflex responses need not be learned and in animals with a central nervous system there are almost endless examples of them. Most reflex arcs have the possiblity of modification because there may be more than one channel of discharge. A complicated act may involve a chain of reflex acts.

Among lower invertebrates a reflex action has a local make-up and does not necessarily involve a more central or general control. The tube foot of a sea star, when severed from the body, will continue to react for some time, but there is central coordination of tube feet in such activities as locomotion or feeding.

Reflexes are less elaborate than instinctive actions. The latter also have a wider range of adaptability and variability. However, as Lorenz stresses, the releasing mechanism that triggers instinctive acts involves reflex action in its pattern. The idea that an instinct is a chain of reflexes is not rigidly held because of the varying intensity of instinctive behavior patterns.

LEARNED BEHAVIOR

Conditioned or learned behavior differs from inherited instinctive behavior in being acquired or modified from experience. Although lower animals are superior in instinctive equipment and higher animals are superior in acquiring new behavior through learning, most animals, even the simplest, are capable of learning. The distinction between unlearned and learned behavior is not easy. Variability occurs in nearly all types of behavior and adds to the complicated nature of behavior studies. Behavior is never exactly predictable, even among the simplest of animals. The concept of learning must then have a variety of meanings. Ordinarily it refers to changes in behavior which are brought about by past experience and which involve more or less permanent modifications of the neural basis of behavior.

The basis of learned experience depends upon many factors, but the most important is the nature or pattern of the nervous system. A particular kind of behavior cannot occur unless there is an established nerve channel for it, neither can it be modified unless there are alternative channels for its expression. Learning implies multiplicity of responses, so that if an organism is frustrated in one response it can try another. This requires adequate nervous interconnections and dominant nerve centers. In many invertebrates the brain is an efficient transmitter rather than an organizing center. When the principal nerve centers can override local reflex patterns, so characteristic of lower organisms, more diverse types of behavior can occur. The capacity for learning depends, then, upon the anatomical and physiological capacities possessed by each group of animals.

To what extent can learning be determined in the animal kingdom? With what accuracy can one say that this particular animal is capable or incapable of such and such a learning process? How valid are the conclusions of the almost endless experimentation which has been done on this problem? One of the greatest difficulties encountered in this field is the impossibility of supplementing objective behavior observations with subjective knowledge. The experimenter cannot know by direct experience what animals of other species feel or perceive. He must depend upon the use of stimuli and the way animals react to them for his knowledge of their behavior. By using controlled experiment, observation, physical analysis of the environment, discriminatory learning, and so forth, the investigator tries to ferret out just what the learning capacity is for a particular animal.

An animal's sensitivity determines how it reacts to its environment. The sensory equipment of animals show enormous differences. Many animals are blind; others live below the surface of the ground in total darkness. Ants live in a world of odors just as other animals live primarily in a world of light and shade. Honeybees are unresponsive to red colors when mixed with gray series but can be taught to distinguish most other colors of the spectrum when interspersed among shades of gray. Cats and dogs are insensitive to colors or hues. Bats emit and react to supersonic vibrations (inaudible to human ears). Male moths are attracted to female odors a mile away. Scores of other examples could be given to indicate that animals have many different sensory abilities, some greater and some less than that found in man.

In studying the varieties of learning found among animals, then, investigators must keep in mind certain basic factors which influence behavior patterns. Among these factors are the animal's external environment both past and present, its present physiological states, its anatomy and physiology, its sensory mechanism, its level of nervous system, and its system of effectors (muscles, endocrine glands, etc.). Any investigation that has little relationship to the biology and natural history of the animal being studied will in general have little significance.

The factors that have done most in the evolution of learning ability are orientation, sensory perception, and skill in manipulation of materials.

Some of the most important varieties or types of learning are conditioned reflexes or associative learning, selective learning, insight learning, and imprinting.

Conditioned reflexes or associative learning. A conditioned reflex is substituting one stimulus for another in bringing about a type of response. It is often considered the simplest form of learning and involves a new stimulus-response connection. We owe this concept mainly to the Russian physiologist I. P. Pavlov, who noted that hungry dogs (and other animals) secrete copious amounts of saliva at the sight or odor of food. By ringing a bell (the conditioned stimulus) at the same time they saw food (unconditioned stimulus), it was possible in time for the conditioned stimulus alone to elicit the response of salivation. The dog could also be conditioned to other forms of stimuli, although there was a definite limit to the number of factors to which an animal could be conditioned for a single response. Animals with higher nervous systems can handle more (and more complex) factors of conditioning. It seems probable that almost any given response may be conditioned when the necessary stimuli are presented together, but it is far more prominent among mammals and some birds. The application of the conditioned reflex concept to human behavior may explain many aspects of our reactions. No doubt many of our likes and dislikes, prejudices and interests, as well as our habits are produced by associations of this kind.

Selective learning (trial and error). This is a higher type of learning and is rarely found below the arthropods. It has nothing to do with an unconditioned stimulus and involves rewards and punishments. With this type the animal does not learn something new but selects a random response on the basis of a reward or punishment. A dog, for instance, finds that a problem box containing food can be opened by pulling on a lever. To get to the food, the animal at first makes many random, useless movements (trial and error), but when it finally succeeds, trials later become fewer until it learns to open the box when confronted with the situation the first time. It has thus mastered a habit of appropriate response. Dogs, and also other animals, vary greatly in mastering problem boxes. Some do so with few trials; others require many.

Mazes and labyrinths are frequently used in selective learning in which a reward or punishment is involved with the right or wrong choice. The maze is often Y or T shaped. When the animal chooses the wrong passage it confronts a blind end, which may involve punishment, or else it fails to achieve a reward which it receives by choosing the right one. Even ants and earthworms can master this type of labyrinth after many trials, but some

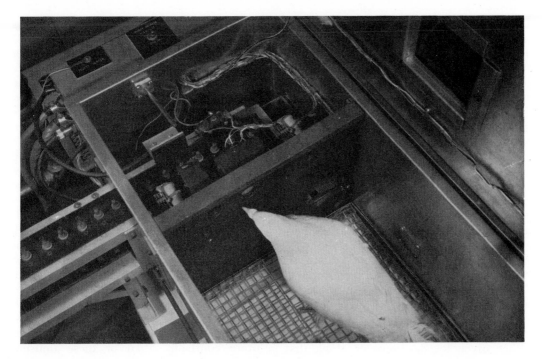

Figure 639. Pigeon taught to do work of a man. This bird has been taught to sort out, for a drug company, inadequately coated capsules by pecking the proper keys for acceptable or nonacceptable capsules as they are brought automatically into view through a tiny window. Birds are trained for this inspection by rewards of food whenever they spot a defective capsule. Birds vary in length of time required for training, but most become expert inspectors in 60 to 80 hours and can easily detect minor flaws overlooked by human inspectors. Principle employed is that of Skinner method, which has been used for many species of animals. (Courtesy T. Verhave, Eli Lilly & Co., Indianapolis, Ind.).

mammals can master the trick with very few attempts. It is a good test to determine an animal's capacity to use acquired behavior in new situations. The widely used Skinner box is based upon a reward of food when the animal presses the right lever (Figure 639).

Insight learning. Insight learning may be considered a modified form of trial and error. When a process is slowly learned by an animal it is often called trial and error; when learned rapidly it is insight, often called "abridged learning." It involves a solution to a problem after an initial survey of the elements involved, getting the idea on the first trial. The facility with which this is done often depends upon previous experience with similar situations. Many cases of selective learning in which animals solve problems

after a few trials may involve a test situation not entirely new to the animal and it profits from previous experience. The capacity for short-cut solutions is rare among most invertebrates but is common in higher mammals.

The concept of latent learning overlaps that of insight learning, and some authorities do not make much distinction between the two. Latent learning refers to learning without definite motivation, such as the random exploration of the immediate surroundings by an animal without the motive of an immediate reward. Later, this learned experience can be used by the organism in its adjustments to specific needs. It is thus a form of transfer training. Birds and mammals probably best display latent learning.

Imprinting. This concept was formulated by O. Heinroth (1910) and refers to a very special type of learning in birds. In the first hours after hatching, a duck or goose is attracted to the first large object it sees and thereafter will follow that object (man, dog, or inanimate) to the exclusion of all others; such birds show no recognition of their parents. When once accomplished, the behavior pattern is very stable and may be irreversible in some cases. Other species of birds may show imprinting. Some psychologists think the type of bird song young hatched birds acquire when exposed to members of different species may be of this nature. The process indicates how learning may be restricted to a critical period of the life cycle. According to Lorenz, when a young bird is imprinted to a member of another species, the imprinted bird will adjust its own functional cycles to that of its adopted parent. Other psychologists, however, think that imprinting is merely a strong early habit and that its socialization to another species is very restricted.

TOOL USING AMONG ANIMALS

The ability to use tools is often considered one of the major achievements of man toward the high evolutionary rank he now holds. Tool using among animals below man is very restricted. Yerkes found that chimpanzees manipulated certain tools in a manner that indicated they had a clear perception of what the tools were for and that their use of them was not a chance trial-and-error method. Many animals rather low in the scale of evolution display amazing feats of craftsmanship, but this usually involves manipulating the materials with bodily parts, beaks, feet, and jaws. In the relatively few cases known among animals the behavior is of an instinctive pattern and no high degree of intelligence need be assigned it. Its action appears to be stereotyped, fixed, and of great antiquity.

One of the early observations of tool using by animals is recorded by the Peckhams in their famous monograph on the solitary wasps. *Ammophila*, a sphegid wasp, seizes a small pebble in her jaws and pounds down (as with a hammer) the earth with which she closes up her burrow. P. and N. Rau reported the same behavior in different species of the same group. In some cases a stone is only used occasionally; more commonly they use only their head and jaws to tramp down the sand.

A widely publicized case of tool using among birds is one of Darwin's finches of the Galápagos Islands. Among these finches, which so well illustrate adaptive radiation, one has the habits of a woodpecker in probing into crevices of bark and trees. To overcome the handicap of a short beak the bird holds a stick or thorn in its beak to pry out its prey. The bower bird of Australia paints the walls of its bower with charcoal and saliva which is applied with a crude brush of fibers. This habit is only one aspect of the elaborate courtship ritual of these unusual birds.

A fascinating account of unique tool using has been found in Malay where a certain red ant (*Oecophylla*) builds its home in leaves. Although the larva of this ant does not weave a cocoon, it does produce silk, an advantage the adults use when they weave leaves together in building or repairing their homes. Some of the workers hold the edges of the leaves together while others hold the larvae in their jaws and pass them back and forth like shuttles from one edge to another, thus closing the gap with a sheet of silk which is secreted by the larvae during the sewing process.

COMMUNICATION AMONG ANIMALS

The idea of communication as applied to animals is not the same as language which involves the symbolic use of certain activities for influencing other members of the group. Every social group of animals has some way for maintaining contact between its members. Communication is simply the influencing of one individual by the behavior of another. This may take the form of bodily contacts (rubbing antennae in bees), scents from glands (mammals at mating season), voice effects (warning cries of birds and mammals), and hosts of others. In some cases, among the higher nonhuman mammals, distinctions between communication and language cannot be rigidly drawn. Yerkes observed in his chimpanzees many sounds and signs which seem to be understood by other members in specific or symbolic ways. Many animal behaviorists believe that many animals have meaningful systems of communication which are not understood by man at all. However, it has been impossible to teach any nonhuman animal a true symbolic language with meaningful association. The reproduction of words and phrases by parrots and mynas has no significant meaning to the birds themselves. A simple form of symbolism of definite meaning is shown whenever a dog assumes a threatening attitude by baring its fangs or raising the hair on its back.

Communication in birds has been extensively studied, and revealing things have been discovered. Bird sounds of a particular species often show a great deal of differentiation. Many of these are thought to be meaningful calls of distress, hunger, warning, etc. W. H. Thorpe, the English investigator, thinks that the sound of birds is to arouse emotional states of warning and courtship and to convey precise information. It is now known since Howard's work that the bird song is actually a warning cry to others of territorial rights. Thorpe has shown that the common English chaffinch has two kinds of warning notes under different circumstances. When mobbing a predator bird chaffinches utter sharp, low-pitched sounds ("chinks") which advertise the presence of the predator. Against a predator on the wing, they utter a high-pitched, thin note ("seeet") which is difficult to locate, so that the hawk or owl has no positional clues of the small birds hiding in the foliage. It is thought that the varied songs of birds are an integration of both innate and learned song patterns and that they sing both for communication and for pleasure.

Bird reactions to calls of various kinds are partly learned and partly inborn. When American crows have been exposed only to the signals of their own group they will not react to the alarm and assembly calls of French crows; when they have mingled with other groups of their own or different species, they learn to respond to the signals of the other groups as though they had learned the meaning of crow calls regardless of species or group differences.

It has been known from the experience of underwater-sound men during World War II that fish and other marine forms make a variety of noises within the sea. Much investigation has been conducted to determine the nature of these sounds in supposedly silent animals. The results have been fascinating. Fish and many other marine forms have no vocal organs but manage to produce a great variety of noises in diverse ways. The chief noise makers are the toadfish, squirrelfish, sea robin, and triggerfish. Many of them use their air bladders to produce sounds. The toadfish and sea robin cause vibrations in their air bladders by muscle contraction; the triggerfish uses its pectoral fins for beating upon a membrane of the air bladder near the body surface; and some, like the squirrelfish, grind together teeth in the back of their mouths and this sound is amplified by the air bladder. Their noises have been recorded on tape for study. Investigators think some of the sounds are made for communication. It is known that fish give different sounds under different physiological states. During spawning, their sounds are different from those at other times.

SOCIAL BEHAVIOR AMONG ANIMALS

Social behavior refers to groups of animals (usually of the same species) living together and exhibiting activity patterns different from what the members would display when living as separate individuals. In this sense, animals are social when their behavior is modified by living together and when they influence and are influenced by other members of the group.

There are many kinds and degrees of social organization and no single definition will apply to all. Mere aggregations of animals such as those in an animal community cannot be called social groups. Animals aggregate for many reasons. They may be attracted by some common favorable environmental factor (e.g., light, shade, moisture) and form natural aggregations. Moths may be attracted to a light or barnacles to a common float. Such animals do not aid each other, but they have a social toleration toward each other and do not prevent others from sharing the same conditions. Some aggregations are the result of more positive reactions to others like themselves, such as schools of fish, flocks of birds roosting together, and the migratory gregarious habits of many birds. Many types of aggregations also have a survival value and, to a certain extent, may be said to serve a social function. The protective circle of giraffe, musk ox, and other herds against predators is an example of this.

Whenever aggregated animals develop division of labor there is the beginning of social behavior. The sexes have division of labor which varies in degree from a mere shedding of gametes into the water by the two parents to the elaborate mating reactions and sex functions of higher forms. Among many kinds of animals, the parents and their offspring may form a closely knit social group while the young are developing; in a wolf pack this family relationship may be more or less permanent. Social relationships may involve only two or three individuals or it may include a whole class of individuals.

In evolution there seems to be a definite trend toward a natural selection of those species which have achieved some degree of mutual cooperation or marked social relationships. Whether a social instinct is transmitted by inheritance from generation to generation is not yet certain. Social organization seems to be the result of the interaction between an inherited behavior pattern and learned experience. Perhaps among invertebrates such as bees, ants, and termites the in-herited pattern would be the dominant factor. Social drives or appetites are usually less intense than those of hunger or sex (which may be considered a form of social behavior), although anyone who has watched schools of small squid in an aquarium and the quick recovery of their organization pattern when broken up is impressed with the force of this social behavior drive.

There seems to be a definite relationship between structural complexity and levels of social integration. This is shown by insects that are at the peak of arthropod evolution and of social organization. The roles of the various members of ant and termite societies are determined by structural differences which result in an inflexible division of labor. Such societies have a long evolutionary history and are so integrated that a member has little chance of survival when separated from its society. Survival here depends upon the fate of the group in meeting the requirements of the environment.

How has social organization arisen? What factors have determined its organization and complexity? No animal lives to itself but is knit to others in some way. Social life in some degree appears to be a universal, normal way of living, ranging from the so-called solitary species to complex associations. Natural selection has operated here as elsewhere in the evolutionary pattern of social aggregations. Various types of societies have arisen, flourished, or become extinct often without any relation to each other. Parallel evolution has been common. Many social organization patterns have followed similar lines because their members have followed similar lines of evolution. Thus any particular social organization is not necessarily in direct evolutionary line with another. Social organization has reached its climax with the arthropods and the mammals. Each of these groups is at the peak of the two main lines of evolution, the annelid-mollusk-arthropod line and the echinoderm-vertebrate line. The social development of these lines has been separately evolved and is not due to common ancestral stock. Each arose from a family unit rather than from aggregation of individuals. Most species of ants, for instance, start a colony by the queen laying eggs which differentiate into the various caste members of workers, soldiers, sexes, etc. Caste determination may be quite complicated and no single plan is followed. In some bees and ants the males develop from haploid (unfertilized) eggs and the other members from diploid eggs. Among termites the males are diploid and the females haploid. Food differences are also determining factors in some cases. Many mammal societies start from the family unit, such as the wolf pack and the societies of the great apes.

According to Allee, a great student of social behavior, vertebrate animal groups have organized their social behavior in accordance with three general principles. These are territorial rights, dominance-subordinance hierarchies, and leadership-followership relations. Much of our knowledge about **territorial rights** dates from Howard's work on birds (1920). This concept involves a restricted area which is taken over, usually by a male, and vigorously defended against trespass by members of other species. The birds sing mainly to proclaim ownership; when a bird's domain is invaded he will fight against the trespasser. Territories may be staked out before or after mating, and there are many variations of behavior among different species. Biological values of such behavior are obvious, for population densities, accessible food supplies, and well-spaced aggregations are promoted to the best advantage. Other groups of animals, including fish, reptiles, and mammals, are known to follow similar territorial rights patterns.

The concept of **dominance-subordinance** refers to a type of social behavior in a group in which one animal is dominant over others. We owe much of this concept to the Norwegian scientist T. Schjelderup-Ebbe, who in 1922 observed that in poultry flocks one hen was dominant over the others and exerted the right to peck other members without being pecked in return.

Further study revealed that flocks were organized on the basis of social hierarchies, that is, there was a whole series of social levels in which members of the higher levels had peck rights over those of lower levels, and so on. The hen of the lowest level is pecked by all the others but does not peck back. Just how many there could be in a peck order has never been ascertained, but these pecking organizations are based largely upon the ability of birds to recognize the members of a flock as individuals. If the population is too large pecking orders may not exist. New members added to a flock, as well as those which are absent from the flock for any length of time, are usually assigned to lower levels. When dominance is once won (usually by fighting) it is relatively permanent. However, it is possible for a lower ranking member to advance to a higher level when its victories are greater than its defeats in challenging the social ranking. A given individual may maintain her social position in many flocks at the same time, although she may occupy a different rank in each flock.

Social hierarchy also exists among the males. One of the best examples of this male dominance is found in the sage grouse of the western American plains. During the breeding season early in spring each male establishes a dominance relation with the other males. The most dominant or master cock takes his position in an area and the less dominant cocks form a guard ring around him. Hens are admitted in the ring, but others are driven away. About 75% of all mating is performed by the master cocks which comprise about 1% of all the males. Dominance hierarchies have been found in all classes of vertebrates, including fish, lizards, mice, and primates. Some arthropods show dominance behavior patterns to a limited extent, but ordinarily the innate, stereotyped behavior of arthropods does not fit into this place of learned behavior.

Leadership behavior refers to the tendency of the members of a group to follow a certain member. It usually involves the selection of an experienced member that stabilizes the other members of the group and holds them together when they are on the move (sheep and deer). Leadership has definite values for the group as a whole and not merely for an individual. The behavior pattern is especially valuable in times of emergency. In some cases the leader may be the dominant member of the group; more often it is an old, experienced female that has the right because of the larger number of offspring that have acquired the habit of following her when they were young. Males, except during the breeding season, are away from the flock, whereas the females are always around.

The relationship between the leader and the followers is different from that of dominance and subordinance. Being the leader does not confer special social privileges, but there is a mutual dependence upon each other of both leader and followers. Besides mammals, certain types of leadership are known to exist among fish, lizards, and birds. In the invertebrates, the arthropods show the behavior here and there. One of the most careful studies ever made on the leadership-followership concept was done by F. F. Darling on Scottish herds of red deer, which he describes vividly in his now classical book, *A Herd of Red Deer* (1937). His observations show the important role of the female (hind) as a leader of a herd and the extreme care she exerts in looking after its welfare. He states that Landseer was a faulty observer in depicting the stag as the "Monarch of the Glen," in his famous picture, for the social system of red deer is definitely matriarchal. Stags form their own companies at times other than the breeding season, but such groups are extremely loose organizations with no apparent leader.

It is apparent that in nearly all groups of animals which show social relations the female is the primary influence in leadership and the center of family life. The aggressive males tend to break up social behavior patterns, and nature, to offset this tendency, either produces males in limited numbers (as in many insects) or the males are kept more or less to themselves except during the breeding season. A notable exception is the termite organization in which males play a role almost as prominent as that of the females.

ANNOTATED REFERENCES

Carthy, J. D. 1958. An Introduction to the Behavior of Invertebrates. New York, The Macmillan Co. *In this work the author stresses the functions of the sensory patterns of invertebrates and their reactions to the various categories of stimuli.*

Darling, F. F. 1937. A Herd of Red Deer. A Study in Animal Behavior. Oxford, Oxford University Press. *This is a notable contribution to animal behavior and represents a careful and penetrating analysis of the movement, population, reproduction, and other aspects of an interesting group of animals. This work has a well-deserved reputation in ecology and animal behavior.*

Griffin, D. R. 1958. Listening in the Dark. New Haven, Yale University Press. *The author subtitles this revealing work, "The Acoustic Orientation of Bats and Men," but other forms are also considered. The author's contribution to the concept of echolocation has fitted him to summarize the mechanisms of accoustic orientation wherever it is found in the animal kingdom, but the major portion of the present treatise is about bats. A bibliography of nearly 500 titles is included.*

Harlow, H. F., and C. N. Woolsey (editors). 1958. Biological and Biochemical Bases of Behavior. Madison, The University of Wisconsin Press. *This volume is based on a symposium held at the University of Wisconsin. Its aim has been to correlate investigations between anatomy, physiology, and biochemistry in their relations to animal behavior. This work will cause one to appreciate the ever-widening field of animal behavior.*

Hooker, D. 1952. The Prenatal Origin of Behavior. Lawrence, University of Kansas Press.

Peckham, G. W., and E. G. Peckham. 1905. Wasps, Social and Solitary. New York, Houghton Mifflin Co. *The careful observations made on an interesting group of insects by these investigators represent a classical study in animal behavior. One of the most revealing observations was the action of some wasps in using pebbles as hammers in pounding down the entrance to their burrows.*

Roe, A., and G. G. Simpson (editors). 1958. Behavior and Evolution. New Haven, Yale University Press. *This well-prepared volume is made up of contributions by eminent authorities on the various problems of integrating evolution and behavior. It tries to fit comparative psychology into the modern synthetic idea of evolution. This outstanding work is further proof of the looming importance of behavior patterns in biological adaptation. It is a work for the serious and advanced student of zoology.*

Schiller, C. H. (editor). 1957. Instinctive Behavior. The Development of a Modern Concept. New York, International Universities Press, Inc. *This distinctive book is made up of the contributions of such eminent authorities as Kuenen, Lorenz, Tinbergen, von Uexkull, and others. It is a comparative study of animal behavior, a subject much in the limelight at present. The work, as a whole, develops the idea that behavior patterns are characteristic of any taxonomic group of animals as are morphological patterns of structure. The basis of learning has its foundation in the combination of these action patterns into more elaborate behavior.*

Scott, J. P. 1958. Animal Behavior. Chicago, University of Chicago Press. *An interesting and well-balanced book on animal behavior written in a simple and direct style. Although formulating some clear-cut principles about the organization and behavior of social groups and populations, the author well recognizes the many problems connected with animal behavior and how difficult it is to form general laws about it without extensive experimentation and observation.*

Scott, J. P. 1958. Aggression. Chicago, University of Chicago Press. *The author attempts to present a picture of the problems of aggression or fighting and the biological and psychological factors which underlie such problems. He points out the application of these principles to human society and how aggressive tendencies can be channeled into constructive activities. The book is interesting and revealing.*

Thorpe, W. H. 1956. Learning and Instinct in Animals. Cambridge, Harvard University Press. *Of the many works on animal behavior in recent years, this book is an excellent synthesis of the behavior concepts and learning processes of animals from protozoans to mammals. In part III the author treats of the learning abilities of those groups on which most investigation has been done.*

Tinbergen, N. 1957. The Study of Instinct. Oxford, The Clarendon Press. *Study of animal behavior is now one of the most active fields of biological investigation. The author of this work is foremost in the field, and this work summarizes his basic concepts. He attempts to show the evolutionary picture of how the rational behavior of animals and man has arisen from innate behavior patterns. The work is a challenging one to all profound students of animal behavior.*

Tinbergen, N. 1958. Curious Naturalists. New York, Basic Books, Inc. *A popular account of the study of animals in their natural habitats by a famous student of animal behavior. Part of the work is devoted to an interesting natural history study in the Arctic.*

Watson, J. B. 1930. Behaviorism, rev. ed. Chicago, The University of Chicago Press. *A classical psychological work which has exerted a great influence on the modern interpretation of behavior patterns.*

Part Six

Development of zoology

Origin of basic concepts and key discoveries in biology, including books that have influenced zoology

It is very difficult to appraise the historical development of any field of study. Discoveries are usually due to the cooperation and investigation of many minds. It is not unusual for several workers to arrive at virtually the same conclusions independently because they have been studying on the same frontier of some particular aspect. One investigator often gets the credit for an important discovery, whereas many others should share in the prestige. No one individual has a monopoly of ideas, and advances in science are built upon the results of many causes and the work of many minds. However, certain important generalizations have been aptly phrased by some one worker who crystalizes the thought on that particular aspect of study.

Certain key discoveries have greatly influenced the progress along certain lines. This list aims to give some of the major landmarks in the development of biology and the individuals whose names are commonly associated with these key discoveries. In this brief outline the student may be able to see some relation between one discovery and another, so that the discoveries do not appear completely isolated. It will be noted that fundamental discoveries in a particular branch of biology tend to be grouped fairly close together chronologically because that interest may have dominated the thought of biological investigators at that time.

384-322 b.c.: *Aristotle. The foundation of zoology as a science.*

Although this great pioneer zoologist and philosopher cannot be appraised by modern standards, there is scarcely a major subdivision of zoology to which he did not make some contribution. He was a true scientist, for he emphasized the observational and experimental method. Despite his lack of scientific background, he was one of the greatest scientists of all time.

130-200 a.d.: *Galen. Development of anatomy and physiology.*

This Roman investigator has been praised for his clear concept of scientific methods and blamed for passing down to others for centuries certain glaring errors. His influence was so great that for centuries after his period students considered him the final authority on anatomical and physiological subjects.

1347: *William of Occam. Occam's razor.*

This principle of logic has received its name from the fact that it is supposed to cut out unnecessary and irrelevant hypotheses in the explanation of phenomena. The gist of the principle is that of several possible explanations the one that is simplest has the fewest assumptions and the one most consistent with the data at hand is the most probable one.

1543: *Vesalius, Andreas. First modern interpretation of anatomical structures.*

With his insight into fundamental structure, Vesalius ushered in the dawn of modern biological investigation. Many aspects of his interpretation of anatomy are just now beginning to be appreciated.

1603: *Platter, F. First description of Diphyllobothrium latum.*

This first published account of the broad tapeworm of man represents an early beginning in the field of parasitology.

1616-1628: *Harvey, William. First accurate description of blood circulation.*

Harvey's classical demonstration of blood circulation was the key experiment which laid the foundation of modern physiology. He explained bodily processes in physical terms, cleared away much of the mental rubbish of mystic interpretation, and gave an auspicious start to experimental physiology.

1627: *Aselli, G. First demonstration of lacteal vessels.*

This discovery, coming at the same time as Harvey's great work, supplemented the discovery of circulation. His name was given to a group of lymph nodes in the mesenteries of mammals, the *pancreas of Aselli.*

1649: *Descartes, R. Early concept of reflex action.* Descartes did not know the functions of the dorsal and ventral roots of the spinal nerves, but he did postulate the idea that impulses originating at the receptors of the body were carried to the central nervous system where they activated muscles and glands by what he called "reflection."

1651: *Harvey, William. Aphorism of Harvey: omne vivum ex ovo (all life from the egg).*

Although Harvey's work as an embryologist is overshadowed by his demonstration of the circulation, his *De Generatione Animalium* published in 1651 contains many sound observations on embryological processes. He was opposed to the preformation theory which was held by many biologists of his and later times.

1652: *Bartholin, Thomas. Discovery of lymphatic system.*

The significance of the thoracic duct in its relation to the circulation was determined in this investigation. Bartholin performed his classical demonstrations mainly on human bodies, material not usually available in his time.

1658: *Swammerdam, Jan. Description of red blood corpuscles.*

This discovery, together with his observations on the valves of the lymphatics and the alterations in shape of muscles during contraction, represented early advancements in the microscopical study of bodily structures.

1660: *Malpighi, Marcello. Demonstration of capillary circulation.*

By demonstrating the capillaries in the lung of a frog, Malpighi was able to complete the scheme of blood circulation, for Harvey never saw capillaries and thus never included them in his description. His name has been given to the Malpighian corpuscles of the kidney and to the deeper portion of the epidermis of the skin.

1665: *Hooke, Robert. Discovery of the cell.*

This was an insignificant discovery at the time and was so regarded for a long time, but how important the cell loomed in the early nineteenth century! Hooke's investigations were made with cork and the term cell fits much better than it does to animal cells. But by tradition the misnomer has stuck.

1672: *de Graaf, R. Description of ovarian follicles.*

De Graaf's name is given to the mature ovarian follicle, but he thought that the follicles were the actual ova, an error corrected by von Baer long after.

1675-1680: *Leeuwenhoek, Anthony van. Discovery of protozoa.*

The discoveries of this eccentric Dutch

microscopist revealed a whole new world of biology.

1693: Ray, J. Concept of species.

Although Ray's work on classification was later overshadowed by Linnaeus, Ray was really the first to make the species concept apply to a particular kind of organism and to point out the variations which exist among the members of a species.

1733: Hales, Stephen. First measurement of blood pressure.

This was further proof that the bodily processes could be measured quantitatively—more than a century after Harvey's momentous demonstration.

1744: Trembley, A. Observations on the structure of Hydra.

Trembley worked out with considerable detail and accuracy the nature of the interesting little animal.

1745: Bonnet, Charles. Discovery of natural parthenogenesis.

Although somewhat unusual in nature, this phenomenon has yielded much information about meiosis and other cytological problems. It is of especial importance in its relation to artificial parthenogenesis, a subject of perennial interest.

1745: Maupertuis, P. M. Early concept of evolutionary process.

Although Maupertuis' ideas are speculative and not based on experimental observation, he foretold many of the concepts of variation and natural selection which Darwin was to demonstrate with convincing evidence.

1753: Reaumur, R. A. F. de. Experiments on digestion.

This was the first recorded account of any note on the nature of the basic principle of nutrition and paved the way for the extensive studies of Beaumont, Pavlov, and Cannon.

1758: Linnaeus, Carolus. Development of binominal nomenclature system of taxonomy.

So important is this work in taxonomy that 1758 is regarded as the starting point in the determination of the generic and specific names of animals. Besides the value of his binomial system, Linnaeus gave taxonomists a valuable working model of conciseness and clearness which has never been surpassed.

1759: Wolff, C. F. Embryological theory of epigenesis.

This embryologist, the greatest before von Baer, did much to overthrow the grotesque preformation theory then in vogue, and, in spite of many shortcomings, laid the basis for the modern interpretation of embryology. The Wolffian ducts are named after him.

1760: Hunter, John. Development of comparative investigations of animal structure.

This vigorous eighteenth century anatomist gave a powerful impetus not only to anatomical observations but also to the establishment of natural history museums.

1763: Koelreuter, J. G. Discovery of quantitative inheritance (multiple genes).

Koelreuter, a pioneer in plant hybridization, found that certain plant hybrids had characters more or less intermediate between the parents in the F_1 generation, but in the F_2 there were many gradations from one extreme to the other. An explanation was not forthcoming until after Mendel's laws were discovered, when it was shown that it was due to the effect of multiple genes.

1768-1779: Cook, James. Influence of geographical exploration on biological development.

This famous sea captain made possible a greater range of biological knowledge because of the able naturalists whom he took on his voyages of discovery. Captain Cook must also be remembered for the practical way he solved the ancient scourge of scurvy.

1774: Priestly, Joseph. Discovery of oxygen.

The discovery of this element is of great biological interest because it helped in determining the nature of oxidation and the exact role of respiration in organisms.

1778: Lavoisier, Antoine. Nature of animal respiration demonstrated.

A basis for the chemical interpretation of the life process was given a great impetus by the careful quantitative studies of the changes during breathing made by this great investigator. His work also meant the final overthrow of the mystical phlogiston theory which had held sway for so long.

1781: *Abildgaard, P. First experimental life cycle of a tapeworm.*

Life cycles of parasites may be very complicated, involving several hosts. This early achievement was followed by many others less than a century later.

1791: *Smith, W. Correlation between fossils and geological strata.*

By observing that certain types of fossils were peculiar to particular strata Smith was able to work out a method for estimating geological age. He laid the basis of stratigraphic geology. His conclusion that fossils constituted a stratified series with unvarying arrangement prepared the way for Cuvier and Lyell.

1792: *Galvani, L. Animal electricity.*

The lively controversy between Galvani and Volta over the twitching of frog legs has led to extensive investigation of precise methods of measuring the various electrical phenomena of animals.

1796: *Cuvier, G. Development of vertebrate paleontology.*

Cuvier compared the structure of fossil forms with that of living ones and concluded that there had been a succession of organisms which had become extinct and were succeeded by the creation of new ones. To account for this extinction, Cuvier held to the theory of catastrophism, or the simultaneous extinction of animal populations by natural cataclysms. His colleague Lamarck, working with the fossils of invertebrates, believed that all populations did not cease at one time but that there was a continuation, with modifications, of life into succeeding geological eras.

1797: *Goethe, J. W. von. Concept of archetypes of animals.*

In this theory, Goethe tried to formulate ideal forms which best fitted animals for their conditions of existence. Although his views were somewhat vaguely expressed, modern biology recognizes the importance of the concept in the way contemporary organisms can best fit into the varied ecological niches of the animal kingdom.

1800: *Bichat, M. F. X. Analysis of body tissues.*

Bichat's studies on body tissues formed the basis of modern histology. He classified the tissues into twenty-one different types, but his failure to use the microscope prevented him from correctly appraising the true minute structure of tissues as we now know them.

1801: *Lamarck, J. B. Evolutionary concept of use and disuse.*

Lamarck gave the first clear-cut expression of a theory to account for organic evolution. His assumption that acquired characters were inherited has been the subject of fierce controversy ever since it was proposed, and although, in general, most evolutionists have refuted this part of his theory, nearly every generation sees a revival of it in some way or other.

1810: *Gall, F. J. Localization of brain functions.*

That different areas of the brain do have different functions was verified by experimental work, a fact which Gall foreshadowed by his crude experiments on skull contours. He should not be blamed for phrenology which quacks quickly developed. His name is recalled by the column of Gall, one of the nerve pathways of the spinal cord.

1814: *Kirchhoff, G. Demonstration of catalytic action.*

Kirchhoff's discovery that starch treated with an extract of barley malt was converted into glucose was the crude beginning of extensive investigations which have been fruitful in understanding the metabolic activities of living protoplasm.

1817: *Pander, C. First description of three germ layers.*

The description of the three germ layers was first made on the chick, and later the concept was extended by von Baer to include all vertebrates.

1822. *Bell C., and F. Magendie. Discovery of the functions of dorsal and ventral roots of spinal nerves.*

This demonstration was a starting point

for an anatomical and functional investigation of the most complex system in the body. The Bell-Magendie law appears simple compared with other aspects of nervous behavior, but it showed that something could be done to unravel the complexity of this system.

1823: Knight, T. Concept of dominance and recessiveness.

Although this investigator worked with the same pea with which Mendel made his classical discoveries, he was unable to formulate clear-cut laws about the mechanism of heredity, but his information about the breeding of peas gave Mendel something to work on later.

1824: Prevost, P., and Dumas, J. B. A. Cell division first described.

The description of the cleavage of the frog egg before the arrival of the cell theory meant that its true significance could not be appreciated at that time. The same observers also showed the true role of the spermatozoan in fertilization.

1825: Raspail, F. V. Beginning of histochemistry.

Raspail devised the iodine test for starch as well as many other histochemical tests for plant and animal tissues. Histochemistry has yielded much information on the location and chemical nature of various cell constituents, such as minerals and enzymes.

1827: Baer, Karl von. Discovery of mammalian ovum.

The very tiny ova of mammals escaped de Graaf's eyes, but von Baer brought mammalian reproduction into line with that of other animals by detecting them and their true relation to the follicles. One of the first achievements of the greatest embryologists of all time was this important discovery.

1828: Brown, Robert. Brownian movement first described.

This interesting phenomenon is characteristic of living protoplasm and sheds some light on the structure of protoplasm.

1828: Thompson, J. V. Nature of plankton.

Thompson's collections of these small forms with a tow net, together with his published descriptions, are the first records of the vast community of planktonic animals. He was also the first to work out the true nature of barnacles.

1828: Wöhler, F. First synthesis of an animal product (urea) in the laboratory.

This was the first synthesis of an organic compound from inorganic material and represents a foundation stone in the great development of organic chemistry and biochemistry.

1829. Vauguelin, N. L. Discovery of carotene.

This important pigment, so widely distributed through the plant and animal kingdoms, has been the source of many investigations to determine its true significance. It is now known to be associated with vitamin A and to have many biological activities. The carotinoids are a complex of many kinds of pigments of similar properties.

1830: Amici, G. B. Discovery of fertilization in plants.

Amici was able to demonstrate the tube given off by the pollen grain and to follow it to the micropyle of the ovule through the style of the ovary. Later it was established that a sperm nucleus of the pollen makes contact and union with the nucleus of the egg.

1830: Baer, Karl von. Biogenetic law formulated.

Von Baer's conception of this law was conservative and sounder in its implication than has been the case with many other biologists (Haeckel, for instance), for von Baer stated that embryos of higher and lower forms resemble each other more the earlier they are compared in their development, and *not* that the embryos of higher forms resemble the adults of lower organisms. This viewpoint of von Baer has gradually come to prevail among most modern biologists.

1830: Lyell, C. Modern concept of geology.

The influence of this concept not only did away with the catastrophic theory but also gave a logical interpretation of fossil life and the correlation between the formation of rock strata and the animal life that existed at the time these formations were laid down. Lyell's great work, *The Principles of Geology*, influenced Darwin and his development of the evolutionary concept.

1831: *Brown, Robert. First description of cell nucleus.*

Others had seen nuclei, but Brown was the first to name the structure and to regard the nucleus as a general phenomenon. This description was an important preliminary to the cell theory a few years later, for Schleiden acknowledged the importance of the nucleus in the development of the cell concept.

1833: *Hall, M. Concept of reflex action.*

Although Hall describes the method by which a stimulus can produce a response independently of sensation or volition, it remained for the outstanding work of the great Sir Charles Sherrington in this century to explain much of the complex nature of reflexes.

1833: *Purkinje, J. E. Discovery of sweat glands.*

This discovery was an important step in histological development. It opened up a new field of investigation into problems of the skin and its structure which have not yet been resolved.

1835: *Bassi, Agostino. First demonstration of a microorganism as an infective agent.*

Bassi's discovery that a certain disease of silkworms was due to a small fungus represents the beginning of the germ theory of disease which was to prove so fruitful in the hands of Pasteur and other able investigators.

1835. *Dujardin, Felix. Description of living matter (protoplasm).*

Dujardin associated the jellylike substance which he found in protozoa and which he called "sarcode" with the life process. This substance was later to be called protoplasm, and the sarcode idea may be considered a significant landmark in the development of the protoplasm concept.

1835: *Owen, R. Discovery of Trichinella.*

This versatile investigator is chiefly remembered for his researches in anatomy, but his discovery of this most common parasite in American people is an important landmark in the history of parasitology.

1837: *Berzelius, J. J. Formulation of catalytic concept.*

Substances which caused chemical conversions by their mere presence he called catalytic in contrast to analytic, which applied to the real chemical affinity between substances in a chemical reaction. This concept was a cornerstone in the development of chemical science and paved the way for an understanding of biocatalysts or enzymes.

1838: *Liebig, Justus. Foundation of biochemistry.*

The idea that vital activity could be explained by chemical and physical factors has given biological investigators their greatest method of attacking the nature of life problems. Liebig's chemical methods of organic analysis have borne fruit as attested by the important role biochemistry has assumed in present-day investigation.

1838-1839: *Schleiden, M. J., and T. Schwann. Formulation of the cell theory.*

The cell doctrine, with its basic idea that all plants and animals were made up of similar units, represents one of the truly great landmarks in biological progress. The theory opened up a new understanding of the life process, for it gave biologists a starting point for studying the structures and functions of the organisms. It must be remembered, however, that the concept of the cell was due to many workers and not merely to the men whose names are commonly associated with its establishment. Many biologists think the work of Schleiden and Schwann has been rated much higher than it deserves in the light of what others did to develop the cell concept.

1839: *Mulder, J. Concept of the nature of proteins.*

Mulder proposed the name protein for the basic constituents of protoplasmic materials because he considered them of first or primary importance in the structure of living matter. All subsequent investigation has proved the correct etymology of this name. It was Verworn who stated that living matter might be defined as the material in which protein metabolism occurs.

1839-1846: *Purkinje, J. E., and Hugo von Mohl. Concept of protoplasm established.*

Purkinje proposed the name protoplasm for living matter, and von Mohl did extensive work on its nature, but it remained for Max Schultze (1861) to give a clear-cut concept of the relations of protoplasm to cells and its essential unity in all organisms. Purkinje's name is perpetuated by the large basket cells of the cerebellum.

1839: *Verhulst, P. F. Logistic theory of population growth.*

According to this theory animal populations have a slow initial growth rate which gradually speeds up until it reaches a maximum and then slows down to a state of equilibrium. By plotting the logarithm of the total number of individuals against time, an S-shaped curve results which is somewhat similar for all populations. Pearl (1920) revived the concept. The principle applies best to population growth of animals with simple life histories.

1840: *Miller, H. Appraisal of geological formation, Old Red Sandstone.*

These Devonian deposits in Scotland and parts of England represent one of the most important vertebrate-bearing sediments ever discovered. From them much knowledge about early vertebrates, such as ostracoderns, placoderms, bony fish, etc., has been obtained. Similar sediments in other parts of the world have also been found rich in fossils (Spitzbergen, Germany, Wyoming, etc.).

1840: *Müller, J. Theory of specific nerve energies.*

This theory states that the kind of sensation experienced depends on the nature of the sense organ with which the stimulated nerve is connected. The optic nerve, for instance, conveys impression of vision however it is stimulated. This concept has been the focal point for many investigations.

1841: *Remak, Robert. Description of direct cell division.*

Remak first described direct cell division, or amitosis, in the red blood corpusles of the chick embryo. The process appears restricted to fully differentiated or senescent tissue cells. Remak's name is carried by the unmyelinated sympathetic nerve fibers.

1842: *Bowman, William. Histological structure of the nephron (kidney unit).*

Bowman's accurate description of the nephron afforded physiologists an opportunity to attack the problem of how the kidney separates waste from the blood, a problem not yet fully solved. His name is given to the capsule of the renal capsule.

1842: *Steenstrup, J. Alternation of generations described.*

Metagenesis, or alternation of sexual and asexual reproduction in the life cycle, exists in many animals and plants. The concept had been introduced before this time by L. A. de Chamisso (1819).

1843: *Owen, Richard. Concepts of homology and analogy.*

Homology as commonly understood refers to similarity in embryonic origin and development, whereas analogy is the likeness between two organs in their functioning. Owen's concept of homology was merely that of the same organ in different animals under all varieties of form and function. Since his time the concept has been broadened to include evolutionary relationships. The concept has been widely used to establish the common ancestry of animals.

1844: *Ludwig, C. Filtration theory of renal excretion.*

About the same time that Bowman described the Malpighian corpuscle, Ludwig showed that the corpuscle functions as a passive filter and that the filtrate which passes through it from the blood carries into the urinary tubules the waste products which are concentrated by the resorption of water as the filtrate moves down the tubules. Other investigators,

Cushny, Starling, and Richards, have confirmed the theory by actual demonstration. This theory has been modified some since the discovery of tubular excretion, especially in the aglomerular marine fish.

1845: *Helmholtz, H., and J. R. Mayer. Formulation of the law of conservation of energy.*

This landmark, in man's thinking, showed that in any system, living or nonliving, the power to perform mechanical work always tends to decrease unless energy is added from without. Physiological investigation could now advance on the theory that the living organism is an energy machine and obeyed the laws of the science of energetics.

1848: *Hofmeister, W. Discovery of chromosomes.*

In the nuclei of pollen mother cells (*Tradescantia*), this investigator made sketches of bodies later known to be chromosomes. Schneider further described these elements in 1873, and Waldeyer named them in 1888.

1848: *Siebold, C. T. E. von. Establishment of the status of protozoa.*

Siebold emphasized the unicellular nature of protozoa, fitted them into the recently developed cell theory, and established them as the basic phylum of the animal kingdom. F. Dujardin had earlier (1841) considered the protozoan body to be composed of a unit mass (sarcode), now known as protoplasm.

1849: *Berthold, A. A. Transplantation of the testis.*

Since progress in endocrinology depends so much upon experimental modification of animals, such as organ transplantation, Berthold's experiment gave workers in this science one of their most important tools of research.

1850: *Bernard, C. Independent irritability of muscle.*

By using the drug curare, which blocks motor impulses through the myoneural junction, Bernard found that the muscle would still respond to direct stimulation, thus proving that the muscle is independently irritable. This curare experiment has had wide applications in physiology.

1851: *Bernard, C. Discovery of vasomotor system.*

Bernard showed how the amount of blood distributed to the various tissues by the small arterioles was regulated by vasomotor nerves of the sympathetic nervous system, as he demonstrated in the ear of a white rabbit.

1851: *Waller, A. V. Importance of nucleus in regeneration.*

When nerve fibers are cut, the parts of the fibers peripheral to the cut degenerate in a characteristic fashion. This Wallerian degeneration enables one to trace the course of fibers through the nervous system. In the regeneration process the nerve cell body (with its nucleus) is necessary for the downgrowth of the fiber from the proximal segment.

1852: *Helmholtz, Herman von. Determination of rate of nervous impulse.*

This landmark in nerve physiology showed that the difficult phenomena of nervous activity could be expressed numerically.

1852: *Kölliker, Albrecht von. Establishment of histology as a science.*

Many histological structures were described with marvelous insight by this great investigator starting with the publication of the first text in histology (*Handbuch der Gewebelehre*). He was far ahead of his time in anticipating the modern trends in molecular biology. His influence in the development of histology cannot be overestimated.

1852: *Stannius, H. F. Stannius' experiment on the heart.*

By tying a ligature as a constriction between the sinus venosus and the atrium in the frog and also one around the atrioventricular groove, Stannius was able to demonstrate that the muscle tissues of the atria and ventricles have independent and spontaneous rhythm. His observations also indicated that the sinus is the pacemaker of the heartbeat. These experiments started many investigations on the nature of the heartbeat.

1854: *Newport, G. Discovery of the entrance of spermatozoan into frog's egg.*

This was a significant step in cellular

embryology, although its real meaning was not revealed until the concept of fertilization as the union of two pronuclei was formulated about 20 years later (Hertwig, 1875).

1854: *Vogt, C. Experimental infestation of man by pork tapeworm.*

A common experiment with parasitologists is to infect a suspected host to determine a life history.

A little later, the great parasitologist R. Leuckart was able to infect a calf with the cysticerci of the beef tapeworm, *Taenia saginata.*

1856: *Discovery of Neanderthal fossil man (Homo neanderthalensis).*

Many specimens of this type of fossil man have been discovered (Europe, Asia, Africa) since the first one was found near Düsseldorf, Germany. His culture was Mousterian, and although of short stature his cranial capacity was as large or larger than that of modern man. Supposed to have lived during the third interglacial stage in late Pleistocene times, he may have been exterminated by the Cro-Magnon man.

1856: *Perkin, W. H. Discovery of the first coal-tar dye.*

The first coal-tar dye, called aniline violet, was formed by oxidizing aniline with potassium bichromate. Rapid development of dyes, many synthetically, followed; their use in microscopical preparations brought rapid strides in cytological and bacteriological investigations.

1857: *Bernard, Claude. Formation of glycogen by the liver.*

Bernard's demonstration that the liver forms glycogen from substances brought to it by the blood showed that the body can build up complex substances as well as tear them down.

1858: *Sclater, P. L. Distribution of animals on basis of zoological regions.*

This was the first serious attempt to study the geographical distribution of organisms, a study which eventually led to the present science of zoogeography. A. R. Wallace worked along similar lines.

1858: *Virchow, Rudolf. Formulation of the concept of disease from the viewpoint of cell structure.*

He laid the basis of modern pathology by stressing the role of the cell in diseased tissue.

1858: *Virchow, Rudolf. Aphorism of Virchow: Omnis cellula e cellula (every cell from a cell).*

1859: *Darwin, Charles. The concept of natural selection as a factor in evolution.*

Although Darwin did not originate the concept of organic evolution, no one has been more influential in the development of evolutionary thought. The publication of *The Origin of Species* represents the greatest single landmark in the history of biology.

1860: *Bernard, Claude. Concept of the constancy of the internal environment (homeostasis).*

This important concept has influenced physiological thinking, for it shows how organisms in their long evolutionary development have been mainly concerned in preserving their stability against environmental forces.

1860: *Pasteur, Louis. Refutation of spontaneous generation.*

Pasteur's experiment with the open S-shaped flask proved conclusively that fermentation or putrefaction resulted from microbes, thus ending the long-standing controversy regarding spontaneous generation.

1860: *Pasteur, Louis. Aphorism of Pasteur: Omne Vivum e Vivo (every living thing from the living).*

We do not doubt the significance of this concept at present, but from what source did life originate?

1860: *Wallace, A. R. The Wallace line of faunal delimitation.*

As originally proposed by Wallace, there was a sharp boundary between the Australian and Oriental faunal regions, so that a geographical line drawn between certain islands of the Malay Archipelago, through the Makassar Strait between Borneo and Celebes, and between the Philippines and the Sanghir Islands separated two distinct and contrasting zoological regions. On one side Australian forms predominated; on the other, Oriental ones. The validity of this division has been questioned by zoogeographers in the light of more extensive knowledge of the faunas of the two regions.

1861: *Claparede, E. Discovery of giant nerve axons of annelids.*

These large nerve fibers were first found and described by Ehrenberg (1836) in the crustacea. As new microscopic techniques were developed, many investigations have been made on the structure and functions of these unique nerve cells. Their chief function is in escape mechanisms involving widespread and synchronous muscular contractions.

1861: *Graham, Thomas. Colloidal states of matter.*

This work on colloidal solutions has resulted in one of the most fruitful concepts regarding protoplasmic systems. Most aspects of cell physiology involve colloidal interpretation in some form or other.

1864: *Haeckel, E. Modern zoological classification.*

The broad features of zoological classification as we know it today were outlined by Haeckel and others, especially R. R. Lankester, in the third quarter of the nineteenth century. B. Hatschek is another zoologist who deserves much credit for the modern scheme which is constantly undergoing revision. Other schemes of classification in the early nineteenth century did much to resolve the difficult problem of classification, such as those of Cuvier, Lamarck, Leuckart, Ehrenberg, Vogt, Gegenbaur, and Schimkevitch. More recently, L. H. Hyman has done invaluable service in the arrangement of animal taxonomy.

1864: *Schultze, Max. Protoplasmic bridges between cells.*

The connection of one cell to another by means of protoplasmic bridges has been demonstrated in both plants and animals, but the concept has never been settled to the satisfaction of histologists. These intercellular connections have been described in many epithelial tissues where some investigators believe them to be artefacts. The concept that cells are definitely separated from each other has been very well established, at least for nervous and muscular tissues.

1865: *Kekule, F. A. Concept of the benzene ring.*

The concept of the benzene ring established the later development of synthetic chemistry; it also aided in understanding the basic structure of life which is so dependent upon the capacity of carbon atoms to form rings and chains.

1866: *Haeckel, E. Nuclear control of inheritance.*

At the time the hypothesis was formed the view that the nucleus transmitted the inheritance of an animal had no evidence to substantiate it. This lucky guess no doubt focused the attention of biologists upon the nucleus for an explanation of heredity.

1866: *Kowalevsky, A. Taxonomic position of tunicates.*

The great Russian embryologist showed in the early stages of development the similarity between *Amphioxus* and the tunicates and how the latter could be considered a degenerate branch of the phylum Chordata. This was a confirmation of the evolutionary theory from an embryological standpoint and must be considered a great landmark in understanding the development of animals.

1866: *Mendel, Gregor. Formulation of the first two laws of heredity.*

These first clear-cut statements of inheritance made possible an analysis of hereditary patterns with mathematical precision. When Mendel published his great laws they were unnoticed by students of heredity because they were looking for an explanation of heredity from a wholly different viewpoint and could not appreciate his findings. Rediscovered in 1900, his paper confirmed the experimental data geneticists had found at that time. Since that time Mendelism has been considered the chief cornerstone of hereditary investigation.

1866: *Schultze, Max. Histological analysis of the retina.*

Schultze's fundamental discovery that

the retina contained two types of visual cells, rods and cones, helped to explain the differences in physiological vision of high and low intensities of light.

1867: *Kowalevsky, A. Germ layers of invertebrates.*

The concept of the primary germ layers laid down by Pander and von Baer was extended to invertebrates by this investigator. He found that the same three germ layers arose in the same fashion as those in vertebrates. Thus an important embryological unity was established for the whole animal kingdom.

1867: *Traube, I. Concept of the semipermeable membrane.*

The nature and role of living membranes in biological systems have been extensively studied in cellular physiology, for the characteristics of the membrane determine the osmotic behavior of cells and the exchanges cells make with their surroundings. Although Traube worked with nonliving membranes, he formulated many principles which have helped in understanding living ones.

1870: *Miescher, F. Isolation of nucleoprotein.*

From pus cells, a pathological product, Miescher was able to demonstrate in the nuclei certain phosphorus-rich substances, nucleic acids, which are bound to proteins to form nucleoproteins. In recent years these complex molecules have been the focal point of significant biochemical investigations on the chemical properties of genes with the wider implications of a better understanding of growth, heredity, and evolution.

1871: *Bowditch, H. P. Discovery of the "all-or-none" law of heart muscle.*

This law states that a minimal stimulus will produce a maximal contraction of the heart musculature. A single skeletal fiber also obeys the law the same as cardiac muscle, but the latter is a continuous protoplasmic mass and an impulse which causes contraction in one part spreads also to other parts. This does not mean, however, that stimulation of any part of the heart will necessarily lead to contraction of the whole heart, for backward con-

duction in the conduction system (Purkinje) does not always occur.

1871: *Quetelet, L. A. J. Foundations of biometry.*

The application of statistics to biological problems is called biometry. By working out the distribution curve of the height of soldiers, Quetelet showed biologists how the systematic study of the relationships of numerical data could become a powerful tool for analyzing data in evolution, genetics, and other biological fields.

1872: *Challenger Expedition.*

Not only did this expedition establish the science of oceanography but it also collected a vast amount of material which greatly extended the knowledge of the variety and range of animal life. No similar expedition has ever equaled this one.

1872: *Dohrn, Anton. Establishment of Naples Biological Station.*

The establishment of this famous station marked the first of the great biological stations, and it rapidly attained international importance as a center of biological investigation. Many of our greatest American investigators conducted studies here, especially toward the end of the nineteenth century and the beginning of the twentieth.

1872: *Ludwig, K., and E. F. W. Pflüger. Gas exchange of the blood.*

By means of the mercurial blood pump, these investigators separated the gases from the blood and thereby threw much light on the nature of gaseous exchange and the place where oxidation occurred (in the tissues).

1873: *Agassiz, L. Establishment of first American marine laboratory.*

Although short-lived, this laboratory on the island of Penikese near Cape Cod was instrumental in the training of an influential group of American biologists and in the establishment of a scientific tradition which gave a great impetus to biological investigation.

1873: *Schneider, Anton. Description of nuclear filaments (chromosomes).*

In his description of cell division, Schneider showed nuclear structures which he termed nuclear filaments, the first recorded description of what are now known as chromosomes. It was not until several years later that they were actually called chromosomes (colored bodies) by Waldeyer in 1888.

1874: *Haeckel, E. Taxonomic position of phylum Chordata.*

The great German evolutionist based many of his conclusions on the work of the Russian embryologist Kowalevsky, who in 1866 showed that the tunicates as well as amphioxus had vertebrate affinities. The embryologist von Baer had considered such animals to be molluscan forms.

1874: *Haeckel, E. H. Gastraea theory of metazoan ancestry.*

According to this theory the hypothetical ancestor of all the Metazoa consisted of two layers (ectoderm and entoderm) similar to the gastrula stage in embryonic development, and the entoderm arose as an invagination of the blastula composed of a single layer of flagellate cells. Thus the diploblastic stage of ontogeny was to be considered as the repetition of this ancestral form. This theory has had wide acceptance but has been criticised on the grounds that the endoderm is not always formed by invagination, such as the inwandering of ectodermal cells in certain forms.

1875: *Hertwig, O. Concept of fertilization as the conjugation of two sex cells.*

The fusion of the pronuclei of the two gametes in the process of fertilization paved the way for the concept that the nuclei contained the hereditary factors and that both maternal and paternal factors are brought together in the zygote.

1875: *Strasburger, Eduard. Description of indirect cell division.*

The accurate description of the processes of cell division which Strasburger made in plants represents a great pioneer work in the rapid development of cytology during the last quarter of the nineteenth century.

1876: *Cohn, F. Significance of the bacterial spore.*

Spore formation among bacteria is restricted mainly to the bacilli. It is an oval body formed within the bacterial cell, and certain environmental conditions favor its formation within a particular kind of bacteria. It may be considered a normal stage in the life history of spore-forming bacteria and an adaptation to harsh survival conditions. Spore-forming bacteria were no doubt responsible for prolonging the belief in spontaneous generation.

1877: *Manson, P. First report of an arthropod vector.*

In working out the life cycle of *Wuchereria bancrofti*, Manson established the role of the mosquito in carrying the larval parasite. The arthropod vector has assumed great importance in the transmission of diseases and parasites.

1877: *Pfeffer, W. Concept of osmosis and osmotic pressure.*

Pfeffer's experiments on osmotic pressure and the determination of the pressure in different concentrations laid the foundation for an understanding of a general phenomenon in all organisms.

1878: *Balfour, F. M. Relationship of the adrenal medulla to the sympathetic nervous system.*

By showing that the adrenal medulla has the same origin as the sympathetic nervous system, Balfour really laid the foundation for the interesting concept of the similarity in the action of epinephrine and sympathetic nervous mediation. Out of this has developed the emergency theory of Cannon and others.

1878: *Brandt, K. Demonstration of vital coloring.*

The belief that only dead cells could be stained was long held by histologists, but Brandt was able to stain the lipid droplets in the cytoplasm of living *Actinosphaerium* (Heliozoa) with the dye Bismark brown and observe the process during the vital staining. Trembley had described vital staining, after a fashion, in the eighteenth century. An important research tool since Brandt's discovery, vital staining is now used less because of the development of phase-contrast and interference microscopy.

900

1878: *Kuhne, W. Nature of enzymes.*

The study of the action of chemical catalysts in an understanding of the fundamental nature of life has steadily increased with biological advancement and now represents one of the most interesting aspects of biochemistry.

1879: *Flemming, W. Chromatin described and named.*

Flemming shares with a few others the description of the details of indirect cell division. The part of the nucleus which stains deeply he called *chromatin* (colored) which gives rise to the chromosomes. This term, as well as certain other ones introduced by the same observer, has been universally accepted by all biologists.

1879: *Fol, Hermann. Penetration of ovum by a spermatozoan described.*

1879: *Kossel, A. Isolation of nucleoprotein.*

Nucleoproteins were isolated in the heads of fish sperm; they make up the major part of chromatin. They are combinations of proteins with nucleic acids, and this study was one of the first of the investigations which interest biochemists at the present time.

Nobel Laureate (1910).

1882: *Flemming, W. First accurate counts of nuclear filaments (chromosomes) made.*

1882: *Flemming, W. Terms mitosis and spireme named.*

1882: *Metchnikoff, Élie. Role of phagocytosis in immunity.*

The theory that microbes are ingested and destroyed by certain white corpuscles (phagocytes) shares with the theory of chemical bodies (antibodies) the chief explanation for the body's natural immunity.

Nobel Laureate (1908).

1882: *Pfitzner, W. Discovery of chromomeres.*

The discrete granules which make up a large part of chromosomes are of especial interest because they are supposed to correspond to the loci of the genes. Some cytologists have even thought that chromomeres correspond to genes, but most agree that each chromomere has more than one gene.

1882: *Strasburger, E. Terms cytoplasm and nucleoplasm named.*

1882-1924: *The "Albatross" of the Fish Commission.*

This vessel, under the direction of the U. S. Fish Commission, was second only to the famed *Challenger* in advancing scientific knowledge about oceanography. Actually, in her long service her collections and investigations greatly surpassed those of the earlier and better-known *Challenger* expedition.

1883: *Golgi, Camillo, and R. Cajal. Silver nitrate technique for nervous elements.*

The development and refinement of this technique gave a completely new picture of the intricate relationships of neurons. Modifications of this method have given valuable information concerning the cellular element, the Golgi apparatus.

Nobel Laureates (1906).

1883: *Leuckart, R., and A. P. Thomas. Life history of sheep liver flukes.*

This investigation is noteworthy in parasitology, for it represents the first time a complete life cycle was worked out for a trematode involving more than one host.

1883: *Roux, W. Allocation of hereditary functions to chromosomes.*

This theory could not be much more than a guess when Roux made it, but how fruitful was the idea ·in the light of the enormous amount of evidence since accumulated!

1884: *Flemming, W., E. Strasburger, and E. Van Beneden. Demonstration that nuclear filaments (chromosomes) double in number by longitudinal division.*

This concept represented a further step in understanding the precise process in indirect cell division.

1884: *Rubner, Max. Quantitative determinations of the energy value of foods.*

Although Liebig and others had estimated calorie values of foods, the investigations of Rubner put their determinations on a sound basis. His work made possible a scientific explanation for metabolism and a basis for the study of comparative nutrition. He also gave a working basis for the relation of basal metabolism to the surface area of the body, a standard of measurement which D. DuBois and other workers have greatly refined.

1884: *Strasburger, E. Terms, prophase, metaphase, and anaphase named.*

1885: *Dubois, R. Nature of light production in animals.*

By his work on luminous clams, Dubois was able to show how a chemical substance, luciferin, could be oxidized with the aid of an enzyme, luciferase, with the production of light. Since this basic discovery, additional work has been done upon the nature of the luciferin molecule.

1885: *Hertwig, O., and E. Strasburger. Concept of the nucleus as basis of heredity.*

The development of this idea occurred before Mendel's laws of heredity were rediscovered in 1900, but it anticipates the important role the nucleus with its chromosomes was to assume in hereditary transmission.

1885: *Rabl, Karl. Concept of the individuality of the chromosomes.*

The view that the chromosomes retain their individuality through all stages of the cell cycle is accepted by all cytologists, and much evidence has accumulated in proof of the theory. However, it has been virtually impossible to demonstrate the chromosome's individuality through all stages. Rabl's suggestion was purely theoretical at the time he made it.

1885: *Roux, W. Mosaic theory of development.*

In the early development of the frog's egg, Roux showed that the determinants for differentiation were segregated in the early cleavage stages and that each cell or groups of cells would form only certain parts of the developing embryo (mosaic or determinate development). Later, other investigators showed that in many forms blastomeres, separated early, would give rise to whole embryos (indeterminate development).

1885: *Weismann, August. Formulation of germ plasm theory.*

Weismann's great theory of the germ plasm stresses the idea that there are two types of protoplasm—germ plasm, which gives rise to the reproductive cells or gametes, and somatoplasm, which furnishes all the other cells. Germ plasm, according to the theory, is continuous from generation to generation, whereas the somatoplasm dies with each generation and does not influence the germ plasm. It is not necessary to point out the influence of the germ plasm upon biological thought, both in the fields of evolution and heredity.

1886: *Establishment of Woods Hole Biological Station.*

This station is by all odds the greatest center of its kind in the world. Here most of the biologists in America have studied and the station has increasingly attracted investigators from many other countries as well. The influence of Woods Hole on the progress of biology cannot be overestimated. Here research is conducted the year round, but during the summer the concentration of biologists is greatly multiplied. Certain courses are offered for the benefit of undergraduates and others who are just beginning active biological study.

1886: *MacMunn, C. A. Discovery of cytochrome.*

This iron-bearing compound was rediscovered in 1925 by D. Keilin and has been demonstrated in most types of cells. Its importance in cellular oxidation as a respiratory enzyme has made possible a workable theory of cell respiration and has stimulated the study of intracellular localization of enzymes and how they behave in metabolic processes.

1887: *Fischer, Emil. Structural patterns of proteins.*

The importance of proteins in biological systems has made their study the central theme of all modern biochemical work. The life process in a large measure revolves around the activities and relations of these complex substances.

Nobel Laureate (1902).

1887: *Haeckel, E. H. Concept of organic form and symmetry.*

Symmetry refers to the spatial relations and arrangements of parts in such a way as to form geometrical designs. Although many others before Haeckel's time had studied and described types of animal form, Haeckel has given us our present concepts of organic symmetry as revealed in his monograph on radiolarians collected on the *Challenger* expedition.

1887: *Van Beneden, E. Demonstration of chromosome reduction during maturation.*

Weismann had predicted this important event before it was actually demonstrated. Only by this method can the constancy of chromosome numbers be maintained.

1887: *Van Beneden, E. Chromsome constancy within a species.*

The number of chromosomes is characteristic for each species, usually within the range of 2 to 200. There are minor exceptions to this rule as in the case of spontaneous polyploidy.

1887: *Weismann, August. Prediction of the reduction division.*

Weismann formulated the hypothesis that the separation of undivided whole chromosomes must take place in one of the maturation divisions (reduction division), or else the number of chromosomes would double in each generation (*reductio ad absurdum*). He predicted this on theoretical grounds, but the hypothesis was later proved true in all particulars and led to an explanation of Mendel's laws of heredity.

1888: *Helriegel, H., and H. Wilfarth. Discovery of nitrogen cycle.*

The description of the course of nitrogen in nature as it is used by plants and animals represents one of the most significant aspects of biological economics.

1888: *Waldeyer, W. Term chromosome named.*

1889: *Hertwig, R., and E. Maupas. True nature of conjugation in paramecium.*

The process of conjugation had been described (even by Leeuwenhoek) many times and its sexual significance interpreted, but these two investigators independently showed the details of pregamic divisions and the mutual exchange of the micronuclei during the process.

1889: *Mering, J. von, and O. Minkowski. Effect of pancreatectomy.*

The classical experiment of removing the pancreas stimulated research which led to the isolation of the pancreatic hormone insulin by Banting (1922).

1891: *Driesch, H. Discovery of totipotent cleavage.*

The discoverey that each of the first several blastomeres, if separated from each other in the early cleavage of the fertilized egg, would develop into a complete embryo stimulated investigation on totipotent and other types of development.

1891: *Dubois, Eugene. Discovery of the fossil man, Pithecanthropus erectus.*

Although not the first fossil man to be found, the Java man represents one of the first significant primitive men which have been discovered in the last half century.

1892: *Ivanovski, D. Discovery of the nature of viruses.*

This discovery was the start of the many investigations on the nature of these important biological agents. It is still too early to appraise the exact role of viruses in the plan of biological life, but they represent one of the most baffling problems with which biologists have to contend.

1894: *Driesch, H. Constancy of nuclear potentiality.*

Driesch's view was that all nuclei of an organism were equipotential but that the activity of nuclei varied with different cells in accordance with the differentiation of tissues. That all genetic factors are present in all cells is supported by the constancy of DNA for each set of chromosomes and the similarity of histone proteins in the different somatic cells of an organism. This theory, however, is being challenged in the much investigated problems of differentiation and growth, and there has been some evidence to show that nuclear potentialities do vary with different stages in development.

1894: *Merriam, C. H. Concept of life zones in North America.*

This scheme is based on temperature criteria and the importance of temperature in the distribution of plants and animals. According to this concept animals and plants are restricted in their northward distribution by the total quantity of heat during the season of growth and reproduction, and their southward distribution by the mean temperature during the hottest part of the year. Although students of birds and mammals have found the concept useful, most biologists at present regard it as oversimplified and believe that biotic distribution should be on the basis of plants and animals.

1894: *Morgan, C. L. Concept of animal behavior.*

The modern interpretation of animal behavior really dates from certain basic principles laid down by this psychologist. Among these principles was the one in which he stated that the actions of an animal should be interpreted in terms of the simplest mental processes (Morgan's canon). He did much to remove the study of animal activities from an anthropomorphic interpretation and place it on an objective basis.

1894: *Oliver, G., and E. A. Sharpey-Schaefer. Demonstration of the action of a hormone.*

The first recorded action of a specific hormone was the demonstration of the effect of an extract of the suprarenal (adrenal) glands upon blood vessels and muscle contraction.

1895: *Bruce, D. Life cycle of protozoan blood parasite (Trypanosoma).*

The relation of this parasite to the tsetse fly and to wild and domestic animal infection in Africa is an early demonstration of the role of arthropods as vectors of disease. This masterly work also threw a light on other protozoan diseases and represents a distinct link between protozoology and medicine.

1895: *Pinkus, F. Discovery of terminal cranial nerve (O).*

This nerve (nervus terminalis) was discovered after the other cranial nerves had been named and numbered. It is sensory and runs from the olfactory membrane to the olfactory lobe of the brain. Its exact significance is unknown. It was first found in the African lungfish, *Protopterus,* but has since been found in all vertebrate classes except birds, although it may be a temporary structure in some. It lies along the anterior border of the olfactory nerve.

1895: *Roentgen, W. Discovery of x-rays.*

This great discovery was quickly followed by its application in the interpretation of bodily structures and processes and represents one of the greatest tools in biological research.

Nobel Laureate (1901).

1896: *Baldwin, J. M. Baldwin evolutionary effect.*

It is the belief that genetic selection of genotypes will be channeled or canalized in the same direction as the adaptive modifications which were formerly nonhereditary. Nonhereditary adaptive modifications are supposed to keep a racial strain in an environmental channel where mutations producing similar phenotypes will be selected. The Baldwin effect emphasizes the genetic assimilation of the originally acquired adaptive characters resulting from reactions with environmental agents. The theory seems to be of limited application but has been revived by evolutionists in recent years.

1896: *Russian Hydrographic Survey. Biology of Lake Baikal.*

This lake in Siberia is more than 500 miles long, 50 miles wide, and has an extreme depth of more than a mile (the deepest lake in the world). Its unique fauna is a striking example of evolutionary results from long-continued isolation. Up to 100% of the species in certain groups are endemic (found nowhere else). This remarkable fauna represents the survival of ancient fresh-water animals which have become extinct in surrounding areas. The lake has been a fertile field for the study of various groups of animals by specialists for the past 50 years.

Lakes Tanganyika and Nyasa in Africa are similar lakes and likewise have unique faunas.

1897: *Born, G. Heteroplastic grafting.*

By joining together parts of embryos of different species, such as frog and toad, Born was able to produce viable individuals which continued to develop as chimaeras. Other investigators, such as Harrison and Spemann, also performed many similar experiments, and the method has been put to practical use by plant workers.

1897: *Buchner, E. Discovery of zymase.*

Buchner's discovery that an enzyme (a nonliving substance) manufactured by yeast cells was responsible for fermentation resolved many problems which had baffled Pasteur and other investigators. Zymase is now known to consist of a number of enzymes.

Nobel Laureate (1907).

1897: *Canadian Geological Survey. Dinosaur fauna of Alberta, Canada.*

In the rich fossil beds along the Red Deer River in Alberta there was found the fauna of the Upper Cretaceous time, and a whole new revelation of dinosaur world has been made from the study of these fossils. The fossils reveal that the dinosaurs had reached the peak of their adaptive radiation at this time and had evolved into many types of diverse morphology and habits. This discovery must rank as one of the most important in the whole field of vertebrate paleontology.

1897: *Eijkman, C. Discovery of the cause of a dietary deficiency disease.*

Eijkman's pioneer work on the causes of beriberi led to the isolation of the antineuritic vitamin (thiamin). This work may be called the key discovery which resulted in the development of the important vitamin concept.

Nobel Laureate (1929).

1897: *Hertwig, O. Influence of yolk on patterns of egg segmentation.*

The mechanical effect of yolk is mainly responsible for the great variety of segmentation types of eggs, a concept that was proved by Hertwig by experimental procedures

1897: *Huot, A. Discovery of the aglomerular fish kidney.*

This discovery in the angler fish (*Loph-*

ius) and later in the toadfish and others proved to renal physiologists that renal tubules of kidneys could excrete as well as resorb substances. By using such a kidney as a test organ it has been possible to ascertain what things can and cannot be excreted by the kidney tubules, and thus a better understanding of many renal functions has been acquired.

1897: *Miescher, F. Discovery of desoxyribonucleic acid (DNA).*

DNA is a constant component of the chromosome and is revealed by a specific staining procedure (Feulgen). The interest in this substance is correlated with the importance biochemistry has assumed in heredity in recent years. Active workers in this field, such as A. E. Mirsky, have shown how an analysis of the germinal substance may throw light upon the chromosomal theory of heredity and how chromosomes may play a part in the functions of the cell.

1897: *Ross, Ronald. Life history of malarian parasite (Plasmodium).*

This notable achievement represents a great landmark in the field of parasitology and the climax of the work of many investigators on the problem. It also marks the important role arthropod vectors play in the transmission of disease.

Nobel Laureate (1902).

1897: *Sherrington, C. S. Concept of the synapse in the nervous system.*

If the nervous system is composed of discrete units or neurons, functional connections must exist between these units. Sherrington showed how individual nerve cells could exert integrative influences on other nerve cells by graded excitatory or inhibitory synaptic actions. The electron microscope has in recent years added much to a knowledge of the synaptic structure.

1898: *Benda, C., and C. Golgi. Discovery of mitochondria and Golgi apparatus.*

These interesting cytoplasmic inclusions were actually seen by various observers before this date, but they were both named in 1898 and the real study of them began at this time. Flemming and R. Altmann first demonstrated mitochondria.

The Golgi apparatus was demonstrated by V. St. George (1867) and G. Platner (1885), but Camillo Golgi with his silver impregnation method gave the first clear description of the apparatus in nerve cells. Mitochondria are now known to play an important role in the synthesis of enzymes in cellular metabolism.

1898: *Osborn, H. F. Concept of adaptive radiation in evolution.* This concept states that starting from a common ancestral type many different forms of evolutionary adaptations may occur. In this way evolutionary divergence can take place, and the occupation of many ecological niches is made possible according to the adaptive nature of the invading species. The concept has been very fruitful in the interpretation of evolutionary progress, and many examples are often cited as evidences for its correctness such as Darwin's finches of the Galápagos Islands, the varied limb structure of mammals, Australian marsupials, etc.

1899: *Bayless, W. H., and E. H. Starling. Law of the intestine.*

As originally formulated, the law stated that the movement of food down the alimentary canal is accomplished by a wave of muscular contraction above the bolus of food and a dilation below it. It is doubtful that there is an inhibition of the muscle below the bolus, but the dilation is simply due to the general opening of the gut by the contraction of the longitudinal muscles.

1899: *Hardy, W. A. Appraisal of conventional fixation methods.*

This investigation showed that the usual preservatives used in killing and fixing cells produced either fibrous networks or fine emulsions and that the method of fixation determined which of these states is produced (artefacts). Thus it is impossible to appraise the structure of dead protoplasm, revealed by such methods, as a true index of the condition of living protoplasm, and the structures found in stained cells needed confirmation by other methods, for the fibrillar, reticular, and other appearances of protoplasm are arte-

facts due to the type of fixation and staining employed.

1900: *Chamberlain, T. C. Theory of the fresh-water origin of vertebrates.*

The evidence for this theory as first proposed was based mainly upon the fact that early vertebrate fossils were found in sediments of fresh-water origin, such as Old Red Sandstone, and were largely absent from marine deposits. Much of these fresh-water deposits were supposed to have been laid down in rivers which drained the higher ranges of the continents Other lines of evidence have also been presented, such as the adaptation of the vertebrate morphological pattern for currents of water and the evolution of the glomerular kidney. The theory has in general been widely accepted by paleontologists.

1900: *Correns, K. E., E. Tschermak, and Hugo de Vries. Rediscovery of Mendel's laws of heredity.*

These three investigators independently in their genetical experiments on plants obtained results similar to Mendel's, and in their survey of the literature found that Mendel had published his now famous laws in 1866. A few years later, W. Bateson and others found that the same laws applied to animals also. The impetus given to genetical study by this rediscovery has resulted in some of the most important contributions in biology.

1900: *Discovery of fossil beds in Fayum Lake province of Egypt.*

The work of C. F. Andrews and others on these fossils has shown how important Africa has been in the evolution of mammals. The many new types which evolved here may have been due to geographical isolation and inbreeding.

1900: *Landsteiner, Karl. Discovery of blood groups.*

This fundamental discovery made possible successful blood transfusions as well as initiated the tremendous amount of work on the biochemistry of blood, an investigation that is more active now than ever before.

1900: *Loeb, J. Discovery of artificial parthenogenesis.*

The possibility of getting eggs which normally undergo fertilization to develop by chemical and mechanical methods has been accomplished in a number of different animals from the sea urchin and frog eggs (Loeb, 1900) to the rabbit egg (Pincus, 1936). The phenomenon has some importance in experimental cytology. As a matter of record, O. Hertwig had mentioned the possibility of parthenogenesis in one of his works many years before.

1901: *Montgomery, T. H. Homologous pairing of maternal and paternal chromosomes in the zygote.*

Sutton, also, showed that in synapsis before the reduction division each pair is made up of a maternal and a paternal chromosome. This phenomenon is of fundamental importance in the segregation of hereditary factors (genes).

1901: *Vries, Hugo de. Mutation theory of evolution.*

De Vries concluded from his study of the evening primrose, *Oenothera lamarckiana,* that new characters appear suddenly and are inheritable Although the variations in *Oenothera* were probably not mutations at all since many of them represented hybrid combinations, yet the evidence for the theory from other sources has steadily mounted until now the theory affords the most plausible explanation for evolutionary progress.

1902: *Kropotkin, P. Mutual aid as a factor in evolution.*

This concept is not new by any means, but Kropotkin elaborated on the importance of social life at all levels of animal life in the survival patterns of the evolutionary process. Population studies in many groups show an underlying element of automatic mutual aid, and many students of animal behavior have stressed the principle since Kropotkin's time.

1902: *McClung, C. E. Discovery of sex chromosomes.*

The discovery in the grasshopper that a certain chromosome (X) had a mate (Y) different in appearance or else lacked a mate altogether gave rise to the theory that certain chromosomes determined sex.

1903: *Bayliss, W. M., and E. H. Starling. Discovery of the first hormone, secretin.*

The isolation of a substance from the mucosa of the duodenum which had a powerful effect on stimulating the secretion of pancreatic juice was a key experiment in the development of the great science of endocrinology.

1903: *Boveri, T., and W. S. Sutton. Parallelism between chromosome behavior and Mendelian segregation.*

This theory states that synaptic mates in meiosis correspond to the Mendelian alternative characters and that the formula of character inheritance of Mendel could be explained by the behavior of the chromosomes during maturation. This is, therefore, a cytological demonstration of Mendelism.

1904: *Cannon, W. B. Mechanics of digestion by x-rays.*

The clever application of x-rays to a study of the movements and other aspects of the digestive system has revealed an enormous amount of information on the physiology of the alimentary canal.

1903: *Sutton, W. S. Constitution of the diploid group of chromosomes.*

The diploid group of chromosomes is made up of two chromosomes of each recognizable size, one member of which is paternal and the other maternal in origin.

1904: *Jennings, H. S. Behavior patterns in Protozoa.*

The careful investigations of this lifelong student of the behavior of these lower organisms lead to concepts such as the trial-and-error behavior and many of our important beliefs about the various forms of tropisms and taxes.

1904. *Macallum, A. B. Similarity of blood salts to sea salts.*

The relative concentration and proportions of the salts (potassium, sodium, and calcium) in the blood of most vertebrates is similar to that found in sea water and is considered to be evidence of the origin of animals in the sea. The higher concentration of salts in the sea today as compared with the Cambrian period when land forms are supposed to have arisen is explained by the constant addition of salt from continental streams.

This hypothesis has been subjected to critical analysis in recent years on the basis that the salt concentration of vertebrate extracellular fluid is proportionally much smaller than the salt concentration of the Cambrian period and that the magnesium content of extracellular fluid is proportionally much smaller than that in the Cambrian seas.

1904: *Nuttall, G. H. F. Serological relationships of animals.*

This method of determining animal relationships is striking evidence of evolution. It has been used in recent years to establish the taxonomic position of animals whose classification has not been determined by other methods.

1905: *Haldane, J. S., and J. G. Priestley. Role of carbon dioxide in the regulation of breathing.*

By their clever technique of obtaining samples of air from the lung alveoli, these investigators showed how the constancy of carbon dioxide concentration in the alveoli and its relation to the concentration in the blood was the chief regulator of the mechanism of respiration.

1905: *Huber, G. C. Dissection of the nephron.*

The isolation of a complete mammalian kidney nephron by maceration and teasing is a landmark in renal histology, for it revealed for the first time the structure of the different parts of the tubule in relation to each other as shown in the sequence of a gross morphological preparation.

1905: *Zsigmondy, R. Application of ultracentrifuge to colloids.*

This has made possible a study of colloidal particles and the finer details of protoplasmic systems.

Nobel Laureate (1925).

1906: *Bateson, W., and R. C. Punnett. Discovery of linkage of hereditary units.*

Although first discovered in sweet peas, it was Morgan and his associates who gave the real meaning to this great genetical concept. All seven pairs of Mendel's alternative characters were in separate chromosomes, a fact that simplified his problem.

1906: *Hopkins, F. G. Analysis of dietary deficiency.*

Hopkins tried to explain dietary deficiency by a biochemical investigation of the lack of essential amino acids in the diet—an approach that has led to many important investigations in nutritional requirements.

1907: *Boveri, T. Qualitative differences of chromosomes.*

Boveri showed in his classical experiment with sea urchin eggs that chromosomes have qualitatively different effects on development. He found that only those cells developed into larva which had one of each kind of chromosomes; those cells which did not have representatives of each kind of chromosome failed to develop.

1907: *Discovery of the Heidelberg fossil man (Homo heidelbergensis).*

This fossil consisted of a lower jaw with all its teeth. The jaw shows many simian characteristics, but the teeth show patterns of primitive men. This type is supposed to have existed during mid-Pleistocene times and is more or less intermediate between the Java man and modern man.

1907: *Hopkins, F. G. Relationship of lactic acid to muscular contraction.*

Hopkins showed that after being formed in muscular contraction a part of the lactic acid is oxidized to furnish energy for the resynthesis of the remaining lactic acid into glycogen. This discovery did much to clarify part of the cyclic reactions involved in the complicated process of muscular contraction.

Nobel Laureate (1929).

1907: *Keith, A., and M. J. Flack. Discovery of the sino-auricular (S-A) node.*

The ancestry of this node is the sinus tissue of the primitive heart of cold-blooded animals. In mammals, this node is embedded in the muscle of the right auricle near the openings of the superior and inferior vena cavae and initiates the

908

beat and sets the pace (pacemaker) for the mammalian heart.

The atrio-ventricular (A-V) node, which lies in the septum of the atria near the A-V valves, was discovered in 1906 by Tawara.

1907: Wilson, H. V. Reorganization of sponge cells.

In this classical experiment, Wilson showed that the disaggregation of sponges by squeezing them through fine silk bolting cloth so that they are separated into minute cell clumps resulted in the surviving cells coming together and organizing themselves into small sponges when they were in sea water. Some cells other than those of sponges have since been found to have the same ability. It is also possible for cells from different species of sponges to reorganize together in the formation of a new sponge.

1908: Hardy, G. H., and W. Weinberg. Hardy-Weinberg population formula.

This important theorem states that in the absence of factors (mutation, selection, etc.) causing change in genes, the proportion of genes in any large population will reach an equilibrium in one generation and thereafter will remain stable regardless of whether the genes are dominant or recessive. Its mathematical expression forms the basis for the calculations of population genetics.

1909: Arrhenius, S., and S. P. L. Sörensen. Determination of hydrogen ion concentration (pH).

The sensitivity of most biological systems to acid and alkaline conditions has made pH values of the utmost importance in biological research.

Arrhenius, Nobel Laureate (1903).

1909: Doublass, E. Discovery of dinosaur fossil bed.

Dinosaur fossils have been found in various parts of the world, such as the deposits in Alberta, Canada, and those in Tendaguru, East Africa, but few have equaled the dinosaur bed near Jensen, Utah. Here one may see the dinosaur skeletons preserved in the rocks just as they were laid down millions of years ago. More than 12 species of dinosaurs have been identified from this bed, including the *Diplodocus* which grew almost 90 feet long. This region is a National Monument, and a large dinosaur museum is now being prepared there.

1909: Janssens, F. A. Chiasmatype theory.

When homologous chromosomes are paired before the reduction division, they or their chromatids form visible crosslike figures or chiasmata, which Janssens interpreted as the visible exchange of parts of two homologous chromatids, although he could not actually prove this point. More than twenty years elapsed before the theory in substance was put on a demonstrable cytological basis. This phenomenon of crossing-over is the key to the genetical mapping of chromosomes so extensively worked out by Morgan and his school with *Drosophila*.

1909: Johannsen, W. Limitations of natural selection on pure lines.

This investigator found that when a hereditary group of characters becomes homogenous, natural selection cannot change the genetic constitution with regard to these characters. Selection was shown to be something that could not create and was effective only in isolating genotypes already present in the group; it therefore could not effect evolutionary changes directly.

1909: Johannsen, W. Terms gene, genotype, and phenotype named.

1910: Ehrlich, Paul. Chemotherapy in the treatment of disease.

The discovery of salvarsan as a cure for syphilis represents the first great discovery in this field. Another was the dye sulfanilamide, discovered by Domagk in 1935. These chemicals, which are more or less harmful to the body, have been generally superseded by the more effective and less harmful antibiotics.

Nobel Laureate (1908).

1910: Heinroth, O. Concept of imprinting as a type of behavior.

This is a special type of learning that is demonstrated by birds (and possibly other animals). It is based on the fact that a goose or bird is attracted to the first large object it sees just after hatching and thereafter will follow that object to the exclusion of all others. Although the behavior pattern appears to be strongly fixed, there is some doubt about its irreversibility.

D. Spalding (1872) had observed and described this behavior also.

1910: *Morgan, T. H. Discovery of sex linkage.*

Morgan and his colleagues discovered that the results of a cross between a white-eyed male with a red-eyed female in *Drosophila* were different from those obtained from the reciprocal cross of a red-eyed male with a white-eyed female. This was a crucial experiment, for it showed for the first time that how a trait behaved in heredity depended upon the sex of the parent in contrast to most Mendelian characters which behave genetically the same way whether introduced by a male or female parent.

1910-1920. *Morgan, T. H. Establishment of the theory of the gene.*

The extensive work of Morgan and his associates on the localization of hereditary factors (by genetical experiments) on the chromosomes of the fruit fly *(Drosophila)* represents the most significant work ever performed in the field of heredity. The next step is to actually see the physical entity known as the gene, and there has been progress along this line.

Nobel Laureate (1933).

1910: *Murray, J., and J. Hjort. Deep-sea expedition of the Michael Sars.*

Of the many expeditions for exploring the depths of the oceans, *Michael Sars* expedition, made in the North Atlantic regions, must rank among the foremost. The expedition yielded an immense amount of information about deep-sea animals, as well as many important concepts regarding the ecological pattern of animal distribution in the sea. This expedition first demonstrated that the ocean was divided vertically and horizontally into many different kinds of environments, each with its characteristic animal population.

1910: *Pavlov, I. P. Concept of the conditioned reflex.*

The idea that acquired reflexes play an important role in the nervous reaction patterns of animals has greatly influenced the development of modern psychology. Nobel Laureate (1904).

1911: *Child, C. M. Axial gradient theory.*

This theory attempts to explain the pattern of metabolism from the standpoint of localized regional differences along the axes of organisms. The differences in the metabolic rate of different areas has made possible an understanding of certain aspects of regeneration, development, and growth.

1911: *Funk, C. Vitamin hypothesis.*

Vitamin deficiency diseases are commonly called avitaminoses and refer to those diseases in which causes can be definitely traced to the lack of some essential constituent of the diet. Thus beriberi is caused by an insufficient amount of thiamine, scurvy by a lack of vitamin C, etc.

Funk is also credited with the name vitamin(e). He also formed a crude preparation of the anti-beriberi substance (thiamine), which was finally synthesized in 1936 by R. R. Williams.

1911: *Walcott, C. D. Discovery of Burgess shale fossils.*

The discovery of a great assemblage of beautifully preserved invertebrates in the Burgess shale of British Columbia and their careful study by an American paleontologist represent a landmark in the fossil record of invertebrates. These fossils date from the Middle Cambrian age and include the striking *Aysheaia* which has a resemblance to the extant *Peripatus*.

1912: *Carrel, A. Technique of tissue culture.*

The culturing of living tissues in vitro, that is, outside of the body, has given biologists an important tool for studying tissue structure and growth. Many facts about cell division and its rate and the processes of senescence and rejuvenation in tissues have been found by this method. R. Harrison in 1907 had found that parts of living tissues in suitable media under

910

suitable conditions could live and multiply.

Nobel Laureate (1912).

1912: *Gudernatsch, J. F. Role of thyroid gland in the metamorphosis of frogs.*

This investigator found that the removal of the thyroid gland of tadpoles prevented metamorphosis into frogs and also that the feeding of thyroid extracts to tadpoles induced precocious metamorphosis. In 1919 W. W. Swingle also showed that the presence and absence of inorganic iodine would produce the same results. These and other investigations did much to clarify the function of an important endocrine gland.

1912: *Kite, G. L. Micrurgical study of cell structures.*

The use of micromanipulators for the microdissection of living cells has greatly enriched our knowledge of the finer microscopic details of protoplasm, chromosomes, cell division, and many other phenomena of cells. The development of the method has been due to many workers, such as H. D. Schmidt (1859), M. A. Barber (1904), and W. Seifriz (1921), but R. Chambers has perhaps done more to refine its use and to employ it in experimental cell research.

1913: *Federley, H. Explanation of hybrid sterility.*

The failure of chromosome pairing in meiosis when different species of moths were crossed was shown to be the primary cause of sterility in hybrids. In such cases the gene arrangement in the chromosomes of different species is so disarranged that homologous loci between pairs no longer exist. Many other cases have since been described.

1913: *Michaelis, L., and M. Menton. Enzyme-substrate complex.*

On theoretical and mathematical grounds these investigators showed that an enzyme formed an intermediate compound with its substrate (the enzyme-substrate complex) which subsequently decomposes to release the free enzyme and the reaction products. Some progress has been made in recent years in demonstrating the nature of this intermediate

compound which is extremely evanescent. D. Keilin of Cambridge University and B. Chance of the University of Pennsylvania have demonstrated the presence of such a complex by color changes and measurements of its rate of formation and breakdown which agree with theoretical predictions. Its clear-cut demonstration will yield further information on the amazing role of enzymes in the life process.

1913: *Miyairi, K., and M. Suzuki. First complete life cycle of a schistosome.*

This work was done with *Schistosoma japonicum,* one of the three common species of blood flukes.

1913: *Reck, H. Discovery of Olduvai Gorge fossil deposits.*

This region in East Africa has yielded an immense amount of early mammalian fossils as well as the tools of the Stone Age man, such as stone axes. Among the interesting fossils discovered were elephants with lower jaw tusks, horses with three toes, and the odd ungulate (chalicothere) with claws on the toes.

1913: *Sturtevant, A. H. Formation of first chromosome map.*

By the method of crossover percentages it has been possible to locate the genes in their relative positions on chromosomes— one of the most fruitful discoveries in genetics, for it led to the extensive mapping of the chromosome in *Drosophila.*

1913: *Tashiro, S. Metabolic activity of propagated nerve impulse.*

The detection of slight increases in carbon dioxide production in stimulated nerves as compared with inactive ones was evidence that conduction in nerves is a chemical change. Later (1926), A. V. Hill was able to measure the heat given off during the passage of an impulse. Oxygen consumption has also been measured in excited nerves.

1914: *Kendall, E. C. Isolation of thyroxin.*

The isolation of thyroxin in crystalline form was a landmark in endocrinology. Its artificial synthesis was done by Harington in 1927.

1914: *Lillie, F. R. Role of fertilizin in fertilization.*

According to this theory, the jelly coat of eggs contains a substance, fertilizin, which combines with the antifertilizin on the surface of sperm and causes the sperm to clump together. Although this theory received little acceptance when first proposed, biologists have in recent years revived the idea and have added new interpretations to it.

1914: Sharp R. Discovery of the neuro-motor apparatus of ciliates.

This demonstration of a system of neurofibrils connected to a motor mass in the anterior part of the organism (*Epidinium*) which was concerned in the coordination of cilia and other motor organelles of the cystostomial region, has been extended to other ciliates and may be considered a universal structural feature of this group.

1914: Shull, G. H. Concept of heterosis.

When two standardized strains or races are crossed, the resulting hybrid generation may be markedly superior to both parents as shown by greater vigor, vitality, and resistance to unfavorable environmental conditions. First worked out in corn (maize), such hybrid vigor may also be manifested by other kinds of hybrids. Although its exact nature is still obscure, the phenomenon may be due to the bringing together in the hybrid of many dominant genes of growth and vigor which were scattered among the two inbred parents, or it may be due to the complementary reinforcing action of genes when brought together. It was first studied in artificial plant hybrids by J. G. Koelreuter in 1763. The concept is an example of the practical utilization of modern genetics.

1916: Bridges, C. B. Discovery of non-disjunction.

Bridges explained an aberrant genetical result by a suggested formula which later he was able to confirm by cytological examination of the failure of a pair of chromosomes to disjoin at the reduction division so that both chromosomes passed into the same cell. It was definite proof that genes are located on the chromosomes.

1916: Lillie, F. R. Theory of freemartin.

The sexually abnormal female calf when it is born as a twin to a normal male had been a baffling problem for centuries until Lillie demonstrated in convincing fashion that hormones from the earlier developing gonads of the male circulate into the blood of the female and alter the sex differentiation of the latter. As a result the gonads of the free-martin never reach maturity and so she remains sterile. Lillie's theory has done much to stimulate investigation into the nature of sex differentiation, especially the role of sex hormones in the process.

1916: Winkler, H. Concept of hetero-ploidy.

Deviations from the normal diploid number of chromosomes are known to occur spontaneously in both plants and animals. It has also been known for some time that heteroploidy can be induced by artifiical means. Intensive investigation of the phenomenon has yielded a great deal of information concerning its relation to such matters as correlation of cell size with number of chromosomes, the viability of organisms possessing abnormal number of chromosomes, nucleoplasmic ratio, etc.

1917: Bloch, N. Discovery of dopa reaction for melanin.

This selective stain for the dendritic melanoblast cells of the skin is based upon the presence of an enzyme (dopa oxidase) in melanoblasts which converts dopa (dihydroxyphenylanine) into a dark brown or black pigment. Such cells are called dopa positive and are to be distinguished from dopa-negative melanophores. The method has clinical application.

1917: Broili, F. Discovery of amphibian-reptilian fossil, Seymouria.

This interesting fossil found near Seymour, Texas, has characteristics of both amphibians and reptiles and thus throws some light on the relations between the two great vertebrate classes.

1917: McCollum, E. V. Discovery of vitamin A.

1918: Starling, E. The law of the heart.

Within physiological limits, the more the ventricles are filled with incoming blood, the greater is the force of their contraction at systole. This is an adaptive mechanism for supplying more blood to tissues when it is needed. This important principle has many implications and relationships to cardiac functions and throws some light upon the nature of muscular action, for both skeletal and cardiac muscle fibers contract with maximal force when they are slightly stretched at the beginning of contraction.

1918: *Szymanski, J. S. Demonstration of time-measuring mechanism of animals.*

Szymanski showed that animals had some means of measuring time independently of such physical factors as light and temperature, for he discovered that 24-hour activity patterns were synchronized with the day-night cycle when animals were kept in constant darkness and temperature. This work has led to the concept (demonstrated by many investigations) that animals have some kind of internal clock whereby they can measure certain cycles independent of external factors.

1918: *Vavilov, N. I. Biological centers of origin as reservoirs of desirable genes.*

The Russian botanist and plant geographer stressed the importance of tracing strains of cultivated plants to the locale of their original cultivation where inferior plants (by present standards) may contain valuable genes already selected by natural selection. Such a pool of genes, he maintained, could by selection and intercrossing afford genetic banks for constructing new and superior genotypes.

1919: *Meyerhof, O. Formation of lactic acid during muscular contraction.*

The discovery that the glycogen content decreases as lactic acid increases was a key discovery in understanding the nature of muscular contraction, a problem which has not yet been solved. Meyerhof also showed that about four-fifths of the lactic acid is resynthesized to glycogen by the energy furnished by the oxidation of the other one-fifth of lactic acid. The relation of lactic acid to muscular fatigue and to oxygen debt was explained also by this discovery.

1920: *Howard, H. E. Territorial patterns of bird behavior.*

A mating pair of birds establishes and defends a specific territory against others of the same species. Usually the male asserts his claim by singing at points close to the boundaries of his staked-out claim. The concept has been confirmed for many species by numerous investigators.

1921: *Hopkins, F. G. Isolation of glutathione.*

The discovery of this sulfur compound gave a great impetus to the study of the complicated nature of cellular oxidation and metabolism, a process far from being solved at present.

1921: *Loewi, O., and H. H. Dale. Isolation of acetylcholine.*

This key demonstration has led to the neurohumoral concept of the transmission of nerve impulses to muscles.

Nobel Laureates (1936).

1921: *Pearl, R. Analysis of population cycles.*

Through experimental population studies, Pearl analyzed such factors as population growth, density, longevity, and expressed the results in quantitative terms. This started a series of similar investigations by many competent scientists on varied aspects of the subject. The concept of the population is important in such fields as speciation, evolution, and animal behavior.

1921: *Richards, A. N. Collection and analysis of glomerular filtrate of the kidney.*

This experiment was direct evidence of the role of the glomeruli as mechanical filters of cell-free and protein-free fluid from the blood and was striking confirmation of the Ludwig-Cushny theory of kidney excretion.

1921: *Spemann, Hans. Organizer concept in embryology.*

The idea that certain parts of the developing embryo known as organizers have a determining influence on the developmental patterns of the organism has completely revolutionized the field of experimental embryology and has afforded many clues into the nature of morphogenesis.

Nobel Laureate (1935).

1922: *Banting, F. Extraction of insulin.*

The great success of this hormone in relieving a distressful disease, diabetes mellitus, and the dramatic way in which active extracts were obtained have made the isolation of this hormone the best known in the field of endocrinology.

Nobel Laureate (1923).

1922: *Kopec, S. Demonstration of hormonal factors in invertebrate physiology.*

This investigation showed that the brain was necessary for insect metamorphosis, for when the brain was removed from the last instar larva of a certain moth, pupation failed to occur; when the brain was grafted into the abdomen, pupation was resumed.

1922: *Schiefferdecker, P. Distinction between eccrine and apocrine sweat glands.*

In mammals certain large sweat glands which develop in connection with the hair follicles in localized regions respond to stresses, such as fear, pain, and sex. This concept has stimulated investigation on the histology and physiology of the glandular activity of the skin. Apocrine glands have been described as early as 1846 by W. E. Horner, an English investigator.

1922: *Schjelderup-Ebbe, T. Social dominance-subordinance hierarchies.*

This observer found certain types of social hierarchies among birds in which higher ranking individuals could peck those of lower rank without being pecked in return. Those of the first rank dominated those of the second rank, who dominated those of the third, and so on. Such an organization, once formed, may be permanent. Dominance orders have also been found in other vertebrate classes as well as in some arthropods. The concept has thrown much light upon the social organization of animals.

1922: *Schmidt, Johannes. Life history of fresh-water eel*

The long, patient work of this oceanographer in solving the mystery of eel migration from the fresh-water streams of Europe to their spawning grounds in the Sargasso Sea near the Bermudas represents one of the most romantic achievements in natural history.

1923: *Andrews, R. C. Discovery of dinosaur eggs.*

The discovery of these fossilized eggs in Mongolia added to information about these reptiles which appeal so much to our imagination.

1923: *Hevesy, G. First isotopic tracer method.*

Tracer methodology has proved especially useful in biochemistry and physiology. For instance, it has been possible by the use of these labeled units to determine the fate of a particular molecule in all steps of a metabolic process and the nature of many enzymatic reactions. The exact locations of many elements in the body have been traced by this method. In physiology this method has been helpful in determining absorption phenomena, blood volume, the nature of permeability, and many others.

Nobel Laureate (1943).

1923: *Taylor, C. V. Isolation of micronucleus in Ciliophora.*

By micromanipulation Taylor removed the micronucleus of Euplotes and discovered that this organelle was necessary for the existence of the organism.

1923: *Warburg, Otto. Manometric methods for studying metabolism of living cells.*

The Warburg apparatus has been useful in measuring the gaseous exchange and other metabolic processes of living tissues. It has proved of great value in the study of enzymatic reactions in living systems and is a standard tool in many biochemical laboratories.

Nobel Laureate (1931).

1924: *Cleveland, L. R. Symbiotic relationships between termites and intestinal flagellates.*

This study was made on one of the most remarkable examples of evolutionary mutualism known in the animal kingdom. Equally important were the observations this observer and others found in the symbiosis between the wood-roach (*Cryp-*

tocercus) and its intestinal Protozoa. This work put such studies on an analytical basis and gave a great impetus to further investigation.

1924: *Feulgen, R. Test for nucleoprotein.*

This microchemical test is widely used by cytologists and biochemists to demonstrate the presence of DNA (desoxyribose nucleic acid), one of the two major types of nucleic acids.

1924: *Houssay, B. A. Role of the pituitary gland in regulation of carbohydrate metabolism.*

This investigator showed that when a dog had been made diabetic by pancreatectomy, the resulting hyperglucemia and glucosuria could be abolished by removing the anterior pituitary gland. This work threw additional light upon the complex cycle of carbohydrate metabolism and the interrelationships of the endocrine system.

Nobel Laureate (1946).

1925: *Baltzer, F. Sex determination in Bonellia.*

This classical discovery of the influence of environmental factors on sex determination with all the potentialities of sex intergrades which it demonstrates has formed the basis for another theory of the development of sex.

1925. *Barcroft, J. Function of the spleen.*

Barcroft and his associates showed that the spleen served as a blood reservoir which in time of stress adds new corpuscles to the circulation. The spleen reservoir is especially important in hemorrhage and shock. This action is effected mainly by the smooth muscle fibers in the elastic capsule which contracts and squeezes out quantities of red corpuscles. The spleen also destroys old and worn-out red cells.

1925: *Dart, Raymond. Discovery of Australopithecus africanus.*

This important fossil is commonly referred to as the ape-man or the "missing-link." This led to the finding of many related ape-men. With many human characteristics and a brain capacity only slightly greater than the higher apes, they have shed a great deal of light on the evolution of the higher primates, since they are placed on or near the main branch of human ancestry.

1925: *Rowan, W. Gonadal hypothesis of bird migration.*

By increasing the hours of light by artificial illumination, Rowan demonstrated that birds subjected to such conditions in winter increased the size of their gonads and showed a marked tendency to migrate out of season. In the development of his theory he laid emphasis on the role of the pituitary gland as well as other aspects of physiological function. The exact relationship of this hypothesis to bird migration is still largely speculative, but Rowan's experiments greatly stimulated investigation in this field.

1926: *Fujii, K. Finer analysis of the chromosome.*

With the development of the smear and squash techniques, it was possible with the light microscope to demonstrate the internal structure of a chromosome which formerly was described as a rod-shaped body. The newer version emphasizes a coiled filament (chromonema) which runs through the matrix of the chromosome and bears the genes. In certain stages of cell division two such threads are spirally coiled around each other so compactly that they appear as one thread. The extensive research on the detailed nature of the chromosome has given rise to many and varied interpretations.

1926: *Hill, A. V. Measurement of heat production in nerve.*

By applying the principle of the thermocouple, which Helmholtz had used to detect the heat of contracting muscle, Hill and other workers were able to measure the different phases of heat release, such as initial heat and recovery heat. The values of heat production in nervous tissue are extremely small when compared with readings of muscle heat.

1926: *Sumner, J. B. Isolation of enzyme urease.*

The isolation of this first enzyme in

crystalline form was a key discovery to be followed by others which have helped unravel the complex nature of these important biological substances.

Nobel Laureate (1946).

1926: *Warburg, O. Discovery of respiratory enzyme, cytochrome oxidase.*

This enzyme catalyzes the oxidation of cytochromes by oxygen, for in the presence of free oxygen and cytochrome oxidase, cytochrome gives up its hydrogen to the oxygen with the formation of water. In this process, cytochrome is a hydrogen acceptor and functions in the union of hydrogen and oxygen.

1927: *Bozler, E. Analysis of nerve net components.*

Bozler's demonstration that the nerve net of coelenterates was made up of separate cells and contained synaptic junctions resolved the old problem of whether or not the plexus in this group of animals was an actual network.

1927: *Coghill, G. E. Innate behavior patterns of Amphibia.*

Coghill's studies on the origin and growth of the behavior patterns of salamanders by following the sequence of the emergence of coordinated movements and nervous connections through all stages of embryonic development have represented one of the most fruitful investigations in animal behavior. He showed how broad, general movements preceded local reflexes and how the probable phylogenetic appearance of behavior patterns originated.

1927: *Eggleton, P., G. P. Eggleton, C. H. Fiske, and Y. Subbarow. Role of phosphagen (phosphocreatine) in muscular contraction.*

The demonstration that phosphagen is broken down during muscular contraction into creatine and phosphoric acid and then resynthesized during recovery gave an entirely new concept of the initial energy necessary for the contraction process. Confirmation of this discovery received a great impetus from the discovery of E. Lundsgaard (1930) that muscles poisoned with mono-iodoacetic acid, which inhibits the production of lactic acid from glycogen, would still contract and that the amount of phosphocreatine broken down was proportional to the energy liberated.

1927: *Heymans, C. Role of carotid and aortic reflexes in respiratory control.*

The carotid sinus and aortic areas contain pressoreceptors and chemoreceptors, the former responding to mechanical stimulation, such as blood pressure, and the latter to oxygen lack. When the pressoreceptors are stimulated, respiration is inhibited; when the chemoreceptors are stimulated, the respiratory rate is increased. These reflexes are of great physiological interest, although their adaptive nature is not as apparent as the vascular control initiated from the same regions.

Nobel Laureate (1938).

1927: *Muller, H. J. Artificial induction of mutations.*

By subjecting fruit flies (*Drosophila*) to mild doses of x-rays Muller found that the rate of mutation could be increased 150 times over the normal rate. This key demonstration has led to an extensive investigation of other forms by these methods and to many fruitful results, such as the biochemical mutations of Beadle and Tatum.

Nobel Laureate (1946).

1927: *Stensio, E. A. Appraisal of the Cephalaspida (Ostracoderm) fish fossil.*

The replacement of *Amphioxus* as a prototype of vertebrate ancestry by the ammocoetes lamprey larva, currently of great interest, has been due to a great extent to this careful fossil reconstruction. It is generally believed that living Agnatha (lamprey and hagfish) are descended from these ancient forms. The best fossils were obtained from Spitsbergen of the Ordovician period.

1928: *Garstang, W. Theory of the ascidian ancestry of chordates.*

According to this theory, primitive chordates were sessile, filter-feeding marine organisms very similar to present-day ascidians which had evolved from pterobranch (Hemichordata) ancestors. The actively swimming prevertebrate was con-

916

sidered a later stage in chordate evolution. The tadpole ascidian larva with its basic organization of a vertebrate had evolved within the group by progressive evolution and by neoteny became sexually mature, ceased to metamorphose into a sessile, mature ascidian, and through adaptation to fresh-water conditions became the true vertebrate. The theory has had added support in recent years, notably from the investigations of Berrill.

1928: *Griffith, F. Discovery of the transforming principle (DNA) in bacteria (genetic transduction).*

By injecting live nonencapsulated bacteria and dead encapsulated bacteria of the *Pneumococcus* strain into mice, it was found that the former acquired the ability to grow a capsule and that this ability was transmitted to succeeding generations. This active agent or transforming principle (from the encapsulated type) was isolated by other workers later and found to consist of DNA. This is excellent evidence that the gene involved is the nucleic acid desoxyribose nucleic acid (DNA).

Sanfelice (1893) had actually found the same principle when he discovered that nonpathogenic bacilli grown in a culture medium containing the metabolic products of true tetanus bacilli would also produce toxins and would do so for many generations. This was the first demonstration that a definite chemical substance had hereditary properties.

1928: *Koller, G., and E. B. Perkins. Hormonal control of color changes in crustaceans.*

These investigators found out independently that the chromatophores of crustaceans were regulated by a substance which originated in the eyestalk and was carried by the blood. Before this time, the common belief was that nerves served as the principal control. This early investigation has stimulated an enormous research in this field since that time and has led not only to a better knowledge of the role of endocrine glands in the animal kingdom but has also thrown much light upon such problems as insect molting and metamorphosis.

1928: *Wieland, H., and A. Windaus. Structure of cholesterol molecule.*

Sterol chemistry has been one of the chief focal points in the investigation of such biological products as vitamins, sex hormones, cortisone, etc. The real role of cholesterol, which is universally present in tissues, has not yet been determined, but it may serve as the precursor for the many forms of steroids whose use is definitely known. Animals make their own steroids but cannot absorb plant ones.

1929: *Berger, Hans. Demonstration of brain waves.*

The science of electroencephalography, or the electrical recording of brain activity, is in its infancy because of the complexity of the subject, but much has been revealed about both the healthy and the diseased brain by this technique. More refinements in technique and better interpretations will no doubt yield more information in this field.

1929: *Butenandt, A., and E. A. Doisy. Isolation of estrone.*

This discovery was the first isolation of a sex hormone and was arrived at independently by the two investigators. Estrone was found to be the urinary and transformed product of estradiol, the actual hormone. The male hormone testosterone was synthesized by Butenandt and L. Ruzicka in 1931. The second female hormone, progesterone, was isolated from the corpora lutea of sow ovaries in 1934.

Doisy, Nobel Laureate (1943).

1929: *Castle, W. B. Discovery of the antianemic factor.*

Castle and his associates showed that the gastric juice contained an enzyme-like substance (intrinsic factor) which reacts with a dietary factor (extrinsic) to produce the antianemic principle. The latter is stored in the liver of healthy individuals and is drawn upon for the maintenance of activity in bone marrow (erythropoietic tissue), i.e., the formation of red blood cells. If the intrinsic factor is missing from gastric juice, pernicious anemia occurs. At present, it is thought that vitamin B_{12} is both the extrinsic factor as well as the antianemic principle (erythrocyte-maturing factor).

1929: *Fleming, A. Discovery of penicillin.*

The chance discovery of this drug from molds and its development by H. Florey a few years later gave us the first of a notable line of antibiotics which have revolutionized medicine. Penicillin, however, still remains the most effective and safest of all.

Nobel Laureate (1945).

1929: *Lohmann, K. Discovery of ATP.*

The discovery of ATP (adenosine triphosphate) culminated a long search for the energy sources in biochemical reactions of many varieties, such as muscular contraction, vitamin action, and many enzymatic systems. Its nature and functions are the focal point of many present-day investigations.

1930: *Fisher, R. A. Statistical analysis of evolutionary variations.*

With Sewall Wright and J. S. B. Haldane, Fisher has analyzed mathematically the interrelationships of the factors of mutation rates, population sizes, selection values, and others in the evolutionary process. Although many of their theories are in the empirical stage, evolutionists in general agree that they have great significance in evolutionary interpretation.

1930: *Lawrence, E. O. Invention of the cyclotron.*

The importance of artificial radioactive isotopes, the synthesis of which is made possible by this invention, to biological research cannot be overestimated. Not only have tagged atoms been of inestimable value in learning about the structure and functioning of the body but many also have been put to medical use.

Nobel Laureate (1939).

1930: *Northrop, J. H. Crystallization of the enzymes pepsin and trypsin.*

This was a further step in the elucidation of the nature of enzymes which form the core of biochemical processes.

Nobel Laureate (1946).

1931: *Lorenz, K., and N. Tinbergen. Theory of instinctive behavior.*

The upsurge of interest (second only to molecular biology) in animal behavior within recent years has been due to the investigations of these men and their school concerning the problems of instinct and instinctive behavior. The interest they have aroused has been a result of their attempt to determine the physiological basis of the animal's reactions to stimuli by focusing attention upon the instinctive behavior pattern which controls innate behavior, by studying the internal conditions of the animal which are organized for particular patterns, and by showing the neural mechanisms which are correlated with these patterns.

1931: *Stern, C., H. Creighton, and B. McClintock. Cytological demonstration of crossing-over.*

Proof that crossing-over in genes is correlated with exchange of material by homologous chromosomes was independently proved by Stern in *Drosophila* and by Creighton and McClintock in corn. By using crosses of strains which had homologous chromosomes distinguishable individually, it was definitely demonstrated cytologically that genetical crossing-over was accompanied by chromosomal exchange.

1932: *Danish Scientific Expedition. Discovery of fossil amphibians (ichthyostegids).*

These fossils were found in the upper Devonian sediments in east Greenland and appear to be intermediate between advanced crossopterygians (*Osteolepis*) and early amphibians. They are the oldest known forms that can be considered amphibians. Many of their characters show primitive amphibian conditions. Only the skulls were found, and these apparently belonged to animals of considerable size.

1932: *Roughton, F. J. W. Discovery of enzyme carbonic anhydrase.*

This enzyme speeds up the reaction of CO_2 with water to form carbonic acid or the reverse reaction. The enzyme is found in red blood corpuscles and contains zinc in its structure. The enzyme plays an important role in the respiratory process.

1932: *Wright, S. Genetic drift as a factor in evolution.*

In small populations the Hardy-Weinberg formula of gene frequency may not apply because chance may determine the presence or absence of certain genes and this tendency will be expressed in the gene frequency of the new population which may be quite different from the original large population.

1933: *Gerard, R. W., and H. K. Hartline. Respiration in nerve.*

With rather simple apparatus, these workers were able to measure the amount of oxygen consumed per gram of nerve tissue during active and inactive conditions. This work shows definitely that nervous activity is a metabolic process. At present, it appears that nerve conduction involves energy-rich phosphate bonds the same as does muscular contraction.

1933, 1938: *Haldane, J. B. S., and A. I. Oparin. Heterotroph theory of the origin of life.*

This theory is based upon the idea that life was generated from nonliving matter under the conditions which existed before the appearance of life and which since have not been duplicated. The theory stresses the idea that living systems at present make it impossible for any incipient life to gain a foothold as primordial life was able to do. That complex organic molecules may arise from nonliving substances under proper conditions has been shown by such experimenters as Urey and Miller (1953), who were able to produce certain amino acids. This theory with variations has aroused much interest and speculation among biologists.

1933: *Holtfreter, J. Chemical nature of embryological inductors.*

Holtfreter and others found that the amphibian organizer retains its capacity to induce a nervous system (after the organizer has been killed by artificial agents) by transplanting fragments of the dead inductor into the blastocoele before gastrulation. They also found that embryonic tissues that cannot induce when alive can do so after they are killed. The agent that induces nerve tube formation seems to be widespread in the embryo and is released by the dead tissue. The great variety of chemical substances that will induce nerve tube formation makes it impossible at present to determine the exact nature of the inducing substance.

1933: *Painter, T. S., E. Heitz, and H. Bauer. Rediscovery of giant salivary chromosomes.*

These interesting chromosomes were first described by Balbiani in 1881, but their true significance was not realized until these investigators rediscovered them. It has been possible in a large measure to establish the chromosome theory of inheritance by comparing the actual cytological chromosome maps of salivary chromosomes with the linkage maps obtained by genetical experimentation.

1933: *Wald, G. Discovery of vitamin A in the retina.*

The discovery that vitamin A is a part of the visual purple molecule of the rods not only gave a better understanding of an important vitamin but also showed how night blindness can occur whenever there is a deficiency of this vitamin in the diet.

1934: *Bensley, R. R., and N. L. Hoerr. Isolation and analysis of mitochondria.*

This demonstration has suggested an explanation for the behavior and possible functions of these mysterious bodies which have intrigued cytologists for a generation, and much has been learned about them in recent years.

1934: *Dam, H., and E. A. Doisy. Identification of vitamin K.*

The isolation and synthesis of this vitamin is important not merely because of its practical value in certain forms of hemorrhage but also because of the light it throws upon the physiological mechanism of blood clotting.

Nobel Laureates (1943).

1934: *Urey, H. Discovery of heavy water (deuterium).*

Water, the most common constituent of protoplasm, has properties which are still not understood. It is not a single substance but is made up of at least 33 substances. Deuterium has furnished the basis for much biological investigation on the structure of water in relation to its role in biological systems.

Nobel Laureate (1934).

1934: *Wigglesworth, V. B. Role of the corpus allatum gland in insect metamorphosis.*

This small gland lies close to the brain of an insect, and it has been shown that during the larval stage this gland secretes a juvenile hormone which causes the larval characters to be retained. Metamorphosis occurs when the gland no longer secretes the hormone. Removal of the gland causes the larva to undergo precocious metamorphosis; grafting the gland into a mature larva will cause the latter to grow into a giant larval form. The gland was first described by A. Nabert in 1913.

1935: *DuShane, G. P. Role of neural crest in pigment cell formation.*

DuShane's discovery that pigment cells in amphibians originated from the neural crest was quickly followed by other investigations which showed that other groups (fish, birds, and mammals) had the same pattern of pigment formation. The current interest in the relation of the pigment cell to certain malignant growths (melanoblastomas), which may be considered immature pigment cells induced by some metabolic error, has been focused on all possible aspects of the pigment cell.

1935: *Hanstrom, B. Discovery of the X-organ in crustaceans.*

This organ, together with the related sinus gland, constitutes an anatomical complex which has proved of great interest in understanding crustacean endocrinology. One view holds that neurosecretory cells in the X organ and the brain produce a molt-preventing hormone which is stored in the sinus gland of the eyestalk; other theories postulate a molt-accelerating hormone produced in a Y organ. The interrelations of these two hormones may be responsible for the molting process.

1935-1936: *Kendall, E. C., and L. H. Sarett. Discovery of cortisone.*

Kendall had first isolated from the adrenals this substance which he called compound E. Its final stages were prepared by Sarett later and involved a long tedious chemical process. A similar hormone, as far as its effects are concerned, was isolated in 1943 from the pituitary and called ACTH (adrenocorticotropic hormone). These hormones are not merely of interest because of their promise in relieving certain diseases, but their relations are of great importance in the development of endocrinology. The use of cortisone in the treatment of arthritis was developed first by Dr. Philip S. Hench of the Mayo Clinic.

Nobel Laureates (1950).

1935: *Needham, J., and C. H. Waddington. Chemical nature of the organizer region in embryology.*

The major effect of the organizer region described by Spemann and others was really due to the production by that region of a specific evocator substance closely related to the sterols and other chemical compounds.

1935: *Stanley, W. M. Isolation of a virus in crystalline form.*

This achievement of isolating a virus (tobacco mosaic disease) is not merely noteworthy in giving information about these small agencies responsible for many diseases but also in affording much speculation on the differences between the living and nonliving. The viruses appear to be a transition stage between the animate and the inanimate.

Nobel Laureate (1946).

1935: *Tansley, A. G. Concept of the ecosystem.*

The relatively recent science of ecology has added many new terms, but the ecosystem is considered the basic functional unit in ecology for it best expresses the environmental relations of organisms in their entirety. It includes both the biotic as well as abiotic factors, and the concept under different terminology had been used by others in the early development of ecology.

1935: *Timofeeff-Ressovsky, N. W. Target theory of induction of gene mutations.*

Timofeeff-Ressovsky's discovery that mutation can be induced in a gene if a single electron is detached by high-energy radiation gave rise to one of the two prevailing theories of how radiation affects mutation rate. The target theory (Treffertheorie) has tried to pinpoint the genetic effect to a certain sensitive volume of matter which is affected by a single ionization or atomic excitation.

1936: *Young, J. Z. Demonstration of giant fibers in squid.*

These giant fibers are formed by the fusion of the axons of many neurons whose cell bodies are found in a ganglion near the head. Each fiber is really a tube, more than a millimeter wide, consisting of an external sheath filled with liquid axoplasm. These giant fibers control the contraction of the characteristic mantle which surrounds these animals. Much information about nervous impulses has been obtained by a study of these fibers.

1937: *Blakeslee, A. F. Artificial production of polyploidy.*

By applying the drug colchicine to dividing cells, it was found that cell division in plants is blocked after the chromosomes have divided (metaphase) and thus the cell has double the normal number of chromosomes. When applied to hybrid plants, it has been possible to produce new plants.

1937: *Krebs, H. A. Citric acid (tricarboxylic) cycle.*

This theory of aerobic carbohydrate oxidation (through stages involving citric acid), which is supposed to occur in most living cells, involves a cycle of linked reactions under the influence of many enzymes (mainly from mitochondria). The scheme consists of many intermediary stages and aims to show how pyruvic acid (a derivative of carbohydrate oxidation) is converted to carbon dioxide and water. The cycle is thought to be the final common path for the oxidation of fatty acids, amino acids, and carbohydrates and represents the chief source of chemical energy in the body. The cycle has been the chief focal point in the study of cellular metabolism.

Nobel Laureate (1953).

1937: *Sonneborn, T. H. Discovery of mating types in paramecium.*

Sonneborn's discovery that only individuals of complimentary physiological classes (mating types) would conjugate opened up a new era of protozoan investigation which bids to shed new light upon the problems of species concept and evolution.

1938-1950: *Cohn, E. J. Blood fractionation.*

Dr. Cohn and his associates have separated more than a score of fractions from plasma, and their investigations have not only yielded medical value but also they have furnished much physiological information on the diversified roles of the blood.

1938: *Kozlowski, R. Analysis of the relationship of fossil graptolites to the pterobranchs.*

Carefully studying graptolites by transmitted light and by serial sections, this investigator found that the skeleton and other features of these wholly extinct forms corresponded with those of *Rhabdopleura*, one of the pterobranchs, which belong to the phylum Hemichordata. Since the hemichordates represent a stock close to vertebrates this analysis throws additional light upon the early ancestry of vertebrates. Formerly classified with the coelenterates or bryozoans, graptolites are now considered an extinct division under Hemichordata.

1938: *Schoenheimer, R. Use of radioactive isotopes to demonstrate synthesis of bodily constituents.*

By labeling amino acids, fats, carbohydrates, etc. with radioactive isotopes it was possible to show how these were incorporated into the various constituents of the body. Such experiments demonstrated that parts of the cell were constantly being synthesized and broken down and that the body must be considered a dynamic equilibrium.

1938: *Skinner, B. F. Measurement of motivation in animal behavior.*

Skinner worked out a technique for measuring the rewarding effect of a stimulus, or the effects of learning on voluntary behavior. His experimental animals (rats) were placed in a special box (Skinner's box) containing a lever which the animal could manipulate. When the rat presses the lever small pellets of food may or may not be released according to the experimental conditions. He found that the frequency with which the lever was pressed by the rat was correlated with the frequency of the reward. Many variant experiments can be done with this box.

1938: *Svedberg, T. Development of ultracentrifuge.*

In biological and medical investigation this instrument has been widely used for the purification of substances, the determination of particle sizes in colloidal systems, the relative densities of materials in living cells, the production of abnormal development, and the study of many problems concerned with electrolytes.

Nobel Laureate (1926).

1939: *Brown, F. A., Jr., and O. Cunningham. Demonstration of molt-preventing hormone in eyestalk of crustaceans.*

Although C. Zeleny (1905) and others had shown that eyestalk removal shortened the intermolt period in crustaceans, Brown and Cunningham were the first to present evidence to explain the effect as being due to a molt-preventing hormone present in the sinus gland. This key discovery has thrown considerable light upon a problem which has been extensively studied but has not yet been resolved.

1939: *Discovery of coelacanth fish.*

The collection of a living specimen of this ancient fish *(Latimeria)* followed later by other specimens, has brought about a complete reappraisal of this "living fossil" with reference to its ancestry of the amphibians and land forms.

1939: *Hoerstadius, S. Analysis of the basic pattern of regulative and mosaic eggs in development.*

The masterful work of this investigator has done much to resolve the differences in the early development of regulative eggs (in which each of the early blastomeres can give rise to a whole embryo) and mosaic eggs (in which isolated blastomeres produce only fragments of an embryo). Regulative eggs were shown to have two kinds of substances and both were necessary in proper ratios to produce normal embryos. Each of the early blastomeres has this proper ratio and thus can develop into a complete embryo; in mosaic eggs the regulative power is restricted to a much earlier time scale in development (before cleavage), and thus each isolated blastomere will give rise only to a fragment.

1939: *Huxley, J. Concept of the cline in evolutionary variation.*

This concept refers to the gradual and continuous variation in character over an extensive area because of adjustments to changing conditions. This idea of character gradients has proved a very fruitful one in the analysis of the mechanism of evolutionary processes, for such a variability helps to explain the initial stages in the transformation of species.

1940: *DDT as a biological control agent.*

DDT, or dichloro-diphenyl-trichloroethane, was synthesized in 1874 by Othmar Leidler but was not put to practical use until the last decade or two. Its value in controlling certain insect pests, such as lice, mosquitoes, potato bugs, and others, has been amply demonstrated. Other agents of more or less selective toxicity have been developed as insecticides. Just how these control agents are going to fit into the biological balances of nature is at present a matter of surmise.

1940: *Landsteiner, Karl, and A. S. Wiener. Discovery of Rh blood factor.*

Not only is a knowledge of the Rh factor of importance in solving a fatal infant's disease but it has also yielded a great deal of information about relationships of human races.

Nobel Laureate (1930).

1941: *Beadle, G. W., and E. L. Tatum. Biochemical mutation.*

By subjecting the bread mold *Neurospora* to x-ray irradiation, it was found

922

that genes responsible for the synthesis of certain vitamins and amino acids were inactivated (mutated) so that a strain of this mold carrying the mutant genes could no longer grow unless these particular vitamins and amino acids were added to the medium on which the mold was growing. This outstanding discovery has revealed as never before the precise way in which a single gene controls the specificity of a particular enzyme and has greatly stimulated similar research on other simple forms of life such as bacteria and viruses.

Nobel Laureates (1958).

1941: *Szent-Györgyi, Albert von. Role of ATP in muscular contraction.*

The demonstration showing that muscles get their energy for contraction from ATP (adenosine triphosphate) has done much to explain many aspects of the puzzling problem of muscle physiology and has been responsible in stimulating research in this and allied fields.

Nobel Laureate (1937).

1942: *McClean, D., and I. M. Rowlands. Discovery of the enzyme hyaluronidase in mammalian sperm.*

This enzyme dissolves the cement substance of the follicle cells which surround the mammalian egg and facilitates the passage of the sperm to the egg. This discovery not only aided in resolving some of the difficult problems of the fertilization process but also offers a logical explanation of cases of infertility in which too few sperm may not carry enough of the enzyme to afford a passage through the inhibiting follicle cells.

1943: *Claude, A. Isolation of cell constituents.*

By differential centrifugation, Claude found it possible to separate, in relatively pure form, particulate components, such as mitochondria, microsomes, and nuclei. These investigations led immediately to a more precise knowledge of the chemical nature of these cell constituents and aided the elucidation of the structure and physiology of the mitochondria—one of the great triumphs in the biochemistry of the cell.

1943: *Holtfreter, J. Tissue synthesis from dissociated cells.*

By dissociating the cells of embryonic tissues of amphibians (by dissolving with enzymes or other agents the intercellular cement that holds the cells together) and heaping them in a mass, it was found that the cells in time coalesced and formed the type of tissue from which they had come. This is an application to vertebrates of the discovery of Wilson with sponge cells. Many variant aspects of the experiment have been performed by numerous investigators, such as mixing together dissociated cells from different tissues and also tissue cells from different organisms. In all cases there was a selective regrouping of cells according to tissue types. There are obvious implications from such experiments to the problems of morphogenesis.

1943: *Sonneborn, T. H. Extranuclear inheritance.*

The view that in paramecia cytoplasmic determiners (plasmagenes) which are self-reproducing and capable of mutation can produce genetic variability has thrown additional light on the role of the cytoplasm in hereditary patterns.

1944: *Robinow, C. F. Discovery of nuclei in bacteria.*

The genetical mechanism of bacteria appears to be similar to those of higher forms, and this discovery has given a great impetus to genetical study of these common organisms. Much of this study has been focused on mutations and the possibility of transforming strains of bacteria by introducing specific hereditary characteristics from another strain. The power to transform bacteria was first demonstrated by the English investigator F. Griffith in 1928, and numerous workers since have realized the significance of such investigation as a laboratory tool in genetics and in the appraisal of the gene.

1944: *Waksman, S. A. Discovery of streptomycin.*

This antibiotic ranks next to penicillin in importance and represents a triumph of carefully planned investigation.

Nobel Laureate (1952).

Basic concepts and key discoveries in biology 923

1945: *Cori, Carl. Hormone influence on enzyme activity.*

The delicate balance insulin and the diabetogenic hormone of the pituitary exercise over the activity of the enzyme hexokinase in carbohydrate metabolism has opened up a whole new field of the regulative action of hormones on enzymes. Nobel Laureate (1947).

1945: *Griffin, D., and R. Galambos. Development of the concept of echolocation.*

Echolocation refers to a type of perception of objects at a distance by which echoes of sound are reflected back from obstacles and detected acoustically. These investigators found that bats generated their own ultrasonic sounds which were reflected back to their own ears so that they were able to avoid obstacles in their flight without the aid of vision. Their work climaxed an interesting series of experiments inaugurated as early as 1793 by Spallanzani, who believed that bats avoided obstacles in the dark by reflection of sound waves to their ears. Others who laid the groundwork for the novel concept were C. Jurine (1794), who proved that ears were the all-important organs in the perception; H. S. Maxim (1912), who advanced the idea that the bat made use of sounds of low frequency inaudible to human ears; and H. Hartridge (1920), who proposed the hypothesis that bats emitted sounds of high frequencies and short wave lengths (ultrasonic sounds).

1946: *Libby, W. F. Radiocarbon dating of fossils.*

The radiocarbon age determination is based on the fact that carbon[14] in the dead organism disintegrates at the rate of one-half in 5,560 years, one-half of the remainder in the next 5,560 years, and so on. This is on the assumption that the isotope is mixed equally through all living matter and that the cosmic rays (which form the isotopes) have not varied much in periods of many thousands of years. The limitation of the method is around 30,000 years. Nobel Laureate (1960).

1946: *White, E. I. Discovery of primitive chordate fossil, Jamoytius.*

The discovery of this fossil in the freshwater deposits of Silurian rock in Scotland bids to throw some light on the early ancestry of vertebrates, for this form seems to be intermediate between *Amphioxus* or *Ammocoetes* larva and the oldest known vertebrates, the ostracoderms. Morphologically, *Jamoytius* represents the most primitive chordate yet discovered. It could well serve as an ancestor of such forms as *Amphioxus* and the jawless ostracoderms.

1948: *Frisch, Karl von. Communication patterns of honeybees.*

Climaxing forty years of patient work on bees, von Frisch has been able to unravel some of the amazing patterns of behavior bees possess in conveying information to each other about the distance, direction, and sources of food supplies—an outstanding demonstration of animal behavior.

1948: *Hess, W. R. Localization of instinctive impulse patterns in the brain.*

By inserting electrodes through the skull, fixing them in position, and allowing such holders to heal in place, it was possible to study the brain of an animal in its ordinary activities. When the rat could automatically and at will stimulate itself by pressing a lever, it did so frequently when the electrode was inserted in the hypothalamus region of the brain, indicating a pleasure center. In this way, by placing electrodes at different centers, rats can be made to gratify such drives as thirst, sex, and hunger.

1948: *Hogeboom, G. H., W. C. Schneider, and G. E. Palade. Separation of mitochondria from the cell.*

This was an important discovery in unravelling the amazing enzymatic activity of the mitochondria in the Krebs cycle. The role mitochondria play in the energy transfer of the cell has earned for these rod-shaped bodies the appellation of the "powerhouse" of the cell.

1948: *Johnson, M. W. Relation between echo-sounding and the deep scattering layer of marine waters.*

The development of a sound transmitter and a receiver coupled with a timing

924

mechanism for recording the time between an outgoing sound impulse and the echo of its return has made possible an accurate method for determining depths in the ocean. By means of this device a deep scattering layer far above the floor of the ocean was discovered which scattered the sound waves and sent back echoes. This scattering layer tends to rise toward the surface at night and sink to a depth of many hundred meters by day. Johnson saw a marked parallelism between the shifting of this scattering layer and the diurnal vertical migration of plankton or pelagic animals. The nature and cause of this layer has been the subject of intense investigation during the past decade and has not yet been fully resolved, although fish and their swim bladders have entered more and more into the picture.

1949: *Barr, M. L., and E. G. Bertram. Sex differences in nuclear morphology— nucleolar satellite.*

The discovery that an intranuclear body (nucleolar satellite) was far better developed in the female mammalian cell has aroused the interesting possibility of detecting the genetic sex of an individual by microscopic examination. The body which is about 1 micron in diameter appears as a satellite to the large nucleolus of the female nucleus. The present explanation is that the two X chromosomes of the female are responsible for the nucleolus. The male satellite (with one X chromosome), if present, is too small to see. Some cells in the body show the phenomenon better than others.

1949: *Pauling, L. Genic control of protein structure.*

Pauling and his colleagues demonstrated a direct connection between specific chemical differences in protein molecules and alterations in genotypes. Making use of the hemoglobin of patients with sickle cell anemia (which is caused by a homozygous condition of an abnormal gene), he was able by the method of electrophoresis to show a marked difference in the behavior of this hemoglobin in an electric field compared with that from a heterozygote or from a normal person.

Nobel Laureate (1954).

1949: *Selye, H. Concept of the stress syndrome.*

In 1937 Selye began his experiments which led to what he called the "alarm reaction" which involved the chain reactions of many hormones, such as cortisone, ACTH, etc., in meeting stress conditions faced by an organism. Whenever the stress experience exceeds the limitations of these body defenses, serious degenerative disorders may result.

1950: *Hadzi, J. Theory of the origin of metazoans.*

The resemblance between multinucleate ciliates and acoelous flatworms has formed the basis of this theory, which was proposed by Sedgwick many years ago and was largely ignored by contemporary zoologists. It has been studied for 50 years by Hadzi, who has brought forth many logical reasons in its support. This new point of view supports the early views of Lankester and Metschnikoff, namely, that the original diploblastic ancestor was solid rather than hollow and that the formation of the archenteron is a secondary process.

1951: *Lewis, E. B. Concept of pseudoallelism in genetics.*

On the basis of a series of mutations in *Drosophila*, Lewis concluded that certain adjacent loci were closely linked, affected the same trait, and probably arose from a common ancestral gene instead of being a single locus with multiple genes.

1952: *Briggs, R., and J. T. King, Demonstration of possible differentiated nuclear genotypes.*

The belief that all cells of a particular organism have the same genetic endowment has been questioned in the light of these investigators, who transplanted nuclei of different ages and sources from blastulae and early gastrulae into enucleated zygotes and got varied abnormal developmental results. This pioneer work bids to shed light upon the difficult problem of cell localization and differentiation.

1952: *Discovery of primitive mollusks.*

The discovery of these interesting forms (class or order Monoplacophora) off the coast of Mexico in deep water represents the most important "living fossils" since the discovery of *Latimeria*. With a round, limpetlike shell and definite segments, this type may represent an intermediate form between the ancestors of annelids and that of mollusks. Its exact status has not been appraised.

1952: *Hayes, W. Discovery of sexual differentiation in bacteria.*

Bacteria chiefly reproduce by simple division, but Hayes and others have shown that the male possesses a sex determinant which, when transferred to the females, transforms them into males. Bacteria have been shown to undergo conjugation, and during this process a portion of genetic material is passed from the male to the female. Bacteria thus seem to fall into the evolutionary pattern of sexual reproduction.

1952: *Kramer, G. Orientation of birds to positional changes of sun.*

This discovery showed that birds (starlings and pigeons) can be trained to find food in accordance with the position of the sun. It was found that the general orientation of the birds shifted at a rate (when exposed to a constant artificial sun) that could be predicted on the basis of the birds' correcting for the normal rotation of the earth. Birds were able to orient themselves in a definite direction with reference to the sun whether the light of the sun reached them directly or was reflected by mirrors. They were capable also of finding food at any time of day, thus indicating an ability to compensate for the sun's motion across the sky.

1952: *Palade, G. E. Analysis of the finer structure of the mitochondrion.*

The important role of mitochondria in enzymatic systems and cellular metabolism has focused much investigation on the structure of these cytoplasmic inclusions. Each mitochondrion is bounded by two membranes; the outer is smooth and the inner is thrown into small folds or cristae which project into a homogenous matrix in the interior. Some modifications of this pattern are found.

1952: *Tuzet, O., R. Loubatieres, and M. Pavans de Ceccatty. Discovery of nerve cells in sponges.*

Bipolar and multipolar cells with long processes have been described on histological and staining grounds in a variety of sponges. The processes connect choanocytes and contractile cells and apparently function in the coordination of pore size and water intake. Although more physiological verification is needed, this finding indicates that sponges must have some integration.

1953: *Crick, F. H. C., and J. D. Watson. Chemical structure of DNA.*

Crick and Watson formulated the hypothesis that the DNA molecule was made up of two chains twisted around each other in a helical structure and cross-linked by pairs of bases—adenine and thymine or guanine and cytosine. Genes are considered to be segments of these molecules. Each of these complementary strands acts as a model or template to form a new strand. The hypothesis has been widely accepted and affords a clue to the chemical structure of inheritance and the way chromosomes duplicate themselves.

1953: *Porter, K. R. Description of the endoplasmic reticulum.*

The endoplasmic reticulum is a very complex cytoplasmic structure consisting of a lacelike network of irregular anastomosing tubules and vesicular expansions within the cytoplasmic matrix. Associated with the reticulum complex are small dense granules of ribonucleoprotein and other granules known as microsomes which are fragments of the endoplasmic reticulum. The reticulum complex is supposed to play an important role in the synthesis of proteins and RNA.

1953: *Urey, H., and S. Miller. Demonstration of the possible primordia of life.*

By exposing a mixture of water vapor, ammonia, methane, and hydrogen gas to electric discharge (to simulate lightning) for several days, these investigators found

926

that several complex organic substances, such as the amino acids, glycine and alanine, were formed when the water vapor was condensed into water. This demonstration offered a very plausible theory to explain how the early beginnings of life substances could have started by the formation of organic substances from inorganic ones.

1954: *Dan, J. C. Acrosome reaction.*

In echinoderms, annelids, and mollusks it has been shown that the acrosome region of the spermatozoan forms a filament and releases an unknown substance at the time of fertilization. Evidence seems to indicate that the filament is associated with the formation of the fertilization cone. Other observers had described similar filaments before Dan made his detailed descriptions. The filament (about 25 microns long) may play an important role in the entrance of the sperm into the cytoplasm.

1954: *Loomis, W. F. Sexual differentiation in Hydra.*

By discovering that high pressures of free carbon dioxide and reduced aeration in stagnant water (and not temperature as formerly supposed) induces sexuality in the hydra, an explanation was found for the large number of sexual forms found in the fall when many individuals crowd together and build up gas pressure generated by their respiration. This work has suggested new methods of attack on some of the problems of growth and differentiation.

1954: *Sanger, F. Structure of the insulin molecule.*

Insulin is the important hormone used in the treatment of diabetes. The discovery of its structure was the first complete description of a protein molecule. The molecule was found to be made up of 17 different amino acids in 51 amino acid units. Although one of the smallest proteins, its formula contains 777 atoms. This achievement has given encouragement for investigating the structure of other protein molecules.

Nobel Laureate (1958).

1955: *Fraenkel-Conrat, H., and R. C.*

Williams. Analysis of the chemical nature of a virus.

In tobacco mosaic virus, these workers were able to separate the protein, which makes up the outer cylinder of the virus, from the nucleic acid, the inner core of the cylinder. Neither the protein fraction nor the nucleic acid by itself was able to grow or infect tobacco, but when the two fractions were recombined, the resulting particle behaved like the original virus. Hybrids were also produced by combining the protein of one strain with the nucleic acid of a different strain. In the case of hybrids, the progeny assume the properties of the virus from which the nucleic acid came. Such investigations throw additional light upon the organization of biologically active material as well as upon certain aspects of inheritance.

1956: *Ingram, V. M. Nature of a mutation.*

By tracing the change in one amino acid unit out of more than 300 units which make up the protein hemoglobin, Ingram was able to pinpoint the difference between normal hemoglobin and the mutant form of hemoglobin which causes sickle cell anemia. This experiment is of great significance in determining the effect of a single genetic mutation on the molecular structure of body materials as well as in throwing some light on the exact mechanism of heredity.

1956: *Peart, W. S., and D. F. Elliot. Isolation of angiotensin.*

Ever since Volhard in 1928 suggested that a substance in the kidney might be responsible for certain cases of hypertension, investigators have been trying to identify this substance. Among the landmarks in the development of the concept were the Goldblatt clamp (an artificial constriction of the renal artery) which caused something in the kidney to elevate blood pressure; the discovery of the enzyme renin by Page and others; the action of this enzyme upon a blood protein (renin substrate) to form an inactive substance (angiotensin I); and finally the conversion of the inactive form into the active angiotensin II by means of a con-

Basic concepts and key discoveries in biology 927

verting enzyme. Although a protective mechanism for the body in times of stress, prolonged release of angiotensin caused by repeated stress could result in types of chronic hypertension.

1956: *Tjio, J. H., and A. Levan. Revision of human chromosome count.*

The time-honored number of chromosomes in man, 48 (diploid), was found by careful cytological technique to be 46 instead. This investigation is of considerable interest because it throws some light on the difficulties of accurate chromosome counts, especially when the number is great or the chromosomes are highly irregular in shape and size.

1957: *Ivanov, A. V. Analysis of phylum Pogonophora (beard worms).*

Specimens of this phylum were collected in 1900 and represent the most recent phylum to be discovered in the animal kingdom. Collections have been made in the waters of Indonesia, the Okhotsk Sea, the Bering Sea, and the Pacific Ocean. They are found mostly in the abyssal depths. They belong to the Deuterostomia division and appear to be related to the Hemichordata. At present twenty-two species divided into two orders have been described.

1957: *Sauer, F. Celestial navigation by birds.*

By subjecting old world warblers to various synthetic night skies of star settings in a planetarium, Sauer was able to demonstrate that the birds made use of the stars to guide them in their migrations. The birds used were hand raised and had never traveled under a natural sky, yet they were able with their precise time sense to adjust their orientation to the geography of the earth and its relation to the heavenly constellations even when the synthetic conditions of the latter were vastly different from their surroundings.

1957: *Taylor, J. H., P. S. Woods, and W. L. Hughes. Application of tracer method to organization and replication of chromosomes.*

By using radioactive materials as markers, these investigators were able to show that each new chromosome consists of one-half of old material and one-half of newly synthesized substances. This was confirmation of the Crick-Watson model of the nucleic acid molecule which is supposed to divide or unwind into two single threads, and each half reduplicates itself to form a complete double thread.

1959: *Leakey, L. S. B. Discovery of Zinjanthropus fossil man.*

This fossil is represented by a skull which shows the morphological characters of a man and is thought to be in direct line of human ancestry. It seems to be definitely more advanced than its fossil relative, Australopithecus, and was a tool maker. It was found in the Olduval Gorge, Tanganyika, South Africa.

1960. *Strell, M., and R. B. Woodward. Synthesis of chlorophyll a.*

Strell and Woodward with the aid of many co-workers finally solved this problem which had been the goal of organic chemists for many generations. Since all biological life depends upon this important pigment, this achievement in molecular biology must have wide implications.

Books and publications that have greatly influenced development of zoology

Aristotle. 336-323 B.C. De Anima, Historia Animalium, De Partibus Animalium, De Generatione Animalium. *These biological works of the Greek thinker have exerted an enormous influence on biological thinking for centuries.*

Vesalius, Andreas. 1543. De Fabrica Corporis Humani. *This work is the foundation of modern anatomy and represents a break with the Galen tradition. His representations of anatomical subjects, such as the muscles, have never been surpassed. Moreover, he treated anatomy as a living whole, a viewpoint present-day anatomists are beginning to copy.*

Fabricius of Aquapendente. 1600-1621. De Formato Foetu and De Formatione Oviet Pulli. *This was the first illustrated work on embryology and may be said to be the beginning of the modern study of development.*

Harvey, William. 1628. Anatomical Dissertation Concerning the Motion of the Heart and Blood. *This great work represents one of the first accurate explanations in physical terms*

928

of an important physiological process. It initiated an experimental method of observation which gave an impetus to research in all fields of biology.

Descartes, Rene. 1637. Discourse on Method. *The physiological section of this book gave a great stimulus to a mechanistic interpretation of biological phenomena.*

Buffon, Georges. 1749-1804. Histoire Naturelle. *This extensive work of many volumes collected together natural history facts in a popular and pleasing style. It had a great influence in stimulating a study of nature. Many eminent biological thinkers, such as Erasmus Darwin and Lamarck, were influenced by its generalizations, which here and there suggest an idea of evolution in a crude form.*

Linnaeus, Carolus. 1758. Systema Naturae. *In this work there is laid the basis for the classification of animals and plants. With few modifications the taxonomic principles outlined therein have been universally adopted by biologists.*

Wolff, Caspar Friedrich. 1759. Theoria Generationis. *The theory of epigenesis was here set forth for the first time in opposition to the preformation theory of development so widely held up to the time of Wolff's work.*

Haller, Albrecht von. 1760. Elementa Physiologiae. *An extensive summary of various aspects of physiology which greatly influenced physiological thinking for many years. Some of the basic concepts therein laid down are still considered valid, especially those on the nervous system.*

Malthus, T. R. 1798. Essay on Population. *This work stimulated evolutionary thinking among such men as Darwin and Wallace.*

Lamarck, Jean Baptiste. 1809. Philosophie Zoologique. *This publication was of great importance in focusing the attention of biologists upon the problem of the role of the environment as a factor in evolution. Lamarck's belief that all species came from other species represented one of the first clear-cut statements on the mutability of species, even though his method of use and disuse has not been accepted by most biologists.*

Cuvier, Georges. 1817. Le Regne Animal. *A comprehensive biological work which dealt with classification and a comparative study of animal structures. Its plates are still of value, but the general plan of the work was marred by a disbelief in evolution and a faith in the doctrine of geological catastrophes. The book, however, exerted an enormous influence upon contemporary zoological thought.*

Audubon, John J. 1828-1838. The Birds of America. *The greatest of all ornithological works, it has served as the model for all monographs dealing with a specific group of animals. The plates, the work of a master artist, have never been surpassed in the field of biological achievement.*

Baer, Karl Ernst von. 1828-1837. Entwickelungsgeschichte der Thiere. *In this important work are laid down the fundamental principles of germ layer formation and the similarity of corresponding stages in the development of embryos which have proved to be the foundation studies of modern embryology.*

Lyell, Charles. 1830-1833. Principles of Geology. *From a biological viewpoint this great work exerted a profound influence on biological thinking, for it did away with the theory of catastrophism and prepared the way for an evolutionary interpretation of fossils and the forms which arose from them.*

Beaumont, William. 1833. Experiments and Observations on the Gastric Juice and the Physiology of Digestion. *In this classical work the observations Beaumont made on various functions of the stomach and digestion were so thorough that only a few details have been added by subsequent research. This book paved the way for the brilliant investigations of Pavlov, Cannon, and Carlson of later generations.*

Müller, Johannes. 1834-1840. Handbook of Physiology. *The principles set down in this work by the greatest of all physiologists have set the pattern for the development of the science of physiology.*

Darwin, Charles. 1839. Journal of Researches (Voyage of the Beagle). *This book reveals the training and development of the naturalist and the material which led to the formulation of Darwin's concept of organic evolution.*

Schwann, Theodor. 1839. Mikroskopische Untersuchungen über die Uebereinstimmung in der Struktur und dem Wachstum der Thiere und Pflanzen. *The basic principles concerning the cell doctrine are laid down in this classic work.*

Kölliker, Albrecht. 1852. Mikroskopische Anatomie. *This was the first textbook in histology and contains contributions of the greatest importance in this field. Many of the histological descriptions Kölliker made have never needed correction. In many of his biological views he was far ahead of his time.*

Maury, M. F. 1855. The Physical Geography of the Sea. *This work has often been called the first textbook on oceanography. This pioneer*

Basic concepts and key discoveries in biology 929

treatise stressed the integration of such knowledge as was then available about tides, winds, currents, depths, circulation, and such matters. Maury's work represents a real starting point in the fascinating study of the oceans and has had a great influence in stimulating investigations in this field.

Virchow, Rudolf. 1858. Cellular Pathologie. *In this work Virchow made the first clear distinction between normal and diseased tissues and demonstrated the real nature of pathological cells. The work also represents the death knell to the old humoral pathology which had held sway for so long.*

Darwin, Charles. 1859. The Origin of Species. *One of the most influential books ever published in biology. Although built around the theme that natural selection is the most important factor in evolution, the great influence of the book has been due to the great array of evolutionary evidence it presented. It also stimulated constructive thinking upon a subject that had been vague and confusing before Darwin's time.*

Owen, Richard. 1866. Anatomy and Physiology of the Vertebrates. *This work contains an enormous amount of personal observation on the structure and physiology of animals, and some of the basic concepts of structure and function, such as homologue and analogue, are here clearly defined for the first time.*

Balfour, Francis M. 1880. Comparative Embryology. *This is a comprehensive summary of embryological work on both vertebrates and invertebrates up to the time it was published. This work is often considered the beginning of modern embryology.*

Butschli, O. 1889. Protozoen (Bronn's Klassen und Ordnungen des Tier-Reichs). *This monograph has been of the utmost importance to students of Protozoa. No other work on a like scale has ever been produced in this field of study.*

Weismann, A. 1892. Das Keimplasma. *Weismann predicted from purely theoretical considerations the necessity of meiosis or reduction of the chromosomes in the germ cell cycle—a postulate that was quickly confirmed cytologically by others.*

Hertwig, R. 1892. Lehrbuch der Zoologie. *A text which has proved to be an invaluable source of material for many generations of zoologists. Its illustrations have been widely used in many other textbooks.*

Hertwig, O. 1893. Zelle und Gewebe. *In this work a clear distinction is made between histology as the science of tissues and cytology as the science of cell structure and function.*

Cytology as a study in its own right really dates from this time.

Korschelt, E., and K. Heider. 1893. Lehrbuch der vergleichender Entwicklungsgeschichte der wirbellosen Thiere, 4 vols. *A treatise which has been a valuable tool for all workers in the difficult field of invertebrate embryology.*

Wilson, Edmund B. 1896. The Cell in Development and Heredity. *This and subsequent editions represented the most outstanding work of its kind in the English language. Its influence in directing the development of cytogenetics cannot be overestimated, and, in summarizing the many investigations in cytology, the book has served as one of the most useful tools in the field.*

Pavlov, Ivan. 1897. Le Travail des Glands Digestive. *This work marks a great landmark in the study of the digestive system, for it describes many of the now classical experiments which Pavlov conducted, such as the gastric pouch technique and the rate of gastric secretions.*

De Vries, Hugo. 1901. Mutationslehre. *The belief that evolution is due to sudden changes or mutations is advanced by one who is commonly credited with the initiation of this line of investigation into the causes of evolution.*

Sherrington, Sir Charles. 1906. The Integrative Action of the Nervous System. *The basic concepts of neurophysiology laid down in this book have been little altered since its publication. Much of the work done in this field has served to confirm the nervous mechanism he here outlines.*

Henderson, L. J. 1913. The Fitness of the Environment. *This book has pointed out in a specific way the reciprocity which exists between living and nonliving nature and how organic matter is fitted to the inorganic environment. It has exerted a considerable influence on ecological aspects of adaptation.*

Bayliss, W. M. 1915. Principles of General Physiology. *If a classical book must meet the requirements of masterly analysis and synthesis of what is known in a particular discipline, then this great work must be called one.*

Morgan, T. H., A. H. Sturtevant, C. B. Bridges, and H. J. Muller. 1915. The Mechanism of Mendelian Heredity. *This book gave an analysis and synthesis of Mendelian inheritance as formulated from the epoch-making investigations of the authors. This classical work will always stand as a cornerstone of our modern interpretation of heredity.*

Doflein, F. 1916. Lehrbuch der Protozoenkunde, ed. 6 (revised by E. Reichenow, 1949). *A standard treatise on Protozoa. Its many edi-*

tions have proved helpful to all workers in this field.

Kukenthal, W., and T. Krumbach. 1923. Handbuch der Zoologie. *An extensive modern treatise on zoology which covers all phyla. The work has been an invaluable tool for all zoologists who are interested in the study of a particular group.*

Barcroft, J. 1934. Features in the Architecture of Physiological Function. *This is a remarkable book of physiological principles dealing with the integration of certain bodily functions and their significance to the organism as a whole.*

Such a work gives the student a bearing and an attitude which he rarely gleans in the ordinary physiological text.

Dobzhansky, T. 1937. Genetics and the Origin of Species. *The vast change in the explanation of the mechanism of evolution which emerged about 1930 is well analyzed in this work by a master evolutionist. Other syntheses of this new biological approach to the evolutionary problems have appeared since this work was published, but none of them has surpassed the clarity and fine integration of Dobzhansky's work.*

Glossary

aboral (ab-o′ral) (L. *ab,* from, + *os,* mouth) A region opposite the mouth.

Acanthocephala (a-kan′tho-sef″a-la) (Gr. *akantho,* a thorn, + *kephale,* head) A phylum composed of spiny-headed worms which are pseudocoelomate parasites.

Acipenser (as′i-pen″ser) (L. a sturgeon) A genus of sturgeon fish.

acoelomate (a-sel′o-mate) (Gr. *a,* not, + *koilos,* cavity) Without a coelom, such as flatworms and proboscis worms.

Actinopterygii (ak′ti-nop′ter-yg″ee-eye) (Gr. *aktinos,* ray, + *pterygion,* fin) One of the two main groups of bony fish, or the ray-finned fish.

adenine (ad′e-nen) A component of nucleotides and nucleic acids.

adenosine (a-den′o-sen) *(di-, tri-) phosphate* (ADP, ATP) Certain phosphorylated compounds which function in the energy cycle of cells.

adipose (ad′i-pos) (L. *adipis,* fat) Fatty tissue.

adrenaline (ad-ren′al-in) (L. *ad,* to, + *renalis,* kidney) A hormone produced by the adrenal or suprarenal gland.

aerobic (a′er-o″bik) (Gr. *aeros,* air, + *bios,* life) Oxygen-dependent form of respiration.

afferent (af′er-ent) (L. *ad,* to, + *ferre,* to bear) A structure (blood vessel, nerve, etc.) leading toward some point.

Agnatha (ag′na-tha) (Cr. *a,* not, + *gnathos,* jaw) A class of vertebrates that includes the modern lampreys and hagfish and the extinct ostracoderms.

allantois (a-lan′toe-is) (Gr. *allas,* sausage, + *eidos,* form) One of the extraembryonic membranes of the amniotes.

allele (al-lel′) (Gr. *allelon,* of one another) One of a pair, or series, of genes which are alternative to each other in heredity and are situated at the same locus in homologous chromosomes. Allele genes may consist of a dominant and its correlated recessive, or two correlated dominants, or two correlated recessives.

alveolus (al-ve′o-lus) (L. dim. of *alveus,* hollow) A small cavity or pit, such as a microscopic air sac of the lungs, terminal part of an alveolar gland, bony socket of a tooth, etc.

amino acid (a-me′no) (amine, an organic compound) An organic acid with an amino radical (NH_2). Makes up the structure of proteins.

amitosis (am′i-to″sis) (Gr. *a,* not, + *mitos,* thread) A form of cell division in which mitotic nuclear changes do not occur; cleavage without separation of daughter chromosomes.

amnion (am′ni-on) (Gr. *amnos,* lamb) One of the extraembryonic membranes forming a sac around the embryo in amniotes.

amylase (am′i-las) (L. *amylum,* starch) An enzyme that breaks down carbohydrates into smaller units.

anaerobic (an-a′er-o″bik) (Gr. *an,* not, + *aeros,* air, + *bios,* life) Not dependent on oxygen for respiration.

androgen (an′dro-jen) (Gr. *andros,* man, + *genes,* born) Any of a group of male sex hormones.

anhydrase (an-hi′dras) (Gr. *an,* not, + *hydor,* water) An enzyme involved in the removal of water from a compound. Carbonic anhydrase promotes the conversion of carbonic acid into water and carbon dioxide.

archenteron (ar-ken′ter-on) (Gr. *archein,* first, + *enteron,* gut) The central cavity of a gastrula which is lined with endoderm, representing the future digestive cavity.

autosome (o′to-som) (Gr. *autos,* self, + *soma,* body) Any chromosome that is not a sex chromosome.

autotroph (o′to-trof″) (Gr. *autos,* self, + *trophos,* feeder) An organism that makes its organic nutrients from inorganic raw materials.

benthos (ben′thos) (Gr. *benthos,* depth of the sea) Those organisms that live along the bottom of seas and lakes.

blastopore (blas′to-por) (Gr. *blastos,* germ, + *porous,* passage) Opening into archenteron of the gastrula; future mouth in some, future anus in others.

buffer (buf′er) Any substance or chemical compound that tends to keep pH constant when acids or bases are added.

carboxyl (kar-bok′sil) (carbon + oxygen + yl) The acid group of organic molecules;—COOH.

carotene (kar′o-ten) (L. *carota*, carrot) A red, orange, or yellow pigment belonging to the group of carotenoids; precursor of vitamin A.

catalyst (cat′a-lyst) (Gr. *kata*, down, + *lysis*, a loosening) A substance that accelerates a chemical reaction but does not become a part of the end product.

cecum (se′kum) (L. *caecus*, blind) A blind pouch at the beginning of the large intestine, or any similar pouch.

cenogenesis (see′no-jen″i-sis) (Gr. *kainos*, new, + *genesis*, origin) In the development of an organism, the new stages which have arisen in adaptive response to the embryonic mode of life, such as the fetal membranes of amniotes.

Cenozoic (se′no-zo″ik) (Gr. *kainos*, recent, + *zoe*, life) The geological era from the Mesozoic to the present (about 75 million years)

centriole (sen′tri-ol) (Gr. dim. of *kentron*, center of a circle) A minute granule, usually found in the centrosome and considered to be the active division center of the cell.

centromere (sen′tro-mer) (Gr. *kentron*, center, + *meros*, part) A small body or constriction on the chromosome where it is attached to a spindle fiber.

Chaetognatha (ke-tog′nath-a) (Gr. *chaite*, hair, + *gnathos*, jaw) Small marine worms, often called arrowworms, with curved bristles on each side of mouth; an enterocoelomate phylum.

chelicera (ke-lis′er-a) (Gr. *chele*, claw) Pincerlike head appendage on the members of the subphylum Chelicerata.

chorion (ko′ri-on) (Gr. membrane) The outer of the double membrane that surrounds the embryo of the amniotes; in mammals it helps form the placenta.

chromatid (kro′ma-tid) (Gr. *chroma*, color, + *-id*, daughter) A half chromosome between early prophase and metaphase in mitosis; a half chromosome between synapsis and second metaphase in meiosis; at the anaphase stage each chromatid is known as a daughter chromosome.

chromomere (kro′mo-mere) (Gr. *chroma*, color, + *meros*, part) The chromatin granules of characteristic size on the chromosome; may be identical with genes or clusters of genes.

coelom (se′lom) (Gr. *koilos*, hollow) The body cavity in triploblastic animals, lined with mesoderm.

cotylosaur (kot″i-lo-sor′) (Gr. *kotyle*, hollow, + *sauros*, lizard) A primitive group of fossil reptiles which arose from the labyrinthodont amphibians and became the ancestral stem of all other reptiles.

Ctenophora (ten-off′o-ra) (Gr. *ktenos*, comb, + *phoros*, bearing) A small phylum of marine animals consisting of three germ layers and eight rows of comb plates by which they move.

cytochrome (si′to-krom) (Gr. *kytos*, vessel, + *chroma*, color) One of the hydrogen carriers in aerobic respiration.

desoxyribose (des-oks′i-ri″bos) (desoxy, loss of oxygen, + ribose, a pentose sugar) A 5-carbon sugar having one oxygen atom less than ribose; a component of desoxyribose nucleic acid (DNA).

diploid (dip′loid) (Gr. *diploos*, double, + *eidos*, form) The somatic number of chromosomes, or twice the number characteristic of a gamete of a given species.

Echiuroidea (ek′i-ur-oi″de-a) (Gr. *echis*, an adder, + *oura*, tail, + *eidos*, form) A phylum of wormlike animals which inhabit marine coastal mud flats.

ectoplasm (ec″to-plaz′m) (Gr. *ektos*, outside, + *plasma*, form) The cortex of a cell or that part of cytoplasm just under cell surface; contrasts with endoplasm.

emulsion (e-mul′shun) (L. *emulsus*, to milk out) A colloidal system in which both phases are liquids.

endocrine (en′do-krin) (Gr. *endon*, within, + *krinein*, to separate) Refers to a gland which is without a duct and which releases its product directly into the blood or lymph.

endoplasm (en″do-plaz′m) (Gr. *endon*, within, + *plasma*, form) That portion of cytoplasm which immediately surrounds the nucleus.

endostyle (en′do-stil) (Gr. *endon*, within, + *stylos*, column) A ciliated groove in the floor of the pharynx of tunicates, amphioxus, and ammocoetes, used for getting food; may be homologous to the thyroid gland of higher forms.

enterocoele (en″ter-o-sel′) (Gr. *enteron*, gut, + *koilos*, hollow) A type of coelom which is formed by the outpouching of a mesodermal sac from the endoderm of the primitive gut.

enterocoelomate (en′ter-o-sel″o-mate) (Gr. *enteron*, gut, + *koilos*, hollow, + *ate*, state of) Those which have an enterocoele, such as the echinoderms and the vertebrates.

Entoprocta (en′to-prok″ta) (Gr. *entos*, within, + *proktos*, anus) A phylum of sessile animals which have the anus enclosed in the ring of ciliated tentacles.

enzyme (en'zym) (Gr. *en*, in, + *zyme*, leaven) A protein substance produced by living cells capable of speeding up specific chemical transformations, such as hydrolysis, oxidation, or reduction, but is unaltered itself in the process; a biological catalyst.

epididymis (ep'i-did"i-mus) (Gr. *epi*, over, + *didymos*, testicle) That part of the sperm duct which is coiled and lying near the testis.

epigenesis (ep'i-jen"e-sis) (Gr. *epi*, over, + *genesis*, origin) The embryological view that an embryo is a new creation which develops and differentiates step by step from an initial stage by the progressive production of new parts that were nonexistent as such in the original zygote.

epigenetics (ep'i-je-net"iks) (Gr. *epi*, over, + *genesis*, origin) That study of the mechanisms by which the genes produce phenotypic effects.

estrogen (es'tro-jen) (Gr. *oistros*, frenzy, + *genes*, born) An estrus-producing hormone; one of a group of female sex hormones.

eurytopic (yu're-top"ic) (Gr. *eurys*, broad, + *topos*, place) Refers to an organism with a wide range of distribution.

exocrine (ek'so-krin) (Gr. *exo*, outside, + *krinein*, to separate) That type of gland which releases its secretion through a duct.

exteroceptor (ek"ster-o-sep'ter) (L. *exterus*, outward, + *capere*, to take) A sense organ near the skin or mucous membrane which receives stimuli from the external world.

fermentation (fur'men-ta"shun) (L. *fermentum*, ferment) The conversion of organic substances into simpler substances under the influence of enzymes with little or no oxygen involved (anaerobic respiration).

fiber, fibril (L. *fibra*, thread) These two terms are often confused. Fiber is a strand of protoplasmic material produced or secreted by a cell and lying outside the cell; or a fiberlike cell. Fibril is a strand of protoplasm produced by a cell and lying within the cell.

Foraminifera (fo-ram'i-nif"er-a) (L. *foramen*, hole, + *ferre*, to bear) An order of sarcodine protozoans with slender, branched pseudopodia (myxopodia) which are extruded through holes in their calcareous shells.

gamete (gam'ete) (Gr. *gamos*, marriage) A mature germ cell, either male or female.

Gastropoda (gas-trop'o-da) (Gr. *gastros*, stomach, + *podos*, foot) A class of mollusks consisting of slugs and snails.

Gastrotricha (gas-trot'ri-ka) (Gr. *gastros*, stom-

ach, + *trichos*, hair) A phylum of aquatic pseudocoelomate animals with cilia or bristles on the body.

gel (jel) (L. *gelare*, to freeze) That state of a colloidal system in which the solid particles form the continuous phase and the fluid medium the discontinuous phase.

gene (jen) (Gr. *genes*, born) That part of a chromosome which is the hereditary determiner and is transmitted from one generation to another. It occupies a fixed chromosomal locus and can best be defined only in a physiological or operational sense.

genotype (jen'o-tip) (Gr. *genos*, race, + *typos*, form) The genetic constitution, expressed and latent, of an organism; the particular set of genes present in the cells of an organism.

genus (je'nus) (L. *genus*, race) A taxonomic rank between family and species.

germ layer In the animal embryo, one of the three basic layers (ectoderm, endoderm, and mesoderm) from which the various organs and tissues arise in the multicellular animal.

gestation (jes-ta'shun) (L. *gestare*, to bear) The period in which offspring are carried in the uterus.

Golgi body (gol'je) (after Golgi, Italian histologist) A cytoplasmic component which may play a role in certain cell secretions or it may represent a region where high energy compounds from the mitochondria collect.

haploid (hap'loid) (Gr. *haploos*, single) The reduced number of chromosomes typical of gametes as opposed to the diploid number of somatic cells.

Hemichordata (hem'i-kor-da"ta) (Gr. *hemi*, half, + L. *chorda*, cord) A phylum of wormlike animals with close affinities to the chordates; body of proboscis, collar, and trunk with stomochord or rudimentary notochord.

hermaphrodite (hur-maf'ro-dit) (Gr. Hermes, + Aphrodite) An organism with both male and female organs. Hermaphroditism commonly refers to an abnormal condition in which male and female organs are found in the same animal; monoecious is a normal condition for the species.

heterotroph (het'er-o-trof) (Gr. *heteros*, another, + *trophos*, feeder) An organism that obtains both organic and inorganic raw materials from the environment in order to live.

heterozygote (het'er-o-zi"got) (Gr. *heteros*, another, + *zygotos*, yolked) An organism in which the pair of alleles for a trait is composed of different genes (usually dominant and recessive); derived from a zygote formed

934

by the union of gametes of dissimilar genetic constitution.

homology (ho-mol'o-ji) (Gr. *homologia,* similarity) Similarity in embryonic origin and adult structure based on descent from a common ancestor.

homozygote (ho'mo-zi"got) (Gr. *homos,* same, + *zygotos,* yolked) An organism in which the pair of alleles for a trait is composed of the same genes (either dominant or recessive but not both).

humoral (hu'mer-al) (L. *humor,* a fluid) Pertaining to a body fluid, such as blood or lymph.

hydrolysis (hi-drol'i-sis) (Gr. *hydor,* water, + *lysis,* a loosening) The decomposition of a chemical compound by the addition of water; the splitting of a molecule into its groupings so that the split products acquire hydrogen and hydroxyl groups.

hydroxyl (hi-drok'sil) (Gr. *hydor,* water, + oxygen, + yl) Containing an OH group, a negatively charged ion formed by alkalies in water.

hypertonic (hi'per-ton"ik) (Gr. *hyper,* over, + *tonos,* tension) Refers to a solution whose osmotic pressure is greater than that of another solution with which it is compared; contains a greater concentration of particles and gains water through a semipermeable membrane from a solution containing fewer particles.

hypotonic (hi'po-ton"ik) (Gr. *hypo,* under, + *tonos,* tension) Refers to a solution whose osmotic pressure is less than that of another solution with which it is compared or taken as standard; contains a lesser concentration of particles and loses water during osmosis.

inductor (in-duk'tor) (L. *inducere,* to introduce) In embryology, a tissue or organ that causes the differentiation of another tissue or organ.

invagination (in-vaj'i-na"shun) (L. *in,* in, + *vagina,* sheath) An infolding of a layer of tissue to form a saclike structure.

isotope (i'so-top) Gr. *isos,* equal, + *topos,* place) One of several different forms of a chemical element, differing from each other physically but not chemically.

Kinorhyncha (kin-o-ring'ka) (Gr. *kineo,* to move, + *rhynchos,* beak) A class of pseudocoelomate animals belonging to the phylum Aschelminthes (Hyman). Same as Echinodera.

labyrinthodont (lab'i-rin"tho-dont) (Gr. *labyrinthos,* labyrinth, + *odous,* tooth) A group of fossil stem amphibians from which most amphibians later arose. They date from the late Paleozoic.

lacteal (lak'te-al) (L. *lactis,* milk) Refers to one of the lymph vessels in the villus of the intestine.

leukocyte (lu'ko-site) (Gr. *leukos,* white, + *kytos,* cell) A common type of white blood cell with beaded nucleus.

lipase (li'pas) (Gr. *lipos,* fat) An enzyme that converts fat into fatty acids and glycerin; it may also promote the reverse reaction.

lipid (lipoid) (lip'id) (Gr. *lipos,* fat) Pertains to certain fattylike substances which often contain other groups such as phosphoric acid.

littoral (lit'o-ral) (L. *litus,* sea shore) The floor of the sea from the shore to the edge of the continental shelf.

luciferase (lu-sif'er-ase) (L. *lux,* light) An enzyme involved in light production in organisms.

macronucleus (mak'ro-nu"kle-us) (Gr. *makros,* long, + *nucleus,* nut) The larger of the two kinds of nuclei in ciliate protozoa; controls all cell functions except reproduction.

marsupial (mar-su'pi-al) (Gr. *marsypion,* pouch) One of the pouched mammals of the subclass Metatheria.

Mastigophora (mas'ti-gof"o-ra) (Gr. *mastix,* whip, + *phorus,* bearing) A protozoan class whose members have flagella for locomotion; sometimes called flagellates.

matrix (ma'trix) (L. *mater,* mother) The intercellular substance of a tissue, or that part of a tissue into which an organ or process is set.

maxilla (mak-sil'a) (L. jaw) One of the upper jawbones in vertebrates; one of the head appendages in arthropods.

maxilliped (mak-sil'i-ped) (L. *maxilla,* jaw, + *pedis,* foot) One of the three pairs of head appendages located just posterior to the maxilla in crustaceans.

medulla (me-dul'a) (L. marrow) The inner portion of an organ in contrast to the cortex or outer portion; hindbrain.

medusa (me-du'sa) (Gr. *Medusa,* a mythological character whose hair was transformed into snakes) A jellyfish or the free-swimming stage in the life cycle of coelenterates.

meiosis (mi-o'sis) (Gr. *meioun,* to make small) That nuclear change by which the chromosomes are reduced from the diploid to the haploid number.

menopause (men'o-poz) (Gr. *menos,* month, + *pauein,* to cease) In the human female that time when reproduction ceases; cessation of the menstrual cycle.

menstruation (men′stroo-a″shun) (L. *mensis,* month) The discharge of blood and uterine tissue from the vagina at the end of a menstrual cycle.

mesoglea (mes′o-gle″a) (Gr. *mesos,* middle, + *gloios,* glutinous substance) The jelly-like gelatinous filling between the ectoderm and endoderm of coelenterates and comb jellies.

metabolism (me-tab″o-liz′m) (Gr. *metabole,* change) A group of processes which includes nutrition, production of energy (respiration), and synthesis of more protoplasm; the sum of the constructive (anabolism) and destructive (catabolism) processes.

metamorphosis (met′a-mor″fo-sis) (Gr. *meta,* beyond, + *morphe,* form) A sudden change in structure after the completion of embryonic development.

micron (mi′kron) (Gr. *micros,* small) One one-thousandth of a millimeter; about 1/25,000 of an inch.

micronucleus (mi′kro-nu″kle-us) A small nucleus found in ciliate protozoa; controls the reproductive functions of these organisms.

microsome (mi′kro-som) (Gr. *soma,* body) A constituent of cytoplasm containing RNA and is the site of protein synthesis.

miracidium (mi′ra-sid″i-um) (Gr. *meirakidion,* youthful person) A minute ciliated larval stage in the life cycle of flukes.

mitochondria (mit′o-kon″dri-a) (Gr. *mitos,* a thread, + *chondros,* a small roundish mass) Minute granules, rods, or threads in the cytoplasm and the seat of important cellular enzymes.

Mollusca, mollusk (mol-lus′ka, mol′usk) (L. *molluscus,* soft) Mollusca is a major phylum of schizocoelomate animals; body typically of visceral mass, foot, and shell; comprises snails, clams, squids, and others.

monosaccharide (mon′o-sak″a-rid) (Gr. *monos,* one, + *sakcharon,* sugar) A simple sugar which cannot be decomposed into smaller sugar molecules; contains 5 or 6 carbons.

morphogenesis (mor′fo-jen″e-sis) (Gr. *morphe,* form, + *genes,* born) Development of the architectural features of organisms.

morphology (mor-fol′o-ji) (Gr. *morphe,* form, + *logos,* study) The science of structure. Includes cytology, or the study of cell structure; histology, or the study of tissue structure; and anatomy, or the study of gross structure.

mutation (mu-ta′shun) (L. *mutare,* to change) A stable and abrupt change of a gene; the heritable modification of a character.

myofibril (mi′o-fi″bril) (Gr. *myos,* muscle) A contractile filament within muscle or muscular fiber.

myosin (mi′o-sin) A protein found in muscle; important component in the contraction of muscle.

myxedema (mik′se-de″ma) (Gr. *myxa,* slime, + *oidema,* a swelling) A disease that results from thyroid deficiency in the adult; characterized by swellings under the skin.

nekton (nek′ton) (Gr. *nektos,* swimming) Term for the actively swimming organisms in the ocean.

Nematomorpha (nem′a-to-mor″fa) (Gr. *nematos,* thread, + *morphe,* form) Hairworms, a pseudocoelomate class of phylum Aschelminthes.

notochord (no′to-kord) (Gr. *noton,* back, + *chorda,* cord) A rod-shaped cellular body along the median plane and ventral to the central nervous system in chordates.

nucleic acid (nu-kle′ik) (L. *nucleus,* nut) One of a class of molecules composed of joined nucleotides; chief types are desoxyribose nucleic acid (DNA), found only in cell nuclei (chromosomes), and ribose nucleic acid (RNA), found both in cell nuclei (chromosomes and nucleoli) and in cytoplasm (microsomes).

nucleolus (nu-kle′o-lus) (dim. of nucleus) A deeply staining body within the nucleus of a cell and containing RNA.

nucleoprotein (nu′kle-o--) A molecule composed of nucleic acid and protein; occurs in two types, depending on whether the nucleic acid portion is DNA or RNA.

nucleotid (nu′kle-o-tid) A molecule consisting of phosphate, 5-carbon sugar (ribose or desoxyribose), and a purine or a pyrimidine; the purines are adenine and guanine, and the pyrimidines are cytosine, thymine, and uracil.

nymph (nimf) (L. *nympha,* a young woman) The immature form of an insect which undergoes a gradual metamorphosis.

ontogeny (on-toj′e-ni) (Gr. *ontos,* being, + *gennao,* to bring forth) The development of an individual from egg to senescence.

operculum (o-pur′ku-lum) (L. a cover) The gill cover in bony fish.

organism (or′gan-iz′m) An individual plant or animal, either unicellular or multicellular.

osmosis (os-mo′sis) (Gr. *osmos,* impulse) The process in which water migrates through a semipermeable membrane, from a side containing a lesser concentration to the side containing a greater concentration of particles. The diffusion of a solvent (usually water) through a semipermeable membrane.

Osteichthyes (os'te-ik"thi-ez) (Gr. *osteon*, bone, + *ichthys*, fish) A class of vertebrates comprising the bony fish.

ostium (os'ti-um) (L. mouth) A mouthlike opening.

oviparity, oviparous (o'vi-par"i-ti, o-vip'a-rus) (L. *ovum*, egg, + *parere*, to bring forth) Reproduction in which eggs are released by the female; development of offspring occurs outside the maternal body.

ovoviviparity, ovoviviparous (o'vo-viv'i-par"i-ti, o'vo-vi-vip"a-rus) (L. *ovum*, egg, + *vivere*, to live, + *parere*, to bring forth) Reproduction in which eggs develop within the maternal body without nutrition by the female parent.

oxidation (ok'si-da"shun) (Gr. *oxys*, acid) Rearrangement of a molecule so as to create a high-energy bond; a chemical change in which a molecule loses one or more electrons.

Paleozoic (pa'le-o-zo"ik) (Gr. *palaios*, old, + *zoe*, life) The geological era between the pre-Cambrian and the Mesozoic, approximately from 550 to 200 million years ago.

palingenesis (pal'in-gen"e-sis) (Gr. *palin*, backward, + *genesis*, origin) The stages in the development or ontogeny of an animal which are inherited from ancestral species, such as gill slits in the unborn of mammals.

papilla (pa-pil'a) (L. nipple) A small nipplelike projection.

parapodia (par'a-po"di-a) (Gr. *para*, bedside, + *podos*, foot) The segmental appendages in polychaete worms which serve in breathing, locomotion, and creation of water currents.

parasympathetic (par'a-sim'pa-thet"ik) (Gr. *para*, beside, + *sympathes*, sympathetic) One of the subdivisions of the autonomic nervous system, whose centers are located in the brain, anterior part of the spinal cord, and posterior part of the spinal cord.

parthenogenesis (par'the-no-jen"e-sis) (Gr. *parthenos*, virgin, + *genesis*, origin) The development of an unfertilized egg; a type of sexual reproduction.

pathogenic (path'o-jen"ic) (Gr. *pathos*, disease, + *gennao*, to produce) Producing a disease.

peduncle (pe-dung'kl) (L. dim. of *pes*, foot) A stalk; a band of white matter joining different parts of the brain.

pelagic (pe-laj'ic) (Gr. *pelagos*, the open sea) Pertaining to the open ocean.

Pelecypoda (pel'e-sip"o-da) (Gr. *pelekus*, hatchet, + *pous*, foot) A class of the phylum Mollusca, comprising clams, mussels, oysters.

pentadactyl (pen'ta-dak"til) (Gr. *pente*, five, + *daktylos*, finger) With five digits.

peptidase (pep'ti-das) (Gr. *peptein*, to digest) An enzyme that breaks down amino acids from a peptide.

peristalsis (per'i-stal"sis) (Gr. *peri*, around, + *stalsis*, contraction) The series of alternate relaxations and contractions by which food is forced through the alimentary canal.

peritoneum (per'i-to-ne"um) (Gr. *peri*, around, + *teinein*, to stretch) The membrane that lines the abdominal cavity and covers the viscera.

petrifaction (pet'ri-fak"shun) (L. *petra*, a stone, + *facere*, to make) The changing of organic matter into stone.

pH A symbol of the relative concentration of hydrogen ions in a solution; pH values are from 0 to 14, and the lower the value, the more acid or hydrogen ions in the solution.

phagocyte (fag'o-sit) (Gr. *phagein*, to eat, + *kytos*, cell) A white blood cell of the body, which devours and destroys microorganisms or other harmful substances.

phenotype (fe'no-tip) (Gr. *phainein*, to show) The visible characters; opposed to genotype of the hereditary constitution.

Phoronidea (for'o-nid"e-a) (Gr. *phoros*, a bearing, + L. *nidus*, nest) A phylum of wormlike, marine, tube-dwelling, schizocoelomate animals.

phosphagen (fos'fa-jen) (phosphate + glycogen) A term for creatine-phosphate and arginine-phosphate, which store and may be sources of high-energy phosphates.

phosphorylation (fos'fo-ri-la"shun) The addition of a phosphate group, such as H_2PO_3, to a compound.

phylogeny (fi-loj'e-ni) (Gr. *phylon*, a tribe, + *gennao*, to bring forth) The evolutionary history of a group of organisms.

phylum (pl. phyla) (fi'lum) (Gr. *phylon*, race, tribe) A chief category of taxonomic classification into which the animal kingdom is divided.

placenta (pla-sen'ta) (L. a cake; fr. Gr. *plax*, *plakos*, anything flat and broad) The vascular structure, embryonic and maternal, through which the embryo and fetus are nourished while in the uterus.

plankton (plangk'ton) (Gr. *planktos*, wandering) The floating animal and plant life of a body of water.

plasma membrane (plaz'ma) (Gr. plasma) The thin membrane that surrounds the cytosome; considered a part of the cytoplasm.

plastid (plas'tid) (Gr. *plastes*, one who forms, + *-id*, daughter) A small body in the cytoplasm which often contains pigment.

Platyhelminthes (plat'i-hel-min"thez) (Gr. *platys*, flat, + *helminthos*, worm) Flatworms; a phylum of acoelomate animals; consists of planarians, flukes, and tapeworms.

pleopod (ple'o-pod) (Gr. *plein*, to swim, + *pous*, foot) One of the swimming feet on the abdomen of a crustacean.

plesiosaur (ple"si-o-sor') (Gr. *plesios*, near, + *sauros*, lizard) A long-necked, marine reptile of Mesozoic times.

pleura (ploor'a) (Gr. side) The membrane that lines each half of the thorax and covers the lungs.

plexus (plek'sus) (L. braid) A network, especially of nerves or of blood vessels.

polarization (po'ler-i-za"shun) (L. *polaris*, pole) The arrangement of positive electric charges on one side of a surface membrane and negative elective charges on the other side (in nerves and muscles).

polymorphism (pol'i-mor"fizm) (Gr. *polys*, many, + *morphe*, form) The presence in a species of more than one type of individual.

polyp (pol'ip) (L. *polypus*, many-footed) The sessile stage in the life cycle of coelenterates.

polypetide (pol'i-pep'tid) (Gr. *polys*, many, + *peptein*, to digest) A molecule consisting of many joined amino acids, not as complex as a protein.

polyphyletic (pol'i-fi-let'ik) (Gr. *polys*, many, + *phylon*, tribe) Derived from more than one ancestral type; contrasts with monophyletic or from one ancestor.

polysaccharide (pol'i-sak"a-rid) (Gr. *polys*, many, + *sakcharon*, sugar) A carbohydrate composed of many monosaccharide units, such as glycogen, starch, and cellulose.

Porifera (po-rif'er-a) (L. *porus*, pore, + *ferre*, to bear) The phylum of sponges.

Priapulida (pri'a-pu"li-da) (Gr. *Priapos*, a Greek god with a large phallus) A small phylum of pseudocoelomate animals.

progesterone (pro-jes'ter-on) (L. *pro*, before, + *gestare*, to carry) Hormone secreted by the corpus luteum and the placenta; prepares the uterus for the fertilized egg and maintains the capacity of the uterus to hold the embryo and fetus.

prothrombin (pro-throm'bin) (L. *pro*, before, + *thrombus*, clot) A constituent of blood plasma which is changed to thrombin by thrombokinase in the presence of calcium ions; involved in blood clotting.

pterosaur (ter'o-sor) (Gr. *pteron*, feather, + *sauros*, lizard) An extinct flying reptile that flourished during the Mesozoic.

pylorus (pi-lo'rus) (Gr. *pyle*, gate, + *ourus*, watcher) The opening between the stomach and duodenum which is guarded by a valve.

pyrenoid (pi're-noid) (Gr. *pyren*, fruit stone, + *eidos*, form) A protein body in the chloroplasts of certain organisms which serves as a center for starch formation.

Radiolaria (ra'di-o-la"ri-a) (L. dim. of radius) A group of sarcodine protozoa, characterized by silicon-containing shells.

redia (re'di-a) (from Redi, Italian biologist) A larval stage in the life cycle of flukes; is produced by a sporocyst larva, and in turn gives rise to many cercariae.

retina (ret'i-na) (L. *rete*, a net) The sensitive, nervous layer of the eye.

rhabdocoele (rab'do-sel) (Gr. *rhabdos*, rod, + *koilos*, a hollow) A member of a group of free-living flatworms possessing a straight, unbranched digestive cavity.

rostrum (ros'trum) (L. a ship's beak) A snout-like projection on the head.

Rotifera (ro-tif'er-a) (L. *rota*, wheel, + *ferre*, to bear) A class of microscopic pseudocoelomate animals belonging to the phylum Aschelminthes.

Sarcodina (sar'ko-di"na) (Gr. *sarkos*, flesh) A class of protozoa; includes *Amoeba*, Foraminifera, Radiolaria, and others; characterized by pseudopodia.

sarcolemma (sar'ko-lem"a) (Gr. *sarkos*, flesh, + *lemma*, skin) The thin noncellular membrane of striated muscle fiber or cell.

schizocoele, schizocoelomate (skiz'o-sel) (Gr. *schizein*, to split) Schizocoele is a coelum formed by a splitting of embryonic mesoderm. Schizocoelomate is an animal with a schizocoele, such as an arthropod or mollusk.

sclerotic (skle-rot'ik) (Gr. *skleros*, hard) The tough outer coat of the eyeball.

scrotum (skro'tum) (L. bag) The pouch that contains the testes and accessory organs in most mammals.

seminiferous (sem'i-nif"er-us) (L. *semen*, semen, + *ferre*, to bear) Pertains to the tubules that produce or carry semen in the testes.

semipermeable (sem'i-pur"me-a-b'l) (L. *semi*, half, + *permeabilis*, that can be passed through) Permeable to small particles, such as water and certain inorganic ions, but not to colloids, etc.

septum (sep'tum) (L. a fence) A wall between two cavities.

serum (ser'um) (L. whey) The plasma of blood that separates on clotting; the liquid that separates from the blood when a clot is formed.

simian (sim'i-an) (L. *simia*, an ape) Pertains to monkeys.

Sipunculoidea (si-pung′ku-loi″de-a) (Gr. *sipun-culus*, small siphon) A phylum of wormlike schizocoelomate animals.

soma (so′ma) (Gr. body) The body of an organism in contrast to the germ cells (germ-plasm).

somatic (so-mat′ik) (Gr. *soma*, body) Refers to the body, such as somatic cells in contrast to germ cells.

speciation (spe′shi-a″shun) (L. *species*, kind, + ation) The evolving of two or more species by the splitting of one ancestral species.

spermatheca (spurm′a-the″ka) (Gr. *sperma*, seed, + *theke*, a case) A sac in the female reproductive organs for the storage of sperm.

sphincter (sfingk′ter) (Gr. *sphingein*, to bind tight) A ring-shaped muscle capable of closing a tubular opening by constriction.

sporocyst (spo′ro-sist) (Gr. *spora*, seed, + *kystis*, pouch) A larval stage in the life cycle of flukes; it originates from a miracidium.

Sporozoa (spo′ro-zo″a) (Gr. *spora*, seed, + *zoon*, animal) A class of parasitic protozoa.

sporozoite (spo′ro-zo″it) (Gr. *spora*, seed, + *zoon*, animal, + -ite, dim.) A motile spore formed from the zygote in many Sporozoa.

stenotopic (sten′o-top″ic) (Gr. *stenos*, narrow, + *topos*, place) Refers to an organism with restricted range.

sterol, steroid (ster′ol, ster′oid) (Gr. *stereos*, solid, + -*ol* [L. *oleum*, oil]) One of a class of organic compounds containing a molecular skeleton of four fused carbon rings; it contains cholesterol, sex hormones, adrenocortical hormones, and vitamin D.

stoma (sto′ma) (Gr. mouth) A mouthlike opening.

substrate (sub′strat) (L. *substratus*, strewn under) A substance that is acted upon by an enzyme.

symbiosis (sim′bi-o″sis) (Gr. *sym*, with, + *bioun*, to live) The living together of two different species in an intimate relationship; includes mutualism, commensalism, and parasitism.

synapse (si-naps′) (Gr. *synapsis*, a union) The place at which a nerve impulse passes from an axon of one nerve cell to a dendrite of another nerve cell.

syncytium (sin-sish′i-um) (Gr. *syn*, together, + *kytos*, cell) A mass of protoplasm containing many nuclei and not divided into cells.

taiga (ti′ga) (Russ.) Habitat zone characterized by large tracts of coniferous forests, long, cold winters, and short summers; most typical in Canada and Siberia.

telencephalon (tel′en-sef″a-lon) (Gr. *telos*, end, + *encephalon*, brain) The most anterior vesicle of the brain.

teleology (tel′e-ol″o-ji) (Gr. *telos*, end, + *logos*, study) The philosophical view that natural events are goal directed and are preordained; contrasts with scientific view of causalism.

template (tem′plet) A pattern or mold guiding the formation of a duplicate; often used with reference to gene duplication.

tentaculocyst (ten-tac″u-lo-cyst′) (L. *tentaculum*, a feeler, + Gr. *kystis*, pouch) A sense organ of several parts along the margin of medusae and derived from a modified tentacle; sometimes called rhopalium.

tetrapoda (te-trap′o-da) (Gr. *tetrapodia*, four feet) Four-legged vertebrates; the group includes amphibians, reptiles, birds, and mammals.

therapsid (the-rap′sid) (Gr. *theraps*, an attendant) Extinct Mesozoic mammal-like reptile, from which true mammals evolved.

thrombokinase (throm′bo-kin″as) (Gr. *thrombos*, lump, + *kinein*, to move) Enzyme, released from blood platelets, that initiates the process of clotting; transforms prothrombin into thrombin, in presence of calcium ions; thromboplastin.

trachea (tra′ke-a) (Gr. *tracheia*, rough) The windpipe; any of the air tubes of insects.

transduction (trans-duk′shun) (L. *trans*, across, + *ducere*, to lead) Transfer of genetic material from one bacterium to another through the agency of virus.

trochophore (trok′o-for) (Gr. *trochos*, wheel, + *phoros*, bearing) A free-swimming ciliated marine larva characteristic of schizocoelomate animals; common to many phyla.

trophozoite (trof′o-zo″it) (Gr. *trephein*, to nourish, + *zoon*, animal, + -ite, dim.) That stage in the life cycle of a sporozoan in which it is actively absorbing nourishment from the host.

tundra (toon′dra) (Russ.) Terrestial habitat zone, between taiga in south and polar region in north; characterized by absence of trees, short growing season, and mostly frozen soil during much of the year.

typhlosole (tif′lo-sol) (Gr. *typhlos*, blind, + *solen*, channel) A longitudinal fold projecting into the intestine in certain invertebrates, such as the earthworm.

urethra (u-re′thra) (Gr. *ourethra*, urethra) The tube from the urinary bladder to the exterior in both sexes.

uriniferous tubule (u′ri-nif″er-us) (L. *urina*, urine, + *ferre*, to bear) One of the tubules in the kidney extending from a Malpighian body to the collecting tubule.

Urochordata (u'ro-kor-da"ta) (Gr. *oura,* tail, + L. *chorda,* cord) A subphylum of chordates; often called the Tunicata.

utricle (u'tri-kl) (L. *utriculus,* little bag) That part of the inner ear containing the receptors for dynamic body balance; the semicircular canals lead from and to the utricle.

vacuole (vak'u-ol) (L. *vacuus,* empty, + *-ole,* dim). A fluid-filled space in a cell.

vestige (ves'tij) (L. *vestigium,* a footprint) A rudimentary structure which is well developed in some other species or in the embryo.

villus (vil'us) (L. a tuft of hair) A small fingerlike process on the wall of the small intestine and on the embryonic portion of the placenta.

virus (vi'rus) (L. slimy liquid poison) A submicroscopic noncellular particle, composed of a nucleoprotein core and a protein shell; parasitic and will grow and reproduce in a host cell.

viscera (vis'er-a) (L. pl. *viscus,* an internal organ) Any organ in the body cavity.

vitalism (vi"tal-iz'm) (L. *vita,* life) The view that natural processes are controlled by supernatural forces and cannot be explained through the laws of physics and chemistry alone; contrasts with mechanism.

vitamin (vi'ta-min) (L. *vita,* life) An organic substance contributing to the formation or action of cellular enzymes; essential for the maintenance of life.

vitelline membrane (vi-tel'in) (L. *vitellus,* the yolk of an egg) The noncellular membrane that encloses the egg cell.

viviparity, viviparous (viv'i-par"i-ti, vi-vip'a-rus) (L. *vivus,* alive, + *parere,* to bring forth) Reproduction in which eggs develop within the female body, with nutritional aid of maternal parent; offspring are born as juveniles.

xanthophyll (zan'tho-fil) (Gr. *xanthos,* yellow, + *phyllon,* leaf) One of a group of yellow pigments found widely among plants and animals; the xanthophylls are members of the carotenoid group of pigments.

zygote (zi'got) (Gr. *zygotos,* yoked) The cell formed by the union of a male and a female gamete; the fertilized egg.

Index

A

Aardvark, 573, 574
Abdomen, 329
Abducens nerve, **502**, 505, 656
Abductor muscle, frog, 499
Abildgaard, P., 892
Abomasum, **557**, 614
Absorption, 617-618
Abyssal, 834
Acanthias, 437
Acanthocephala, 29, 234-238
  biological principles, 234
  characteristics, 235
  classification, 235-236
  epidermis, **589**
  genital selective apparatus, 237
  internal structure, 236-**237**
  life cycle, 238
  origin and position, 234-235
Acanthodian, 408
Acanthopterygii, 444
Acclimatization, 95
Accommodation, 669
Acellular, 185
Acerentulus, 335
Acetabulum, 196, 598, 601
Acetyl coenzyme A, 67
Acetylcholine isolation, 913
Achorutes, 335
Aciculi, **267**
Acinetopsis, 134
Acinonyx, **572**
Acipenser, **442**
Acipenseroidei, 442
Acoela, 185, 186, **187**
Acoelomate, **88**
Acontia, 172, **173**
Acorn worm (*see* Tongue worms)
Acquired characters, 780-781
Acrania, 420
Acrodont, **613**
Acromegaly, 695
Acrosome reaction, 927
Actinophrys, **114**
Actinopterygii, 410, 442-444
Actinosphaerium, **830**
Actinozoa, 172
Action current, 628
  potential, 659
Adaptations, 851-868
  bird bills, **524**
  feet, **525**
  environmental, 95
  nature, 851
  physiological, 820

Adaptive radiation, concept, 906
  mammal locomotion, 549, **550**
  mammals, **417**
  pelecypods, 364
  reptiles, **414**, 415
Adductor longus, 501
  magnus, **499**, 501
  muscles, **358**, 360, 499
Adenine, 727
Adenohypophysis, 690, **691**, 692, 696, 699
Adenosine triphosphate, 67, 605
Adhesive pad, 166
  tube, 221
ADP, 605
Adrenal cortex, **694**, 698
  gland, 530
  medulla, 694, 698, 900
Adrenalin, 694
Adrenergic, 658
Adrenocorticotropin (ACTH), **691**, 699
Aëdes, 230
Aeolis, **352**, 355
Aeolosoma, 253, 264, **265**
Aerobic, 605
Aestivation, 565, 815
African man-apes, 800
Agamete, 240
Agamidae, 485
Agassiz, L., 899
Age determinations, geological, 761-762
  distribution, 822
Agglutinin, 633
Agglutinogen, 633
Aging and death, 718-719
Agkistrodon, 478
Aglomerular kidney, discovery, 905
Agnatha, 404, 420
Agriolimax, 355
Air bladder, evolution, 449, **450**
  capillaries, 528
  composition (breathing), 639
  sac, 528
Alarm reaction, 867-868, 925
Albatross, 531, 539
Albinism, 554
Albumin, 44, 530
  gland, 356
Aldosterone, 694
Allantois, **705**
Allantosoma, 134
Allele, 734

Allen's rule, 796
Alligator, **483**, 485
Alloeocoela, 186, **187**
Allolobophora, 253
Allopatric, 794
"All-or-none" law, 627, 899
Alternation of generations, 895
Altricial, 533, 567
Alula, 522, 526
Alveolus, **512**, 638
Alytes, **858**
Ambergris, 576
Ambulacral groove, 378, **379**, 381, 390
Ambystoma, **463**, 469
Ambystomidae, 469
Ameba, 103, **110**-114
  behavior, 114
  binary fission, **113**
  habitat, 110
  locomotion, **110, 112**, 113
  metabolism, 112-113
  mitosis, **113**
  pseudopodia, **110**-111, **112**
  reproduction, 113-114
  respiration, 113
  structure, **110**-112
Amebocyte, 140, 379, **624**
Ameboid movement, **112**, 607
Ametabola, 320
Amia, **409**, 443, 449, 859
Amici, G. B., 893
Amictic egg, 221
Amino acids, 44-45, 615
  artificial creation, 773
  essential, 45
  formula, 44
Amitosis, 60-61
Ammocoete larva, 426-430, **427**
  circulatory system, 428
  digestive system, **427**, 428
  excretory system, 428
  nervous system, 429-430
  reproductive system, 429
  respiratory system, **427**
Ammocoetes, 426-430, 433
Ammonoidea, 366
Ammophila, 880
Amnion, **705, 707**
Amniota, 431, 704-711
  development, 708-710
  embryology, 704-711
Amniotic cavity, 706, 707
  egg, 413, **705**
Amoeba, 103, **110**-114 (*see also* Ameba)
Amoebina, **114**

Numbers in boldface refer to pages that contain illustrations or diagrams of the entries. Scientific names of genera are given in italics.

Amphiaster, 63
Amphibia, 458-469 (*see also* Frog; Salamander)
  brain, **654**
  characteristics, 459
  circulation, 625
  classification, 459, 468-469
  evolution, **411, 412,** 413
  frog, as a vertebrate type, 488-516
  natural history, 460-468
  origin and relations, 459-460
Amphibians, Age of, 32
Amphiblastula, 144, **146**
Amphid, 223
Amphilina, 203
Amphineura, 349, 350, 351
Amphiodia, 383
Amphioxus, 404, **423-425,** 426, 603
Amphipholis, 383
Amphiplatyan, 560
Amphipoda, 308, **309**
Amphiporus, **213-215**
Amphisbaenidae, 485
Amphitrite, 253, **268**
Amphiuma, 460, **461,** 469
Amphiumidae, 469
Amplexus, **468,** 515, **516**
Ampulla, **380, 381,** 667
Amylopsin, 508, 616
Anabas, 443
Anabolism, 609
Anaconda, 478
Anadromous, 453
Anaerobic, 605
Anal cone, 390
  spot, 126
Analogy, principle of, 85, 86
Anamnia, 431
Anaphase, **62,** 63, **65, 66,** 113, 902
Anarma, 134
Anatomy, 22, 890
Ancylostoma, 227, 228
Andrews, R. C., 914
Androgen, 695-698
Androgenic, 694
Androsterone, 699
Aneides, 462
Anemone, sea, 172-**174**
Anestrum, 566
Angiotensin, isolation, 927-928
Angler fish, **446**
Anguidae, 485
Anguilla, 444, **446,** 453, 855
Anguispira, 355, 356
Angulifera moth, **322**
Angulosplenial, **496**
Animal, acellular, 71
  adjustment to land, 457-458
  aquatic and osmotic problems, 59
  archetype concept, 892
  architectural pattern, 71-89
  behavior patterns, 869-884
  breeding habits, 686-687
  classification, 24-29
  communication, 880-881
  cooperation, 882
  definition, 19

Animal—cont'd
  dispersion, 848-849
    Krakatao, 848-849
    Lake Baikal, 849
  electricity, 892
  grades of structure, 71
  habitats, 19, 825-833
  kingdom, divisions, 88
  metazoan, 71
  methods of information, 20
  morphology and function, 92
  phylogeny, 29-33
  place of origin, 844
  populations, 820-823
  range, 846
  serological relationship, 908
  size, 87
  somatic, **405**
  unity, 71, 72
  variety, 20
  visceral, **405**
Animalcula, 102
Anisogamete, 675
Annelida, 29, 251-271
  biological principles, 251
  blood cells, **624**
  characteristics, 253
  circulation, **623**
  classes, 253
  excretion, **642**
  metamerism, 252
  nervous system, **649**
  origin and relation, 251-252
Anodonta, 349, 357-364
Anolis, **474,** 485
Anomalops, 864
Anopheles, 121, **122,** 341
Anopola, 213
Anoplura, 334, 337
Anostraca, 305, **306**
Anseriformes, **540**
Ant cows, 324
  lion, **334, 338, 339**
Anteater, **575-576**
Antedon, 376
Antelope horns, 594
Antenna, 280, **295, 296, 328, 332, 333**
Antennae cleaner, **333**
Antennary artery, **298,** 299
Antennule, **295, 296**
Anterior pituitary, **691,** 699
Anthonomus, 339
Anthozoa, 152, **153,** 172-176
Anthropoid, 581-582
Anthropopithecus, 582
Antianemic factor, discovery, 917-918
Antibody, 633
Antigen, 633
Antler, 594, **595**
Ants, 323-324, 341
Anura, 459, 463-469, 488
Anus, **214, 220, 226,** 255, 299, 614
Aorta, 361, **509,** 510, 528
Aortic arch, **257,** 428, 473, 528 **626**
Ape, 579-580
Aphasmidia, 223-224

Aphid, **338**
  lion, **325**
Aphrodite, 253, 268
Aphycus, **325**
Aplacophora, 350
Aplectana, 492
Aplodontia, 574
Aplysia, 355
Apocrine gland, **554**
Apoda, **412,** 459, 460, 468
Apodes, 444
Apodiformes, **544**
Apo-enzymes, 48
Apopyle, 145
Appendage, 274, **294, 295,** 296-298, 601
Applied genetics, 746-758
Aptenodytes, **538**
Apteria, **522**
Apterygiformes, 538
Apterygota, 335
Apteryx, **537**
Aqueduct of Sylvius, **503,** 504
Aqueous chamber, **667,** 668
  humor, 668
Aquila, 540
Arachnida, 277, 283-291
  characteristics, 284
  economic, 283
  relations, 283-284
Arachnoid, 652
Arbacia, 376, 384, **386**
Arcella, **114,** 116, **830**
Archaeoceti, 576
Archaeopteryx, **416,** 518, 519
Archaeornis, 518
Archaeornithes, 519
Archenteron, 76, **77**
Archeocyte, 143, 144, 146
Archeozoic era, 32, 764
Archiacanthocephala, 236
Archiannelida, 253, 271
Archinephros, 428, 429
Architeuthis, 364, 369
Archosauran, 415
Arenicola, 253, **268**
Areolar connective tissue, 80, 82
Argonauta, 366, 370
Argulus, **306**
Aristotle, 703, 869, 889
Aristotle's lantern, 385, **386, 387**
Armadillium, **309**
Armadillo, **575-576**
Army worm moth, **326**
Arrector pili, 553
Arrhenius, S., 909
Arrowworm, 248-**249**
Artemia, **274**
Arterial system, frog, **509,** 510-511
Arteriole, 511
Artery, 628, **629**
Arthrobranchia, 299, **300**
Arthropod vector, concept, 900
Arthropoda, 29, 273-344
  and Annelida, 278-279
  behavior, 276
  beneficial, 278
  biological principles, 273
  body plan, 274

Arthropoda—cont'd
  characteristics, 276
  classification, 276-278, 304-
      308, 335-342
  economic, 278
  exoskeleton, 275
  harmful, 278
  locomotion, 276
  number of species, 274
  origin and position, 273-274
  reproduction, 276
Articular bone, **665**
  process, 496, **599**
Articulation, 498
Artiodactyla, 578-580
Ascaphidae, 469
Ascaphus, **466,** 468, 469
Ascaris, 219, **224-227**
  digestive system, 225, **226**
  excretory system, 225
  life cycle, 227
  locomotion, 226
  metabolism, 226
  nervous system, **225**
  reproductive system, 225-226
  structure, **224, 225, 226**
Aschelminthes, 29, 217-233, **623**
  biological principles, 217
  circulation, **623**
  characteristics, 218
  classes, 218-219
  origin and relations, 217-218
Ascidiacea, 421
Ascidian, 421-423
  tadpole, 404-405, **422,** 423
  theory, 404
Asconoid, sponge, **141**
Aselli, G., 622, 890
Asellus, 277, 308, **309, 828,** 829
Asexual reproduction, 119, **160**
Ash of body, 54
Aspidobranchia, 354
Asplanchna, 219
Assimilation, 610
Association areas of brain, 655
Astacus, 293
Aster, 63
Asterias, 376, 378-382 (*see also*
      Sea star)
Asteroid, **375**
Asteroidea, 376, 378-382
Astragalus, **495, 497**
Astrangia, **153, 175**
Astroscopus, 864
Astylosternus, 465, **466**
Ateles, 581
Athecanephria, 398
Atlas, **495, 598, 600**
Atoll, 175
Atoms, 35
  tagged, 37
ATP, 67, 69, 605, 862, 918
Atrio-ventricular node (A-V),
      627, 628
Atrium, **423,** 424, **508,** 509
Auditory canal, **664**
  nerve, **502, 505,** 656, **664**
  organs, grasshopper, 331
Aurelia, 152, **153, 170, 171**
Auricle, flatworm, 188
  heart, **359, 360,** 625

Auricularia, **377, 389**
Auriculoventricular groove, 509
Australian zoological realm, 847
Australopithecus, 800, 915
Autocatalytic reaction, 616
Autogamy, 109, 127, 129
Autonomic nervous system, 331,
      502, 505, 651, 652,
      657-658
Autotomy, 294, 382
Autotroph, 773
Aves, 415, 518-545 (*see also*
      Bird)
Avicularium, 246
Avoiding reaction, **127**
Axial gland, **380,** 382, **389**
  gradient, 95, 194, 717, 910
  sinus, **380,** 382
Axis, **598, 600**
Axolotl, **463**
Axon, 650
Aysheaia, 281, 910

B

Babesia, 291
Bacteria, discovery of nuclei,
      923
  sexual differentiation, 926
  transduction, 729
Bacterial spore, 900
Bacteriophage, 729
Bactrian camel, **579**
Badger, 573
Baer, K. von, 704, 893
Bagworms, 321
Bainbridge reflex, 628
Balaenoptera, 576
Balancers, 317
Balanoglossus, 373, 393, 394
Balantidium, **132**
Balanus, **307**
Baldwin, J. M., 904
Balfour, F. M., 900
Ball-and-socket joint, 497
Baltzer, F., 915
Banting, F., 689, 914
Barb, **520**
Barber, H. S., 874
Barbicel, **520**
Barbule, **520**
Barcroft, J., 915
Barn owl, **544**
Barnacle, **306, 307**
Barr, M. L., 925
Barred owl, **543**
Barrier Reef, 175
Bartholin, T., 622, 890
Basal granule, 126
Basic concepts, key discoveries,
      889-931
Basilar membrane, **666**
Basipodite, 296
Basket star, 383
Basophil, **630**
Bassi, A., 894
Bastard wing, **522**
Bat, 549, **550, 570**-571, **814**
  skeleton, **597**
Bateson, W., 908

Bathyal, 834
Bathynomus, 308
Batoidei, 437, 440
Batrachoseps, 463
Bauer, H., 919
Bayliss, W. H., 688, 689, 906,
      907
Bdellostoma, 432
Bdelloura, 186, **192**
Beadle, G. W., 922
Bear, **565,** 573
Beard worms, 397-400, **399**
Beaumont, William, 609
Beaver, **574**
Bedbugs, 337
Bees, 323-324, 341
Beetles, **325, 326,** 339, **340**
Behavior, 869-884
  analysis of innate patterns,
      916
  annelid, 263-264, 267-268,
      270
  arthropod, 276, 293-294, 318-
      319, 865-867
  bird, 535
  breeding, 856-859
  dominance-subordinance
      hierarchies, 914
  echinoderm, 382, 384, 387
  frog, 490
  heredity, 873
  historical, 869-870
  hydra, 162-163
  imprinting, 879-880, 909-910
  leadership, 883-884
  learned, 877-880
  mammal, 565-566
  measurement of motivation,
      921-922
  methods, 870-871
  molluscan, 357, 365-366, 369
  motivation centers, 875-876
  nervous organization, 872
  planaria, 194-195
  Pleurobrachia, 182
  protozoan, 114, 118, 130-132
  social, 881-884
  taxonomy, 873
  territorial patterns, 913
  tropisms and taxes, 872-873
Bell, C., 892
Bell toad, 466
Belts, 398, **399**
Benda, C., 905
Bensley, R. R., 919
Benthonic animals, 834
Benthos, 828, 831
Benzene ring, concept, 898
Berger, H., 917
Bergmann's rule, **795, 796**
Bernard, C., 896, 897
Beroë, 180, 183
Berthold, A. A., 896
Bertram, E. G., 925
Berzelius, J. J., 894
Best, C. H., 689
Biceps femoris, 501, **606**
Bichat, M. F. X., 892
Bicuspid teeth, 612
  valve, 627
Bilateria, 185

Bile, 616
  duct, 507, 527
Bilharzia (*see Schistosoma*)
Bilharziasis, 199
Bilirubin, 616
Biliverdin, 616
Bills, bird, 524
Binary fission, 128, 673
Biochemical genetics, 747-748
Biochemistry, 22, 894
Biogenesis, 91
Biogenetic law, 94, 308-309, 310, 311, 704, 893
Biological clocks, concept, 913
  drives, 876
  principles, 90-97
Biology, definition, 17
Biomass, 818, 839
Biome, 833-836, 839
Biometry development, 899
Bionomial nomenclature, 25, 27-28
Biosphere, 19
Biotic communities, 823-824
  factors, 817-820
  potential, 821
Biotin, 620
Bipalium, 186
Biparental reproduction, 673
Bipinnaria, 377
Biramous appendage, 296, 298
Bird, 518-545
  advancements, 523, 524
  banding, 536
  behavior, 535, 536
  bills, 524
  brain, 654
  care of young, 533, 534
  carinate, 519
  celestial navigation, 928
  characteristics, 520
  circulatory system, 527-528
  classification, 519, 536-545
  coloration, 532
  digestive system, 526-527
  economic importance, 536
  embryology, 705-706
  endocrine system, 530
  excretory system, 527, 529
  feather, 520-523
    tracts, 522
  feet, 525
  flight, 530-532
    muscles, 526
  food, 532
  hibernation, 434-435
  internal structure, 527
  migration, 851-854
    gonadal hypothesis, 915
  milk, 527
  muscular system, 526
  nervous system, 527, 529
  nests, 533, 534
  orientation, theory of sun position, 926
  origin and relationships, 415, 416, 418, 518-519
  pecking order, 883
  perching mechanism, 526
  population, 535
  ratite, 519, 537

Bird—cont'd
  reproductive system, 527, 529, 530
  respiratory system, 527, 528, 529
  sensory system, 529
  skeleton, 523, 524-526
  song, 532
  structure, 524-530
  territory selection, 535, 883
  wing, 522
Birth, 710-711
  rate, 822
Biston, 794
Biting lice, 337
Bittern, 529, 539
Bivalves, 349, 357-364
Black, D., 799
Black widow spider, 288
Blacksnake, 475
Bladder, urinary, development, 710
  frog, 495, 507, 513
  man, 643, 678
Bladder worm, 206, 207
Blakeslee, A. F., 921
Blarina, 570
Blastema, 717
Blastocoele, 76, 77, 706
Blastoderm, 76, 706
Blastodisc, 706
Blastomere, 74, 75
Blastophaga, 325
Blastopore, 76
Blastula, 76
Blepharoplast, 116, 117
Blind snake, 485
  spot, 668
Block, N., 912
Blood, amount, 630
  bird, 528
  cells, invertebrate, 624
  coagulation, 632-633
  corpuscles, compared, 631
  crayfish, 300
  differential white cell count, 632
  earthworm, 259
  formed elements, 53, 81, 630-632, 890
  fractionation, development, 921
  frog, 508
  gas exchange, 899
  groups, 633
    discovery, 906
    heredity, 750-751
  human, 630-632
  plasma, 81
  pressure, 629-630
    diastolic, systolic, 630
    first measured, 622, 891
  rate of flow, 629
  Rh factor, 634
  serum, 632
  similarity to sea water, 907-908
  types, 633-634
  vessel, 628, 629, 710
Blood fluke (*see Schistosoma*)
Bloom, R., 800

Boa constrictor, 479, 485
Body cavity, 86-87, 88, 96
  stalk, 706, 707
Boidae, 485
Bonasa, 540, 542
Bonellia, 243, 244
Bones, 595, 596-601
  number in man, 601-602
  primitive nature, 426
Bonnet, C., 891
Bony fish, 441-455
  adaptive radiation, 446
  air bladder, 449-450
  characteristics, 441-442
  classification, 442-444
  coloration, 453
  evolution, 410-411, 444-449
  fins, 450-451
  osmoregulation, 451-453
  reproduction, 454-455
  scales, 453, 454
  structural adaptations, 449
  structure, 452
Booby, 539
Book louse, 334, 337
  lung, 284, 285
Boöphilus, 291
Boreus, 339
Born, G., 905
Botaurus, 540
Bothriocyrtum, 287
Bothrops, 480
Bouditch, H. P., 899
Boveri, T., 907-908
Bowfin, 443
Bowman, W., 895
Bowman's capsule, 643, 644
Box elder bug, 337
Bozler, E., 916
Brachial artery, 509, 510, 528
  enlargement, 504
  plexus, 502, 504, 652
  vein, 510, 511
Brachiopoda, 29, 247-248
Brain, 301, 503-504, 653-656, 872
  comparative vertebrate, 654
  cortex, 654, 655
  divisions, 652
  evolution, 653-654
  localization centers, 876, 924
    of function, 655, 892
  median section, 654
  sand, 687
  waves, 656, 917
Branchiocardiac canal, 300
Branchiopoda, 304, 305
Branchiostegite, 294, 295, 298, 300
Branchiostoma (*see Amphioxus*)
Branchiura, 306
Brandt, K., 900
Breathing, 529, 638, 639
Breeding behavior, 856-859
  places, 816
Bridges, C. B., 912
Bridle, 398, 399
Briggs, R., 925
Bristle, 553
Bristletails, 335

Brittle star, **383, 384**
  behavior, 384
  larva, **377**
  structure, **383, 384**
Broili, F., 912
Bronchiole, 528, 638
Bronchus, **512,** 528, **638**
Brontotherium, 766
Brook rapids, **827**
Brow spot, 492, 503
Brown body, 246
Brown, F. A., Jr., 922
Brown, R., 893, 894
Brownian movement, 40, 56, 893
Bruce, D., 904
Bryozoa, 29, 242, **245-247**
Buchner, E., 905
Budding, 108, 154-155, **160,** 206, **673**
Bufo, **465**
Bufonidae, 469
Bug, **325, 326,** 337
Bugula, **246, 247**
Bulinus, 200
Bullfrog, 488, **489**
Bumblebee, **325, 334**
Burgess shale fossils, 910
Bursa, 383, **384, 498**
Bushmaster, 478
Busycon, **354**
Butenandt, A., 917
Butterfly, 340, **341**
  migration, 856

C

Caddis fly, **334,** 341
Caducibranch, 461
Caecilians, 459, **460**
Caeciliidae, 469
Caiman, 485
Cajal, R., 901
Calcaneus, **495,** 497
Calcarea, 140
Calciferol, 46
Calciferous gland, 255
Calcispongiae, 140, 145-146
Calcium, 619
Callosamia, **322**
Caloric values, 618
Calorie (*see* Kilocalorie)
Calorimetry, 619
Calyx, 389, 390
Cambarus, 277, 293
Cambrian period, 32, 764
Camel, **579**
Camelus, **579**
Campeloma, 355
Canal, incurrent, 145
Candiru, 451
Candidae, 573
Canine teeth, 612
Cannibalism, 819
Cannon, W. B., 610, 907
Capillaries, 511
  air, 528
  cross-sectional area, 629
  function, 629
Capillary circulation, 890
Caprimulgiformes, 543
Capsular filtrate, 644

Captacula, **351**
Capuchin, 581
Carapace, 295, 296
Carapus, **388**
Caravan formation, **566**
Carbohydrate metabolism, 915
Carbohydrates, 43-44, 618
Carbon cycle, 836, **837**
  dioxide, 67, 640, 641
Carbon-14 dating, 761-762
Carbonic acid, 640
  anhydrase, 640, 918
Carboxypeptidase, 616
Carcharodon, 437
Carcinoscorpius, 282
Carderia, 355
Cardiac muscle, **499**
  stomach, 299, 379, **380,** 614
Cardinal nest, **534**
Caribou, **578**
Carinate, 519
Carlson, A. J., 610
Carnivora, 572-573, 817
Carnivorous animal, 563, 618
Carotene, discovery, 893
Carotid arteries, **509,** 510
  gland, **508, 509,** 510
Carp, 444
Carpals, **495,** 497, **523,** 526
Carpenter ant, **326**
Carpometacarpus, 526
Carrel, A., 910
Cartilage, hyaline, **80**
Cartilaginous fish, 431-440
Casein, 615
Cassiopeia, 152
Cassowary, **537,** 538
Castle, W. B., 917
Castor, **574**
Castoridae, **574**
Castration, 696
Casuariiformes, 538
Casuarius, **537**
Cat, 572-573
Catabolism, 609
Catadromous, 453
Catalase, 49
Catalyst, 46-47
Catalytic action, 892
  concept, 894
Catarrhinii, 581
Catastrophism, 777
Caterpillar, **319,** 322
Catfish, 444, **446**
Catostomus, 444
Cattle fever tick, **291**
Cauda equina, 559, **652**
Caudata, 459, 460-463, 469
Cave animals, 833
Ceboidea, 581
Cebus, 581
Ceccatty, M. P. de, 926
Cecum, 527, 558
Cell(s), 41, 51-70, 895, 923
  and age, 60
  chemical analysis, 54
  constancy in rotifers, 221
  cycle, 59-69
  discovery of, 890
  division, 60-**66,** 893, 895

Cell(s)—cont'd
  examples of, 53
  exchange with environment, 55
  germ, 60
  historical, 51
  how studied, 54
  isolation of constituents, 923
  nucleus first described, 894
  number, 55
  physiology, 55-59
  shape, 53-55
  size, 53
  sponge types, 143
  structure, 51-53
  synthesis of dissociated, **715**
  theory, 51, 894
  wall, 51
Cell-tissue organization, 72
Cellular metabolism, 55, 66-69
  organization, 72, 139
  respiration, 641
Cellulose, 43
Cement gland, 220, **237**
Cementum, 556
Cenozoic era, 31, 765
Census, 821
Centipede, 278, **310,** 311-312
Central canal, 504
  nervous system, 652-656
Centriole, **52,** 55, 63
Centroderes, 219
Centromere, 62, 63, **64**
Centrosome, **64**
Centrum, 496
Centruroides, 290
Centrurus, **289**
Cephalaspis, **407**
Cephalization, 85
Cephalocardia, 305
Cephalochordata, 404, 420, 423-425
Cephalodiscus, 394, **396,** 397
Cephalogonimus, 492
Cephalopod eye, 667
Cephalopoda, 349, 364-370
  evolution, 767
  natural history, 365-366
Cephalothorax, 284
Ceratium, 119, **830**
Ceratodus, 449
Ceratomorpha, 579
Cercaria, **196, 198,** 199, 200
Cercopithecoidea, 581-582
Cercus, 329
Cerebellum, **502,** 503, **527,** 529, **652, 654,** 656
Cerebral ganglia, **190, 260**
  hemispheres, **503**
  localization, **655**
Cerebratulus, 213
Cerebrosides, 46
Cerebrospinal fluid, 504
Cerebrum, **652, 654**
Cermatia, 278, **311,** 312
Cervical plexus, **652**
Cervix, **679**
Cestoda, 186, **203-209**
Cestodaria, 203
Cestum, 180, 183
Cetacea, 576

Chaenocephalus, 453
Chaetoderma, 351
Chaetogaster, **265**
Chaetognatha, 29, 248-249, 589
Chaetonotus, 219, 222
Chaetopleura, 351
Chaetopterus, 253, **269**
Chaetura, 544
Chalazae, 705, **706**
Chalcid wasp, **325**
Challenger expedition, 899
Chamaeleo, 485
Chamaeleontidae, 485
Chamberlain, T. C., 404, 906
Chameleon, **474,** 485
Chaoborus, **830**
Chaos, 114
Charadriiformes, 541
Cheetah, **572**
Cheirolopis, 445
Chela, 294, 295
Chelicerae, 284
Chelicerata, 277, **282-291**
Cheliped, **296**
Chelonethida, **289**
Chelonia, **482,** 480-483
Chelonidae, 484
Chelydra, 133, 483
Chelydridae, 484
Chemical elements, 35
  properties, 42
  receptors, 663
Chemotaxis, 131
Chiasmatype theory, 909
Chiggers, 290
Child, C. M., 910
Chilomonas, 119
Chilopoda, 278, 311-312
Chimaera, 437
Chimpanzee, **581**
Chinch bug, **326**
Chinook salmon eggs, **455**
Chironomus, 724
Chiroptera, **570,** 571
Chitin, 275, **596**
Chiton, 349, **350,** 351
Chloragogue cell, 255, **256**
Chloride shift, 640, 641
Chlorocruorin, 624
Chlorohydra, 153, 156
Chlorophyll, 635
  synthesis, 928
Chloroplast, **116**
Choanichthyes, 410, 444, 447
Choanocytes, 139, 140, 143, 145
Choanoflagellates, 119, **121**
Cholecystokinin, 616, **695,** 698
Cholesterol, 46, 917
Cholinergic, 658
Chondrichthyes, **409,** 436-440
  classification, 437
  dogfish shark, 437-440
  evolution, 410
Chondrocranium, 439
Chondrostei, 442
Chordata, 29, 401-594
  adjustment to land life, 457-458
  advancement, 419, 420
  ammocoete larva as archetype, 426-428

Chordata—cont'd
  amphibians, 457-469
  ancestry and evolution, 403-418
  ascidian theory, 404, **405,** 916-917
  biological principles, 401
  birds, 518-545
  bony fish, 441-455
  change to land, 457
  characteristics, 418
  Chondrichthyes, 436-440
  comparison with invertebrate, 420
  Craniata, 420, 425-430
  Cyclostomata, 431-436
  dual organization, **405**
  early chordates, 404
  echinoderm theory, 403
  integument, **590-591, 592-595**
  mammals, 547-582
  origin and relations, 401-403
  protochordates, 420-425
  reptiles, 469-486
  subphyla, 420
  taxonomic position, 900
  vertebrates, 420, 425-430, 458-485
Chorion, **705, 706, 707**
Chorionic gonadotropin, 699
Choroid coat, 506, **667,** 668
  plexus, 504
Chromatid, 63, **64, 683**
Chromatin, **52,** 55, 61, 901
Chromatophore, 118, 365, 369, **493,** 554, 592, **594**
Chromocenter, 725
Chromomere, 62, 723, 901
Chromonema, 62, 63, **64,** 723
Chromosome, **61-62,** 160, 722-724, 744
  aberrations, 744
  constancy, 723
  historical, 896, 899-900, 901, 902, 903, 907, 908, 911, 915, 928
  salivary gland, **724**-725
  structure, **61-62, 722-723**
Chrysaora, **153**
Chrysemys, 133, **482**
Chymotrypsin, 616
Cicada, **326,** 334, 338
Ciconiiformes, **539**
Cilia, 125, **126,** 607-608
  movement, 607
  process, 506
Ciliata, 103, 125-134
Ciliophora, 103
Cinclide, 172
Ciona, 404
Circulatory system, 82, 508-512, 621-635
  ammocoetes, 428
  bird, **527,** 528
  clam, **360,** 361
  comparative schemes, **623**
  crayfish, **298,** 299-300
  earthworm, **257**-259

Circulatory system—cont'd
  frog, **508, 509, 510,** 508-512
  grasshopper, 330
  historical, 621-622, 890
  invertebrate, **623, 624**
  plan of, 622
  reptile, **472,** 473
  Rhynchocoela, 214
  sea star, 379
  snail, 356
  spider, 285
  tongue worm, 395
  vertebrate, 508-512, 558, 624-635
Circumesophageal connective, 301
Cirri, buccal, **423,** 424
Cirripedia, **306**
Cisterna magna, 512, 513
Citric acid cylic, 67, 921
Civit, 573
Cladocera, 305, **306**
Clam, fresh-water, 357-364
  circulatory system, **359, 360,** 361
  development, 362, 363
  digestive system, **359,** 360-361
  excretory system, 362
  external features, 357-359
  feeding mechanism, **358**
  internal structure, **359, 360,** 361-362
  long-neck, **352**
  natural history, 363-364
  nervous system, 362
  pearl formation, **358,** 359
  respiratory system, **360, 361,** 362
  shell, **358, 359**
Clamworm, **266**-268
  behavior, 267
  cross-section, 267
  locomotion, 267
  structure, **266**
Claperede, E., 898
Clark, LeGros, 802
Clasper, 438
Class, 25
Classification, 24-29, 88-89
Claude, A., 923
Clavicle, 497, **600**
Claws, 329, 594
Cleavage, 73, 74-76, 515, **516,** 712-713
  determinate, **75, 712**
  holoblastic, 75
  indeterminate, **75, 712**
  meroblastic, 75
  partial, 705
  radial, **75,** 76
  spiral, **75,** 76
  superficial, 75
Clelia, 480
Cleveland, L. R., 914
Cliff swallow, nest, 533
Climatius, 408
Climax community, 839
Cline, 776-777
Clinostomum, 492

946

Cliona, 140, 148
Clione, 355
Clitellum, 254, 256
Clitoris, **678**, 680
Cloaca, 492, 495, 508, **513**, **527**, 529, 558, 677
Cloacal opening, **507**, **508**, **513**
Clone, 128
Clonorchis, 197 (*see also Opisthorchis*)
Clot, 508, 632
Clothes moth, **326**, **327**
Clupea, **444**
Clypeus, 328
Cnidaria, 28, 150-178, **623**, **642**, **649**
Cnidoblast, **154**, 155, **156**, 157
Cnidocil, **154**, 157
C-O sole, 443
Coal-tar dye, discovery, 897
Cobra, 480
Coccidia, 107, 124-125
Coccidiosis, 124
Coccygeoiliacus, 500
Coccygeosacralis, 500
Coccyx, **598**, **599**, **600**
Cochlea, **664**, **665**, 666
Cochlear duct, **666**
Cockroach, **326**, 335
Cocoon, **194**, 262, **263**, 322
Codfish, 444
Coelacanth, **409**, 411, 922
Coelacanthini, 444
Coelenterata, 28, 150-178
  biological principles, 150
  characteristics, 151-152
  classes, 152
  corals, 174-176
  economic, 176
  epidermis, **588**
  habitat, 153
  origin and relations, 150-151
  types of individuals, 152
Coeliac artery, **509**, 510
Coeliacomesenteric artery, **509**, 510
Coelom, 77, 86-87, 96, 223, 244, 494, 614
  enterocoelus, **77**, 87
  formation, **77**
  schizocoelous, **77**, 87
  types, **88**
Coelomic cavity, 298
  fluid, 255
Coelomocyte, 379
Coeloplana, 180, 183
Coenosarc, **164**
Coenzymes, 48, 67
Coghill, G. E., 870, 871, 875, 916
Cohn, E. J., 921
Cohn, F., 900
Coleoptera, 339, **340**
Colic cecum, 611, 614
Coliiformes, 544
Colinus, 540
Collar (squid), **368**
Collecting tubule, **644**
Collembola, **334**, 335
Collenchyma, 79, 170, 172, 182

Colloblast, 181
Collocalia, 544
Colloidal state, 898
Colloids, 38, 39, 40, 908
Colon, 558, **613**, 617
Colonies, 109, **119**, 167-188, 323-327
Color vision, 670
Colorado potato beetle, **340**
Coloration, bird, 532
  hormonal control of, 917
  insect, 318
  mammal, 553, 554
Colubridae, 485
Columbiformes, 541
Columella, 506, **665**
Colymbiformes, 539
Comb jellies, 179-183 (*see also* Ctenophora)
  plates, **181**
Commensalism, 106, **388**
Communication, 880-881
  honeybee, 865, **866**, **867**
  bird, 881
Community, biotic, 823-824, 839
  climax, 824
  major, minor, 823
  periodicity, 824
Comparative anatomy, development, 891
Complemental air, 639
Compound eye, 302, **303**
Compounds, 35, 42
Conchostraca, 305
Conditioned reflex, concept, 910
Condor, **541**
Condylura, 570
Conepatus, 480
Cones, eye, 506, **668**, 669
Congo eel, **461**
Coniferous forests, 835
Conjugation, 109, **128**, 673, 675
Conjunctiva, 507
Connective tissue, 78, **79-80**, 82, 83
Conservation, 838-839
Consumers (primary, secondary), 823
Contour feather, 521, **522**
Contractile tissue (*see* Muscular system)
  vacuole, 72, 112, **116**, 117, **126**
Contraction period, 604
Conus arteriosus, 625
Cony, 577
Cook, J., 891
Coot, 541
Copepoda, **306**
Cope's law, 795
Copperhead snake, 478
Copulation, 193, 200, **262**
Copulatory organ, bird, 529
  snake, **473**
Coracidium, 208
Coraciiformes, 544-545
Coracoid, 560
  process, **600**

Coral, 153, 174, **175**, 176
  atoll, 175
  reefs, 175
  snake, **477**
Cori, C., 924
Corium, 552, 592
Cormorant, 539
Cornea, 506, **667**, 668
Corneagen cell, 303
Corona, 220
Corpora allata, 323
  arenacea, 700
  quadrigemina, 559
Corpus callosum, **654**
  luteum, **688**, 696, **697**, 699
Corpuscle, renal, 513
  sense, 506
Correns, K. E., 906
Corrodentia, 334, 337
Corticotropic release factor, 692
Cortisone, 694, 920
Corydalis, 338
Cotton boll weevil, **326**
Cotylosaur, 413, **414**, 470, 547
Cougar, 573
Coupled reaction, 48
Courtship ritual, spiders, 286
Coverts, 521, **522**
Cow, 549, **550**
Cowbird, 533
Cowper's gland, 679
Cowries, 348
Coxa, **328**, 329
Coxopodite, **296**
Coyote, **571**
Crane, 541
Cranial nerve, 504, 505, 656
  terminal, 904
Craniata, 420, 425-430
Cranium, frog, **495**, **496**
Crappie, 444
Craspedacusta, **168-169**
Craspedomonadidae, 139
Crassostrea, **363**
Crayfish, 293-304
  appendages, **294**, **295**, **296-**298
  behavior, 293
  circulatory system, **288**, 299-**300**
  digestive system, **298**, 299
  endocrine system, 303-304
  excretory system, **298**, 301
  external features, **294**, **295**, **296**
  habitat, 293
  internal features, **298-304**
  metabolism, 299
  muscular system, 298
  nervous system, 301, **302**
  regeneration, 294
  reproductive system, 300-301
  respiratory system, 298-299, **300**
  sensory system, 302, **303**
Creighton, H., 918
Crenation, 58
Creodont, 573
Crepidula, 354
Cretaceous period, 31, 104, 765
Cretinism, 692

Crick, F. H. C., 926
Crickets, 335
Crinoidea, **375**, 376, **388**, **389**,
    390
    larvae, **377**
Crisscross inheritance, **741-742**
Crocidura, 566
Crocodile, 483, 485
Crocodilia, 471, **483**, 485
Crocodylidae, 485
Crocodylus, 483, 485
Cro-Magnon man, 801-802
Crop, 255, **271**, 329, **527**
Crossing-over, 726, **742-743**,
    918
Crossopterygian fish, **409, 410**,
    411, **412**
Crossopterygii, 444
Crotalidae, 485
Crotalus, **478, 479**, 485
Crustacea, 277, 293-311
    blood cells, **624**
    Malacostracans, **309**
    shrimp, life history, **310**
Cryoscopy, 59
Cryptobranchidae, 469
Cryptobranchus, 463, 469
Cryptocercus, 106
Cryptochiton, 350, 351
Cryptorchidism, 696
Cryptotis, 570
Cryptozoite, 121
Crystalline style, 361
Crystalloids, 40
Ctenidia, 360, 361
Ctenoid scale, 453
Ctenophora, 29, 179-183
    biological principles, 179
    characteristics, 180
    classes, 180
    comparison with coelenter-
        ates, 180
    economic importance, 183
    habitat, 180
Ctenoplana, 180, 183
Cuckoo, 534, 541, 543
Cuculiformes, 541, 543
Cuculus, 541
Cucumaria, 387, 389
Culex, 230, **341**
Cunningham, O., 922
Currents, ocean, 833-834
Cusp, 556
Cuticle, 125, 224, 587, **589**
Cuttlefish, 370
Cutworm moth, **326**
Cuvier, G., 892
Cuvier, ducts of, 428
Cyanea, 157, **170**
Cyanocobalamin, 621
Cycloid scale, 453
Cyclops, 208, 231, 277, **306**,
    830
Cyclostomata, 406, **409**, 431-
    436
Cyclotron, invention, 918
Cynocephalus, 572
Cynognathus, **416**, 418, 547
Cypraea, 348
Cyprinus, 444
Cypselurus, **451**

Cysticercus, 205, 206
Cytochrome, 47, 67, 902, 916
Cytogamy, 129
Cytology, 22
Cytopharynx, 126
Cytoplasm, 41, 52, 901
Cytoplasmic inclusions, **52**,
    905-906
    inheritance, 745
Cytosine, 727
Cytostome, 126

D

Dale, H. H., 913
Dam, H., 919
Damsel flies, 337
Dan, J. C., 927
Danaüs, 856
Daphnia, 277, 305, **306, 830**
Darling, F. F., 884
Dart, R., 800, 915
Darwin, C., 263, 762, 778, 870,
    897
    natural selection theory, 781-
        784
Darwin, E., 778, 870
Darwin's finches, 793
Dasyatis, 437
Dasypeltis, 861
Dasypus, **575**
Day vision, 669
DDT synthesis, 922
Decapoda, 308, **309**, 367
Deciduous forests, 835-836
Decomposer organisms, 824
Deer antlers, 594
Deletion, 744
Deltoid, **606**
Deme, 777
Demodex, 275
Demospongiae, 140, **147**-148
Dendrites, 650
Dendrobates, 465
Dendrosoma, 134
Dental formula, 557
Dentalium, 349, **351**, 352
Dentary bone, **496, 665**
Dentine, 438
Depressor mandibuli, **499**, 500
    muscle, 502
Dermacentor, **290**, 291
Dermal branchiae, 378, **380**,
    381, 635
    plica, 493
Dermaptera, **334**, 336
Dermasterias, **385**
Dermis, 552, **592, 595**
Dermochelidae, 484
Dermocranium, 598
Dermoptera, 571, 572
Dero, **265**
Descartes, R., 890
Desert, 835
Desmodus, 571, 861
Desmognathus, 463
Desoxycorticosterone, 694
Desoxyribonucleic acid (DNA),
    45, 727, **728**, 905
Desoxyribose, 45, 727, **728**
Determinate cleavage, **712**

Deuterostomia, 89, 249
Development, embryonic, 703-
    719, 902
    determinate, **712**
    indeterminate, **712**
    patterns analysis, 922
Devonian period, 764
Diabetes mellitus, 693
Diabetogenic hormone, 49
Diacodexis, 579
Diadophis, **477**
Dialysis, 58
Diamondback terrapin, 482
Diapause, 323
Diapedesis, 511
Diaphragm, **558**, 559, 560, 614,
    638
Diarthrosis joint, 497, **498**
Diastole, 510, 628
Dibranchia, 366-367
Dichromatism, 554
Dicyema, **241**
Didelphis, **569**, 570
Didinium, 111
Diemictylus, 463, 469
Diencephalon, **503**, 652
Dietary   deficiency,   analysis,
    908
Differentiation, 73, 78, 711-716
Difflugia, **114**, 116, **830**
Diffusion pressure, 56
Digenea, 195, 196, 202
Digestion, 610-618, 891
    ameba, 112
    extracellular, 610
    hormones, 695
    intracellular, 189, 610
    invertebrate, 610-**611**
    physiology, 614-618
    vertebrate, 611-618
Digestive system, 82, 609-618
    ammocoetes, **427**-428
    Ascaris, 225, **226**
    comparative, **611**
    crayfish, **298**, 299
    development, **709**, 710
    earthworm, 255, **256**, 257,
        611
    echinoderm, 379, **380, 388**
    flatworm, 189, **190**, 197,
        611
    frog, **507**-508
    grasshopper, 329-**330**
    histology, **612**
    historical, 609-610
    hydra, 152, **154**, 155-166,
        158
    mammal, 557-**558**, **611**-614
    mollusk, 355, **358**, **359**,
        360-361, 368
    Peripatus, 280
    Protozoa, 112, 126, 611
    reptile, **472**-473
    ribbon worm, 214
    secretion, 614-617
    spider, 284-**285**
    sponge, 144, 146
    tongue worm, **395**
    vertebrate, **611**, **612**, **613**,
        614
Digits, 497, **523**, 526

Dihybrid, 734
Dimorphic, 167
Dinobryon, 107, **120**
Dinophilus, 253
Dinosaur, **414**, 415
  eggs, discovery, 914
  fauna (Alberta), 905
  fossil bed (Utah), 909
Dioctophyma, 219
Dioecious, 73, 160, 676
Dioecocestus, 203
Diphycercal tail, **444**, 447
Diphyletic origin, 519
Diphylla, 861
Diphyllobothrium, 186, 206,
  208, 890
Dipleurula, 374, 375
Diploblastic, 76
Diplopoda, 277, 278, 312
Dipnoi, 444, 447-449
Diptera, **334**, 340, **341**
Dipterus, 449
Dipylidium, 206, 208
Disaccharides, 43
Discorbis, **114**
Disease vector, arthropod, 327
  mammal, 568
Disease-resistant strains, 747
Diseases, concept, 897
Dispersal factors, 844-845
Distribution of animals, 843-
  849
  continuous, discontinuous,
    843
  mammal, 561
  present vs. past, 843-844
  zoological zonation, 897
Diuretic, 646
Diverticulum, 189, **190**
Diving beetle, giant, **340**
Divisions of animal kingdom, 88
DNA, 45, **728**, 729, 926
Dobson flies, **334**, 338
  fly larva, **325**, 338
Dobzhansky, T., 314, 789
Dog, 572-573
  skeleton, **598**
Dogfish shark, 437-440
  characteristics, 437, **438**,
    439, 440
  external anatomy, 437, **438**
  integument, 438, **590**
  internal anatomy, **438**, 439
  nervous system, 440
  placoid scale, 438, **590**
  urogenital system, 439
Dohrn, A., 899
Doisy, E. A., 917
Doliolaria larva, **377**, 390
Doliolum, 421
Dollo's law, 795
Dolomedes, 286
Dolphin, 576
Domestic fowl, 540
Dominance, 732
  and recessiveness, 893
  complete, 734
  incomplete, 734, **736**
Dominance-subordinance, 883
Dominant, 734, 824

Dorsal abdominal artery, 299
  fissure, 504
  sensory root, 504
Dorsalis scapulae, **499**, 500
Dorsolumbar vein, **510**, 511
Doublass, E., 909
Dove, 541
Down feather, **521**, **522**
Draco, 474, 485
Dracunculus, 231
Dragonfly, **325**, **334**, 337
Driesch, H., 903
Drone, 324
Drosophila, 314, **722**, 724
Drymarchon, 485
Dryopithecus, 797, 798
Dubois, E., 903
Dubois, R., 902
Duck, 529, 533, 540, **814**
Dugesia, 186, 187-195 (*see also*
    Planaria)
Dugong, 577
Dujardin, F., 894
Dumas, J. B. A., 893
Duodenum, **507**, **558**, **613**, 614
Duplication (chromosome), 744,
    928
Dura mater, 503, 652
DuShane, G. P., 920
Dwarfism, 695
Dyad, **683**, **684**
Dytiscus, **340**
  larva, **829**

E

Eagle, bald, **540**
  harpy, **541**
Ear, 663-667
  chamber, 24
  evolution, **665**
  frog, 506
  inner, **664**, 665-667
  mammal, 551
  man, **664**
  middle, **664**, 665
  ossicles, 559, **664**, **665**
Earthworm, 253-264
  aortic arches, **257**
  behavior, 263-264
  body plan, 255
  circulatory system, **257**-259
  cross section, **256**
  digestive system, 255, **256**
  economic importance, 264
  excretory system, **258**, 259
  external features, **254**
  farming, 264
  giant, 265
    fibers, **260**, 261
  habitat, 253-254
  integument, **261**
  internal features, **255**, **256**
  locomotion, 254-255
  openings, 254
  reflex arc, **260**
  reproductive system, **261**, 262
  respiratory system, 259
  setae, **255**
  sporozoan parasite, 123
Earwig, **334**, **336**
Eccrine gland, **554**

Ecdysis, 275, 301, 320
Echidna, **417**, 561
Echinarachnius, **386**
Echinococcus, 186, 206, **208**,
    209
Echinodera, 222
Echinoderella, 219, 222
Echinoderes, 222
Echinoderm theory, 403
Echinodermata, 29, 372-390,
    642
  biological principles, 372
  characteristics, 373, 374
  classification, 374-376
  digestive system, **375**
  economic importance, 374
  larvae, 376, **377**, 378
  origin and relations, 372, 373
  skeleton, **375**
  water-vascular system, **375**
Echinoidea, 375, 376, 384-**387**
Echinopluteus, **377**
Echiuroidea, 243-**244**
Echiurus, 244
Echolocation, concept, 924
Ecological density, 562
  equivalent, 823, 839
  niche, 824, 839
  succession, 824-**825**
  terms, 839-840
Ecology, 22, 809-840
  and conservation, 838-839
  biomes, 833-836
  definition, 809
  factors, 810-820
  habitats, 825-833
Ecosystem, 823, 839, 920
Ecotone, 823, 839
Ectoderm, **76**, **77**, 96, 161, 706
  derivatives, 77
Ectomesoderm, 151
Ectoplasm, 41, **110**, 111, **116**,
    117, 125, **126**, 588
Ectoprocta (Bryozoa), 29, 245,
    246, **247**
  behavior, 246-247
  brown body, 246
  characteristics, 245
  structure, 245-**246**, **247**
Edentata, 575-576
Eel, fresh-water, 444, 446, 855,
    914
Effector, 650
eft, 463
Egestion, 508
Egg(s), amniotic, 413, 458, **705**
  Amphioxus, **711**
  bird, **706**
  centrolecithal, **74**
  crayfish, **301**
  fish, **455**
  fresh-water, 74
  holoblastic, 74
  intrauterine, 74
  isolecithal, 74
  jelly, 74
  marine, 74
  meroblastic, 74
  pinworm, **230**
  salamander, **462**
  salmon, **455**

Egg(s)—cont'd
  segmentation, **75, 76, 77,** 905
  telolecithal, **74**
  terrestrial, 74
  toad, **467**
  types, **74**
Eggleton, G. P., 916
Eggleton, P., 916
Eijkman, C., 905
Eimeria, 107, **124-125**
Einstein equation, 37
Eisenia, 253
Ejaculatory duct, **678**
  tube, 226
Elaphe, **475**
Elapidae, 479, 485
Elasmobranchii, 436-440 (*see* Chondrichthyes)
Electric eel, 444
  organ, 864-**865**
  ray, 440, 864, **865**
Electricity, animal, 607, 892
Electrocardiograph, 628
Electroencephalograph, 6 5 6, 917
Electrolyte, 37, 40
Electrons, 36
Electrophorus, 444, 864
Elements, chemical, 35
Eleocyte, 255, **624**
Elephant, 551, 576, 577
  evolution, 767, **768**
  tusk shells, 349, **351**
Elephantiasis, 230, **231**
Elephas, 577, **768**
Eleutherozoa, 373, 376
Elliot, D. F., **927**
Elytra, 317
Embia, 337
Embiids, 337
Embioptera, 337
Embolomeri, **412,** 460
Embolus, 633
Embryological inductor, **713,** 714, 919
Embryology, 22, **74-78,** 703-719
  amniote, 704-711
  bird, 705, **706**
  definition, 73
  frog, **515-517**
  historical, 703-704, 913-914, 920
  hydra, 161, **162**
  man, **706, 707, 709**
  pig, **708**
  reptile, 705, 706
Embryos, comparative vertebrate, **704**
  formation of, **74-78**
Emigration, 564
Emperor penguin, **538**
Emu, 538
Emulsion, 39
Endamoeba, 115
Endocardium, 626
Endocranium, 598
Endocrine system, 83, 559, 687, 700
  bird, 530
  crayfish, 303
  frog, 513

Endocrine system—cont'd
  historical, 688, 689, 896, 903, 904, 907, 915, 917
  invertebrate, 690
  location of glands, **687**
  vertebrate, **691-697,** 698-700
Endocrinology, 22, 687, 688
Endoderm, **76, 77,** 96, 161, 706
Endolymph, 506
Endometrium, 680, **697,** 698, 699
Endomixis, 109, 129
Endoplasm, 41, 42, **110,** 111, **116,** 117, 125, **126**
Endoplasmic reticulum, 42, 69, 926
Endopodite, **296**
Endopterygota, 338-342
Endoskeleton, 419, 596, **597-602,** 708-709
  chordate, **402**
  echinoderm, **375**
  frog, **495-498**
  sea star, 378, **380**
Endosmosis, 58
Endostyle, 421, 424, **427**
Endothelium, 511, 629
Endothermal, 560
Energy, 35-38, 93
  conservation of, 38, 896
  kinetic, 38
  laws, 37
  potential, 38
  requirements, 618
  values, determination, 619, 901-902
Enopla, 213-215
Ensis, **352**
Entamoeba, 107, 108, **111,** 492
Enterobius, 219, 224, **229, 230**
Enterocoelous coelom, **77,** 87
Enterocrinin, 617
Enterogastrone, 617, **695,** 698
Enteropneusta, 393, **394, 395**
Entodiniomorphina, 107
Entomology, 22, 314
Entomostraca, 304, **306**
Entoprocta, 29, 241-242
Entosphenus, 432
Environment, 95, 809-840
  factors, 810
  types (habitats), 825-833
Environmental resistance, 821
Enzymes, 46-50,
  action, 48
  catalytic power, 49
  chemical nature, 47
  coupled reaction, 48
  digestive, 615-617
  frog, 507-508
  functions, 47
  historical, 47, 901, 915-916, 924
  intestine, 616
  location, 47
  molecular weight, 47
  pancreatic, 616
  relation to mitochondria, 52
  reversibility, 49

Enzymes—cont'd
  sensitivity, 49
  specificity, 48
  terminology, 47
  vitamin relations, 48
Enzyme-substrate complex, 48, 911
Eoanthropus, 799
Eocanthocephala, 236
Eocene epoch, 765
Eogyrinus, **412**
Eorhynchus, 235
Eosinophil, **624, 630**
Ephelota, 134
Ephemera, 337
Ephemerida, **334,** 336, 337
Ephemeroptera, 320
Ephydata, 144
Ephydra, 274
Ephyra, **171,** 172
Epiceratodus, 444, **448,** 449
Epicoracoid, 497
Epicranium, 328
Epidermis, **154,** 155, **189, 261,** 378, **493,** 552, 587, **588-592,** 595
Epididymis, **674**
Epidinium, 132, **133**
Epigastric artery, **509,** 511
Epigenesis, 703, 891
Epinephrine, 694, 698
Epiphanes, 219, 220
Epipodium, 364
Episternum, 497
Epistylis, 492
Epithelial tissue, **78, 79, 83**
Epitheliomuscular cells, **154,** 155
Epithelium, types of, 79, **82**
Epochs, 31-32
Eptesicus, **570,** 571
Equidae, 577
Equilibrium, 667
Equus, 770
Erepsin, 508, 616
Erethizontidae, 574
Ergosterol, 46
Eryops, **411, 412,** 413
Erythroblastosis fetalis, 634
Erythrocruorin, 259, 624
Erythrocyte, 508, **631**
Esophagus, **298,** 299, 507, **527,** **613**
Esox, 444
Estradiol, 696, **697,** 698, 699
Estrogen, 695
Estrogenic, 694
Estrone, 917
Estrus cycle, 566-567, 697
Ethiopian realm, 847
Ethology, 870
Eubranchipus, 277, **304, 305**
Eucestoda, 203-204
Euchlora, 179, 180
Eucoelomate, **88**
Eudorina, 119
Eugenics, 755-756
Euglena, 103, 108, **116-118**
  behavior, 118
  habitat, 116-117
  locomotion, 118

Euglena—cont'd
  metabolism, 117-118
  reproduction, 118
  structure, 116, 117
Euglenoid movement, 118
Eumeces, 474, 485
Eumicrosoma, 325
Eunice, 269
Eunuchism, 696
Euplectella, 140, **142,** 147
Euplotes, 131, 132
Eupnea, 639
Eupomatus, 196
Eurybathic, 816-817
Eurycea, **464, 465**
Euryhaline, 453
Eurypterida, 277, 282
Eurypterus, 277, **763**
Eurythermal, 810
Eurytopic, 843
Eustachian tube, **494, 664, 665**
Eutheria, 569, 570-582
Eutrombicula, 290
Euzoic, 119
Evolution, 20, 772-804
  adaptation, 787-789
  amphibian, **411, 412,** 413
  Baldwin effect, 904
  birds, 415, **416,** 418
  brain, 653-654
  cephalopods, 767
  cline concept, 776, 777, 922
  convergent, **548,** 845
  elephants, 767-**768**
  evidences, 778-780
  fish, **407, 408, 409, 410, 411**
  future, 803-804
  history, 777-778, 916, 918,
    919, 922
  horse, 768, **769,** 770
  human, record of, 797-803
  in action, 794
  kidney nephron, 645
  mammals, **417,** 418
  man, 796-803, **799**
  meaning, 774-777
  middle ear and ossicles, **665**
  modern synthesis, 775-777
  mutual cooperation, 907
  natural selection theory, 781-
    784
  rate, 787
  reptiles, 413, 414, 415
  statistical analysis, 918
  theories, 780-787
  use and disuse theory, 892
  vertebrate kidney, 428, **429**
Evolutionary blueprint, 30
  concept, 94, 891
  generalizations, 794, **795,** 796
Excretion, nature of, 642
  hydra, 158, **642**
  Protozoa, 112, **642**
Excretory system, 642-646, 821
  ammocoetes, 428, **429**
  bird, **527,** 529
  clam, 362
  comparative, **642**
  crayfish, 301
  earthworm, **256, 258,** 259,
    642

Excretory system—cont'd
  frog, 512, **513**
  grasshopper, **330**
  invertebrate, 642-643
  mammal, **559, 643**
  planaria, **190, 191, 642**
  reptile, **472,** 473
  ribbon worm, 214
  spider, **285**
  tapeworm, **204,** 206
  vertebrate, **643-646**
Existence, basic requirements,
    809-810
Exoccipital, **495, 496**
Exocrine gland types, 593
Exopodite, **296**
Exopterygota, 335-338
Exoskeleton, **102, 104, 105,** 275,
    294, 382, 471, 595-
    597
Exosmosis, 58
Experimental methods, 23
  zoology, 21
Expiration, 512, 528, 639
Expressivity, 736
Extensor cruris muscle, **499,** 501
  muscle, 502
External acoustic meatus, 598
  oblique muscle, **499,** 500
  of eye, 506
Extracellular digestion, 158
Extraembryonic coelom, 706
  membrane, 705
Exumbrella, 166, 171
Eye, 667-670
  accommodation, 669
  Amphiporus, 213
  crayfish, 302-**303**
  frog, **494,** 506
  grasshopper, **328**
  muscles, 506
  Nautilus, 367
  parietal, **484**
  planaria, **188**
  spider, **285**
  squid, **369**
  variations (vertebrate), 669-
    670
  vertebrate, 551, **667-670**
Eyelid, **667**
Eyespot, **188,** 191, 378, 380,
    660

F

Facial nerve, **502,** 505, 656
Fairy shrimp, **304, 305, 306**
Falcustra, 492
Falconiformes, **540**
Fallopian tube, 560, **678,** 680
Family, 25
Fangs, 477, **478,** 479
Fascia, 499
Fasciola, 186, **196,** 197, 202-
    203
Fasciolopsis, 203
Fat, 46, 618
  bodies, 495, **513,** 514
Fatty acids, 46
Fauces, 557
Faunal delimitation, 897-898
  realms, 846-848

Fayum Lake fossil beds, 906
Feather, 520-523
  barb, **520-521**
  barbicel, **520**
  barbule, **520**
  bud, 520, **521**
  contour, 521
  coverts, 521, **522**
  down, **521**
  interlocking mechanism, **520**
  molting, 522
  number, 523
  origin and development, 520-
    521
  quill, 520
  structure, **520**
  tracts, **522**
Feather star (sea lily), **388,**
    389, 390
Feces, 508
Federley, H., 911
Feeblemindedness, inheritance,
    752
Feedback, 692
Felidae, 573
Female sex hormones, 696, **697,**
    698
Femoral artery, **509,** 511
  vein, **510,** 511
Femur, **328,** 329, **495,** 497, **523,**
    525, **598, 600**
Fertilization, 73, 124, 672, **673,**
    682, 685-686, 893, 900
  frog, 515, **516**
  grasshopper, 331
  types, 686
Fertilizin, 685, 911-912
Fetal pig, structure, **558, 559**
Fetus, human, **707**
Feulgen, R., 915
Fiber, 79, 655, **657**
Fibrin, 508
Fibrinogen, 632
Fibula, **598, 600**
Fiddler crab, 309
Fierasfer, 388
Filarial worm, 230-231
Filoplume feather, **522**
Filter feeding, clam, 361, 363
Filtration, 58
  pressure, 630
Filum terminale, 504
Fingerling, salmon, **455**
Fins, **445,** 450, 451
Firefly, 863
Fischer, E., 902
Fish, 431-456
  "bloodless," 453
  bony, 441-456
  brain, **654**
  cartilaginous, 431-440
  caudal fins, **445**
  circulation, 625
  evolutionary pattern, 444,
    446, 447, 449
  tree, **409**
  sounds, 881
  structural adaptations, 449-
    455
Fisher, R. A., 789, 918
Fishes, Age of, 32

Fiske, C. H., 916
Fission, 108, **118, 128,** 674
Fissipedia, 573
Fissure, dorsal and ventral, 504
Fissurella, 354
Fixation methods, 24, 906
Flack, M. J., 908
Flagella, 608
Flagellata (*see* Mastigophora)
Flagellum, **116,** 117
Flame cells, 186, **190, 191,** 206, 642
Flamingo, 539
Flatworms, 184-210, **588, 589, 642, 649**
Flavoprotein, 67
Flea, **334,** 341
Flemming, A., 918
Flemming, W., 901
Flexor muscle, 499
Flies, **325, 326,** 340
Flight (birds), 530, 531, 532
Flounder, **443, 446**
Flukes, 195-203, **491,** 492
Flying fish, **446, 451,** 860-861
lemur, 571
nature's experiments, **814**
phalanger, **548**
squirrel, **548,** 549, **550**
Fol, H., 901
Foliaceous appendage, 298
Folic acid, 620
Follicle cell, **674**
ovarian, 890
Follicle-stimulating hormone, FSH, **696-699**
Food chains, 817, 839
classification, 618
cycle, 836-838
getting, 861-862
pyramid, 817, **818**
vacuole, **110,** 112, **126, 133,** 610
Foot, bird, **525**
horse, **769**
man, **600**
mollusk, 345, **346, 351,** 355, **358**
rotifer, **220**
Foramen, interventricular, 504
magnum, 496
of Monro, 504
Foramina, intervertebral, 496
Foraminifera, **104**-106, 115
Foregut, 330
Forficula, 336
Fossils, 760-770
age determination, 761-762
Archaeopteryx, **416**
coprolite, 761
Cynognathus, **416**
entire remains, 760
evidence of evolution, 766-767
geological correlation, 892
record, 762-766
hard parts, 760
Hesperornis, **519**
Ichthyostega, 459
Jamoytius, **406**
labyrinthodont, **411**

Fossils—cont'd
location, 761
molds and casts, 761
nature of, 760-761
Osteolepis, **410**
ostracoderm, **407**
petrification, 760-761
placoderm, 408
representative, **763**
Seymouria, **413**
significance, 762
trilobite, **281,** 282
Four-o'clock flowers, genetics, **736**
Fovea centralis, **667,** 669
Fox, 573
Fraenkel-Conrat, H., 927
Fragmentation, **673,** 675
Freemartin concept, 912
Freezing point, 59
Freezing-drying fixation, 24
Fresh-water streams, 826, **827**
Frisch, Karl von, 866, 924
Frog, 463-469, 488-517
behavior, 490
bell, **466**
blood, 508
bullfrog, **489**
classification, 28, 468-469
development, **515, 516,** 517
distribution, 488-490
external features, 492-494
flying, **466**
green, **489**
hairy, 465, **466**
hibernation, 490
integument, 493-494
internal structures, 494-495
leopard, **489**
life cycle, **514, 515, 516,** 517
lung, **637**
morphological type, 492
parasites, 490, **491,** 492
spring peeper, **467, 489**
swamp cricket, **489**
systems, circulatory, 508-512
digestive, **494,** 507-508
endocrine, 513
excretory, 512, **513**
muscular, 498-502
nervous, **502**-506
reproductive, **513-514**
respiratory, 512
sensory, 505-507
skeleton, **495-498**
tree, **489**
Frons, 328
Frontal bone, **598**
Frontoparietal, **495,** 496
Fujii, K., 915
Fulmar, 539
Fulton, B. B., 874
Funk, C., 910
Funiculus, 246, **247**
Fur seal, 563, **564**

G

Galambos, R., 924
Galathealinum, 398

Galen, 889
Galeopithecus, 572
Gall, F. J., 892
Gallbladder, 428, 495, **507, 527, 613**
Galliformes, **540**
Gallinule, 541
Galvani, L., 892
Galvanotaxis, 131
Gambusia, 454
Gametes, **674, 675, 676,** 685
Gametocyte, 122
Gametogenesis, 681-685, **682**
Gammarus, **309**
Ganglion, 83, **330,** 648
autonomic, **657**
cerebropleural, **359,** 362
dorsal root (spinal), **651,** 652
pedal, **359,** 362
subpharyngeal, **260, 302**
supraesophageal, **302**
sympathetic, 505, **651**
visceral, 359, 362
Gannet, 539
Ganoid scales, 444, 453
Gar, **442**
Garpike, **409,** 443
Garstang, W., 404, 916
Gas, partial pressure, 640
Gases, transport, 640, 641
Gasterosteus, 859
Gastrea theory of metazoans, 900
Gastric ceca, 330
filament, 172
ligament, 379
lipase, 616
mill, 299
mucosa, 698
pouch, 172
Gastrin, 617, **695,** 698
Gastrocnemius muscle, **499,** 501, **606**
Gastrocolic reflex, 617
Gastrodermis, 151, **154,** 155, **170**
Gastrointestinal mucosa, hormones, **695**
Gastrolith, 299
Gastropoda, 349, **352-357**
habitat, 352
major groups, 354-355
size, 353
snail, 355-**357**
torsion, **353,** 354
Gastrotheca, 857, **858**
Gastrotricha, 218, 219, **221-222**
Gastrovascular cavity, 151, **154,** 155, 158, 164, 166, 181, 189, **190,** 610, **611**
Gastrozooid, 168
Gastrula, **76**
Gastrulation, **76**
Gause's rule, 796
Gavia, **539**
Gavial, 485
Gavialidae, 485
Gavialis, 485
Gaviiformes, **539**

952

Gecko, 485
Geese, 540
Gegenbaur, K., 185
Gekkonidae, 485
Gel, 39
Gemmule, 144, **145, 673,** 675
Genae, 328
Gene, 72, 725-729
  biological centers, 913
  lethal, 739
  multiple, 737
  named, 909
  number, 726
  theory, 725-729, 910
Genetics, 22, 721-759 (*see also* Heredity*)
  applied, 746-758
  biochemical, 747-748
  drift, 776, 791-792, 919
  radiation effects, 754-755
  terminology, 734-735
  transduction, 917
Genioglossus muscle, 500
Geniohyoid muscle, 500
Genital atrium, 192
  bursa, **237**
  ligament, 237
  pore, 300
Genotype, 733, 909
Genus, 25
Geographical equivalents, 845
  exploration, 891
Geological time, divisions, 764
  time scale, 31-32
Geology, modern concept, 893-894
Geomyidae, 574
Geophilus, 278
Geotaxis, 132
Gephyrea, 245
Gerard, R. W., 919
Germ cell, 60, **676,** 681
  cells, origin, 681, **682**-685
  layers, 76-78, 96, 892, 899
  plasm, 96, 681, 902
Germinal disc, 705
Gestation, 567
Giant anteater, **575**
  fossil men, 800, 801
  nerve axons, **260,** 261, 898, 921
  squid, 369
Giardia, 120
Gibbon, 582
Gigantism, 695
Gigantopithecus, 800
Gila monster, 475, 861
Gills, 635-**636**
  ammocoetes, 427
  clam, **358**-362
  crayfish, 298
  hagfish, **435**
  lamprey, 434, **435**
  pharyngeal, 401
  slits, 394, 419, 422, **423,** 424, **435, 436, 438**
  squid, **368**
Ginglymodi, 443
Giraffe, horns, 594
Gizzard, 255, **256,** 527

Gland, **154**-156, **593,** 894
  apocrine, **554**
  cutaneous, **591**
  digestive, **359**
  eccrine, **554**
  endocrine, 687-690
  exocrine types, **593**
  holocrine, **555**
  intestinal, 614
  lacrimal, 555
  mammary, **555**
  mental hedonic, **461**
  mucous, **493**
  parotid, 615
  poison, **493**
  reproductive, **678,** 679
  salivary, 615
  scent, 555
  sebaceous, **554**
  sweat, **554,** 555, **592,** 595
Glenoid fossa, 497, **598**
Gliding, 860
Globigerina, 104-106, **115**
Globin, 640
Glochidium, **362**
Gloger's rule, 795, 796
Glomerular filtrate analysis, 913
Glomerulus, **644**
Glossina, 120
Glossopharyngeal nerve, **502,** 505, 656
Glottis, **512,** 527, 528, 557
Glowworm, **863**
Glucagon, 698
Glucocorticoid, **694,** 698
Glucose, 44, 618
Glutathione, 158, 913
Gluteus, **499,** 501
  maximus, **606**
Glycerol, 46
Glycogen, 43, 605, 618
Glycolysis, 67
Glycolytic cycle, **68**
Glypthelmins, 492
Gnathostoma, 420
Gnats, 340
Goatsucker, 543
Goethe, J. W. von, 892
Goiter, 692, 693
Golgi bodies, **52**
Golgi, C., 901, 905
Gomphus, 337
Gonad, **161, 165,** 167, 212, **380,** 381, **421,** 424, 676, 677
Gonadotropic release factor, 692
Gonadotropin, **691**
Gonangium, **164,** 165
Goniobasis, 355
Gonionemus, **153,** 163, 164, **165**
Gonium, 119
Gonophore, 165, **166,** 168
Gonopore, **164,** 165, **388,** 389
Gonyaulax, **108**
Gordiacea, 492
Gordius, 232
Gorgodera, 492
Gorgoderina, 492
Gorgonia, **153**
Gorgonocephalus, 383
Gorilla, 28, 582

Graaf, R. de, 890
Graafian follicle, **675**
Gracilis major muscle, **499,** 501
  minor muscle, **499**
Gradient, axial, 95
Graham, T., 898
Grantia, 145
Graptolite fossils, 921
Grasshopper, 327-334, **328,** 335
  circulatory system, 330
  development, 331
  digestive system, 329-330
  excretory system, 330
  external features, **328**-329
  habitat, 327
  internal features, 329, **330,** 331
  mouth parts, **328, 329**
  muscular system, 329
  nervous system, **330,** 331
  plagues, 327, 328
  reproductive system, **330, 331**
  respiratory system, **330**
  sense organs, 331
  sound, 318
Grasslands, 835
Gray matter, 504, **653**
Grebe, **534,** 539
Green frog, 488, **489**
  gland, **298,** 301
Gregarina, 107
Gregarinida, **123**-124
Griffin, D., 924
Griffith, F., 917
Ground beetle, **325, 334**
Grouse, 534, 540, **542**
Growth, 92, 717-718
  and development hormones, 695
  correlation, 93
  curve, individual, **718**
    population, **821**
  hydra, 162, **163**
  insect, 319
  stimulator (STH), 699
Gruiformes, 541
Gryllotalpe, **335**
Guanine, 453, 727
Guano, 529
Guanophore, 493
Gudernatsch, J. F., 911
Guinea worm, 231
Gull, 531, 541
Gymnodinium, 108
Gymnophiona, 459, 460, 468
Gymnotus, **864**
Gynandromorph, 740
Gynecophoric canal, 199
Gyri, 655
Gyrodactylus, 196

H

Habitats, 457-458, 825-833, 839
  fresh-water, 826-831
  marine, 833-834
  terrestrial, 831-833
Hadzi, J., 925
Haeckel, E., 898, 900, 903
Haematoloechus, **491,** 492
Haemogregarina, 492

Hagfish, 431, 432, **435**, **436**
Hair, 552, **553**, **554**, **591**, **592**
  cells, 666
  follicle, 552, 553, **592**
Haldane, J. B. S., 789, 919
Haldane, J. S., 908
Hales, Stephan, 622, 891
Haliaeetus, 540
Haliclystus, **166**
Halicore, 577
Haliotis, 354
Halipegus, 492
Hall, M., 894
Halobates, 314
Halteres, 317, 340
Hamingia, 244
Hanstrom, B., 920
Hardy, G. H., 909
Hardy, W. A., 906
Hardy-Weinberg formula, 791, 909
Hare, **548**, 574
Hare-Wallaby, **548**
Harpia, **541**
Hartline, H. K., 919
Harvey, W., 621, 703, 890
Haustra, **611**
Haversian system, **80**
Hawk, **524**, 529, 530, 531, 536
Hayes, W., 926
Head, mammal, 551
Headfish, **446**
Heart, 626, **627**, 628
  bird, **527**, 528
  branchial, **368**
  clam, **359**, **360**
  conducting system, 627
  development, 710
  evolution, 625
  frog, 495, **508**, 509
  grasshopper, **330**
  law of, 628, 912
  lymph, 512
  physiology, 626-628
  snail, 356
  Stannius' experiment, 896
  tissues, 83
  valves, **627**
Heartbeat cycle, 628
Hectocotylized arm, **366**
Hedgehog, 570
Heidelberg fossil man, 800, 908
Heinroth, O., 880, 909
Heitz, E., 919
Heliozoa, **114**
Helisoma, 355
Helix, 349, 355
Hellgrammite, **338**
Helmholtz, H., 896
Helminthology, 22
Heloderma, 485, 861
Helodermatidae, 485
Helriegel, H., 903
Hemal system, 379, 381, **388**
Hematin, 640
Hemerythrin, 624
Hemichordata, 29, 392-397
  biological principles, 392
  characteristics, 393, 394
  classes, 394

Hemichordata—cont'd
  origin and relations, 392, 393
  structure, **394**, **395**, **396**
Hemimetabola, 320
Hemipenes, **473**
Hemiptera, **334**, 337, **338**
Hemocoel, 298, 329, 330
Hemocyanin, 299, 624
Hemoglobin, 508, 631
Hemolysis, 58
Hepatic artery, 299
  cecum, **423**, 424
  portal system, **510**, 511, 528, 625
  vein, **509**, 511
Heptabrachia, 398
Herbivore, 817
Herbivorous, 562, 618
Heredity, 94, 721-755
  application to medicine, 754
  behavior, 873
  blood groups, 750-751
  complementary factor, 738
  crossing-over, 742-**743**
  cumulative factors, 738-739
  cytological background, **722**
  environment, 749-750
  first laws, 898
  hair and eye color, 750
  human, 748-755
  linkage, 742-743
  meaning, 721
  mental traits, 751-752
  nucleus role, 902
  pseudoalleles, 739
  rediscovery of Mendel's laws, 906
  special forms, 737-739
  supplementary factors, 737-738
  traits in man, 743
  vs. environment, 749-750
Hermaphroditic, 73
  duct, 356
Hermaphroditism, 677
Hermit crab, **308**
Heron, 539
Herpestes, 480
Herpetology, 22
Herring, 444
Hertwig, O., 900, 902, 905
Hertwig, R. 903
Hesperornis, **519**
Hess, W. R., 876, 924
Heterocercal tail, 437, **444**
Heterodera, 232
Heterodon, **476**
Heterodont teeth, 556
Heteromorphosis, 294
Heteroplastic grafting, 905
Heteroploidy, concept, 912
Heterosis, 744-745, 912
Heterostelea, 373
Heterothermal, 560
Heterotroph, 773
Heterozygous trait, 735
Hevesy, G., 914
Hexactinellida, 140
Hexamita, 492
Hexokinase, 49
Heymans, C., 916

Hibernation, bird, 534-535
  frog, 490, 514
  mammal, 564-565
Hickory horned devil, **319**
Hill, A. V., 915
Hindgut, 330
Hindwing, 329
Hinge joint, 497
Hippocampus, **444**, 859
Hippomorpha, 579
Hippopotamus, 579-**580**
Hirudinea, 253, 269, **270**, 271
Hirudo, 253, **269**, **270**, 271
His-Tawara bundle, **627**
Histochemistry, 893
Histogenesis, **78**
Histology, 22, 78, 896
Hjort, J., 910
Hoerr, N. L., 919
Hoerstadius, S., 922
Hofmeister, W., 896
Hogeboom, G. H., 924
Hog-nosed snake, **476**
Holdfast, 203
Holoblastic, 75
Holocephali, 437
Holometabola, 321
Holophytic nutrition, 102, 117
Holostei, 443
Holothuroid, **375**
Holothuroidea, 376, 387-390
Holozoic nutrition, 102, 117
Holtfreter, J., 919, 923
Homarus, 277, 293, **309**
Home range, mammal, 561
Homeostasis, 93, 897
Hominidae, 582, 797
Hominoidea, 582
Homo, 420, 582, **799**, 800, **802**
Homocercal tail, **444**
Homodont teeth, 556
Homologous appendages, **296**
Homology, 85, 298
  and analogy, 85, 895
Homoptera, **334**, **338**
Homozygous trait, 735
Honeybee, casts, 324, **325**
  communication, 865, **866**, **867**, 924
  legs, **333**
  stinger, **341**
Hoof, 594
Hoofed mammals, 577-**579**, 580
Hooke, R., 51, 890
Hookworm, **227**, 228
Hopkins, F. G., 908, 913
Hormones, 513, 687-700, 907, 922
  adrenal medula, 694
  adrenocortical, 694
  categories, 690
  diabetogenic, 49
  enzyme relation, 49-50
  female, 696-**697**, 698
  gastrointestinal, 695
  glands and hormones, table of, 698-699
  growth and development, 323, 691-692, 695
  historical, 688-689, 922
  insulin, 693-694

Hormones—cont'd
  interrelations, 689
  juvenile, 323
  male, 695, 696
  metabolism, 692
  molting, 323, 922
  parathyroid, 693
  pituitary, 690, **691**, 692
  thyroid, 692-693
Hornbill, 544
Horned toad, 475
Hornet nest, **324**
Horns, 594, **595**
Horse, 549, **550**, 577
  evolution, 768, **769**, 770
Horsefly larva, **829**
Horsehair worms, 232
Horseshoe crab, **282**, 283
House mouse, **548**
Housefly, **326**, **334**
Houssay, B. A. 915
Howard, H. E. 913
Howler monkey, 581
Huber, G. C., 908
Hughes, W. L., 928
Human heredity, 748-755
Humerus, **495**, 497, **598**, **600**
Hummingbird, 523, 533, **544**
Hunter, J., 891
Hunting spider, 286
Huot, A., 905
Huxley, J. S., 775, 789, 922
Hyaline cap, 110
Hyalonema, 140
Hyaloplasm, 41
Hyalospongiae, **142**, 146-147
Hyaluronic acid, 685, 686
Hyaluronidase enzyme, 685, 686, 923
Hybrid sterility, 911
  varieties, 746-747
  vigor, 744-745
Hydatid cyst, 209
  worm, 208-209
Hydatina, 219, 220
Hydra, 153-163
  behavior, 162-163
  budding, 159
  embryology, 161, **162**
  excretion, 158
  feeding reaction, 158-**159**
  growth pattern, 162, **163**
  histology, **154**
  life cycle, **162**
  locomotion, 158-159, **160**
  metabolism, 158
  nematocyst, **154**, **156**, 157
  nerve net, 157, **158**
  nervous system, 155, 157-**158**
  nutrition, 158, **159**
  regeneration, 161-162, **163**
  reproduction, 159-160, **161**
  sexual differentiation, 927
  structure, 153-157, 891
Hydractinia, **166**, 167
Hydranth, 164
Hydrocaulus, 164
Hydrocortisone, 694
Hydrogen, 67
  ion concentration, 40
Hydrolysis, 615

Hydrorhiza, **164**
Hydrotheca, **164**, 165
Hydrozoa, 152, 153-169
Hyena, **572**
Hyla, **467**, 469, **489**, 858
Hylidae, 469
Hylobates, 582
Hyman, L. H., 185, 218
Hymenolepis, 206, 208
Hymenoptera, 318, 341, 342
Hyoid arch, **599**
Hyomandibular arch, **599**
  bone, **665**
Hyperbranchial groove, 424
Hypermetamorphosis, 339
Hyperoartii, 432
Hypertonic, 58
Hypoglossal nerve, 656
Hypoglossus muscle, 500
Hypopharynx, 328
Hypophysis, 503
Hypostome, 153, **154**, **164**
Hypothalamus, 655, 690, **691**, 692, 876
Hypotonic, 58
Hyracoidea, 577
Hyracotherium, 579, **769**
Hyrax, 577

I

Ibis, 539
Ichneumon wasp, **325**, **342**
Ichthyology, 22
Ichthyomyzon, 432
Ichthyophis, 460, 469
Ichthyornis, 519
Ichthyosaur, **414**, 415
Ichthyostega, **412**, 413, 459, 918
Ictalurus, 444
Iguanidae, **474**, 485
Ileum, 507, 614
Iliac artery, **509**, 511
Iliacus, 501
Ilium, **495**, 497, **598**, **600**, 601
Immigration, 564
Immovable-fang snake, 485
Imprinting, 879-880, 909
Improvement of human race, 755-756
Incisor teeth, 612
Incus, 559, **664**, **665**
Indeterminate cleavage, **712**
Individuality, 72
Inductor, 713-714
Infraspinatus, **606**
Infundibulum, **503**, 530
Infusoria (*see* Ciliata)
Ingestion, 610
Ingram, V. M., 927
Inheritance, 721-745, 746-759
  cytoplasmic, 745, 923
  nuclear control, 898
  of traits in man, 753
Inner cell mass, **706**
Innominate vein, **510**, 511
Insect, 314-342
  adaptability, 315, 316
  behavior, 318, 319
  beneficial, 324-**325**, 326
  body form, 332

Insect—cont'd
  characteristics, 315
  coloration, 318
  disease vectors, 327
  distribution, 314-315
  flight, 317-318
  food habits, 316
  harmful, **326**, 327
  light production, 334-335, 863, 902
  metamorphosis, 319-323
  mouth parts, **329**, 332
  neuromuscular, 318
  number of species, 314
  orders, 335-342
  origin and relations, 315
  parasitic, 316-317
  protection, 318
  relations to man, 324
  reproduction, 319, **331**
  size, 315
  social, 323-324
  sound production, 318
  wings, **316**
Insecta, 278, 314-342
Insectivora, 570
Insectivorous animals, 563
Insight learning, 879
Inspiration, 512, 528, 639
Instar, 320
Instinct, 874-875
  appetitive behavior, 874
  final consummatory act, 874-875
  innate releasing mechanism, 874
  social, 323-324
Instinctive behavior, 875, 918
Insulin, 44, 45, 50, 689, 693, 698, 914, 927
Integument, 82, 587-595
  cornified, **591**
  earthworm, **261**
  frog, 493-494
  invertebrate, 587, **588**, **589**, 592
  keratin, 590, 593
  mammal, 552, **554**, 592
  mucous gland, **590**
  vertebrate, 590-595
Interatrial septum, 509
Intercellular bridges, 79
Intermedin, 691, 699
Internal oblique muscle, eye, 506
Interphase, **62**, 63, **64**, 113, **683**
Interradii, 378
Interstitial cell, 155, 156
  stimulating hormone (ICSH), 699
  tissue, 678, 695, 696, 699
Interventricular foramen, 496, 504
Intestinal juice, 508, 616
  mucosa, 612, 698
Intestine, *Ascaris*, **225**, **226**
  bird, **527**
  clam, **359**, 360-361
  crayfish, **298**, 299
  earthworm, 255, **256**

Intestine—cont'd
  frog, 495, **507**
  law, 906
  man, **613**, 614
Intracellular digestion, **111**, 158,
  Rhynchocoela, **214**
  189
Intra-vitam staining, 24
Introvert, 244, **245**
Inversion, 744
Invertebrates, Age of, 32
  hormonal factors, 914
Iodopsin, 669
Iridocyte, 592
Iris, 506, **667**, 668
Ischium, **495**, 497, **598, 600,
  601**
Island faunas, 847
Islets of Langerhans, 530, **688**,
  693, 698
Isociella, 492
Isogamete, 675
Isolation factor in evolution,
  783-784
Isopoda, 306
Isoptera, **334**, 336
Isospondyli, 443
Isotonic, 58
Isotopes, 37, 914
Isotopic tracer method, 24, 914
Ivanov, A. V., 928
Ivanovski, D., 903

J

Jaeger, E. C., 534
Jamoytius, **406**-407, 924
Janssens, F. A., 909
Java man, **798-799**
Jaw, **266, 279, 368**, 496
  origin, **599**
Jejunum, **558**, 614
Jellyfish (*see* Coelenterata; Me-
  dusa)
Jennings, H. S., 870, 873, 907
Johannsen, W., 909
Johnson, M. W., 924
Joint, 497, **498**
Jordan's rule, 796, 855
Jugular veins, **510**, 511, 528
Julus, 278, 312
June beetle, **326**
Jurassic period, 31, 765
Juvenile, 193, 516

K

Kallima, **317**
Kangaroo, 549, **550**, 569
Kaola, 569
Kappa particles, 134
Katydid, classification, 28
Keith, A., 908
Kekule, F., 898
Kellia, 364
Kendall, E. C., 911, 920
Keratin, 521, 593, 595
Kerona, 106, 163
Kidney and osmoregulation,
  451-453
  clam, 362

Kidney—cont'd
  evolution, 428, **429**, 451, 452,
    453
  frog, 495, **513**
  histology, 643, **644**
  mammal, **559**
  man, **643**
  squid, 368
  structure, **643-644**
Killer strain, 134
  whale, 576
Kilocalorie, 619
Kinetochore, 62
King, J. T., 925
King snakes, 480
Kingfisher, 533, 544-545
Kinorhyncha, 219, 222
Kinosternidae, 484
Kirchhoff, G., 892
Kite, G. L., 911
Kiwi, **537**, 538
Knight, T., 893
Koelreuter, J. G., 891
Koller, G., 917
Kölliker, A. von, 896
Kopec, S., 914
Kossel, A., 901
Kowalevsky, A., 898, 899
Kozlowski, R., 921
Kramer, G., 926
Krause's corpuscle, **661**, 662
Krebs citric acid cycle, 67, **68**,
  69
Krebs, H. A., 921
Kropotkin, P., 907
Kuhne, W., 901
Kuryus, 859
Kymograph, 23

L

Labia majora, **678**, 680
  minora, **678**, 680
Labial palp, **328**, 329
Labium, 328, **329**
Labyrinth, bony, 665
  membranous, 665
Labyrinthodont, **411**, **412**, 413,
  460
Lacerta, 485
Lacertidae, 485
Lacertilia, 474, 484
Lacewings, 338
Lachesis, 478, 479
Lachnosterna, 238
Lack, D., 793, 875
Lactase, 616
Lacteals, 622, **634**, 890
Lacunar system, 299, **589**
Ladybird beetle, **325**
Lagomorpha, 574, 575
Lake Baikal, 844, 904
Lakes, 830-831
Lama, **579**
Lamarck, J. B., 19, 51, 780-781,
  820, 870, 892
Lamarckianism, 780-781
Lamellae, **361**
Lamellibranchiata, 357-364
  (*see also* Clam;
  Pelecypoda)
Lamp shells, 247-248

Lampetra, 432, **433**
Lamprey, 431-436
  characteristics, 434
  gill arrangement, **435**
  natural history, 432-434
  parasitic relations, 434
  spawning, 433
  species, 432
Lampropeltis, 480
Lampsilis, 357, 364
Lampyris, 863
Landsteiner, K., 906, 922
Larva, echinoderm classes, 376,
  377, 378
  dipleurula, 374, 375
  pilidium, 212
  plerocercoid, 208
  trochophore, **240**
Larvacea, 421
Laryngeal vein, 510
Larynx, **512**, 528, **638**
Latent period, 604
Lateral canal, **381**
  line, 506
Latimeria, 411, 444, 447
Latissimus dorsi muscle, **499**,
  500, **606**
Latrodectus, **288**
Lavoisier, A., 891
Lawrence, E. O., 918
Laws of probability, 734
Leadership behavior, 883-884
Leaf hopper, 338
Leakey, L. S. B., 801, 928
Learning, 263, 877-880
  associative, 878
  insight, 879
  selective, 878
Leatherback turtle, 484
Leech, 269-270, **271**
Leeuwenhoek, A. van, 101, 622,
  890-891
Legs, insect, **333**
Lehman, D. S., 870
Leishmania, 120
Lemming, 564
Lemmus, 564
Lemnisci, 237
Lemur, 579-580, 860
Lemuroidea, 581
Lens, 506, **667**, 668, 669
Leodice, 269
Leopard frog, 488, **489**
Leopold, Aldo, 838
Lepas, **307**
Lepidoptera, 340, **341**
Lepidosiren, 444, **448**, 449
Lepidosteus, 442, 443, 449
Lepisma, 335
Lepospondyli, **412**, 413
Leptinotarsa, 340
Leptocephalia, 855
Leptodactylus, 858
Leptolepis, **446**
Leptor, 364
Leptorhynchoides, 236
Leptotyphlopidae, 485
Leptotyphlops, 485
Lethal genes, 739, 747
Leuckart, R., 901
Leucochloridium, **202**

Leuconoid sponge, **141**
Leucosolenia, 140, **142**
Leukocyte, 508, 624, **630**, 632
Levan, A., 928
Levator muscle, 502
Lewis, E. B., 925
Leydig cells, 696
Libby, W. F., 924
Libnia, 308
Liebig, J., 894
Life, criteria of, 19
  cycle, 93-94
    Ascaris, 227
    blood fluke, **200**
    Craspedacusta, **169**
    filarial worm, 230
    frog, 514, **515**, **516**, 517
    hookworm, 228
    hydra, **162**
    liver fluke, **198**, 199
    Metridium, **174**
    Obelia, **164**
    pinworm, 230
    planaria, **193**
    Protozoa, 109, 121-124
    tapeworm, **205**, 206
  distribution, 20
  origin, 772-774, 919
  possible primordia, 926-927
  rhythmic patterns, 92
  terrestrial, adjustment to, 457-458
  zones, 846, 903-904
Ligament sac, **237**
Light production, 334-335, 862-864, 902
Lillie, F. R., 911, 912
Lima, 364
Limax, 355
Limb, 551, 552, **709**
  adaptive radiation, **550**
  bud, **709**
Limnology, 828
Limnoscelis, 469
Limulus, 277
Lineus, 212, 215
Linguatula, 277, 291
Linkage, 726, 735, 742-743, 908
Linnaeus, C., 25, 891
Lion, 573
Liopelma, 468
Lipase, 507, 616
Lipids, 45-46
Lipophore, 493
Liriope, **166**, 167
Lithobius, 278
Littoral, 834
Littorina, 349, 354
Liver, frog, 495
  functions, 616-617
  glycogen relation, 897
  man, **613**
  pig, **558**
Liver flukes, 195-199, 901
Lizard, **474**-480
  body temperature, 475
  classification, 484-485
  structure, **472**-475
Llama, **579**

Locomotion, 859-861
  adaptive radiation, 549, **550**
  ameba, **112**, 113
  arthropod, 276
  clamworm, 267
  earthworm, 254-255
  Euglena, 118
  hydra, 158-159
  Paramecium, **127**
  planaria, 193-194
  Pleurobrachia, 182
  sea star, 382
Loeb, J., 870, 873, 906
Loewi, O., 913
Lohmann, K., 918
Loligio, 347, 349, **367**, 368, 369
Longissmus dorsi muscle, 500
Long-neck clam, **352**
Loomis, W. F., 927
Loon, **539**
Lophius, 449
Lophophore, 246, **247**, 393, **396**, 397
Lorenz, K., 870, 874, 876, 880, 918
Loricata (*see* Crocodilia)
Loubatieres, R., 926
Louse, **334**, 337
Loxodonta, 577
Loxogenes, 492
Loxosoma, 242
Lucanus, 340
Luciferase, 862
Luciferin, 862
Ludwig, C., 895
Ludwig, K., 899
Lugworm, **268**
Lumbar arteries, 571
  plexus, **652**
Lumbricus, 253-264 (*see also* Earthworm)
Luminous insects, 334-335
Lung, bird, **527**, 528
  book, 284, 285
  comparative, **637**
  evolution, 449, **450**
  frog, **512**
  gaseous exchange, 639-640
  lizard, **637**
  mammal, 559, 638
  reptile, 473
  snail, 356
Lung fluke, **201**
Lungfish, 444, 447, **448**, 449
Lunule, **386**, 387
Luteinizing hormone, **696**, **697**, 699
Lycosa, 286
Lyell, C., 778, 893
Lymnaea, 202, 355
Lymph, 81, 634-635
  heart, 512
  sinuses, 511-512
Lymphatic system, 511-512, **622**, **634**, 635, 809, 890
  vessels, **634**
Lymphocyte, **630**
Lymphoid cell, **624**
Lynceus, 305
Lynx, 573

M

Macacus, 582
Macallum, A. B., 907
Mackerel, 446
Mackie, G. O., 157
Macleod, J. J. R., 689
MacMunn, C. A., 902
Macracanthorhynchus, **236**, 237, 238
Macrobdella, 253
Macrobiotus, 277
Macrocheira, 275
Macrodasys, 219
Macroevolution, 785
Macrogamete, 119
Macrogametocyte, 122
Macronucleus, 126
Macrophage, **624**
Madreporite, **378**, **380**, 381, 383, 385, **386**
Magendie, F., 892
Maggots, 321
Magicicada, 338
Malaclemys, 482
Malacostraca, 304, 306-308, **310**
Malania, 444
Malapterurus, 864
Malaria, 122
Male sex hormones, 695, 696
Malleus, 559, **664**, **665**
Mallophaga, **334**, 337
Malpighi, M., 621-622, 890
Malpighian tubule, **330**, 643
Maltase, 508, 615, 616
Maltose, 615
Mammal, 547-582
  adaptive radiation, 549, **550**
  advancements, 551
  behavior, 560-567
  brain, **654**
  caravan formation, **566**
  characteristics, 551
  coloration, 553, 554
  comparison with reptiles, 549
  convergent evolution, **548**
  disease vector, 568
  distribution, 561
  economic importance, 567, 568
  enemies, 565
  evolution, **417**, 418
  external features, 551-557
  food, 562
  gestation, 567
  gland, **554**, **555**, 556
  hair, 552, **553**
  hibernation, 564-565
  migration and emigration, 563-564
  number of species, 547
  orders, 568-582
  organ systems, 552-553, 557-560
    circulatory, **558**, 559, 627-630
    digestive, 557-**558**, 612-614
    endocrine, 559, 687-700
    excretory, **559**, 643-646

Mammal—cont'd
    integument, 552-556,
      592-595
    muscular, 560, 602-604
    nervous, 559, 649-658
    reproductive, **559**, 560,
      674-687
    respiratory, 559, 637-
      642
    sensory, 559, 661-669
    skeleton, 560, **596-602**
  origin and relations, 547, 549
  pelage, 553
  population, 561, 562
  range, 561
  shelters, 562
  size ranges, 551
  teeth, **556**
  temperature, 560
  territory patterns, 561
Mammalia, 547-582
  origin, **416**, **417**, 418
Mammals, Age of, 31
Mammary gland, **555**, 556
Mammoth, 766
Man, circulatory system, **627**,
    631, 632-634
  classification, 28, 579-582
  digestive system, **611**, **613**
  endocrine system, **687**, 690-
    700
  evolution, 796-803
  excretory system, 642-646
  heredity, 748-755
  integument, **592**
  muscular system, **606**
  nervous sytem, **652**, **655**
  reproductive system, 677,
    678, 679
  respiratory system, **638**-641
  sensory system, **664**, **667**
  skeletal system, **599**, **600**,
    601
Manatee, **577**
Mandible, **296**, **328**, **329**, **598**
Mandibular arch, **599**
Mandibulata, 277, 293-342
Mandrill, 554
Manson, P., 900
Mantle, 345, 355, **358**, **368**
Manubrium, **165**, 166, 171
Margaritifera, **358**
Marine habitats, 833-834
  realm, 847-848
Marsupial mole, **548**
Marsupialia, **569**, 570
Marsupium, 362, 570
Marten, 573
Masseter, 500
Mastax, 220
Mastigophora, 103, 116-120
Mating, birds, 534
  types, *Paramecium,* 129-130
Matrix, 79
Matter, 35
Maturation, hydra, 160
  sex cells, 681-684
Maupas, E., 903
Maupertuis, P. M., 891
Maxilla, **296**, **329**, **495**, **496**,
    598

Maxilliped, 295, **296**
Mayer, J. R., 896
Mayfly, **334**, 336, 337
McClean, D., 923
McClintock, B., 918
McClung, C. E., 907
McCollum, E. V., 912
"Measly" pork, **207**
Mecoptera, 339
Medulla oblongata, **502**, **503**,
    654
Medusa, **152**, **165**, 168-169,
    171
Megaceryle, 544
Megalodiscus, 492
Meganthropus, 800
Megascolides, 265
Megellania, 248
Meiosis, 60, 681-685
Meissner's corpuscle, **661**, 662
Melanin, dopa reaction, 912
Melanism, 554
Melanophore, 493, 554
Meleagrina, 348
Meleagris, 541
Membrane, basement, 79
  fertilization, 685
  impermeable, 57
  moist, 81
  mucous, 81
  permeable, 57
  semipermeable, 57
    concept, 899
  serous, 81
  undulating, 126
  vitelline, 74
  zona pellucida, 74
Mendel, G., 730-732, 898
  investigations, **730**-731
  law of independent assort-
    ment, 732
    of segregation, 731
  modifications of laws, 735
  postulates, **730**, 731, 732
Mendelian ratios, explanation,
    732-734
Mendelism, cytological basis,
    735
  parallelism with chromosome,
    907
Meninges, 503, 652
Menopon, 337
Menstrual cycle, **697**, 698-700
Menstruation, 698
Mental gland, **461**
Mentomeckelian, **496**
Menton, M., 911
Mering, J. von, 903
Mermaid's purse, **438**, 439
Meroblastic, 75
Merostomata, 277, 282
Merozoite, 121, 124-125
Merriam, C. H., 903
Merychippus, **769**
Mesencephalon, 652
Mesenchyme, 79, 140, **146**, 170,
    172
Mesenteric artery, **509**, 510,
    511
Mesentery, 614
Mesichthyes, **444**

Mesoderm, 76, **77**, 98, 185, 706
  derivatives, 77
  types, **77**
Mesogaster, 507
Mesoglea, 151, 156
Mesorectum, 508
Mesosternum, 497
Mesothorax, **328**, 329
Mesovarium, 514
Mesozoa, 28, 240-241
Mesozoic era, 31, 765
Metabolism, 609-612, 614-620
  Ascaris, 226
  basal, 618
  carbohydrate, 67
  cellular, 55, 66-69, **68**
  crayfish, 299
  Euglena, 117-118
  hormone control, **692**, **693**,
    694
  hydra, 158
  Paramecium, 126-127
  Pleurobrachia, 182
  Protozoa, 112-113
  ribbon worms, 215
  sequence of stages, 610
  sponge, 143, 144
Metacarpals, **495**, 497
Metacercaria, **196**, **198**, **199**
Metagenesis, 673
Metamere, 85, 251, 254
Metamerism, 72, 85, **86**
  Annelida, 251-252
  arthropod, 274
  significance of, 251, 252
Metamorphosis, complete, 321,
    322
  frog, **516**, 517
  gradual, 320-321
  incomplete, 320
  insect, 319
  physiology, 322, 323
  role of corpus allatum, 920
  of thyroid gland, 911
Metanauplius, 308
Metaphase, **62**, 63, **65**, **66**, **683**,
    902
Metapleural fold, **423**
Metatarsals, **495**, 497, **598**, **600**
Metatheria, 547, 569
Metathorax, **328**, 329
Metazoa, 71, 102
  theory of origin, 925
Metchnikoff, E., 901
Metencephalon, 652
Metestrum, 566
Methods, experimental, 23
Metridium, 152, **153**, 172, **173**,
    174
Meyenia, 140
Meyerhof, O., 913
Miacid, 573
Miastor, 319, 677, 681
Michael Sars deep-sea explora-
    tion, 910
Michaelis, L., 911
Michelinoceras, 365
Microcyema, **241**
Microevolution, 785
Microfilariae, 230
Microgadus, **451**

Microgamete, 119
Microgametocyte, 122
Microhydra, 168
Micro-incineration, 24, 54
Micromanipulation, 24, 54
Micronucleus isolation (ciliates), 914
Microorganism, infective, 894
Micropyle, 331
Microscope, 23, 54
Microsomes, 69
Microsorex, 570
Microstomum, 186
Microtome, 24
Micrurgical methods, 911
Micrurus, **477**
Mictic egg, 221
Midbrain, 503
Midges, 340
Midgut, 330
Miescher, F., 899, 905
Migration and sporadic dispersal, 848
    birds, 851-854
    butterflies, 856
    eels, 855
    mammals, 563-564
    salmon, 855-856
Milk, bird, **527**
    lines, 555
Miller, H., 895
Miller, S., 926
Millipede, 278, 312
Mimicry, 788
Mineral metabolism, 618, 619
    salts, 43
Mineralocorticoid, **694**, 698
Mink, 573
Minkowski, O., 903
Minor phyla, 239-250
    contributions, 239-240
Miocene epoch, 765
Miohippus, **769**
Miracidia, 202
Miracidium, 199
Miranda, **284-286**
Mississippian period, 32, 765
Mitella, **307**
Mites, 290
Mitochondria, **52**, 67, 924, 926
Mitosis, 60-**65**, **66**
    ameba, **113**
    comparison with meiosis, 683
    duration, 66
    function, 60
    named, 901
    purpose, 61
    significance, 65-66
    stages in whitefish, **66**
    theory of mechanism, 64
"Mittelschmerz," 697
Mixtures, 38
Miyairi, K., 911
Mnemiopsis, 183
Models, reconstruction, 24
Modern synthesis of evolution, 789-794
Moeritherium, 767
Mohl, H. von, 895
Molar teeth, 612
Molds, slime, 41, 102

Mole, 548, **550**, **552**, 570
    cricket, **335**
Molecules, 35, 56
Molgula, 420, 421-423
Mollusca, 29, 345-370
    Amphineura, **349**, **350**, 351
    biological principles, 345
    blood cells, **624**
    Cephalopoda, 349, 364-370
    characteristics, 347, 348
    circulation, **623**
    classes, 348, 349
    distribution, 346
    economic importance, 348
    evolution, 346-347
    gastropoda, 349, 352-**357**
    hypothetical ancestor, **346**
    life cycle, 347
    origin and relations, 345-347
    Poelecypoda, 349, 357-364
    Scaphopoda, 349, **351**-352
    segmentation, 348
Mollusk, 345-370 (*see also* Mollusca)
    discovery of primitive, 925-926
Molting, 320, 322-323, 522, 532
Monestrus, 567
Mongoose, 480
Moniezia, **203**, 206, 209
Monionina, **104**
Monkey, 579-580
Monocystis, 103, 123
Monocyte, **630**
Monodon, 576
Monoecious, 73, 146, 160, 677
Monogenea, 195
Monohybrid, 734
Monophydont teeth, 556
Monophyletic origin, 519
Monoplacophora, 349
Monosaccharides, 43
Monotremata, **568**, 569
Montgomery, T. H., 907
Moonfish, **446**
Morgan, C. L., 870, 904
Morgan, T. H., 722, 735, 785, 910
Morgan's canon, 870, 904
Morphogenesis, 92
Morphology, 21, 22, 92
Mortality rate, 822
Mosaic cleavage, **712**
Mosquito, **326**, **341**
Moths, 34, **319**-320, **326**
    clothes, 327
    life history, **322**
Motivation, 875-876
Motor end plate, 603, **604**
    neuron, 81
    root, 504
    unit, 603, **604**
Mountain beaver, 574
Mousebird, 544
Mouth, frog, 507
Movement, ameboid, 60, **112**, 607
    breathing, 638
    Brownian, 40
    ciliary, 60, 607

Movement—cont'd
    euglenoid, **118**
    flagellate, 608
    hydra, 158-**160**
    muscular, 60, 602-608
    protoplasmic, 607
    sponge, 144
Mucosa, 507, 612
Mucous membrane, 81
Mulder, J., 894-895
Mule deer, **580**
Muller, H. J., 789, 916
Müller, J., 895
Müllerian duct, 514
Muller's larva, 187
Multiple alleles, 737
    fission, 673
    genes, discovery, 891
Murex, 348, 355
Murgantia, **338**
Muridae, **574**
Murray, J., 910
Muscle(s), action, 499-502
    belly, 499, **606**
    cardiac, **498**, 499
    chemistry, 604-606
    development, **709**
    electricity, 607
    eye, 506
    fiber, 80
    frog, **499**
    gross structure, 499, 502, **606**
    independent irritability, 896
    involuntary, 80, 607
    myofibrils, 80
    origin and insertion, **499**, 500-501
    segmented, 560, **603**
    skeletal, **498**
    smooth, 53, 80, **82**, 498, 499
    striated, 53, 80, **82**, 329
    tonus, 604
Muscular contraction, 603-607, 908, 913, 923
    system, 83, 498-502, 602-607
        birds, 526
        chordate, 602-608
        comparative, **602**
        crayfish, **298**
        frog, 498-502, **499**
        human, **606**
        invertebrate, **602**, 603
        mammal, 560
        physiology, 603-606
        vertebrate, **603**, **606**, 607
    tissue, 78, 80, **82**, **83**, 602-603
Muscularis, 507, **612**
Musculocutaneous vein, **510**, 511
Musk turtle, 484
Muskrat, **574**
Mussel (*see* Clam)
Mustelidae, 573
Mutation, 94, 726-727, 907, 916, 921, 922-923, 927
    causes, 786-787
    gene, 743, 744
    nature, 785

Mutation—cont'd
point, 727
pressure, 726
rate, 776
recessive nature, 790
types, 786
Mutual cooperation, 882
Mutualism, 106
Mya, 352, 364
Mycetozoa, 102
Myelencephalon, 652
Myenia, 148
Mylohyoid, 499, 500
Myocardium, 626
Myocyte, 144
Myoneme, 155
Myotis, 571
Myotome, 423, 424
Myrmecophaga, 575
Myrmeleon, 339
Mysidacea, 309
Mysis, 309, 310
Mysticeti, 576
Mytilus, 307, 364
Myxedema, 692
Myxine, 432, 436
Myxinoidea, 432, 436
Myxomycetes, 41
Myzostomata, 271
Myzostomum, 271

N

Nacre, 359
Naiad, 320
Naja, 485
Naples Biological Station, 899
Nares, 492, 494, 512, 528, 638
Narwhol, 576
Nasal bone, 495, 496
cavities, 512
Nasalis, 582
Nasohypophyseal canal, 430
Nasolabial groove, 461
Natality, 822
Natural selection, 776, 781-784, 792-793
appraisal, 783-784
concept, 897
limitations of pure lines, 909
nature, 792-793
theory, 781-784
Nauplius larva, 305, 306, 308, 310, 830
Nautiloidea, 366
Nautilus, 365, 366
Neanderthal fossil man, 799, 800, 897
Neanthes, 253, 266-268
Necator, 219, 228
Nectonema, 232
Nectophore, 168
Nectophrynoides, 468
Necturus, 460, 637, 769
Needham, J., 920
Needham, J. T., 671
Negativity, wave of, 659
Nekton, 828
Nemathelminthes, 217

Nematocyst, 154, 155, 156-157
Nematoda, 219, 223-232, 492
Nematogen, 240, 241
Nematomorpha, 219, 232-233
Nemertina, 211-215 (*see also* Rhynchocoela)
Neoarctic realm, 847
Neoascaris, 224
Neoblast, 194
Neoechinorhynchus, 236
Neognathous, 525
Neomenia, 351
Neopilina, 348, 349
Neornithes, 519
Neoteny, 405, 673
salamander, 462, 463
Neotropical realm, 847
Nephridia, 251, 259, 424, 513, 644
Nephridiopore, 254, 258, 259
Nephridium, 256, 258, 356
Nephron, 452, 513, 643, 644, 895, 908
evolution, 645
Nephrostome, 258, 259, 513
Nereis, 266 (*see also* Neanthes)
Neritic, 834
Nerve, 80, 502, 504, 664, 895, 915
cell, 81, 653
cord, 256, 271, 298, 301, 419, 423, 424
cross-section, 260, 651
fiber, 80, 81
impulse, 658-659, 896, 911
net, 73, 157-158, 165, 649, 871-872, 916
tracts, 652
trunk, cross-section, 656
Nervous components, 651
organization levels, 871-872
system, 83, 502-506, 648-659
ammocoete, 427, 429-430
autonomic, 502, 505, 652, 653, 657-658
bird, 527, 529
clam, 359, 362
coelenterate, 157-158, 165, 649
comparative, 649
crayfish, 301-302
development, 652, 709
earthworm, 256, 259-261
flatworms, 190, 191-192, 197, 204, 206, 649
frog, 502-506
functional components, 651
grasshopper, 330-331
invertebrate, 648
linear type, 648
mammal, 559
man, 651, 652, 653
nerve impulse, nature, 658-659
neuron, structural unit, 81, 650
parasympathetic, 628, 657
peripheral, 502, 504-505, 656-658
reflex arc, 650, 651, 652

Nervous system—cont'd
reptile, 473-474
Rhynchocoela, 214
sea star, 380, 381
sea urchin, 386
snail, 356
spider, 285
spinal cord, 652-653
sympathetic, 628, 657
tongueworm, 395, 396
vertebrate, 649, 659
tissue, 78, 80, 81, 82, 83, 901
Nervus terminalis, 505, 656
Nestor, 533
Nests, bird, 533, 534
hornet, 324
Neural arch, 496
crest and pigment formation, 920
plate, 708, 709
spine, 496
tube development, 709
Neuroblast, 80
Neurochord, 259
Neurohumor, 651, 652
Neurohypophysis, 690, 691, 699
Neuromotor apparatus, 126, 127, 133, 648, 912
Neuromuscular coordination, insect, 318
system, 158
Neuron, 80, 81, 259, 502, 650, 653
Neuropodium, 266, 267
Neuroptera, 338, 339
Neurotendinous spindle, 661
Neutrons, 36
Neutrophil, 630
New World lizard, 474, 485
Newport, G., 896
Newts, 460-463
Niacin, 620
Nictitating membrane, 494, 507, 529
Night vision, 669
Nighthawk, 543
Nipple, 555, 556
Nitrogen cycle, 837, 838, 903
Noctiluca, 119, 863
Nodosaria, 104
Nomeus, 168
Nondisjunction, 740, 912
Norepinephrine, 694, 698
Northrop, J. H., 918
Notiosorex, 570
Notochord, 394, 402, 419, 422, 423, 424, 427, 435, 597, 706
Notostraca, 305, 306
Nuclear differentiation, 714
genotype, 925
membrane, 51, 52
Nuclei, constancy, 221
potential constancy, 903
Nucleic acid, 45
Nucleolar satellite, 925
Nucleolus, 52, 65, 729
Nucleoplasm, 52, 901
ratio, 60

Nucleoproteins, 45, 899, 901, 915
Nucleotides, 45, 727, **728**, 729
Nucleus, 41, 51, 55, 72, **110, 116**, 117, **126**, 722, 896
Nucula, 363, 364
Nuda, 180
Nudibranch, 347, **352**
Nudibranchia, 355
Nuptial pad, frog, 492
Nutallina, 351
Nutcracker fossil man, 801
Nutrition, 618-621 (*see also* Food)
  balanced diet, 619
  energy requirements, 618
  Protozoa, 102
  vitamins, 619-621
Nutritive-muscular cells, **154**
Nuttall, G. H. F., 908
Nyctotherus, 132, 492
Nymph, 320, **321**, 331

O

Obelia, 152, **153**, 163, 164, 165, 167, 587
  life cycle, **164**
  medusa, **165**
  skeleton, 596
Occam's razor, 21, 889-890
Occipital bone, **598, 600**
  condyle, 496
Occipitovertebral artery, **509**, 510
Ocean currents, 833-834
Ocellus, 192, 213, **330**, 378
Ochotona, 575
Octopoda, 367
Octopus, 349, 365, **366, 369**, 370
Oculina, **175**
Oculomotor, 656
  nerve, **502**, 505
Odonata, 320, **334**, 337
Odontoceti, 576
Oecophylla, 880
Oikopleura, 421
Old Red Sandstone, 447, 895
Old World lizard, 485
Olduvai Gorge fossil deposits, 911
Olfactory epithelium, 506
  lobe, **503, 657**
  nerve, **502**, 505, 656
  organs, 369
Oligobrachia, 398
Oligocene epoch, 765
Oligochaeta, 253-265
Oliver, G., 904
Omasum, **557**, 614
Ommatidia, 302, **303**, 667
Ommatidia, 302, **303**, 667
Omnivore, 817
Omnivorous, 563, 618
Omosternum, 497
Onchosphere, **205**, 206, 208
Oncorhynchus, 444
Onychophora, 252, 277, **279-281**
Oöcyst, 122, 124-125

Oöcyte, **682**, 684
Oögenesis, **682**, 684
Oögonia, 681, **682**
Oökinete, 122
Oötheca, **321**
Oötid, 684
Opalina, **131**, 132, 490, 492
Oparin, A. I., 919
Opercularia, 492
Operculum, 156
Ophidia, 474, 475-480, 485
Ophioderma, 383
Ophioplocus, 383
Ophiopluteus, **377**, 383
Ophiotaenea, 492
Ophiothrix, 383
Ophisaurus, 485
Ophiura, 376
Ophiuroid, **375**
Ophiuroidea, 376, 382, **383, 384**
Ophthalmic artery, 299, 510
Opisthobranchia, 355
Opisthoglypha, 479
Opisthonephric kidney, 425, **429**, 439
Opisthonephros, 428, **429**, 451, **513**
Opisthorchis, 186, **197, 198, 199**
Opossum, **569**, 570
Opsarus, 452
Optic chiasma, **503, 654**
  lobe, **502**, 503, **527**, 529, **654**, 655
  nerve, **502**, 505, 654, 656, **667**, 669
Oral groove, 125, **126**
  hood, **423**, 424, 427
  papillae, 427
Orangutan, 582
Orbital fossa, **496**
Orcinus, 576
Orconectes, 293
Order, 25
Ordovician period, 32, 764
Organ, definition, 81
  of Corti, **666**
Organelle, 111
Organic compounds, 42, 43-46
  symmetry, concept, 903
Organism, basic requirements, 93
  biological system, 96-97
  characteristic form, 92
  cooperation, 96
  energy relations, 93
  sensitivity to environment, 95
Organization grades, 72
Organizer theory, **713**, 714
Organology, 82
Oriental realm, 847
Origin of life, 772-774
Oriole, nest, 533, **534**
Ornithology, 22
Ornithorhynchus, **568**, 569
Orohippus, 769
Orthasterias, 383
Orthoceras, 365
Orthogenesis, 784
Orthoptera, **321, 334, 335, 336**

Os priapi, 560
Osborn, H. F., 906
Oscillograph, 24
Osculum, 140, **141**, 145
Osmoregulation, 451-453
Osmosis, 56-59, 112, 900
Osmotic pressure, 57, 59
  value, 57
Osprey, **541**
Ossicles, 378, **380, 664, 665**
Ostariophysi, 444
Osteichthyes, 441-445
  evolution, **410, 411**
Osteolepis, 410, 447
Ostium (ostia), 140, **141**, 145, 361, **513, 514**
Ostracoda, 305, **306**
Ostracoderm, 406, **407-408, 409**, 916
Ostrea, 363, 364
Ostrich, 534, **537**
Oswaldocruzia, 492
Otocelis, 186
Otolith, 667
Otter, 573
Ova, **674**
Ovarian (genital) vein, **510**, 511
Ovaries, fish, 454
Ovariole, **331**
Ovary, 676, 699
  Ascaris, **226**
  bird, 530
  development, 710
  dog tapeworm, **204**
  frog, **513, 514**
  grasshopper, **330**
  hydra, 160, **161**
  man, **678**, 679, 680
  planaria, **190**
Oviduct, **190**, 193, **226**, 262, 300, **678**, 680
  frog, 495, **513, 514**
  grasshopper, **331**
  mammal, **558**, 560, **678**
  vestigial, **513, 514**
Oviparous, 319, 686
Ovipositor, 329
Ovisac, **513, 514**
Ovotestis, 356, **357**
Ovoviviparous, 439, 687
Ovulation, 696, **697**, 699
Ovum, 74, 672, **673, 674, 675**, 676, 677, 893
Owen, R., 894, 895
Owl, 529, 530, 536, **543, 544**
Oxaloacetic acid, 67
Oxidations, 38, 610, 641
Oxygen, 67, 457, 639-640, 672, 891
  cycle, 837-838
  debt, 605, 606
Oxyhemoglobin, 640
Oxytocin, 690, 699
Oxytricha, 108, **131**
Oxyuris, 229
Oyster, 358, **363**
  borer, **352**
  catcher, 541

P

Pachyderm, 552
Pacinian corpuscle, **661, 662**
Paddlefish, 442
Paedogenesis, 673, 677
Pagurus, **308**
Painted turtle, **482**
Painter, T. S., 919
Palade, G. E., 924, 926
Palaeacanthocephala, 236
Palaemonetes, **309**
Palaeognathous, 525
Palaeomastodon, **768**
Palate, hard and soft, 557
Palatine artery, 510
Palearctic realm, 847
Paleocene epoch, 765
Paleogenesis, 94
Paleontology, 22, 760-770, 892
Paleozoic era, 32, 764
Pallial groove, 350
  line, **359**
Palps, **358**, 360
Paludina, 355
Pancreas, 495, **613**
Pancreatectomy, effect, 903
Pancreatic duct, **507**
  juice, 616
  lipase, 616
Panda, **571**
Pander, C., 892
Pandorina, 109, 119
Pangolin, 574
Panniculus carnosus, 560
Pantopoda, 283
Pantothenic acid, 67, 620
Pantotheria, 547
Paper nautilus, 370
Papilio, **341**
Papillae, 494, 557
Papillary muscle, 627
Papulae, 378, **380**, 635
Paragastric canal, **181**, 182
Paragonimus, **201**, 202
Paragordius, 219, 232
Parahippus, 769
Parakeet, 541
Paramecium, 103, 105, 125-132, 134
  avoiding reaction, **127**
  behavior, 130-132
  binary fission, **128**
  conjugation, **128**, 129, 903
  cytogamy, 129
  habitat, 125
  locomotion, **127**
  mating types, 129-130, 921
  metabolism, 126-127
  pellicle, **127**
  reproduction, 127, **128**
  structure, **125-126**
  taxes, **130-132**
Paramylum body, **116**, 117
Parapodia, 251, **266**
Parascalops, 570
Parasitic animals, candiru fish, 451
  filarial worm, 230
  flukes, 195-203
  frog, 490-492

Parasitic animals—cont'd
  guinea worm, 231
  hookworm, **227**
  insects, 316, 317
  intestinal worm, *Ascaris,* **224**, 227
  nematode, 492
  pinworm, **229**
  protozoan, 119-**120**, 121-124, 192
  sea lamprey, **434**
  spiny-headed worms, 234-**237**
  trematode, **196-200**, 492
  trichina worm, **228**
Parasitism, 107, 819
Parasitology, 22
Parasphenoid, **496**
Parasympathetic system, **657**, 658
Parathormone, **693**, 698
Parathyroid gland, **687**, 693, 698
Parazoa, 139
Parenchyma, 79, 82, 186, **189**, 206, 213
Parietal bone, **598**, 600
Parotid gland, **613**, 615
Parra, 860
Parrot, 533, 541
Parthenogenesis, 73, 109, 319, **673**, 676, 677, 891, 906-907
Parturition, 710
Passeriformes, 545
Pasteur, L., 897
Patella, 354, 525, **598, 600**
Pauling, L., 925
Paunch, **557**
Paurometabola, 320
Pauropoda, 278
Pauropus, 278
Pavlov, I., 609, 870, 878, 910
Pearl formation, **358**
Pearl, R., 913
Peart, W. S., 927
Peckham, E. G., 870
Peckham, G. W., 870
Pecquet, Jean, 622
Pecten, **352**, 364, 529
Pectinatella, 247
Pectinibranchia, 354
Pectoral artery, 528
  girdle, **495**, 497
Pectoralis muscle, **499**, 500, 526, **606**
Pedicellariae, 378, **379**, **380**, **381**, 385
Pediculus, 337
Pedinaspis, 288
Pedipalp, 284, 289
Pedogenesis, 319
Peduncle, 396
Peking man, 799
Pelage, 553
Pelagic animals, 834
Pelecaniformes, 539
Pelecypoda, 349, 357-364
Pelican, **524**, 539
Pellicle, 62, **116**, 117, 125, **127**
Pelmatohydra, 153, 160

Pelmatozoa, 373, 376
Pelobatidae, 469
Pelomyxa, **110, 114**
Pelvic vein, **510**, 511
Pelvis, **598, 600, 601**
Pen, **368**
Penaeus, 308
Pendrostoma, 245
Penetrance, 736
Penetrant, **156**, 157
Penguin, **538**
Penial spicule, 224, **226**
Penicillin discovery, 918
Penikese laboratory, 899
Penis, **190**, 192, 560, 678
Pennsylvanian period, 32, 765
Pentadactyl, 601
Pentastomida, 277, 291
Pepsin, 507, 615
Pepsinogen, 615
Peptones, 507
Peranema, **120**
Perca, 444, **452**
Perch, 444
  climbing, **443**
  structure, **452**
  yellow, **452**
Perching mechanism, **526**
Perennibranch, 461
Pericardial cavity, 614
  sac, 495
  sinus, **300**
Pericardium, 509, 627
Perimysium, **606**
Periodic table, 36
Periosteum, **498**
Periostracum, 359
Peripatus, 262, 277, **279**, 280
  digestive system, 280
  distribution, 279
  evolutionary status, 281
  external features, **279**, 280
  internal features, 280
  nervous system, 280
  reproductive system, 280
Peripheral nervous system, 504, **652**, 656-658
Periproct, **306**, 385
Perisarc, 164
Perissodactyla, 577, **578**, 579
Peristalsis, 617
Peristomial membrane, 378
  tentacles, **266**
Peristomium, **266**
Peritoneum, 255, 379, 494
Perkin, W. H., 897
Perkins, E. B., 917
Permian period, 32, 765
Peroneus muscle, **499**, 501
Petrel, 539
Petromyzon, 420, 432, 434
Petromyzontia, 432-435
Pfeffer, W., 900
Pfizner, W., 901
Pflüger, E. F. W., 899
pH, 40, 909
Phagocytosis role, 901
Phalanges, **495**, 497, **598**, 600
Pharyngeal chamber, **190**
  sheath, **189**

Pharynx, 190, 612, **613**
  bird, 527
  frog, 494, 507
  planaria, **188**
Phascolion, 245
Phasmid, 223
Phasmidia, 223
Pheasant, **542**
Phenotype, 733, 909
Philodina, 219, **220**, 221
Phoebe, nest, 534
Pholas, **352**, 364
Pholidota, 574
Phoronida, 242-243
Phoronis, **242**
Phoronopsis, 243
Phosphagen, 916
Phosphocreatine, 605
Phospholipids, 46
Phosphorus, 69
Phosphorylation, 67
Photinus, **863**
Photoblepharon, 864
Photochemical theory, 669
Photoperiodicity, 812
Photoreceptor, **261**, 667
Photosynthesis, 43
Phototaxis, 131
Phrynosoma, 475
Phthirius, 337
Phyla, 25, 28-29
Phyllobates, 468
Phyllodactylus, 485
Phylogenetic tree, 30
Phylogeny, 29-33, 94
Physa, 349, 355
Physalia, 152, **153**, 167, **168**
Physeter, 576
Physical factors, 811-817
Physiology, 21, 22
  digestion, 614-617
  heart, 626-628
  muscle, 603-606
Physoclisti, 449
Physostomi, 449
Phytomonadina, 118
Phytophagous, 316
Pia mater, 503, 652
Piciformes, 545
Pickerel frog, 488, 490
Pig, visceral organs, **558**
Pigeon, 527, 541, **637**
Pigment cells, **594**
  skin, 592
Pika, 574, 575
Pike, 444
Pilidium larva, 212
Pill bug, **309**
Pinacocyte, 140, 143, **588**
Pineal body, 503, **687**, 700
Pinfeather, 522
Pinkus, F., 904
Pinna, 559, **664**
Pinnipedia, 573
Pinnule, **388**, 390
Pinworm, **229-230**
Pipa, **468**, 857
Piranha, **443**
Pisaster, **385**
Pisces, 409, 431
Pit vipers, 478-480, 485

Pithecanthropus, 798-**799**, 903
Pitocin, 690
Pitressin, 690
Pituitary gland, 430, **503**, 530, **654**, 690-**692**, 695, **697**
Pituitrin, 690
Placenta, 699, **707**
Placobdella, 253, **270**
Placoderm, **408**-410, **599**
Placoid scale, **590**, **595**
Planaria, 187-195, **188**
  behavior, 194-195
  digestion, 189-191, **190**
  excretory system, **190**, **191**
  habitat, 187-188
  histology, **189**
  life cycle, **193**
  locomotion, 193-194
  nervous system, **190**
  regeneration, 194, **195**
  reproductive system, **190**, 192-193
  respiration, 191
  skin, 189
  species, 187-188
Planes of symmetry, 84
Plankton, 106, **830**, 834, 893
Planocera, 186, 187
Planorbis, 201, 203, 356
Planula, **164**, **171**
Plasma, 81, 259, 508, 631, 633-634
  membrane, 41, 51, 55
Plasmagel, **110**, 111
Plasmalemma, **110**, 111
Plasmasol, **110**, 111
Plasmodium, 52, 109, 121-123
  life cycle, **122**, 905
Plasmodroma, 103
Plastid, **52**
Plated lizard, 485
Platelets, 81, **630**, 632
Platichys, 443
Platter, F., 890
Platyhelminthes, 29, 184-210, **623**
  biological principles, 184
  characteristics, 185-186
  classes, 186
  origin and relations, 184-185
  representative types, 186-210
    (*see also* Fluke; Planaria; Tapeworm; etc.)
Platypus, **568**, **569**
Platyrhinii, 581
Plecoptera, 320, **334**, 336
Pleistocene epoch, 766
Pleodorina, 119
Plerocercoid larva, 208
Plesianthropus, 800
Plesiosaur, 414
Plethodon, 462, 464, 469
Plethodontidae, 461, 462, 469, 636
Pleura, **638**
Pleural cavity, 614, 638, 639
Pleurobrachia, 180, **181**-183
Pleurodont, **613**
Pleuron, 294, 295, 329
Pleuronichthys, 443
Pleuroperitoneal cavity, 614

Plexus, Auerbach, 658
  brachial, **652**, 657
  cervical, **652**, 657
  choroid, 504
  lumbar, **652**, 657
  sciatic, **502**, 504
Pliocene epoch, 765
Pliohippus, 770
Plover, 541
Plumage, 522
Plumatella, **246**
Pluteus, 386
Pneumatophore, **167**, **168**
Pneumobites, **491**, 492
Pneumogastric nerve, 505
Pocket gopher, 574
Podobranchiae, 298
Podophrya, 103, **111**, 134
Pogonophora, 29, 397-400, 928
  biological principles, 397
  characteristics, 398
  classification, 398
  natural history, 399, 400
  origin and relations, 397, 398
  structure, 398, **399**
Poikilothermous animal, 514
Poisonous lizard, 485
Polar body, **682**, 684
Polarity, 85
Polian vesicle, **388**
Polistes, 339
Polistotrema, 436
Pollen basket, **333**
  brush, **333**
  comb, **333**
  Packer, **333**
Polocyte, 684
Polyandry, 534
Polychaeta, 253, 265-269
  clamworm, 266-268
  common forms, 268-269
  compared with Oligochaeta, 265-266
Polycladida, **187**
Polyembryony, 319
Polyergus, 819
Polyestrus, 567
Polygordius, 253, 271
Polygyny, 534
Polygyra, 355, **832**
Polyhybrid, 734
Polymorphism, 72, 167-168
Polyodon, 442
Polypedates, **466**
Polyplacophora, 350
Polyploidy, 744, 747, 921
Polyps, **152**, **169**
Polypterini, 442
Polypterus, **409**, 443, 449
Polysaccharides, 43
Polyspermy, 686
Polystoma, 196
Polytene, 725
Pond, **826**, **828**, **829**, **830**
Pongidae, 582, 797
Pons, **654**, 655
Poorwills, 543
Population(s), animal, 820-823, 913
  bird, 535

Population(s)—cont'd
dynamics, 821
evolutionary factors, 776-777
fluctuations, 562
genetics, 789-792
growth curve, **821**
pressure, 822
survey, 561-562
theory of growth, 895
turnover, 823
Porcellio, 308
Porcupine, **553,** 574
Porifera, 28, 138-148, **649**
biological principles, 138
characteristics, 139-140
classes, 140
economic, 148
fresh-water sponges, **147**-148
glass sponges, 142, 146-147
habitat, 140
metabolism, 143-144
origin and relation, 138-139
reproduction, 144-145, 146
Scypha, **145**-146
skeleton, 141-**142, 143**
structure, 140-**141, 142, 145-146**
types of cells, 143
Porocephalus, 291
Porocyte, 143
Porpoise, 576
Portal systems, 511
Porter, K. R., 926
Portuguese man-of-war, 167, **168**
Postanal tail, 249
Posterior pituitary, 699
Potato bettle, **326, 340**
Pouched mouse, 548
Prairie dog, **573**
Prawn, **309**
Praying mantis, **321**
Precambrian era, 32, 104
Precocial Young, 533, 567
Predaceous insects, 325
Predation, 819
Preformation, 703
Premaxilla, **495, 496, 598**
Prepotency, 748-749
Presbyopia, 669
Presoma, 223
Pressure, water, 816
Prevertebrates, 404-406, 658
Prevost, P., 893
Priapulida, 219, 223
Priapulus, 219
Priestly, J., 891, 908
Primates, 579-582, 797
Primitive streak, 706
Principles, biological, 90-97
Priority, law of, 26
Prismatic layer, 359
Probability laws, 734
Proboscidea, 576, 577
Proboscis, 188, 212, 236, **237,** 243, **394, 395**
monkey, 582
sheath, **213**
Procellariiformes, 539
Producer organisms, 823
Proestrum, 566

Progeny selections, 747
Progesterone, 696, **697,** 698, 699
Proglottid, **203, 204, 205,** 206
Prolactin, 691, **697,** 699
Prometaphase, **64**
Pronghorn, 554
Prootic, **496**
Prophase, **62,** 63, **64,** 113, **683,** 902
Prosencephalon, 652
Prosobranchia, **354,** 355
Prostate gland, **678,** 679
Prostoma, 215
Prostomial tentacles, **266**
Prostomium, 254, 256, **260,** 266
Protandry, 677
Protective coloration, 788
Proteidae, 469
Proteins, 44-45, 618, 894-895, 902, 925
Proteocephalidae, 492
Proterospongia, 119, **121,** 139
Proterozoic era, 32, 104, 764
Prothorax, **328,** 329
Prothrombin, 632
Protista, 19, 102
Protocercal, **444**
Protochordata, 420-425
Protochordates, 403
Protogyny, 677
Protomonadina, 119
Protonephridia, 186, **191,** 221, 241
Protoneuron, 648
Protons, 36
Protoplasm, 19, 41-50, 90, 91, 894, 895
Protoplasmic bridge, 898
grade of organization, 72
organization, 72
streaming, 607
Protopodite, **296**
Protopterus, 444, **448,** 449
Protospondyli, 443
Protostomia, 89
Prototheria, 547, 569
Prototrich, 553
Protozoa, 28, 101-137 (*see also* Ameba; Euglena; Paramecium; Parasitic animals; etc.
behavior, 114, 118, 130-132
biological principles, 101
characteristics, 102
classes, 103
colonies, 109
earth deposits, 104-106, 115-116
evolution, 103
habitat, 102, 110, 116-117, 125, **127,** 133
historical, 101-102, 890-891, 896, 907
investigation, 134
life cycles, *Eimeria,* **124**-125
Monocystis, **123**-124
Plasmodium, 121, **122,** 123
Volvox, 119

Protozoa—cont'd
locomotion, **112**-113, 118
metabolism, 112-113, 117-118
number of species, 102-103
plankton, 106
reproduction, 108, **113**-114, **118,** 119, **123**-124, 127-130
symbiotic relationships, 106-107
types, 109-134
water contamination, 107-108
Protozoea, 308, **310**
Protractor muscle, **359,** 360, 387
Protura, 335
Proventriculus, 329, **527**
Pselaphid beetle, **832**
Psephenus, **827**
Pseudacris, **489**
Pseudicyema, 241
Pseudoalleles, 739, 925
Pseudocoel, 217, 220, 221, 225
Pseudocoelomate, **88**
Pseudopodium, **110**
Pseudoscorpion, **289**
Psittaciformes, 541
Ptarmigan, 540, **542**
Pterobranchia, 393, 394, **396**
Pterodactyl, **414,** 415, **814**
Pteropus, 571
Pterosaur, 414, 415
Pterygoid, **495, 496**
Pterygota, 335-342
Pteryla, **522**
Ptyalin, 615
Pubis, **598, 600, 601**
Puffbird, 545
Pulmocutaneous, **508, 509, 510**
Pulmonary artery, **509,** 510, 625
fluke, **201**
vein, **508, 510,** 511
Pulmonata, 355-357
Pulvillus, 329
Punnett, R.C., 908
Punnett square, 732
Pupa, 322
Pupil, 506, **668**
Purine base, 727
Purkinje cells, 656
fiber system, **627**
Purkinje, J. E., 894
Pycnogonida, 277, 283, **385**
Pycnogonum, 277
Pycnophyes, 222
Pygostyle, 523
Pyloric ceca, 611
sphincter, **507**
stomach, 299, 614
Pyramid, biomass, 818
food, 817, 818
Pyridoxine, 620
Pyrimidine base, 727
Pyruvic acid, 67, 69
Python, 85, 478

Q

Quadrate bone, **665**
Quadratojugal, **496**
Quadrula, 364

Quail, 533, 540
Quartz-rod illumination, 24
Quaternary period, 31, 765
Quetelet, L. A. J., 899
Quill, 520

R

Rabbit, 574
Rabl, K., 902
Raccoon, **573**
Races, (Caucasoid, Mongoloid, Negroid), 803
Radial canal, 145, **165**, 166, **170**, **172**, **380**, **381**
Radiata, 185, 373
Radiating canal, **126**
Radiation effect on heredity, 754-755
Radioactive tracers, 24
Radioactivity, 37
Radiocarbon dating, 924
Radiography (x-rays), 24
Radiolaria, 104-106, **105**, **114**, 115-116
Radioulna, **495**, 497
Radius, 423, 526, **598**, **600**
Radula, 345, 353, 355, **356**, **368**
Rail, 541
Raja, 439
Ramak, R., 895
Rami comunicans, 505, 653
Rana, 468, 469, **489**, 488-492
Rancho La Brea, 519
Range of animal, 843, 845
Ranidae, 469
Raspail, F. V., 893
Rat, 568, 574, **637**
Ratite birds, 519, **537**
Rat-tailed maggot, **829**
Rattlesnake, **478**, **479**
Rau, N., 880
Rau, P., 880
Ray, J., 25, 891
Ray-finned fish, 442, 443, **444**
Razor-shell clam, **352**
Reaumur, R. A. F., 891
Recapitulation, **310** (*see also* Biogenetic law)
Recent period, 766
Receptor, 81, 650
   chemical, **663**
   classification, 662
   sensory, 505-507, **660**, **661**
Recessive, 734
Recessiveness, 732
Reck, H., 911
Reconstruction models, 24
Rectal ceca, 379, **380**
Rectovesical artery, 511
Rectum, 330, **527**, 613
Rectus abdominis muscle, **499**, 500
   femoris muscle, **606**
Red blood corpuscles, **630**
   comparative sizes and shapes, **631**
   bugs, 290
   tide, 107
"Red" meat, 526
Redi, Francesco, 671

Redia, **196**, **198**, 199
Reduction division, **683**, 723, 724, 903
Reflex act, 650
   action, 876-877, 890, 894
   arc, **260**, 650, **651**, 652
   conditioned, 878
Refractory period, 607, 627
Regeneration, **163**, 716-717
   crayfish, 294
   hydra, 161-162
   planaria, 194, **195**
   sea star, 382
   sponge, 143, 909
Relationships of animal groups, 30
Relaxation period, 604
Relaxin, 697, 699
Remige, 521
Remora, **446**
Renal excretion, 895-896
   portal system, **510**, **511**, 626
   vein, **510**, 511
Rennin, 615
Reproduction, ameba, 113-114
   asexual, 672, **673**, 674-675
   biparental, 73, 676
   bony fish, 454-455
   crayfish, 300-301
   division of parent, 91-92
   earthworm, 262
   Euglena, 118
   gamete formation, **674**
   hormones, 695
   hydra, 159-160, 165
   insect, 319
   mammal, 566-567
   Obelia, **164**
   Paramecium, 127-128
   planaria, 192-193
   Pleurobrachia, 182
   Protozoa, 108-109, **113-114**, 118, 119, 127-130
   Rhynchocoela, 215
   Scypha, 146
   sea star, 380, 381
   sexual, 73, 672, **673**, **675**, **676**, 677
   spider, 285
   Spongilla, **145**
   Sporozoa, 121-122
   tongue worm, 395-396
   types, **673**
   Volvox, 118-119
Reproductive cycle in female, **697**
   system, 83, 671-687
      Acanthocephala, 237-238
      bird, **527**, 529, 530
      earthworm, **256**, **261**-263
      frog, **513**, 514
      grasshopper, 331
      human, 677-681
      invertebrate, 677
      mammal, **559**, 560
      Peripatus, 280
      uterus, comparative, **679**
      vertebrate plan, 677
Reptilia, 469-485
   adaptive radiation, **414**, 415

Reptilia—cont'd
   advancements, 471
   brain, **654**
   characteristics, 470
   classification, 470-471, 484-485
   embryology, 705-706
   evolution, **413**, **414**, **415**
   organ systems, **472**, 471-474
      circulatory, 473
      digestive, **472**, 473
      epidermis, **591**, **595**
      excretory, 473
      exoskeleton, 471
      muscles, 472
      nervous, **472**, 473, 474
   origin and relations, 469-470
Reptiles, Age of, 31
Reservoir, **116**, 117
Residual air, 639
Respiration, 635-643, 908, 916, 919
   ameba, 113
   ammocoetes, 427
   buccopharyngeal, 461
   cellular, 641
   clam, 361-362
   comparative, **636**
   control factors, 641
   direct, indirect, 635
   formula, 67
   gaseous exchange, 639-640
   hydra, 158
   internal, external, 635
   invertebrate, 635-636
   man, 638-642
   nature, 891-892
   nerve, 919
   Paramecium, 126
   rhythm, 641
   transport of gases, 640-641
   utilization coefficient, 641
   vertebrate, **636**-641
Respiratory center, 641
   pigments, 624
   quotient, 635
   system, 82, 635-641
      bird, **527**, 528-529
      comparative, **636**
      crayfish, 298-300
      earthworm, 259, **636**
      frog, **512**
      grasshopper, 330, **636**
      human, **638**-639
      lung, comparative, **637**
      mammal, 559, 638
      spider, 285
      tree, **388**, 636
Rete mirabile, 629
Reticulum, **557**, 614
Retina, 506, **667**, **668**, 669, 898-899, 919
Retractor, sea urchin, 387
Retrice, 521
Rh factor, 634, 922
Rhabdias, 492
Rhabdites, 185, **189**, 212
Rhabditis, 223
Rhabdocoela, 186. 187
Rhabdome, **303**

Rhabdopleura, 394, 396, 397
Rhachitomi, **412**
Rhagon, 141
Rhea, **537**, 538
Rheiformes, 538
Rheotaxis, 131, 319
Rhesus monkey, 582
    inheritance, 751
Rhineura, 485
Rhinoceros, 577, 578
Rhinoderma, 858
Rhizoplast, **116**, 117
Rhizopoda (*see* Sarcodina)
Rhodesian man, 800
Rhodeus, 454
Rhodopsin, 669
Rhombencephalon, 652
Rhombogen, 241
Rhopalura, **241**
Rhynchocephalia, 483-484
Rhynchocoela, 29, 211-215, **623**
    biological principles, 211-212
    characteristics, 212-213
    classes, 213
    digestion, 214
    habitat, 213
    locomotion, 215
    metabolism, 215
    origin and relations, 212
    reproduction, 215
Rhynchodaeum, 213
Rhythm in nature, 92
Rhythmic patterns of life, 92
Ribbon worms, 212-215
Riboflavin, 620
Ribonucleic acid (RNA), 45, 727
Ribose nucleic acid (RNA), 45, 727
Ribs, **598**, **600**
Richards, A. N., 913
Rickettsia, 291
Rictal bristle, 522
Rigor mortis, 605
Ring canal, 172, **381**
Ring-necked snake, **477**
RNA, 45, 727
Roadrunner, 541
Robin, 535
    nest, **534**
Robinow, C. F., 923
Rock borer, **352**
Rocky Mountain spotted fever, 290, 291
Rodentia, **573**, 574
Rods, eye, 506, **668**, 669
Roentgen, W., 904
Romelea, 327-334 (*see also* Grasshopper)
Root sheath, 552
Ross, R., 905
Rossia, 364
Rostellum, 206
Rostrum, **294**, 295
Rotator muscle, 502
Rotifer, **830**
Rotifera, 218, 219-221
Roughton, F. J. W., 918
Round dance, **867**
Roundworms, 217-233, **224**-227

Roux, W., 711, 901, 902
Rove beetle, **325**
Rowan, W., 915
Rowlands, I. M., 923
Rubner, M., 901
Ruffed grouse, **542**
Rugae, 611
Rumen, **557**, 614
Ruminant stomach, **557**
Ruminantia, 579

S

Saccoglossus, 394, **395**, 396
Saccosoma, 244
Saccule, 667
Sacculina, **308**, 690
Sacral plexus, **652**
Sacrum, **495**, 497, **598**, **599**, **600**
Sagitta, 248, **249**, 681
Sagittal axis, 84
Salamander, 460-463
    cave, **465**
    eggs, **462**
    long-tailed, **464**
    red-backed, **464**
    slimy, **464**
    spotted, **463**
    tiger, **463**
    two-lined, **464**
    zigzag, **464**
Salamandra, 462, **463**
Salamandridae, 469
Salientia, 459, 463-469, 488
Saliva, 615
Salivary gland chromosome, 724-725, 919
    glands, 329, 615
    development, **455**
Salmon, 444, **455**, 855-**856**
Salpa, 421
Salt water, drinking by birds, 533
San Jose scale, **326**
Sand dollar, **386**, 384-387
Sandpiper, 541
Sandworm (*Neanthes*), **266-268**
Sanger, F., 927
Saprophagous, 316
Saprophytic nutrition, 102, 117
Sarcodina, 103, 110-116
Sarcoplasm, 80
Sarcosomes, 628
Sardine, 444
Sardinops, 444
Sarett, L. H., 920
Sartorius muscle, **499**, 501, **606**
Sauer, F., 928
Sauria, 484
Scala tympani, **666**
    vestibuli, **666**
Scale insects, 338
Scales, **591**, **595**
    bony, **595**
    cosmoid, 410, 447
    ctenoid, 453, **454**
    cycloid, 447, 453, **454**
    epidermal, **595**
    ganoid, 444, **454**
Scallop, **352**
Scalopus, 570

Scapanus, 570
Scaphiopus, 469
Scaphopoda, 349, **351**, 352
Scapula, 497, **598**, **600**
Scattering layer of sea, 924-925
Schiefferdecker, P., 914
Schistosoma, 199, **200**, **201**, 186, 911
Schistosomiasis, 199, 201
Schizocoelous, coelom, 87
Schizogony, 121, **124**
Schizont, 121, **124**
Schjelderup-Ebbe, T., 883, 914
Schleiden, M. J., 894
Schmidt, J., 855, 914
Schneider, A., 899
Schneider, W. C., 924
Schneirla, T. C., 870
Schoenheimer, R., 921
Schultze, M., 898
Schwann, T., 894
Sciatic artery, **509**, 511
    enlargement, 504
    nerve, **652**
    plexus, **502**, 504
    vein, **510**, 511
Scincidae, 485
Sciuridae, 574
Sclater, P. L., 897
Sclera, **667**, 668
Sclerite, 328
Scleroblast, 142, 143, 145
Sclerotic coat, 506
Scolex, 203
Scolopendra, **310**
Scorpion flies, 339
Scorpions, **289**, 290
Scrotum, 559
Scute, 476
Scutigera, **311**
Scutigerella, 278
Scypha, 44, 140, **145**, **146**
Scyphistoma, **171**, 172
Scyphomedusae, 170-172
Scyphozoa, 152, 153, **170**-172
Sea anemone, 172-**174**
    biscuit, **386**
    butterflies, 355
    cow, **577**
    cucumber, 375, **385**, **388**
        behavior, 389-390
        digestive system, **375**, **388**
        larva, **377**
        nervous system, **388**
        reproductive system, **388**, 389
        respiratory tree, **388**
        structure, 387-389, **388**
        water-vascular system, **375**, **388**
    horse, **444**, **446**
    lily, **388**, **389**, 390
    lion, 573
    slugs, 355
    spiders, 283
    squirt, 421-423
    star, 378-382
        behavior, 382
        circulatory system, 379, 381

Sea star—cont'd
digestive system, 379, **380**
endoskeleton, **375, 378,
380**
external features, **378-379**
internal structure, 379-382,
380, 381
larva, **377**
locomotion, 382
nervous system, **380,** 381
Pacific purple, **385**
regeneration, 382
reproductive system, **380,**
381
21-rayed, **385**
water-vascular system, **380,
381,** 382
turtle, **482**
urchin, 384, **385, 386, 387**
walnuts, 179
water and protoplasm, 42
Seal, 549, **550,** 573
rookery, **564**
Sebaceous gland, **554**
Secretin, 616, 617, 689, **695,**
698
Segment, 251
Segmentation, **86,** 252, 275, 617
Segmentina, 203
cavity, **706**
Selachii, 437
Selye, H., 867, 925
Semicircular canal, 506, **664,**
667
Semilunar valve, **627**
Semimembranosus muscle, **499,**
501
Seminal receptacle, **190,** 193,
262, 254, **256,** 330,
331
vesicle, **190, 226, 331, 513,**
514, 529, **678**
Seminiferous tubules, 514, **674,**
678
Semipermeable membrane, **57**
Semitendinosus muscle, 501
Semotilus, 859
Sense organs, 659-670
chemical, **663**
ear, 663, **664, 665, 666,** 667
earthworm, **260, 261**
eye, **188,** 213, **285,** 302-
303, **328,** 506, 551,
367, 369, **667-670**
grasshopper, 331
invertebrate, **660,** 662-663
Ruffini, 662
smell, 663
tactile, **661, 662**
vertebrate, 661-670
Sensory neuron, 81
organs, transition from water
to land, 458
root, 504, **651, 653**
system, 83, 659-670, **660-661**
bird, 529
equilibrium, 667
frog, 505-507
hydra, 157
mammal, 559, **661, 662-668**
Sepia, 349, 370

Septa, heart, **508,** 509
Sere, 824, 839
Serial homology, 85, **296,** 298,
601
Serosa, **312,** 507
Serous membrane, 81
Serpentes, 485
Serranidae, 454
Serrasalmo, 443
Sertoli cell, **674**
Seta, **252,** 254
Sewellel, 574
Sex chromosomes, **722,** 740,
741, 907
determination, 739-741, 915
hormones, 694, 695, **696,** 697
mosaic, 740
organs, accessory, 676, **678**
homology, 680, 681
Sex-linked inheritance, **741-742,**
910
Sexual dimorphism, 532
selection, 788
Seymouria, **413,** 469, 912
Shaft, **520**
Shark skin, **595**
Sharp, R., 912
Sharpey-Schaefer, E. A., 904
Shearwater, 539
Shell, chitinous, 74
gland, **204**
snail, 353, 355, **357**
Shelters, 562, 816
Sherrington, C. S., 905
Shrew, 551, 570, **566**
Shrimp, life history, **310**
Shull, G. H., 912
Siboglinum, 398
Siebold, C. T. E. von, 896
Sign stimuli, 875
Silkworm, 324
moth, **325**
Silurian period, 32, 764
Silver impregnation, 24
Silverfish, **334**
Sima, 364
Simia, 582
Sinanthropus, **799**
Sino-atrial (auricular) node
(S-A), **627,** 628, 908-
909
Sinus gland, 303
lymph, 511-512
pericardial, **359**
venosus, **508,** 509, **510,** 511,
625
Sinuses, 299
Sinusoid, 629
Siphon, clam, **358, 359**
squid, **368**
tunicate, **421**
Siphonaptera, 341
Siphonoglyph, 172, **173**
Siphonophora, 167
Siphuncle, **365,** 370
Sipunculoidea, 244-**245**
Sipunculus, **245**
Siren, 460, 469
Sirenia, **577**
Sirenidae, 469
Skate, **439**

Skeletal muscle, **498**
system, 82, 595-602, **596**
Skeleton, appendicular, **495,
496**
axial, **495,** 496
bat, **597**
bird, **523,** 524-526
comparative, **596**
dog, **598**
frog, **495-498**
mammal, **597, 598, 600-601**
reptile, 471-472, **597**
sponge, 141-142
turtle, **597**
Skin, **588-595,** 709
frog, **493**
invertebrate, **587-589**
mammal, 552, **592**
reptile, **595**
sense organs, 506
shark, **595**
teleost, **595**
vertebrate, **590-595**
Skink, **474,** 485
Skinner, B. F., 921
Skinner box, 879
Skull, bird, **523,** 524
frog, **495, 496**
mammal, **598**
man, **497, 600**
Skunk, 573
Slime eel, 432, **435, 436**
glands, *Peripatus,* 280
molds, 41, 102
tube, 262, **263**
Sloth, 575, 576
Smell, 506
Smith, H. W., 404, 426, 645
Smith, W., 892
Snail, 349, 352-357
circulatory system, 356, **357**
digestive system, 355, 356,
357
excretory system, 356
land, **832**
natural history, 357
nervous system, 356, **357**
reproductive system, **354,** 356,
357
structure, 355-357
Snakes, 474-480
classification, 485
copperhead, 478
coral, **477, 478**
fangs, 477, **478**
hog-nosed, **476**
poisonous, 477-480
rattle, 478, **479**
ring-necked, **477**
scales, 476
structure, 476-478
venom, 480
Snapping turtle, 484
Social behavior, 881-884
instincts, insect, 323-324
Soft-shelled turtle, 484
Soil, 814
Sol, 39
Sole, **443,** 444
Sole (sea cucumber), 387
Solemya, 364

Solenocyte, **191**, 223, **642**
Solenogastres, 350
Solution, colloidal, 39, 40
  hypotonic, isotonic, 58
  molecular, 38
Somaplasm (somatoplasm), 96,
  681
Somatic cell, 60
Somatotropin (STH), **691**, 695
Somite, 85, 251
  muscle, **709**
Song, bird, 532
Sonneborn, T. H., 134, 921, 923
Sörensen, S. P. L., 909
Sorex, 551, 561, 570
Sound, 666, 667
Spallanzani, L., 671-672
Sparrow, **524**
Spats, 363
Specialization and division of
  labor (principle), 91
Speciation, 793-794
Species, 25, 27, 891
  specificity, 45
Spemann, H., 711, 913
Spencer, H., 870
Sperm, 60, **674**
  duct, **674**
Sperm whale, 576
Spermatic (genital) vein, **510**,
  511
Spermatid, **674**
Spermatocyte, **674**, **682**, 684
Spermatogenesis, **682**, 684
Spermatogonia, **674**, 681
Spermatophore, 270, 366, **462**
Spermatozoa, human, **53**
Spermatozoan, 672, **674**, 675,
  676, 677, 896, 897,
  901
Sphaerophrya, 134
Sphenethmoid, **495**, **496**
Sphenisciformes, **538**
Sphenodon, **414**, 471, 473, 483,
  484
Sphincter, pyloric, 507, **613**,
  614
  vesical, external and internal,
  643, 646
Sphygmomanometer, 630
Sphyrna, 437
Spicules, **142-143**, 145
  penial, 224, **226**
Spider, **284-288**
  black widow, **288**
  external features, **284**, **286**
  organ systems, 284-**285**
  trap-door, **287**-288
  web, 286-**287**
Spinal accessory nerve, 656
  cord, **502**, 504, 651, **652-653**
  nerve, **502**, 504, **652**, 892-893
Spindle, 63, **64**, **65**
Spine, porcupine, **553**
  sea star, 378, **380**
Spinneret, 284, **285**, 286
Spiny anteater, 569
Spiny-headed worms, 234-238
  (*see also* Acantho-
  cephala)

Spiracle, 284, **328**, 329, 330,
  516, 517, **599**, **665**
Spiral valve, **508**, 509
Spireme, named, 901
Spirillina, **104**
Spirobolus, 278, **312**
Spiromonas, **120**
Spirotricha, 107
Spirotrichonympha, **106**
Splanchnocranium, 598
Spleen, 495, **507**, **509**, **558**, 915
Sponges, 138-149, 926 (*see also*
  Porifera)
  fresh-water, **142**, **147**-148
  glass, **142**, 146-147
  Scypha, **145-146**
Spongiidae, 148
Spongilla, **140**, 144, **145**, **147**,
  148
Spongillidae, 148
Spongin, **142**, **143**
Spongioblast, 142, 143
Spongioplasm, 41
Spongocoel, 140, **141**, 145, **146**
Spontaneous generation, 671-
  672, 897
Spoonbill, 539
Sporocyst, **196**, **198**, 199, 200
Sporogony, **124**
Sporozoa, 103, 121-125, **122**,
  123, **124**
Sporozoite, 121, **123**, **124**
Sporulation, 108, 114, **123**, 124,
  675
Spring peeper, **467**, **489**
Springtail, **334**, 335
Squalorophrya, 134
Squalus, 437, **438**
Squamata, 470, **472**, 474-480,
  484
Squash bug, **326**
Squid, 349, 367-369
  behavior, 369
  circulatory system, **368**
  coloration, 369
  digestive system, **368**
  external features, 367, **368**
  eye, **369**
  gills, **368**
  internal structures, **368**, 369
Squirrel, 550, 574
Squirrelfish, 881
Stag beetle, **340**
Staining, intra-vitam, 24
Stanley, W. M., 920
Stannius, H. F., 896
Stapedius muscle, **664**, 665
Stapes, 559, **664**, **665**
Starfish (*see* Sea star)
Stargazer, 864
Starling, E. H., 688-689, 906,
  907, 912
Strasburger, E., **900**, 901, 902
Statoblast, **247**
Statocyst, 167, 181, 302, 356,
  362, 369, **660**
Statolith, 182, 302, **660**
Steenstrup, J., 895
Stenohaline, 453
Stenothermal, 810
Stenotopic, 843

Stensio, E. A., 426, 916
Stentor, 106, **131**, 132, 134, 873
Stereoline glutinant, 157
Stern, C., 918
Sternal artery, 299-300
  sinus, **300**
Sternohyoid, 500
Sternum, **328**, 329, 497, **598**,
  600
Stichopus, **385**, 387, 389
Stigma, **116**, 117
Stimulus, 658-659
Stingray, **439**, 440
Stomach, bird, **527**
  frog, 495, **507**
  grasshopper, 330
  man, **613**
  pig, **558**
  ruminant, **557**
  vertebrate, 614
Stomochord, 393, 394, **395**
Stomodaeum, 172, **181**
Stone canal, **380**, **381**
Stonefly, **334**, 336
Stork, **539**
Stratification, 823
Stratum, 839
  corneum, 493, **592**
  germinativum, 493, **592**
Streamline form, **813**
Strell, M., 928
Strepsiptera, 339
Streptoline glutinant, **156**, 157
Streptomycin, 923
Stress reaction, 867-868, 925
  syndrome, 925
Strigiformes, **543**
Strobila, **171**, 172, 206
Stroma, 82
Strombus, 353, 354
Strongylocentrotus, 384, **385**
Struthio, **537**
Struthioniformes, 537
Sturgeon, **409**, **442**
Sturtevant, A. H., 911
Stylaria, 264, **265**
Stylops, 339
Subbarow, Y., 916
Subclavian artery, **509**, 510
Subesophageal ganglion, **302**
Subkingdoms, 89
Sublingual gland, **613**, 615
Submaxillary gland, **613**, 615
Submucosa, 507, **612**
Subpharyngeal gland, **427**
Subscapular vein, **510**, 511
Substratum, 813-814
Subumbrella, **165**, 166, 171
Subvertebral lymph sinus, 512
Succinea, **202**, 355
Sucker-mouthed worms (*see*
  Myzostomata)
Sucking lice, 337
Sucrase, 616
Suctoria, 103, **111**, 132-134
Suina, 579
Sulci, 655
Sumner, J. B., 915
Sun star, **385**
Super female, 740
  male, 740

Supplemental air, 639
Support, 595-602
Supra-anal plate, 329
Suprascapula, **495**, 497
Surface-volume ratio, 87
Surinam toad, **468, 857**
Suspensions, 38
Suspensory ligament, **667**, 669
Sutton, W. S., 907
Sutton-Boveri hypothesis, 735
Suzuki, M., 911
Svedberg, T., 922
Swallowing, 615
Swallow-tailed butterfly, 334, 341
Swammerdam, J., 890
Swamp cricket frog, **489**
Swan, 540
Sweat gland, **554**, 555, 914
Swift, 544
Swim bladder, 449, **450**, 452
Swimmeret, **295, 296**
Swimmer's itch, 201
Swordfish, **446**
Syconoid sponge, **141**
Symbiosis, 106, 819, 839
Symmetry, **84**, 85
Sympathetic nervous system, **502**, 505, **657**, 658
trunk, **653**
Sympatric, 794
Symphyla, 278
Synapase, 80, 650, **651**, 905
Synapsida, 418
Synapsis, **682, 683**, 907
Synarthrosis joint, **497**
Syncoryne, **166**
Syncytium, 52, 60, 499
Syngamy, **682**, 685, 686
Syngeographs, 845
Synovial fluid, **498**
membrane, **498**
Synsacrum, 525
Synthesis of bodily constituents, 921
tissue, **715**
Synura, 107
Syrinx, 528
Syrphid fly, **325**
Systematic zoology, 21
Systemic artery, **508, 509**, 510
blood pressure, 625
Systems and organs (survey), 81-84
Systole, 510, 628
Szent, Gvörgyi, A., 923
Szymanski, J. S., 913

T

Tachinid fly, **325**
Tachyglossus, 569
Tachypleus, 282
Tactile organs, 302
Tadarida, 571
Tadpole, ascidian, **422**, 423
frog, **515, 516**, 517
shrimp, **306**
Taenia, 186, **204-207** (*see also* Tapeworm)
beef, 204-206, **205**
life cycle, **205**, 206

Taenia—cont'd
dog, **204**, 209
pork, 206, **207**, 208
Taeniae coli, 614
Tagged atoms, 37
Taiga, 835
Tail fins, **445**
mammal, 551
Tansley, A. G., 920
Tapeworm, 203-209, 892
beef, 204, **205**, 206
life history, **205**
dog, **204**, 208, 209
dwarf, 208
experimental infestation, 897
fish, 208
frog, 492
hydatid, **208-209**
pork, 206, **207**, 208
sheep, 209
Tapir, 577, **578**
Tapirella, 578
Tapirus, 578
Tarantula, 286
Tardigrada, 277, **291**, 292
Taricha, 463
Tarsals, **495**, 497, **598, 600**
Tarsioidea, 581
Tarsius, 581
Tarsometatarsus, **523**, 525
Tarsus, **328**, 329
Tashiro, S., 911
Tasmanian wolf, 570
Taste buds, 506, 557, **663**
sensation, 663
Tatum, E. L., 922
Taxes, 130-132, 319, 872-873
Taxonomy, 22, 24-29
behavior relations, 873-874
binomial nomenclature, 25, 891
history, 25
rules, 27-28
synonyms, 26
variations, 26
Taylor, C. V., 914
Taylor, J. H., 928
Teeth, canine, **598**
clam, 359
heterodont, 556
homodont, 556
mammal, **556**-557
maxillary, **494**
milk, 612
monophyodont, 556
permanent, 612
sea urchin, 387
vomerine, **494**
Tegmina, 317
Telegony, 748
Telencephalon, 652
Teleost fish, adaptive radiation, 446
skin, 595
Teleostei, **409**, 443
Telophase, 63, **65, 66, 683**
Temperature, bird, 528
lethal, 561
mammal, 560, 561
Template duplication, 729
Temporal muscle, **499**, 500

Tendon, 499, **606**
Tensor fasciae latae, **606**
tympani muscle, **364**, 665
Tent caterpillar moth, **326**
Tentacle, Pogonophora, 398, **399**
sea cucumber, 387, **388**
snail, 355
velar, **423**, 424
Tentacular bulb, 167
Tentaculata, 180, **181**, 183
Tentaculocyst, **170**
Terebratulina, **248**
Teredo, 348, 349, 364
Teres major, **606**
Tergum, **294**, 295, **316, 328**, 329
Terminal nerve, 505
Terminology, genetics, 734-735
Termite, 106, 324, **326, 334**, 336, 914-915
Tern, 541
Terrapene, **482**
Terrestrial habitats, 831-833
Terrigenous bottom, 831
Territorial rights, 883
Territory selection, bird, 535
Tertiary period, 31, 104, 765
Test, 384, **387**
Testacea, **114**, 116
Testcross, 735-736
Testes, 192, **676, 678**, 699, 896
Ascaris, **226**
bird, **527**, 529
crayfish, 300
development, 710
dog tapeworm, 204
earthworm, **261**
fish, 454
frog, 495, **513**, 514
grasshopper, **331**
hydra, 160, **161**
mammal, **559**
planaria, **190**
Testosterone, 695, **696**, 699
Testudinata, 471, 480, **481, 482**, 483, 484
Testudinidae, 484
Tetanus, 604
Tethys, 355
Tetrabranchia, 366
Tetrad, 682, **683**, 684
Tetrapoda, 431
Textularia, **104**
Thalamus, 655
Thalassicolla, **114**
Thaliacea, 421
Theca, externa, interna, **674, 675**
Thecanephria, 398
Thecodont, **414, 613**
Thenea, 140
Therapsid, **416, 417**
Theria, 547, 566
Thermobia, 335
Thermocline, 831
Thermodynamics, laws, 38
Thermotaxis, 131
Thiamine, 620
isolation, 905
Thigmocyte, **624**
Thigmotaxis, 131, 319
Thomas, A. P., 901

Thompson, J. V., 893
Thoracic duct, **634**
Thoracica, 306
Thorax, 329
Thorpe, W. H., 870, 881
Thrips, 337
Thrombin, 508, 632
Thrombocyte, 508
Thromboplastin, 632
Thymine, 727
Thymus, **558**, 700
Thyone, 376, 387, 389
Thyroid gland, 427, 530, **688**,
    698
  hyper-, hypofunction, 692
  relation to thyrotropin, **692**
Thyrotropic hormone (TSH),
    699
  release factor, **691**, 692
Thyrotropin (TSH), **691**
Thyroxin, **692**, **693**, 698, 911
Thysanoptera, **334**, 337
Thysanura, 335
Tibia, **328**, 329, **598**, **600**
Tibialis anticus, **499**, 501
  posticus, **499**, 501
Tibiofibula, **495**, 497
Tibiotarsus, **523**, 525
Ticks, 290
Tidal air, 639
Tiedemann's bodies, **381**, 382
Tiger, 373
Tiger salamander, **463**
Time scale, geological, 31-32
Timofeeff-Ressovsky, N.W., 921
Tinamiformes, 538
Tinamous, 538
Tinbergen, N., 870, 874, 876,
    918
Tinea, 327
Tissue(s), **78-81**, **715**, 892, 923
  connective, 79-**80**, 82
  culture, 24, 54, 910-911
  differentiation, **78**
  epithelial, 78-**79**, 82
  instability, 83
  isolation, 54
  level organization, 150
  muscular, 80, **82**
  nervous, 80, **81**, 82
  synthesis, **715**, 923
  types of, **78**, **82**
  vascular, **78**, 81, 82, **83**
Tjio, J. H., 928
Toad, 463-469
  eggs, **467**
  giant South American, **465**
  Surinam, **468**, **857**
Toadfish, 452, 881
Tolerance, 810, 839
Tomcod, **451**
Tone, loudness, 666
  timbre, 667
Tongue, 612
  bird, **527**
  chameleon, 472, 475
  frog, **494**
  mammal, 557
  snake, 476, 477, **478**
Tongue worms, 277, 291, **394**,
    395, 396

Tongue worms—cont'd
  digestive system, **395**
  nervous system, **395**, 396
  reproductive system, **395**,
    396
  structure, **394**, **395**, 396
  vascular system, **395**
Tool using, 880
Tooth attachment, types of, 613
  shells, **351**, 352
Tornaria larva, 393, 396
Torpedo, 864, **865**
Torsion (snail), **353**
Tortoise, **482**, 484
Totipotent cleavage, **712**, 903
Toucan, 524, 545
Toxocara, 224
Trabecular net, 147
Trachea, **527**, 528, **613**
Tracheae, 280, **330**, 636
Tracheal gills, **636**
  system, 275, **636**
Trachydemus, 222
Trachylina, 168
Transduction, 729
Translocation, 726
Transverse process, 496
Transversus muscle, 500
Trap-door spider, **287**, 288
Trapezius muscle, 606
Traube, I., 899
Tree frog, **467**, **489**
Tree-hole habitat, **832**
Trematoda, 186, **196-202**, 492
  blood flukes, 199, **200**, **201**
  human liver fluke, **197**, **198**
  sheep liver fluke, **196**
Trembley, A., 161, 891
Treppe, 604
Trial and error, 130, 878-879
Triarthrus, 277, **281**
Triassic period, 31, 765
Triatoma, 120
Tricarboxylic acid cycle, 67, **68**
Triceps femoris, **499**, 501
Trichechus, 577
Trichina worm, **228-229**
Trichinella, 219, **228-229**, 894
  life cycle, 229
Trichinosis, 228
Trichocyst, **126**, **127**
Trichodina, 106, 163, **187**, 492
Trichomonas, 120, 492
Trichonumpha, 106
Trichophrya, 134
Trichoptera, **334**, 341
Tricuspid valve, 627
Trigeminal nerve, **502**, 505, 656
Trihybrid, 734
Triiodothyronine, 698
Trilobita, 277, **281**, 282
Trilobite, 277, **763**
Trinomial nomenclature, 26
Trionychidae, 484
Triops, 305, **306**
Triploblastic, 76
Trochanter, **328**, 329
Trochelminthes, 217
Trochlear nerve, **502**, 505, 656
Trochophore larva, **240**, 248,
    253, 352

Trochozoon, 240
Troctes, 337
Trogon, 544
Trogoniformes, 544
Trophoderm, **706**
Trophozoite, 121, **123**, **134**
Tropical rain forests, 836
Tropisms, 872-873
Trumpeter swan, **540**
Truncus arteriosus, **508**, **509**,
    510
Trypanosoma, 107, 119, **121**,
    492, 904
Trypanosomiasis, 121
Trypsin, 507, 616
Tschermak, E., 906
Tsetse fly, 120, 121
Tuatara, 483, **484**
Tube feet, 378, **380**, 383, 385,
    387, 390
Tube-within-a-tube organiza-
    tion, 87
Tubifera, 829
Tubifex, 253, **265**
Tubipora, 175
Tubularia, 166
Tubulidentata, 573, 574
Tundra, 834-835
Tunica externa, 628, **629**
  interna, 628, **629**
  media, 628, **629**
Tunicata, 420-423, 898
Turbatrix, 231
Turbellaria, 186-195 (*see also*
    Planaria)
Turkey, 540
Turtles, 480, **481**, **482**, 483, 484,
    597
  classification, 484
  life history, **481**
  skeleton, **597**
Tusk, **556**, 557
Tuzet, O., 926
Twining, heredity, 752-753
Twins, fraternal, 752
  identical, 753
Tylopoda, 579
Tympanic membrane, 329, 492,
    494, **506**, **660**, **665**
Typhlonectes, 460
Typhlosole, 255, **256**, 361
Typhlotriton, 462

U

Uca, 308, **309**
Ulna, **523**, 526, **598**, **600**
Ultracentrifuge, 922
Umbilicus, 521
Umbo, 358, 359
Uncinate process, 526
Underwater sound, 881
Unguiculata, 579
Ungulate, 577
Uniformitarianism, 778
Unio, 347, 357, 364
Uniramous appendage, 298
Uracil, 727
Urea, 618, 893
Urechis, 244
Ureter, **513**
Urethra, **559**, **678**, **679**

Urey, H., 919, 926
Urine, 513, 529, 644-646
Uriniferous tubule, 513, 643, **644**
Urnatella, 242
Urochordata, 404, 420-423
  classes, 421
  structure, **421**
Urochrome, 646
Urodela, 459, 460, **461, 462, 463, 464,** 469
Urogenital arteries, **509,** 510
  papilla, 429
  system, **513, 559,** 677
Uroglena, 107
Urosalpinx, 348, **352**
Urostyle, **495,** 496
Ursidae, 573
Uterus, **204, 237,** 560, 678-680, **708**
  bicornuate (horse) 560, **679**
  bipartite, 560
  comparative types, **679**
  dog, **708**
  duplex (rodent), 560, **679**
  mammal, **558,** 560
  marsupial type, **679**
  monotreme type, **679**
  simplex (human) 560, **678, 679,** 680
Utilization coefficient, 641
Utricle, 667

V

Vacuole, contractile, **110,** 112, 117, 126
  food, 110, 112, 126, 146, **154,** 155, 610
Vagility, 839-840
Vagina, **190, 331,** 560, **679,** 680
Vagus nerve, **502,** 505, 656
Valves (clam), 357
Vampire bat, 571, 861
Van Beneden, E., 901, 903
Vane, **520**
Varanope, 547
Variation, 782
Variety, 26
Vas deferens, **190,** 192, **226,** 300, **331, 527,** 529, **678**
  efferens, **190,** 192, 261, **513,** 514, **678**
  epididymis, **678**
Vascular tissue, 78, 81, **82, 83,** 624, **630, 631-632**
Vasomotor system, 630, 896
Vasopressin, 690, 699
Vastus lateralis muscle, **606**
Vauquelin, N. L., 893
Vavilov, N. I., 913
Vector, 568
Vein(s), 628, **629**
  of insect wing, 329
Velella, 153, 157, **158,** 167
  giant fiber system, **158**
Veliger larva, 364
Velum, **165,** 166, **423,** 424
Velvet, 552, **595**

Vena cava, **508, 510,** 511
Venom, black widow, 289
  snake, 480
Venomous snakes, 477-480
Venous system, frog, **510,** 511
  mammal, 625
Ventral abdominal vein, **510,** 511
  fissure, 504
  motor root, 504, **651**
Ventricle, brain, **503,** 504
  heart, **359, 360, 508,** 509, 625, **627-628**
Venule, 511
Venus, 349, 364
Venus's girdle, 183
Verhulst, P. F., 895
Vermiform appendix, 611, **613**
Vertebra, 560, **598, 599, 600, 653**
  articulations, **599**
Vertebral column, 402, **598, 599, 600**
Vertebrata, 425-430, 458-485
  characteristics, 425, 426
  circulatory system, 624-635
  classification, 420
  digestive system, 611-614
  epidermis, **590-591, 592-595**
  excretion, 643-646
  fresh-water origin, 404, **405,** 906
  frog as a type, 488-517
  jaws, 599
  nervous system, 649-659
  reproduction, **674, 675, 676, 677-687**
  respiration, 636-641
  sequence of origin, **405, 406-** 418, 906
Vesalius, A., 890
Vespa, 324
Vibrissae, 553
Villus, 611, **612,** 617, 707
Virchow, R., 897
Vireo's nest, **534**
Virus, 19, **45,** 729, 903, 920, 927
Vision (compound eye), day and night adapted, 303
Visual purple, 669
  violet, 669
Vital capacity, 639
  staining, 900
Vitamins, 618, 619-621
  A, 620, 912
  B complex, 620
  C, D, E, 621
  K, 621, 919
  deficiency, 620-621
  enzyme relations, 48
  hypothesis, 910
Vitelline membrane, 74, **706**
Viterous humor, **667,** 668
Vitrodentine, 438, **590, 595**
Viviparous, 439, 687
Vocal cords, 494, 512
Vogt, C., 897
Volvent, 157
Volvox, 109, 118, **119, 120**

Vomer, **495,** 496
Vorticella, 106, **131, 132,** 492
Vries, H. de, 785, 906, 907
Vultur, **541**
Vulture, vision, 529
Vulva, 680

W

Waddington, C. H., 920
Waggle dance, **866**
Waksman, S. A., 923
Walcott, C. D., 910
Wald, G., 919
Waldeyer, W., 903
Walking stick, **336**
Wallace, A. R., 897
Waller, A. V., 896
Walnut moth, **326**
Walrus, 573
Warburg apparatus, 914
Warburg, O., 914, 916
Wart hog, 556
Wasp, **325, 341, 342**
  Ichneumon, **342**
  Pedinaspis, 288
Water, 42, 618, 815
  capacity for heat, 42
  contamination, 107
  density, 42
  heavy, 919-920
  importance, 42
  percentage, 60
  properties, 815
  relation to protoplasm, 42
  solvent power, 42
Water bear, 277, **291-292**
  bug, **334,** 337
  fleas, 305, **306**
  penny, **827**
  tube, **361**
  vascular system, **375, 380, 381,** 382, **389,** 390
Watson, J. D., 926
Watson-Crick model, **728,** 729
Weasel, 572-573
Weather effects, 815-816
Web, spider, **287**
Weberian ossicles, 664
Web-spinning, 286
Weevils, **326,** 339
Weinberg, W., 909
Weismann, A., 902, 903
Whale, 576
Whalebone whale, 576
Wheel organ, **423,** 424
Whelk, 354
Whirligig beetle, **325**
White blood corpuscles, **630,** 631, 632
  matter, 504, **653**
White, E. I., 924
White, G., 264
"White" meat (bird), 526
Wieland, H., 917
Wiemer, A. S., 922
Wigglesworth, B. V., 920
Wilfarth, H., 903
William of Occam, 889
Williams, R. C., 927
Wilson, H. V., 143, 909

Wind, 815, 816
Windaus, A., 917
Window, oval and round, **666**
Winkler, H., 912
Wing, structure, **522**
Wöhler, F., 42, 893
Wolf, 572, 573
Wolff, C. F., 703, 891
Wolffian duct, **429**, 439, **513**, 677
Wolverine, 573
Wombat, **548**, 570
Wood frog, 488
  tick, **290**
Woodchuck, **548**, 574
Woodcock, **524**, 529, **543**
Woodpecker, 531, 532, 545
Woods Hole Biological Station, 902
Woods, P. S., 928
Woodward, R. B., 928
Wool, 553
Worm lizard, 485
Wright, S., 789, 919
Wuchereria, 219, 230-231, 812

X

X chromosome, **722**, 740, 741
  organ, 304, 920
Xanthophore, 493, 554
Xenos, 339
Xiphisternum, 497
Xiphosura, **282**-283
Xiphosurida, 277, **282**, 283
X-rays, 24, 904, 907

Y

Y organ, 304
Yoldia, 364
Yolk, 74
  gland, **190**, 193, **204**
  sac, **705**, **706**, 707
Young, J. Z., 921

Z

Zaglossus, 569
Zebra, 577
Zelleriella, 108
Zinjanthropus, 801, 928
Zoea, 308, **310**

Zoecium, 245
Zona granulosa, **675**
  pelucida, **675**
Zonitoides, 355
Zoochlorella, 106, 153, 156
Zoogeographical realms, 847
Zoogeography, 22, 843-849
Zooid, 118, **167**, **246**, **247**, 265
Zoological classification, modern, 898
  realms, 847
Zoology, aspects of, 17-22
  definition, 17
  experiment and investigation, 21, 22
  major subdivisions, 21, 22
  relation to other sciences, 17
  value of, 17
Zooxanthella, 106
Zoraptera, 338
Zsigmondy, R., 908
Zygapophyses, 496
Zygote, 60, 73, 74, 672, **673**, 685, 735
Zymase discovery, 905
Zymogens, 48